TABLES ON THE THERMOPHYSICAL PROPERTIES OF LIQUIDS AND GASES

In Normal and Dissociated States

ADVANCES IN THERMAL ENGINEERING

Editors:

JAMES P. HARTNETT
THOMAS F. IRVINE, JR.

I	Blackshear	• **Heat Transfer in Fires: Thermophysics, Social Aspects, Economic Impact***
II	Afgan and Beer	• **Heat Transfer in Flames***
III	de Vries and Afgan	• **Heat and Mass Transfer in the Biosphere: Part I Transfer Processes in Plant Environment***
IV	Vargaftik	• **Tables on the Thermophysical Properties of Liquids and Gases**
V	Veziroglu	• **Remote Sensing: Energy-Related Studies**
	Begell	• **Glossary of Terms in Heat Transfer: English, Russian, German, French, and Japanese** (in preparation)
	Chang	• **Control of Flow Separation** (in preparation)
	Chi	• **Heat Pipe Theory and Practice** (in preparation)
	Denton	• **Future Energy Production*** (in preparation)
	Eckert and Goldstein	• **Heat Transfer Measurement 2nd revised and augmented edition** (in preparation)
	Ginoux	• **Two-Phase Flows with Application to Nuclear Reactor Design Problems†** (in preparation)
	Gutfinger	• **Topics in Transport Phenomena: Bioprocesses, Mathematical Treatment, Mechanisms** (in preparation)
	Hartnett	• **Heat and Mass Transfer Problems in Future Energy Production*** (in preparation)
	Hsu and Graham	• **Transport Processes in Boiling and Two-Phase Systems, Including Near-Critical Fluids** (in preparation)
	Pfender	• **High-Temperature Phenomena in Electric Arcs** (in preparation)
	Richards	• **Measurement of Unsteady Fluid Dynamic Phenomena†** (in preparation)
	Sieverding	• **Two-Phase Fluid Dynamics in Turbines: Engineering, Instrumentation, Theory†** (in preparation)
	Yovanovich	• **Advanced Heat Conduction** (in preparation)

*A publication of the International Centre for Heat and Mass Transfer, Belgrade.
†A von Karman Institute Book, Brussels.

TABLES ON THE THERMOPHYSICAL PROPERTIES OF LIQUIDS AND GASES

In Normal and Dissociated States

SECOND EDITION

BY

N. B. VARGAFTIK

WITH A FOREWORD TO THE ENGLISH EDITION BY

Y. S. Touloukian

PURDUE UNIVERSITY

HEMISPHERE PUBLISHING CORPORATION

Washington – London

A HALSTED PRESS BOOK

JOHN WILEY & SONS, INC.

New York London Sydney Toronto

Originally published by Nauka Press, Moscow as Spravochnik po
Teplofizicheskim Svoitstvam Gazov i Zhidkostey

Hemisphere Publishing Corporation
1025 Vermont Ave., N.W., Washington, D.C. 20005

Distributed solely by Halsted Press, a Division of John Wiley & Sons, Inc.,
New York.

Library of Congress Cataloging in Publication Data

Vargaftik, N B
Tables on the thermophysical properties of liquids and gases.

Translation of Spravochnik po teplofizicheskim svoĭstvam gazov i zhidkosteĭ.
Bibliography: p.
Includes index.
1. Gases—Thermal properties—Tables, etc.
2. Liquids—Thermal properties—Tables. I. Title.
QC145.4.T5V3713 1975 530.4'2 75-14260
ISBN 0-470-90310-4

Printed in the United States of America

CONTENTS

PART II
MIXTURES

FOREWORD TO THE ENGLISH TRANSLATION–SECOND EDITION

I am indeed pleased to write a foreword to this extensive work. This book is a translation of the second, most recent edition of Professor Vargaftik's "Spravochnik po Teplofizicheskim Svoitstvam Gazov i Zhidkostey," which first appeared in this format in 1963. The primary contribution of the translated version comes from the author's extensive presentation, primarily from the Russian literature, on a wide range of materials of technological importance, in the liquid, vapor, gaseous, dissociated, and ionized states. The thermodynamic and transport properties presented, often over a wide range of temperatures and pressures, are basically reproductions from other data sources. In several instances, the tabular material is unique, and this reasonably up-to-date compendium would be most welcome by many in the English-speaking world to whom much of the data would otherwise remain unobtainable.

In the absence of any evaluative commentary in the presentation of the data, those who use this work will have to rely at this time on the author's judgment in the selection of the data and his internationally acknowledged reputation for his many valuable and original contributions to the field. I very much hope, however, that this work, together with others, may constitute the basis for future cooperative endeavors for the generation of an internationally agreed-upon set of thermophysical properties tables for gases and liquids such as that currently sponsored by special Task Groups within CODATA/ICSU, IUPAC, and the International Association for the Properties of Steam.

In this translation the corrections found on the errata page of the original work have been incorporated as have additional corrections noted since it was published. As an added feature the translated edition presents a thorough index to both the substances and the properties covered in the volume. The reader will find these conveniences most helpful in using this extensive reference work.

Y. S. Touloukian, Director
Center for Information and
Numerical Data Analysis and Synthesis
and
Distinguished Atkins Professor of Engineering
Purdue University
West Lafayette, Indiana

FOREWORD TO THE SECOND EDITION

Since the publication of the first edition of this Handbook (in 1963) a large amount of material on thermophysical properties of different substances has been published. The following changes and additions have been incorporated in the present edition:

1. New, detailed data are given for two types of hydrogen, both in the liquid and in the gaseous states. The present tables contain data up to 6,000°K and 1,000 bar, that is, the data include the region of high temperatures where hydrogen exists in a dissociated state. New tables of transport properties of hydrogen have been provided for both the liquid and the gaseous states at different pressures up to a temperature of 2,000°K.

2. The thermophysical properties of nitrogen, oxygen, air and argon are given over a much wider range of parameters. Detailed new data at high temperatures are given for these substances, for both the liquid as well as for the gaseous states, ranging from extremely low to very high pressures (up to 1,000 bar).

3. The tables of thermophysical properties of carbon dioxide (CO_2) have been reworked, expanded and rendered more accurate. This section contains new detailed data for liquid carbon dioxide at high temperatures (up to 4,000°K) in the critical region, where it exists in the dissociated state.

4. More detailed tables are given for alkali metals and mercury. Thermodynamic properties have been determined on the basis of new, more accurate data on the dissociation energy of diatomic molecules of alkali metals. The thermodynamic properties tables have been expanded to 3,000°K, taking into account both dissociation and ionization. Thermodynamic properties for ionized lithium at high temperatures are given in a separate set of tables. Viscosity and thermal conductivity of alkali metals in the gas phase are reported here for the first time.

5. Information on thermophysical properties of monatomic substances has been significantly expanded. In particular, new tables for helium include data for both liquid and gas phases at extremely low and high temperatures (up to 3,000°K) at different pressures. Thermophysical properties of neon, krypton and xenon are given for a wide range of temperatures and pressures.

6. Thermophysical properties of water and steam are given here on the basis of new international tables adapted in 1963–1964. For dissociated steam, data are given up to 6,000°K and 1,000 bar taking into account true properties of dissociated steam.

7. New data are given on diffusion in binary gas mixtures, on viscosity and thermal conductivity of mixtures and solutions; data at different pressures are included.

8. The majority of tables for the remaining substances cite more accurate and newer data over a wider range of parameters.

9. The editors have not included in the present edition data on thermophysical properties of compounds of boron, nitrogen oxide, gallium, deuterium and individual hydrocarbons, due to the fact almost no new information for these substances has been published since the appearance of the original edition of this handbook.

10. All thermophysical properties are given in SI units, with the exception of the data for ionized lithium, argon and nitrogen.

The author is grateful to the entire faculty of the Department of Physics at Moscow Institute of Aviation for their help in the preparation of this handbook. The author was helped in many aspects in the preparation of the present edition by Prof. P. M. Kesselman, Docents L. D. Volyak, Y. K. Vinogradov and N. D. Kosov and Assistant E. L. Studnikov, to whom he wishes to express his appreciation.

The author is very grateful to Academician A. S. Predvoditelev and Professor L. P. Filippov for valuable comments and to E. I. Gaydul for great help in the preparation of the manuscript.

N. B. Vargaftik

FOREWORD TO THE FIRST EDITION

The requirements of modern science and technology necessitate the knowledge of thermophysical properties of gases and liquids.

This area of science, in addition to experimental work, centers on research in diffusion, thermal conductivity and viscosity of gases, as well as on the derivation of equations of state for real gases. Over the recent years, a large amount of data on thermophysical properties of gases and liquids have been collected; these data are of great practical interest.

The present book attempts to provide a systematic presentation of data obtained over the last 5–10 years. Most reliable data for pure substances, gas mixtures and solutions are presented. The data are essentially based on experimental results. Most often, the data are given for whole-number temperatures and pressures, and in the cases of mixtures for concentrations convenient for practical calculations.

The handbook gives data for thermophysical properties of a number of gases: hydrogen, lithium, nitrogen, argon and steam; data are given at high temperatures and take into account the dissociation of the given gas. Data on thermophysical properties of vapors of lithium, sodium and potassium up to 2,000°K take into account the dimerization of these substances in the gaseous state. The book gives I-S [entropy-enthalpy] charts for these substances in the range of high temperatures.

In the compilation of this handbook, data reported in both monographic and periodical literature has been cited.

The author would like to express his appreciation to the entire faculty of the Department of Physics at the Moscow Institute of Aviation for their help in the preparation of this book.

Special thanks are due to Docent L. D. Volyak who arranged and correlated the data and compiled the tables on thermodynamic properties of potassium in the gas phase, to Assistant Yu. D. Vasilevskaya who worked on diffusion in binary mixtures, to V. V. Rybakov for thermodynamic properties of lithium at high temperatures in the gas phase. Candidate of Technical Sciences L. S. Zaytseva prepared the graphical presentation of thermodynamic properties of air at high temperatures.

The author is deeply grateful to Academician A. S. Predvoditelev and Candidate of Physical-Mathematical Sciences L. P. Filippov for their very valuable comments, and to E. I. Gaydul for great help in the preparation of the manuscript.

N. B. Vargaftik

USEFUL CONVERSION TABLES AND SYMBOLS

Dimensionless Groups

Group*	Symbol	Name
$\Delta p/\rho V^2$	Eu	Euler number
$\alpha t/r_0^2$	Fo	Fourier number
$(L/d)(k/Vd\rho c_p)$	Gz [= (L/d)/RePr]	Graetz number
$g\beta(\Delta T)L^3\rho^2/\mu^2$	Gr	Grashof number
λ/L	Kn	Knudsen number
α/D	Le	Lewis number
V/V_{sound}	Ma	Mach number
hL/k, hd/k	Nu	Nusselt number
$Vd\rho c_p/k$	Pe (= RePr)	Peclet number
$c_p\mu/k$	Pr	Prandtl number
$g\beta(\Delta T)L^3\rho^2 c_p/\mu k$	Ra (= GrPr)	Rayleigh number
$\rho VD/u$, $\rho VL/\mu$	Re	Reynolds number
$\mu/\rho D$	Sc	Schmidt number
$h_p d/D$	Sh	Sherwood number
$h/c_p G$	St (= Nu/RePr)	Stanton number
$V_\infty^2/C_p(\Delta T)_0$	E	Eckert number
V^2/gL	Fr	Froude number
$f_r d/V$	St	Strouhal number
$\rho V^2 L/\sigma$	We	Weber number

*f_r = frequency of oscillation
σ = surface tension.

Conversion Table

	To convert number of	To	Multiply by
Length	inch	cm	2.540
	ft	m	0.3048
Area	ft^2	m^2	0.0929
Volume	ft^3	m^3	0.02832
Mass	lbm	kg	0.45359
	Slugs	kg	14.594
Force	lbf	Newtons	4.4482
Density	lbm/ft^3	kg/m^3	16.02
Work	ft-lbf	mkg	0.1383
	hp-hr	mkg	273,700
Heat	Btu	kcal	0.2520
	Chu	Btu	1.800
	Btu	Joules	1054.35
	Btu	ft-lbf	778.26
	kw-hr	Btu	3412.75
Specific heat	Btu/lbm-°F	cal/gC	1.000
	Btu/lbm-°F	Wsec/kgmC	4184.0
Pressure	lbf/in^2, psi	kgf/cm^2	0.070309
	psi	atm	0.068046
	psi	bars	0.068948
	psi	dynes/cm^2	68947.0
Surface tension	lbf/ft	dynes/cm	6.8519×10^{-5}

Heat Flux, q/A

Multiply number of → by ↘ To obtain ↓	$\frac{\text{Btu}}{\text{ft}^2\text{-hr}}$	$\frac{\text{W}}{\text{cm}^2}$	$\frac{\text{kcal}}{\text{hr-m}^2}$	$\frac{\text{cal}}{\text{sec-cm}^2}$
Btu/ft^2-hr	1	3,170.75	0.36865	13,277.26
W/cm^2	3.154×10^{-4}	1	1.163×10^{-4}	4.1868
kcal/hr-m^2	2.7126	8,600	1	2.778×10^{-5}
cal/sec-cm^2	7.536×10^{-5}	0.2389	36,000	1

Heat Transfer Coefficient, h

Multiply number of → by ↘ To obtain ↓	$\frac{\text{Btu}}{\text{hr-ft}^2\text{-°F}}$	$\frac{\text{W}}{\text{cm}^2\text{-°C}}$	$\frac{\text{cal}}{\text{sec-cm}^2\text{-°C}}$	$\frac{\text{kcal}}{\text{hr-m}^2\text{-°C}}$
Btu/hr-ft^2-°F	1	1761	7376	0.20489
W/cm^2-°C	5.6785×10^{-4}	1	4.186	1.163×10^{-4}
cal/sec-cm^2-°C	1.356×10^{-4}	0.2391	1	2.778×10^{-5}
kcal/hr-m^2-°C	4.8826	8600	36000	1

Thermal Conductivity, k

Multiply number of → by ↘ To obtain ↓	$\frac{\text{Btu}}{\text{hr-ft-°F}}$	$\frac{\text{W}}{\text{cm-°C}}$	$\frac{\text{cal}}{\text{sec-cm-°C}}$	$\frac{\text{kcal}}{\text{hr-m-°C}}$	$\frac{\text{Btu in}}{\text{hr-ft}^2\text{-°F}}$
Btu/hr-ft-°F	1	57.793	241.9	0.6722	0.08333
W/cm-°C	0.01730	1	4.186	0.01171	1.442×10^{-3}
cal/sec-cm-°C	4.134×10^{-3}	0.2389	1	2.778×10^{-3}	3.445×10^{-4}
kcal/hr-m-°C	1.488	86.01	360	1	0.1240
Btu in./hr-ft^2-°F	12	693.5	2903	8.064	1

Viscosity, μ

Multiply number of → by ↘ To obtain ↓	$\frac{\text{lbm}}{\text{ft-hr}}$	$\frac{\text{lbf-sec}}{\text{ft}^2}$	Centipoise	$\frac{\text{kgm}}{\text{m-hr}}$	$\frac{\text{kgf-sec}}{\text{m}^2}$
lbm/ft-hr	1	116,000	2.42	0.672	23733
lbf-sec/ft^2	0.00000862	1	0.00002086	0.00000579	0.2048
Centipoise	0.413	47,880	1	0.278	9807
kgm/m-hr	1.49	172,000	3.60	1	35305
kgf-sec/m^2	0.0000421	4.882	0.0001020	0.0000284	1

100 centipoise = 1 Poise = 1g/sec-cm = 1 dyne sec/cm^2.

Kinematic Viscosity, υ

To obtain ↓ / Multiply number of → by ↘	$\frac{ft^2}{hr}$	Stokes	$\frac{m^2}{hr}$	$\frac{m^2}{sec}$
ft^2/hr	1	3.875	10.764	38,751
Stokes	0.25806	1	2.778	10^4
m^2/hr	0.092903	0.3599	1	3600
m^2/sec	0.00002581	10^{-4}	0.0002778	1

Conversion Factors

The following tables of conversion factors are convenient. In order to convert the numerical value of a property expressed in one of the units in the left-hand column of the table to the numerical value of the same property expressed in one of the units in the tow row of the table, multiply the former vvalue by the factor in the block common to both units.

In tables involving energy, *cal* denotes the thermochemical calorie; *IT cal* denotes the International Steam Table calorie. The thermochemical calorie (cal) equals 4.184 joule. The International Steam Table calorie (IT cal) equals 4.186 joule. The Btu is the International Steam Table Btu and it equals 1055.04 joule.

Conversion Factors for Mass

	lbm	slugs	gm	kg	ton
1 lbm =	1	0.03108	453.59	0.45359	0.0005
1 slug =	32.174	1	1.4594×10^4	14.594	0.016087
1 gm =	2.2046×10^{-3}	6.8521×10^{-5}	1	10^{-3}	1.1023×10^{-6}
1 kg =	2.2046	6.8521×10^{-3}	10^3	1	1.1023×10^{-3}
1 ton =	2000	61.162	9.0718×10^5	907.18	1

SOURCE: Modified and extended from "Selected Values of Properties of Hydrocarbons," National Bureau of Standards.

Conversion Factors for Density

	lbm/ft^3	$slug/ft^3$	$lbm/in.^3$	lbm/gal	gm/cc
1 lbm/ft^3 =	1	0.03108	5.787×10^{-4}	0.13368	0.01602
1 $slug/ft^3$ =	32.174	1	0.1862	4.3010	0.51543
1 $lbm/in.^3$ =	1728	53.706	1	231	27.680
1 lbm/gal =	7.4805	0.2325	4.329×10^{-3}	1	0.11983
1 gm/cc =	62.428	1.9403	0.03613	8.345	1

SOURCE: Modified and extended from "Selected Values of Properties of Hydrocarbons," National Bureau of Standards.

Conversion Factors for Pressure

		lbf/ft^2	lbf/in.^{2}	atm	in. Hg	in. H_2O	mm Hg	bar
1 lbf/ft^2	=	1	0.006944	4.726×10^{-4}	0.014139	0.19243	0.3591	4.788×10^{-4}
1 lbf/in.^{2}	=	144	1	0.06805	2.036	27.71	51.715	0.06895
1 atm	=	2116.2	14.696	1	29.921	407.18	760	1.01325
1 in. Hg	=	70.726	0.49116	0.033421	1	13.608	25.40	0.03386
1 in. H_2O	=	5.197	0.036092	0.002456	0.07348	1	1.8665	0.002488
1 mm Hg	=	2.7845	0.019337	1.315×10^{-3}	0.03937	0.53577	1	1.333×10^{-3}
1 mm H_2O	=	2.0886×10^4	14.504	0.98692	29.530	401.85	750.06	1

Conversion Factors for Energy

		abs joule	cal	IT cal	Btu	int. kw-hr	hp-hr	ft-lb	liter-atm
1 abs joule	=	1	0.239005	0.238848	0.947827×10^{-3}	2.77731×10^{-7}	3.72505×10^{-7}	0.737561	9.86896×10^{-3}
1 cal	=	4.18401	1	0.999344	3.96572×10^{-3}	1.162028×10^{-6}	1.558566×10^{-6}	3.08596	4.12918×10^{-2}
1 IT cal	=	4.18676	1.000657	1	3.96832×10^{-3}	1.162791×10^{-6}	1.559590×10^{-6}	3.08799	4.13189×10^{-2}
1 Btu	=	1055.045	252.161	251.996	1	2.93018×10^{-4}	3.93010×10^{-4}	778.16	10.41220
1 int. kw-hr	=	3,600,612	860,565	860,000	3412.76	1	1.341247	2,655,669	35534.3
1 hp-hr	=	2,684,525	641.615	641.194	2544.46	0.745575	1	1,980,000	26493.5
1 ft-lb	=	1.355821	0.324048	0.323836	1.285083×10^{-3}	3.76553×10^{-7}	5.05051×10^{-7}	1	1.338054×10^{-2}
1 liter-atm	=	101.3278	24.2179	24.2020	0.0960412	2.81418×10^{-5}	3.77452×10^{-5}	74.7354	1

Conversion Factors for Specific Energy

		abs joule/gm	cal/gm	IT cal/gm	Btu/lb	ft-lbf/lbm	int. kw-hr/gm	hp-hr/lb	ft^2/sec^2
abs joule/gm	=	1	0.2390	0.2388	0.4299	334.53	2.777×10^{-7}	1.690×10^{-4}	10763
cal/gm	=	4.184	1	0.9993	1.7988	1399.75	1.162×10^{-6}	7.069×10^{-4}	4.504×10^4
IT cal/gm	=	4.186	1.0007	1	1.8	1400.69	1.163×10^{-6}	7.074×10^{-4}	4.506×10^4
Btu/lb	=	2.326	0.5559	0.5556	1	778.16	6.460×10^{-7}	3.930×10^{-4}	25,037
ft-lbf/lbm	=	2.989×10^{-3}	7.144×10^{-4}	7.139×10^{-4}	1.285×10^{-3}	1	8.302×10^{-10}	5.051×10^{-7}	32.174
int. kw-hr/gm	=	3.610×10^6	860,565	860,000	1.548×10^6	1.2046×10^9	1	608.4	3.876×10^{10}
hp-hr/lb	=	5919	1414.5	1413.6	2545	1.980×10^6	0.001644	1	6.370×10^7
ft^2/sec^2	=	9.291×10^{-5}	2.220×10^{-5}	2.219×10^{-5}	3.994×10^{-5}	0.03108	2.580×10^{-11}	1.567×10^{-8}	1

Conversion Factors for Specific Energy per Degree

	abs joule/gm-°K	cal/gm-°K	IT cal/gm-°K	Btu/lb-°R	w-sec/kg-°K
abs joule/gm-°K =	1	0.2390	0.2388	0.2388	10^3
cal/gm-°K =	4.184	1	0.9993	0.9993	4184
IT cal/gm-°K =	4.186	1.0007	1	1	4186
Btu/lb-°R =	4.186	1.0007	1	1	4186
w-sec/kg-°K =	10^{-3}	2.390×10^{-4}	2.388×10^{-4}	2.388×10^{-4}	1

Conversion Factors for Thermal Conductivity

	cal/sec-cm-°C	Btu/hr-ft-°F	Btu/hr-ft^2-°F/in.	w/cm-°C
1 cal/sec-cm-°C =	1	241.9	2903	4.183
1 Btu/hr-ft-°F =	4.13×10^{-3}	1	12	0.0173
1 Btu/hr-ft^2-°F/in. =	3.45×10^{-4}	0.0833	1	1.44×10^{-3}
1 w/cm^2-°C =	0.239	57.8	694	1

Conversion Factors for Dynamic Viscosity

	poise or g/cm-sec, or dyn-sec/cm^2	lbm/ft-hr or pdl-hr/ft^2	lbm/ft-sec or pdl-sec/ft^2
1 poise =	1	242	0.0672
1 lbm/ft-hr =	4.13×10^{-3}	1	2.78×10^{-4}
1 lbm/ft-sec =	14.87	3600	1

Conversion Factors for Kinematic Viscosity

	ft^2/hr	stokes	m^2/hr	m^2/sec
ft^2/hr =	1	0.25806	0.092903	2.58×10^{-5}
stokes =	3.885	1	0.36	10^{-4}
m^2/hr =	10.764	2.778	1	2.778×10^{-4}
m^2/sec =	38,750	10^4	3600	1

CONVERSION OF UNITS FROM SI TO OTHER SYSTEMS

Quantity	Symbol	Units, in SI	Units, in other systems	To convert from SI to other system, multiply by
Pressure	P	N/m^2	$dyne/cm^2$	10
			bar	10^{-5}
			atm (phys)	$0.9869 \cdot 10^{-5}$
		bar $= 10^5$ N/m^2	atm (phys)	0.9869
			kg/cm^2 (atm. abs)	1.0197
			mm Hg	750
Density	ϱ	kg/m^3	g/cm^3	10^{-3}
Specific volume	V	m^3/kg	cm^3/g	10^3
Heat capacity	C	$kJ/kg \cdot deg$	$Kcal/kg \cdot deg$	0.2388
Enthalpy	i	kJ/kg	$Kcal/kg$	0.2388
Entropy	S	$kJ/kg \cdot deg$	$Kcal/kg \cdot deg$	0.2388
Latent heat of vaporization	r	kJ/kg	$Kcal/kg$	0.2388
Thermal conductivity	λ	$W/m \cdot deg$	$cal/cm \cdot s \cdot deg$	$2.388 \cdot 10^{-3}$
			$Kcal/m \cdot hr \cdot deg$	0.86
Viscosity	η	$N \cdot s/m^2$ (kg/m ·)		
			$g/cm \cdot s$ (poise)	10
			$kg \cdot s/m^2$	0.102
Kinematic viscosity	$\nu = \frac{\eta}{\varrho}$	m^2/s	cm^2/s (stokes)	10^4
Surface tension	δ	N/m	$dyne/cm$ (erg/cm^2)	10^3

NOTATION

a — thermal diffusivity
C_p, c_p — heat capacity at constant pressure
C_v — heat capacity at constant volume
D — diffusion coefficient
I, i — enthalpy
K_T — thermodiffusion ratio
p — pressure
Pr — prandtl number
q — heat of melting
R, r — heat of vaporization
r_i, X_i — volumetric component fractions in a gas mixture
S, s — entropy
u — velocity of sound
V — specific volume
z — compressibility factor (pV/RT)
α — volumetric expansion coefficient $\left(\frac{1}{V}\frac{\delta V}{\delta T}\right)_p$
β — coefficient of thermal compressibility $\left(-\frac{1}{V}\frac{\delta V}{\delta p}\right)_T$
η — viscosity
λ — thermal conductivity
$\Delta\lambda$ — coefficient of thermodiffusional separation of the gas mixture
ν — kinematic viscosity
ϱ — density
σ — surface tension, electrical conductivity

Subscript *cr* and superscript *o* refer, respectively, to critical and ideal states of the gas. A prime and a double prime refer, respectively, to liquid and vapor at saturation. In all tables a horizontal line indicates the separation of liquid and vapor states.

PART I

PURE SUBSTANCES

Chapter 1

HYDROGEN AND HYDROGEN COMPOUNDS

HYDROGEN (H_2)

Molecular weight 2.0160

Parahydrogen (p-H_2): T_{melt} = 13.8 °K; T_{boil} = 20.28 °K at 760 mm Hg; T_{cr} = 32.98 °K; p_{cr} = 12.93 bar; ρ_{cr} = 31.4 kg/m³.

Hydrogen: (n-H_2; 25% p-H_2 + 75% o-H_2): T_{melt} = 13.95 °K; $T_{boiling}$ = 20.38 °K at 760 mm Hg; T_{cr} = 32.23 °K; p_{cr} = 13.16 bar; ρ_{cr} = 31.6 kg/m³.

THERMOPHYSICAL PROPERTIES OF HYDROGEN

Molecules of hydrogen exist in two modifications, differing from each other by the orientation of the nuclear spin of the atoms. At low temperatures (0 to 20 °K) hydrogen is practically in the form of pure paramodification (p-H_2). At somewhat higher temperatures, parahydrogen undergoes partial isomerization into orthohydrogen (o-H_2) and remains in equilibrium with the latter. The ratio of the concentrations of the two forms of hydrogen is basically temperature-dependent and is almost independent of pressure [1]. Figure 1 shows the equilibrium concentration of parahydrogen as a function of temperature. In the absence of catalysts, the equilibrium composition corresponding to a given temperature, is established quite slowly, giving rise to the possibility of prolonged coexistence of components in a mixture different from equilibrium [2]. The most widely used compositions are those reaching equilibrium at 300 °K (Fig. 1) and boiling temperature of liquid hydrogen at a pressure of 1 atmosphere (20.3 °K). The first is referred to as (normal) hydrogen (n-H_2: 25% p-H_2 + 75% o-H_2), and the second represents practically pure parahydrogen. Experiments show [3] that the thermal properties $V = f(p, T)$ of the mentioned compositions, while differing at lower temperatures, become practically identical at temperatures above Boyle temperature of 110 °K. However, caloric values (heat capacity, enthalpy, entropy) above 110 °K for both compositions differ at each temperature by a constant value. At temperatures above 500 °K, both the thermal and the caloric properties of both hydrogen compositions become practically equal.

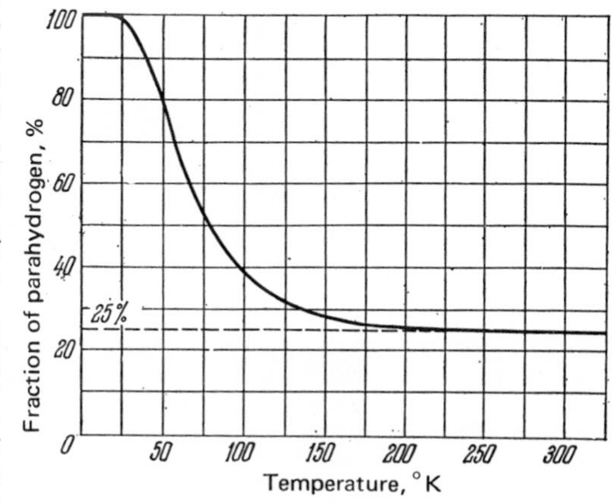

Fig. 1. Equilibrium concentration of parahydrogen as a function of temperature.

Serduyk and Kazavchinsky [3, 4] derived equations of state for parahydrogen and normal hydrogen describing with sufficient accuracy the entire complex of thermodynamic properties of these compositions over a range of of temperatures from the triple point to the appearance of noticeable dissociation, and in the range of reduced densities $\omega = V_{cr}/V$ from 0 to 2.8. These equations [3, 4] were used to compile detailed data of thermodynamic properties of parahydrogen [5, 6] which are used in the present book.

The tables below give thermodynamic properties of hydrogen at saturation, as well as values of V, I and S from 14–1500 °K and pressures from 1 to 1000 bar. Up to 500 °K the data for parahydrogen and normal hydrogen are given separately.

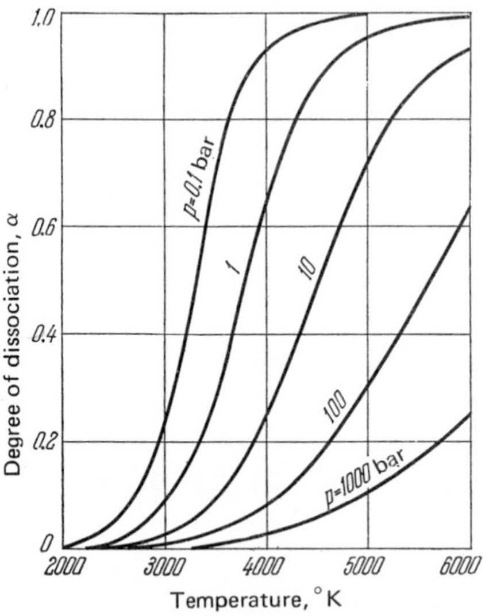

For the first time, we are publishing here the data on thermodynamic properties of dissociated hydrogen from 1500 to 6000 °K at pressures ranging from 0.1 to 1000 bar as calculated by Kesselman and Gorykin [8, 9]. The curves in Figs. 1 and 3 describe the degree of dissociation of and heat capacity of dissociated hydrogen as a function of temperature at different pressures.

For the first time, the handbook includes the values of viscosity and thermal conductivity for dissociated hydrogen [13] as calculated by Vargaftik and Vasilevskaya in the range of temperatures from 1400–6000 °K and pressures from 10^{-5} to 200 bar without taking ionization into account. Figures 4 and 5 give the viscosity and thermal conductivity as a function of temperature at different pressures.

A table is also given for viscosity of ionized hydrogen at temperatures ranging from 6000 to 30000 °K and pressures from 0.001 to 10 bar. These data were compiled by Belov [14] on the basis of theoretical calculations.

Fig. 2. Degree of dissociation of hydrogen as a function of temperature at different pressures.

Melting temperature of normal hydrogen and parahydrogen as a function of pressure [7, 396, 399, 400]

T, °K	p, bar		T, °K	p, bar	
	normal hydrogen	para-hydrogen		normal hydrogen	para-hydrogen
13. 803*	—	0.0704*	25	457.2	463.1
13. 947*	0.072*	—	26	509.4	515.4
14	1.66	5.96	28	618.3	624.7
15	32.9	37.4	30	733.4	740.0
16	66.5	71.1	35	1047	1055
17	102.3	107.1	40	1398	1405
18	140.1	145.1	45	1785	1794
19	180.0	185.1	50	2206	2215
20	221.8	227.1	55	2663	2672
21	265.4	270.8	60	3154	3164
22	310.8	316.4	65	3679	3689
23	357.9	363.8	70	4238	4249
24	406.8	412.6	80	5460	5472

*Triple point.

Thermodynamic properties of normal hydrogen at saturation V(cm³/mole), I and R (J/mole), S and C_p (J/mole · deg)[1, 7]

T, °K	p, bar	V'	V''	I'	I''	R	S'	S''	C_p'	C_p''
14	0.07451	25.17	15 380	425	1348	923	16.49	82.18	13.41	20.90
15	0.1274	26.44	9 564.5	438	1366	928	17.45	79.07	14.10	21.23
16	0.2054	26.74	6 269.0	453	1384	931	18.35	76.31	14.80	21.56
17	0.3150	27.05	4 294.6	468	1400	932	19.33	73.95	15.52	21.91

continued

T, °K	p, bar	V′	V″	I′	I″	R	S′	S″	C_p′	C_p″
18	0.4629	27.40	3 052.7	485	1416	931	20.27	71.81	16.48	22.30
19	0.6561	27.78	2 237.7	502	1429	927	21.18	69.84	17.68	22.77
20	0.9021	28.20	1 682.6	522	1443	921	22.17	68.10	19.06	23.35
21	1.209	28.65	1 292.1	541	1453	912	23.08	66.39	20.56	24.07
22	1.584	29.15	1 009.5	563	1461	898	24.06	64.84	22.13	24.99
23	2.036	29.70	800.1	587	1469	882	25.03	63.32	23.81	26.15
24	2.574	30.32	641.5	613	1474	861	26.03	61.88	25.62	27.63
25	3.206	31.02	519.2	640	1476	836	27.09	60.50	27.67	29.53
26	3.942	31.81	423.2	670	1476	806	28.18	59.14	30.08	32.02
27	4.789	32.72	346.9	701	1471	770	29.27	57.75	33.07	35.35
28	5.755	33.80	285.2	735	1462	727	30.43	56.36	37.01	40.01
29	6.848	35.10	234.5	774	1450	676	31.66	54.92	42.63	46.93
30	8.077	36.75	191.9	819	1431	612	32.99	53.37	51.52	58.21
30.5	8.747	37.79	173.0	842	1417	575	33.70	52.52	58.35	67.03
31	9.455	38.98	155.1	868	1400	532	34.46	51.59	68.23	79.94
31.5	10.20	40.49	138.1	898	1379	431	35.33	50.58	83.88	100.66
32	11.00	42.47	121.3	933	1352	419	36.32	49.40	112.5	139.29
32.5	11.84	45.39	103.9	977	1313	336	37.56	47.90	181.8	235.59
33	12.73	51.15	83.01	1045	1245	200	39.48	45.54	560.3	817.7
33.23	13.16	63.86	63.86	1131	1131	0	41.99	41.99	∞	∞

Thermodynamic properties of parahydrogen at saturation
V(cm^3/mole), I and R (J/mole), S and C_p (J/mole · deg)

T, °K	p, bar	V′	V″	I′	I″	R	S′	S″	C_p′	C_p″
14	0.07880	26.26	14 529	−623	285	908	10.05	74.80	13.25	20.90
15	0.1342	26.54	9 072.9	−609	303	912	11.01	71.75	13.97	21.25
16	0.2154	26.84	5 968.9	−594	321	915	11.93	69.04	14.59	21.60
17	0.3291	27.17	4 102.5	−580	337	917	12.84	66.65	15.33	21.97
18	0.4820	27.53	2 924.5	−563	352	915	13.77	64.53	16.35	22.38
19	0.6812	27.92	2 148.8	−545	367	912	14.69	62.60	17.61	22.87
20	0.9342	28.35	1 618.9	−526	379	905	15.71	60.91	19.04	23.47
21	1.249	28.82	1 245.2	−506	389	895	16.62	59.21	20.56	24.24
22	1.633	29.34	974.1	−484	398	882	17.56	57.62	22.15	25.20
23	2.095	29.91	772.7	−460	404	864	18.56	56.14	23.81	26.43
24	2.645	30.55	619.8	−435	409	844	19.57	54.70	25.63	28.01
25	3.290	31.27	501.7	−408	410	818	20.61	53.90	27.69	30.05
26	4.039	32.10	409.0	−378	409	787	21.70	51.94	30.18	32.73
27	4.901	33.05	335.0	−346	404	750	22.79	50.54	33.27	36.37
28	5.883	34.18	275.1	−310	395	705	23.97	49.14	37.45	41.52
29	6.993	35.57	225.7	−272	380	653	25.15	47.63	43.61	49.32
30	8.240	37.34	184.2	−228	359	587	26.55	46.08	53.64	62.39
30.5	8.920	38.45	165.5	−203	344	547	27.24	45.16		
31	9.638	39.81	147.8	−176	325	501	28.05	44.19	73.79	89.25
31.5	10.399	41.53	130.7	−144	301	445	28.97	43.12		
32	11.205	43.90	113.6	−107	269	376	30.07	41.82	136.04	174.52
32.5	12.068	47.77	94.88	−56	220	276	31.50	39.99		
32.98	12.933	64	64	61	61	0	34.90	34.90	∞	∞

Thermodynamic properties of normal hydrogen at different temperatures
and pressures V(cm^3/mole), I (J/mole), S and C_p (J/mole · deg) [5, 7]

p, bar	V	I	S	C_p	V	I	S	C_p
	T = 14 °K				T = 16 °K			
1	26.14	426	16.47	13.40	26.71	455	18.33	14.76
2					26.68	456	18.30	14.72
4					26.61	461	18.24	14.64
6					26.55	466	18.18	14.56

continued

p, bar	V	I	S	C_p	V	I	S	C_p
8					26.48	470	18.12	14.49
10					26.42	474	18.07	14.41
12					26.38	479	18.01	14.34
14					26.30	483	17.96	14.27
16					26.24	488	17.90	14.21
18					26.19	492	17.85	14.14
20					26.13	496	17.80	14.08
30					25.87	518	17.55	13.79
40					25.62	540	17.32	13.54
50					25.40	563	17.10	13.32
60					25.19	585	16.90	13.11
	$T = 18$ °K				$T = 20$ °K			
1	27.38	486	20.25	16.45	28.19	552	22.16	19.05
2	27.34	488	20.21	16.39	28.14	524	22.11	18.96
4	27.26	493	20.14	16.27	28.04	528	22.03	18.79
6	27.18	497	20.07	16.16	27.94	532	21.94	18.62
8	27.11	501	20.00	16.05	27.85	536	21.86	18.46
10	27.03	505	19.93	15.94	27.76	540	21.78	18.32
12	26.96	509	19.89	15.84	27.67	544	21.70	18.18
14	26.89	514	19.80	15.75	27.59	548	21.62	18.04
16	26.82	518	19.74	15.65	27.50	552	21.55	17.91
18	26.76	522	19.68	15.57	27.42	556	21.48	17.79
20	26.69	526	19.62	15.48	27.34	560	21.41	17.67
30	26.38	548	19.33	15.09	26.98	580	21.07	17.16
40	26.10	569	19.08	14.75	26.65	601	20.76	16.73
50	25.84	591	18.81	14.46	26.35	622	20.48	16.36
60	25.61	612	18.58	14.19	26.08	643	20.22	16.04
80	25.18	655	18.18	13.74	25.60	685	19.74	15.51
100	24.80	698	17.78	13.35	25.18	727	19.32	15.08
150					24.33	833	18.43	14.26
200					23.64	938	17.70	13.67
	$T = 22$ °K				$T = 24$ °K			
1	1 690.5	1 484	69.31	23.03	1 875.8	1 530	71.29	22.59
2	29.12	563	24.04	22.07	869.7	1 497	64.60	25.30
4	28.99	567	23.94	21.79	30.19	614	25.95	25.28
6	28.89	571	23.83	21.54	30.02	617	25.81	24.83
8	28.75	574	23.73	21.30	29.86	620	25.67	24.43
10	28.63	577	23.63	21.07	29.70	623	25.50	24.07
12	28.52	581	23.54	20.88	29.56	626	25.45	23.74
14	28.41	585	23.45	20.69	29.42	629	25.33	23.43
16	28.31	588	23.36	20.48	29.28	632	25.22	23.15
18	28.21	592	23.27	20.31	29.15	636	25.12	22.89
20	28.11	596	23.19	20.15	29.03	639	25.02	22.65
30	27.69	615	22.79	19.44	28.47	657	24.55	21.64
40	27.28	635	22.44	18.87	28.00	675	24.14	20.89
50	26.93	655	22.12	18.40	27.59	694	23.77	20.26
60	26.62	675	21.82	18.01	27.22	713	23.44	19.75
80	26.07	716	21.29	17.36	26.59	753	22.84	18.96
100	25.60	758	20.83	16.88	26.08	798	22.33	18.36
150	24.66	862	19.85	15.95	25.02	896	21.27	17.30
200	23.32	966	19.08	15.32	24.22	998	20.42	16.60
250	23.31	1 069	18.39	14.84	23.57	1 101	19.71	16.08
300					23.02	1 202	19.09	15.67
	$T = 26$ °K				$T = 28$ °K			
1	2 058.4	1 575	73.09	22.29	2 234.8	1 619	74.74	22.05
2	970.5	1 546	66.61	24.32	1 067.4	1 593	68.40	23.66
4	31.80	670	28.17	30.05	476.2	1 533	61.21	28.84
6	31.54	671	27.99	29.15	33.74	735	30.40	36.73
8	31.30	673	27.82	28.88	33.32	735	30.14	34.75
10	31.07	675	27.65	27.71	32.94	734	29.90	33.22

continued

p, bar	V	I	S	C_p	V	I	S	C_p
12	30.88	677	27.50	27.15	32.61	735	29.68	31.97
14	30.69	680	27.36	26.61	32.31	736	29.48	30.94
16	30.48	682	27.22	26.14	32.03	738	29.30	30.07
18	30.31	685	27.09	25.72	31.76	739	29.13	29.31
20	30.14	687	26.96	25.34	31.52	740	28.98	28.65
30	29.43	703	26.39	23.64	30.57	752	28.30	26.27
40	28.84	719	25.91	22.79	29.82	766	27.68	24.74
50	28.34	737	25.49	21.96	29.20	782	27.18	23.64
60	27.90	755	25.11	21.31	28.67	798	26.75	22.80
80	27.17	792	24.44	20.32	27.81	834	26.00	21.59
100	26.59	832	23.88	19.59	27.12	871	25.38	20.69
150	25.41	982	22.73	18.36	25.83	969	24.10	19.25
200	24.54	1 033	21.82	17.55	24.88	1 068	23.16	18.33
250	23.85	1 134	21.06	16.99	24.13	1 168	22.35	17.68
300	23.26	1 235	20.40	16.52	23.52	1 268	21.68	17.19
		$T = 30$ °K				$T = 32$ °K		
1	2 411.2	1 664	76.27	21.88	2 588.1	1 707	77.68	21.71
2	1 161.8	1 642	70.03	23.17	1 254.1	1 689	71.51	22.79
4	532.3	1 590	63.14	26.89	585.1	1 642	64.83	25.63
6	315.8	1 527	58.29	33.95	358.2	1 590	60.35	30.12
8	195.9	1 439	53.58	56.18	239.9	1 526	56.51	38.68
10	35.91	813	32.55	45.30	160.2	1 434	52.40	64.59
12	35.23	809	32.18	41.29	40.82	917	35.67	80.97
14	34.67	806	31.88	38.49	38.93	899	34.86	59.68
16	34.19	805	31.58	36.38	37.72	889	34.31	50.61
18	33.78	804	31.33	34.75	36.83	882	33.89	45.33
20	33.41	804	31.10	33.42	36.12	878	33.50	41.80
30	31.99	809	30.18	29.26	33.80	871	32.19	33.28
40	30.98	819	29.47	26.96	32.39	875	31.29	29.62
50	30.20	832	28.89	25.44	31.38	884	30.59	27.49
60	29.56	847	28.39	24.33	30.56	897	30.01	26.00
80	28.53	880	27.54	22.80	29.33	926	29.06	24.08
100	27.73	915	26.87	21.75	28.40	959	28.29	22.83
150	26.28	1 009	25.50	20.06	26.78	1 050	26.82	20.92
200	25.24	1 109	24.43	19.05	25.63	1 145	25.71	19.77
250	24.44	1 204	23.61	18.33	24.78	1 242	24.81	18.98
300	23.78	1 304	22.88	17.79	24.03	1 340	24.05	18.40
400					22.98	1 534	22.77	17.62
		$T = 34$ °K				$T = 36$ °K		
1	2 759.6	1 751	79.01	21.59	2 932.2	1 794	80.22	21.48
2	1 345.0	1 733	72.90	22.49	1 434.8	1 777	74.16	22.25
4	635.7	1 693	66.38	24.75	684.7	1 741	67.75	24.09
6	396.8	1 648	62.12	27.93	433.1	1 702	63.66	26.51
8	274.8	1 597	58.67	32.87	305.8	1 659	60.44	29.84
10	198.3	1 535	55.47	41.79	227.8	1 610	57.61	34.78
12	142.0	1 451	52.01	63.66	173.7	1 552	54.91	42.87
14	88.06	1 293	46.68	210.04	132.5	1 481	52.07	58.18
16	47.95	1 044	39.00	142.32	98.08	1 384	48.75	92.25
18	43.19	993	37.42	80.25	69.91	1 257	44.75	138.79
20	40.96	978	36.55	62.25	54.62	1 155	41.59	118.41
30	36.27	943	34.39	39.18	39.89	1 029	36.85	48.29
40	34.14	938	33.21	32.96	36.38	1 007	35.19	37.21
50	32.75	942	32.35	29.82	34.42	1 004	34.11	32.56
60	31.72	951	31.66	27.85	33.07	1 008	33.29	29.90
80	30.22	976	30.58	25.43	31.22	1 028	32.06	26.85
100	29.13	1 006	29.73	23.94	29.94	1 055	31.11	25.08
150	27.28	1 093	28.14	21.77	27.84	1 137	29.39	22.63
200	26.03	1 186	26.95	20.51	26.46	1 227	28.13	21.27
250	25.10	1 281	26.00	19.66	25.45	1 321	27.13	20.35
300	24.35	1 378	25.20	19.03	24.66	1 416	26.29	19.69
400	23.20	1 570	23.88	18.21	23.44	1 607	24.92	18.82

continued

p, bar	V	I	S	C_p	V	I	S	C_p
	T=38 °K				T=40 °K			
1	3 104.0	1 837	81.39	21.40	3 275.0	1 880	82.47	21.32
2	1 523.7	1 821	75.36	22.06	1 611.8	1 866	76.48	21.90
4	732.5	1 789	69.05	23.59	779.5	1 836	70.24	23.19
6	467.8	1 754	65.07	25.50	501.4	1 805	66.35	24.75
8	334.5	1 717	62.01	27.95	361.8	1 772	63.40	26.64
10	253.6	1 676	59.40	31.20	277.4	1 737	60.93	29.00
12	198.7	1 630	57.02	35.74	220.7	1 698	58.74	32.00
14	158.3	1 579	54.72	42.38	179.6	1 657	56.70	35.92
16	127.0	1 519	52.39	52.51	148.3	1 611	54.74	41.08
18	101.6	1 448	49.94	67.60	123.5	1 561	52.81	47.82
20	81.47	1 370	47.39	84.48	103.5	1 506	50.88	56.06
30	45.69	1 138	39.79	60.16	54.56	1 266	43.05	65.38
40	39.35	1 087	37.34	42.40	43.33	1 178	39.64	47.62
50	36.47	1 072	35.96	35.69	39.00	1 148	37.86	39.01
60	34.66	1 071	34.97	32.14	36.54	1 138	36.67	34.50
80	32.34	1 083	33.55	28.33	33.61	1 142	35.04	29.85
100	30.83	1 107	32.51	26.24	31.80	1 161	33.87	27.40
150	28.43	1 183	30.64	23.49	29.06	1 232	31.86	24.33
200	26.92	1 271	29.31	22.02	27.40	1 316	30.44	22.75
250	25.83	1 363	28.25	21.05	26.21	1 406	29.34	21.73
300	24.97	1 456	27.38	20.35	25.30	1 498	28.43	21.00
400	23.69	1 645	25.97	19.43	23.94	1 685	26.96	20.04
500					22.94	1 872	25.77	19.52
	T=50 °K				T=60 °K			
1	4 123.8	2 092	87.20	21.13	4 966.0	2 303	91.06	21.14
2	2 045.2	2 082	81.31	21.44	2 471.7	2 296	85.21	21.34
4	1 005.8	2 062	75.27	22.11	1 224.8	2 281	79.27	21.74
6	659.4	2 041	71.62	22.82	809.2	2 264	75.72	22.19
8	486.2	2 020	68.94	23.60	601.5	2 250	73.14	22.61
10	382.2	1 999	66.79	24.45	477.0	2 235	71.11	23.08
12	313.0	1 977	64.97	25.37	394.1	2 214	69.41	23.54
14	263.5	1 954	63.38	26.39	334.7	2 203	67.94	24.03
16	226.4	1 932	61.95	27.45	290.6	2 189	66.65	24.53
18	197.8	1 909	60.64	28.62	256.2	2 174	65.48	25.06
20	174.8	1 885	59.43	29.87	228.7	2 158	64.42	25.59
30	106.6	1 765	54.31	36.78	141.0	2 082	60.12	28.43
40	75.43	1 655	50.33	41.39	107.2	2 010	56.02	31.14
50	59.77	1 575	47.31	41.57	84.58	1 946	54.17	33.11
60	51.19	1 523	45.24	39.68	70.55	1 893	52.01	34.06
80	42.53	1 473	42.39	35.33	55.02	1 823	48.78	33.82
100	38.18	1 461	40.54	32.12	47.02	1 788	46.51	32.58
150	32.87	1 493	37.68	27.78	37.78	1 781	42.93	29.45
200	30.17	1 559	35.86	25.71	33.54	1 826	40.71	27.36
250	28.41	1 637	34.51	24.48	31.00	1 891	39.12	26.01
300	27.13	1 722	33.42	23.64	29.25	1 969	37.87	25.10
400	25.33	1 899	31.72	22.53	26.90	2 132	35.96	23.93
500	24.08	2 079	30.39	21.84	25.33	2 305	34.51	23.17
600	23.14	2 261	29.30	21.47	24.18	2 482	33.33	22.63
700					23.29	2 660	32.34	22.29
	T=70 °K				T=80 °K			
1	5 804.8	2 515	94.32	21.31	6 641.6	2 730	97.19	21.64
2	2 894.9	2 509	88.50	21.45	3 316.0	2 726	91.38	21.75
4	1 440.0	2 497	82.61	21.79	1 653.3	2 716	85.53	21.95
6	955.3	2 486	79.11	22.01	1 099.2	2 707	82.06	22.16
8	713.0	2 474	76.60	22.30	822.2	2 698	79.56	22.36
10	567.7	2 462	74.62	22.60	656.2	2 689	77.63	22.57
12	470.9	2 451	72.98	22.89	545.5	2 679	76.02	22.78
14	401.8	2 439	71.57	23.20	466.5	2 671	74.65	22.99
16	350.1	2 428	70.34	23.50	407.3	2 662	73.45	23.20
18	309.9	2 417	69.23	23.81	361.4	2 653	72.38	23.41
20	277.8	2 405	68.24	24.13	324.5	2 644	71.42	23.62

continued

p, bar	V	I	S	C_p	V	I	S	C_p
30	182.1	2 350	64.26	25.72	214.8	2 602	67.62	24.67
40	135.0	2 299	61.29	27.27	160.5	2 563	64.81	25.69
50	107.3	2 251	58.89	28.64	128.3	2 527	62.57	26.62
60	89.51	2 209	56.90	29.69	107.3	2 494	60.70	27.43
80	68.52	2 145	53.75	30.71	81.82	2 440	57.70	28.54
100	57.06	2 104	51.39	30.71	67.36	2 403	55.38	29.02
150	43.53	2 075	47.48	29.40	49.74	2 367	51.36	28.74
200	37.46	2 103	44.98	27.95	41.76	2 383	48.72	27.95
250	33.96	2 155	43.19	26.77	37.20	2 425	46.80	27.13
300	31.62	2 222	41.50	25.87	34.21	2 483	45.30	26.38
400	28.61	2 375	39.71	24.66	30.45	2 625	43.04	25.23
500	26.67	2 540	38.14	23.89	28.11	2 783	41.36	24.45
600	25.29	2 712	36.87	23.31	26.47	2 948	40.02	23.88
800	23.40	3 060	34.92	22.50	24.26	3 288	37.96	22.99
1000					22.84	3 635	36.42	22.32
	T=90 °K				T=100 °K			
1	7 477.2	2 949	99.76	22.09	8 311.8	3 172	102.11	22.63
2	3 735.8	2 945	93.96	22.17	4 154.7	3 169	96.32	22.69
4	1 865.2	2 938	88.13	22.33	2 076.3	3 163	90.50	22.82
6	1 230.3	2 930	84.69	22.49	1 383.5	3 156	87.08	22.94
8	930.2	2 923	82.22	22.64	1 037.3	3 150	84.63	23.06
10	743.3	2 916	80.30	22.80	829.5	3 145	82.72	23.19
12	618.8	2 908	78.71	22.96	691.1	3 139	81.15	23.31
14	529.8	2 901	77.36	23.12	592.3	3 133	79.81	23.43
16	463.2	2 894	76.18	23.27	518.2	3 127	78.65	23.55
18	411.4	2 887	75.14	23.43	460.6	3 122	77.61	23.67
20	370.0	2 880	74.19	23.58	414.6	3 116	76.68	23.79
30	246.2	2 847	70.49	24.34	276.7	3 090	73.06	24.37
40	184.7	2 816	67.79	25.07	208.2	3 065	70.42	24.93
50	148.2	2 788	65.64	25.74	167.4	3 043	68.33	25.44
60	124.1	2 762	63.85	26.35	140.3	3 023	66.60	25.92
80	94.64	2 719	60.98	27.32	107.0	2 988	63.82	26.73
100	77.55	2 687	58.73	27.92	87.51	2 962	61.63	27.31
150	56.13	2 652	54.71	28.19	62.57	2 931	57.66	27.88
200	46.28	2 662	52.00	27.82	50.90	2 939	54.93	27.78
250	40.65	2 698	50.00	27.32	44.21	2 971	52.88	27.50
300	36.98	2 750	48.42	26.79	39.86	3 019	51.26	27.17
400	32.42	2 880	46.04	25.83	34.48	3 141	48.80	26.46
500	29.64	3 030	44.28	25.09	31.23	3 284	46.95	25.81
600	27.71	3 190	42.87	24.53	29.01	3 438	45.49	25.30
800	25.16	3 522	40.70	23.68	26.11	3 762	43.24	24.53
1000	23.53	3 861	39.07	22.93	24.26	4 094	41.53	23.84
	T=120 °K				T=140 °K			
1	9 979.4	3 637	106.35	23.80	11 645	4 124	110.11	24.92
2	4 990.8	3 635	100.57	23.84	5 325.5	4 122	104.33	24.96
4	2 496.6	3 631	94.77	23.93	2 915.5	4 120	98.54	25.02
6	1 665.3	3 627	91.36	24.01	1 945.6	4 117	95.15	25.08
8	1 249.7	3 623	88.93	24.09	1 460.7	4 114	92.73	25.14
10	1 000.3	3 619	87.04	24.18	1 169.7	4 112	90.85	25.20
12	834.2	3 615	85.49	24.26	975.8	4 109	89.30	25.25
14	715.5	3 612	84.17	24.34	837.3	4 107	88.00	25.31
16	626.5	3 608	83.02	24.42	733.5	4 105	86.86	25.37
18	557.3	3 604	82.01	24.50	652.7	4 102	85.86	25.42
20	502.0	3 600	81.10	24.58	588.1	4 100	84.96	25.48
30	336.3	3 583	77.55	24.96	394.5	4 089	81.46	25.75
40	253.6	3 568	75.00	25.32	297.9	4 080	78.96	26.01
50	204.3	3 554	72.99	25.66	240.0	4 072	76.99	26.25
60	171.5	3 551	71.33	25.97	201.6	4 065	75.37	26.47
80	130.9	3 520	68.67	26.54	153.8	4 054	72.79	26.88
100	106.8	3 505	66.58	27.01	125.3	4 046	70.76	27.24
150	75.36	3 488	62.73	27.76	87.86	4 044	67.03	27.92
200	60.27	3 498	60.02	28.02	69.55	4 060	64.36	28.29

continued

p, bar	V	I	S	C_p	V	I	S	C_p
250	51.50	3 527	57.95	28.03	58.83	4 091	62.31	28.45
300	45.80	3 571	56.30	27.96	51.81	4 135	60.65	28.51
400	38.78	3 684	53.75	27.72	43.19	4 246	58.08	28.51
500	34.57	3 818	51.81	27.40	38.04	4 376	56.12	28.41
600	31.74	3 968	50.27	27.07	34.53	4 517	54.54	28.27
800	28.11	4 273	47.89	26.52	30.18	4 818	52.10	27.94
1000	25.81	4 594	46.09	26.09	27.45	5 132	50.24	27.67
		T=160 °K				T=180 °K		
1	13 311	4 632	113.49	25.87	14 975	5 158	116.60	26.66
2	6 659.2	4 631	107.72	25.89	7 492.4	5 157	110.83	26.68
4	3 333.5	4 630	101.94	25.94	3 751.0	5 156	105.05	26.72
6	2 325.0	4 628	98.55	25.98	2 503.9	5 155	101.66	26.75
8	1 670.8	4 627	96.14	26.03	1 880.3	5 155	99.25	26.78
10	1 338.3	4 625	94.26	26.07	1 506.2	5 154	97.38	26.82
12	1 116.6	4 624	92.73	26.11	1 256.8	5 153	95.85	26.85
14	958.3	4 622	91.43	26.16	1 078.7	5 153	94.55	26.89
16	839.6	4 621	90.30	26.20	945.1	5 152	93.43	26.92
18	747.2	4 619	89.30	26.24	841.2	5 151	92.44	26.95
20	673.4	4 618	88.40	26.28	758.2	5 151	91.55	26.98
30	452.0	4 612	84.94	26.49	508.9	5 148	88.11	27.14
40	341.4	4 607	82.47	26.68	384.4	5 147	85.65	27.29
50	275.1	4 603	80.53	26.86	309.8	5 146	83.73	27.43
60	231.1	4 600	78.93	27.03	260.1	5 146	82.16	27.56
80	176.2	4 596	76.40	27.84	198.2	5 147	79.65	27.80
100	143.4	4 595	74.41	27.61	161.1	5 151	77.70	28.02
150	100.1	4 605	70.76	28.17	112.0	5 171	74.10	28.47
200	78.72	4 629	68.15	28.55	87.74	5 202	71.53	28.81
250	66.11	4 664	66.12	28.77	73.31	5 242	69.54	29.04
300	57.82	4 709	64.48	28.88	68.79	5 290	67.91	29.18
400	47.61	4 821	61.91	28.98	52.01	5 404	65.36	29.33
500	41.53	4 951	59.95	29.02	45.03	5 535	63.40	29.41
600	37.46	5 090	59.36	29.01	40.36	5 675	61.82	29.46
800	32.30	5 387	55.89	28.88	34.44	5 971	59.33	29.47
1000	29.12	5 697	54.00	28.71	30.80	6 278	57.43	29.39
		T=200 °K				T=220 °K		
1	16 640	5 697	119.43	27.29	18 303	6 248	122.06	27.79
2	8 825.2	5 697	113.66	27.31	9 147.7	6 248	116.29	27.80
4	4 168.0	5 697	107.89	27.33	4 584.8	6 249	110.52	27.82
6	2 782.3	5 696	104.50	27.36	3 060.5	6 249	107.14	27.85
8	2 089.5	5 696	102.10	27.39	2 298.4	6 249	104.74	27.87
10	1 673.8	5 696	100.23	27.42	1 841.1	6 250	102.87	27.89
12	1 396.7	5 696	98.71	27.44	1 536.3	6 250	101.35	27.91
14	1 198.8	5 696	97.41	27.47	1 318.6	6 250	100.06	27.93
16	1 050.3	5 696	96.39	27.50	1 155.3	6 251	98.94	27.96
18	934.9	5 696	95.30	27.52	1 023.3	6 251	97.95	27.98
20	842.5	5 696	94.41	27.55	926.7	6 252	97.06	28.00
30	565.5	5 697	90.99	27.67	621.9	6 254	93.65	28.10
40	427.1	5 697	88.55	27.79	469.6	6 258	91.22	28.20
50	344.2	5 699	86.64	27.90	378.3	6 261	89.32	28.29
60	388.9	5 701	85.08	28.01	317.4	6 265	87.77	28.38
80	219.9	5 707	82.60	28.21	241.5	6 275	85.30	28.54
100	178.6	5 715	80.66	28.38	196.0	6 286	83.38	28.68
150	123.8	5 743	77.11	28.75	135.5	6 321	79.86	28.99
200	96.64	5 780	74.57	29.04	105.4	6 363	77.35	29.24
250	80.43	5 825	72.60	29.26	87.48	6 412	75.40	29.43
300	69.70	5 876	70.98	29.40	75.57	6 466	73.80	29.58
400	56.42	5 993	68.45	29.57	60.79	6 587	71.28	29.75
500	48.51	6 125	66.51	29.66	51.98	6 721	69.34	29.84
600	43.24	6 267	64.93	29.73	46.11	6 864	67.77	29.91
800	36.58	6 563	62.44	29.82	38.73	7 162	65.30	30.09
1000	32.50	6 870	60.54	29.81	34.21	7 469	63.40	30.08

continued

p, bar	V	I	S	C_p	V	I	S	C_p
	T=240 °K				T=260 °K			
1	19 967	6 807	124.48	28.18	21 681	7 375	126.76	28.53
2	9 990.0	6 808	118.71	28.19	10 822	7 375	120.99	28.53
4	5 001.3	6 808	112.94	28.20	5 417.8	7 376	115.22	28.55
6	3 338.5	6 809	109.57	28.22	3 616.3	7 377	111.84	28.57
8	2 507.1	6 810	107.17	28.24	2 715.6	7 378	109.45	28.58
10	2 008.2	6 811	105.80	28.26	2 175.2	7 379	107.59	28.60
12	1 675.7	6 811	103.78	28.28	1 814.9	7 381	106.06	28.61
14	1 438.1	6 812	102.49	28.30	1 557.6	7 382	104.78	28.63
16	1 260.0	6 813	101.37	28.31	1 364.6	7 383	103.66	28.64
18	1 121.4	6 814	100.39	28.33	1 214.5	7 384	102.67	28.66
20	1 010.6	6 815	99.50	28.35	1 094.4	7 385	101.79	28.67
30	678.1	6 819	96.10	28.48	734.2	7 391	98.39	28.74
40	511.9	6 824	93.67	28.51	554.1	7 398	95.97	28.81
50	412.3	6 829	91.78	28.59	446.1	7 404	94.09	28.87
60	345.8	6 835	90.24	28.66	374.1	7 411	92.55	28.94
80	262.9	6 848	87.79	28.90	284.2	7 426	90.11	29.05
100	213.2	6 862	85.87	28.92	230.3	7 443	88.21	29.16
150	147.1	6 902	82.38	29.18	158.5	7 488	84.73	29.38
200	114.1	6 949	79.89	29.39	122.8	7 539	82.26	29.56
250	94.47	7 001	77.95	29.56	101.4	7 594	80.83	29.71
300	81.40	7 058	76.36	29.70	87.18	7 653	78.75	29.84
400	65.14	7 182	78.86	29.87	69.46	7 781	76.27	30.01
500	55.48	7 318	71.98	29.97	58.87	7 919	74.34	30.10
600	48.98	7 462	70.37	30.08	51.83	8 064	72.78	30.17
800	40.86	7 763	67.91	30.15	42.99	8 368	70.33	30.27
1000	35.90	8 072	66.01	30.28	37.60	8 678	68.44	30.37
	T=280 °K				T=300 °K			
1	23 294	7 946	128.37	28.70	24 958	8 522	180.86	28.85
2	11 654	7 946	123.41	28.71	12 466	8 523	125.09	28.86
4	5 834.0	7 948	117.34	28.72	6 250.2	8 524	119.33	28.87
6	3 894.0	7 949	113.96	28.73	4 171.6	8 526	115.95	28.88
8	2 924.0	7 950	111.57	28.75	3 132.3	8 528	118.55	28.89
10	2 342.0	7 952	109.71	28.76	2 506.8	8 529	111.70	28.90
12	1 954.0	7 953	108.19	28.77	2 093.1	8 531	110.18	28.92
14	1 676.9	7 955	106.90	28.78	1 796.1	8 533	108.89	28.93
16	1 469.0	7 956	105.78	28.80	1 573.4	8 534	107.77	28.94
18	1 307.4	7 958	104.80	28.81	1 400.2	8 536	106.79	28.95
20	1 178.1	7 959	103.92	28.82	1 261.7	8 538	105.91	28.96
30	790.1	7 966	100.52	28.88	846.0	8 546	102.52	29.01
40	596.2	7 974	98.11	28.94	638.2	8 555	100.11	29.07
50	479.8	7 982	96.23	29.00	513.5	8 564	98.53	29.11
60	402.3	7 990	94.69	29.05	430.4	8 573	96.70	29.15
80	305.4	8 007	92.26	29.15	326.5	8 592	94.37	29.24
100	247.3	8 025	90.37	29.24	264.3	8 612	92.39	29.32
150	170.0	8 075	86.91	29.43	181.4	8 665	88.94	29.51
200	131.4	8 129	84.45	29.59	140.0	8 742	86.49	29.68
250	108.3	8 187	82.58	29.69	115.2	8 783	84.58	29.75
300	92.94	8 249	80.96	29.82	98.67	8 877	83.02	29.85
400	73.77	8 380	78.48	30.00	78.06	8 981	80.55	30.00
500	62.30	8 520	76.57	30.09	65.72	9 153	78.65	30.09
600	54.67	8 667	75.01	30.16	57.51	9 271	77.09	30.15
800	45.10	8 972	72.57	30.25	47.22	9 578	74.66	30.24
1000	39.29	9 284	70.69	30.35	40.98	9 892	72.78	30.33
	T=350 °K				T=400 °K			
1	29 116	9 971	135.34	29.09	33 273	11 428	189.33	29.19
2	14 565	9 972	129.57	29.09	16 645	11 429	133.47	29.19
4	7 290.4	9 974	123.81	29.10	8 390.3	11 432	127.70	29.20
6	4 866.4	9 976	120.43	29.11	6 558.8	11 434	124.33	29.20
8	3 652.8	9 978	118.04	29.12	4 172.1	11 436	121.94	29.21
10	2 925.3	9 980	116.18	29.13	3 341.6	11 439	120.08	29.21
12	2 440.3	9 982	114.66	29.13	2 787.3	11 441	118.56	29.22

continued

p, bar	V	I	S	C_p	V	I	S	C_p
14	2 093.9	9 985	113.38	29.14	2 301.1	11 444	117.28	29.22
16	1 834.1	9 987	112.27	29.15	2 094.5	11 446	116.17	29.23
18	1 632.0	9 989	111.28	29.16	1 863.5	11 449	115.19	29.23
20	1 470.3	9 991	110.40	29.16	1 678.8	11 454	114.31	29.24
30	935.4	10 002	107.02	29.20	1 124.5	11 463	110.93	29.27
40	742.9	10 012	104.62	29.24	847.3	11 476	108.58	29.29
50	597.4	10 023	102.75	29.27	681.0	11 488	108.66	29.32
60	500.0	10 035	101.22	29.30	570.2	11 501	105.14	29.34
80	379.2	10 057	98.80	29.37	431.7	11 526	102.73	29.39
100	306.5	10 080	96.93	29.43	348.5	11 552	100.86	29.44
150	209.6	10 141	93.51	29.55	237.7	11 618	97.45	29.53
200	161.2	10 204	91.07	29.66	182.3	11 686	95.03	29.61
250	132.2	10 281	89.18	29.75	149.1	11 756	93.15	29.68
300	112.9	10 338	87.63	29.82	127.0	11 826	91.61	29.74
400	88.72	10 479	85.19	29.95	99.30	11 974	89.18	29.84
500	74.23	10 626	83.29	30.03	82.68	12 124	87.30	29.92
600	64.57	10 777	81.65	30.09	71.60	12 278	85.76	29.97
800	52.47	11 088	79.33	30.17	60.49	12 513	83.89	30.04
1000	45.17	11 405	47.46	30.22	51.10	12 832	81.92	30.08
		T=450 °K				T=500 °K		
1	37 431	12 883	142.66	29.24	41 588	14 350	145.75	29.27
2	18 724	12 889	136.90	29.24	20 803	14 352	139.97	29.27
4	9 369.9	12 892	131.13	29.25	10 410	14 355	134.21	29.27
6	6 252.1	12 894	127.76	29.25	6 945.2	14 358	130.85	29.27
8	4 693.1	12 897	125.37	29.26	5 213.0	14 360	128.45	29.28
10	3 757.7	12 900	123.51	29.26	4 173.7	14 363	126.60	29.28
12	3 134.2	12 902	121.99	29.27	3 480.9	14 366	125.08	29.28
14	2 688.7	12 905	120.71	29.27	2 986.0	14 369	123.80	29.29
16	2 354.7	12 908	119.60	29.27	2 614.8	14 372	122.69	29.29
18	2 094.9	12 911	118.62	29.28	2 326.1	14 375	121.71	29.29
20	1 887.0	12 913	117.74	29.28	2 095.1	14 378	120.83	29.30
30	1 263.4	12 927	114.36	29.30	1 402.3	14 392	117.45	29.31
40	951.6	12 940	111.97	29.32	1 055.8	14 406	115.06	29.33
50	764.6	12 954	110.10	29.34	848.0	14 421	113.20	29.34
60	640.0	12 967	108.58	29.36	709.4	14 435	111.68	29.36
80	484.0	12 995	106.18	29.40	536.2	14 464	109.28	29.39
100	390.4	13 022	104.31	29.43	432.2	14 494	107.42	29.41
150	265.7	13 093	100.92	29.51	293.6	14 587	104.03	29.48
200	203.4	13 164	98.50	29.57	224.3	14 642	101.62	29.53
250	166.0	13 237	96.63	29.63	182.7	14 717	99.75	29.57
300	141.0	13 312	95.10	29.65	155.0	14 794	98.22	29.61
400	109.8	13 468	92.68	29.76	120.3	14 948	95.81	29.68
500	91.10	13 617	90.80	29.82	99.48	15 105	93.94	29.73
600	78.59	13 773	89.27	29.87	85.57	15 264	92.42	29.77
800	62.93	14 090	86.87	29.93	68.13	15 584	90.02	29.83
1000	53.48	14 412	85.01	29.96	57.63	15 907	88.16	29.85

Thermodynamic properties of parahydrogen at different temperatures and pressures
V(cm³/mole), I (J/mole), S and C_p (J/mole · deg) [5, 7]

p, bar	V	I	S	C_p	V	I	S	C_p
		T=14 °K				T=16 °K		
1	26.23	−621	10.02	13.23	26.82	−593	11.90	14.57
2	26.20	−618	9.99	13.21	26.78	−591	11.87	14.52
4	26.14	−614	9.96	13.17	26.71	−586	11.81	14.44
6					26.64	−582	11.75	14.36
8					26.58	−578	11.69	14.28
10					26.51	−573	11.63	14.20
12					26.45	−569	11.57	14.13
14					26.39	−564	11.52	14.06

continued

p, bar	V	I	S	C_p	V	I	S	C_p
16					26.33	−560	11.46	13.99
18					26.27	−556	11.41	13.92
20					26.21	−551	11.35	13.86
30					25.94	−529	11.10	13.57
40					25.68	−507	10.86	13.31
50					25.45	−465	10.64	13.08
60					25.23	−463	10.43	12.87
		T=18 °K				T=20 °K		
1	27.51	−562	13.75	16.32	28.35	−526	15.71	19.03
2	27.47	−560	13.71	16.25	28.29	−524	15.66	18.94
4	27.38	−556	13.64	16.13	28.19	−520	15.57	18.75
6	27.30	−552	13.56	16.01	28.09	−516	15.49	18.58
8	27.22	−548	13.49	15.90	27.99	−512	15.40	18.42
10	27.14	−543	13.42	15.79	27.89	−508	15.32	18.27
12	27.07	−539	13.36	15.69	27.80	−504	15.24	18.12
14	27.00	−535	13.29	15.59	27.71	−500	15.16	17.98
16	26.92	−531	13.23	15.50	27.62	−496	15.08	17.85
18	26.85	−526	13.16	15.40	27.54	−492	15.01	17.72
20	26.79	−522	13.10	15.32	27.46	−488	14.94	17.61
30	26.46	−501	12.60	14.92	27.08	−468	14.58	17.08
40	26.17	−480	12.53	14.58	26.74	−447	14.28	16.64
50	25.91	−458	12.28	14.28	26.43	−426	13.99	16.27
60	25.66	−437	12.04	14.01	26.15	−405	13.72	15.95
80	25.22	−393	11.61	13.55	25.66	−363	13.24	15.42
100	24.84	−350	11.23	13.17	25.23	−321	12.81	14.99
150					24.35	−215	11.91	14.17
200					23.66	−110	11.17	13.58
		T=22 °K				T=24 °K		
1	1 609.7	422	62.41	23.03	1 875.5	468	64.40	22.59
2	29.31	−484	17.54	22.09	869.8	434	57.73	25.31
4	29.17	−480	17.43	21.79	30.42	−433	19.47	25.29
6	29.04	−477	17.32	21.52	30.24	−431	19.33	24.82
8	28.91	−473	17.22	21.27	30.06	−428	19.20	24.39
10	28.79	−470	17.12	21.04	29.90	−425	19.08	24.01
12	28.67	−466	17.02	20.82	29.74	−422	18.95	23.66
14	28.56	−462	16.93	20.62	29.59	−419	18.84	23.35
16	28.45	−459	16.83	20.43	29.45	−415	18.72	23.05
18	28.35	−455	16.75	20.25	29.32	−412	18.62	22.78
20	28.25	−451	16.66	20.08	29.19	−409	18.51	22.53
30	27.78	−432	16.26	19.36	28.61	−391	18.03	21.50
40	27.38	−413	15.89	18.78	28.12	−373	17.61	20.72
50	27.02	−393	15.57	18.31	27.69	−354	17.24	20.11
60	26.70	−372	15.27	17.91	27.31	−335	16.90	19.60
80	26.13	−331	14.73	17.27	26.66	−295	16.30	18.81
100	25.65	−290	14.25	16.77	26.12	−255	15.78	18.21
150	24.69	−186	13.27	15.87	25.05	−153	14.71	17.17
200	23.94	− 82	12.47	15.25	24.24	− 50	13.85	16.47
250	23.32	21	11.79	14.77	23.59	52	13.13	15.96
300					23.03	153	12.50	15.55
		T=26 °K				T=28 °K		
1	2 056.6	513	66.22	22.29	2 235.0	558	67.88	22.05
2	970.6	483	59.74	24.33	1 067.6	532	61.54	23.66
4	414.7	410	52.07	32.45	476.4	472	54.34	28.86
6	31.82	−377	21.51	29.21	34.15	−311	23.95	37.32
8	31.56	−375	21.33	28.38	33.68	−312	23.67	35.07
10	31.32	−373	21.16	27.67	33.27	−312	23.42	33.36
12	31.09	−371	21.00	27.04	32.91	−312	23.19	32.00
14	30.89	−369	20.85	26.49	32.59	−311	22.98	30.89
16	30.69	−366	20.71	26.01	32.29	−310	22.79	29.95
18	30.51	−364	20.57	25.57	32.02	−308	22.61	29.16

continued

p, bar	V	I	S	C_p	V	I	S	C_p
20	30.33	−361	20.44	25.17	31.77	−307	22.44	28.47
30	29.58	−346	19.86	23.63	30.75	−296	21.72	26.00
40	28.97	−330	19.37	22.54	29.96	−282	21.13	24.44
50	28.45	−312	18.94	21.72	29.32	−266	20.63	23.33
60	28.00	−294	18.55	21.07	28.78	−250	20.19	22.49
80	27.25	−256	17.88	20.09	27.90	−214	19.43	21.26
100	26.63	−217	17.31	19.37	27.19	−177	18.80	20.39
150	25.45	−118	16.15	18.15	25.87	−79	17.54	18.97
200	24.57	−16	15.23	17.36	24.91	20	16.57	18.06
250	23.86	85	14.47	16.78	24.15	120	15.76	17.43
300	23.27	185	13.81	16.34	23.53	220	15.06	16.94
		T=30 °K				T=32 °K		
1	2 411.4	602	69.42	21.87	2 586.2	645	70.83	21.71
2	1 161.9	579	63.17	23.17	1 254.3	625	64.66	22.79
4	532.5	528	56.28	26.90	585.2	580	57.98	25.64
6	316.0	465	51.44	33.96	358.4	528	53.50	30.13
8	196.4	374	46.74	55.66	240.2	464	49.66	38.60
10	36.46	−234	26.11	46.67	160.9	373	45.59	63.42
12	35.69	−239	25.71	41.93	42.07	−125	29.40	92.89
14	35.07	−242	25.37	38.77	39.69	−147	28.45	62.67
16	34.54	−244	25.08	36.47	38.30	−159	27.83	51.79
18	34.09	−245	24.82	34.71	37.30	−167	27.36	45.83
20	33.70	−245	24.58	33.30	36.52	−172	26.98	41.96
30	32.19	−241	23.63	28.96	34.05	−180	25.62	32.99
40	31.14	−231	22.91	26.61	32.57	−176	24.71	29.25
50	30.33	−218	22.32	25.08	31.51	−166	24.00	27.07
60	29.67	−203	21.81	23.97	30.68	−154	23.41	25.61
80	28.62	−170	20.96	22.44	29.42	−125	22.45	23.69
100	27.80	−135	20.27	21.40	28.48	−92	21.68	22.44
150	26.32	−41	18.90	19.75	26.81	−1	20.20	20.55
200	25.27	57	17.86	18.74	25.66	94	19.09	19.42
250	24.46	155	17.00	18.03	24.78	191	18.19	18.65
300	23.80	254	16.27	17.50	24.08	289	17.42	18.07
400					22.97	483	16.14	17.30
		T=34 °K				T=36 °K		
1	2 759.8	689	72.13	21.50	2 932.4	732	73.36	21.48
2	1 345.2	670	66.02	22.49	1 435.0	715	67.30	22.25
4	635.8	630	59.50	24.75	684.8	680	60.89	24.09
6	397.0	586	55.25	27.94	433.3	640	56.80	26.51
8	275.0	535	51.79	32.85	306.0	598	53.58	29.84
10	198.6	473	48.60	41.63	228.0	549	50.76	34.73
12	142.7	390	45.18	62.40	174.0	492	48.06	42.65
14	91.25	245	40.22	171.37	133.1	421	45.26	57.23
16	50.25	7	32.83	160.93	99.25	328	42.03	87.80
18	44.22	−46	30.98	83.42	71.81	209	38.24	128.34
20	41.66	−70	30.04	63.49	56.14	110	35.14	115.08
30	36.58	−108	27.78	38.91	40.30	−21	30.24	47.97
40	34.35	−114	26.57	32.57	36.62	−44	28.55	36.79
50	32.91	−110	25.70	29.40	34.60	−48	27.46	32.13
60	31.85	−101	25.01	27.43	33.22	−44	26.63	29.47
80	30.32	−76	23.92	25.02	31.33	−24	25.40	26.44
100	29.21	−45	23.06	23.54	30.02	3	24.44	24.68
150	27.33	41	21.46	21.39	27.89	85	22.71	22.25
200	26.07	134	20.28	20.15	26.50	176	21.45	20.90
250	25.12	230	19.33	19.30	25.48	269	20.45	20.00
300	24.37	326	18.52	18.69	24.67	364	19.61	19.34
400	23.21	518	17.19	17.86	23.45	555	18.23	18.47

continued

p, bar	V	I	S	C_p	V	I	S	C_p
		T=38 °K				T=40 °K		
1	3 104.1	775	74.54	21.39	3 275.2	818	75.63	21.34
2	1 523.8	759	68.52	22.05	1 611.8	803	69.63	21.91
4	732.7	727	62.20	23.59	779.6	774	63.39	23.21
6	468.0	692	58.22	25.50	501.5	743	59.50	24.76
8	334.7	655	55.16	27.94	361.9	710	56.55	26.65
10	253.8	614	52.55	31.18	277.6	674	54.08	29.00
12	198.9	569	50.18	35.66	220.8	636	51.87	31.98
14	158.7	517	47.89	42.14	179.8	595	49.86	35.84
16	127.5	458	45.58	51.85	148.5	550	47.92	40.87
18	102.3	390	43.18	65.93	123.9	500	46.00	47.36
20	82.41	313	40.69	81.37	104.0	446	44.09	55.19
30	46.20	86	33.16	59.36	55.08	211	36.36	54.08
40	39.62	37	30.68	41.89	43.64	123	32.98	46.97
50	36.66	20	29.29	35.24	39.21	93	31.17	38.52
60	34.81	17	28.30	31.71	36.90	83	29.98	34.07
80	32.45	30	26.87	27.92	33.72	87	28.34	29.46
100	30.91	53	25.83	25.85	31.88	106	27.17	27.03
150	28.48	130	23.96	23.12	29.12	178	25.16	23.90
200	26.95	218	22.63	21.66	27.44	262	23.74	22.42
250	25.85	310	21.57	20.70	26.24	352	22.64	21.41
300	24.99	403	20.69	20.00	25.32	444	21.72	20.66
400	23.70	592	19.26	19.09	23.96	631	20.25	19.72
500					20.95	813	19.08	19.20
		T=50 °K				T=60 °K		
1	4 123.9	1 030	80.37	21.25	4 966.1	1 244	84.27	21.59
2	2 045.2	1 020	74.47	21.56	2 471.8	1 236	78.42	21.79
4	1 005.9	1 000	68.44	22.22	1 224.8	1 221	74.48	22.20
6	659.5	979	64.79	22.94	809.3	1 206	68.93	22.62
8	486.3	958	62.12	23.72	601.6	1 191	66.35	23.06
10	382.3	937	59.96	24.57	477.1	1 176	64.32	23.51
12	313.1	915	58.14	25.48	394.1	1 170	62.62	23.99
14	263.6	893	56.55	26.48	335.0	1 145	61.16	24.47
16	226.5	870	55.12	27.55	290.7	1 130	59.86	24.98
18	197.7	847	53.81	28.71	256.3	1 115	58.70	25.59
20	174.7	824	52.60	29.95	228.8	1 099	57.64	26.04
30	106.8	704	47.49	36.74	147.1	1 024	53.33	28.85
40	75.60	596	43.54	41.25	107.3	952	50.05	31.53
50	59.91	516	40.60	41.39	84.66	888	47.40	33.48
60	51.32	464	38.46	39.48	70.63	835	45.24	34.40
80	42.63	415	35.62	35.14	55.09	766	42.02	34.14
100	38.26	403	33.78	31.94	47.07	731	39.75	32.88
150	32.92	436	30.92	27.63	37.82	725	36.18	29.75
200	30.20	503	29.10	25.56	33.58	770	33.97	27.66
250	28.44	582	27.75	24.34	31.03	836	32.38	26.32
300	27.15	666	26.66	23.53	29.27	912	31.13	25.42
400	25.35	843	24.96	22.43	26.91	1 077	29.22	24.25
500	24.09	1 024	23.63	21.70	25.34	1 250	27.76	23.50
600	23.15	1 205	22.55	21.36	24.19	1 427	26.59	22.96
		T=70 °K				T=80 °K		
1	5 804.9	1 464	87.65	22.44	5 641.7	1 694	90.73	23.72
2	2 894.9	1 458	81.83	22.57	3 316.0	1 689	84.92	23.83
4	1 440.1	1 445	75.94	22.85	1 653.3	1 680	79.06	24.03
6	955.3	1 434	72.44	23.13	1 099.2	1 671	75.60	24.23
8	713.0	1 423	69.93	23.42	822.3	1 662	73.11	24.44
10	567.7	1 411	67.95	23.71	656.2	1 652	71.17	24.65
12	471.0	1 400	66.31	24.01	545.6	1 643	69.56	24.86
14	401.8	1 388	64.90	24.31	466.6	1 634	68.19	25.07
16	350.2	1 377	63.67	24.62	407.4	1 626	66.99	25.23
18	310.0	1 365	62.57	24.93	361.4	1 617	65.92	25.49
20	277.9	1 354	61.57	25.24	324.6	1 608	64.96	25.70
30	182.2	1 299	57.59	26.82	214.9	1 566	61.15	26.74

continued

p, bar	V	I	S	C_p	V	I	S	C_p
40	135.0	1 248	54.62	28.36	160.5	1 527	58.35	27.75
50	107.4	1 201	52.23	29.72	128.4	1 491	56.11	28.68
60	89.56	1 159	50.24	30.77	107.3	1 456	54.24	29.48
80	68.57	1 094	47.09	31.78	81.85	1 405	51.24	30.59
100	57.11	1 055	44.74	31.77	67.40	1 367	48.92	31.06
150	43.57	1 027	40.82	30.44	49.76	1 333	44.91	30.78
200	37.49	1 054	38.34	28.98	41.79	1 349	42.27	29.98
250	33.98	1 107	36.55	27.81	37.22	1 391	40.35	29.15
300	31.64	1 179	35.16	26.91	34.23	1 450	38.85	28.41
400	28.62	1 327	33.07	25.70	30.47	1 591	36.60	27.26
500	26.68	1 492	31.49	24.93	28.13	1 749	34.92	26.48
600	25.30	1 663	30.23	24.36	26.47	1 915	33.58	25.91
800	23.41	2 012	28.28	23.55	24.26	2 255	31.51	25.03
	T=90 °K				T=100 °K			
1	7 477.2	1 939	93.61	25.33	8 311.2	2 201	96.37	27.07
2	3 735.8	1 935	87.81	25.41	4 154.7	2 198	90.58	27.13
4	1 865.2	1 928	81.98	25.57	2 076.3	2 192	84.76	27.26
6	1 241.8	1 920	78.53	25.72	1 383.6	2 186	81.33	27.38
8	930.2	1 913	76.07	25.88	1 037.3	2 180	78.88	27.51
10	743.3	1 906	74.15	26.04	829.6	2 174	76.97	27.63
12	618.8	1 898	72.56	26.19	691.1	2 168	75.40	27.75
14	529.9	1 891	71.21	26.35	592.3	2 162	74.07	27.87
16	463.2	1 884	70.03	26.51	518.2	2 157	72.90	27.99
18	411.4	1 877	69.99	26.66	460.6	2 151	71.87	28.11
20	370.1	1 870	68.04	26.82	414.6	2 145	70.94	28.23
30	246.2	1 837	64.34	27.57	276.8	2 119	67.31	28.81
40	184.8	1 807	61.64	28.29	208.2	2 095	64.68	29.36
50	148.2	1 778	59.50	28.97	167.4	2 072	62.59	29.88
60	124.2	1 753	57.71	29.58	140.4	2 052	60.86	30.35
80	94.67	1 710	54.83	30.54	107.1	2 018	58.07	31.16
100	77.57	1 678	52.58	31.13	87.53	1 992	55.89	31.73
150	56.15	1 643	48.57	31.41	62.59	1 962	51.92	32.30
200	46.30	1 653	45.86	31.03	50.92	1 970	49.19	32.20
250	40.67	1 690	43.86	30.52	44.23	2 002	47.15	31.92
300	36.99	1 742	42.29	29.99	39.87	2 050	45.53	31.58
400	32.43	1 873	39.91	29.03	34.49	2 172	43.06	30.88
500	29.65	2 023	38.14	28.29	31.24	2 316	41.22	30.23
600	27.72	2 183	36.73	27.74	29.02	2 470	39.76	29.72
800	25.17	2 514	34.56	26.90	26.12	2 793	37.51	28.96
1000	23.53	2 854	32.93	26.15	24.26	3 126	35.81	28.27
	T=120 °K				T=140 °K			
1	9 979.4	2 775	101.59	30.19	11 645	3 402	106.37	32.11
2	4 990.8	2 773	95.81	30.23	5 825.5	3 400	100.59	32.15
4	2 496.6	2 769	90.01	30.32	2 915.5	3 398	94.80	32.21
6	1 665.3	2 765	86.60	30.40	1 945.6	3 395	91.41	—
8	1 249.7	2 761	84.17	30.48	1 460.7	3 392	88.99	32.33
10	1 000.3	2 757	82.28	30.57	1 169.7	3 390	87.11	32.39
12	834.2	2 753	80.73	30.65	975.8	3 387	85.56	32.44
14	715.5	2 750	79.41	30.73	837.3	3 385	84.26	—
16	626.5	2 746	78.26	30.81	733.5	3 383	83.12	32.56
18	557.3	2 742	77.25	30.89	652.7	3 380	82.12	—
20	502.0	2 738	76.34	30.97	588.1	3 378	81.22	32.67
30	336.3	2 721	72.79	31.35	394.5	3 367	77.72	32.94
40	253.6	2 706	70.24	31.71	297.9	3 358	75.22	33.20
50	204.9	2 692	68.23	32.05	240.0	3 350	73.25	33.44
60	171.5	2 689	66.57	32.36	201.6	3 343	71.63	33.66
80	130.9	2 658	63.91	32.93	153.8	3 332	69.05	34.07
100	106.8	2 643	61.82	33.40	125.3	3 324	67.02	34.43
150	75.36	2 626	57.97	34.15	87.86	3 322	63.29	35.11
200	60.27	2 636	55.26	34.41	69.55	3 338	60.62	35.48
250	51.50	2 665	53.19	34.42	58.83	3 369	58.57	35.64
300	45.80	2 709	51.54	34.35	51.81	3 413	56.91	35.70

continued

p, bar	V	I	S	C_p	V	I	S	C_p
400	38.78	2 822	48.99	34.11	43.19	3 524	54.34	35.69
500	34.57	2 956	47.05	33.79	38.04	3 654	52.38	35.60
600	31.74	3 101	45.51	33.46	34.58	3 795	50.80	35.46
800	28.11	3 411	43.13	32.91	30.18	4 096	48.36	35.13
1000	25.81	3 732	41.33	32.48	27.45	4 410	46.50	34.86
		T=160 °K				T=180 °K		
1	13 311	4 045	110.74	32.89	14 975	4 712	114.64	32.82
2	6 659.2	4 044	104.97	32.91	7 492.4	4 711	108.87	32.84
4	3 333.5	4 043	99.19	32.96	3 751.0	4 710	103.09	32.88
6	2 225.0	4 041	95.80		2 503.9	4 709	99.70	—
8	1 670.8	4 040	93.39	33.05	1 880.3	4 709	97.29	32.94
10	1 338.3	4 038	91.51	33.09	1 506.2	4 708	95.42	32.98
12	1 116.6	4 037	89.98	33.19	1 256.8	4 707	93.89	33.01
14	958.3	4 035	88.68		1 078.7	4 707	92.59	
16	839.6	4 034	87.55	33.22	945.1	4 706	91.47	33.08
18	747.2	4 032	86.55		841.2	4 705	90.48	
20	673.4	4 031	85.65	33.30	758.1	4 705	89.59	33.14
30	452.0	4 025	82.19	33.51	508.9	4 702	86.15	33.30
40	341.4	4 020	79.72	33.70	384.4	4 701	83.69	33.45
50	275.1	4 016	77.78	33.88	309.8	4 700	81.77	33.59
60	231.1	4 013	76.18	34.05	260.1	4 700	80.20	33.72
80	176.2	4 009	73.65	34.36	198.2	4 701	77.69	33.96
100	143.4	4 008	71.66	34.63	161.1	4 705	75.74	34.18
150	100.1	4 018	68.01	35.19	112.0	4 725	72.14	34.63
200	78.72	4 042	65.40	35.57	87.74	4 756	69.57	34.97
250	66.11	4 077	63.37	35.79	73.31	4 796	67.58	35.20
300	57.82	4 122	61.73	35.90	63.79	4 844	65.95	35.34
400	47.61	4 234	59.16	36.00	52.01	4 958	63.40	35.49
500	41.53	4 364	57.20	36.04	45.03	5 089	61.44	35.57
600	37.46	4 503	55.61	36.03	40.35	5 229	59.86	35.62
800	32.30	4 800	53.14	35.90	34.44	5 525	57.37	35.63
1000	29.12	5 110	51.25	35.73	30.80	5 832	55.47	35.55
		T=200 °K				T=220 °K		
1	16 640	5 367	118.10	32.41	18 303	6 004	121.15	31.76
2	8 325.2	5 367	112.33	32.43	9 157.7	6 004	115.38	31.77
4	4 168.0	5 367	106.56	32.45	4 584.8	6 005	109.61	31.79
6	2 782.3	5 366	103.17		3 060.5	6 005	106.23	
8	2 089.5	5 366	100.77	32.51	2 298.4	6 005	103.83	31.84
10	1 673.8	5 366	98.90	32.54	1 841.1	6 006	101.96	31.86
12	1 396.7	5 366	97.38	32.56	1 536.3	6 006	100.44	31.88
14	1 198.8	5 366	96.08		1 318.6	6 006	99.15	
16	1 050.3	5 366	94.96	32.62	1 155.3	6 007	98.03	31.93
18	934.9	5 366	93.97		1 028.3	6 007	97.04	
20	842.5	5 366	93.08	32.67	926.7	6 008	96.15	31.97
30	565.5	5 366	89.66	32.79	621.9	6 010	92.74	32.07
40	427.1	5 367	87.22	32.91	469.6	6 014	90.31	32.17
50	344.2	5 369	85.31	33.02	378.3	6 017	88.41	32.26
60	288.9	5 371	83.75	33.13	317.4	6 021	86.86	32.35
80	219.9	5 377	81.27	33.33	241.5	6 031	84.39	32.51
100	178.6	5 385	79.33	33.50	196.0	6 042	82.47	32.65
150	123.8	5 413	75.78	33.87	135.5	6 077	78.95	32.96
200	96.64	5 450	73.24	34.16	105.4	6 119	76.44	33.21
250	80.43	5 495	71.27	34.38	87.48	6 168	74.49	33.40
300	69.70	5 546	69.65	34.52	75.57	6 222	72.89	33.55
400	56.42	5 663	67.12	34.69	60.79	6 343	70.37	33.72
500	48.51	5 795	65.18	34.78	51.98	6 477	68.43	33.81
600	43.24	5 937	63.60	34.85	46.11	6 620	66.86	33.88
800	36.58	6 233	61.11	34.94	38.73	6 918	64.39	34.00
1000	32.50	6 540	59.21	34.93	34.21	7 225	62.49	34.05

continued

p, bar	V	I	S	C_p	V	I	S	C_p
	T=240 °K				T=260 °K			
1	19 967	6 631	123.88	31.16	21 631	7 248	126.41	30.67
2	9 990.0	6 632	118.11	31.17	10 822	7 248	120.64	30.67
4	5 001.3	6 632	112.34	31.18	5 417.8	7 249	114.87	30.69
6	3 338.5	6 633	108.97		3 616.3	7 250	111.49	
8	2 507.1	6 634	106.57	31.22	2 715.6	7 251	109.10	30.72
10	2 008.2	6 635	104.70	31.24	2 175.2	7 252	107.24	30.74
12	1 675.7	6 635	103.18	31.26	1 814.9	7 254	105.71	30.75
14	1 438.1	6 636	101.89		1 557.6	7 255	104.43	
16	1 260.0	6 637	100.77	31.29	1 364.6	7 256	103.31	30.78
18	1 121.4	6 638	99.79		1 214.5	7 257	102.32	
20	1 010.6	6 639	98.90	31.33	1 094.4	7 258	101.44	30.81
30	678.1	6 643	95.50	31.41	734.2	7 264	98.04	30.88
40	511.9	6 648	93.07	31.49	554.1	7 271	95.62	30.95
50	412.2	6 653	91.18	31.57	446.1	7 277	93.74	31.01
60	345.8	6 659	89.64	31.64	374.1	7 284	92.20	31.08
80	262.9	6 672	87.19	31.78	284.2	7 299	89.76	31.19
100	213.2	6 686	85.27	31.90	230.3	7 316	87.86	31.30
150	147.1	6 726	81.78	32.16	158.5	7 361	84.38	31.52
200	114.1	6 773	79.29	32.37	122.8	7 412	81.91	31.70
250	94.47	6 825	77.35	32.54	101.4	7 467	79.98	31.85
300	81.40	6 882	75.76	32.68	87.18	7 526	78.40	31.98
400	65.14	7 006	73.26	32.85	69.46	7 654	75.92	32.15
500	55.43	7 142	71.33	32.95	58.87	7 792	73.99	32.24
600	48.98	7 286	69.77	33.01	51.83	7 937	72.43	32.31
800	40.86	7 587	67.31	33.13	42.99	8 241	69.98	32.41
1000	35.90	7 896	65.41	33.21	37.60	8 551	68.09	32.51
	T=280 °K				T=300 °K			
1	23 294	7 851	128.65	30.27	24 958	8 466	130.70	29.94
2	11 654	7 851	122.89	30.28	12 466	8 467	124.93	29.94
4	5 834.0	7 853	117.12	30.29	6 250.2	8 468	119.17	29.95
6	3 894.0	7 854	113.74		4 171.6	8 470	115.79	
8	2 924.0	7 855	111.35	30.32	3 132.3	8 472	113.39	29.97
10	2 342.0	7 857	109.49	30.33	2 506.8	8 473	111.54	29.98
12	1 954.0	7 858	107.97	30.34	2 093.1	8 475	110.02	30.00
14	1 676.9	7 860	106.68		1 796.1	8 477	108.73	
16	1 469.0	7 861	105.56	30.37	1 573.4	8 478	107.61	30.02
18	1 307.4	7 863	104.58		1 400.2	8 480	106.63	
20	1 178.1	7 864	103.70	30.39	1 261.7	8 482	105.75	30.04
30	790.1	7 871	100.30	30.45	846.0	8 490	102.36	30.09
40	596.2	7 879	97.89	30.51	638.2	8 499	99.95	30.15
50	479.8	7 887	96.01	30.57	513.5	8 508	98.37	30.19
60	402.3	7 895	94.47	30.62	430.4	8 517	96.54	30.23
80	305.4	7 912	92.04	30.72	326.5	8 536	94.21	30.32
100	247.3	7 930	90.15	30.81	264.3	8 556	92.23	30.40
150	170.0	7 980	86.69	31.00	181.4	8 609	88.78	30.59
200	131.4	8 034	84.23	31.16	140.0	8 686	86.33	30.71
250	108.3	8 092	82.31	31.29	115.2	8 727	84.42	30.83
300	92.94	8 154	80.74	31.41	98.67	8 791	82.86	30.93
400	73.77	8 285	78.26	31.57	78.06	8 925	80.39	31.08
500	62.30	8 425	76.35	31.66	65.72	9 097	78.49	31.17
600	54.67	8 572	74.79	31.79	57.51	9 215	76.93	31.23
800	45.10	8 877	72.35	31.82	47.22	9 522	74.50	31.32
1000	39.29	9 189	70.47	31.92	40.98	9 836	72.62	31.41
	T=350 °K				T=400 °K			
1	29 116	9 950	135.28	29.50	33 273	11 420	139.20	29.34
2	14 565	9 951	129.51	29.50	16 645	11 421	133.44	29.34
4	7 290.4	9 953	123.75	29.51	8 330.3	11 424	127.67	29.35
6	4 866.4	9 955	120.37		5 558.8	11 426	124.30	
8	3 652.8	9 957	117.98	29.53	4 173.1	11 428	121.91	29.36
10	2 925.3	9 959	116.12	29.54	3 341.6	11 431	120.05	29.36
12	2 440.3	9 961	114.60	29.54	2 787.3	11 433	118.53	29.37

continued

p, bar	V	I	S	C_p	V	I	S	C_p
14	2 093.9	9 964	113.32		2 391.4	11 436	117.25	
16	1 834.1	9 966	112.21	29.56	2 094.5	11 438	116.14	29.38
18	1 632.0	9 968	111.22		1 863.5	11 441	115.16	
20	1 470.3	9 970	110.24	29.57	1 678.8	11 443	114.28	29.39
30	985.4	9 981	106.96	29.61	1 124.5	11 455	110.90	29.42
40	742.9	9 991	104.56	29.65	847.3	11 468	108.50	29.44
50	597.4	10 002	102.69	29.68	681.0	11 480	106.63	29.47
60	500.0	10 014	101.16	29.71	570.2	11 493	105.11	29.49
80	379.2	10 036	98.74	29.78	431.7	11 518	102.70	29.54
100	306.5	10 059	96.87	29.84	348.5	11 544	100.83	29.59
150	209.6	10 120	93.45	29.96	237.7	11 610	97.42	29.68
200	161.2	10 183	91.01	30.07	182.3	11 678	95.00	29.76
250	132.2	10 259	89.12	30.16	149.1	11 748	93.12	29.83
300	112.9	10 317	87.57	30.23	127.0	11 819	91.58	29.89
400	88.72	10 458	85.13	30.36	99.30	11 966	89.15	29.99
500	74.23	10 605	83.23	30.44	82.68	12 116	87.27	30.07
600	64.57	10 756	81.69	30.50	71.60	12 270	85.73	30.12
800	52.47	11 067	79.27	30.57	57.71	12 584	83.32	30.19
1000	45.17	11 384	77.40	30.63	49.33	12 904	81.46	30.23
		T=450 °K				T=500 °K		
1	37 431	12 884	142.58	29.29	41 588	14 349	145.74	29.29
2	18 724	12 885	136.82	29.29	20 803	14 351	139.97	29.29
4	9 369.9	12 888	131.05	29.30	10 410	14 354	134.21	29.29
6	6 252.1	12 890	127.68		6 945.2	14 357	130.84	
8	4 693.1	12 893	125.29	29.31	5 213.0	14 359	128.44	29.30
10	3 757.7	12 896	123.43	29.31	4 173.7	14 362	126.59	29.30
12	3 134.2	12 898	121.91	29.32	3 480.9	14 365	125.07	29.30
14	2 688.7	12 901	120.63		2 986.0	14 368	123.79	
16	2 354.7	12 904	119.52	29.32	2 614.8	14 371	122.68	29.31
18	2 094.9	12 907	118.54		2 326.1	14 374	121.70	
20	1 887.0	12 909	117.66	29.33	2 095.1	14 377	120.82	29.32
30	1 263.4	12 923	114.28	29.35	1 402.3	14 391	117.44	29.33
40	951.6	12 936	111.89	29.37	1 055.8	14 405	115.05	29.35
50	764.6	12 950	110.02	29.39	848.0	14 420	113.19	29.36
60	640.0	12 963	108.50	29.41	709.4	14 434	111.67	29.38
80	484.0	12 991	106.10	29.45	536.2	14 463	109.27	29.41
100	390.4	13 018	104.23	29.48	432.2	14 493	107.41	29.43
150	265.7	13 089	100.84	29.56	293.6	14 586	104.02	29.50
200	203.4	13 160	98.42	29.62	224.3	14 641	101.61	29.55
250	166.0	13 233	96.55	29.68	182.7	14 716	99.74	29.59
300	141.0	13 308	95.02	29.73	155.0	14 793	98.21	29.63
400	109.8	13 459	92.60	29.81	120.3	14 947	95.80	29.70
500	91.10	13 613	90.72	29.87	99.48	15 104	93.93	29.75
600	78.59	13 769	89.19	29.92	85.57	15 263	92.41	29.79
800	62.93	14 086	86.79	29.98	68.13	15 583	90.01	29.85
1000	53.48	14 408	84.93	30.01	57.63	15 906	88.15	29.87

Thermodynamic properties of hydrogen at high temperatures
V(cm³/mole), I (J/mole), S and C_p (J/mole · deg) [5, 7]

p, bar	V	I	S	C_p	V	I	S	C_p
		T=550 °K				T=600 °K		
1	45 746	15 815	148.54	29.30	49 903	17 280	151.09	29.34
2	22 881	15 816	142.78	29.30	24 960	17 281	145.32	29.34
4	11 449	15 819	137.01	29.30	12 788	17 284	139.56	29.34
6	7 638.2	15 822	133.64	29.31	8 331.2	17 287	136.19	29.34
8	5 732.9	15 825	131.25	29.31	6 252.6	17 291	133.80	29.34
10	4 589.6	15 828	129.39	29.31	5 005.5	17 294	131.94	29.34
12	3 827.5	15 831	127.87	29.31	4 174.0	17 297	130.42	29.35
14	3 283.1	15 834	126.59	29.31	3 580.2	17 300	129.14	29.35

continued

p, bar	V	I	S	C_p	V	I	S	C_p
16	2 874.8	15 837	125.48	29.32	3 134.7	17 303	128.03	29.35
18	2 557.2	15 840	124.50	29.32	2 788.3	17 306	127.05	29.35
20	2 303.2	15 843	123.63	29.32	2 511.2	17 309	126.17	29.35
30	1 541.0	15 858	120.25	29.34	1 679.7	17 325	122.80	29.36
40	1 159.9	15 873	117.86	29.35	1 264.0	17 340	120.41	29.37
50	931.3	15 888	116.00	29.36	1 014.5	17 356	118.55	29.38
60	778.8	15 904	114.48	29.37	848.2	17 371	117.03	29.39
80	588.3	15 934	112.08	29.40	640.2	17 403	114.64	29.41
100	474.0	15 964	110.22	29.42	515.6	17 434	112.78	29.43
150	321.5	16 041	106.84	29.47	349.3	17 513	109.40	29.47
200	245.2	16 118	104.44	29.51	266.1	17 592	107.00	29.51
250	199.5	16 195	102.57	29.55	216.2	17 671	105.14	29.54
300	169.0	16 274	101.05	29.58	182.9	17 751	103.62	29.57
400	130.8	16 431	98.64	29.64	141.2	17 911	101.22	29.61
500	107.8	16 590	96.78	29.68	116.2	18 092	99.35	29.65
600	92.53	16 751	95.25	29.71	99.47	18 334	97.84	29.68
800	73.33	17 014	92.86	29.76	78.52	18 559	95.64	29.72
1000	61.77	17 561	90.22	29.79	65.90	18 885	93.60	29.74
	$T=650$ °K				$T=700$ °K			
1	54 060	18 747	153.43	29.39	58 218	20 218	155.61	29.45
2	27 039	18 749	147.67	29.39	29 117	20 219	149.85	29.45
4	13 528	18 752	141.91	29.39	14 567	20 223	144.08	29.45
6	9 024.2	18 755	138.54	29.39	9 717.1	20 226	140.71	29.45
8	6 772.4	18 758	136.14	29.39	7 292.1	20 229	138.32	29.45
10	5 421.3	18 761	134.29	29.39	5 837.0	20 233	136.46	29.45
12	4 520.6	18 765	132.77	29.39	4 867.0	20 236	134.95	29.46
14	3 877.2	18 768	131.49	29.39	4 174.2	20 239	133.67	29.46
16	3 394.6	18 771	130.38	29.40	3 654.5	20 242	132.56	29.46
18	3 019.3	18 774	129.40	29.40	3 250.3	20 246	131.58	29.46
20	2 719.1	18 776	128.52	29.40	2 927.0	20 249	130.70	29.46
30	1 818.4	18 794	125.15	29.41	1 957.0	20 265	127.33	29.46
40	1 368.0	18 810	122.76	29.41	1 472.0	20 282	124.94	29.47
50	1 097.8	18 826	120.90	29.43	1 180.9	20 298	123.08	29.48
60	917.6	18 842	119.39	29.44	986.9	20 315	121.56	29.49
80	692.4	18 874	116.99	29.45	744.4	20 348	119.17	29.50
100	557.3	18 906	115.13	29.46	598.9	20 381	117.31	29.51
150	377.1	18 987	111.76	29.50	404.8	20 463	113.94	29.54
200	286.9	19 068	109.36	29.53	307.8	20 545	111.54	29.56
250	232.9	19 148	107.50	29.55	249.5	20 627	109.69	29.59
300	196.8	19 229	105.98	29.58	210.7	20 709	108.17	29.61
400	151.6	19 392	103.58	29.62	162.0	20 873	105.77	29.64
500	124.5	19 554	101.73	29.65	132.8	21 037	103.92	29.67
600	106.4	19 718	100.21	29.67	113.3	21 201	102.40	29.69
800	83.71	20 044	97.82	29.70	88.89	21 530	100.02	29.71
1000	70.03	20 371	95.97	29.72	74.16	21 858	98.17	29.73
	$T=750$ °K				$T=800$ °K			
1	62 375	21 691	157.64	29.53	66 532	23 169	159.55	29.63
2	31 196	21 693	151.88	29.53	33 275	23 171	153.79	29.63
4	15 606	21 696	146.12	29.53	18 646	23 174	148.02	29.63
6	10 410	21 700	142.74	29.53	11 103	23 178	144.65	29.63
8	7 811.7	21 703	140.95	29.53	8 331.4	23 181	142.26	29.64
10	6 252.8	21 707	138.50	29.53	6 668.5	23 185	140.41	29.64
12	5 213.5	21 710	136.98	29.54	5 559.9	23 188	138.89	29.64
14	4 471.1	21 713	135.70	29.54	4 768.1	23 191	137.61	29.64
16	3 914.4	21 717	134.59	29.54	4 174.2	23 195	136.50	29.64
18	3 481.3	21 720	133.61	29.54	3 712.3	23 198	135.52	29.64
20	3 134.9	21 723	132.73	29.54	3 342.8	23 202	134.64	29.64
30	2 095.6	21 740	129.36	29.55	2 234.2	23 219	131.27	29.65
40	1 575.9	21 757	126.97	29.55	1 679.9	23 236	128.98	29.65
50	1 264.1	21 774	125.11	29.56	1 347.3	23 252	127.02	29.65
60	1 056.2	21 790	123.60	29.56	1 125.5	23 269	125.51	29.66
80	796.4	21 824	121.21	29.57	848.4	23 303	123.12	29.67

continued

p, bar	V	I	S	C_p	V	I	S	C_p
100	640.5	21 857	119.35	29.58	682.1	23 337	121.26	29.68
150	432.6	21 940	115.98	29.60	460.3	23 422	117.89	29.70
200	328.6	22 024	113.58	29.63	349.4	23 506	115.50	29.71
250	266.2	22 107	111.73	29.65	282.8	23 590	113.64	29.73
300	224.5	22 190	110.21	29.66	238.4	23 674	112.12	29.74
400	172.4	22 355	107.82	29.69	182.8	23 841	109.74	29.77
500	141.2	22 521	105.96	29.71	149.5	24 017	107.88	29.79
600	120.3	22 686	104.45	29.73	127.2	24 173	106.37	29.80
800	94.06	23 016	102.07	29.76	99.23	24 504	103.99	29.82
1000	78.29	23 344	100.22	29.77	82.41	24 833	102.14	29.83
		$T = 850$ °K				$T = 900$ °K		
1	76 689	24 655	161.35	29.75	74 846	26 145	162.95	29.89
2	35 353	24 657	155.59	29.75	37 432	26 146	157.29	29.89
4	17 685	24 660	149.82	29.75	16 724	26 150	151.52	29.89
6	11 796	24 664	146.45	29.76	12 489	26 153	148.15	29.89
8	8 851.0	24 667	144.06	29.76	9 370.7	26 157	145.76	29.89
10	7 084.2	24 670	142.21	29.76	7 499.9	26 160	143.91	29.89
12	6 906.4	24 674	140.69	29.76	6 252.8	26 163	142.39	29.89
14	5 065.0	24 677	139.41	29.76	5 361.9	26 167	141.11	29.89
16	4 434.0	24 681	138.30	29.76	4 693.8	26 171	140.00	29.89
18	3 943.2	24 684	137.32	29.76	4 174.2	26 174	139.02	29.89
20	3 550.6	24 688	136.44	29.76	3 758.4	26 178	138.14	29.89
30	2 372.7	24 705	133.07	29.76	2 411.3	26 195	134.77	29.90
40	1 783.8	24 722	130.68	29.77	1 887.7	26 210	132.38	29.90
50	1 430.4	24 739	128.83	29.77	1 613.5	26 230	130.53	29.90
60	1 194.8	24 756	127.31	29.78	1 264.1	26 247	129.01	29.90
80	900.3	24 791	124.92	29.78	952.3	26 282	126.62	29.91
100	723.6	24 825	123.06	29.79	765.2	26 316	124.77	29.92
150	488.1	24 910	119.69	29.81	515.7	26 402	121.40	29.93
200	370.1	24 995	117.30	29.82	390.9	26 409	119.01	29.94
250	299.4	25 080	115.45	29.83	316.0	26 574	117.15	29.95
300	252.2	25 165	113.93	29.85	266.1	26 659	115.64	29.97
400	193.2	25 333	111.45	29.87	203.6	26 828	113.25	29.99
500	157.1	25 500	109.69	29.89	166.0	26 996	111.40	30.00
600	134.1	25 667	108.18	29.90	141.0	27 163	109.89	30.01
800	104.4	25 998	105.80	29.92	109.7	27 496	107.51	30.03
1000	86.53	26 328	103.86	29.93	90.66	27 826	105.66	30.03
		$T = 950$ °K				$T = 1000$ °K		
1	79 004	27 643	164.67	30.04	83 161	29 149	166.22	30.21
2	39 510	27 645	158.91	30.04	41 589	29 151	160.45	30.21
4	19 754	27 649	153.15	30.05	26 803	29 154	154.69	30.21
6	13 181	27 652	149.77	30.05	13 874	29 158	151.32	30.21
8	9 890.3	27 656	147.38	30.05	10 410	29 162	148.93	30.21
10	7 915.6	27 659	145.53	30.05	8 331.3	29 165	147.17	30.21
12	6 599.2	27 663	144.01	30.05	6 945.6	29 169	145.56	30.21
14	5 658.9	27 666	142.73	30.05	5 955.8	29 173	144.27	30.21
16	4 953.6	27 668	141.62	30.05	5 213.4	29 176	143.16	30.21
18	4 405.1	27 673	140.64	30.05	4 636.0	29 179	142.19	30.21
20	3 966.3	27 677	139.76	30.05	4 174.1	29 183	141.31	30.21
30	2 649.8	27 694	136.40	30.05	2 788.4	29 200	137.94	30.22
40	1 991.6	27 712	134.00	30.05	2 095.5	29 218	135.55	30.22
50	1 596.6	27 729	132.15	30.06	1 679.8	29 235	133.69	30.22
60	1 333.3	27 747	130.63	30.06	1 402.6	29 253	132.18	30.22
80	1 004.2	27 781	128.24	30.06	1 056.1	29 288	129.79	30.23
100	806.7	27 816	126.39	30.07	848.3	29 323	127.93	30.23
150	543.2	27 903	123.02	30.08	571.1	29 410	124.57	30.24
200	411.7	27 989	120.63	30.09	432.4	29 497	122.18	30.25
250	332.6	28 095	118.78	30.10	349.2	29 584	120.32	30.26
300	279.9	28 161	117.26	30.11	293.7	29 670	118.81	30.27
400	214.0	28 331	114.88	30.13	224.3	29 841	116.43	30.28
500	174.3	28 500	113.00	30.14	182.6	30 010	114.58	30.29

continued

p, bar	V	I	S	C_p	V	I	S	C_p
600	147.4	28 608	111.52	30.15	154.7	30 179	113.07	30.30
800	114.7	29 001	109.13	30.16	119.9	30 512	110.69	30.31
1000	94.78	29 331	107.29	30.17	98.90	30 843	108.84	30.31
		T=1100 °K				T=1200 °K		
1	91 475	32 189	169.12	30.58	99 789	35 265	171.79	30.99
2	45 746	32 190	163.36	30.58	49 903	35 267	166.03	30.99
4	22 881	32 194	157.59	30.58	24 960	35 270	160.27	30.99
6	15 260	32 198	154.22	30.59	16 646	35 274	156.90	30.99
8	11 449	32 201	151.83	30.59	12 488	35 278	154.50	30.99
10	9 162.7	32 205	149.98	30.59	9 994.0	35 281	152.65	30.99
12	7 638.4	32 208	148.46	30.59	8 331.4	35 285	151.13	30.99
14	6 549.6	32 212	147.28	30.59	7 143.4	35 288	149.85	30.99
16	5 733.0	32 215	146.07	30.59	6 252.5	35 292	148.74	30.99
18	5 097.9	32 219	145.09	30.59	5 559.7	35 296	147.76	30.99
20	4 589.7	32 222	144.21	30.59	5 005.4	35 299	146.89	30.99
30	3 065.4	32 240	141.04	30.59	3 342.5	35 317	143.62	31.00
40	2 303.3	32 258	138.45	30.59	2 511.0	35 335	141.13	31.00
50	1 846.0	32 276	136.60	30.59	2 012.2	35 353	139.27	31.00
60	1 541.1	32 293	135.08	30.59	1 679.6	35 371	137.76	31.00
80	1 160.0	32 329	132.69	30.60	1 263.8	35 406	135.37	31.00
100	931.3	32 364	130.84	30.60	1 014.4	35 442	133.51	31.00
150	626.4	32 452	127.47	30.60	681.8	35 530	130.15	31.01
200	473.9	32 540	125.08	30.61	515.4	35 619	127.76	31.01
250	382.4	32 627	123.23	30.62	415.6	35 706	125.91	31.01
300	321.4	32 714	121.72	30.62	349.0	35 794	124.40	31.02
400	245.0	32 886	119.34	30.63	265.8	35 967	122.01	31.03
500	199.2	33 057	117.49	30.64	215.8	36 138	120.16	31.03
600	168.6	33 226	115.98	30.65	182.4	36 308	118.65	31.04
800	130.2	33 560	113.60	30.66	140.6	36 643	116.28	31.05
1000	107.0	33 891	111.76	30.66	115.4	36 974	114.43	31.05
		T=1300 °K				T=1400 °K		
1	108 100	38 386	174.29	31.43	116 420	41 551	176.64	31.87
2	54 060	38 388	168.53	31.43	58 217	41 553	170.88	31.87
4	27 038	38 392	162.76	31.43	29 117	41 556	165.11	31.87
6	16 031	38 395	159.39	31.43	19 417	41 560	161.74	31.87
8	13 527	38 399	157.00	31.43	14 567	41 564	159.35	31.87
10	10 825	38 403	155.15	31.43	11 667	41 567	157.50	31.87
12	9 023.9	38 406	153.63	31.43	9 716.7	41 571	155.98	31.87
14	7 737.1	38 410	152.35	31.43	8 330.9	41 574	154.70	31.87
16	6 772.1	38 413	151.24	31.43	7 291.6	41 578	153.59	31.87
18	6 021.5	38 417	150.26	31.43	6 483.3	41 582	152.61	31.87
20	5 421.0	38 421	149.38	31.43	5 836.6	41 585	151.73	31.87
30	3 619.5	38 439	146.01	31.43	3 896.6	41 603	148.36	31.87
40	2 718.8	38 457	143.62	31.43	2 926.6	41 621	145.97	31.87
50	2 178.4	38 474	141.77	31.43	2 344.5	41 639	144.12	31.87
60	1 818.1	38 492	140.25	31.44	1 956.5	41 657	142.60	31.87
80	1 367.7	38 528	137.96	31.44	1 471.5	41 693	140.21	31.87
100	1 097.4	38 564	136.01	31.44	1 180.5	41 729	138.36	31.88
150	737.1	38 653	132.64	31.44	792.4	41 818	134.99	31.88
200	556.9	38 741	130.26	31.44	598.4	41 907	132.61	31.88
250	448.8	38 830	128.41	31.45	481.9	41 995	130.76	31.88
300	376.7	38 917	126.90	31.45	404.3	42 083	129.25	31.88
400	286.5	39 091	124.51	31.45	307.2	42 257	126.86	31.89
500	232.3	39 263	122.66	31.46	248.9	42 430	125.01	31.89
600	196.2	39 433	121.16	31.46	209.9	42 600	123.51	31.89
800	150.9	39 769	118.78	31.47	161.2	42 936	121.13	31.90
1000	123.6	40 100	116.93	31.47	131.9	43 267	119.39	31.90

p, bar	V	I	S	C_p	p, bar	V	I	S	C_p
				T=1500 °K					
1	124 730	44 759	178.85	32.30	50	2510.7	44 848	146.33	32.31
2	62 374	44 761	173.09	32.30	60	2095.0	44 866	144.82	32.31
4	31 185	44 765	167.33	32.30	80	1575.3	44 902	142.43	32.31
6	20 802	44 768	163.96	32.30	100	1263.5	44 937	140.58	32.31
8	15 606	44 772	161.57	32.30	150	847.8	45 027	137.21	32.31
10	12 488	44 776	159.71	32.30	200	639.9	45 116	134.82	32.31
12	10 409	44 779	158.20	32.30	250	515.1	45 204	132.97	32.31
14	8 924.7	44 782	156.91	32.30	300	431.9	45 282	131.46	32.31
16	7 811.2	44 786	155.80	32.30	400	327.9	45 467	129.08	32.31
18	6 945.1	44 791	154.82	32.30	500	265.4	45 639	127.23	32.31
20	6 252.2	44 794	153.95	32.30	600	223.7	45 810	125.72	32.32
30	4 173.6	44 812	150.58	32.31	800	171.5	46 147	123.34	32.32
40	3 134.3	44 830	148.19	32.31	1000	140.1	46 477	121.50	32.32

Sound velocity u (m/s) in hydrogen [7]*

T, °K → / p, bar	15	20	22	24	26	28	30	32
1	1245.3	1135.8	375.7	395.5	413.1	431.1	447.8	463.4
5	1260.3	1156.4	1090.3	1016.8	932.0	393.8	417.7	439.0
10	1278.4	1180.7	1118.6	1051.1	976.0	886.1	765.2	397.5
12	1285.7	1190.0	1129.3	1063.9	992.0	907.5	798.9	627.9
14	1292.4	1199.1	1139.8	1078.2	1007.1	927.3	827.8	687.3
16	1299.2	1208.0	1149.9	1088.1	1021.6	945.8	853.7	731.4
18	1306.0	1216.7	1159.8	1099.6	1035.4	963.2	877.2	767.9
20	1312.6	1225.3	1169.5	1110.8	1048.7	979.7	898.9	799.2
25	1328.8	1245.9	1192.6	1137.2	1079.7	1017.8	946.6	863.6
30	1344.5	1265.6	1214.5	1162.0	1108.3	1051.1	987.7	915.8
40		1302.7	1255.2	1207.3	1159.5	1110.1	1057.1	998.8
50		1337.1	1292.6	1248.2	1204.9	1161.1	1115.0	1065.3
60		1369.2	1327.1	1285.8	1246.0	1208.4	1165.3	1121.7
80		1428.1	1390.0	1353.0	1318.5	1284.9	1250.9	1213.3
100		1481.1	1446.0	1412.5	1381.8	1352.5	1323.2	1292.8
150		1594.6	1565.3	1538.2	1514.2	1492.0	1470.2	1447.5
200		1687.0	1662.7	1640.8	1622.2	1605.2	1588.5	1570.7
250			1742.2	1725.8	1712.4	1700.5	1688.4	1674.9
300				1794.6	1787.4	1781.2	1774.2	1765.1
400								1911.2

T, °K → / p, bar	34	36	38	40	50	60	80	100
1	478.6	493.3	507.5	521.3	584.5	640.2	733.4	808.8
5	458.4	476.4	493.3	509.3	579.8	639.1	735.4	811.9
10	428.9	453.9	475.6	495.2	575.5	638.9	738.6	816.2
12	415.4	444.7	468.9	490.1	574.3	639.3	740.0	818.0
14	407.7	436.4	462.8	485.6	573.5	639.9	741.6	819.9
16	533.7	433.6	458.6	482.3	573.2	640.7	743.4	821.8
18	614.3	454.4	458.9	480.9	573.3	641.9	745.2	823.9
20	669.0	511.7	468.8	483.0	574.0	643.3	747.2	826.0
25	764.4	648.7	549.2	515.1	578.7	648.4	752.7	831.5
30	733.0	740.5	648.1	583.3	588.9	655.1	758.9	837.5
40	734.8	865.6	794.4	728.0	628.6	675.7	773.8	850.6

*The difference between speed of sound in hydrogen and parahydrogen in the liquid state is less than 1% [392]. This difference is even smaller in the gas phase.

continued

p, bar \ T, °K →	34	36	38	40	50	60	80	100
50	1011.9	955.1	896.6	839.3	689.3	705.8	791.4	865.2
60	1075.3	1026.3	975.9	925.9	758.3	743.6	811.8	881.1
80	1177.8	1138.6	1098.2	1057.6	891.3	832.8	859.6	916.5
100	1260.9	1227.5	1193.1	1158.4	1004.6	925.1	914.7	955.8
150	1423.6	1398.4	1372.3	1345.6	1219.2	1129.2	1063.5	1066.1
200	1551.6	1530.9	1509.2	1486.7	1377.6	1292.1	1204.7	1181.2
250	1659.5	1642.2	1623.5	1603.9	1505.8	1426.3	1331.2	1291.2
300	1753.4	1739.4	1723.3	1705.8	1615.5	1540.9	1444.6	1393.3
400	1909.2	1902.8	1892.8	1880.0	1801.6	1732.7	1640.2	1576.5
500				2026.7	1962.4	1895.0	1804.8	1737.4
600					2110.8	2043.4	1948.4	1880.0
700						2188.3	2080.5	2008.0
800							2210.1	2125.9
900							2344.8	2239.9
1000							2490.0	2356.5

p, bar \ T, °K →	120	140	160	180	200	250	300	350
1	873.4	932.1	987.3	1039.8	1090.2	1209.0	1319.3	1422.5
2	874.3	933.0	988.2	1040.7	1091.2	1209.8	1320.2	1423.3
5	877.0	935.8	991.0	1043.5	1094.0	1212.5	1322.7	1425.8
10	881.6	940.5	995.8	1048.3	1098.7	1217.0	1327.0	1429.8
20	891.6	950.6	1005.7	1058.0	1108.2	1226.0	1335.5	1437.8
30	902.7	961.3	1018.1	1068.1	1118.0	1235.1	1344.0	1445.9
40	914.8	972.6	1026.9	1078.4	1127.9	1244.3	1352.6	1454.0
50	927.8	984.6	1038.1	1089.1	1138.1	1253.6	1361.3	1462.1
60	941.5	997.1	1049.7	1100.0	1148.5	1263.0	1370.0	1470.1
80	971.2	1023.4	1073.9	1122.5	1169.8	1282.0	1387.4	1488.4
100	1003.1	1051.3	1099.1	1145.8	1191.6	1301.3	1404.9	1502.6
150	1090.5	1125.6	1165.2	1208.3	1247.9	1350.4	1449.2	1543.4
200	1184.3	1204.6	1234.4	1268.8	1305.5	1400.0	1493.6	1584.0
250	1278.2	1285.5	1305.4	1332.5	1363.9	1449.6	1537.9	1624.5
300	1368.3	1365.3	1376.6	1396.8	1422.7	1499.3	1581.9	1664.6
400	1533.3	1515.2	1513.8	1523.1	1539.5	1598.2	1669.1	1743.6
500	1681.6	1651.3	1640.3	1641.7	1651.3	1695.2	1754.4	1821.1
600	1817.0	1776.8	1757.0	1751.7	1755.9	1788.6	1838.7	1897.2
700	1941.0	1894.1	1868.6	1854.7	1853.8	1877.2	1919.7	1971.4
800	2054.9	2003.8	1970.4	1952.6	1946.6	1961.1	1997.3	2043.3
900	2160.6	2106.1	2068.9	2048.2	2035.4	2041.0	2071.4	2112.6
1000	2261.6	2202.0	2162.0	2136.8	2121.0	2117.7	2142.3	2179.2

p, bar \ T, °K →	400	450	500	600	800	1000	1200	1500
1	1519.6	1611.2	1697.9	1859.1	2142.1	2386.0	2601.2	2886.6
2	1520.4	1611.9	1698.6	1859.7	2142.7	2386.4	2601.6	2887.0
5	1522.7	1614.1	1700.7	1861.6	2144.3	2387.9	2602.9	2888.1
10	1528.5	1617.7	1704.1	1864.7	2147.0	2390.2	2605.0	2890.0
20	1534.1	1624.9	1711.0	1871.0	2152.4	2395.0	2609.2	2893.6
30	1541.8	1632.2	1717.9	1877.3	2157.8	2399.7	2613.4	2897.3
40	1549.4	1639.4	1724.8	1883.6	2163.2	2404.4	2617.7	2901.0
50	1557.0	1648.6	1731.7	1889.8	2168.5	2409.1	2621.9	2904.6
60	1564.6	1653.8	1738.5	1896.2	2173.9	2413.8	2628.1	2908.3
80	1579.8	1668.2	1752.2	1908.6	2184.5	2423.2	2634.4	2915.5

continued

p, bar \ T, °K →	400	450	500	600	800	1000	1200	1500
100	1595.1	1682.6	1765.8	1921.0	2195.1	2432.5	2642.8	2922.8
150	1633.0	1718.3	1799.6	1951.7	2221.4	2455.6	2663.5	2940.8
200	1670.8	1753.7	1833.1	1982.1	2247.3	2478.4	2684.0	2958.7
250	1708.3	1788.8	1866.1	2011.9	2272.8	2500.9	2704.2	2976.4
300	1745.4	1823.4	1898.8	2041.4	2297.9	2523.1	2724.2	2993.9
400	1818.3	1891.5	1962.8	2099.1	2347.6	2566.4	2763.3	3028.2
500	1889.6	1958.0	2025.3	2155.4	2394.7	2608.4	2801.1	3061.6
600	1959.6	2023.1	2086.4	2210.3	2441.1	2649.2	2837.9	3094.0
700	2028.0	2088.8	2148.2	2264.0	2486.5	2689.0	2873.7	3125.5
800	2094.7	2149.1	2204.7	2316.5	2530.9	2727.9	2908.6	3158.2
900	2159.6	2209.8	2261.9	2367.9	2574.3	2766.0	2942.7	3186.1
1000	2222.3	2268.9	2317.7	2418.2	2617.0	2803.5	2976.2	3215.4

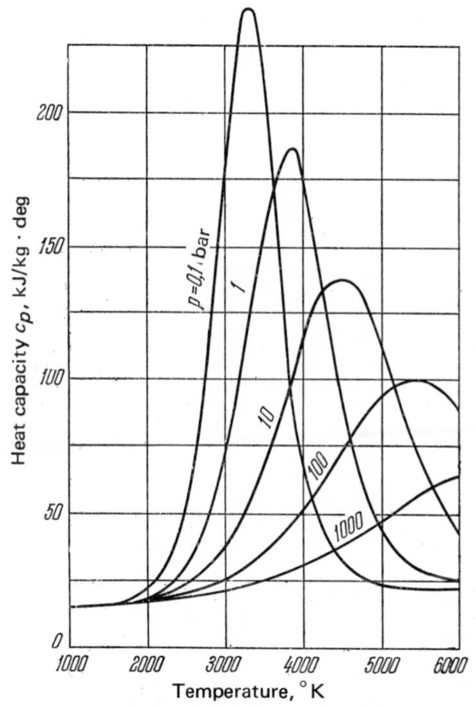

Fig. 3. Heat capacity of dissociated hydrogen as a function of temperature with pressure as parameter.

Thermodynamic properties of dissociated hydrogen at different temperatures and pressures: v (m³/kg), i (kJ/kg), s and c_p (kJ/kg · deg) [8, 9]

T, °K	v	i	s	c_p	v	i	s	c_p
	$p=0.1$ bar				$p=1$ bar			
1500	618.7	22 210	98.216	16.08	61.87	22 207	88.718	16.03
1600	659.9	23 834	99.259	16.42	66.00	23 822	89.759	16.28
1700	701.3	25 499	100.259	16.91	70.12	25 464	90.751	16.58
1800	742.8	27 226	101.226	17.69	74.26	27 140	91.701	16.96
1900	784.6	29 053	102.177	18.95	78.40	28 860	92.618	17.49
2000	826.9	31 041	103.136	20.97	82.56	30 646	93.510	18.25
2200	915.4	35 911	105.214	28.77	90.99	34 534	95.267	20.96

continued

T, °K	v	i	s	c_p	v	i	s	c_p
2400	1015	43 101	107.873	44.90	99.78	39 201	97.101	26.27
2600	1137	54 734	111.786	73.97	109.3	45 320	99.207	35.74
2800	1303	73 810	117.892	119.7	120.2	53 883	101.865	50.99
3000	1537	103 537	127.192	178.8	133.5	66 198	105.436	73.42
3200	1856	144 786	139.964	229.0	150.4	83 753	110.327	103.3
3400	2237	191 826	154.445	230.8	172.2	107 836	116.890	137.9
3600	2612	233 335	167.151	178.2	199.8	138 688	125.195	169.1
3800	2928	262 452	175.972	114.9	232.6	174 349	134.723	183.7
4000	3183	280 651	181.369	70.96	267.9	210 397	144.300	172.5
4200	3398	292 158	184.650	46.73	302.0	241 669	152.630	141.1
4400	3590	300 125	186.793	34.35	332.6	266 551	159.048	105.1
4600	3771	306 297	188.341	28.07	359.1	284 474	163.646	75.61
4800	3944	311 550	189.566	24.81	382.3	297 412	166.875	55.21
5000	4114	316 321	190.607	23.07	403.1	307 055	169.189	42.24
5200	4282	320 828	191.534	22.10	422.5	314 639	170.921	34.26
5400	4449	325 187	192.385	21.54	440.9	320 962	172.285	29.37
5600	4616	329 460	193.180	21.21	458.6	326 510	173.415	26.35
5800	4781	333 682	193.934	21.02	476.0	331 577	174.390	24.46
6000	4947	337 875	194.654	20.91	493.1	336 342	175.259	23.27
		$p=5$ bar				$p=10$ bar		
1500					6.194	22 213	79.222	16.01
1600					6.607	23 825	80.262	16.23
1700					7.019	25 460	81.252	16.47
1800					7.432	27 120	82.197	16.73
1900					7.845	28 807	83.105	17.03
2000	16.51	30 547	86.843	17.56	8.258	30 528	83.979	17.39
2200	18.18	34 185	88.528	18.96	9.089	34 106	85.647	18.48
2400	19.87	38 207	90.174	21.50	9.931	37 975	87.253	20.38
2600	21.64	42 911	91.870	25.89	10.79	42 344	88.859	23.56
2800	23.52	48 739	93.734	32.88	11.70	47 522	90.549	28.57
3000	25.63	56 285	95.920	43.19	12.69	53 931	92.430	35.95
3200	28.06	66 273	98.610	57.37	13.79	62 086	94.628	46.09
3400	30.97	79 501	102.001	75.55	15.06	72 572	97.283	59.26
3600	34.53	96 716	106.278	97.02	16.57	85 982	100.535	75.28
3800	38.88	118 385	111.558	119.6	18.38	102 822	104.504	93.35
4000	44.09	144 337	117.805	138.9	20.54	123 339	109.251	111.6
4200	50.07	173 397	124.743	149.7	23.07	147 298	114.726	127.1
4400	56.55	203 360	131.850	147.6	25.94	173 777	120.725	136.2
4600	63.10	231 620	138.509	133.2	29.05	201 177	126.890	136.1
4800	69.37	256 179	144.249	111.7	32.23	227 591	132.794	126.6
5000	75.12	276 261	148.887	89.38	35.34	251 400	138.075	110.7
5200	80.32	292 150	152.495	70.23	38.26	271 734	142.539	92.57
5400	85.02	304 654	155.267	55.56	40.95	288 506	146.169	75.55
5600	89.35	314 650	157.413	45.02	43.42	302 147	149.065	61.40
5800	93.39	322 876	159.112	37.69	45.70	313 283	151.369	50.47
6000	97.23	329 880	160.496	32.67	47.83	325 526	153.222	42.39
		$p=20$ bar				$p=30$ bar		
2000	4.133	30 520	81.116	17.28	2.758	30 521	79.442	17.21
2200	4.547	34 056	82.774	18.15	3.034	34 039	81.096	18.00
2400	4.965	37 817	84.352	19.58	3.313	37 752	82.662	19.22
2600	5.392	41 948	85.894	21.91	3.594	41 778	84.182	21.18
2800	5.834	46 667	87.471	25.53	3.885	46 294	85.705	24.18
3000	6.303	52 271	89.146	30.81	4.191	51 541	87.293	28.54
3200	6.813	59 125	91.011	38.08	4.519	57 817	89.017	34.51
3400	7.385	67 648	93.164	47.53	4.881	65 466	90.954	42.29
3600	8.040	78 285	95.705	59.20	5.288	74 859	93.190	51.94
3800	8.805	91 460	98.731	72.82	5.756	86 357	95.803	63.32
4000	9.704	107 497	102.316	87.67	6.298	100 273	98.863	76.01
4200	10.76	126 519	106.491	102.3	6.929	116 796	102.413	89.21
4400	11.97	148 310	111.211	114.9	7.656	135 905	106.452	101.6
4600	13.33	172 208	116.340	123.1	8.481	157 278	110.917	111.5
4800	14.80	197 106	121.644	124.8	9.391	180 237	115.670	117.2

continued

T, °K	v	i	s	c_p	v	i	s	c_p
5000	16.34	221 648	126.836	119.6	10.36	203 798	120.512	117.4
5200	17.87	244 561	131.649	108.8	11.36	226 842	125.215	112.1
5400	19.34	264 975	135.898	95.03	12.36	248 371	129.576	102.6
5600	20.73	282 542	139.512	80.74	13.33	267 711	133.458	90.61
5800	22.03	297 357	142.514	67.73	14.24	284 586	136.806	78.21
6000	23.23	309 776	144.980	56.84	15.10	299 059	139.634	66.75
		$p=40$ bar				$p=50$ bar		
1500					1.245	22 248	72.586	16.01
1600					1.328	23 860	73.626	16.22
1700					1.410	25 493	74.615	16.44
1800					1.493	27 148	75.560	16.67
1900					1.575	28 827	76.465	16.91
2000	2.070	30 525	78.256	17.18	1.658	30 531	77.335	17.16
2200	2.277	34 032	79.906	17.91	1.823	34 030	78.984	17.85
2400	2.485	37 716	81.466	19.01	1.989	37 695	80.539	18.87
2600	2.696	41 680	82.970	20.74	2.158	41 616	82.033	20.45
2800	2.913	46 075	84.465	23.37	2.330	45 928	83.508	22.83
3000	3.139	51 109	86.002	27.18	2.510	50 817	85.011	26.25
3200	3.380	57 040	87.643	32.39	2.699	56 513	86.597	30.93
3400	3.642	64 168	89.457	39.16	2.904	63 284	88.327	37.02
3600	3.935	72 814	91.513	47.58	3.131	71 420	90.264	44.59
3800	4.266	83 303	93.883	57.55	3.386	81 215	92.471	53.58
4000	4.647	96 921	96.631	68.81	3.676	72 936	95.008	63.81
4200	5.086	110 875	99.801	80.79	4.009	106 790	97.917	74.82
4400	5.592	128 224	103.409	92.56	4.391	122 873	101.222	85.94
4600	6.168	147 800	107.424	102.8	4.824	141 103	104.910	96.12
4800	6.807	169 160	111.759	110.1	5.308	161 176	108.923	104.1
5000	7.499	191 576	116.271	113.2	5.839	182 537	113.154	108.8
5200	8.228	214 122	120.777	111.4	6.403	204 421	117.454	109.3
5400	8.970	235 852	125.088	105.2	6.986	225 977	121.663	105.6
5600	9.703	255 987	129.051	95.76	7.571	246 418	125.622	98.35
5800	10.41	274 050	132.572	84.76	8.145	265 167	129.222	88.90
6000	11.08	289 887	135.621	73.69	8.696	281 922	132.405	78.63
		$p=60$ bar				$p=70$ bar		
2000	1.383	30 537	76.583	17.15	1.186	30 544	75.947	17.14
2200	1.520	34 031	78.231	17.81	1.304	34 033	77.594	17.77
2400	1.659	37 682	79.782	18.76	1.423	37 673	79.143	18.68
2600	1.799	41 571	81.269	20.23	1.542	41 538	80.625	20.06
2800	1.942	45 822	82.730	22.42	1.665	45 741	82.075	22.11
3000	2.090	50 603	84.209	25.57	1.792	50 439	83.534	25.04
3200	2.247	56 126	85.755	29.86	1.924	55 827	85.049	29.03
3400	2.414	62 634	87.423	35.44	2.066	62 130	86.671	34.21
3600	2.599	70 393	89.273	42.38	2.221	69 596	88.454	40.65
3800	2.805	79 673	91.361	50.64	2.394	78 475	90.451	48.34
4000	3.038	90 726	93.743	60.06	2.587	89 006	92.713	57.14
4200	3.304	103 754	96.460	70.32	2.807	101 385	95.281	66.77
4400	3.607	118 871	99.539	80.83	3.057	115 735	98.183	76.76
4600	3.952	136 049	102.976	90.77	3.341	132 061	101.422	86.39
4800	4.337	155 071	106.734	99.09	3.659	150 208	104.971	94.79
5000	4.762	175 503	110.729	104.7	4.009	169 829	108.766	100.9
5200	5.217	196 700	114.842	106.7	4.389	190 388	112.708	104.0
5400	5.693	217 932	118.927	104.9	4.788	211 213	116.671	103.6
5600	6.177	238 416	122.842	99.46	5.197	231 596	120.521	99.70
5800	6.656	257 543	126.467	91.49	5.607	250 909	124.141	93.06
6000	7.122	274 921	129.730	82.16	6.009	268 703	127.446	84.70
		$p=80$ bar				$p=90$ bar		
2000	1.039	30 552	75.397	17.13	0.9244	30 559	74.911	17.12
2200	1.142	34 037	77.043	17.75	1.015	34 042	76.556	17.78
2400	1.246	37 668	78.589	18.61	1.108	37 665	78.102	18.56
2600	1.351	41 513	80.067	19.92	1.201	41 493	79.575	19.81
2800	1.457	45 678	81.508	21.85	1.296	45 627	81.010	21.64

continued

T, °K	v	i	s	c_p	v	i	s	c_p
3000	1.568	50 309	82.953	24.61	1.394	50 203	82.442	24.26
3200	1.683	55 588	84.443	28.36	1.495	55 391	83.912	27.80
3400	1.806	61 726	86.028	33.22	1.604	61 393	85.466	32.40
3600	1.939	68 955	87.757	39.27	1.721	68 425	87.152	38.11
3800	2.087	77 510	89.681	46.48	1.850	76 712	89.016	44.94
4000	2.252	87 618	91.848	54.76	1.993	86 469	91.104	52.78
4200	2.439	99 470	94.296	63.87	2.155	97 880	93.453	61.44
4400	2.651	113 191	97.055	73.39	2.358	111 075	96.093	70.55
4600	2.891	128 811	100.131	82.72	2.545	126 096	99.034	79.60
4800	3.159	146 216	103.507	91.10	2.777	142 864	102.263	87.89
5000	3.457	165 127	107.131	97.62	3.034	161 148	105.739	94.62
5200	3.779	185 084	110.921	101.4	3.313	180 552	109.392	98.99
5400	4.121	205 493	114.765	102.1	3.610	200 546	113.125	100.4
5600	4.474	225 693	118.542	99.41	3.920	220 518	116.826	98.78
5800	4.831	245 067	122.137	93.93	4.235	239 871	120.385	94.33
6000	5.184	263 134	125.461	86.50	4.549	258 108	123.711	87.77
		$p=100$ bar				$p=150$ bar		
1500	0.6267	22 292	69.730	16.01	0.4205	22 336	68.060	16.01
1600	0.6679	23 903	70.769	16.22	0.4479	23 947	69.099	16.22
1700	0.7091	25 536	71.759	16.43	0.4754	25 580	70.089	16.43
1800	0.7503	27 190	72.703	16.65	0.5028	27 233	71.033	16.65
1900	0.7915	28 867	73.608	16.88	0.5303	28 909	71.938	16.87
2000	0.8328	30 567	74.477	17.10				
2200	0.9153	34 047	76.122	17.70				
2400	0.9982	37 664	77.665	18.51				
2600	1.082	41 479	79.136	19.71				
2800	1.167	45 585	80.565	21.46				
3000	1.254	50 114	81.986	23.96	0.8376	49 827	80.244	22.94
3200	1.346	55 226	83.440	27.33	0.8972	54 681	81.642	25.73
3400	1.442	61 112	84.968	31.70	0.9599	60 174	83.086	29.34
3600	1.546	67 978	86.617	37.14	1.027	66 476	84.612	33.83
3800	1.661	76 038	88.431	43.63	1.099	73 763	86.258	39.19
4000	1.788	85 496	90.452	51.11	1.178	82 206	88.059	45.38
4200	1.930	96 533	92.719	59.38	1.266	91 961	90.047	52.28
4400	2.091	109 278	95.258	68.13	1.364	103 153	92.248	59.71
4600	2.272	123 785	98.083	76.90	1.473	115 857	94.677	67.35
4800	2.475	139 998	101.186	85.07	1.595	130 081	97.339	74.83
5000	2.700	157 724	104.533	91.91	1.730	145 743	100.221	81.63
5200	2.945	176 622	108.064	96.67	1.879	162 652	103.293	87.22
5400	3.208	196 213	111.693	98.77	2.039	180 514	106.504	91.08
5600	3.483	215 934	115.317	97.96	2.210	198 940	109.786	92.80
5800	3.764	235 211	118.833	94.39	2.388	217 481	113.062	92.23
6000	4.045	253 542	122.150	88.63	2.571	235 686	116.254	89.49
		$p=200$ bar				$p=300$ bar		
1500	0.3174	22 380	66.876	16.01	0.2142	22 467	65.208	16.00
1600	0.3379	23 991	67.915	16.22	0.2279	24 078	66.248	16.22
1700	0.3585	25 623	68.905	16.43	0.2416	25 710	67.237	16.43
1800	0.3791	27 277	69.849	16.64	0.2553	27 363	68.181	16.64
1900	0.3997	28 952	70.753	16.86	0.2691	29 038	69.085	16.85
2000	0.4203	30 649	71.622	17.08	0.2828	30 734	69.953	17.06
2200	0.4615	34 116	73.263	17.60	0.3102	34 194	71.594	17.55
2400	0.5028	37 698	74.800	18.26	0.3377	37 761	73.127	18.15
2600	0.5445	41 377	76.254	19.19	0.3654	41 467	74.575	18.95
2800	0.5866	45 399	77.652	20.50	0.3933	45 364	75.959	20.07
3000	0.6295	49 673	79.019	22.33	0.4217	49 525	77.303	21.61
3200	0.6738	54 372	80.384	24.78	0.4508	54 042	78.630	23.65
3400	0.7199	59 632	81.778	27.94	0.4809	59 024	79.968	26.27
3600	0.7688	65 598	83.234	31.85	0.5126	64 590	81.342	29.50
3800	0.8213	72 422	84.782	36.53	0.5461	70 867	82.779	33.37
4000	0.8783	80 257	86.456	41.94	0.5822	77 978	84.304	37.84
4200	0.9408	89 241	88.281	47.99	0.6213	86 040	85.940	42.87
4400	1.009	99 489	90.282	54.56	0.6639	95 156	87.709	48.35

continued

T, °K	v	i	s	c_p	v	i	s	c_p
4600	1.087	111 083	92.475	61.41	0.7108	105 401	89.625	54.15
4800	1.171	124 052	94.869	68.25	0.7625	116 822	91.696	60.07
5000	1.266	138 360	97.459	74.73	0.8194	129 421	93.933	65.88
5200	1.369	153 893	100.228	80.43	0.8816	143 147	96.322	71.30
5400	1.482	170 449	103.143	84.90	0.9494	157 894	98.849	76.02
5600	1.603	187 746	106.158	87.78	1.022	173 490	101.488	79.76
5800	1.730	205 436	109.214	88.80	1.100	189 112	104.204	82.24
6000	1.862	223 139	112.248	87.91	1.182	206 290	106.955	83.30
		$p=400$ bar				$p=600$ bar		
1500	0.1627	22 553	64.027	16.00	0.1110	22 725	62.364	16.00
1600	0.1729	24 164	65.066	16.22	0.1179	24 336	63.404	16.21
1700	0.1832	25 797	66.055	16.42	0.1247	25 968	64.393	16.42
1800	0.1935	27 450	67.000	16.63	0.1315	27 621	65.337	16.63
1900	0.1637	29 124	67.903	16.84	0.1384	29 294	66.240	16.84
2000	0.2140	30 819	68.771	17.05	0.1452	30 989	67.108	17.04
2200	0.2346	34 276	70.411	17.52	0.1589	34 441	68.746	17.49
2400	0.2552	37 834	71.942	18.08	0.1726	37 988	70.275	18.00
2600	0.2759	41 520	73.386	18.82	0.1864	41 650	71.714	18.65
2800	0.2967	45 378	74.762	19.82	0.2002	45 463	73.082	19.52
3000	0.3179	49 472	76.093	21.18	0.2142	49 477	74.396	20.67
3200	0.3396	53 879	77.399	22.98	0.2285	53 755	75.678	22.18
3400	0.3619	58 696	78.703	25.27	0.2431	58 375	76.945	24.09
3600	0.3852	64 024	80.030	28.10	0.2583	63 421	78.217	26.44
3800	0.4097	69 973	81.402	31.48	0.2742	68 983	79.514	29.24
4000	0.4358	76 652	82.841	35.39	0.2909	75 148	80.855	32.48
4200	0.4639	84 163	84.368	39.79	0.3087	82 003	82.255	36.13
4400	0.4945	92 597	86.001	44.61	0.3278	89 624	83.732	40.13
4600	0.5277	102 026	87.755	49.73	0.3484	98 073	85.297	44.41
4800	0.5640	112 498	89.640	55.01	0.3707	107 398	86.960	48.87
5000	0.6039	124 029	91.660	60.29	0.3950	117 623	88.727	53.39
5200	0.6474	136 598	93.814	65.35	0.4213	128 749	90.600	57.85
5400	0.6947	150 138	96.094	69.96	0.4498	140 747	92.577	62.08
5600	0.7457	164 536	98.483	73.89	0.4806	153 557	94.650	65.94
5800	0.8004	179 635	100.958	76.93	0.5136	167 086	96.807	69.26
6000	0.8583	195 234	103.489	78.88	0.5488	181 213	99.031	71.90
		$p=800$ bar				$p=1000$ bar		
1500	0.08521	22 894	61.188	16.00	0.06969	23 061	60.277	16.00
1600	0.09033	24 506	62.227	16.21	0.07378	24 673	61.316	16.21
1700	0.09545	26 138	63.215	16.42	0.07787	26 305	62.305	16.42
1800	0.1006	27 790	64.159	16.63	0.08196	27 958	63.248	16.63
1900	0.1057	29 464	65.062	16.83	0.08605	29 631	64.152	16.93
2000	0.1108	31 157	65.930	17.03	0.09014	31 325	65.018	17.02
2200	0.1210	34 607	67.568	17.46	0.09833	34 773	66.656	17.45
2400	0.1313	38 148	69.095	17.95	0.1065	38 309	68.182	17.92
2600	0.1416	41 796	70.531	18.55	0.1147	41 947	69.616	18.48
2800	0.1520	45 581	71.894	19.34	0.1230	45 714	70.975	19.21
3000	0.1624	49 547	73.199	20.37	0.1313	49 647	72.274	20.16
3200	0.1730	53 848	74.466	21.70	0.1398	53 796	73.531	21.38
3400	0.1839	58 251	75.711	23.39	0.1484	58 219	74.762	22.91
3600	0.1951	63 129	76.952	25.45	0.1573	62 982	75.982	24.78
3800	0.2068	68 459	78.206	27.91	0.1665	68 154	77.207	26.99
4000	0.2190	74 319	79.489	30.75	0.1761	73 805	78.452	29.56
4200	0.2319	80 782	80.817	33.94	0.1862	80 001	79.732	32.45
4400	0.2458	87 916	82.203	37.45	0.1969	86 802	81.057	35.61
4600	0.2604	95 777	83.659	41.20	0.2083	94 261	82.439	39.01
4800	0.2763	104 409	85.192	45.14	0.2205	102 417	83.886	42.58
5000	0.2934	113 839	86.810	49.17	0.2336	111 297	85.404	46.24
5200	0.3119	124 074	88.516	53.18	0.2477	120 913	86.997	49.92
5400	0.3319	135 102	90.310	57.06	0.2629	131 259	88.665	53.52
5600	0.3534	146 884	92.187	60.71	0.2792	142 311	90.407	56.96
5800	0.3765	159 366	94.141	64.00	0.2967	154 027	92.219	60.15
6000	0.4011	172 454	96.162	66.83	0.3153	166 347	94.094	62.99

Thermodynamic properties of dissociated hydrogen at different temperatures and pressures: x_2—mole fraction H_2, M—molecular weight of the mixture, u—sound velocity (m/s) and k—adiabatic exponent [8, 9]

T, °K	x_2	M	u	k	x_2	M	u	k
	$p=0,1$ bar				$p=1$ bar			
1500	0.9999	2.016	2885	1.345			2887	1.347
1600	0.9998	2.016	2970	1.337			2974	1.340
1700	0.9996	2.016	3049	1.326	0.9998	2.016	3057	1.332
1800	0.9988	2.015	3120	1.311	0.9996	2.016	3135	1.323
1900	0.9974	2.013	3182	1.291	0.9992	2.015	3208	1.313
2000	0.9948	2.011	3235	1.266	0.9984	2.014	3276	1.300
2200	0.9824	1.998	3328	1.210	0.9944	2.010	3394	1.266
2400	0.9508	1.966	3439	1.166	0.9841	2.000	3497	1.226
2600	0.8855	1.901	3602	1.141	0.9623	1.978	3606	1.190
2800	0.7723	1.786	3840	1.131	0.9212	1.937	3744	1.166
3000	0.6095	1.622	4170	1.131	0.8539	1.869	3923	1.153
3200	0.4219	1.433	4595	1.137	0.7553	1.769	4155	1.148
3400	0.2538	1.264	5071	1.150	0.6285	1.642	4449	1.150
3600	0.1370	1.146	5527	1.170	0.4860	1.498	4805	1.155
3800	0.0706	1.079	5937	1.204	0.3475	1.358	5206	1.165
4000	0.0364	1.045	6327	1.257	0.2317	1.242	5620	1.179
4200	0.0195	1.028	6728	1.332	0.1471	1.156	6018	1.199
4400	0.0108	1.019	7133	1.417	0.0913	1.100	6389	1.227
4600	0.0063	1.014	7509	1.495	0.0567	1.065	6743	1.266
4800	0.0038	1.012	7833	1.555	0.0357	1.044	7092	1.316
5000	0.0024	1.010	8104	1.596	0.0230	1.031	7442	1.374
5200	0.0016	1.010	8336	1.622	0.0152	1.023	7783	1.434
5400	0.0011	1.009	8539	1.639	0.0103	1.018	8103	1.489
5600	0.0008	1.009	8723	1.649	0.0072	1.015	8392	1.536
5800	0.0005	1.009	8894	1.654	0.0051	1.013	8649	1.572
6000	0.0004	1.008	9055	1.657	0.0037	1.012	8876	1.595
	$p=5$ bar				$p=10$ bar			
1500							2890	1.349
1600							2978	1.342
1700							3062	1.336
1800							3143	1.329
1900					0.9998	2.016	3222	1.322
2000	0.9992	2.015	3290	1.311	0.9994	2.015	3295	1.315
2200	0.9976	2.014	3423	1.289	0.9982	2.014	3432	1.296
2400	0.9928	2.009	3540	1.261	0.9950	2.011	3554	1.272
2600	0.9829	1.999	3648	1.230	0.9879	2.004	3666	1.245
2800	0.9631	1.979	3761	1.202	0.9743	1.990	3777	1.219
3000	0.9316	1.947	3892	1.182	0.9501	1.966	3897	1.197
3200	0.8818	1.897	4050	1.169	0.9148	1.930	4037	1.182
3400	0.8113	1.826	4245	1.163	0.8624	1.877	4204	1.173
3600	0.7201	1.734	4480	1.162	0.7605	1.775	4402	1.169
3800	0.6125	1.625	4761	1.165	0.7059	1.720	4637	1.170
4000	0.4968	1.509	5084	1.172	0.6068	1.620	4910	1.174
4200	0.3838	1.395	5439	1.181	0.5017	1.514	5219	1.180
4400	0.2836	1.294	5811	1.194	0.3991	1.410	5556	1.190
4600	0.2025	1.212	6181	1.210	0.3064	1.317	5969	1.202
4800	0.1414	1.151	6535	1.231	0.2286	1.238	6263	1.217
5000	0.0981	1.107	6874	1.258	0.1672	1.177	6608	1.236
5200	0.0681	1.077	7199	1.291	0.1211	1.130	6939	1.258
5400	0.0478	1.056	7518	1.329	0.0877	1.097	7258	1.286
5600	0.0340	1.042	7832	1.373	0.0638	1.072	7567	1.319
5800	0.0245	1.033	8139	1.418	0.0468	1.055	7870	1.355
6000	0.0180	1.026	8431	1.465	0.0348	1.043	8166	1.397
	$p=20$ bar				$p=30$ bar			
2000	0.9996	2.016	3300	1.318	0.9998	2.016	3304	1.320
2200	0.9988	2.015	3441	1.302	0.9990	2.015	3446	1.305
2400	0.9964	2.012	3568	1.282	0.9970	2.013	3576	1.287
2600	0.9914	2.007	3684	1.258	0.9930	2.009	3694	1.266

continued

T, °K	x_2	M	u	k	x_2	M	u	k
2800	0.9818	1.998	3795	1.234	0.9851	2.001	3807	1.243
3000	0.9652	1.981	3910	1.213	0.9716	1.987	3920	1.222
3200	0.9389	1.954	4037	1.196	0.9499	1.965	4042	1.205
3400	0.9006	1.916	4183	1.185	0.9179	1.933	4179	1.192
3600	0.8481	1.863	4354	1.179	0.8741	1.889	4336	1.185
3800	0.7813	1.796	4552	1.177	0.8170	1.832	4517	1.181
4000	0.7011	1.715	4782	1.178	0.7478	1.762	4725	1.181
4200	0.6111	1.624	5043	1.182	0.6681	1.681	4962	1.184
4400	0.5165	1.529	5335	1.189	0.5813	1.594	5227	1.189
4600	0.4234	1.435	5652	1.198	0.4992	1.504	5518	1.197
4800	0.3373	1.348	5984	1.209	0.4061	1.417	5831	1.207
5000	0.2623	1.272	6322	1.223	0.3272	1.338	6154	1.218
5200	0.2005	1.210	6655	1.239	0.2586	1.269	6482	1.232
5400	0.1516	1.161	6979	1.259	0.2014	1.211	6805	1.249
5600	0.1141	1.123	7292	1.282	0.1556	1.165	7120	1.268
5800	0.0861	1.095	7594	1.309	0.1198	1.129	7424	1.290
6000	0.0654	1.074	7887	1.339	0.0924	1.101	7719	1.311
		p=40 bar				p=50 bar		
1500							2905	1.355
1600							2992	1.348
1700							3076	1.342
1800							3157	1.336
1900							3239	1.329
2000	0.9998	2.016	3308	1.321	0.9998	2.016	3311	1.323
2200	0.9992	2.015	3451	1.307	0.9992	2.016	3455	1.309
2400	0.9974	2.013	3582	1.290	0.9978	2.014	3586	1.293
2600	0.9940	2.010	3702	1.270	0.9946	2.011	3708	1.274
2800	0.9871	2.003	3815	1.249	0.9885	2.004	3822	1.254
3000	0.9753	1.991	3928	1.229	0.9778	1.994	3934	1.234
3200	0.9564	1.972	4047	1.211	0.9610	1.977	4052	1.217
3400	0.9286	1.944	4179	1.198	0.9359	1.951	4180	1.203
3600	0.8900	1.905	4328	1.190	0.9010	1.916	4324	1.194
3800	0.8396	1.854	4498	1.185	0.8551	1.870	4486	1.189
4000	0.7773	1.792	4692	1.184	0.7982	1.813	4671	1.187
4200	0.7046	1.718	4913	1.186	0.7309	1.745	4881	1.188
4400	0.6242	1.637	5161	1.191	0.6555	1.669	5115	1.192
4600	0.5396	1.552	5434	1.197	0.5749	1.587	5375	1.197
4800	0.4553	1.467	5729	1.206	0.4930	1.505	5656	1.205
5000	0.3756	1.387	6040	1.216	0.4138	1.425	5955	1.215
5200	0.3103	1.321	6359	1.228	0.3407	1.351	6266	1.226
5400	0.2419	1.252	6679	1.243	0.2759	1.286	6580	1.239
5600	0.1905	1.200	6993	1.260	0.2207	1.230	6893	1.255
5800	0.1492	1.158	7299	1.279	0.1753	1.185	7199	1.272
6000	0.1167	1.126	7595	1.298	0.1386	1.148	7496	1.291
		p=60 bar				p=70 bar		
2000	0.9998	2.016	3315	1.324	0.9998	2.016	3318	1.326
2200	0.9992	2.015	3458	3.311	0.9994	2.015	3462	1.312
2400	0.9980	2.014	3591	1.295	0.9980	2.014	3595	1.297
2600	0.9950	2.011	3713	1.277	0.9954	2.011	3717	1.280
2800	0.9895	2.005	3828	1.257	0.9902	2.006	3833	1.261
3000	0.9798	1.996	3941	1.238	0.9812	1.997	3946	1.242
3200	0.9643	1.980	4057	1.221	0.9670	1.983	4061	1.224
3400	0.9412	1.957	4182	1.207	0.9455	1.961	4185	1.211
3600	0.9091	1.924	4322	1.198	0.9155	1.931	4320	1.200
3800	0.8669	1.882	4479	1.192	0.8760	1.891	4474	1.195
4000	0.8139	1.828	4657	1.189	0.8263	1.841	4646	1.192
4200	0.7510	1.765	4857	1.190	0.7671	1.781	4839	1.192
4400	0.6797	1.693	5080	1.193	0.6991	1.713	5056	1.194
4600	0.6027	1.616	5330	1.198	0.6252	1.638	5295	1.199
4800	0.5232	1.535	5600	1.205	0.5481	1.560	5556	1.205
5000	0.4450	1.457	5889	1.214	0.4711	1.483	5836	1.214
5200	0.3714	1.382	6192	1.225	0.3977	1.409	6131	1.224

continued

T, °K	x_2	M	u	k	x_2	M	u	k
5400	0.3050	1.315	6500	1.237	0.3302	1.341	6434	1.235
5600	0.2472	1.257	6810	1.251	0.2706	1.281	6740	1.249
5800	0.1985	1.208	7115	1.267	0.2196	1.229	7044	1.264
6000	0.1587	1.168	7413	1.285	0.1771	1.177	7341	1.279
		p=80 bar				p=90 bar		
2000	0.9998	2.016	3321	1.327	0.9998	2.016	3324	1.328
2200	0.9994	2.015	3465	1.314	0.9994	2.015	3468	1.315
2400	0.9982	2.014	3598	1.299	0.9984	2.014	3602	1.301
2600	0.9956	2.012	3722	1.282	0.9960	2.012	3726	1.284
2800	0.9908	2.007	3838	1.263	0.9914	2.007	3843	1.266
3000	0.9824	1.998	3951	1.245	0.9833	1.999	3955	1.247
3200	0.9683	1.985	4066	1.228	0.9706	1.986	4070	1.231
3400	0.9489	1.964	4187	1.214	0.9518	1.967	4190	1.216
3600	0.9209	1.936	4321	1.203	0.9251	1.941	4322	1.206
3800	0.8836	1.899	4471	1.197	0.8898	1.905	4468	1.199
4000	0.8365	1.851	4638	1.194	0.8450	1.860	4632	1.196
4200	0.7802	1.794	4825	1.193	0.7913	1.806	4814	1.195
4400	0.7154	1.765	5035	1.195	0.7291	1.743	5018	1.196
4600	0.6441	1.657	5267	1.199	0.6602	1.673	5243	1.200
4800	0.5692	1.582	5520	1.205	0.5873	1.600	5490	1.206
5000	0.4937	1.506	5793	1.213	0.5132	1.525	5755	1.213
5200	0.4206	1.432	6080	1.223	0.4407	1.452	6036	1.222
5400	0.3526	1.363	6378	1.234	0.3726	1.384	6329	1.233
5600	0.2917	1.302	6680	1.247	0.3107	1.321	6628	1.245
5800	0.2388	1.249	6982	1.261	0.2563	1.266	6927	1.259
6000	0.1941	1.204	7278	1.276	0.2098	1.219	7223	1.274
		p=100 bar				p=150 bar		
1500			2923	1.363			2941	1.372
1600			3009	1.356			3027	1.364
1700			3093	1.349			3110	1.356
1800			3174	1.343			3190	1.349
1900			3268	1.336			3283	1.342
2000	0.9998	2.016	3327	1.330				
2200	0.9994	2.015	3472	1.317	0.9996	2.016		
2400	0.9984	2.014	3605	1.302	0.9987	2.014		
2600	0.9962	2.012	3730	1.286	0.9969	2.013		
2800	0.9918	2.008	3847	1.268	0.9934	2.010		
3000	0.9843	2.000	3960	1.250	0.9871	2.003	3978	1.260
3200	0.9722	1.988	4074	1.233	0.9773	1.993	4091	1.244
3400	0.9541	1.970	4193	1.219	0.9623	1.978	4208	1.229
3600	0.9288	1.944	4323	1.208	0.9414	1.957	4332	1.218
3800	0.8950	1.910	4467	1.201	0.9135	1.929	4466	1.210
4000	0.8524	1.867	4627	1.197	0.8776	1.893	4615	1.205
4200	0.8007	1.815	4805	1.196	0.8339	1.849	4779	1.202
4400	0.7408	1.755	5004	1.197	0.7824	1.797	4960	1.202
4600	0.6743	1.688	5224	1.200	0.7241	1.738	5159	1.205
4800	0.6032	1.616	5464	1.206	0.6607	1.674	5378	1.208
5000	0.5305	1.543	5724	1.213	0.5940	1.607	5614	1.214
5200	0.4587	1.470	5999	1.222	0.5263	1.539	5867	1.221
5400	0.3905	1.402	6287	1.232	0.4597	1.471	6134	1.230
5600	0.3280	1.339	6582	1.244	0.3965	1.408	6411	1.240
5800	0.2725	1.283	6878	1.257	0.3381	1.349	6695	1.251
6000	0.2245	1.234	7173	1.271	0.3023	1.313	6981	1.262
		p=200 bar				p=300 bar		
1500			2959	1.380			2995	1.396
1600			3044	1.371			3079	1.386
1700			3127	1.363			3160	1.377
1800			3206	1.356			3238	1.369
1900			3299	1.349			3330	1.361
2000	0.9998	2.016	3358	1.342			3388	1.353
2200	0.9996	2.016	3502	1.328	0.9996	2.016	3530	1.339

continued

T, °K	x_2	M	u	k	x_2	M	u	k
2400	0.9988	2.015	3636	1.315	0.9990	2.015	3664	1.325
2600	0.9972	2.013	3762	1.300	0.9978	2.014	3791	1.311
2800	0.9942	2.010	3881	1.284	0.9952	2.011	3910	1.295
3000	0.9889	2.005	3995	1.267	0.9908	2.007	4024	1.280
3200	0.9802	1.996	4107	1.252	0.9837	2.000	4135	1.264
3400	0.9673	1.983	4221	1.237	0.9732	1.989	4247	1.250
3600	0.9489	1.961	4342	1.226	0.9581	1.971	4363	1.238
3800	0.9246	1.940	4471	1.217	0.9378	1.953	4486	1.228
4000	0.8930	1.908	4612	1.211	0.9117	1.927	4619	1.221
4200	0.8543	1.869	4767	1.208	0.8790	1.894	4762	1.217
4400	0.8083	1.823	4938	1.206	0.8403	1.855	4919	1.215
4600	0.7556	1.770	5124	1.208	0.7952	1.810	5090	1.214
4800	0.6978	1.711	5328	1.211	0.7447	1.759	5275	1.216
5000	0.6360	1.649	5549	1.216	0.6900	1.704	5475	1.220
5200	0.5721	1.585	5786	1.222	0.6323	1.645	5691	1.224
5400	0.5080	1.520	6037	1.230	0.5728	1.585	5920	1.230
5600	0.4456	1.457	6300	1.238	0.5135	1.526	6162	1.238
5800	0.3866	1.398	6572	1.248	0.4557	1.467	6414	1.246
6000	0.3323	1.343	6848	1.258	0.4008	1.412	6674	1.254
		p=400 bar				p=600 bar		
1500			3030	1.411			3100	1.442
1600			3113	1.401			3179	1.429
1700			3192	1.391			3257	1.417
1800			3269	1.381			3332	1.406
1900			3360	1.373			3435	1.396
2000			3418	1.365			3476	1.387
2200	0.9998	2.016	3558	1.350	0.9998	2.016	3614	1.370
2400	0.9992	2.015	3692	1.335	0.9994	2.015	3745	1.354
2600	0.9980	2.014	3817	1.320	0.9984	2.014	3869	1.339
2800	0.9958	2.012	3936	1.305	0.9966	2.013	3987	1.323
3000	0.9920	2.008	4050	1.289	0.9934	2.009	4099	1.307
3200	0.9859	2.002	4161	1.275	0.9885	2.004	4209	1.292
3400	0.9767	1.993	4272	1.260	0.9808	1.997	4318	1.278
3600	0.9635	1.979	4385	1.248	0.9701	1.986	4428	1.265
3800	0.9459	1.961	4504	1.238	0.9554	1.971	4542	1.254
4000	0.9229	1.938	4631	1.230	0.9363	1.952	4662	1.245
4200	0.8943	1.909	4768	1.224	0.9124	1.928	4789	1.238
4400	0.8598	1.875	4916	1.222	0.8836	1.899	4926	1.234
4600	0.8197	1.834	5076	1.221	0.8498	1.865	5074	1.231
4800	0.7743	1.788	5249	1.221	0.8109	1.825	5232	1.231
5000	0.7246	1.738	5437	1.224	0.7680	1.782	5402	1.232
5200	0.6714	1.685	5638	1.227	0.7213	1.735	5585	1.234
5400	0.6160	1.629	5852	1.232	0.6718	1.685	5779	1.237
5600	0.5597	1.572	6079	1.239	0.6206	1.634	5985	1.242
5800	0.5039	1.516	6316	1.246	0.5688	1.581	6201	1.248
6000	0.4497	1.461	6562	1.253	0.5172	1.529	6426	1.253
		p=800 bar				p=1000 bar		
1500			3167	1.471			3233	1.499
1600			3244	1.456			3307	1.483
1700			3319	1.443			3380	1.467
1800			3392	1.430			3452	1.454
1900			3493	1.419			3660	1.441
2000			3533	1.408			3589	1.429
2200	0.9998	2.016	3668	1.389	0.9998	2.016	3721	1.408
2400	0.9994	2.015	3796	1.372	0.9994	2.015	3847	1.389
2600	0.9986	2.015	3919	1.355	0.9988	2.015	3967	1.372
2800	0.9970	2.013	4035	1.339	0.9974	2.013	4082	1.355
3000	0.9944	2.010	4147	1.323	0.9948	2.011	4193	1.338
3200	0.9899	2.006	4255	1.308	0.9910	2.007	4299	1.322
3400	0.9833	1.999	4362	1.293	0.9851	2.001	4404	1.307
3600	0.9739	1.990	4469	1.280	0.9765	1.992	4510	1.293
3800	0.9612	1.977	4580	1.268	0.9650	1.981	4618	1.281

continued

T, °K	x_2	M	u	k	x_2	M	u	k
4000	0.9444	1.960	4695	1.258	0.9501	1.966	4730	1.270
4200	0.9236	1.939	4817	1.251	0.9311	1.947	4847	1.262
4400	0.8981	1.913	4947	1.245	0.9080	1.923	4972	1.256
4600	0.8681	1.883	5084	1.242	0.8809	1.896	5105	1.251
4800	0.8337	1.848	5235	1.240	0.8495	1.864	5247	1.248
5000	0.7950	1.809	5394	1.239	0.8141	1.829	5398	1.247
5200	0.7528	1.767	5564	1.240	0.7753	1.790	5559	1.247
5400	0.7078	1.721	5745	1.243	0.7334	1.747	5731	1.249
5600	0.6604	1.674	5937	1.247	0.6892	1.703	5912	1.252
5800	0.6119	1.625	6139	1.251	0.6434	1.657	6102	1.255
6000	0.5630	1.576	6349	1.255	0.5968	1.610	6301	1.258

Viscosity η (N · s/m²) of parahydrogen and hydrogen at saturation [393]

T, °K	Parahydrogen		T, °K	Hydrogen		T, °K	Parahydrogen		T, °K	Hydrogen	
	$\eta' \cdot 10^8$	$\eta'' \cdot 10^8$		$\eta' \cdot 10^8$	$\eta'' \cdot 10^8$		$\eta' \cdot 10^8$	$\eta'' \cdot 10^8$		$\eta' \cdot 10^8$	$\eta'' \cdot 10^8$
14	2310	76	14	2450	76	26	826	152	26	846	149
15	2050	80	15	2140	80	27	776	160	27	784	156
16	1840	86	16	1910	86	28	716	169	28	729	165
17	1660	92	17	1720	92	29	667	179	29	676	174
18	1510	98	18	1560	98	30	617	190	30	627	186
19	1390	104	19	1420	102	31	560	206	31	567	200
20	1270	111	20	1310	109	31.5	531	216	31.5	535	209
21	1180	118	21	1200	117	32	500	230	32	500	219
22	1090	126	22	1120	124	32.5	460	252	32.5	454	235
23	1020	133	23	1050	130	32.7	434	260	32.7	432	243
24	945	139	24	970	137	32.976	346	346	33.22	338	338
25	886	145	25	905	143						

Viscosity $\eta \cdot 10^8$ (N · sec/m²) of hydrogen at temperatures from 15 - 1000°K and pressures from 1 - 1000 bar [349]*

T, °K \ p, bar →	1	10	20	50	100	150	200	300	500	750	1000
15	2100	2239	2405								
16	1860	1988	2130	2570							
17	1680	1784	1911	2286	2940						
18	1520	1596	1711	2065	2638						
19	1400	1484	1588	1895	2407	2995					
20	1300	1381	1470	1740	2200	2700	3240				
21	116	1265	1350	1609	2038	2475	2955				
22	121	1172	1255	1495	1876	2302	2740				
23	125	1100	1175	1390	1760	2125	2525	3350			
25	135	960	1025	1230	1555	1875	2201	2900			
27	145	811	900	1091	1379	1654	1952	2539			
30	160	638	730	930	1200	1444	1690	2195			
33	175	220	598	805	1056	1275	1481	1901			
36	188	205	405	705	945	1140	1329	1704			
40	207	222	275	585	828	1000	1170	1506	2330		
45	228	236	265	470	717	880	1024	1311	1982		
50	249	254	280	420	625	790	925	1177	1741		

*The difference in viscosities of parahydrogen and hydrogen in the liquid phase does not exceed 2–3%. Above critical temperature, their viscosities may be considered equal.

continued

p, bar → / T, °K	1	10	20	50	100	150	200	300	500	750	1000
60	288	294	299	380	537	665	783	995	1324	2115	
80	358	362	368	400	480	570	655	810	1131	1561	2092
100	421	423	424	442	500	562	634	763	995	1307	1680
150	560	562	564	574	600	633	669	746	898	1082	1288
200	681	682	685	691	706	723	750	802	913	1047	1186
300	896	896	898	902	910	921	933	962	1030	1121	1210
500	1264	1264	1265	1267	1271	1275	1283	1296	1329	1379	1434
750	1660	1660	1660	1662	1664	1667	1670	1678	1697	1726	1759
1000	2013	2013	2013	2015	2017	2018	2020	2025	2036	2057	2079

Viscosity $\eta \cdot 10^8$ ($N \cdot s/m^2$) of hydrogen at low temperatures and different pressures [10]

p, bar → / t, °C	1	40	60	80	100	120	140	160	180	200
—200	335	369	404	446	491	537	582	621	662	700
—180	399	419	445	465	494	522	550	580	612	644
—160	460	475	489	505	522	545	567	589	611	635
—140	516	527	539	550	563	579	594	611	629	648
—120	568	579	583	595	605	617	630	643	657	672
—100	620	629	637	643	651	660	670	682	693	704
—80	665	673	680	687	694	701	709	718	727	736
—60	711	718	723	729	736	743	749	757	766	774
—40	756	762	766	773	778	785	792	797	801	807
—20	800	805	810	814	820	825	832	838	843	848
0	840	845	848	853	857	862	867	874	880	886
20	880	884	888	891	895	900	905	911	916	922

Viscosity $\eta \cdot 10^8$ ($N \cdot s/m^2$) of hydrogen at elevated temperatures and different pressures [11, 12]

p, bar → / t, °C	1	100	200	300	400	500
0	840	857	886	917	948	982
100	1033	1044	1062	1084	1107	1130
200	1213	1221	1234	1250	1267	1285
300	1382	1388	1398	1410	1424	1439
400	1538	1543	1551	1561	1572	1584
500	1686	1690	1696	1705	1714	1724
600	1828	1831	1837	1844	1852	1860
700	1965	1968	1973	1979	1986	1993
800	2103	2105	2110	2115	2121	2127
900	2235	2237	2241	2245	2251	2257
1000	2355	2357	2360	2364	2369	2374

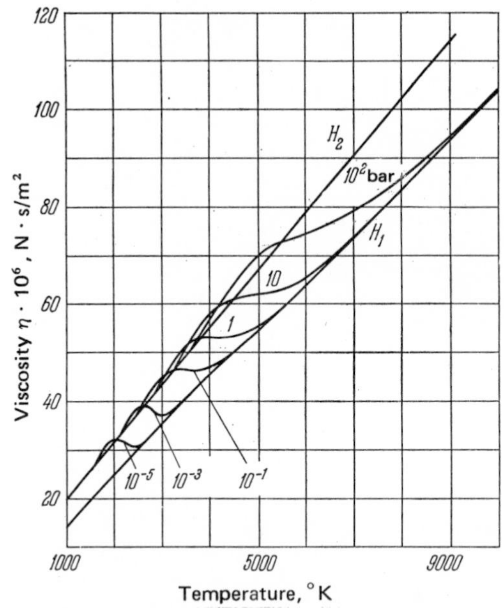

Fig. 4. Viscosity of dissociated hydrogen (H_1 – atomic and H_2 – molecular)

Viscosity $\eta \cdot 10^8$ (N·s/m²) of dissociated hydrogen [13]

T, °K \ p, bar →	10^{-5}	10^{-4}	10^{-3}	10^{-2}	0.1	1	10	100	200
1000	1997	1997	1997	1997	1997	1997	1997	1997	1997
1200	2262	2262	2262	2262	2262	2262	2262	2262	2262
1400	2507	2507	2507	2507	2507	2507	2507	2507	2507
1600	2740	2738	2737	2737	2737	2737	2737	2737	2737
1800	2988	2972	2965	2962	2962	2961	2961	2961	2961
2000	3215	3227	3200	3188	3183	3182	3181	3181	3181
2200	3123	3459	3475	3441	3425	3419	3417	3417	3417
2400	3038	3413	3728	3721	3682	3665	3659	3657	3657
2600	3172	3308	3770	3995	3957	3919	3904	3899	3898
2800	3359	3365	3423	3762	4207	4234	4180	4154	4150
3000	3565	3576	3675	4131	4497	4474	4421	4398	4395
3200	3773	3777	3813	4073	4636	4756	4690	4651	4645
3400	3973	3974	3988	4112	4642	5008	4966	4906	4896
3600	4164	4165	4171	4229	4601	5189	5245	5168	5152
3800	4348	4348	4351	4379	4604	5271	5514	5437	5415
4000	4529	4529	4531	4545	4674	5273	5749	5708	5680
4200	4708	4708	4708	4716	4791	5255	5934	5981	5951
4400	4886	4886	4886	4891	4935	5266	6054	6247	6221
4600	5061	5061	5061	5064	5091	5319	6114	6499	6486
4800	5237	5237	5237	5239	5256	5411	6138	6727	6742
5000	5414	5414	5414	5415	5426	5533	6152	6925	6981
5200	5591	5591	5591	5592	5600	5674	6178	7087	7199
5400	5770	5770	5770	5770	5776	5828	6229	7214	7390
5600	5950	5950	5950	5951	5955	5993	6306	7309	7548
5800	6136	6136	6136	6136	6139	6167	6412	7384	7681
6000	6326	6326	6326	6327	6329	6350	6541	7449	7790

Viscosity $\eta \cdot 10^7$ (N · s/m²) of ionized hydrogen at high temperatures [14]

p, atm → / T, °K	0.001	0.01	0.1	1	10
6 000	628	632	633	633	633
7 000	669	716	729	731	732
8 000	489	718	804	825	831
9 000	214	537	796	898	925
10 000	62.0	273	639	913	1000
11 000	21.4	115.0	402	805	1037
12 000	10.1	53.0	218	625	1016
13 000	7.5	23.0	111	420	923
14 000	7.4	15.0	59.0	263	764
15 000	8.6	11.8	36.0	162	594
16 000			26.9	104	426
17 000	11.5	14.0	24.3	72.0	306
18 000			24.1	55.6	226

p, atm → / T, °K	0.001	0.01	0.1	1	10
19 000	14.6	18.0		41.0	170
20 000	16.0	20.0	26.0	44.5	135
21 000	18.0	22.0	28.0	44.6	115
22 000				45.3	103
23 000	22.0	27.0	33.0		96.4
24 000				50.8	93.3
25 000	26.0	32.0	40.0		93.6
26 000				58.0	95.1
27 000	32.0	38.0	47.0		97.8
28 000				66.0	96.5
29 000	37.0	44.0	54.0	71.0	122
30 000	39.0	47.0	57.0	76.0	119

Viscosity η of liquid hydrogen at saturation [16, 349]

T, °K	15	16	17	18	19	20	21	22	23	25	27	30
$\eta \cdot 10^8$, N · s/m²	2100	1860	1680	1520	1400	1300	1170	1100	1030	920	765	620

Thermal conductivity λ (W/m · deg) of hydrogen at a pressure of 1 bar [15]

T, °K	λ · 10³	T, °K	λ · 10³	T, °K	λ · 10³	T, °K	λ · 10³
80	53.2	210	137	340	200	950	430
90	60.1	220	142	350	204	1000	448
100	67.0	230	147	400	226	1100	488
110	74.3	240	152	450	247	1200	528
120	81.5	250	157	500	266	1300	568
130	87.8	260	162	550	285	1400	610
140	94.6	270	167	600	305	1500	655
150	101	280	172	650	323	1600	697
160	107	290	178	700	342	1700	742
170	113	300	183	750	360	1800	786
180	119	310	187	800	378	1900	835
190	125	320	191	850	395	2000	878
200	131	330	196	900	412		

Thermal conductivity λ · 10³ (W/m · deg) of hydrogen at different temperatures and pressures

p, bar → / T, °K	1	10	20	30	40	50	60	70	80	90	100	150	200	250	300	350	400	450	500	550	600
80	53.2	55.8	60.0	63.2	66.9	69.8	74.7	78.8	81.8	86.3	90.2										
90	60.1	63.2	66.1	69.2	72.3	75.1	78.0	81.3	84.7	88.0	91.1	108									
100	67.0	70.7	72.6	75.7	67.8	80.9	83.6	86.5	89.2	91.6	94.8	109	119	128	138	147	156	165	174	—	—
110	74.3	77.6	79.7	81.6	83.8	86.7	89.8	92.6	93.8	95.7	98.6	112	122	132	141	150	159	168	176	184	—
120	81.5	83.5	85.6	87.7	89.5	91.6	94.7	96.8	98.7	101	104	115	125	134	143	152	161	170	178	186	194
130	87.8	89.2	91.8	93.7	95.9	97.6	100	102	104	106	108	118	128	137	146	154	162	171	179	188	196
140	94.6	96.4	98.2	100	102	104	106	108	110	111	113	122	131	140	149	157	165	174	182	190	198
150	101	103	105	106	108	109	111	113	115	116	117	126	135	146	153	161	169	177	185	192	199
160	107	109	110	112	113	115	116	118	120	121	122	130	138	146	154	162	170	178	186	194	200
170	113	115	116	118	119	120	121	123	124	125	126	134	141	148	156	164	172	180	187	195	202
180	119	121	122	123	125	126	127	129	129	130	131	138	145	153	160	167	174	181	188	196	203
190	125	127	128	129	130	132	133	134	135	136	137	144	150	157	164	171	177	183	189	197	204
200	131	132	134	135	136	137	139	140	141	142	143	149	156	163	170	176	181	186	192	198	205

continued

p, bar → / T, °K	1	10	20	30	40	50	60	70	80	90	100	150	200	250	300	350	400	450	500	550	600
210	137	138	139	141	142	143	144	145	147	148	149	154	160	166	172	177	183	188	193	199	206
220	142	143	144	145	147	148	149	150	150	151	152	158	164	170	176	181	187	192	197	202	207
230	147	148	149	150	151	152	154	155	156	157	158	163	168	173	178	184	189	194	199	204	209
240	152	153	154	155	156	157	158	159	160	161	162	167	173	178	183	189	194	198	202	207	212
250	157	158	159	160	161	162	163	164	165	167	168	172	177	181	186	191	196	201	205	209	214
260	162	163	164	165	166	167	168	169	170	171	172	177	181	185	189	193	197	202	207	211	216
270	167	168	169	170	171	172	173	174	175	176	177	181	185	189	193	197	201	205	208	212	218
280	172	173	174	175	176	176	177	178	179	180	181	186	190	194	198	202	206	210	214	217	221
290	178	179	180	181	182	182	183	184	185	186	187	191	195	199	203	206	210	214	218	221	224
300	183	183	184	185	186	187	188	189	190	191	192	195	198	201	204	208	212	216	220	224	227
350	204	204	205	206	207	208	209	209	210	211	212	215	218	221	224	227	231	235	238	241	244
400	226	226	227	228	229	229	230	230	231	232	232	235	238	241	244	247	250	253	256	259	262
450	247	247	248	249	249	250	250	251	252	252	253	256	258	261	264	267	269	272	275	278	280
500	266	266	267	268	268	269	269	270	270	271	271	274	276	278	281	283	286	288	291	294	295
550	285	285	286	286	287	287	288	288	289	289	290	292	294	296	298	300	302	304	306	308	309
600	305	305	306	306	307	307	307	308	308	309	309	311	313	315	316	317	319	320	322	323	325
700	342				343				344		345	346	347	348	349	350	351	352	354	355	356
800	378				379				380		381	382	383	384	385	386	387	388	389	390	391
900	412				413				414			415	416	417	418	419	420	421	422	423	424
1000	448				449				450			451	452	453	454	455	456	457	458	459	460
1100	488				489				490			491	492		493	494	495	496	497	498	499
1200	528								529		530	531	532		533	534	535	536	537	538	539

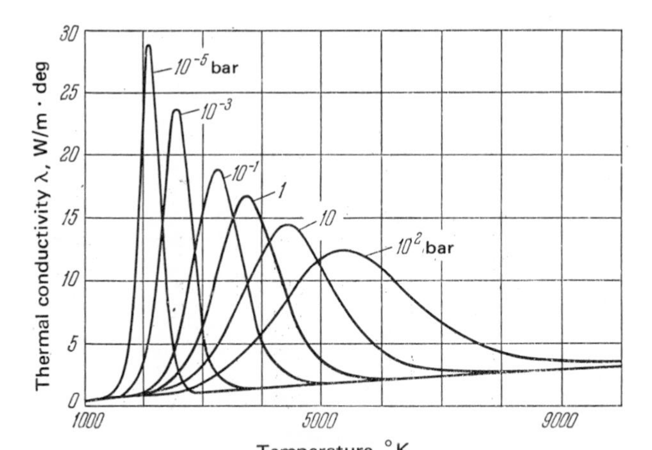

Fig. 5. Thermal conductivity of dissociated hydrogen as a function of temperature with pressure as a parameter.

Thermal conductivity λ (W/m · deg) of dissociated hydrogen [13]

p, bar → / T, °K	10^{-5}	10^{-4}	10^{-3}	10^{-2}	0.1	1	10	100	200
1400	0.7222	0.6304	0.6013	0.5921	0.5892	0.5883	0.5880	0.5879	0.5879
1600	1.951	1.071	0.7910	0.7021	0.6739	0.6650	0.6622	0.6613	0.6612
1800	7.848	3.080	1.485	0.9724	0.8095	0.7578	0.7415	0.7363	0.7356
2000	23.07	9.687	3.795	1.770	1.114	0.9050	0.8387	0.8178	0.8149
2200	24.72	22.12	9.589	3.834	1.838	1.190	0.9829	0.9174	0.9085
2400	7.330	23.93	19.07	8.149	3.381	1.745	1.215	1.047	1.024
2600	2.154	9.991	23.51	14.87	6.203	2.755	1.597	1.224	1.173
2800	1.285	3.347	14.80	20.75	10.49	4.418	2.203	1.474	1.374
3000	1.165	1.711	6.255	19.43	15.49	6.871	3.115	1.827	1.649
3200	1.186	1.349	2.890	12.12	18.78	10.02	4.396	2.311	2.018

continued

T, °K \ p, bar →	10^{-5}	10^{-4}	10^{-3}	10^{-2}	0.1	1	10	100	200
3400	1.235	1.291	1.837	6.269	17.72	13.40	6.067	2.951	2.500
3600	1.291	1.312	1.523	3.456	13.09	16.00	8.077	3.763	3.110
3800	1.346	1.355	1.444	2.301	8.326	16.68	10.26	4.747	3.853
4000	1.402	1.406	1.447	1.847	5.185	15.05	12.31	5.887	4.725
4200	1.457	1.459	1.479	1.677	3.477	11.99	13.87	7.145	5.712
4400	1.512	1.513	1.523	1.627	2.612	8.849	14.56	8.461	6.785
4600	1.566	1.567	1.572	1.630	2.186	6.387	14.22	9.748	7.902
4800	1.620	1.621	1.624	1.657	1.983	4.715	12.97	10.89	8.996
5000	1.675	1.675	1.677	1.697	1.895	3.663	11.19	11.80	10.01
5200	1.730	1.730	1.731	1.744	1.868	3.022	9.297	12.38	10.87
5400	1.785	1.785	1.786	1.794	1.875	2.642	7.596	12.57	11.52
5600	1.841	1.841	1.842	1.847	1.901	2.421	6.214	12.37	11.90
5800	1.898	1.898	1.899	1.903	1.939	2.300	5.158	11.84	12.01
6000	1.957	1.957	1.958	1.960	1.986	2.241	4.384	11.05	11.83

Thermal conductivity* of liquid hydrogen [16]

T, °K	16	17	18	19	20	21	22	23	24	25	26	27	28	29	30
$\lambda \cdot 10^3$, W/m · deg	108	111	113	116	118	120	123	125	127	129	132	134	137	139	141

*Within experimental accuracy (±2%) [395] The values are independent of ortho–para composition.

Surface tension of normal hydrogen* [16, 395, 396]

T, °K	15	16	17	18	19	20	21	22	23	24
$\sigma \cdot 10^3$, N/m	2.83	2.66	2.49	2.32	2.15	1.98	1.81	1.64	1.47	1.30
T, °K	25	26	27	28	29	30	31	32	32.5	32.77
$\sigma \cdot 10^3$, N/m	1.13	0.960	0.796	0.648	0.483	0.333	0.207	0.106	0.062	0.046

*Measurements at 17–20 °K [397] showed that the values of surface tension for para-hydrogen are 2% lower than for normal hydrogen.

WATER (H_2O)

Molecular weight 18.016

t_{cr} = 100.0 °C at 760 mm Hg; t_{melt} = 0.0 °C;
t_{boil} = 374.12 °C; p_{cr} = 221.2 bar; ρ_{cr} = 317.8 kg/m³

Thermodynamic properties of water and steam at saturation
p (bar), v (m³/kg), i and r (kJ/kg) and s (kJ/kg · deg) [17]

t, °C	p	$v' \cdot 10^3$	$v'' \cdot 10^3$	i'	i''	r	s'	s''
0.00	0.006108	1.0002	206 321	−0.04	2501.0	2501.0	−0.00016	9.1565
0.01	0.006112	1.00022	206 175	0.000614	2501.0	2501.0	0.00005	9.1562
2	0.007054	1.0001	179 935	8.39	2504.7	2496.3	0.0306	9.1035
4	0.008129	1.0000	157 267	16.80	2508.3	2491.5	0.0611	9.0514
6	0.009346	1.0000	137 768	25.21	2512.0	2486.8	0.0913	9.0003
8	0.010721	1.0001	120 952	33.60	2515.7	2482.1	0.1213	8.9501
10	0.012271	1.0003	106 419	41.99	2519.4	2477.4	0.1510	8.9009
12	0.014015	1.0004	93 828	50.38	2523.0	2472.6	0.1805	8.8525

continued

t, °C	p	$v' \cdot 10^3$	$v'' \cdot 10^3$	i'	i''	r	s'	s''
14	0.015974	1.0007	82 893	58.75	2526.7	2467.9	0.2098	8.8050
16	0.018170	1.0010	73 376	67.13	2530.4	2463.3	0.2388	8.7583
18	0.020626	1.0013	65 080	75.50	2534.0	2458.5	0.2677	8.7125
20	0.023368	1.0017	57 833	83.86	2537.7	2453.8	0.2963	8.6674
22	0.026424	1.0022	51 488	92.22	2541.4	2449.2	0.3247	8.6232
24	0.029824	1.0026	45 923	100.59	2545.0	2444.4	0.3530	8.5797
26	0.033600	1.0032	41 031	108.95	2548.6	2439.6	0.3810	8.5370
28	0.037785	1.0037	36 726	117.31	2552.3	2435.0	0.4088	8.4950
30	0.042417	1.0043	32 929	125.66	2555.9	2430.2	0.4365	8.4537
32	0.047536	1.0049	29 572	134.02	2559.5	2425.5	0.4640	8.4132
34	0.053182	1.0056	26 602	142.38	2563.2	2420.8	0.4913	8.3733
36	0.059401	1.0063	23 968	150.74	2566.8	2416.1	0.5184	8.3341
38	0.066240	1.0070	21 629	159.09	2570.4	2411.3	0.5453	8.2955
40	0.073749	1.0078	19 548	167.45	2574.0	2406.5	0.5721	8.2576
42	0.081983	1.0086	17 694	175.81	2577.6	2401.8	0.5987	8.2203
44	0.090998	1.0094	16 039	184.17	2581.1	2396.9	0.6252	8.1836
46	0.100854	1.0103	14 559	192.53	2584.7	2392.2	0.6514	8.1475
48	0.11161	1.0112	13 236	200.89	2588.3	2387.4	0.6776	8.1121
50	0.12335	1.0121	12 048	209.26	2591.8	2382.5	0.7035	8.0771
52	0.13612	1.0131	10 982	217.62	2595.4	2377.8	0.7293	8.0427
54	0.15001	1.0140	10 024	225.98	2598.9	2372.9	0.7550	8.0089
56	0.16510	1.0150	9 160.9	234.35	2602.4	2368.1	0.7804	7.9756
58	0.18146	1.0161	8 383.1	242.72	2606.0	2363.3	0.8058	7.9428
60	0.19919	1.0171	7 680.7	251.09	2609.5	2358.4	0.8310	7.9106
62	0.21837	1.0182	7 045.8	259.46	2613.0	2353.5	0.8560	7.8788
64	0.23910	1.0193	6 471.1	257.84	2616.4	2348.6	0.8809	7.8475
66	0.26148	1.0205	5 950.2	276.21	2619.9	2343.7	0.9057	7.8167
68	0.28561	1.0217	5 477.5	284.59	2623.3	2338.7	0.9303	7.7864
70	0.31161	1.0228	5 047.9	292.97	2626.8	2333.8	0.9548	7.7565
72	0.33957	1.0241	4 657.4	301.36	2630.2	2328.8	0.9792	7.7270
74	0.36963	1.0253	4 301.5	309.74	2633.6	2323.9	1.0034	7.6980
76	0.40190	1.0266	3 977.1	318.13	2637.0	2318.9	1.0275	7.6694
78	0.43650	1.0279	3 681.1	326.52	2640.4	2313.9	1.0514	7.6413
80	0.47359	1.0292	3 410.4	334.92	2643.8	2308.9	1.0752	7.6135
82	0.51328	1.0305	3 162.9	343.31	2647.1	2303.8	1.0990	7.5862
84	0.55572	1.0319	2 936.2	351.71	2650.4	2298.7	1.1225	7.5592
86	0.60107	1.0333	2 728.4	360.12	2653.7	2293.6	1.1460	7.5326
88	0.64947	1.0347	2 537.6	368.53	2657.0	2288.5	1.1693	7.5064
90	0.70108	1.0361	2 362.4	376.94	2660.3	2283.4	1.1925	7.4805
92	0.75607	1.0376	2 201.2	385.36	2663.5	2278.1	1.2156	7.4550
94	0.81460	1.0391	2 052.9	393.78	2666.8	2273.0	1.2386	7.4299
96	0.87685	1.0406	1 916.3	402.20	2670.0	2267.8	1.2615	7.4051
98	0.94301	1.0421	1 790.2	410.63	2673.2	2262.6	1.2842	7.3806
100	1.01325	1.0437	1 673.8	419.06	2676.3	2257.2	1.3069	7.3564
105	1.20799	1.0477	1 420.0	440.17	2684.1	2243.9	1.3630	7.2974
110	1.4326	1.0519	1 210.6	461.32	2691.8	2230.5	1.4185	7.2402
115	1.6905	1.0562	1 036.9	482.50	2699.3	2216.8	1.4733	7.1848
120	1.9854	1.0606	892.02	503.7	2706.6	2202.9	1.5276	7.1310
125	2.3209	1.0652	770.67	525.0	2713.8	2188.8	1.5813	7.0788
130	2.7012	1.0700	668.51	546.3	2720.7	2174.4	1.6344	7.0281
140	3.6136	1.0801	508.75	589.1	2734.0	2144.9	1.7390	6.9307
150	4.7597	1.0908	392.61	632.2	2746.3	2114.1	1.8416	6.8381
160	6.1804	1.1022	306.85	675.5	2757.7	2082.2	1.9425	6.7498
170	7.9202	1.1145	242.59	719.1	2768.0	2048.9	2.0416	6.6652
180	10.027	1.1275	193.81	763.1	2777.1	2014.0	2.1393	6.5838
190	12.552	1.1415	158.31	807.5	2784.9	1977.4	2.2356	6.5052
200	15.551	1.1565	127.14	852.4	2791.4	1939.0	2.3307	6.4289
210	19.079	1.1726	104.22	897.8	2796.4	1898.6	2.4247	6.3546
220	23.201	1.1900	86.02	943.7	2799.9	1856.2	2.5178	6.2819
230	27.979	1.2087	71.43	990.3	2801.7	1811.4	2.6102	6.2104
240	33.480	1.2291	59.64	1037.6	2801.6	1764.0	2.7021	6.1397
250	39.776	1.2513	50.02	1085.8	2799.5	1713.7	2.7936	6.0693
260	46.940	1.2756	42.12	1135.0	2795.2	1660.2	2.8850	5.9989
270	55.051	1.3025	35.57	1185.4	2788.3	1602.9	2.9766	5.9278

continued

t, °C	p	$v' \cdot 10^3$	$v'' \cdot 10^3$	i'	i''	r	s'	s''
280	64.191	1.3324	30.10	1237.0	2778.6	1541.6	3.0687	5.8555
290	74.448	1.3659	25.51	1290.3	2765.4	1475.1	3.1616	5.7811
300	85.917	1.4041	21.62	1345.4	2748.4	1403.0	3.2559	5.7038
305	92.136	1.4252	19.89	1373.9	2738.3	1364.4	3.3037	5.6637
310	98.697	1.4480	18.29	1402.9	2726.8	1323.9	3.3522	5.6224
315	105.613	1.4726	16.81	1432.7	2714.0	1281.3	3.4013	5.5798
320	112.90	1.4995	15.44	1463.4	2699.6	1236.2	3.4513	5.5356
325	120.57	1.5289	14.16	1494.9	2683.6	1188.7	3.5023	5.4896
330	128.65	1.5614	12.96	1527.5	2665.5	1138.0	3.5546	5.4414
335	137.14	1.5977	11.84	1561.4	2645.4	1084.0	3.6084	5.3908
340	146.08	1.6390	10.78	1596.8	2622.3	1025.5	3.6638	5.3363
345	155.48	1.6859	9.779	1633.7	2596.2	962.5	3.7211	5.2782
350	165.37	1.7407	8.822	1672.9	2566.1	893.2	3.7816	5.2149
355	175.77	1.8073	7.895	1715.5	2530.5	815.0	3.8467	5.1442
360	186.74	1.8930	6.970	1763.1	2485.7	722.6	3.9189	5.0603
362	191.29	1.9357	6.593	1784.3	2463.5	679.2	3.9509	5.0204
364	195.94	1.9861	6.209	1807.2	2438.1	630.9	3.9856	4.9758
366	200.69	2.0472	5.815	1832.6	2409.3	576.7	4.0238	4.9262
368	205.55	2.125	5.404	1861.6	2376.1	514.5	4.0676	4.8701
370	210.53	2.230	4.958	1896.2	2335.7	439.5	4.1198	4.8031
371	213.06	2.298	4.710	1916.5	2310.7	394.2	4.1503	4.7624
372	215.62	2.392	4.432	1942.0	2280.1	338.1	4.1891	4.7130
373	218.21	2.524	4.090	1974.5	2238.3	263.8	4.2385	4.6467
374	220.84	2.834	3.482	2039.2	2150.7	111.5	4.3374	4.5096
374.12	221.145	3.147	3.147	2095.2	2095.2	0	4.4237	4.4237

Heat capacity c_p (kJ/kg · deg) for water and steam at different temperatures and pressures

t, °C \ p, bar →	0.1	1	10	20	40	60	80	100
0	4.218	4.217	4.212	4.207	4.196	4.186	4.176	4.165
50	1.929	4.181	4.179	4.176	4.172	4.167	4.163	4.158
100	1.910	2.038	4.214	4.211	4.207	4.202	4.198	4.194
120	1.913	2.007	4.243	4.240	4.235	4.230	4.226	4.221
140	1.918	1.984	4.283	4.280	4.275	4.269	4.263	4.258
160	1.926	1.977	4.337	4.334	4.327	4.320	4.313	4.307
180	1.933	1.974	2.613	4.403	4.395	4.386	4.378	4.370
200	1.944	1.975	2.433	4.494	4.483	4.472	4.461	4.450
220	1.954	1.979	2.316	2.939	4.601	4.586	4.571	4.557
240	1.964	1.985	2.242	2.674	4.763	4.741	4.720	4.700
260	1.976	1.993	2.194	2.505	3.582	4.964	4.932	4.902
280	1.987	2.001	2.163	2.395	3.116	4.514	5.25	5.20
300	1.999	2.010	2.141	2.321	2.834	3.679	5.31	5.70
320	2.011	2.021	2.126	2.268	2.649	3.217	4.118	5.79
340	2.024	2.032	2.122	2.239	2.536	2.943	3.526	4.412
350	2.030	2.038	2.125	2.235	2.504	2.861	3.350	4.043
360	2.037	2.044	2.127	2.231	2.478	2.793	3.216	3.769
365	2.040	2.048	2.128	2.227	2.462	2.759	3.134	3.655
370	2.043	2.050	2.128	2.222	2.446	2.725	3.072	3.546
375	2.046	2.053	2.127	2.218	2.428	2.690	3.018	3.446
380	2.049	2.056	2.127	2.212	2.412	2.657	2.964	3.356
385	2.052	2.059	2.126	2.207	2.396	2.627	2.913	3.274
390	2.056	2.061	2.125	2.202	2.381	2.600	2.867	3.201
395	2.059	2.065	2.125	2.200	2.369	2.575	2.826	3.137
400	2.062	2.068	2.126	2.197	2.358	2.553	2.789	3.078
405	2.066	2.071	2.127	2.195	2.349	2.534	2.756	3.025
410	2.069	2.074	2.128	2.193	2.340	2.517	2.727	2.979
415	2.072	2.077	2.129	2.192	2.334	2.501	2.700	2.936

continued

t, °C \ p, bar →	0.1	1	10	20	40	60	80	100
420	2.076	2.080	2.131	2.192	2.327	2.487	2.675	2.898
425	2.079	2.083	2.132	2.190	2.321	2.474	2.653	2.863
430	2.082	2.086	2.134	2.190	2.316	2.462	2.632	2.830
440	2.089	2.093	2.138	2.190	2.307	2.441	2.596	2.773
450	2.095	2.099	2.141	2.191	2.300	2.424	2.565	2.726
460	2.102	2.106	2.146	2.192	2.294	2.409	2.538	2.684
480	2.116	2.119	2.154	2.196	2.286	2.385	2.496	2.618
500	2.129	2.132	2.164	2.201	2.281	2.368	2.464	2.569
520	2.142	2.146	2.175	2.208	2.280	2.357	3.441	2.531
540	2.156	2.159	2.185	2.216	2.280	2.349	2.423	2.502
560	2.170	2.173	2.197	2.226	2.285	2.349	2.416	2.487
580	2.184	2.187	2.208	2.233	2.285	2.342	2.401	2.465
600	2.198	2.200	2.219	2.240	2.287	2.336	2.389	2.445
620	2.212	2.213	2.230	2.250	2.291	2.334	2.381	2.431
640	2.226	2.227	2.243	2.260	2.298	2.337	2.379	2.423
660	2.240	2.241	2.256	2.272	2.307	2.343	2.381	2.421
680	2.254	2.255	2.270	2.286	2.317	2.352	2.388	2.424
700	2.268	2.270	2.283	2.299	2.330	2.362	2.398	2.429
800	2.339	2.341	2.352	2.364	2.389	2.414	2.440	2.465

t, °C \ p, bar →	150	175	200	210	220	225	230	240
0	4.141	4.129	4.117	4.113	4.108	4.106	4.103	4.099
50	4.148	4.142	4.137	4.135	4.133	4.132	4.131	4.129
100	4.183	4.178	4.173	4.171	4.169	4.168	4.167	4.165
120	4.209	4.204	4.198	4.196	4.194	4.193	4.192	4.189
140	4.245	4.238	4.232	4.229	4.227	4.226	4.224	4.222
160	4.291	4.283	4.276	4.273	4.270	4.268	4.267	4.264
180	4.350	4.340	4.331	4.328	4.324	4.322	4.320	4.317
200	4.425	4.413	4.402	4.397	4.393	4.390	4.388	4.384
220	4.523	4.508	4.492	4.486	4.481	4.478	4.475	4.469
240	4.653	4.632	4.611	4.603	4.595	4.591	4.588	4.580
260	4.832	4.801	4.772	4.760	4.749	4.744	4.738	4.728
280	5.09	5.04	4.997	4.979	4.963	4.955	4.947	4.931
300	5.50	5.41	5.33	5.31	5.28	5.26	5.25	5.23
320	6.23	6.05	5.89	5.84	5.79	5.76	5.74	5.69
340	8.14	7.45	7.01	6.87	6.74	6.68	6.63	6.53
350	8.68	9.27	9.10	7.81	7.56	7.45	7.35	7.17
360	6.86	12.57	11.37	10.18	9.40	9.10	8.84	8.41
365	6.15	9.84	19.72	13.77	11.62	10.94	10.40	9.58
370	5.69	8.36	18.38	75.67	18.38	15.56	13.84	11.79
375	5.33	7.40	12.71	19.03	52.7	81.49	29.52	17.44
380	5.02	6.68	10.19	13.14	19.19	25.71	40.95	68.4
385	4.750	6.13	8.68	10.49	13.38	15.62	18.88	33.4
390	4.520	5.68	7.65	8.90	10.68	11.88	13.42	18.21
395	4.325	5.32	6.90	7.83	9.06	9.84	10.77	13.29
400	4.155	5.02	6.33	7.06	7.97	8.53	9.16	10.76
405	4.007	4.770	5.87	6.46	7.18	7.60	8.06	9.20
410	3.879	4.556	5.50	5.99	6.57	6.90	7.26	8.12
415	3.764	4.371	5.19	5.61	6.09	6.36	6.65	7.32
420	3.664	4.211	4.933	5.29	5.70	5.92	6.16	6.71
425	3.573	4.069	4.711	5.02	5.37	5.56	5.77	6.22
430	3.491	4.945	4.520	4.795	5.10	5.26	5.44	5.83
440	3.350	3.734	4.205	4.424	4.664	4.791	4.927	5.22
450	3.235	3.564	3.959	4.139	4.333	4.435	4.544	4.77
460	3.138	3.424	3.761	3.912	4.074	4.159	4.247	4.43
480	2.986	3.210	3.465	3.576	3.695	3.756	3.819	3.95
500	2.875	3.056	3.257	3.343	3.434	3.481	3.529	3.63
520	2.791	2.940	3.104	3.174	3.247	3.284	3.322	3.40
540	2.726	2.852	2.989	3.046	3.106	3.136	3.167	3.23

continued

t, °C \ p, bar →	150	175	200	210	220	225	230	240
560	2.683	2.791	2.906	2.954	3.003	3.028	3.054	3.10
580	2.638	2.733	2.833	2.875	2.918	2.939	2.961	3.01
600	2.598	2.682	2.770	2.807	2.844	2.863	2.882	2.92
620	2.566	2.640	2.717	2.709	2.781	2.798	2.814	2.85
640	2.542	2.607	2.675	2.703	2.731	2.746	2.760	2.79
660	2.528	2.585	2.644	2.669	2.694	2.707	2.719	2.75
680	2.520	2.572	2.625	2.646	2.669	2.680	2.691	2.71
700	2.518	2.565	2.613	2.632	2.652	2.662	2.672	2.69
800	2.531	2.564	2.598	2.611	2.625	2.632	2.639	2.65

t, °C \ p, bar →	250	270	300	400	500	600	800	1000
0	4.095	4.086	4.073	4.032	3.993	3.956	3.882	3.800
50	4.127	4.123	4.117	4.098	4.080	4.064	4.035	4.010
100	4.163	4.159	1.153	4.135	4.117	4.100	4.068	4.039
120	4.187	4.183	4.177	4.156	4.137	4.119	4.085	4.054
140	4.220	4.215	4.208	4.185	4.163	4.143	4.105	4.071
160	4.261	4.255	4.247	4.220	4.196	4.172	4.130	4.092
180	4.313	4.306	4.296	4.265	4.235	4.208	4.159	4.116
200	4.379	4.371	4.358	4.319	4.284	4.252	4.195	4.145
220	4.464	4.452	4.437	4.388	4.344	4.305	4.237	4.180
240	4.572	4.558	4.537	4.474	4.419	4.371	4.290	4.223
260	4.717	4.697	4.669	4.584	4.514	4.453	4.354	4.276
280	4.916	4.886	4.845	4.728	4.633	4.555	4.432	4.340
300	5.20	5.16	5.09	4.920	4.788	4.683	4.524	4.411
320	5.65	5.57	5.46	5.19	4.996	4.848	4.633	4.485
340	6.43	6.27	6.07	5.60	5.30	5.08	4.766	4.552
350	7.02	6.76	6.45	5.81	5.45	5.20	4.871	4.663
360	8.07	7.56	7.03	6.10	5.64	5.34	4.954	4.719
365	8.99	8.18	7.43	6.27	5.73	5.40	4.987	4.737
370	10.56	9.12	7.98	6.48	5.84	5.47	5.03	4.764
375	13.76	10.67	8.76	6.70	5.96	5.56	5.08	4.802
380	23.37	13.51	9.90	6.97	6.10	5.65	5.14	4.843
385	73.1	20.07	11.68	7.30	6.26	5.75	5.20	4.884
390	28.04	38.02	14.60	7.71	6.43	5.84	5.25	4.919
395	17.31	33.71	19.68	8.19	6.61	5.94	5.30	4.949
400	13.02	21.11	25.71	8.78	6.81	6.05	5.34	4.974
405	10.67	15.32	24.85	9.47	7.04	6.16	5.38	4.996
410	9.17	12.22	19.59	10.25	7.29	6.27	5.42	5.02
415	8.12	10.30	15.45	11.12	7.57	6.40	5.46	5.04
420	7.35	8.99	12.70	12.00	7.87	6.54	5.51	5.06
425	6.74	8.04	10.83	12.73	8.18	6.69	5.56	5.08
430	6.26	7.32	9.49	13.13	8.50	6.84	5.61	5.10
440	5.54	6.28	7.73	12.54	9.08	7.17	5.72	5.15
450	5.02	5.58	6.62	10.89	9.48	7.47	5.84	5.20
460	4.631	5.08	5.87	9.28	9.52	7.71	5.97	5.26
480	4.089	4.389	4.902	7.08	8.55	7.87	6.19	5.40
500	3.731	3.951	4.316	5.81	7.20	7.48	6.31	5.51
520	3.481	3.650	3.926	5.02	6.13	6.76	6.28	5.58
540	3.295	3.431	3.650	4.487	5.37	6.03	6.10	5.56
560	3.158	3.268	3.442	4.095	4.796	5.38	5.75	5.43
580	3.051	3.144	3.290	3.823	4.387	5.890	5.39	5.28
600	2.960	3.040	3.165	3.614	4.082	4.510	5.03	5.08
620	2.882	2.952	3.060	3.446	3.845	4.216	4.724	4.871
640	2.819	2.880	2.974	3.308	3.654	3.981	4.465	4.669
660	2.771	2.824	2.906	3.197	3.500	3.791	4.249	4.485
680	2.736	2.783	2.855	3.110	3.376	3.637	4.068	4.322
700	2.713	2.755	2.819	3.044	3.279	3.513	3.916	4.178
800	2.666	2.694	2.736	2.879	3.024	3.168	3.441	3.669

Thermophysical properties of water and steam at saturation: viscosity η ($N \cdot s/m^2$), thermal conductivity λ ($W/m \cdot deg$), heat capacity c_p ($kJ/kg \cdot deg$) and Prandtl number P_r [17, 18]

t, °C	Liquid				Steam			
	$\eta \cdot 10^7$	$\lambda \cdot 10^3$	c_p	P_r	$\eta \cdot 10^7$	$\lambda \cdot 10^3$	c_p	P_r
0	17 525	569	4.217	12.99	80.4	17.6	1.864	0.85
10	12 992	586	4.193	9.30	84.5	18.2	1.868	0.87
20	10 015	602	4.182	6.96	88.5	18.8	1.874	0.88
30	7 970	617	4.179	5.40	92.6	19.4	1.883	0.90
40	6 513	630	4.179	4.32	96.6	20.1	1.894	0.91
50	5 440	643	4.181	3.54	100	20.9	1.907	0.92
60	4 630	653	4.185	2.97	105	21.6	1.924	0.94
70	4 005	662	4.190	2.54	109	22.3	1.944	0.95
80	3 510	669	4.197	2.20	113	23.1	1.969	0.96
90	3 113	675	4.205	1.94	117	23.9	1.999	0.98
100	2 790	680	4.216	1.73	121	24.8	2.034	0.99
110	2 522	683	4.229	1.56	124	25.8	2.075	1.00
120	2 300	685	4.245	1.43	128	26.7	2.124	1.02
130	2 110	687	4.263	1.31	132	27.8	2.180	1.04
140	1 950	687	4.285	1.22	135	28.8	2.245	1.05
150	1 810	686	4.310	1.14	139	30.0	2.320	1.08
160	1 690	684	4.339	1.07	142	31.3	2.406	1.09
170	1 585	681	4.371	1.02	146	32.6	2.504	1.12
180	1 493	676	4.408	0.97	149	34.1	2.615	1.14
190	1 412	671	4.449	0.94	153	35.7	2.741	1.17
200	1 338	664	4.497	0.91	156	37.5	2.883	1.20
210	1 273	657	4.551	0.88	160	39.4	3.043	1.24
220	1 215	648	4.614	0.86	163	41.5	3.223	1.27
230	1 162	639	4.686	0.85	167	43.9	3.426	1.30
240	1 114	629	4.770	0.85	171	46.5	3.656	1.34
250	1 070	617	4.869	0.84	174	49.5	3.918	1.38
260	1 030	604	4.985	0.85	178	52.8	4.221	1.42
270	994	589	5.13	0.86	182	56.6	4.574	1.47
280	961	573	5.30	0.89	187	60.9	4.996	1.53
290	930	557	5.51	0.92	193	66.0	5.51	1.61
300	901	540	5.77	0.96	198	71.9	6.14	1.69
310	865	522	6.12	1.01	205	79.1	6.96	1.80
320	830	503	6.59	1.09	214	87.8	8.05	1.96
330	790	482	7.25	1.19	225	98.9	9.59	2.18
340	748	460	8.27	1.34	238	113	11.92	2.51
350	700	435	10.08	1.62	256	130	15.95	3.14
360	644	401	14.99	2.41	282	150	26.79	5.04
370	564	338	53.9	8.99	335	183	112.9	20.66

Viscosity $\eta \cdot 10^7$ ($N \cdot s/m^2$) of water and steam at different temperatures and pressures [17, 18]

t, °C \ p, bar →	1	20	40	60	80	100	150	200	210
0	17 525	17 514	17 502	17 491	17 480	17 468	17 439	17 411	17 405
10	12 992	12 986	12 980	12 975	12 969	12 963	12 948	12 934	12 931
20	10 015	10 013	10 010	10 008	10 005	10 003	9 997	9 991	9 990
30	7 971	7 970	7 970	7 970	7 970	7 969	7 968	7 968	7 968
40	6 513	6 514	6 515	6 516	6 517	6 519	6 521	6 524	6 525
50	5 441	5 443	5 445	5 447	5 449	5 451	5 456	5 461	5 462
60	4 630	4 633	4 636	6 638	4 641	4 644	4 650	4 657	4 658
70	4 004	4 007	4 010	4 013	4 016	4 019	4 027	4 036	4 038
80	3 509	3 513	3 516	3 520	3 523	3 527	3 535	3 544	3 546
90	3 113	3 116	3 120	3 124	3 128	3 131	3 141	3 150	3 152
100	121	2 793	2 797	2 801	2 805	2 809	2 819	2 828	2 830
110	125	2 526	2 530	2 534	2 538	2 542	2 552	2 563	2 565
120	129	2 303	2 307	2 311	2 315	2 319	2 330	2 340	2 342

continued

t, °C \ p, bar →	1	20	40	60	80	100	150	200	210
130	133	2 114	2 118	2 123	2 127	2 131	2 142	2 152	2 154
140	137	1 953	1 957	1 962	1 966	1 970	1 981	1 992	1 994
150	141	1 814	1 818	1 823	1 827	1 832	1 843	1 854	1 856
160	146	1 693	1 698	1 702	1 707	1 711	1 722	1 734	1 736
170	150	1 588	1 592	1 597	1 601	1 606	1 617	1 628	1 631
180	154	1 495	1 500	1 504	1 509	1 513	1 525	1 536	1 538
190	158	1 413	1 417	1 422	1 426	1 431	1 442	1 454	1 456
200	162	1 339	1 343	1 348	1 353	1 358	1 369	1 381	1 383
210	166	1 275	1 278	1 282	1 287	1 292	1 303	1 315	1 317
220	170	164	1 218	1 223	1 228	1 232	1 244	1 256	1 258
230	174	169	1 164	1 169	1 174	1 179	1 190	1 202	1 204
240	178	174	1 115	1 120	1 125	1 129	1 141	1 153	1 156
250	182	179	1 070	1 075	1 080	1 084	1 096	1 108	1 111
260	186	183	180	1 033	1 039	1 043	1 055	1 067	1 069
270	190	188	185	995	1 000	1 005	1 017	1 029	1 031
280	194	193	191	189	964	969	981	993	996
290	198	197	196	194	931	936	948	960	963
300	202	202	201	200	199	904	917	929	932
310	207	206	206	206	206	866	881	895	898
320	211	211	211	212	212	213	843	859	862
330	215	216	216	218	219	221	800	820	824
340	219	220	222	224	226	229	749	777	782
350	223	225	227	229	232	236	248	727	734
360	227	229	231	234	237	241	255	661	673
370	231	233	236	239	243	246	259	298	335
380	235	238	240	243	246	250	263	288	297
390	239	242	244	247	250	254	266	286	292
400	243	246	248	251	254	258	268	286	290
410	247	250	252	255	258	261	272	287	291
420	251	254	256	259	262	265	275	288	292
430	255	258	260	263	266	269	278	290	294
440	260	262	264	267	269	272	281	293	296
450	264	266	268	270	273	276	285	296	298
460	268	270	272	274	277	280	288	298	301
470	272	274	276	278	281	284	292	301	304
480	276	278	280	282	285	288	295	304	307
490	280	282	284	286	289	291	299	308	310
500	284	286	288	290	293	295	302	311	313
520	292	294	296	298	301	303	310	318	320
540	300	302	304	306	308	311	317	324	326
560	308	310	312	314	316	319	325	332	333
580	316	318	320	322	324	326	332	339	340
600	325	326	328	330	332	334	340	346	347
620	333	334	336	338	340	342	348	353	355
640	341	342	344	346	348	350	355	361	362
660	349	351	352	354	356	358	363	368	370
680	357	359	360	362	364	366	371	376	377
700	365	367	368	370	372	374	378	384	385

t, °C \ p, bar →	220	230	240	250	300	400	500	600	800
0	17 399	17 394	17 388	17 382	17 353	17 296	17 239	17 182	17 067
10	12 928	12 925	12 922	12 919	12 905	12 875	12 846	12 817	12 759
20	9 988	9 987	9 986	9 985	9 979	9 967	9 954	9 942	9 918
30	7 967	7 967	7 967	7 967	7 966	7 965	7 963	7 962	7 959
40	6 225	6 526	6 526	6 527	6 529	6 535	6 540	6 546	6 557
50	5 463	5 464	5 465	5 466	5 471	5 481	5 491	5 502	5 522
60	4 660	4 661	4 662	4 664	4 670	4 684	4 697	4 711	4 737
70	4 038	4 040	4 041	4 043	4 051	4 066	4 082	4 098	4 129

continued

t, °C \ p, bar →	220	230	240	250	300	400	500	600	800
80	3 548	3 549	3 551	3 553	3 561	3 579	3 596	3 614	3 648
90	3 154	3 155	3 157	3 159	3 168	3 187	3 206	3 224	3 261
100	2 832	2 834	2 836	2 838	2 848	2 867	2 887	2 906	2 945
110	2 567	2 569	2 571	2 573	2 583	2 603	2 623	2 644	2 684
120	2 344	2 347	2 349	2 351	2 361	2 382	2 403	2 424	2 465
130	2 157	2 159	2 161	2 163	2 174	2 195	2 216	2 237	2 280
140	1 996	1 998	2 000	2 003	2 013	2 035	2 057	2 078	2 122
150	1 858	1 860	1 862	1 865	1 876	1 898	1 920	1 941	1 985
160	1 738	1 740	1 742	1 745	1 756	1 778	1 800	1 822	1 867
170	1 633	1 635	1 637	1 640	1 651	1 674	1 696	1 718	1 763
180	1 540	1 543	1 545	1 547	1 559	1 581	1 604	1 627	1 672
190	1 458	1 461	1 463	1 465	1 477	1 500	1 523	1 546	1 591
200	1 385	1 388	1 390	1 392	1 404	1 427	1 450	1 473	1 519
210	1 320	1 322	1 324	1 327	1 338	1 362	1 385	1 408	1 455
220	1 261	1 263	1 265	1 268	1 279	1 303	1 326	1 350	1 397
230	1 207	1 209	1 212	1 214	1 226	1 249	1 273	1 297	1 344
240	1 158	1 160	1 163	1 165	1 177	1 201	1 225	1 248	1 296
250	1 113	1 116	1 118	1 120	1 132	1 156	1 180	1 204	1 252
260	1 072	1 074	1 077	1 079	1 091	1 115	1 140	1 164	1 212
270	1 034	1 036	1 038	1 041	1 053	1 077	1 102	1 126	1 175
280	998	1 001	1 003	1 006	1 018	1 042	1 067	1 091	1 140
290	965	968	970	972	985	1 009	1 034	1 059	1 108
300	934	937	939	941	954	978	1 004	1 028	1 078
310	901	904	906	909	922	948	972	997	1 045
320	865	868	871	874	888	915	940	964	1 012
330	827	831	834	837	853	881	908	932	980
340	786	790	794	798	817	848	876	901	949
350	740	745	751	756	779	815	845	871	920
360	683	692	700	707	738	781	814	842	891
370	596	617	633	646	692	746	784	813	864
380	311	340	468	537	630	703	748	783	840
390	300	310	324	348	561	667	721	759	817
400	296	303	311	321	458	627	692	735	797
410	295	300	306	313	380	580	660	710	777
420	296	300	304	310	352	529	626	683	758
430	297	300	304	309	340	479	591	656	737
440	299	302	305	309	334	438	555	628	716
450	301	304	307	310	331	411	521	599	695
460	303	306	309	312	330	394	495	572	674
470	306	308	311	314	330	383	466	546	654
480	309	311	313	316	331	376	446	522	633
490	312	314	316	318	332	371	432	502	614
500	315	317	319	321	334	369	421	485	596
520	321	323	325	327	338	367	408	460	563
540	328	330	331	333	343	368	402	444	537
560	335	336	338	340	348	370	399	435	516
580	342	343	345	346	354	374	399	430	502
600	349	350	352	353	361	379	401	428	491
620	356	357	359	360	367	384	404	428	484
640	363	365	366	367	374	389	408	429	480
660	371	372	373	374	381	395	412	432	477
680	378	379	380	382	388	401	418	435	477
700	386	387	388	389	395	408	422	439	478

Thermal conductivity $\lambda \cdot 10^3$ (W/m · deg) for water and steam at different temperatures and pressures [15, 17, 18]

t, °C \ p, bar →	1	20	40	60	80	100	150	200
0	569	570	572	574	575	577	581	585
10	588	589	590	592	594	595	599	603
20	603	605	607	608	610	612	616	620
30	617	620	622	623	625	627	631	634
40	630	633	635	637	638	640	644	648
50	643	645	647	648	650	651	655	659
60	653	655	657	658	660	661	665	669
70	662	664	665	667	668	670	674	677
80	669	671	673	674	676	677	681	684
90	675	677	679	680	682	683	687	690
100	24.5	682	684	685	686	688	691	694
110	25.2	686	687	688	690	691	694	698
120	26.0	688	689	691	692	693	697	700
130	26.9	689	690	692	693	694	698	701
140	27.7	689	690	692	693	694	698	701
150	28.6	688	689	690	692	693	696	700
160	29.5	685	687	688	690	691	694	698
170	30.4	682	683	685	686	688	691	695
180	31.3	677	679	680	682	683	687	691
190	32.2	672	673	675	677	678	682	686
200	33.1	665	667	668	670	672	676	681
210	34.1	657	659	661	663	665	670	674
220	35.1	40.0	650	652	654	656	662	667
230	36.1	40.3	640	643	645	647	653	658
240	37.1	40.8	629	632	634	637	643	649
250	38.1	41.4	616	619	622	625	632	639
260	39.1	42.1	48.9	606	609	612	620	628
270	40.1	42.9	48.7	590	594	598	607	616
280	41.2	43.8	48.8	58.1	578	582	593	602
290	42.3	44.7	49.1	56.8	560	565	577	587
300	43.3	45.7	49.6	56.1	66.9	545	559	571
310	44.4	46.7	50.3	55.8	64.7	523	539	553
320	45.5	47.7	51.0	55.9	63.3	75.2	516	532
330	46.7	48.8	51.8	56.2	62.5	72.0	491	509
340	47.8	49.9	52.7	56.7	62.1	69.9	462	483
350	49.0	51.0	53.7	57.3	62.1	68.8	104	454
360	50.1	52.1	54.7	58.0	62.3	68.1	94.8	420
370	51.3	53.2	55.7	58.8	62.7	67.8	89.3	163
380	52.5	54.4	56.7	59.7	63.3	67.8	85.9	129
390	53.6	55.5	57.8	60.6	64.0	68.1	83.6	115
400	54.8	56.7	58.9	61.6	64.7	68.6	82.2	107
410	56.0	57.9	60.1	62.6	65.6	69.1	81.2	102
420	57.3	59.1	61.2	63.7	66.5	69.8	80.8	98.3
430	58.5	60.3	62.4	64.8	67.5	70.6	80.6	95.7
440	59.7	61.5	63.6	65.9	68.5	71.4	80.6	94.1
450	61.0	62.8	64.8	67.0	69.5	72.4	81.0	93.3
460	62.2	64.0	66.0	68.2	70.6	73.3	81.5	92.4
470	63.5	65.3	67.2	69.4	71.7	74.3	82.0	92.1
480	64.8	66.5	68.5	70.6	72.9	75.4	82.7	92.1
490	66.0	67.8	69.7	71.8	74.0	76.5	83.5	92.2
500	67.3	69.1	71.0	73.0	75.2	77.6	84.3	92.6
520	69.9	71.7	73.5	75.5	77.6	79.9	86.2	93.7
540	72.5	74.3	76.1	78.1	80.1	82.3	88.2	95.2
560	75.2	76.9	78.7	80.6	82.7	84.7	90.4	96.9
580	77.8	79.6	81.4	83.3	85.2	87.3	92.7	98.8
600	80.5	82.3	84.1	85.9	87.8	89.8	95.1	101
620	83.2	85.0	86.7	88.6	90.5	92.4	97.6	103
640	85.9	87.7	89.5	91.3	93.2	95.1	100	105

continued

t, °C \ p, bar →	1	20	40	60	80	100	150	200
660	88.7	90.4	92.2	94.0	95.8	97.7	103	108
680	91.4	93.1	94.9	96.7	98.5	100	105	110
700	94.2	95.9	97.7	99.5	101	103	108	113

t, °C \ p, bar →	210	220	230	240	250	300	400	500
0	586	586	587	588	589	592	599	606
10	604	605	606	606	607	611	617	624
20	620	621	622	623	623	627	634	640
30	635	636	637	637	638	642	648	654
40	648	649	650	650	651	654	661	666
50	660	660	661	662	662	666	672	678
60	670	670	671	672	672	676	682	687
70	678	679	679	680	681	684	690	695
80	685	686	686	687	688	691	697	702
90	691	691	692	693	693	696	702	708
100	695	696	696	697	698	701	707	713
110	698	699	700	700	701	704	710	716
120	700	701	702	702	703	706	712	718
130	702	702	703	703	704	707	714	720
140	701	702	703	703	704	707	714	720
150	700	701	702	702	703	706	713	720
160	698	699	700	700	701	705	711	718
170	696	696	697	698	698	702	709	716
180	692	692	693	694	695	698	706	713
190	687	688	688	689	690	694	702	709
200	681	682	683	684	685	689	697	704
210	675	676	677	678	678	683	691	699
220	668	669	670	671	672	676	685	693
230	660	661	662	663	664	669	678	686
240	650	652	653	654	655	660	670	679
250	640	642	643	644	646	651	662	671
260	630	631	632	634	635	642	653	663
270	617	619	621	622	624	631	643	653
280	604	606	608	609	611	619	633	643
290	590	592	594	595	597	606	622	633
300	573	576	578	580	582	592	609	622
310	555	558	561	563	566	577	596	610
320	535	538	541	544	547	560	582	597
330	513	516	520	523	526	541	566	583
340	488	491	495	499	503	520	548	568
350	458	463	467	472	476	496	529	552
360	425	430	435	440	445	468	504	537
370	206	392	385	396	406	437	479	514
380	147	170	185	269	322	398	453	490
390	126	140	150	165	188	338	423	465
400	115	124	134	144	156	262	388	439
410	108	114	124	132	141	206	348	411
420	103	108	116	123	130	177	307	382
430	99.8	104	109	116	122	160	271	352
440	97.6	101	105	110	116	148	241	323
450	96.0	99.2	103	106	111	139	217	297
460	95.0	97.9	101	104	108	131	198	274
470	94.5	97.0	99.7	103	106	125	184	253
480	94.2	96.5	99.0	102	104	120	172	236
490	94.2	96.4	98.7	101	103	118	163	220
500	94.4	96.4	98.5	101	103	116	155	207
520	95.3	97.1	98.9	101	103	113	142	186
540	96.6	98.2	99.8	102	103	112	136	170
560	98.3	99.7	101	103	104	112	133	159
580	100	101	103	104	106	113	131	153

continued

t, °C \ p, bar →	210	220	230	240	250	300	400	500
600	102	103	105	106	107	114	130	149
620	104	105	107	108	109	116	130	147
640	106	108	109	110	111	117	131	147
660	109	110	111	112	113	119	132	146
680	111	112	113	115	116	121	133	147
700	114	115	116	117	118	124	135	148

Surface tension σ (dyne/cm) of water [19]

t, °C	σ	t, °C	σ	t, °C	σ	t, °C	σ
0	75.50	130	52.90	260	23.73	362	1.53
10	74.40	140	50.79	270	21.33	363	1.37
20	72.88	150	48.68	280	18.94	364	1.22
30	71.20	160	46.51	290	16.60	365	1.07
40	69.48	170	44.38	300	14.29	366	0.93
50	67.77	180	42.19	310	12.04	367	0.79
60	66.07	190	40.00	320	9.84	368	0.66
70	64.36	200	37.77	330	7.69	369	0.54
80	62.69	210	35.51	340	5.61	370	0.42
90	60.79	220	33.21	350	3.64	371	0.31
100	58.91	230	30.88	355	2.71	372	0.20
110	56.97	240	28.52	360	1.85	373	0.10
120	54.96	250	26.13	361	1.68	374.15	0

Thermodynamic properties of dissociated steam*:
v (m³/kg), i (kJ/kg), s and c_p (kJ/kg · deg) [20, 21]

T, °K	v	i	s	c_p	v	i	s	c_p
	p=0.1 bar				p=0.2 bar			
1250	57.69	—10 670	14.517	2.483	28.84	—10 670	14.197	2.481
1300	60.00	—10 546	14 615	2.524	30.00	—10 546	14.295	2,520
1400	64.62	—10 290	14.804	2.619	32.31	—10 291	14.484	2.608
1500	69.24	—10 027	14.986	2.747	34.62	—10 028	14.665	2.722
1600	73.88	—9 752	15.163	2.928	36.94	—9 756	14.841	2.877
1700	78.55	—9 463	15.338	3.193	39.27	—9 470	15.014	3.097
1800	83.27	—9 153	15.515	3.578	41.61	—9 167	15.187	3.412
1900	88.08	—8 812	15.700	4.127	44.00	—8 839	15.364	3.858
2000	93.03	—8 427	15.897	4.890	46.44	—8 476	15.550	4.459
2200	103.8	—7 439	16.367	7.295	51.63	—7 580	15.976	6.339
2400	116.7	—5 927	17.022	11.34	57.65	—6 290	16.536	9.440
2600	133.4	—3 428	18.019	17.64	65.38	—4 279	17.338	14.20
2800	161.5	—834	19.593	26.99	76.43	—1 020	18.542	21.09
3000	205.4	7 916	22.029	40.31	93.42	4 254	20.357	30.76
3200	272.3	18 357	25.393	55.54	119.6	12 298	22.948	43.36
3400	355.0	30 196	28.983	59.48	155.7	22 817	26.134	54.10
3600	431.3	39 669	31.696	44.62	195.8	33 395	29.159	51.87
3800	489.8	45 512	33.280	26.47	231.1	41 395	31.326	37.38
4000	543.2	48 834	34.133	14.96	258.6	46 435	32.621	22.92
4200	570.6	50 829	34.621	9.12	280.4	49 472	33.364	13.77
4400	602.8	52 182	34.949	6.33	298.3	51 404	33.814	8.87
4600	633.0	53 224	35.168	4.98	314.6	52 765	34.117	6.37

*For tables of thermodynamic properties of water and steam below 1250 °K at different pressures, consult Ref. [17].

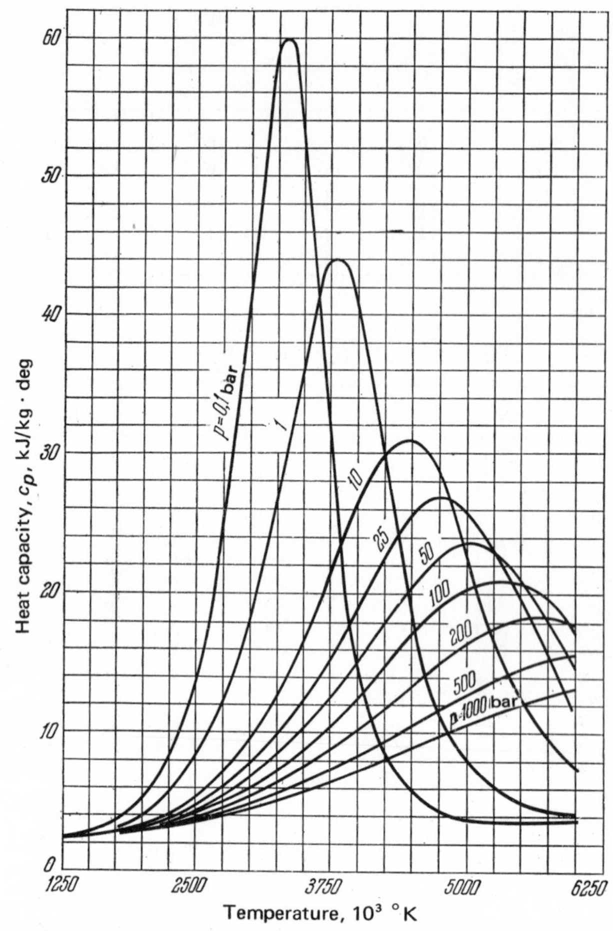

Fig. 6. Heat capacity c_p for dissociated steam as a function of temperature at different pressures.

continued

T, °K	v	i	s	c_p	v	i	s	c_p
4800	662.2	54 112	35.357	4.32	329.9	53 832	34.344	5.09
5000	690.7	54 921	35.522	3.97	344.6	54 744	34.530	4.42
5500	760.9	56 798	35.880	3.66	380.1	56 733	34.910	3.79
6000	830.4	58 603	36.194	3.59	415.1	58 576	35.231	3.64
		p=0.4 bar				p=0.6 bar		
1250	14.42	—10 670	13.877	2.479	9.615	—10 671	13.690	2.478
1300	15.00	—10 546	13.975	2.516	9.999	—10 546	13.788	2.515
1400	16.15	—10 291	14.163	2.600	10.77	—10 292	13.976	2.595
1500	17.31	—10 029	14.344	2.702	11.54	—10 030	14.157	2.692
1600	18.47	—9 758	14.519	2.836	12.31	—9 759	14.331	2.817
1700	19.63	—9 476	14.690	3.022	13.08	—9 479	14.501	2.985
1800	20.80	—9 179	14.860	3.280	13.86	—9 184	14.670	3.217
1900	21.98	—8 861	15.032	3.638	14.65	—8 871	14.839	3.534
2000	23.19	—8 514	15.210	4.122	15.45	—8 533	15.012	3.960
2200	25.72	—7 688	15.603	5.601	17.12	—7 740	15.390	5.250
2400	28.56	—6 561	16.092	7.998	18.96	—6 688	15.846	7.317
2600	32.03	—4 903	16.753	11.61	21.15	—5 189	16.445	10.70
2800	36.69	—2 348	17.698	16.76	24.00	—2 947	17.273	14.76
3000	43.43	1 635	19.068	23.82	27.98	466	18.448	20.66

continued

T, °K	v	i	s	c_p	v	i	s	c_p
3200	53.53	7 685	21.016	33.18	33.80	5 586	20.096	28.44
3400	68.09	16 139	23.576	43.91	42.21	12 845	22.294	37.91
3600	86.53	26 142	26.434	50.21	53.35	21 963	24.898	46.02
3800	105.7	35 487	28.963	45.17	65.92	31 415	27.454	46.33
4000	122.3	42 467	30.756	32.54	77.80	39 311	29.482	37.43
4200	135.6	47 035	31.872	20.87	87.44	44 909	30.850	25.86
4400	146.3	49 493	32.550	13.25	95.80	48 596	31.709	16.84
4600	155.5	51 881	32.981	8.021	102.5	51 039	32.253	11.19
4800	163.8	53 284	33.280	6.567	108.4	52 753	32.618	7.937
5000	171.5	54 395	33.507	5.287	113.8	54 052	32.883	6.113
5500	189.7	56 604	33.929	4.047	126.3	56 477	33.346	4.298
6000	207.4	58 520	34.263	3.726	138.2	58 465	33.693	3.814
		p=0.8 bar				p=1 bar		
1250	7.211	—10 671	13.557	2.477	5.769	—10 671	13.454	2.477
1300	7.499	—10 546	13.655	2.514	5.999	—10 546	13.552	2.513
1400	8.077	—10 292	13.843	2.593	6.461	—10 292	13.740	2.591
1500	8.654	—10 030	14.024	2.686	6.923	—10 030	13.921	2.682
1600	9.233	—9 760	14.198	2.804	7.386	—9 761	14.094	2.795
1700	9.813	—9 480	14.368	2.962	7.850	—9 482	14.264	2.946
1800	10.40	—9 188	14.535	3.177	8.316	—9 190	14.430	3.148
1900	10.98	—8 878	14.702	3.468	8.787	—8 882	14.597	3.422
2000	11.58	—8 544	14.873	3.858	9.263	—8 552	14.756	3.786
2200	12.82	—7 772	15.241	5.030	10.25	—7 794	15.127	4.874
2400	14.18	—6 767	15.677	6.894	11.32	—6 822	15.549	6.597
2600	15.77	—5 364	16.237	9.663	12.57	—5 486	16.082	9.142
2800	17.79	—3 309	16.997	13.54	14.12	—3 560	16.794	12.69
3000	20.55	—237	18.054	18.75	16.20	—720	17.772	17.43
3200	24.51	4 322	19.522	25.57	19.14	3 455	19.116	23.58
3400	30.19	10 805	21.484	34.03	23.33	9 385	20.911	31.28
3600	37.86	19 183	23.877	42.38	29.05	17 170	23.134	39.43
3800	46.96	28 408	26.371	45.51	36.03	26 079	25.542	44.07
4000	56.99	36 730	28.507	39.88	43.36	34 573	27.722	40.99
4200	64.07	43 038	30.047	29.39	50.02	41 365	29.381	31.91
4400	70.63	47 349	31.053	19.79	55.61	46 190	30.505	22.24
4600	76.08	50 237	31.696	13.21	60.24	49 471	31.235	15.01
4800	80.77	52 238	32.122	9.21	64.19	51 737	31.718	10.40
5000	85.00	53 717	32.424	6.904	67.71	53 388	32.055	7.660
5500	94.56	56 351	32.928	4.546	75.53	56 225	32.598	4.789
6000	103.5	58 411	33.287	3.903	82.78	58 356	32.970	3.990
		p=2 bar				p=3 bar		
1250	2.884	—10 671	13.133	2.477	1.922	—10 672	12.946	2.477
1300	3.000	—10 546	13.232	2.512	2.000	—10 547	13.044	2.512
1400	3.231	—10 292	13.420	2.586	2.154	—10 293	13.233	2.584
1500	3.462	—10 031	13.600	2.670	2.308	—10 032	13.413	2.665
1600	3.693	—9 763	13.773	2.772	2.462	—9 763	13.586	2.761
1700	3.924	—9 485	13.944	2.903	2.616	—9 487	13.753	2.881
1800	4.157	—9 197	14.106	3.073	2.771	—9 200	13.917	3.036
1900	4.392	—8 895	14.270	3.298	2.927	—8 901	14.079	3.238
2000	4.628	—9 574	14.434	3.594	3.085	—8 585	14.241	3.502
2200	5.115	—7 854	14.777	4.464	3.407	—7 883	14.575	4.266
2400	5.635	—6 966	15.162	5.816	3.748	—7 035	14.944	5.443
2600	6.219	—5 802	15.627	7.783	4.126	—5 950	15.377	7.142
2800	6.916	—4 200	16.220	10.49	4.567	—4 495	15.915	9.458
3000	7.804	—1 936	16.999	14.04	5.113	—2 490	16.606	12.47
3200	8.995	1 281	18.035	18.57	5.826	302	17.505	16.27
3400	10.64	5 783	19.398	24.20	6.785	4 154	18.671	20.96
3600	12.88	11 820	21.121	30.80	8.083	9 317	20.145	26.54
3800	15.79	19 290	23.140	37.06	9.785	15 849	21.909	32.44
4000	19.20	27 460	25.235	39.86	11.87	23 378	23.839	36.76
4200	22.72	35 146	27.111	36.83	14.14	31 044	25.710	36.95
4400	25.96	41 433	28.575	29.52	16.39	37 883	27.302	32.43
4600	28.75	46 106	29.615	21.60	18.42	43 848	28.518	25.49

continued

T, °K	v	i	s	c_p	v	i	s	c_p
4800	31.12	49 440	30.325	15.29	20.18	47 430	29.388	18.81
5000	33.16	51 832	30.814	10.98	21.69	50 411	29.997	13.67
5500	37.46	55 612	31.538	5.950	24.78	55 020	30.880	7.021
6000	41.25	58 086	31.970	4.419	27.40	57 819	31.369	4.833
		$p=4$ bar				$p=5$ bar		
1250	1.442	—10 672	12.814	2.477	1.153	—10 672	12.710	2.477
1300	1.500	—10 547	12.911	2.512	1.200	—10 547	12.808	2.512
1400	1.615	—10 293	13.100	2.583	1.292	—10 293	12.996	2.583
1500	1.731	—10 032	13.280	2.662	1.385	—10 032	13.176	2.660
1600	1.846	—9 764	13.453	2.754	1.477	—9 764	13.349	2.749
1700	1.962	—9 488	13.620	2.868	1.570	—9 489	13.517	2.858
1800	2.078	—9 202	13.783	3.013	1.663	—9 204	13.679	2.996
1900	2.195	—8 904	13.944	3.201	1.756	—8 907	13.840	3.174
2000	2.313	—8 591	14.105	3.443	1.850	—8 596	13.999	3.402
2200	2.554	—7 901	14.433	4.143	2.042	—7 914	14.324	4.055
2400	2.807	—7 078	14.791	5.211	2.244	—7 108	14.674	5.046
2600	3.085	—6 041	15.205	6.743	2.463	—6 105	15.075	6.462
2800	3.405	—4 676	15.710	8.821	2.713	—4 803	15.557	8.373
3000	3.794	—2 826	16.347	11.51	3.013	—3 060	16.157	10.84
3200	4.292	—290	17.164	14.88	3.391	—698	16.918	13.91
3400	4.951	3 173	18.212	19.00	3.885	2 498	17.885	17.64
3600	5.833	7 794	19.531	23.91	4.540	6 741	19.096	22.09
3800	6.990	13 686	21.123	29.33	5.397	12 169	20.562	27.08
4000	8.429	20 660	22.911	34.02	6.473	18 689	22.233	31.79
4200	10.07	28 092	24.724	35.86	7.729	25 841	23.978	34.50
4400	11.76	35 111	26.357	33.44	9.063	32 872	25.614	33.57
4600	13.35	41 037	27.686	27.82	10.36	39 066	26.992	29.20
4800	14.75	45 653	28.659	21.38	11.54	44 069	28.058	23.27
5000	15.98	49 106	29.365	15.86	12.57	47 903	28.841	17.66
5500	18.45	54 448	30.389	8.010	14.65	53 897	29.990	8.926
6000	20.48	57 558	30.931	5.232	16.33	57 300	30.584	5.619
		$p=6$ bar				$p=8$ bar		
1250	0.9611	—10 672	12.626	2.478	0.7207	—10 673	12.493	2.479
1300	0.9996	—10 548	12.724	2.512	0.7497	—10 548	12.591	2.513
1400	1.077	—10 293	12.912	2.582	0.8075	—10 294	12.779	2.582
1500	1.154	—10 033	13.092	2.658	0.8653	—10 033	12.959	2.656
1600	1.231	—9 765	13.265	2.745	0.9232	—9 765	13.132	2.740
1700	1.308	—9 489	13.432	2.851	0.9811	—9 490	13.299	2.841
1800	1.385	—9 205	13.595	2.984	1.039	—9 206	13.461	2.966
1900	1.463	—8 909	13.754	3.154	1.097	—8 912	13.620	3.137
2000	1.542	—8 600	13.913	3.370	1.156	—8 605	13.777	3.325
2200	1.701	—7 923	14.235	3.988	1.275	—7 938	14.095	3.891
2400	1.868	—7 131	14.579	4.922	1.400	—7 164	14.431	4.741
2600	2.049	—6 154	14.970	6.249	1.533	—6 234	14.807	5.941
2800	2.253	—4 898	15.434	8.086	1.683	—5 035	15.247	7.549
3000	2.497	—3 235	16.007	10.33	1.858	—3 435	15.781	9.605
3200	2.800	—1 002	16.727	13.18	2.072	—1 434	16.441	12.14
3400	3.191	1 995	17.639	16.63	2.344	1 284	17.264	15.19
3600	3.705	5 957	18.765	20.72	2.696	4 847	18.281	18.78
3800	4.376	11 029	20.134	25.37	3.152	9 401	19.511	22.90
4000	5.222	17 175	21.710	29.97	3.730	14 974	20.940	27.20
4200	6.225	24 054	23.388	33.14	4.426	21 366	22.498	30.74
4400	7.316	31 016	25.008	33.26	5.209	28 098	24.064	32.15
4600	8.403	37 360	26.419	29.98	6.020	34 542	25.498	30.53
4800	9.413	42 645	27.544	24.66	6.800	40 182	26.699	26.43
5000	10.31	46 789	28.391	19.13	7.513	44 789	27.640	21.36
5500	12.12	53 363	29.651	9.774	8.967	52 347	29.088	11.29
6000	13.56	57 046	30.294	5.992	10.11	56 550	29.822	6.701
		$p=10$ bar				$p=20$ bar		
1250	0.5765	—10 674	12.389	2.480	0.2880	—10 677	12.067	2.486
1300	0.5997	—10 549	12.487	2.514	0.2997	—10 551	12.166	2.519

continued

T, °K	v	i	s	c_p	v	i	s	c_p
1400	0.6460	−10 294	12.676	2.582	0.3229	−10 296	12.355	2.585
1500	0.6923	−10 033	12.856	2.655	0.3461	−10 035	12.535	2.653
1600	0.7386	−9 766	13.028	2.737	0.3693	−9 768	12.707	2.728
1700	0.7849	−9 491	13.195	2.834	0.3925	−9 493	12.874	2.815
1800	0.8313	−9 208	13.357	2.958	0.4157	−9 212	13.035	2.920
1900	0.8779	−8 915	13.515	3.103	0.4390	−8 921	13.192	3.048
2000	0.9248	−8 609	13.672	3.292	0.4624	−8 619	13.346	3.206
2200	1.020	−7 948	13.987	3.822	0.5097	−7 975	13.653	3.640
2400	1.119	−7 187	14.317	4.612	0.5585	−7 249	13.969	4.274
2600	1.225	−6 273	14.683	5.724	0.6099	−6 403	14.307	5.152
2800	1.342	−5 130	15.106	7.207	0.6657	−5 380	14.686	6.310
3000	1.478	−3 659	15.612	9.095	0.7284	−4 108	15.124	7.768
3200	1.642	−1 734	16.232	11.41	0.8016	−2 501	15.642	9.538
3400	1.848	793	16.998	14.13	0.8899	−454	16.262	11.62
3600	2.111	4 081	17.936	17.44	0.9988	2 146	17.004	14.03
3800	2.450	8 272	19.068	21.17	1.135	5 409	17.885	16.77
4000	2.879	13 423	20.388	25.17	1.305	9 421	18.913	19.80
4200	3.401	19 414	21.849	28.78	1.515	14 193	20.077	22.93
4400	3.999	25 886	23.355	30.86	1.763	19 617	21.388	25.71
4600	4.636	32 297	24.780	30.38	2.045	25 433	22.631	27.42
4800	5.267	38 120	26.020	27.36	2.347	31 265	23.872	27.40
5000	5.856	43 040	27.025	22.88	2.652	36 730	24.988	25.55
5500	7.082	51 393	28.625	12.598	3.346	47 372	27.024	16.96
6000	8.035	56 069	29.442	7.364	3.901	53 865	28.159	10.10
		$p=30$ bar				$p=40$ bar		
1250	0.1919	−10 680	11.878	2.492	0.1438	−10 683	11.743	2.499
1300	0.1997	−10 554	11.977	2.525	0.1497	−10 557	11.842	2.531
1400	0.2152	−10 298	12.166	2.588	0.1614	−10 300	12.032	2.593
1500	0.2307	−10 037	12.346	2.654	0.1730	−10 038	12.213	2.656
1600	0.2462	−9 769	12.519	2.726	0.1847	−9 771	12.386	2.725
1700	0.2617	−9 495	12.685	2.808	0.1963	−9 497	12.552	2.804
1800	0.2772	−9 214	12.846	2.904	0.2079	−9 215	12.712	2.895
1900	0.2927	−8 924	13.003	3.021	0.2196	−8 926	12.869	3.005
2000	0.3083	−8 625	13.156	3.164	0.2313	−8 628	13.021	3.139
2200	0.3398	−7 988	13.460	3.552	0.2548	−7 996	13.322	3.497
2400	0.3721	−7 280	13.767	4.111	0.2790	−7 299	13.626	4.009
2600	0.4059	−6 465	14.093	4.879	0.3042	−6 504	13.943	4.708
2800	0.4422	−5 498	14.451	5.884	0.3310	−5 571	14.289	5.617
3000	0.4825	−4 319	14.851	7.141	0.3605	−4 449	14.675	6.751
3200	0.5286	−2 856	15.329	8.658	0.3938	−3 074	15.118	8.113
3400	0.5830	−1 026	15.883	10.43	0.4327	−1 375	15.633	9.699
3600	0.6489	1 264	16.537	12.46	0.4791	728	16.233	11.50
3800	0.7299	4 106	17.304	14.75	0.5353	3 816	16.932	13.52
4000	0.8298	7 580	18.195	17.28	0.6040	6 460	17.738	15.76
4200	0.9520	11 723	19.205	19.98	0.6876	10 207	18.652	18.15
4400	1.098	16 500	20.315	22.61	0.7877	14 550	19.662	20.57
4600	1.267	21 768	21.486	24.72	0.9045	19 404	20.740	22.72
4800	1.455	27 276	22.658	25.77	1.036	24 592	21.844	24.17
5000	1.652	32 690	23.768	25.35	1.177	29 863	22.920	24.52
5500	2.131	44 255	25.975	19.19	1.528	41 748	25.191	20.32
6000	2.533	51 941	27.317	12.10	1.855	50 243	26.674	13.59
		$p=50$ bar				$p=60$ bar		
1250	0.1150	−10 686	11.639	2.505	0.09575	−10 689	11.552	2.512
1300	0.1197	−10 559	11.737	2.537	0.09970	−10 562	11.651	2.543
1400	0.1291	−10 302	11.928	2.598	0.1075	−10 304	11.843	2.602
1500	0.1384	−10 040	12.109	2.659	0.1153	−10 042	12.024	2.662
1600	0.1477	−9 772	12.282	2.726	0.1231	−9 773	12.197	2.727
1700	0.1571	−9 498	12.448	2.801	0.1309	−9 499	12.363	2.800
1800	0.1664	−9 217	12.608	2.889	0.1387	−9 218	12.523	2.885
1900	0.1757	−8 928	12.764	2.994	0.1464	−8 930	12.679	2.986
2000	0.1850	−8 631	12.916	3.121	0.1542	−8 633	12.831	3.107
2200	0.2039	−8 002	13.216	3.458	0.1700	−8 007	13.130	3.428

continued

T, °K	v	i	s	c_p	v	i	s	c_p
2400	0.2232	—7 312	13.516	3.936	0.1860	—7 322	13.427	3.881
2600	0.2432	—6 531	13.828	4.586	0.2026	—6 552	13.735	4.494
2800	0.2644	—5 623	14.165	5.429	0.2202	—5 663	13.981	5.287
3000	0.2876	—4 541	14.538	6.477	0.2392	—4 610	14.427	6.269
3200	0.3136	—3 227	14.961	7.730	0.2605	—3 342	14.836	7.441
3400	0.3436	—1 619	15.448	9.185	0.2848	—1 802	15.303	8.798
3600	0.3791	356	16.012	10.83	0.3133	77	15.839	10.33
3800	0.4216	2 769	16.664	12.67	0.3473	2 360	16.456	12.03
4000	0.4732	5 686	17.411	14.69	0.3881	5 108	17.160	13.90
4200	0.5355	9 154	18.257	16.87	0.4373	8 367	17.954	15.91
4400	0.6101	13 183	19.194	19.11	0.4960	12 154	18.835	18.00
4600	0.6974	17 717	20.201	21.20	0.5647	16 434	19.786	20.01
4800	0.7966	22 628	21.246	22.82	0.6433	21 110	20.781	21.68
5000	0.9051	27 714	22.284	23.59	0.7301	26 017	21.782	22.69
5500	1.190	39 676	24.568	20.87	0.9642	37 925	24.055	21.08
6000	1.452	48 729	26.148	14.70	1.186	47 369	25.703	15.54
		p=80 bar				p=100 bar		
1250	0.07172	—10 695	11.415	2.525	0.05730	—10 701	11.308	2.538
1300	0.07470	—10 567	11.515	2.555	0.05970	—10 572	11.409	2.567
1400	0.08062	—10 308	11.707	2.611	0.06447	—10 312	11.601	2.620
1500	0.08650	—10 045	11.889	2.668	0.06920	—10 048	11.784	2.675
1600	0.09236	—9 776	12.062	2.730	0.07390	—9 778	11.958	2.734
1700	0.09820	—9 500	12.229	2.799	0.07859	—9 503	12.124	2.800
1800	0.1040	—9 220	12.389	2.880	0.08327	—9 222	12.285	2.877
1900	0.1099	—8 932	12.545	2.975	0.08795	—8 935	12.440	2.968
2000	0.1157	—8 637	12.697	3.088	0.09264	—8 639	12.592	3.075
2200	0.1275	—8 014	12.993	3.386	0.1021	—8 020	12.887	3.356
2400	0.1395	—7 338	13.237	3.802	0.1117	—7 348	13.179	3.745
2600	0.1519	—6 583	13.589	4.361	0.1215	—6 605	13.476	4.267
2800	0.1649	—5 720	13.908	5.080	0.1319	—5 760	13.789	4.934
3000	0.1790	—4 710	14.256	5.968	0.1430	—4 780	14.129	5.756
3200	0.1945	—3 508	14.644	7.024	0.1551	—3 625	14.499	6.730
3400	0.2120	—2 064	15.081	8.241	0.1687	—2 247	14.917	7.850
3600	0.2323	—321	15.579	9.611	0.1844	—598	15.387	9.106
3800	0.2562	1 777	16.146	11.12	0.2027	1 373	15.920	10.49
4000	0.2846	4 285	16.789	12.77	0.2241	3 715	16.520	11.99
4200	0.3185	7 246	17.510	14.54	0.2496	6 468	17.191	13.59
4400	0.3587	10 682	18.309	16.39	0.2797	9 658	17.933	15.28
4600	0.4059	14 582	19.176	18.24	0.3149	13 283	18.738	16.98
4800	0.4600	18 884	20.091	19.90	0.3554	17 303	19.594	18.58
5000	0.5206	23 475	21.028	21.14	0.4010	21 634	20.478	19.89
5500	0.6897	35 109	23.248	20.99	0.5312	32 924	22.630	20.61
6000	0.8590	45 015	24.975	16.66	0.6667	43 042	24.394	17.30
		p=150 bar				p=200 bar		
1250	0.03808	—10 716	11.110	2.571	0.02847	—10 731	10.967	2.605
1300	0.03971	—10 585	11.213	2.598	0.02972	—10 597	11.071	2.629
1400	0.04294	—10 322	11.408	2.644	0.03218	—10 331	11.268	2.669
1500	0.04613	—10 055	11.592	2.692	0.03460	—10 062	11.454	2.710
1600	0.04929	—9 784	11.767	2.745	0.03700	—9 790	11.630	2.757
1700	0.05244	—9 508	11.934	2.805	0.03936	—9 513	11.798	2.812
1800	0.05558	—9 227	12.095	2.876	0.04173	—9 231	11.959	2.877
1900	0.05871	—8 939	12.250	2.958	0.04409	—8 945	12.115	2.955
2000	0.06185	—8 645	12.401	3.056	0.04645	—8 649	12.266	3.046
2200	0.06815	—8 029	12.695	3.308	0.05129	—8 035	12.558	3.280
2400	0.07453	—7 367	12.982	3.655	0.05598	—7 379	12.843	3.599
2600	0.08108	—6 640	13.273	4.114	0.06088	—6 663	13.129	4.019
2800	0.08789	—5 826	13.574	4.698	0.06596	—5 868	13.424	4.550
3000	0.09513	—4 894	13.896	5.412	0.07132	—4 966	13.735	5.197
3200	0.1030	—3 812	14.245	6.255	0.07708	—3 929	14.069	5.959
3400	0.1117	—2 541	14.630	7.219	0.08341	—2 723	14.435	6.827
3600	0.1215	—1 041	15.058	8.295	0.09049	—1 314	14.837	7.793
3800	0.1327	729	15.536	9.471	0.09852	334	15.282	8.845

continued

T, °K	v	i	s	c_p	v	i	s	c_p
4000	0.1458	2810	16.069	10.74	0.1077	2 256	15.775	9.971
4200	0.1610	5 236	16.661	12.08	0.1184	4 483	16.318	11.16
4400	0.1789	8 032	17.311	13.50	0.1308	7 039	16.912	12.41
4600	0.1996	11 207	18.017	14.95	0.1451	8 934	17.555	13.69
4800	0.2235	14 746	18.769	16.37	0.1615	13 165	18.243	14.97
5000	0.2506	18 604	19.557	17.66	0.1802	16 702	18.965	16.18
5500	0.3301	29 066	21.550	19.37	0.2357	26 486	20.829	18.21
6000	0.4182	39 231	23.322	17.82	0.2994	36 448	22.563	17.70
		p=400 bar				p=600 bar		
1250	0.01408	—10 790	10.604	2.738	0.009307	—10 848	10.375	2.872
1300	0.01475	—10 649	10.715	2.752	0.009785	—10 698	10.493	2.876
1400	0.01605	—10 369	10.923	2.766	0.01070	—10 405	10.710	2.863
1500	0.01731	—10 091	11.115	2.782	0.01157	—10 118	10.909	2.855
1600	0.01855	—9 812	11.295	2.809	0.01242	—9 833	11.093	2.862
1700	0.01977	—9 531	11.465	2.847	0.01325	—9 547	11.266	2.885
1800	0.02098	—9 246	11.628	2.897	0.01407	—9 260	11.431	2.923
1900	0.02218	—8 957	11.785	2.960	0.01488	—8 968	11.588	2.976
2000	0.02338	—8 662	11.936	3.035	0.01569	—8 672	11.740	3.041
2200	0.02577	—8 051	12.227	3.230	0.01731	—8 062	12.031	3.213
2400	0.02818	—7 405	12.508	3.491	0.01892	—7 420	12.311	3.445
2600	0.03063	—6 711	12.786	3.830	0.02056	—6 735	12.585	3.745
2800	0.03314	—5 953	13.066	4.254	0.02224	—5 994	12.859	4.116
3000	0.03576	—5 111	13.357	4.766	0.02397	—5 181	13.139	4.562
3200	0.03854	—4 164	13.662	5.364	0.02580	—4 276	13.431	5.081
3400	0.04153	—3 088	13.988	6.041	0.02774	—3 261	13.739	5.667
3600	0.04481	—1 858	14.339	6.789	0.02985	—2 114	14.066	6.312
3800	0.04844	—448	14.720	7.597	0.03216	—815	14.417	7.007
4000	0.05251	1 167	15.134	8.454	0.03471	658	14.795	7.741
4200	0.05712	3 007	15.583	9.352	0.03757	2 321	15.201	8.506
4400	0.06235	5 093	16.068	10.28	0.04078	4 191	15.635	9.293
4600	0.06830	7 436	16.589	11.23	0.04438	6 279	16.099	10.09
4800	0.07505	10 041	17.143	12.19	0.04844	8 591	16.591	10.90
5000	0.08267	12 902	17.727	13.14	0.05300	11 125	17.108	11.70
5500	0.1056	21 020	19.273	15.20	0.06665	18 352	18.484	13.56
6000	0.1334	29 940	20.825	16.14	0.08345	26 493	19.900	14.78
		p=800 bar				p=1000 bar		
1250	0.006940	—10 904	10.199	3.005	0.005534	—10 958	10.054	3.135
1300	0.007318	—10 745	10.324	2.997	0.005852	—10 790	10.187	3.117
1400	0.008033	—10 439	10.552	2.958	0.006446	—10 471	10.425	3.052
1500	0.008710	—10 142	10.757	2.926	0.007003	—10 167	10.636	2.996
1600	0.009362	—9 852	10.946	2.914	0.007536	—9 870	10.828	2.966
1700	0.01000	—9 562	11.122	2.923	0.008055	—9 576	11.007	2.962
1800	0.01062	—9 272	11.288	2.951	0.008564	—9 283	11.176	2.979
1900	0.01124	—8 978	11.447	2.995	0.009066	—8 967	11.335	3.015
2000	0.01246	—8 681	11.599	3.052	0.009563	—8 688	11.489	3.066
2200	0.01308	—8 069	11.891	3.209	0.01055	—8 076	11.731	3.210
2400	0.01430	—7 429	12.170	3.422	0.01154	—7 436	12.059	3.408
2600	0.01554	—6 750	12.441	3.695	0.01253	—6 761	12.330	3.668
2800	0.01680	—6 020	12.712	4.033	0.01354	—6 038	12.598	3.977
3000	0.01809	—5 224	12.986	4.438	0.01457	—5 254	12.868	4.351
3200	0.01945	—4 346	13.270	4.907	0.01566	—4 395	13.146	4.785
3400	0.02089	—3 369	13.566	5.435	0.01680	—3 444	13.433	5.273
3600	0.02244	—2 273	13.879	6.016	0.01802	—2 385	13.736	5.808
3800	0.02412	—1 042	14.212	6.641	0.01934	—1 201	14.056	6.383
4000	0.02597	343	14.567	7.299	0.02078	123	14.396	6.988
4200	0.02801	1 899	14.946	7.988	0.02236	1 602	14.756	7.616
4400	0.03029	3 637	15.350	8.684	0.02412	3 249	15.139	8.257
4600	0.03284	5 569	15.770	9.366	0.02607	5 073	15.545	8.907
4800	0.03568	7 700	16.233	10.11	0.02824	7 079	15.971	9.559
5000	0.03885	10 032	16.709	10.83	0.03064	9 269	16.418	10.20
5500	0.04833	16 686	17.976	12.50	0.03779	15 515	17.608	11.75
6000	0.06003	24 266	19.294	13.77	0.04662	22 670	18.852	13.01

Thermouynamic properties of dissociated steam:
molecular weight M, sound velocity u (m/s) and adiabatic exponent k [20, 21]

T, °K	M	u	k	M	u	k	M	u	k
	p=0.1 bar			p=0.2 bar			p=0.4 bar		
1300	18.015	856.9	1.224	18.016	857.1	1.224	18.016	857.2	1.225
1400	18.014	885.8	1.214	18.015	886.2	1.215	18.015	886.5	1.216
1500	18.010	912.8	1.203	18.011	913.6	1.205	18.012	914.2	1.207
1600	18.006	937.3	1.190	18.008	939.1	1.194	18.010	940.1	1.196
1700	17.900	960.9	1.175	17.995	962.8	1.180	18.000	964.4	1.185
1800	17.973	982.5	1.159	17.982	985.1	1.166	17.989	987.3	1.172
1900	17.924	1003.6	1.144	17.943	1006.7	1.151	17.959	1009.2	1.158
2000	17.875	1025.6	1.130	17.905	1028.1	1.138	17.929	1031.0	1.146
2200	17.630	1074.6	1.113	17.715	1075.5	1.120	17.781	1077.1	1.128
2400	17.099	1141.2	1.116	17.308	1135.9	1.119	17.467	1132.9	1.123
2600	16.087	1243.8	1.151	16.533	1222.8	1.143	16.872	1208.5	1.140
2800	14.417	1412.1	1.235	15.230	1358.5	1.207	15.865	1320.3	1.188
3000	12.147	1663.1	1.347	13.351	1563.8	1.309	14.360	1487.4	1.273
3200	9.770	1955.1	1.404	11.126	1824.4	1.392	12.427	1711.5	1.368
3400	7.963	2211.5	1.378	9.078	2087.0	1.399	10.379	1958.3	1.408
3600	6.941	2381.8	1.315	7.644	2302.1	1.353	8.648	2188.6	1.384
3800	6.451	2500.7	1.277	6.837	2451.8	1.301	7.476	2375.7	1.335
4000	6.226	2620.3	1.285	6.431	2570.6	1.278	6.891	2515.9	1.294
4200	6.121	2759.6	1.335	6.231	2692.5	1.294	6.440	2635.7	1.281
4400	6.069	2913.0	1.408	6.131	2829.7	1.342	6.250	2758.0	1.300
4600	6.042	3062.3	1.481	6.078	2976.8	1.408	6.149	2891.4	1.344
4800	6.027	3193.5	1.540	6.049	3119.9	1.475	6.093	3032.2	1.404
5000	6.019	3303.6	1.580	6.033	3247.8	1.581	6.060	3169.9	1.465
5500	6.010	3515.2	1.624	6.015	3483.1	1.605	6.025	3454.4	1.572
6000	6.007	3683.0	1.633	6.010	3674.5	1.626	6.014	3658.5	1.613
	p=0.6 bar			p=0.8 bar			p=1 bar		
1300	18.016	857.3	1.225	18.016	857.3	1.225	18.016	857.3	1.223
1400	18.015	886.6	1.217	18.015	886.7	1.217	18.015	886.8	1.217
1500	18.013	914.4	1.208	18.013	914.6	1.208	18.013	914.8	1.209
1600	18.011	940.6	1.198	18.011	941.0	1.199	18.011	941.2	1.199
1700	18.002	965.3	1.187	18.003	965.8	1.188	18.003	966.2	1.189
1800	17.993	988.5	1.175	17.995	989.2	1.176	17.996	989.8	1.178
1900	17.966	1010.7	1.162	17.972	1011.6	1.164	17.974	1012.3	1.166
2000	17.940	1032.5	1.150	17.947	1033.6	1.152	17.952	1034.4	1.155
2200	17.812	1078.1	1.132	17.832	1079.0	1.135	17.845	1079.6	1.137
2400	17.542	1131.9	1.126	17.588	1131.5	1.128	17.621	1131.3	1.130
2600	17.032	1202.5	1.139	17.131	1198.9	1.139	17.201	1196.6	1.139
2800	16.168	1303.4	1.180	16.356	1293.3	1.175	16.488	1286.4	1.172
3000	14.857	1451.8	1.255	15.171	1430.1	1.244	15.394	1415.1	1.236
3200	13.119	1654.6	1.350	13.572	1618.4	1.336	13.900	1592.7	1.325
3400	11.163	1888.2	1.408	11.707	1841.6	1.404	12.116	1807.3	1.400
3600	9.351	2116.0	1.399	9.883	2065.1	1.408	10.306	2026.1	1.414
3800	7.987	2315.7	1.356	8.410	2268.3	1.370	8.769	2230.2	1.380
4000	7.125	2473.9	1.311	7.413	2437.7	1.324	7.671	2406.2	1.335
4200	6.634	2601.3	1.285	6.814	2573.8	1.292	6.982	2549.8	1.300
4400	6.365	2723.0	1.288	6.474	2694.5	1.285	6.579	2673.5	1.285
4600	6.218	2846.0	1.317	6.284	2816.0	1.303	6.350	2793.5	1.295
4800	6.135	2980.3	1.365	6.177	2945.0	1.342	6.218	2918.7	1.327
5000	6.087	3117.6	1.423	6.114	3079.6	1.395	6.140	3050.3	1.374
5500	6.035	3421.5	1.545	6.045	3393.1	1.522	6.056	3368.3	1.502
6000	6.018	3643.4	1.601	6.022	3629.1	1.590	6.027	3615.7	1.579
	p=2 bar			p=3 bar			p=4 bar		
1300	18.016	857.4	1.225	18.016	857.5	1.226	18.016	857.5	1.226
1400	18.015	887.0	1.218	18.015	887.1	1.218	18.015	887.1	1.218
1500	18.013	915.1	1.210	18.014	915.8	1.210	18.014	915.5	1.211
1600	18.012	941.9	1.201	18.013	942.2	1.202	18.013	942.5	1.203
1700	18.006	967.2	1.191	18.007	967.8	1.193	18.008	968.2	1.194
1800	18.000	991.3	1.182	18.002	992.1	1.184	18.004	992.7	1.185
1900	17.983	1014.4	1.171	17.987	1015.4	1.174	18.990	1016.1	1.176
2000	17.966	1036.7	1.161	17.972	1038.0	1.164	17.976	1038.9	1.166

continued

T, °K	M	u	k	M	u	k	M	u	k
2200	17.882	1081.8	1.144	17.899	1083.0	1.148	17.910	1083.9	1.150
2400	17.707	1131.3	1.135	17.748	1131.5	1.139	17.774	1131.9	1.141
2600	17.383	1191.1	1.141	17.469	1188.9	1.142	17.522	1187.7	1.143
2800	16.833	1269.4	1.165	16.996	1261.9	1.162	17.078	1257.4	1.161
3000	15.983	1377.1	1.215	16.264	1359.9	1.206	16.440	1349.4	1.200
3200	14.791	1524.8	1.292	15.227	1492.7	1.275	15.501	1473.0	1.264
3400	13.288	1711.5	1.377	13.890	1663.2	1.359	14.277	1632.3	1.345
3600	11.617	1915.7	1.424	12.345	1856.5	1.421	12.832	1817.2	1.415
3800	10.003	2112.7	1.413	10.765	2048.4	1.429	11.303	2005.1	1.438
4000	8.661	2295.0	1.372	9.348	2227.8	1.394	9.866	2181.7	1.412
4200	7.687	2457.9	1.329	8.231	2394.9	1.351	8.672	2347.0	1.368
4400	7.048	2597.9	1.300	7.441	2543.2	1.315	7.779	2499.8	1.329
4600	6.653	2722.3	1.289	6.922	2675.0	1.295	7.165	2637.3	1.303
4800	6.413	2841.8	1.298	6.594	2796.5	1.292	6.763	2762.2	1.293
5000	6.268	2963.6	1.324	6.390	2915.6	1.306	6.505	2881.4	1.299
5500	6.105	3279.3	1.435	6.154	3222.7	1.397	6.200	3182.4	1.372
6000	6.048	3558.5	1.535	6.069	3513.6	1.502	6.089	3477.0	1.476
		p=5 bar			p=6 bar			p=8 bar	
1300	18.016	857.5	1.226	18.016	857.5	1.226	18.016	857.6	1.226
1400	18.016	887.2	1.218	18.016	887.2	1.218	18.016	887.3	1.219
1500	18.014	915.6	1.211	18.014	915.7	1.211	18.015	915.8	1.211
1600	18.013	942.6	1.203	18.013	942.8	1.203	18.014	943.0	1.204
1700	18.009	968.5	1.195	18.009	968.7	1.196	18.010	969.0	1.196
1800	18.005	993.1	1.186	18.005	993.4	1.187	18.006	993.9	1.188
1900	17.992	1016.7	1.177	17.993	1017.1	1.178	17.995	1017.7	1.180
2000	17.979	1039.5	1.168	17.981	1040.0	1.169	17.984	1040.7	1.171
2200	17.918	1084.6	1.152	17.924	1085.2	1.154	17.933	1086.1	1.156
2400	17.792	1132.3	1.143	17.806	1132.6	1.144	17.826	1133.1	1.147
2600	17.560	1187.0	1.144	17.589	1186.5	1.145	17.630	1185.9	1.146
2800	17.169	1254.4	1.160	17.223	1252.2	1.160	17.301	1249.2	1.159
3000	16.563	1342.2	1.196	16.656	1337.0	1.193	16.792	1329.5	1.189
3200	15.696	1459.2	1.256	15.844	1448.9	1.250	16.059	1434.2	1.241
3400	14.557	1610.2	1.335	14.771	1593.4	1.326	15.084	1569.0	1.313
3600	13.190	1788.2	1.409	13.470	1765.6	1.402	13.884	1731.8	1.391
3800	11.712	1972.8	1.442	12.038	1947.1	1.444	12.534	1907.9	1.444
4000	10.278	2147.3	1.425	10.617	2120.1	1.435	11.158	2078.7	1.448
4200	9.039	2310.8	1.382	9.352	2281.8	1.394	9.865	2237.7	1.414
4400	8.074	2464.5	1.340	8.336	2435.1	1.351	8.782	2388.7	1.369
4600	7.385	2605.4	1.311	7.587	2578.0	1.318	7.944	2532.7	1.332
4800	6.920	2733.7	1.296	7.068	2708.9	1.299	7.338	2667.2	1.308
5000	6.616	2854.2	1.296	6.721	2831.0	1.296	6.918	2792.3	1.297
5500	6.247	3151.3	1.356	6.242	3126.2	1.344	6.381	3086.7	1.328
6000	6.110	3446.6	1.455	6.130	3420.6	1.438	6.170	3378.4	1.411
		p=10 bar			p=20 bar			p=30 bar	
1300	18.016	857.6	1.226	18.016	857.7	1.227	18.016	857.8	1.228
1400	18.016	887.4	1.219	18.016	887.6	1.220	18.016	888.0	1.221
1500	18.015	915.9	1.212	18.015	916.3	1.213	18.016	916.6	1.214
1600	18.014	943.2	1.204	18.014	943.8	1.206	18.015	944.2	1.207
1700	18.010	969.3	1.197	18.011	970.1	1.199	18.012	970.7	1.200
1800	18.007	994.2	1.189	18.009	995.4	1.192	18.010	996.2	1.193
1900	17.997	1018.2	1.181	18.001	1019.7	1.184	18.003	1020.7	1.186
2000	17.987	1041.4	1.173	17.993	1043.2	1.177	17.996	1044.4	1.179
2200	17.939	1086.8	1.158	17.955	1089.0	1.163	17.963	1090.4	1.166
2400	17.840	1133.5	1.148	17.879	1135.2	1.154	17.896	1136.5	1.157
2600	17.659	1185.5	1.148	17.736	1185.2	1.152	17.773	1185.5	1.154
2800	17.356	1247.2	1.159	17.501	1242.5	1.160	17.569	1240.8	1.160
3000	16.887	1324.3	1.187	17.136	1311.6	1.181	17.255	1306.1	1.179
3200	16.211	1423.9	1.235	16.611	1397.9	1.219	16.802	1386.1	1.212
3400	15.306	1551.7	1.303	15.900	1506.7	1.276	16.185	1485.8	1.262
3600	14.184	1707.3	1.381	14.998	1640.6	1.347	15.398	1608.1	1.328
3800	12.901	1878.7	1.441	13.930	1794.9	1.419	14.450	1751.4	1.401
4000	11.557	2047.7	1.456	12.750	1956.4	1.465	13.379	1906.3	1.460

continued

T, °K	M	u	k	M	u	k	M	u	k
4200	10.272	2204.1	1.430	11.538	2110.8	1.471	12.244	2059.1	1.485
4400	9.151	2353.5	1.385	10.381	2253.2	1.439	11.118	2200.5	1.470
4600	8.253	2496.7	1.345	9.357	2388.5	1.395	10.070	2331.8	1.430
4800	7.580	2632.8	1.316	8.507	2521.0	1.354	9.154	2459.0	1.386
5000	7.100	2760.3	1.301	7.827	2651.2	1.325	8.397	2585.2	1.349
5500	6.465	3055.8	1.319	6.851	2955.3	1.305	7.172	2890.8	1.307
6000	6.209	3344.9	1.392	6.396	3239.2	1.345	6.568	3175.5	1.327
	$p=40$ bar			$p=50$ bar			$p=60$ bar		
1300	18.016	857.9	1.229	18.016	858.0	1.230	18.016	858.1	1.231
1400	18.016	888.0	1.221	18.016	888.2	1.222	18.016	888.3	1.223
1500	18.016	916.9	1.215	18.016	917.1	1.215	18.016	917.4	1.216
1600	18.015	944.6	1.208	18.015	945.0	1.209	18.015	945.8	1.210
1700	18.012	971.2	1.201	18.013	971.7	1.202	18.013	972.1	1.203
1800	18.010	996.8	1.195	18.011	997.4	1.196	18.011	997.9	1.197
1900	18.004	1021.4	1.188	18.005	1022.1	1.189	18.005	1022.7	1.190
2000	17.998	1045.3	1.181	17.999	1046.0	1.183	18.000	1046.7	1.184
2200	17.968	1091.4	1.169	17.971	1092.4	1.170	17.974	1093.2	1.172
2400	17.907	1137.5	1.159	17.915	1138.4	1.161	17.921	1139.2	1.163
2600	17.796	1186.0	1.156	17.813	1186.6	1.158	17.825	1187.1	1.159
2800	17.613	1240.0	1.161	17.643	1239.7	1.162	17.666	1239.6	1.163
3000	17.330	1303.0	1.178	17.380	1301.0	1.177	17.421	1299.7	1.177
3200	16.921	1379.2	1.208	17.005	1374.5	1.205	17.069	1371.1	1.203
3400	16.365	1473.0	1.254	16.491	1464.2	1.248	16.588	1457.8	1.244
3600	15.650	1587.8	1.316	15.830	1573.6	1.307	15.966	1563.0	1.299
3800	14.783	1723.3	1.336	15.022	1703.1	1.376	15.230	1687.7	1.367
4000	13.791	1872.6	1.451	14.090	1847.6	1.443	14.321	1828.1	1.435
4200	12.720	2023.4	1.489	13.071	1996.4	1.489	13.346	1974.7	1.486
4400	11.631	2165.0	1.488	12.018	2133.0	1.498	12.326	2116.3	1.505
4600	10.588	2294.9	1.456	10.990	2267.8	1.475	11.315	2246.4	1.489
4800	9.645	2418.3	1.411	10.038	2389.0	1.433	10.363	2366.5	1.451
5000	8.838	2540.4	1.370	9.201	2507.6	1.390	9.509	2482.5	1.407
5500	7.455	2942.7	1.314	7.705	2804.7	1.322	7.930	2773.8	1.330
6000	6.728	3128.6	1.319	6.876	3091.0	1.316	7.016	3059.5	1.315
	$p=80$ bar			$p=100$ bar			$p=150$ bar		
1300	18.016	858.3	1.233	18.016	858.6	1.235	18.016	859.3	1.240
1400	18.016	888.7	1.225	18.016	889.1	1.226	18.016	890.2	1.230
1500	18.016	917.9	1.218	18.016	918.5	1.219	18.016	919.9	1.223
1600	18.015	946.0	1.211	18.015	946.7	1.213	18.015	948.4	1.216
1700	18.013	972.9	1.205	18.013	973.8	1.206	18.013	975.7	1.210
1800	18.012	996.9	1.199	18.012	999.8	1.200	18.012	1002.1	1.204
1900	18.007	1023.8	1.192	18.007	1024.8	1.194	18.008	1027.4	1.199
2000	18.002	1048.0	1.186	18.003	1049.2	1.188	18.004	1051.9	1.193
2200	17.978	1094.7	1.175	17.981	1096.0	1.177	17.986	1099.1	1.182
2400	17.930	1140.7	1.166	17.937	1142.1	1.163	17.947	1145.2	1.173
2600	17.844	1188.2	1.162	17.857	1189.4	1.164	17.878	1192.2	1.169
2800	17.700	1239.8	1.165	17.724	1240.3	1.167	17.763	1242.2	1.170
3000	17.480	1298.2	1.177	17.502	1297.5	1.178	17.521	1297.4	1.179
3200	17.162	1366.6	1.201	17.227	1363.9	1.199	17.334	1360.5	1.198
3400	16.728	1448.8	1.238	16.827	1442.8	1.234	16.988	1434.4	1.228
3600	16.166	1547.9	1.289	16.307	1537.6	1.282	16.538	1522.0	1.271
3800	15.473	1665.4	1.353	15.665	1649.8	1.343	15.978	1625.3	1.327
4000	14.662	1799.1	1.422	14.307	1778.2	1.411	15.312	1744.3	1.391
4200	13.756	1941.6	1.480	14.054	1917.0	1.472	14.553	1875.5	1.456
4400	12.793	2082.5	1.511	13.138	2056.8	1.513	13.723	2011.7	1.508
4600	11.818	2213.5	1.509	12.197	2188.5	1.521	12.852	2144.0	1.535
4800	10.877	2333.1	1.479	11.273	2308.7	1.500	11.974	2266.2	1.532
5000	10.009	2445.0	1.436	10.404	2420.0	1.460	11.122	2377.5	1.504
5500	8.318	2726.2	1.347	8.645	2691.3	1.364	9.287	2634.5	1.402
6000	7.270	3008.5	1.317	7.497	2968.6	1.322	7.978	2897.3	1.338

continued

T, °K	M	u	k	M	u	k	M	u	k
	p=200 bar			p=400 bar			p=600 bar		
1300	18.016	860.3	1.245	18.016	865.9	1.271	18.016	874.5	1.302
1400	18.016	891.4	1.235	18.016	897.7	1.255	18.016	906.1	1.279
1500	18.016	921.4	1.227	18.016	928.5	1.245	18.016	937.3	1.266
1600	18.015	950.2	1.220	18.015	958.1	1.237	18.016	967.5	1.256
1700	18.014	977.8	1.214	18.014	986.5	1.231	18.015	996.3	1.249
1800	18.013	1004.3	1.208	18.013	1013.7	1.225	18.014	1023.9	1.242
1900	18.009	1029.8	1.203	18.010	1039.8	1.219	18.011	1050.4	1.235
2000	18.006	1054.5	1.197	18.008	1065.0	1.213	18.009	1075.9	1.229
2200	17.988	1102.0	1.186	17.995	1113.2	1.202	17.998	1124.5	1.218
2400	17.954	1148.2	1.178	17.968	1159.8	1.193	17.975	1171.3	1.208
2600	17.891	1195.0	1.173	17.919	1206.3	1.188	17.933	1217.8	1.202
2800	17.788	1244.4	1.174	17.839	1254.6	1.187	17.864	1265.5	1.200
3000	17.630	1298.4	1.182	17.716	1306.3	1.193	17.759	1316.1	1.204
3200	17.401	1359.5	1.199	17.539	1363.0	1.206	17.607	1371.3	1.215
3400	17.090	1430.3	1.226	17.297	1427.9	1.227	17.399	1432.9	1.233
3600	16.683	1513.4	1.266	16.980	1502.1	1.259	17.126	1502.9	1.261
3800	16.176	1611.0	1.317	16.583	1587.9	1.301	16.783	1583.1	1.299
4000	15.570	1723.6	1.379	16.104	1686.6	1.354	16.367	1674.8	1.347
4200	14.874	1848.9	1.443	15.545	1797.9	1.415	15.870	1778.4	1.403
4400	14.106	1981.5	1.500	14.916	1919.3	1.477	15.324	1892.6	1.464
4600	13.288	2113.3	1.589	14.231	2045.9	1.532	14.713	2014.2	1.523
4800	12.452	2237.2	1.549	13.508	2171.2	1.570	14.059	2137.8	1.572
5000	11.623	2349.9	1.532	12.766	2289.1	1.585	13.379	2257.8	1.603
5500	9.770	2600.4	1.435	10.973	2539.7	1.527	11.672	2516.4	1.584
6000	8.639	2850.1	1.356	9.445	2759.4	1.427	10.132	2726.4	1.485

T, °K	M	u	k	T, °K	M	u	k	T, °K	M	u	k
					p=800 bar						
1300	18.016	885.8	1.340	2400	17.979	1183.1	1.223	4000	16.534	1671.8	1.345
1400	18.016	916.5	1.307	2600	17.942	1229.4	1.216	4200	16.092	1770.4	1.398
1500	18.016	947.8	1.289	2800	17.880	1276.8	1.213	4400	15.587	1879.5	1.458
1600	18.016	978.1	1.277	3000	17.736	1326.7	1.216	4600	15.026	1996.9	1.518
1700	18.015	1007.2	1.268	3200	17.650	1380.7	1.225	4800	14.421	2118.5	1.572
1800	18.014	1035.1	1.260	3400	17.463	1440.5	1.242	5000	13.785	2238.9	1.613
1900	18.012	1061.7	1.253	3600	17.219	1507.9	1.267	5500	12.155	2504.7	1.623
2000	18.010	1087.4	1.246	3800	16.910	1584.5	1.301	6000	10.631	2713.0	1.533
2200	18.000	1136.2	1.234								
					p=1000 bar						
1300	18.016	899.6	1.383	2400	17.982	1195.1	1.238	4000	16.655	1673.1	1.347
1400	18.016	928.7	1.338	2600	17.948	1241.3	1.230	4200	16.246	1768.0	1.398
1500	18.016	959.6	1.315	2800	17.892	1288.4	1.226	4400	15.777	1873.4	1.455
1600	18.016	989.9	1.301	3000	17.806	1337.7	1.228	4600	15.254	1987.5	1.515
1700	18.015	1019.1	1.289	3200	17.861	1390.8	1.235	4800	14.686	2107.0	1.572
1800	18.014	1047.0	1.280	3400	17.510	1449.3	1.250	5000	14.085	2227.0	1.619
1900	18.012	1073.8	1.272	3600	17.286	1514.8	1.274	5500	12.519	2496.5	1.652
2000	18.010	1099.4	1.264	3800	17.002	1589.0	1.306	6000	11.020	2708.4	1.573
2200	18.001	1148.3	1.250								

Equilibrium composition of dissociated steam [20, 21]

T, °K	x_{O_2}	x_O	x_{H_2}	x_{OH}	x_H	x_{H_2O}
			p=0.1 bar			
2000	0.0051	0.0001	0.0124	0.0046	0.0006	0.9772
2200	0.0122	0.0009	0.0304	0.0136	0.0031	0.9398
2400	0.0242	0.0043	0.0624	0.0323	0.0126	0.8642
2600	0.0407	0.0148	0.1079	0.0632	0.0399	0.7335
2800	0.0572	0.0410	0.1549	0.1011	0.1020	0.5438

continued

T, °K	x_{O_2}	x_O	x_{H_2}	x_{OH}	x_H	x_{H_2O}
3000	0.0648	0.0911	0.1791	0.1281	0.2116	0.3253
3200	0.0566	0.1620	0.1593	0.1233	0.3550	0.1438
3400	0.0374	0.2324	0.1083	0.0893	0.4871	0.0455
3600	0.0200	0.2816	0.0607	0.0523	0.5740	0.0114
3800	0.0097	0.3082	0.0315	0.0278	0.6202	0.0026
4000	0.0047	0.3210	0.0163	0.0146	0.6428	0.0006
4200	0.0023	0.3270	0.0087	0.0079	0.6539	0.0002
4400	0.0012	0.3300	0.0048	0.0044	0.6596	
4600	0.0007	0.3314	0.0028	0.0026	0.6625	
4800	0.0004	0.3322	0.0017	0.0016	0.6641	
5000	0.0002	0.3326	0.0011	0.0010	0.6651	
5500		0.3331	0.0004	0.0004	0.6661	
6000		0.3332	0.0002	0.0002	0.6664	
			$p=1$ bar			
2000	0.0024		0.0058	0.0021	0.0001	0.9896
2200	0.0057	0.0002	0.0145	0.0064	0.0007	0.9725
2400	0.0117	0.0009	0.0308	0.0158	0.0028	0.9380
2600	0.0208	0.0034	0.0569	0.0329	0.0092	0.8768
2800	0.0329	0.0098	0.0927	0.0593	0.0250	0.7803
3000	0.0459	0.0242	0.1336	0.0930	0.0578	0.6455
3200	0.0562	0.0511	0.1691	0.1266	0.1157	0.4813
3400	0.0598	0.0929	0.1856	0.1478	0.2017	0.3122
3600	0.0543	0.1468	0.1745	0.1461	0.3077	0.1706
3800	0.0420	0.2028	0.1406	0.1224	0.4146	0.0776
4000	0.0282	0.2500	0.0995	0.0891	0.5029	0.0303
4200	0.0173	0.2831	0.0647	0.0591	0.5651	0.0107
4400	0.0102	0.3037	0.0405	0.0374	0.6045	0.0037
4600	0.0060	0.3157	0.0252	0.0235	0.6283	0.0013
4800	0.0036	0.3226	0.0159	0.0149	0.6425	0.0005
5000	0.0022	0.3266	0.0103	0.0097	0.6510	0.0002
5500	0.0007	0.3310	0.0038	0.0036	0.6609	
6000	0.0003	0.3323	0.0017	0.0016	0.6641	
			$p=2$ bar			
2000	0.0019		0.0046	0.0017		0.9918
2200	0.0046	0.0001	0.0116	0.0051	0.0004	0.9782
2400	0.0093	0.0006	0.0247	0.0126	0.0018	0.9510
2600	0.0168	0.0021	0.0462	0.0266	0.0058	0.9025
2800	0.0270	0.0063	0.0766	0.0488	0.0160	0.8253
3000	0.0388	0.0157	0.1138	0.0790	0.0377	0.7150
3200	0.0499	0.0340	0.1515	0.1128	0.0774	0.5744
3400	0.0571	0.0642	0.1794	0.1420	0.1402	0.4171
3600	0.0576	0.1069	0.1873	0.1559	0.2255	0.2668
3800	0.0507	0.1577	0.1716	0.1488	0.3239	0.1473
4000	0.0392	0.2082	0.1387	0.1239	0.4198	0.0702
4200	0.0271	0.2504	0.1011	0.0923	0.4994	0.0297
4400	0.0174	0.2808	0.0689	0.0638	0.5574	0.0117
4600	0.0108	0.3006	0.0454	0.0425	0.5962	0.0045
4800	0.0067	0.3128	0.0297	0.0280	0.6210	0.0018
5000	0.0042	0.3203	0.0196	0.0186	0.6366	0.0007
5500	0.0014	0.3287	0.0075	0.0072	0.6551	0.0001
6000	0.0006	0.3314	0.0033	0.0031	0.6616	
			$p=4$ bar			
2000	0.0015		0.0037	0.0014		0.9934
2200	0.0036		0.0092	0.0041	0.0003	0.9828
2400	0.0074	0.0004	0.0198	0.0101	0.0011	0.9612
2600	0.0135	0.0014	0.0372	0.0214	0.0037	0.9228
2800	0.0219	0.0040	0.0626	0.0398	0.0103	0.8614
3000	0.0322	0.0101	0.0953	0.0659	0.0244	0.7721
3200	0.0430	0.0223	0.1315	0.0976	0.0510	0.6546
3400	0.0519	0.0433	0.1645	0.1296	0.0949	0.5158
3600	0.0566	0.0749	0.1856	0.1538	0.1587	0.3704
3800	0.0552	0.1163	0.1881	0.1624	0.2398	0.2382

continued

T, °K	x_{O_2}	x_O	x_{H_2}	x_{OH}	x_H	x_{H_2O}
4000	0.0481	0.1632	0.1709	0.1525	0.3296	0.1357
4200	0.0377	0.2088	0.1403	0.1283	0.4161	0.0688
4400	0.0271	0.2473	0.1061	0.0986	0.4891	0.0318
4600	0.0183	0.2760	0.0758	0.0713	0.5447	0.0159
4800	0.0120	0.2958	0.0526	0.0497	0.5840	0.0059
5000	0.0078	0.3087	0.0361	0.0343	0.6106	0.0025
5500	0.0028	0.3241	0.0146	0.0139	0.6442	0.0004
6000	0.0011	0.3295	0.0065	0.0062	0.6567	
			$p=6$ bar			
2000	0.0013		0.0032	0.0012		0.9943
2200	0.0032		0.0081	0.0035	0.0002	0.9850
2400	0.0065	0.0003	0.0173	0.0088	0.0009	0.9662
2600	0.0119	0.0010	0.0328	0.0188	0.0028	0.9327
2800	0.0194	0.0031	0.0555	0.0352	0.0079	0.8789
3000	0.0288	0.0078	0.0853	0.0589	0.0189	0.8003
3200	0.0390	0.0173	0.1198	0.0887	0.0397	0.6955
3400	0.0483	0.0341	0.1535	0.1207	0.0749	0.5685
3600	0.0545	0.0600	0.1794	0.1484	0.1274	0.4303
3800	0.0557	0.0954	0.1905	0.1643	0.1971	0.2970
4000	0.0516	0.1380	0.1834	0.1635	0.2788	0.1847
4200	0.0432	0.1825	0.1606	0.1469	0.3635	0.1033
4400	0.0331	0.2234	0.1294	0.1206	0.4410	0.0525
4600	0.0237	0.2567	0.0977	0.0921	0.5049	0.0249
4800	0.0162	0.2813	0.0708	0.0672	0.5531	0.0114
5000	0.0109	0.2983	0.0502	0.0478	0.5877	0.0051
5500	0.0040	0.3199	0.0212	0.0202	0.6339	0.0008
6000	0.0017	0.3276	0.0096	0.0092	0.6518	0.0001
			$p=8$ bar			
2000	0.0012		0.0029	0.0011		0.9948
2200	0.0029		0.0073	0.0032	0.0002	0.9864
2400	0.0059	0.0003	0.0158	0.0080	0.0007	0.9693
2600	0.0108	0.0009	0.0299	0.0171	0.0024	0.9389
2800	0.0177	0.0026	0.0509	0.0322	0.0065	0.8901
3000	0.0265	0.0065	0.0787	0.0543	0.0157	0.8183
3200	0.0362	0.0145	0.1116	0.0826	0.0332	0.7219
3400	0.0455	0.0287	0.1452	0.1141	0.0631	0.6034
3600	0.0525	0.0510	0.1734	0.1431	0.1085	0.4715
3800	0.0553	0.0823	0.1894	0.1631	0.1701	0.3396
4000	0.0531	0.1212	0.1891	0.1684	0.2451	0.2231
4200	0.0464	0.1639	0.1726	0.1579	0.3262	0.1330
4400	0.0373	0.2053	0.1452	0.1354	0.4046	0.0722
4600	0.0278	0.2409	0.1142	0.1079	0.4728	0.0364
4800	0.0197	0.2688	0.0856	0.0815	0.5269	0.0175
5000	0.0136	0.2889	0.0624	0.0596	0.5673	0.0082
5500	0.0053	0.3157	0.0262	0.0274	0.6241	0.0013
6000	0.0022	0.3257	0.0126	0.0121	0.6471	0.0003
			$p=10$ bar			
2000	0.0011		0.0027	0.0010		0.9952
2200	0.0027		0.0068	0.0030	0.0002	0.9873
2400	0.0055	0.0002	0.0147	0.0075	0.0006	0.9715
2600	0.0101	0.0007	0.0278	0.0160	0.0020	0.9434
2800	0.0165	0.0022	0.0475	0.0301	0.0057	0.8980
3000	0.0248	0.0056	0.0739	0.0509	0.0136	0.8312
3200	0.0342	0.0126	0.1055	0.0779	0.0289	0.7409
3400	0.0434	0.0250	0.1387	0.1088	0.0551	0.6290
3600	0.0507	0.0449	0.1680	0.1386	0.0955	0.5023
3800	0.0546	0.0731	0.1872	0.1610	0.1513	0.3728
4000	0.0538	0.1091	0.1915	0.1706	0.2207	0.2543
4200	0.0485	0.1498	0.1802	0.1649	0.2981	0.1585
4400	0.0403	0.1908	0.1565	0.1461	0.3758	0.0905
4600	0.0311	0.2277	0.1271	0.1203	0.4459	0.0479

continued

T, °K	x_{O_2}	x_O	x_{H_2}	x_{OH}	x_H	x_{H_2O}
4800	0.0227	0.2578	0.0979	0.0935	0.5041	0.0240
5000	0.0160	0.2804	0.0730	0.0700	0.5489	0.0117
5500	0.0064	0.3118	0.0332	0.0319	0.6148	0.0019
6000	0.0027	0.3239	0.0156	0.0149	0.6425	0.0004
			p=20 bar			
2000	0.0009		0.0021	0.0008		0.9962
2200	0.0022		0.0054	0.0024		0.9900
2400	0.0044	0.0001	0.0117	0.0059	0.0004	0.9775
2600	0.0080	0.0005	0.0223	0.0128	0.0013	0.9551
2800	0.0133	0.0014	0.0383	0.0242	0.0036	0.9192
3000	0.0202	0.0036	0.0603	0.0414	0.0087	0.8658
3200	0.0283	0.0081	0.0877	0.0646	0.0186	0.7927
3400	0.0369	0.0163	0.1183	0.0926	0.0360	0.6999
3600	0.0447	0.0298	0.1487	0.1294	0.0635	0.5909
3800	0.0506	0.0498	0.1742	0.1495	0.1032	0.4727
4000	0.0533	0.0768	0.1901	0.1690	0.1555	0.3553
4200	0.0521	0.1098	0.1933	0.1770	0.2184	0.2494
4400	0.0475	0.1465	0.1835	0.1718	0.2877	0.1630
4600	0.0404	0.1836	0.1634	0.1555	0.3577	0.0994
4800	0.0324	0.2178	0.1377	0.1324	0.4226	0.0571
5000	0.0248	0.2468	0.1109	0.1076	0.4786	0.0313
5500	0.0114	0.2940	0.0579	0.0562	0.5741	0.0064
6000	0.0051	0.3153	0.0291	0.0281	0.6210	0.0014
			p=40 bar			
2000	0.0007		0.0017	0.0006		0.9970
2200	0.0017		0.0043	0.0019		0.9921
2400	0.0035		0.0093	0.0047	0.0003	0.9822
2600	0.0064	0.0003	0.0178	0.0102	0.0008	0.9645
2800	0.0106	0.0009	0.0308	0.0194	0.0023	0.9360
3000	0.0163	0.0023	0.0489	0.0335	0.0055	0.8935
3200	0.0232	0.0052	0.0720	0.0529	0.0119	0.8348
3400	0.0308	0.0106	0.0991	0.0773	0.0233	0.7589
3600	0.0384	0.0195	0.1280	0.1051	0.0417	0.6673
3800	0.0451	0.0332	0.1555	0.1332	0.0690	0.5640
4000	0.0498	0.0525	0.1779	0.1580	0.1064	0.4554
4200	0.0518	0.0774	0.1919	0.1756	0.1539	0.3494
4400	0.0508	0.1071	0.1953	0.1831	0.2099	0.2538
4600	0.0469	0.1399	0.1880	0.1796	0.2713	0.1743
4800	0.0411	0.1734	0.1718	0.1664	0.3339	0.1134
5000	0.0343	0.2050	0.1500	0.1466	0.3937	0.0704
5500	0.0187	0.2662	0.0924	0.0909	0.5133	0.0185
6000	0.0093	0.2999	0.0515	0.0503	0.5844	0.0046
			p=60 bar			
2000	0.0006		0.0015	0.0005		0.9974
2200	0.0015		0.0038	0.0016		0.9931
2400	0.0031		0.0081	0.0041	0.0002	0.9845
2600	0.0056	0.0002	0.0156	0.0089	0.0006	0.9691
2800	0.0094	0.0007	0.0270	0.0170	0.0017	0.9442
3000	0.0144	0.0018	0.0431	0.0295	0.0042	0.9070
3200	0.0205	0.0040	0.0639	0.0469	0.0092	0.8555
3400	0.0276	0.0081	0.0888	0.0691	0.0180	0.7884
3600	0.0348	0.0152	0.1161	0.0951	0.0325	0.7063
3800	0.0415	0.0261	0.1434	0.1227	0.0541	0.6122
4000	0.0469	0.0416	0.1676	0.1488	0.0844	0.5107
4200	0.0502	0.0622	0.1858	0.1699	0.1237	0.4082
4400	0.0509	0.0876	0.1953	0.1832	0.1714	0.3116
4600	0.0490	0.1167	0.1952	0.1867	0.2258	0.2266
4800	0.0448	0.1479	0.1859	0.1806	0.2837	0.1571
5000	0.0392	0.1786	0.1696	0.1664	0.3420	0.1042
5500	0.0238	0.2452	0.1156	0.1146	0.4688	0.0320
6000	0.0127	0.2867	0.0693	0.0684	0.5540	0.0089

continued

T, °K	x_{O_2}	x_O	x_{H_2}	x_{OH}	x_H	x_{H_2O}
			$p=80$ bar			
2000	0.0006		0.0013	0.0005		0.9976
2200	0.0014		0.0034	0.0015		0.9937
2400	0.0028		0.0074	0.0038	0.0002	0.9860
2600	0.0051	0.0002	0.0142	0.0080	0.0005	0.9720
2800	0.0085	0.0006	0.0246	0.0155	0.0014	0.9494
3000	0.0131	0.0014	0.0394	0.0269	0.0035	0.9157
3200	0.0188	0.0033	0.0586	0.0429	0.0077	0.8687
3400	0.0254	0.0068	0.0819	0.0636	0.0150	0.8073
3600	0.0323	0.0127	0.1079	0.0883	0.0271	0.7317
3800	0.0390	0.0219	0.1347	0.1151	0.0454	0.6439
4000	0.0447	0.0352	0.1595	0.1414	0.0713	0.5479
4200	0.0486	0.0530	0.1797	0.1643	0.1054	0.4490
4400	0.0503	0.0754	0.1927	0.1808	0.1475	0.3533
4600	0.0496	0.1018	0.1971	0.1888	0.1965	0.2662
4800	0.0467	0.1307	0.1927	0.1876	0.2502	0.1921
5000	0.0420	0.1606	0.1808	0.1779	0.3057	0.1330
5500	0.0275	0.2284	0.1323	0.1318	0.4344	0.0456
6000	0.0156	0.2752	0.0840	0.0833	0.5281	0.0138
			$p=100$ bar			
2000	0.0005		0.0012	0.0005		0.9978
2200	0.0012		0.0032	0.0014		0.9942
2400	0.0026		0.0068	0.0035	0.0001	0.9870
2600	0.0047	0.0002	0.0131	0.0075	0.0004	0.9741
2800	0.0079	0.0005	0.0229	0.0144	0.0012	0.9531
3000	0.0126	0.0013	0.0379	0.0259	0.0033	0.9190
3200	0.0176	0.0029	0.0548	0.0400	0.0066	0.8781
3400	0.0238	0.0059	0.0768	0.0597	0.0130	0.8208
3600	0.0305	0.0110	0.1018	0.0832	0.0235	0.7500
3800	0.0370	0.0191	0.1279	0.1092	0.0396	0.6672
4000	0.0428	0.0308	0.1529	0.1355	0.0625	0.5755
4200	0.0482	0.0467	0.1742	0.1592	0.0928	0.4799
4400	0.0495	0.0670	0.1894	0.1777	0.1309	0.3855
4600	0.0497	0.0911	0.1969	0.1887	0.1758	0.2978
4800	0.0477	0.1182	0.1962	0.1911	0.2258	0.2211
5000	0.0439	0.1467	0.1877	0.1851	0.2787	0.1579
5500	0.0304	0.2148	0.1448	0.1448	0.4065	0.0587
6000	0.0181	0.2649	0.0962	0.0960	0.5057	0.0191
			$p=200$ bar			
2000	0.0004		0.0010	0.0004		0.9982
2200	0.0010		0.0025	0.0011		0.9954
2400	0.0021		0.0054	0.0027		0.9898
2600	0.0037	0.0001	0.0104	0.0059	0.0003	0.9796
2800	0.0063	0.0003	0.0182	0.0113	0.0008	0 9631
3000	0 0098	0 0008	0 0293	0.0198	0.0019	0.9384
3200	0.0142	0.0018	0.0441	0.0320	0.0042	0.9037
3400	0.0194	0.0037	0.0625	0.0483	0.0083	0.8578
3600	0.0252	0.0071	0.0840	0.0683	0.0152	0.8002
3800	0.0312	0.0124	0.1076	0.0914	0.0257	0.7317
4000	0.0369	0.0202	0.1317	0.1162	0.0410	0.6540
4200	0.0419	0.0312	0.1544	0.1407	0.0619	0.5699
4400	0.0457	0.0455	0.1740	0.1629	0.0888	0.4831
4600	0.0479	0.0633	0.1886	0.1806	0.1218	0.3978
4800	0.0484	0.0842	0.1971	0.1923	0.1602	0.3178
5000	0.0472	0.1077	0.1989	0.1969	0.2031	0.2462
5500	0.0384	0.1706	0.1778	0.1796	0.3188	0.1148
6000	0.0265	0.2271	0.1362	0.1380	0.4258	0.0464
			$p=300$ bar			
2000	0.0003		0.0009	0.0003		0.9985
2200	0.0008		0.0022	0.0009		0.9961
2400	0.0018		0.0047	0.0023		0.9912

continued

T, °K	x_{O_2}	x_O	x_{H_2}	x_{OH}	x_H	x_{H_2O}
2600	0.0033		0.0090	0.0051	0.0002	0.9824
2800	0.0055	0.0002	0.0158	0.0098	0.0006	0.9681
3000	0.0085	0.0006	0.0256	0.0172	0.0015	0.9466
3200	0.0124	0.0014	0.0387	0.0280	0.0032	0.9163
3400	0.0171	0.0029	0.0551	0.0424	0.0064	0.8761
3600	0.0224	0.0054	0.0746	0.0604	0.0117	0.8255
3800	0.0280	0.0096	0.0963	0.0816	0.0199	0.7646
4000	0.0335	0.0157	0.1192	0.1049	0.0320	0.6947
4200	0.0386	0.0244	0.1418	0.1288	0.0485	0.6179
4400	0.0428	0.0360	0.1624	0.1517	0.0701	0.5370
4600	0.0458	0.0505	0.1795	0.1717	0.0971	0.4554
4800	0.0474	0.0681	0.1918	0.1870	0.1293	0.3764
5000	0.0475	0.0882	0.1986	0.1967	0.1659	0.3031
5500	0.0418	0.1454	0.1909	0.1937	0.2701	0.1581
6000	0.0314	0.2020	0.1581	0.1614	0.3750	0.0721
			p=400 bar			
2000	0.0003		0.0008	0.0003		0.9986
2200	0.0008		0.0019	0.0008		0.9965
2400	0.0016		0.0042	0.0021		0.9921
2600	0.0030		0.0082	0.0045	0.0002	0.9841
2800	0.0050	0.0002	0.0143	0.0088	0.0005	0.9712
3000	0.0078	0.0005	0.0231	0.0156	0.0012	0.9518
3200	0.0113	0.0011	0.0352	0.0253	0.0027	0.9244
3400	0.0156	0.0024	0.0503	0.0385	0.0053	0.8879
3600	0.0206	0.0045	0.0683	0.0551	0.0097	0.8418
3800	0.0258	0.0080	0.0888	0.0748	0.0166	0.7860
4000	0.0312	0.0131	0.1106	0.0970	0.0267	0.7214
4200	0.0362	0.0205	0.1327	0.1202	0.0407	0.6497
4400	0.0406	0.0303	0.1536	0.1430	0.0592	0.5733
4600	0.0440	0.0429	0.1717	0.1639	0.0824	0.4951
4800	0.0462	0.0582	0.1861	0.1812	0.1104	0.4179
5000	0.0471	0.0760	0.1957	0.1937	0.1428	0.3447
5500	0.0436	0.1286	0.1970	0.2002	0.2378	0.1928
6000	0.0347	0.1837	0.1717	0.1761	0.3387	0.0951
			p=500 bar			
2000	0.0003		0.0007	0.0002		0.9988
2200	0.0007		0.0018	0.0008		0.9967
2400	0.0015		0.0039	0.0019		0.9927
2600	0.0027		0.0075	0.0042	0.0002	0.9854
2800	0.0046	0.0002	0.0132	0.0081	0.0004	0.9735
3000	0.0072	0.0004	0.0215	0.0143	0.0010	0.9556
3200	0.0106	0.0010	0.0326	0.0233	0.0023	0.9302
3400	0.0146	0.0020	0.0467	0.0356	0.0046	0.8965
3600	0.0192	0.0039	0.0637	0.0512	0.0084	0.8536
3800	0.0242	0.0069	0.0831	0.0698	0.0144	0.8016
4000	0.0294	0.0114	0.1041	0.0909	0.0232	0.7410
4200	0.0344	0.0179	0.1256	0.1134	0.0355	0.6732
4400	0.0388	0.0266	0.1464	0.1360	0.0519	0.6003
4600	0.0425	0.0377	0.1651	0.1573	0.0724	0.5250
4800	0.0451	0.0514	0.1807	0.1757	0.0974	0.4497
5000	0.0464	0.0676	0.1921	0.1900	0.1267	0.3772
5500	0.0445	0.1164	0.1998	0.2032	0.2144	0.2217
6000	0.0369	0.1696	0.1807	0.1859	0.3111	0.1158
			p=1000 bar			
2000	0.0002		0.0005	0.0002		0.9991
2200	0.0005		0.0014	0.0005		0.9976
2400	0.0011		0.0030	0.0014		0.9945
2600	0.0021		0.0058	0.0031		0.9890
2800	0.0036	0.0001	0.0102	0.0061	0.0003	0.9797
3000	0.0057	0.0003	0.0166	0.0108	0.0007	0.9659
3200	0.0083	0.0006	0.0255	0.0178	0.0015	0.9463

continued

T, °K	x_{O_2}	x_{O_2}	x_{H_2}	x_{OH}	x_H	x_{H_2O}
3400	0.0116	0.0013	0.0368	0.0274	0.0029	0.9200
3600	0.0155	0.0025	0.0507	0.0398	0.0053	0.8862
3800	0.0197	0.0044	0.0669	0.0551	0.0092	0.8447
4000	0.0243	0.0073	0.0849	0.0729	0.0149	0.7957
4200	0.0289	0.0116	0.1041	0.0925	0.0230	0.7399
4400	0.0333	0.0174	0.1237	0.1133	0.0339	0.6784
4600	0.0372	0.0250	0.1427	0.1342	0.0479	0.6130
4800	0.0406	0.0346	0.1602	0.1541	0.0652	0.5453
5000	0.0431	0.0461	0.1753	0.1718	0.0861	0.4776
5500	0.0454	0.0832	0.1986	0.2013	0.1519	0.3196
6000	0.0420	0.1281	0.1986	0.2049	0.2317	0.1947

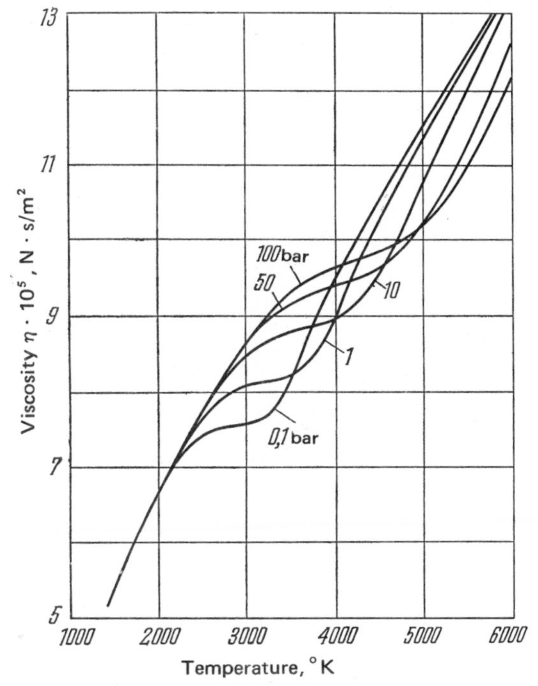

Fig. 7. Viscosity of dissociated steam as a function of temperature at different pressures.

Viscosity $\eta \cdot 10^7$ ($N \cdot s/m^2$) of dissociated steam [20–22]

T, °K \ p, bar →	0.1	0.2	0.4	0.6	0.8	1.0	2.0	5.0	10	20	30	40	50	60	80	100
1400	512	512	512	512	512	512	512	512	512	512	512	512	512	512	512	512
1600	563	563	563	563	563	563	563	563	563	563	563	563	563	563	563	563
1800	612	612	612	612	612	612	612	612	612	612	612	612	612	612	612	612
2000	657	658	658	659	659	659	659	659	660	660	660	660	660	660	660	660
2200	698	700	702	702	702	703	704	704	705	705	706	706	706	706	706	706
2400	731	735	739	740	742	742	744	746	748	749	749	749	750	750	750	750
2600	752	760	767	771	776	775	779	784	788	789	790	790	791	791	792	792
2800	754	772	784	791	795	798	806	815	820	824	826	828	828	829	830	831
3000	756	774	790	800	806	810	824	838	846	854	858	860	861	863	865	865
3200	763	774	778	801	809	814	832	852	866	877	882	886	889	891	894	896
3400	795	791	796	804	810	816	834	859	877	893	901	906	910	913	918	921
3600	804	832	822	821	822	825	838	863	883	903	913	920	926	930	936	941

continued

T, °K \ p, bar →	0.1	0.2	0.4	0.6	0.8	1.0	2.0	5.0	10	20	30	40	50	60	80	100
3800	903	886	867	851	854	851	852	868	887	908	921	929	936	941	949	955
4000	953	940	922	910	901	895	882	882	894	914	932	936	943	949	958	965
4200	997	989	976	965	956	949	927	909	910	922	933	942	949	955	965	973
4400	1030	1035	1025	1055	1010	1005	980	950	937	939	945	952	958	963	972	980
4600	1080	1075	1070	1065	1060	1055	1035	999	976	965	965	968	972	975	983	989
4800	1115	1115	1110	1005	1105	1100	1085	1055	1025	1000	995	993	993	994	998	1005
5000	1155	1155	1160	1145	1080	1145	1130	1105	1075	1045	1035	1025	1025	1020	1020	1020
5200	1190	1190	1190	1185	1185	1185	1175	1155	1130	1095	1080	1070	1060	1055	1050	1050
5400	1230	1230	1225	1225	1225	1220	1215	1200	1180	1150	1130	1115	1105	1100	1090	1080
5600	1265	1265	1265	1265	1260	1260	1255	1245	1225	1200	1180	1165	1155	1145	1130	1125
5800	1300	1300	1300	1300	1300	1300	1295	1285	1270	1250	1230	1215	1205	1195	1180	1170
6000	1340	1340	1340	1340	1335	1335	1335	1320	1315	1295	1280	1265	1255	1245	1230	1215

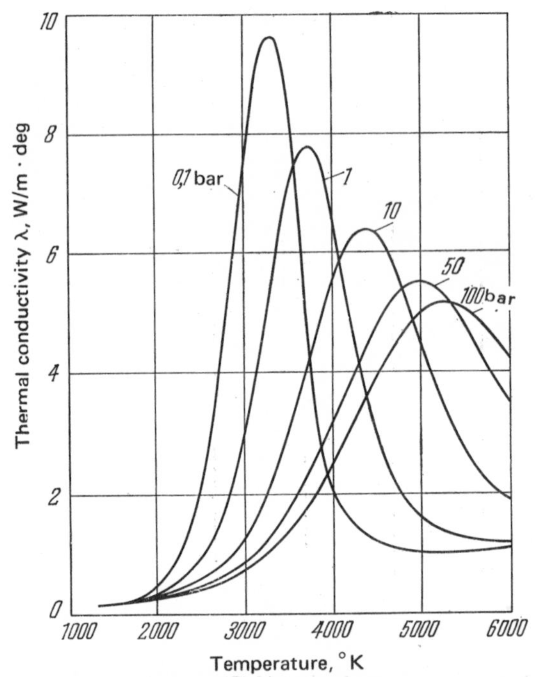

Fig. 8. Thermal conductivity of dissociated steam as a function of temperature at different pressures.

Thermal conductivity $\lambda \cdot 10^3$ (W/m · deg) of dissociated steam [20–22]

T, °K \ p, bar →	0.1	0.2	0.4	0.6	0.8	1.0	2.0	5.0
1400	188	188	188	187	187	187	187	187
1600	227	224	222	220	220	219	218	217
1800	291	280	271	267	265	263	258	253
2000	423	387	359	347	339	333	316	304
2200	711	606	530	495	474	459	421	384
2400	1330	1060	865	779	726	690	599	515
2600	2590	1935	1495	1305	1545	1110	910	730
2800	4610	3465	2595	2210	1980	1820	1430	1045
3000	7450	5090	4295	3625	3220	2940	2240	1605
3200	9380	8060	5945	5505	4915	4495	3400	2375
3400	8470	8935	8155	7365	6745	6265	4855	7835

continued

p, bar → / T, °K	0.1	0.2	0.4	0,6	0.8	1.0	2.0	5.0
3600	6870	7460	8300	8210	7925	7610	6335	4600
3800	3440	5055	6720	6825	7690	7765	7305	5795
4000	2160	3210	4685	5620	6235	6635	7280	6650
4200	1535	2140	3135	3905	7395	4995	6300	6840
4400	1240	1580	2190	3040	3170	3565	4930	6315
4600	1110	1305	1665	2000	2300	2580	3685	5335
4800	1055	1170	1385	1595	1790	1975	2770	4270
5000	1042	1110	1245	1370	1525	1615	2160	3355
5200	1050	1090	1175	1255	1335	1415	1780	2665
5400	1065	1090	1145	1200	1255	1305	1850	2190
5600	1090	1105	1145	1180	1215	1245	1415	1870
5800	1115	1130	1155	1175	1200	1225	1340	1665
6000	1145	1555	1905	1190	1205	1220	1305	1555

p, bar → / T, °K	10	20	30	40	50	60	80	100
1400	186	186	186	186	186	186	186	186
1600	216	215	215	215	215	215	215	214
1800	251	248	247	247	246	246	245	245
2000	296	290	287	285	264	283	281	280
2200	304	348	341	336	333	331	327	324
2400	469	435	419	409	402	396	389	383
2600	636	566	534	515	501	490	476	465
2800	896	765	706	669	644	625	598	579
3000	1285	1055	953	890	846	814	768	751
3200	1845	1470	1300	1195	1125	1075	999	948
3400	2600	2020	1760	1605	1495	1415	1305	1225
3600	3535	2725	2345	2125	1970	1850	1690	1575
3800	4580	3550	3060	2755	2540	2385	2160	2005
4000	5565	4435	3880	3465	3200	2995	2705	2505
4200	6255	5250	4630	4205	3895	3660	3310	3060
4400	6445	5835	5295	4885	4565	4310	3925	3640
4600	6095	6060	5725	5400	5120	4880	4495	4120
4800	5355	5875	5830	5560	5470	5280	4950	4640
5000	4480	5365	5805	5625	5560	5465	5240	5025
5200	3660	4885	5135	5325	5395	5400	5320	5195
5400	2990	3985	4530	4845	5030	5130	5200	5190
5600	2485	3355	3915	4285	4540	4710	4910	4995
5800	2130	2845	3360	3735	4020	4230	4515	4680
6000	1885	2455	2895	3245	3525	3710	4080	4300

HEAVY WATER (DEUTERIUM OXIDE D_2O)

Molecular weight 20.02942

t_{boil} = 101.43 °C at 760 mm Hg; t_{melt} = 371.5 °C; p_{cr} = 218.3 bar;
ρ_{cr} = 338 kg/m³ Thermodynamic properties of heavy water at saturation
v (m³/kg), i and r (kJ/kg) and s (kJ/kg · deg) [23, 25]

t, °C	p, bar	v'	v''	i'	i''	s'	s''	r
3.8	0.00668	0.0009047	172.2	0.0	2322.4	0.0000	8.3857	2322.4
5.0	0.00720	0.0009045	160.4	5.0	2324.1	0.0193	8.3564	2319.1
10	0.01030	0.0009042	114.1	26.0	2332.5	0.0929	8.2384	2306.5
20	0.02011	0.0009047	60.45	67.8	2349.2	0.2391	8.0211	2281.4
30	0.03731	0.0009063	33.71	109.7	2365.5	0.3818	7.8230	2255.8
40	0.06598	0.0009091	19.66	151.6	2382.3	0.5187	7.6417	2230.7
50	0.11198	0.0009127	11.93	193.4	2398.2	0.6506	7.4730	2204.8
60	0.18305	0.0009170	7.517	234.9	2414.9	0.7762	7.3198	2180.1
70	0.2894	0.0009220	4.890	276.7	2431.7	0.8997	7.1787	2154.9
80	0.4440	0.0009274	3.273	318.6	2446.8	1.0212	7.0468	2128.2

continued

t, °C	p, bar	v′	v″	i′	i″	s′	s″	r
90	0.6627	0.0009336	2.249	360.5	2461.4	1.1396	6.9250	2100.9
100	0.9646	0.0009403	1.582	402.4	2476.5	1.2535	6.8119	2074.1
110	1.3728	0.0009476	1.138	444.6	2490.7	1.3653	6.7056	2046.1
120	1.9134	0.0009556	0.8326	486.9	2504.5	1.4742	6.6064	2017.6
130	2.6170	0.0009643	0.6212	528.8	2517.9	1.5809	6.5142	1989.1
140	3.518	0.0009736	0.4705	571.1	2530.9	1.6835	6.4267	1959.8
150	4.653	0.0009835	0.3616	612.9	2543.5	1.7823	6.3451	1930.5
160	6.066	0.0009942	0.2815	655.2	2556.0	1.8782	6.2660	1900.8
170	7.802	0.0010055	0.2218	697.9	2566.5	1.9741	6.1906	1868.6
180	9.911	0.0010175	0.1765	741.1	2574.9	2.0691	6.1165	1833.8
190	12.445	0.0010303	0.1422	784.2	2581.6	2.1642	6.0453	1797.4
200	15.462	0.0010439	0.1153	827.3	2587.4	2.2575	5.9771	1760.1
210	19.028	0.0010584	0.09420	875.5	2592.5	2.3488	5.9109	1721.2
220	23.194	0.0010749	0.07746	916.1	2596.6	2.4401	5.8477	1680.6
230	28.031	0.0010910	0.06411	962.1	2600.0	2.5301	5.7853	1637.9
240	33.606	0.0011106	0.05340	1008.6	2601.3	2.6197	5.7234	1592.7
250	39.993	0.001133	0.04470	1055.9	2600.4	2.7093	5.6614	1544.5
260	47.280	0.001159	0.03756	1104.1	2597.5	2.7985	5.5994	1493.4
270	55.527	0.001186	0.03162	1153.0	2592.5	2.8872	5.5370	1439.4
280	64.834	0.001214	0.02667	1203.3	2584.5	2.9760	5.4726	1381.2
290	75.288	0.001244	0.02253	1254.8	2572.8	3.0652	5.4060	1318.0
300	86.968	0.001276	0.01906	1307.5	2557.3	3.1548	5.3357	1249.8
305	93.323	0.001294	0.01751	1334.8	2548.1	3.2004	5.2988	1213.3
310	100.01	0.001314	0.01607	1362.0	2537.2	3.2456	5.2611	1175.2
315	107.07	0.001338	0.01474	1389.6	2524.6	3.2824	5.2209	1135.0
320	114.54	0.001364	0.01351	1418.1	2510.4	3.3373	5.1791	1092.3
325	122.38	0.001392	0.01235	1446.5	2494.1	3.3838	5.1351	1047.5
330	130.65	0.001424	0.01128	1476.7	2476.1	3.4311	5.0882	999.4
335	139.37	0.001459	0.01028	1507.2	2455.1	3.4788	5.0371	947.9
340	148.54	0.001498	0.009336	1538.2	2430.9	3.5265	4.9823	892.6
345	158.20	0.001543	0.008413	1571.3	2402.4	3.5768	4.9212	831.1
350	168.35	0.001596	0.007537	1608.1	2368.0	3.6333	4.8529	759.9
355	178.98	0.001660	0.006692	1648.3	2326.2	3.6961	4.7750	677.8
360	190.16	0.001750	0.005869	1696.9	2270.5	3.7757	4.6817	573.6
365	202.12	0.00189	0.00497	1758.9	2186.8	3.8854	4.5347	427.0
370	214.68	0.00222	0.00383	1864.8	2049.0	4.0696	4.3559	184.2
371	217.22	0.00251	0.00343	1910.9	2006.3	4.1533	4.3024	95.5

Thermodynamic properties of heavy water and superheated steam at different temperatures and pressures: v (m^3/kg), i (kJ/kg) and s (kJ/kg · deg) [23–25]

t, °C	v	i	s	v	i	s
	p=0.1 bar			p=1 bar		
3.8	0.0009047	0.0	0.0000	0.0009047	0.0	0.0000
10	0.0009045	26.0	0.0921	0.0009044	26.0	0.0921
20	0.0009050	67.8	0.2395	0.0009050	67.8	0.2395
30	0.0009063	109.7	0.3818	0.0009063	109.7	0.3818
40	0.0009090	151.6	0.5187	0.0009090	151.6	0.5187
50	13.36	2399.4	7.5212	0.0009127	193.4	0.6502
60	13.78	2416.6	7.5768	0.0009170	235.3	0.7766
70	14.20	2434.2	7.6271	0.0009219	276.7	0.8997
80	14.62	2451.8	7.6778	0.0009274	318.6	1.0207
90	15.05	2469.8	7.7276	0.0009335	360.5	1.1384
100	15.46	2487.4	7.7757	0.0009403	402.4	1.2535
110	15.88	2505.0	7.8230	1.569	2495.3	6.8462
120	16.30	2523.0	7.8687	1.613	2514.2	6.8952
130	16.71	2541.0	7.9135	1.656	2533.0	6.9426
140	17.13	2558.6	7.9574	1.700	2551.4	6.9882
150	17.54	2576.6	8.0001	1.742	2570.3	7.0326
160	17.96	2594.6	8.0424	1.784	2588.7	7.0765
170	18.38	2613.0	8.0839	1.826	2607.5	7.1192

continued

t, °C	v	i	s	v	i	s
180	18.79	2631.4	8.1245	1.869	2626.4	7.1607
190	19.21	2649.4	8.1643	1.911	2644.8	7.2013
200	19.62	2667.8	8.2036	1.953	2663.6	7.2415
210	20.04	2686.2	8.2426	1.996	2682.5	7.2808
220	20.45	2704.7	8.2806	2.038	2700.9	7.3194
230	20.86	2723.1	8.3179	2.080	2719.7	7.3570
240	21.29	2741.9	8.3543	2.122	2739.0	7.3943
250	21.70	2760.8	8.3903	2.164	2758.3	7.4312
260	22.11	2779.6	8.4259	2.206	2777.1	7.4663
270	22.53	2798.5	8.4611	2.247	2795.9	7.5019
280	22.95	2817.3	8.4958	2.288	2815.2	7.5371
290	23.36	2836.6	8.5298	2.330	2834.0	7.5714
300	23.78	2855.8	8.5637	2.373	2853.3	7.6053
310	24.20	2875.1	8.5968	2.414	2873.0	7.6384
320	24.61	2894.3	8.6294	2.456	2892.7	7.6715
330	25.03	2913.6	8.6616	2.497	2911.9	7.7041
340	25.44	2933.3	8.6939	2.539	2931.6	7.7364
350	25.86	2952.5	8.7257	2.582	2950.9	7.7682
360	26.27	2972.2	8.7567	2.623	2970.5	7.7996
370	26.68	2991.9	8.7877	2.664	2990.2	7.8306
380	27.09	3012.0	8.8187	2.706	3010.3	7.8611
390	27.51	3031.7	8.8488	2.747	3030.0	7.8917
400	27.92	3051.8	8.8785	2.789	3050.1	7.9214
410	28.34	3071.8	8.9078	2.830	3070.6	7.9512
420	28.76	3092.0	8.9371	2.873	3090.7	7.9805
430	29.17	3112.0	8.9664	2.914	3110.8	8.0093
440	29.59	3132.6	8.9953	2.956	3131.3	8.0382
450	30.01	3152.7	9.0238	2.997	3151.4	8.0667
460	30.42	3173.2	9.0519	3.038	3172.3	8.0948
470	30.84	3193.7	9.0795	3.080	3192.8	8.1228
480	31.25	3214.6	9.1071	3.122	3213.8	8.1504
490	31.66	3235.1	9.1348	3.164	3234.3	8.1781
500	32.08	3256.1	9.1620	3.205	3255.2	8.2053
510	32.49	3277.0	9.1888	3.247	3276.2	8.2321
520	32.90	3297.9	9.2156	3.288	3297.1	8.2589
530	33.32	3318.9	9.2419	3.330	3318.0	8.2853
540	33.73	3340.2	9.2679	3.371	3339.4	8.3112
550	34.14	3361.6	9.2934	3.412	3360.7	8.3372
		p=5 bar			p=10 bar	
3.8	0.0009045	0.4	0.0000	0.0009043	0.8	0.0000
10	0.0009043	26.4	0.0921	0.0009041	26.8	0.0921
20	0.0009048	68.2	0.2395	0.0009045	68.7	0.2395
30	0.0009061	110.1	0.3818	0.0009059	110.5	0.3814
40	0.0009088	152.0	0.5187	0.0009086	152.4	0.5183
50	0.0009125	193.8	0.6502	0.0009123	194.3	0.6498
60	0.0009169	235.7	0.7766	0.0009167	236.1	0.7762
70	0.0009218	277.2	0.8997	0.0009216	277.6	0.8993
80	0.0009273	319.0	1.0207	0.0009271	319.4	1.0203
90	0.0009334	360.9	1.1380	0.0009332	361.3	1.1380
100	0.0009401	403.2	1.2531	0.0009399	403.6	1.2527
110	0.0009475	445.1	1.3649	0.0009472	445.5	1.3645
120	0.0009555	487.3	1.4742	0.0009552	487.8	1.4742
130	0.0009642	529.2	1.5809	0.0009639	529.6	1.5805
140	0.0009735	571.1	1.6835	0.0009732	571.5	1.6831
150	0.0009835	612.9	1.7823	0.0009832	613.8	1.7819
160	0.3451	2562.3	6.3602	0.0009940	655.6	1.8782
170	0.3547	2583.3	6.4083	0.0010054	697.9	1.9737
180	0.3641	2602.9	6.4544	0.0010175	741.1	2.0691
190	0.3731	2623.9	6.4992	0.1803	2594.6	6.1617
200	0.3821	2644.0	6.5427	0.1854	2618.0	6.2111
210	0.3912	2664.5	6.5850	0.1905	2641.0	6.2584
220	0.4002	2684.6	6.6264	0.1953	2662.8	6.3045

continued

t, °C	v	i	s	v	i	s
230	0.4091	2704.7	6.6666	0.2001	2684.6	6.3484
240	0.4179	2724.8	6.7056	0.2047	2706.3	6.3912
250	0.4265	2744.9	6.7437	0.2093	2727.7	6.4330
260	0.4351	2765.0	6.7814	0.2139	2748.6	6.4728
270	0.4439	2784.6	6.8182	0.2186	2769.1	6.5113
280	0.4526	2804.3	6.8546	0.2230	2790.9	6.5490
290	0.4612	2824.0	6.8902	0.2275	2811.4	6.5862
300	0.4698	2844.1	6.9250	0.2320	2832.4	6.6227
310	0.4784	2863.8	6.9593	0.2364	2852.9	6.6578
320	0.4870	2883.9	6.9928	0.2408	2873.4	6.6934
330	0.4955	2904.8	7.0263	0.2452	2893.9	6.7269
340	0.5039	2924.9	7.0589	0.2496	2914.4	6.7604
350	0.5125	2944.6	7.0916	0.2540	2934.5	6.7935
360	0.5210	2964.7	7.1234	0.2585	2955.0	6.8262
370	0.5295	2984.4	7.1552	0.2627	2975.6	6.8584
380	0.5379	3004.4	7.1866	0.2670	2996.1	6.8906
390	0.5464	3024.5	7.2172	0.2713	3017.0	6.9220
400	0.5549	3045.1	7.2474	0.2756	3037.5	6.9526
410	0.5633	3065.6	7.2771	0.2799	3058.0	6.9832
420	0.5718	3086.1	7.3068	0.2842	3079.0	7.0133
430	0.5802	3105.8	7.3365	0.2884	3100.0	7.0426
440	0.5886	3126.7	7.3654	0.2927	3120.4	7.0719
450	0.5969	3147.2	7.3943	0.2970	3141.8	7.1008
460	0.6053	3168.2	7.4228	0.3013	3162.7	7.1293
470	0.6137	3189.1	7.4508	0.3055	3183.6	7.1578
480	0.6221	3210.0	7.4789	0.3098	3204.6	7.1858
490	0.6306	3230.1	7.5065	0.3140	3225.5	7.2139
500	0.6390	3251.9	7.5341	0.3182	3246.4	7.2415
510	0.6474	3272.4	7.5609	0.3224	3268.2	7.2691
520	0.6557	3293.8	7.5877	0.3268	3289.6	7.2959
530	0.6642	3315.1	7.6141	0.3310	3310.9	7.3227
540	0.6725	3336.5	7.6405	0.3352	3332.3	7.3491
550	0.6809	3357.8	7.6664	0.3394	3354.0	7.3750
		$p=20$ bar			$p=30$ bar	
3.8	0.0009038	1.7	0.0000	0.0009034	2.5	0.0000
10	0.0009037	27.6	0.0921	0.0009033	28.5	0.0921
20	0.0009042	69.5	0.2391	0.0009038	70.3	0.2391
30	0.0009056	111.4	0.3814	0.0009052	112.2	0.3810
40	0.0009083	153.2	0.5179	0.0009079	154.1	0.5179
50	0.0009119	195.1	0.6494	0.0009116	195.9	0.6490
60	0.0009163	237.0	0.7758	0.0009159	237.8	0.7754
70	0.0009212	278.8	0.8989	0.0009208	279.7	0.8985
80	0.0009266	320.7	1.0195	0.0009262	321.5	1.0191
90	0.0009327	362.6	1.1371	0.0009323	363.4	1.1367
100	0.0009394	404.4	1.2523	0.0009390	405.3	1.2514
110	0.0009468	446.3	1.3641	0.0009463	447.2	1.3632
120	0.0009548	488.2	1.4733	0.0009543	489.0	1.4725
130	0.0009634	530.0	1.5797	0.0009629	530.9	1.5784
140	0.0009727	571.9	1.6823	0.0009721	572.8	1.6810
150	0.0009826	613.8	1.7806	0.0009821	614.6	1.7798
160	0.0009933	656.1	1.8774	0.0009927	656.5	1.8761
170	0.0010047	698.8	1.9728	0.0010040	698.8	1.9720
180	0.0010168	741.5	2.0679	0.0010161	741.9	2.0670
190	0.0010298	784.6	2.1629	0.0010290	785.0	2.1616
200	0.0010435	827.7	2.2567	0.0010426	828.1	2.2554
210	0.0010583	871.3	2.3488	0.0010572	871.7	2.3475
220	0.09205	2614.2	5.9394	0.0010729	916.5	2.4392
230	0.09506	2641.0	5.9913	0.0010907	962.1	2.5301
240	0.09780	2666.2	6.0411	0.06140	2619.7	5.7991
250	0.1005	2690.4	6.0884	0.06354	2649.0	5.8565
260	0.1030	2714.7	6.1341	0.06559	2677.0	5.9097
270	0.1055	2738.2	6.1776	0.06757	2703.4	5.9586

continued

t, °C	v	i	s	v	i	s
280	0.1080	2761.6	6.2191	0.06944	2729.4	6.0055
290	0.1105	2784.2	6.2593	0.07128	2754.9	6.0508
300	0.1129	2807.2	6.3024	0.07304	2779.6	6.0947
310	0.1153	2829.4	6.3409	0.07480	2803.5	6.1366
320	0.1177	2851.6	6.3773	0.07650	2827.3	6.1772
330	0.1201	2873.4	6.4133	0.07817	2851.2	6.2170
340	0.1223	2894.7	6.4481	0.07984	2874.2	6.2551
350	0.1247	2916.1	6.4833	0.08149	2896.8	6.2919
360	0.1269	2937.5	6.5176	0.08310	2919.0	6.3279
370	0.1292	2959.2	6.5511	0.08468	2942.1	6.3627
380	0.1315	2980.6	6.5837	0.08624	2964.2	6.3970
390	0.1337	3001.9	6.6164	0.08781	2986.4	6.4301
400	0.1359	3023.7	6.6478	0.08938	3008.2	6.4627
410	0.1382	3045.1	6.6792	0.09093	3030.4	6.4954
420	0.1405	3066.4	6.7102	0.09247	3052.6	6.5276
430	0.1426	3087.3	6.7412	0.09398	3074.4	6.5599
440	0.1448	3108.7	6.7717	0.09551	3096.1	6.5925
450	0.1470	3130.0	6.8019	0.09700	3117.9	6.6235
460	0.1492	3151.0	6.8312	0.09849	3139.7	6.6537
470	0.1513	3172.3	6.8601	0.1000	3161.4	6.6830
480	0.1535	3193.7	6.8885	0.1014	3183.6	6.7119
490	0.1557	3215.0	6.9166	0.1029	3205.4	6.7403
500	0.1579	3236.8	6.9442	0.1044	3227.2	6.7684
510	0.1601	3258.6	6.9714	0.1058	3249.0	6.7964
520	0.1622	3280.4	6.9986	0.1074	3271.1	6.8245
530	0.1643	3302.1	7.0259	0.1088	3293.3	6.8521
540	0.1666	3323.9	7.0522	0.1104	3315.1	6.8797
550	0.1688	3345.7	7.0786	0.1117	3337.3	6.9061
		p=40 bar			p=50 bar	
3.8	0.0009029	3.35	0.0000	0.0009025	4.2	0.0004
10	0.0009028	29.3	0.0921	0.0009024	30.1	0.0921
20	0.0009034	71.2	0.2391	0.0009030	72.0	0.2386
30	0.0009048	113.0	0.3810	0.0009045	113.9	0.3806
40	0.0009075	154.9	0.5175	0.0009072	155.7	0.5171
50	0.0009112	196.8	0.6485	0.0009108	197.6	0.6481
60	0.0009155	238.6	0.7750	0.0009151	239.1	0.7746
70	0.0009204	280.1	0.8976	0.0009200	280.9	0.8972
80	0.0009258	322.0	1.0186	0.0009254	322.8	1.0178
90	0.0009319	363.8	1.1359	0.0009314	364.7	1.1355
100	0.0009386	405.7	1.2510	0.0009381	406.5	1.2498
110	0.0009458	447.6	1.3624	0.0009454	448.0	1.3615
120	0.0009538	489.4	1.4712	0.0009533	489.9	1.4704
130	0.0009624	531.3	1.5776	0.0009618	531.7	1.5767
140	0.0009716	573.2	1.6802	0.0009710	573.6	1.6793
150	0.0009815	615.0	1.7790	0.0009809	615.5	1.7781
160	0.0009921	656.9	1.8753	0.0009915	657.3	1.8740
170	0.0010033	699.6	1.9707	0.0010027	699.6	1.9695
180	0.0010154	742.3	2.0658	0.0010146	742.7	2.0645
190	0.0010281	785.0	2.1604	0.0010273	785.9	2.1591
200	0.0010417	828.1	2.2542	0.0010408	829.0	2.2525
210	0.0010561	872.1	2.3463	0.0010551	872.5	2.3446
220	0.0010715	916.5	2.4371	0.0010704	916.9	2.4355
230	0.0010889	962.1	2.5280	0.0010873	962.1	2.5259
240	0.0011089	1008.6	2.6180	0.0011069	1008.6	2.6155
250	0.0011340	1055.9	2.7093	0.001130	1055.9	2.7063
260	0.04654	2633.5	5.7246	0.001157	1104.1	2.7976
270	0.04830	2664.5	5.7824	0.03651	2620.1	5.6229
280	0.04993	2694.6	5.8368	0.03802	2654.8	5.6865
290	0.05146	2722.7	5.8862	0.03952	2687.1	5.7443
300	0.05296	2750.3	5.9340	0.04089	2717.2	5.7975
310	0.05436	2777.1	5.9796	0.04204	2747.0	5.8477
320	0.05578	2802.2	6.0235	0.04328	2775.0	5.8958

continued

t, °C	v	i	s	v	i	s
330	0.05715	2827.8	6.0658	0.04446	2801.8	5.9411
340	0.05847	2852.5	6.1069	0.04561	2828.6	5.9846
350	0.06079	2876.3	6.1462	0.04673	2854.1	6.0265
360	0.06109	2899.8	6.1843	0.04783	2879.7	6.0667
370	0.06234	2923.6	6.2216	0.04890	2904.4	6.1060
380	0.06360	2947.1	6.2580	0.04995	2929.1	6.1433
390	0.06483	2970.1	6.2940	0.05099	2953.4	6.1797
400	0.06607	2993.1	6.3283	0.05201	2977.2	6.2157
410	0.06728	3016.2	6.3618	0.05303	3001.1	6.2505
420	0.06849	3038.8	6.3941	0.05405	3024.5	6.2848
430	0.06968	3061.4	6.4259	0.05505	3047.6	6.3187
440	0.07085	3084.0	6.4577	0.05601	3071.0	6.3514
450	0.07200	3106.2	6.4891	0.05697	3093.6	6.3836
460	0.07314	3128.4	6.5201	0.05792	3116.6	6.4150
470	0.07427	3150.6	6.5502	0.05886	3139.7	5.4456
480	0.07541	3172.8	6.5796	0.05978	3162.3	6.4761
490	0.07655	3194.9	6.6089	0.06072	3184.5	6.5067
500	0.07768	3217.1	6.6382	0.06164	3207.5	6.5356
510	0.07881	3239.3	6.6666	0.06256	3230.1	6.5645
520	0.07993	3261.5	6.6980	0.06348	3252.3	6.5934
530	0.08106	3283.7	6.7236	0.06440	3274.9	6.6218
540	0.08218	3305.9	6.7512	0.06532	3297.5	6.6491
550	0.08330	3328.5	6.7784	0.06622	3320.6	6.6771
		$p=60$ bar			$p=70$ bar	
3.8	0.0009020	5.0	0.0004	0.0009016	5.9	0.0004
10	0.0009019	31.0	0.0921	0.0009015	31.8	0.0921
20	0.0009025	72.8	0.2386	0.0009022	73.7	0.2386
30	0.0009040	114.7	0.3806	0.0009037	115.6	0.3802
40	0.0009067	156.6	0.5166	0.0009063	157.4	0.5162
50	0.0009104	198.4	0.6477	0.0009100	199.3	0.6477
60	0.0009147	239.9	0.7741	0.0009143	241.2	0.7737
70	0.0009195	281.8	0.8968	0.0009191	283.0	0.8964
80	0.0009249	323.2	1.0174	0.0009245	324.5	1.0170
90	0.0009309	365.1	1.1346	0.0009305	366.3	1.1342
100	0.0009376	407.0	1.2489	0.0009371	407.8	1.2485
110	0.0009448	448.8	1.3607	0.0009444	449.2	1.3599
120	0.0009527	490.7	1.4700	0.0009522	491.1	1.4691
130	0.0009612	532.6	1.5759	0.0009607	533.0	1.5755
140	0.0009704	574.4	1.6781	0.0009698	574.8	1.6772
150	0.0009802	616.3	1.7769	0.0009796	616.7	1.7760
160	0.0009907	658.2	1.8728	0.0009901	658.6	1.8719
170	0.0010019	700.4	1.9682	0.0010013	700.9	1.9670
180	0.0010138	743.2	2.0632	0.0010131	743.6	2.0620
190	0.0010265	785.9	2.1579	0.0010257	786.7	2.1566
200	0.0010399	829.0	2.2512	0.0010391	829.8	2.2500
210	0.0010541	872.5	2.3434	0.0010532	872.9	2.3421
220	0.0010693	917.3	2.4334	0.0010682	917.3	2.4317
230	0.0010861	962.1	2.5230	0.0010847	962.1	2.5209
240	0.0011051	1008.6	2.6121	0.0011035	1008.6	2.6100
250	0.001127	1055.9	2.7030	0.001125	1055.5	2.6996
260	0.001153	1103.6	2.7938	0.001150	1103.6	2.7897
270	0.001183	1153.0	2.8851	0.001179	1152.6	2.8801
280	0.02988	2608.8	5.5416	0.001211	1202.9	2.9722
290	0.03123	2646.5	5.6103	0.02519	2600.0	5.4776
300	0.03252	2681.6	5.6718	0.02650	2641.0	5.5496
310	0.03373	2714.3	5.7284	0.02767	2678.7	5.6145
320	0.03487	2745.7	5.7811	0.02878	2713.9	5.6740
330	0.03591	2774.6	5.8301	0.02981	2746.1	5.7284
340	0.03699	2803.5	5.8766	0.03079	2777.5	5.7790
350	0.03799	2831.1	5.9214	0.03173	2807.2	5.8276
360	0.03895	2857.5	5.9645	0.03261	2835.7	5.8737
370	0.03990	2884.7	6.0060	0.03347	2863.8	5.9176

continued

t, °C	v	i	s	v	i	s
380	0.04084	2911.1	6.0470	0.03431	2891.4	5.9595
390	0.04175	2936.2	6.0847	0.03513	2917.8	6.0001
400	0.04264	2960.9	6.1219	0.03594	2943.3	6.0390
410	0.04353	2985.6	6.1579	0.03673	2969.3	6.0767
420	0.04440	3009.5	6.1931	0.03750	2995.2	6.1131
430	0.04526	3033.3	6.2279	0.03827	3020.4	6.1487
440	0.04611	3057.2	6.2618	0.03902	3044.6	6.1835
450	0.04694	3081.1	6.2944	0.03975	3069.3	6.2174
460	0.04776	3104.5	6.3267	0.04048	3093.2	5.2505
470	0.04856	3128.0	6.3577	0.04120	3117.1	6.2831
480	0.04936	3151.0	6.3886	0.04190	3140.9	6.3150
490	0.05015	3174.0	6.4192	0.04260	3164.4	6.3459
500	0.05093	3197.5	6.4498	0.04329	3187.8	6.3765
510	0.05172	3220.5	6.4799	0.04398	3211.3	6.4066
520	0.05247	3243.1	6.5092	0.04466	3234.3	6.4359
530	0.05327	3266.1	6.5381	0.04534	3257.3	6.4653
540	0.05406	3289.2	6.5662	0.04600	3280.4	6.4941
550	0.05482	3312.2	6.5938	0.04667	3303.4	6.5222
		$p=80$ bar			$p=90$ bar	
3.8	0.0009012	6.7	0.0004	0.0009008	7.5	0.0004
10	0.0009011	32.7	0.0921	0.0009007	33.5	0.0921
20	0.0009018	74.5	0.2386	0.0009014	75.4	0.2382
30	0.0009033	116.4	0.3802	0.0009029	117.2	0.3797
40	0.0009060	158.3	0.5158	0.0009056	159.1	0.5158
50	0.0009096	200.1	0.6473	0.0009092	201.0	0.6469
60	0.0009139	241.6	0.7733	0.0009135	242.8	0.7729
70	0.0009187	283.4	0.8960	0.0009183	284.3	0.8951
80	0.0009241	324.9	1.0161	0.0009237	325.7	1.0157
90	0.0009301	366.3	1.1334	0.0009297	367.2	1.1329
100	0.0009367	408.2	1.2477	0.0009362	409.0	1.2472
110	0.0009439	450.1	1.3594	0.0009434	450.9	1.3590
120	0.0009517	491.5	1.4683	0.0009512	492.4	1.4679
130	0.0009602	533.4	1.5738	0.0009597	534.2	1.5726
140	0.0009693	575.3	1.6764	0.0009687	576.1	1.6756
150	0.0009790	617.1	1.7752	0.0009785	618.0	1.7739
160	0.0009895	659.4	1.8707	0.0009889	659.8	1.8698
170	0.0010006	701.7	1.9657	0.0009999	702.1	1.9649
180	0.0010124	744.4	2.0607	0.0010117	744.4	2.0595
190	0.0010249	787.1	2.1554	0.0010241	787.1	2.1537
200	0.0010382	834.0	2.2487	0.0010373	829.8	2.2471
210	0.0010522	873.4	2.3404	0.0010513	873.4	2.3387
220	0.0010671	917.7	2.4304	0.0010660	917.7	2.4288
230	0.0010835	962.1	2.5196	0.0010822	962.1	2.5179
240	0.0011020	1008.6	2.6080	0.0011004	1008.6	2.6059
250	0.001123	1055.1	2.6971	0.001121	1055.1	2.6942
260	0.001148	1103.2	2.7859	0.001146	1102.8	2.7825
270	0.001176	1152.2	2.8747	0.001173	1151.8	2.8700
280	0.001207	1202.4	2.9659	0.001203	1201.6	2.9592
290	0.001241	1253.9	3.0610	0.001236	1252.7	3.0522
300	0.02183	2595.0	5.4252	0.001271	1306.7	3.1514
310	0.02301	2638.9	5.5014	0.01931	2592.9	5.3863
320	0.02414	2678.3	5.5693	0.02041	2638.5	5.4650
330	0.02512	2714.7	5.6308	0.02143	2680.8	5.5345
340	0.02606	2749.5	5.6865	0.02235	2718.9	5.5965
350	0.02696	2780.9	5.7388	0.02322	2752.8	5.6538
360	0.02779	2812.3	5.7882	0.02402	2786.3	5.7070
370	0.02859	2842.8	5.8347	0.02480	2818.6	5.7577
380	0.02939	2872.1	5.8791	0.02554	2850.4	5.8054
390	0.03015	2900.2	5.9214	0.02625	2879.3	5.8506
400	0.03089	2926.6	5.9624	0.02694	2907.7	5.8925
410	0.03161	2953.0	6.0018	0.02762	2935.4	5.9327
420	0.03231	2978.9	6.0399	0.02827	2962.6	5.9720

continued

t, °C	v	i	s	v	i	s
430	0.03301	3004.9	6.0771	0.02891	2989.4	6.0110
440	0.03369	3030.0	6.1127	0.02954	3015.8	6.0487
450	0.03436	3055.1	6.1479	0.03015	3041.7	6.0847
460	0.03501	3079.4	6.1818	0.03076	3067.2	6.1194
470	0.03567	3103.7	6.2149	0.03135	3092.4	6.1533
480	0.03630	3128.4	6.2471	0.03193	3117.1	6.1864
490	0.03693	3152.7	6.2785	0.03250	3141.8	6.2195
500	0.03755	3176.5	6.3095	0.03306	3166.1	6.2517
510	0.03816	3200.4	6.3405	0.03362	3190.3	6.2835
520	0.03877	3223.8	6.3710	0.03418	3214.2	6.3141
530	0.03937	3247.7	6.4012	0.03474	3238.1	6.3438
540	0.03997	3271.6	6.4305	0.03528	3262.4	6.3723
550	0.04056	3295.4	6.4590	0.03581	3286.2	6.4008
		$p=100$ bar			$p=120$ bar	
3.8	0.0009004	8.4	0.0004	0.0008994	10.0	0.0000
10	0.0009003	34.3	0.0917	0.0008994	36.0	0.0917
20	0.0009011	76.2	0.2382	0.0009003	77.9	0.2378
30	0.0009026	118.1	0.3793	0.0009018	119.7	0.3789
40	0.0009053	159.9	0.5154	0.0009045	161.6	0.5146
50	0.0009089	201.4	0.6464	0.0009081	203.1	0.6456
60	0.0009132	243.2	0.7725	0.0009123	244.5	0.7716
70	0.0009180	284.7	0.8951	0.0009174	286.4	0.8939
80	0.0009234	326.2	1.0153	0.0009224	327.8	1.0140
90	0.0009293	367.6	1.1325	0.0009284	369.3	1.1313
100	0.0009359	409.5	1.2468	0.0009349	410.7	1.2456
110	0.0009430	450.9	1.3582	0.0009420	452.2	1.3565
120	0.0009508	492.4	1.4670	0.0009497	494.0	1.4662
130	0.0009592	534.2	1.5726	0.0009581	535.9	1.5713
140	0.0009682	576.1	1.6747	0.0009671	577.4	1.6735
150	0.0009779	618.0	1.7731	0.0009767	618.8	1.7710
160	0.0009883	659.8	1.8690	0.0009870	660.7	1.8673
170	0.0009993	702.1	1.9640	0.0009979	703.0	1.9619
180	0.0010110	744.4	2.0586	0.0010095	745.2	2.0561
190	0.0010233	787.1	2.1524	0.0010218	788.0	2.1503
200	0.0010364	830.2	2.2458	0.0010348	831.1	2.2437
210	0.0010503	873.8	2.3375	0.0010485	874.2	2.3350
220	0.0010650	917.7	2.4271	0.0010629	918.6	2.4242
230	0.0010811	962.1	2.5163	0.0010787	962.1	2.5129
240	0.0010990	1008.6	2.6038	0.0010964	1008.6	2.5996
250	0.001120	1055.1	2.6917	0.001116	1055.1	2.6862
260	0.001144	1102.8	2.7792	0.001139	1102.4	2.7721
270	0.001171	1151.4	2.8654	0.001165	1150.5	2.8571
280	0.001201	1201.2	2.9542	0.001194	1199.9	2.9429
290	0.001232	1251.8	3.0442	0.001224	1250.6	3.0296
300	0.001266	1305.4	3.1393	0.001257	1303.4	3.1200
310	0.01606	2537.2	5.2632	0.001298	1359.0	3.2192
320	0.01730	2593.7	5.3570	0.001360	1416.8	3.3285
330	0.01838	2642.3	5.4370	0.01355	2545.2	5.2247
340	0.01932	2684.6	5.5077	0.01459	2604.6	5.3227
350	0.02015	2723.5	5.5714	0.01548	2655.3	5.4047
360	0.02097	2759.9	5.6300	0.01631	2699.2	5.4759
370	0.02170	2793.4	5.6844	0.01702	2740.7	5.5400
380	0.02242	2826.9	5.7351	0.01772	2779.2	5.5986
390	0.02311	2859.2	5.7828	0.01838	2813.9	5.6526
400	0.02374	2888.5	5.8276	0.01899	2847.4	5.7028
410	0.02442	2918.2	5.8691	0.01959	2879.7	5.7506
420	0.02506	2945.8	5.9101	0.02016	2911.1	5.7962
430	0.02565	2973.0	5.9503	0.02068	2940.4	5.8393
440	0.02622	3000.3	5.9888	0.02121	2970.1	5.8795
450	0.02677	3027.5	6.0256	0.02172	2998.6	5.9185
460	0.02733	3053.8	6.0616	0.02221	3026.6	5.9561
470	0.02787	3080.2	6.0968	0.02270	3054.3	5.9930

continued

t, °C	v	i	s	v	i	s
480	0.02841	3104.9	6.1270	0.02318	3080.6	6.0290
490	0.02895	3130.5	6.1638	0.02364	3107.0	6.0646
500	0.02949	3156.0	6.1965	0.02410	3133.4	6.0993
510	0.02997	3180.7	6.2287	0.02455	3158.1	6.1328
520	0.03046	3204.6	6.2605	0.02510	3184.9	6.1651
530	0.03095	3228.9	6.2907	0.02543	3210.0	6.1965
540	0.03146	3253.1	6.3196	0.02587	3235.1	6.2270
550	0.03197	3277.8	6.3489	0.02630	3260.3	6.2568
		$p=140$ bar			$p=160$ bar	
3.8	0.0008986	12.1	0.0000	0.0008977	13.8	0.0000
10	0.0008986	38.1	0.0917	0.0008978	39.8	0.0913
20	0.0008994	80.0	0.2378	0.0008986	81.6	0.2374
30	0.0009011	121.8	0.3785	0.0009004	123.5	0.3781
40	0.0009038	163.7	0.5137	0.0009031	165.0	0.5133
50	0.0009073	204.7	0.6448	0.0009066	206.4	0.6439
60	0.0009116	246.2	0.7708	0.0009108	247.9	0.7700
70	0.0009163	288.0	0.8926	0.0009155	289.3	0.8918
80	0.0009216	329.5	1.0128	0.0009208	330.8	1.0124
90	0.0009275	371.0	1.1296	0.0009267	372.2	1.1288
100	0.0009340	412.4	1.2439	0.0009331	413.7	1.2426
110	0.0009411	453.8	1.3548	0.0009402	455.1	1.3536
120	0.0009488	495.3	1.4641	0.0009478	496.6	1.4620
130	0.0009571	536.7	1.5696	0.0009561	538.0	1.5675
140	0.0009660	578.6	1.6714	0.0009649	579.9	1.6697
150	0.0009755	620.1	1.7689	0.0009744	621.3	1.7672
160	0.0009857	661.9	1.8648	0.0009845	662.8	1.8627
170	0.0009966	703.8	1.9594	0.0009952	704.6	1.9573
180	0.0010081	746.1	2.0536	0.0010066	746.9	2.0515
190	0.0010203	788.8	2.1474	0.0010187	789.6	2.1453
200	0.0010331	831.9	2.2408	0.0010314	832.3	2.2383
210	0.0010466	875.0	2.3316	0.0010448	875.5	2.3287
220	0.0010609	918.6	2.4208	0.0010589	919.0	2.4175
230	0.0010764	962.5	2.5091	0.0010741	963.0	2.5058
240	0.0010937	1008.6	2.5954	0.0010911	1008.6	2.5920
250	0.001113	1054.6	2.6808	0.001110	1054.2	2.6766
260	0.001135	1101.5	2.7658	0.001132	1101.1	2.7599
270	0.001161	1149.7	2.8491	0.001156	1148.9	2.8416
280	0.001188	1198.7	2.9328	0.001183	1197.8	2.9241
290	0.001217	1248.5	3.0166	0.001211	1247.2	3.0057
300	0.001250	1300.8	3.1041	0.001243	1299.2	3.0903
310	0.001288	1356.1	3.1979	0.001279	1353.6	3.1795
320	0.001343	1413.5	3.2984	0.001328	1410.1	3.2732
330	0.001415	1474.2	3.4156	0.001395	1470.0	3.3854
340	0.01083	2496.6	5.1050	0.001483	1533.6	3.5077
350	0.01191	2569.9	5.2251	0.00887	2447.2	4.9940
360	0.01279	2628.5	5.3181	0.00997	2537.6	5.1372
370	0.01359	2678.3	5.3964	0.01084	2604.6	5.2435
380	0.01429	2723.9	5.4654	0.01159	2661.1	5.3306
390	0.01493	2765.0	5.5282	0.01226	2710.1	5.4060
400	0.01552	2803.5	5.5860	0.01287	2754.9	5.4717
410	0.01611	2839.1	5.6392	0.01343	2787.2	5.5316
420	0.01663	2873.4	5.6890	0.01394	2832.8	5.5873
430	0.01713	2906.9	5.7359	0.01443	2869.2	5.6392
440	0.01763	2937.9	5.7803	0.01490	2904.4	5.6873
450	0.01809	2968.4	5.8230	0.01535	2937.0	5.7326
460	0.01855	2998.2	5.8636	0.01580	2973.5	5.7765
470	0.01902	3027.1	5.9030	0.01624	2999.4	5.8180
480	0.01945	3055.5	5.9406	0.01665	3029.1	5.8582
490	0.01989	3083.2	5.9775	0.01704	3058.5	5.8971
500	0.02029	3110.4	6.0131	0.01739	3086.9	5.9344
510	0.02070	3137.2	6.0482	0.01775	3115.0	5.9704
520	0.02109	3164.0	6.0813	0.01813	3142.6	6.0055

continued

t, °C	v	i	s	v	i	s
530	0.02148	3190.0	6.1144	0.01849	3170.2	6.0399
540	0.02186	3215.9	6.1462	0.01884	3197.5	6.0721
550	0.02224	3241.8	6.1772	0.01919	3223.8	6.1035
		$p=180$ bar			$p=200$ bar	
3.8	0.0008969	15.5	0.0000	0.0008959	16.7	0.0000
10	0.0008970	41.4	0.0913	0.0008960	43.1	0.0908
20	0.0008978	83.3	0.2370	0.0008970	85.0	0.2366
30	0.0008996	125.2	0.3776	0.0008988	126.9	0.3768
40	0.0009023	166.6	0.5125	0.0009015	168.3	0.5120
50	0.0009059	208.1	0.6431	0.0009050	209.8	0.6427
60	0.0009101	249.5	0.7691	0.0009092	251.2	0.7683
70	0.0009148	291.0	0.8914	0.0009139	292.7	0.8905
80	0.0009200	332.4	1.0115	0.0009191	333.7	1.0107
90	0.0009258	373.9	1.1279	0.0009249	375.1	1.1267
100	0.0009323	415.3	1.2410	0.0009313	416.2	1.2401
110	0.0009393	456.8	1.3523	0.0009383	457.2	1.3511
120	0.0009469	497.8	1.4608	0.0009458	498.6	1.4591
130	0.0009550	539.3	1.5663	0.0009540	540.1	1.5646
140	0.0009638	580.7	1.6676	0.0009627	581.5	1.6659
150	0.0009732	622.2	1.7652	0.0009721	623.0	1.7635
160	0.0009833	663.6	1.8610	0.0009820	664.4	1.8589
170	0.0009939	705.5	1.9552	0.0009926	706.3	1.9531
180	0.0010052	747.8	2.0494	0.0010037	748.2	2.0473
190	0.0010171	790.5	2.1432	0.0010156	790.9	2.1407
200	0.0010297	833.2	2.2362	0.0010280	833.6	2.2337
210	0.0010429	875.9	2.3266	0.0010410	876.3	2.3245
220	0.0010568	919.4	2.4149	0.0010548	919.8	2.4128
230	0.0010719	963.4	2.5024	0.0010697	963.4	2.4995
240	0.0010886	1008.6	2.5883	0.0010861	1008.6	2.5845
250	0.001107	1054.2	2.6720	0.001105	1054.2	2.6678
260	0.001129	1101.1	2.7545	0.001125	1100.3	2.7495
270	0.001153	1148.0	2.8353	0.001149	1148.0	2.8290
280	0.001179	1196.6	2.9161	0.001174	1196.2	2.9090
290	0.001206	1246.0	2.9961	0.001201	1244.7	2.9881
300	0.001237	1297.1	3.0781	0.001231	1295.4	3.0685
310	0.001271	1350.7	3.1640	0.001264	1348.6	3.1514
320	0.001317	1407.2	3.2544	0.001306	1404.2	3.2385
330	0.001376	1465.0	3.3603	0.001361	1460.8	3.3402
340	0.001456	1526.9	3.4792	0.001432	1520.2	3.4549
350	0.001566	1601.0	3.6140	0.001528	1590.6	3.5856
360	0.00738	2402.0	4.8965	0.001697	1668.4	3.7547
370	0.00853	2510.4	5.0660	0.00631	2369.7	4.8249
380	0.00940	2586.6	5.1828	0.00751	2490.3	5.0116
390	0.01013	2647.7	5.2766	0.00832	2572.4	5.1364
400	0.01073	2700.5	5.3545	0.00899	2637.7	5.2331
410	0.01131	2747.0	5.4236	0.00959	2692.9	5.3139
420	0.01182	2790.1	5.4864	0.01010	2742.8	5.3859
430	0.01231	2830.3	5.5446	0.01059	2787.6	5.4500
440	0.01276	2868.0	5.5982	0.01105	2829.4	5.5094
450	0.01320	2903.1	5.6467	0.01147	2867.5	5.5638
460	0.01362	2937.9	5.6936	0.01187	2904.4	5.6145
470	0.01403	2970.5	5.7384	0.01226	2940.0	5.6622
480	0.01441	3001.9	5.7807	0.01264	2973.9	5.7070
490	0.01478	3032.9	5.8217	0.01300	3006.1	5.7502
500	0.01514	3063.5	5.8607	0.01334	3038.4	5.7924
510	0.01549	3094.9	5.8988	0.01366	3068.9	5.8322
520	0.01583	3120.8	5.9352	0.01400	3099.5	5.8711
530	0.01616	3149.3	5.9708	0.01431	3128.4	5.9080
540	0.01648	3177.4	6.0055	0.01461	3157.3	5.9427
550	0.01680	3205.4	6.0395	0.01490	3185.7	5.9767

continued

t, °C	v	i	s	v	i	s
		$p=225$ bar			$p=250$ bar	
3.8	0.0008949	19.7	0.0000	0.0008938	22.2	0.0000
10	0.0008950	45.6	0.0908	0.0008940	48.1	0.0904
20	0.0008960	87.5	0.2357	0.0008950	89.6	0.2353
30	0.0008979	129.0	0.3760	0.0008970	131.0	0.3756
40	0.0009006	170.4	0.5112	0.0008997	172.5	0.5104
50	0.0009041	211.8	0.6414	0.0009032	213.9	0.6406
60	0.0009083	252.9	0.7670	0.0009073	255.0	0.7662
70	0.0009129	294.3	0.8893	0.0009119	296.4	0.8880
80	0.0009181	335.8	1.0090	0.0009171	337.5	1.0078
90	0.0009238	376.8	1.1254	0.0009228	378.5	1.1242
100	0.0009302	417.8	1.2389	0.0009291	419.5	1.2376
110	0.0009371	459.3	1.3494	0.0009360	460.5	1.3477
120	0.0009446	500.7	1.4578	0.0009434	501.6	1.4566
130	0.0009527	541.8	1.5625	0.0009514	543.0	1.5604
140	0.0009613	583.2	1.6638	0.0009600	584.5	1.6617
150	0.0009705	624.7	1.7610	0.0009691	625.5	1.7589
160	0.0009804	666.1	1.8564	0.0009789	667.0	1.8539
170	0.0009909	707.6	1.9506	0.0009893	708.4	1.9477
180	0.0010019	749.4	2.0444	0.0010002	750.3	2.0415
190	0.0010136	791.7	2.1378	0.0010118	792.6	2.1353
200	0.0010259	834.4	2.2303	0.0010238	834.8	2.2278
210	0.0010388	877.1	2.3216	0.0010366	877.6	2.3182
220	0.0010524	920.3	2.4108	0.0010500	920.7	2.4070
230	0.0010670	963.8	2.4970	0.0010642	963.8	2.4928
240	0.0010831	1008.6	2.5807	0.0010800	1008.6	2.5766
250	0.001101	1053.8	2.6632	0.001098	1053.8	2.6590
260	0.001122	1099.9	2.7436	0.001118	1099.4	2.7390
270	0.001145	1146.8	2.8227	0.001140	1146.3	2.8173
280	0.001169	1194.5	2.9006	0.001164	1193.7	2.8943
290	0.001195	1243.5	2.9789	0.001190	1242.6	2.9726
300	0.001224	1293.7	3.0580	0.001218	1292.5	3.0501
310	0.001256	1346.1	3.1384	0.001249	1343.5	3.1292
320	0.001295	1400.9	3.2234	0.001285	1397.6	3.2117
330	0.001344	1456.2	3.3197	0.001331	1452.0	3.3030
340	0.001407	1513.1	3.4286	0.001388	1507.7	3.4055
350	0.001490	1579.3	3.5538	0.001460	1569.2	3.5249
360	0.001606	1653.4	3.7066	0.001553	1637.9	3.6618
370	0.001871	1803.7	3.9469	0.001708	1735.0	3.8284
380	0.00515	2304.0	4.6808	0.00218	1896.2	4.0821
390	0.00632	2452.2	4.9283	0.00434	2263.4	4.6231
400	0.00713	2545.2	5.0664	0.00548	2424.6	4.8634
410	0.00779	2616.3	5.1707	0.00628	2524.6	5.0103
420	0.00834	2676.2	5.2586	0.00690	2599.6	5.1209
430	0.00884	2729.0	5.3340	0.00740	2663.6	5.2126
440	0.00929	2777.1	5.4010	0.00787	2719.7	5.2909
450	0.00971	2820.2	5.4625	0.00830	2769.6	5.3599
460	0.01010	2861.7	5.5186	0.00869	2815.6	5.4227
470	0.01048	2900.2	5.5701	0.00906	2857.9	5.4805
480	0.01083	2936.6	5.6191	0.00941	2898.1	5.5341
490	0.01118	2972.2	5.6660	0.00974	2936.2	5.5844
500	0.01151	3006.1	5.7104	0.01006	2972.2	5.6321
510	0.01183	3038.4	5.7527	0.01036	3007.0	5.6773
520	0.01213	3070.2	5.7929	0.01065	3040.4	5.7196
530	0.01242	3101.6	5.8314	0.01093	3073.1	5.7598
540	0.01270	3131.3	5.8686	0.01120	3104.9	5.7991
550	0.01208	3161.0	5.9046	0.01146	3135.9	5.8364
		$p=300$ bar			$p=400$ bar	
3.8	0.0008917	26.8	−0.0004	0.0008874	36.0	−0.0008
10	0.0008921	52.8	0.0896	0.0008879	61.1	0.0879
20	0.0008931	94.2	0.2345	0.0008892	102.2	0.2328
30	0.0008952	135.6	0.3739	0.0008914	143.2	0.3714
40	0.0008979	176.7	0.5083	0.0008942	184.2	0.5053

continued

t, °C	v	i	s	v	i	s
50	0.0009014	217.7	0.6385	0.0008976	225.2	0.6347
60	0.0009054	258.7	0.7637	0.0009016	266.3	0.7595
70	0.0009100	300.2	0.8855	0.0009060	306.9	0.8809
80	0.0009151	340.8	1.0044	0.0009110	347.5	0.9994
90	0.0009207	381.8	1.1208	0.0009165	388.5	1.1154
100	0.0009269	422.9	1.2343	0.0009225	429.6	1.2284
110	0.0009337	463.9	1.3448	0.0009290	470.2	1.3385
120	0.0009410	504.9	1.4528	0.0009361	510.8	1.4461
130	0.0009488	546.0	1.5583	0.0009437	551.4	1.5504
140	0.0009572	587.0	1.6584	0.0009519	592.4	1.6508
150	0.0009662	628.0	1.7551	0.0009605	633.0	1.7476
160	0.0009758	669.5	1.8497	0.0009697	674.1	1.8422
170	0.0009860	711.3	1.9439	0.0009794	715.5	1.9360
180	0.0009967	753.2	2.0373	0.0009896	757.0	2.0293
190	0.0010081	795.1	2.1302	0.0010003	798.4	2.1223
200	0.0010197	836.9	2.2224	0.0010116	839.9	2.2140
210	0.0010321	878.8	2.3132	0.0010232	881.7	2.3040
220	0.0010449	921.5	2.4011	0.0010352	923.6	2.3911
230	0.0010587	964.2	2.4865	0.0010481	965.9	2.4752
240	0.0010740	1008.6	2.5699	0.0010622	1009.0	2.5581
250	0.001091	1053.4	2.6515	0.001078	1052.6	2.6385
260	0.001110	1098.6	2.7306	0.001095	1096.9	2.7172
270	0.001131	1144.7	2.8077	0.001114	1142.2	2.7930
280	0.001154	1192.4	2.8839	0.001135	1188.6	2.8692
290	0.001179	1240.1	2.9609	0.001158	1235.9	2.9454
300	0.001205	1288.7	3.0379	0.001182	1284.1	3.0216
310	0.001234	1339.4	3.1158	0.001207	1333.9	3.0982
320	0.001267	1391.7	3.1945	0.001236	1384.2	3.1753
330	0.001307	1444.4	3.2799	0.001269	1434.0	3.2527
340	0.001355	1498.0	3.3704	0.001307	1484.6	3.3318
350	0.001414	1552.5	3.4771	0.001350	1535.7	3.4177
360	0.001485	1612.3	3.5906	0.001402	1587.2	3.5073
370	0.001580	1674.7	3.7062	0.001461	1639.1	3.6002
380	0.00173	1763.1	3.8255	0.00154	1692.7	3.7032
390	0.00202	1871.1	4.0097	0.00163	1762.6	3.8188
400	0.00271	2076.2	4.3158	0.00176	1845.1	3.9448
410	0.00371	2273.4	4.6072	0.00193	1938.9	4.0813
420	0.00450	2407.0	4.8035	0.00220	2051.1	4.2366
430	0.00514	2507.9	4.9463	0.00256	2166.7	4.4100
440	0.00566	2588.3	5.0581	0.00296	2281.4	4.5711
450	0.00611	2654.4	5.1510	0.00340	2384.0	4.7143
460	0.00651	2712.6	5.2318	0.00381	2473.1	4.8378
470	0.00688	2767.1	5.3026	0.00417	2551.8	4.9438
480	0.00723	2813.1	5.3671	0.00450	2621.8	5.0363
490	0.00755	2860.0	5.4265	0.00481	2684.2	5.1196
500	0.00785	2899.8	5.4814	0.00510	2741.5	5.1933
510	0.00813	2940.4	5.5324	0.00536	2793.8	5.2607
520	0.00840	2978.5	5.5810	0.00560	2842.4	5.3231
530	0.00867	3014.9	5.6262	0.00584	2888.0	5.3800
540	0.00914	3050.9	5.6693	0.00607	2931.6	5.4336
550	0.00916	3084.4	5.7112	0.00629	2972.6	5.4839

t, °C	v	i	s	t, °C	v	i	s
			$p = 500$ bar				
3.8	0.0008831	45.2	−0.0013	70	0.0009022	314.0	0.8763
10	0.0008838	69.5	0.0867	80	0.0009069	354.6	0.9952
20	0.0008853	110.5	0.2307	90	0.0009123	395.2	1.1108
30	0.0008877	151.6	0.3693	100	0.0009182	435.4	1.2238
40	0.0008905	192.2	0.5028	110	0.0009244	476.0	1.3339
50	0.0008938	232.8	0.6310	120	0.0009313	516.6	1.4411
60	0.0008977	273.4	0.7553	130	0.0009387	557.3	1.5445

continued

t, °C	v	i	s	t, °C	v	i	s
140	0.0009466	597.9	1.6433	350	0.001304	1528.6	3.3905
150	0.0009548	638.5	1.7404	360	0.001345	1579.3	3.4675
160	0.0009637	679.1	1.8342	370	0.001394	1629.9	3.5496
170	0.0009729	720.1	1.9272	380	0.00144	1680.6	3.6350
180	0.0009827	761.2	2.0205	390	0.00151	1731.2	3.7296
190	0.0009928	802.2	2.1135	400	0.00159	1792.0	3.8330
200	0.0010035	843.2	2.2052	410	0.00167	1861.9	3.9419
210	0.0010145	884.7	2.2948	420	0.00177	1934.7	4.0470
220	0.0010256	926.1	2.3827	430	0.00192	2012.2	4.1596
230	0.0010377	967.6	2.4664	440	0.00208	2098.0	4.2785
240	0.0010508	1009.0	2.5481	450	0.00228	2186.3	4.4012
250	0.001066	1051.7	2.6276	460	0.00249	2274.3	4.5222
260	0.001082	1095.7	2.7051	470	0.00277	2358.4	4.6369
270	0.001100	1139.6	2.7817	480	0.00302	2438.0	4.7453
280	0.001118	1185.7	2.8571	490	0.00329	2510.4	4.8420
290	0.001138	1233.4	2.9324	500	0.00354	2577.8	4.9287
300	0.001160	1282.0	3.0078	510	0.00378	2641.4	5.0091
310	0.001182	1330.1	3.0857	520	0.00403	2700.9	5.0844
320	0.001209	1379.1	3.1627	530	0.00421	2755.8	5.1535
330	0.001236	1428.5	3.2381	540	0.00440	2806.8	5.2172
340	0.001269	1478.4	3.3143	550	0.00460	2855.4	5.2758

Heat capacity c_p (kJ/kg · deg) of heavy water vapor [25]

p, bar \ t, °C →	120	140	160	180	200	220	240	260	280	300	320
1	1.884	1.867	1.859	1.859	1.863	1.876	1.888	1.897	1.910	1.926	1.943
20						2.71	2.48	2.34	2.25	2.18	2.14
40								3.42	2.91	2.65	2.48
60									4.23	3.40	3.00
80										4.78	3.82
100											5.26

p, bar \ e, °C →	340	360	380	400	420	440	460	480	500	520	540
1	1.956	1.973	1.986	2.001	2.022	2.039	2.056	2.077	2.094	2.111	2.128
20	2.12	2.11	2.11	2.12	2.13	2.14	2.14	2.15	2.16	2.17	2.18
40	2.39	2.33	2.29	2.26	2.24	2.24	2.23	2.23	2.23	2.24	2.24
60	2.77	2.61	2.51	2.44	2.38	2.35	2.33	2.32	2.31	2.30	2.30
80	3.28	2.98	2.78	2.65	2.56	2.49	2.45	2.42	2.40	2.39	2.38
100	4.10	3.49	3.15	2.93	2.76	2.66	2.58	2.54	2.49	2.46	2.44
120	5.52	4.23	3.61	3.24	3.02	2.85	2.73	2.66	2.59	2.56	2.52
140		5.32	4.19	3.63	3.29	3.05	2.90	2.80	2.72	2.66	2.62
160		7.52	5.08	4.13	3.62	3.28	3.09	2.95	2.85	2.77	2.71
180			6.44	4.83	4.04	3.58	3.32	3.14	3.00	2.90	2.81
200			9.00	5.79	4.59	3.96	3.58	3.33	3.16	3.03	2.93
220			13.94	7.20	5.28	4.41	3.88	3.55	3.32	3.16	3.03
240				9.63	6.15	4.91	4.22	3.80	3.50	3.29	3.14
260				13.15	7.29	5.48	4.57	4.04	3.68	3.43	3.25
280				18.68	8.82	6.12	4.95	4.31	3.86	3.58	3.36
300					10.51	6.90	5.37	4.60	4.05	3.72	3.48
320					12.45	7.77	5.83	4.88	4.28	3.88	3.60
340						8.69	6.36	5.20	4.52	4.04	3.73
360						9.63	6.94	5.54	4.76	4.22	3.87
380						10.54	7.54	5.91	5.02	4.41	4.00
400							8.17	6.32	5.28	4.60	4.14
420							8.78	6.74	5.58	4.78	4.27

continued

e, °C → / p, bar	340	360	380	400	420	440	460	480	500	520	540
440							9.28	7.21	5.88	5.00	4.44
460								7.68	6.18	5.23	4.61
480								8.14	6.48	5.46	4.78
500									6.80	5.71	4.96

Heat capacity c_p (kJ/kg · deg) for liquid heavy water [25, 27]

p, bar → / t, °C	1	20	40	60	80	100	150	200	250	300	350	400	450	500
20	4.208	4.203	4.199	4.195	4.191	4.187	4.178	4.166	4.157	4.145	4.132	4.120	4.111	4.103
40	4.191	4.187	4.183	4.178	4.174	4.170	4.162	4.149	4.141	4.128	4.116	4.103	4.086	4.074
60	4.183	4.178	4.174	4.170	4.166	4.162	4.149	4.137	4.128	4.116	4.099	4.086	4.070	4.057
80	4.178	4.174	4.170	4.166	4.162	4.157	4.145	4.132	4.120	4.107	4.095	4.082	4.065	4.053
100	4.178	4.174	4.170	4.162	4.157	4.153	1.141	4.128	4.116	4.103	4.090	4.078	4.061	4.049
120		4.178	4.174	4.166	4.162	4.153	4.141	4.128	4.116	4.100	4.086	4.074	4.057	4.044
140		4.191	4.183	4.174	4.170	4.166	4.153	4.141	4.128	4.111	4.090	4.074	4.057	4.044
160		4.216	4.208	4.199	4.191	4.183	4.170	4.157	4.141	4.124	4.103	4.082	4.065	4.049
180		4.266	4.258	4.250	4.241	4.229	4.208	4.187	4.162	4.145	4.124	4.103	4.082	4.061
200		4.350	4.337	4.325	4.312	4.304	4.275	4.241	4.212	4.187	4.162	4.137	4.107	4.078
220			4.434	4.417	4.404	4.392	4.358	4.321	4.287	4.254	4.220	4.187	4.153	4.116
240			4.572	4.551	4.534	4.518	4.471	4.230	4.388	4.346	4.304	4.258	4.216	4.178
260				4.744	4.718	4.689	4.631	4.584	4.534	4.484	4.434	4.384	4.333	4.291
280					4.986	4.957	4.882	4.811	4.739	4.677	4.618	4.564	4.505	4.446
300						5.451	5.254	5.120	5.012	4.924	4.848	4.777	4.710	4.647

Ratio η_{D_2O}/η_{H_2O} for the gas phase at different temperatures

t, °C	η_{D_2O}/η_{H_2O}	Reference	t, °C	η_{D_2O}/η_{H_2O}	Reference
80	1.051	35	600	1.027	70
100	1.068		700	1.025	
130	1.075		800	1.025	
200	1.024	70	900	1.018	
300	1.028		1000	1.013	
400	1.030		1200	1.011	
500	1.033		1400	1.01	

Viscosity η (N · s/m²) for heavy water and ratio η_{D_2O}/η_{H_2O} in the liquid phase at saturation [387]

t, °C	$\eta_{D_2O} \cdot 10^5$	η_{D_2O}/η_{H_2O}	t, °C	$\eta_{D_2O} \cdot 10^5$	η_{D_2O}/η_{H_2O}	t, °C	$\eta_{D_2O} \cdot 10^5$	η_{D_2O}/η_{H_2O}
4	208.1	1.33	90	36.7	1.16	190	16.2	1.13
7	186.9	1.30	100	32.7	1.16	200	15.3	1.12
10	169.1	1.28	110	29.8	1.15	210	14.6	1.12
15	145.0	1.26	120	27.2	1.15	220	13.9	1.12
20	125.1	1.25	130	24.9	1.14	230	13.3	1.12
30	101.3	1.23	140	22.9	1.14	240	12.8	1.12
40	79.1	1.21	150	21.2	1.14	250	12.3	1.11
50	65.8	1.20	160	19.6	1.13	260	11.8	1.11
60	55.7	1.19	170	18.4	1.13	270	11.3	1.11
70	47.8	1.18	180	17.3	1.13	280	10.9	1.11
80	41.6	1.17						

Ratio $\eta_{D_2O}\eta/_{H_2O}$ in the liquid phase at different temperatures and pressures [26]

t, °C \ p, bar →	1	10	100	300	500	800	1000
20	1.257	1.257	1.255	1.248	1.247	1.246	1.243
50	1.191	1.191	1.192	1.187	1.187	1.191	1.192
100		1.151	1.152	1.163	1.162	1.165	1.169

Ratio $\lambda_{D_2O}/\lambda_{H_2O}$ in the gas phase at different temperatures and pressures [388, 389]

t, °C \ p, kg/cm² →	1	100	150	200	225	250
150	0.985					
200	1.00					
250	1.01					
300	1.02					
320	1.024					
340	1.028	0.997				
360	1.032	1.012	0.998			
380	1.036	1.023	1.008	0.972		
400	1.04	1.026	1.010	1.002	0.981	0.971
420	1.044	1.027	1.016	1.008	1.001	0.994
440	1.047	1.035	1.024	1.013	1.007	0.999
460	1.050	1.037	1.028	1.019	1.014	1.008
480	1.053	1.039	1.030	1.025	1.018	1.016
500	1.055	1.041	1.034	1.027	1.023	1.021

Ratio $\lambda_{D_2O}/\lambda_{H_2O}$ in the liquid phase at saturation [390]

t, °C	$\lambda_{D_2O}/\lambda_{H_2O}$	t, °C	$\lambda_{D_2O}/\lambda_{H_2O}$	t, °C	$\lambda_{D_2O}/\lambda_{H_2O}$	t, °C	$\lambda_{D_2O}/\lambda_{H_2O}$
10	0.988	100	0.933	190	0.905	280	0.865
20	0.975	110	0.930	200	0.904	290	0.862
30	0.968	120	0.927	210	0.900	300	0.859
40	0.961	130	0.925	220	0.896	310	0.855
50	0.954	140	0.922	230	0.891	320	0.851
60	0.952	150	0.919	240	0.887	330	0.848
70	0.947	160	0.916	250	0.881	340	0.844
80	0.944	170	0.911	260	0.875	350	0.852
90	0.938	180	0.906	270	0.870		

Chapter 2

METALS

THERMODYNAMIC PROPERTIES OF ALKALI METALS

The thermodynamic tables for vapors of alkali metals have been compiled for the pressure range from 10^{-5} to 10 bar and from the saturation temperature to 3000 °K. The tables have been compiled using the scheme of a dissociated gas and taking into account single ionization of atoms. Within the indicated range of temperatures and pressures it appeared possible to neglect double ionization of the atoms and ionization of the diatomic component. The equations used for computation were taken from Ref. [29]. Corrections for true properties of vapor components have not been made, and, as a result, the calculations have been limited by the pressure of 10 bar.

Table 1 gives the values of dissociation energy D^0 of diatomic molecules of alkali metals and their heats of sublimation ΔH^0_1 into a monatomic vapor at 0 °K. These values were used in calculations; they were arrived at by determining the values obtained by various methods (optical, thermodynamic, etc) and reviewed in Refs. [28, 405, 406, 420, 421]. More recent data [407–410] have also been taken into account. The necessary standard functions of alkali metals were taken from Refs. [37, 41, 346]. As shown in [28], at pressures above 1 bar, the presence of vapor components becomes apparent, so that the calculated values of saturated vapor pressure are somewhat lower than the experimental ones. Therefore, at such pressures the calculated saturated pressure values have been replaced by experimental data: for sodium, potassium and cesium from Ref. [41] and for rubidium from Ref. [350]. The density of saturated vapor has been proportionately adjusted.

Enthalpy and entropy are calculated from the base state of condensed (solid) phase at 0 °K. In the calculation we took 1 calorie = 4.1868 Joule and 1 ev/molecule = 23 063 calories/mole.

Table 1

Values of D^0 and ΔH^0_1 for alkali metals

Metal	D^0			ΔH^0_1	
	eV/molecule	cal/mole	J/mole	cal/mole	J/mole
Lithium	1.117±0,012	25 750±300	107 800±1300	37 940±60	158 850±250
Sodium	0.740±0,008	17 050±200	71 380±850	25 760±30	107 850±130
Potassium	0.558±0,008	12 850±200	53 800±850	21 545±30	90 200±130
Rubidium	0.503±0,01	11 600±250	48 570±1000	19 610±30	82 100±130
Cesium	0.460±0,01	10 600±250	44 380±1000	18 720±30	78 380± 30

The handbook gives tables for the saturated vapor pressures above 10 bar. For sodium, potassium, rubidium and cesium the tables have been compiled from experimental data [350, 404, 414–417] which can be described by the following equation:

$$\log p = A - \frac{B}{T} - C \log T,$$

where the pressure is given in bar, and temperature in °K. The values of A, B, and C for these metals are given in Table 2.

Table 2

Metal	A	B	C
Sodium	4.54597	5242.1	
Potassium	7.74887	4812.3	1.0216
Rubidium	4.09838	3873.8	0.0194
Cesium	5.7345	3909	0.5329

The experimental data for saturated vapor pressure of lithium are available up to 2160 °K and correspondingly to 16 bar. The values $p_s = f(T_s)$ for higher temperatures have been calculated using the method of similarity [415].

The critical values for alkali metals given in this handbook have been calculated (cf. Ref. [28]) and taken from experimental values [411–414].

LITHIUM (Li)

Atomic weight 6.940
T_{melt} = 453.7 °K; T_{boil} = 1615 °K at 760 mm Hg; T_{cr} = 3800 °K;
P_{cr} = 970 bar ρ_{cr} = 100 kg/m³

Thermodynamic properties of liquid lithium at saturation [28]: ρ (kg/m³), c_p (kJ/kg · deg), i (kJ/kg), s (kJ/kg · deg) and r (kJ/kg)

T, °K	p, bar	ϱ'	c_p'	i'	s'	r
453.7	$1.779 \cdot 10^{-13}$	523	4.30	1703	6.776	22 556
500	$8.207 \cdot 10^{-12}$	514	4.34	1905	7.199	22 485
600	$4.184 \cdot 10^{-9}$	503	4.23	2334	7.983	22 340
700	$3.51 \cdot 10^{-7}$	493	4.19	2697	8.633	22 172
800	$9.572 \cdot 10^{-6}$	483	4.17	3174	9.192	21 989
850	$3.723 \cdot 10^{-5}$	478	4.16	3382	9.444	21 877
900	$1.242 \cdot 10^{-4}$	473	4.16	3590	9.682	21 751
950	$3.645 \cdot 10^{-4}$	468	4.16	3798	9.907	21 616
1000	$9.598 \cdot 10^{-4}$	463	4.16	4006	10.120	21 471
1050	$2.301 \cdot 10^{-3}$	457	4.16	4214	10.323	21 317
1100	$5.090 \cdot 10^{-3}$	452	4.15	4421	10.516	21 156
1150	$1.051 \cdot 10^{-2}$	447	4.15	4628	10.700	20 989
1200	$2.04 \cdot 10^{-2}$	442	4.14	4835	10.876	20 818
1250	$3.752 \cdot 10^{-2}$	437	4.15	5043	11.046	20 644
1300	$6.583 \cdot 10^{-2}$	432	4.16	5251	11.209	20 466
1350	0.1108	427	4.17	5459	11.366	20 288
1400	0.1794	422	4.19	5668	11.518	20 110
1450	0.2810	416	4.19	5878	11.665	19 933
1500	0.4269	411	4.20	6088	11.808	19 757
1550	0.6310	406	4.22	6299	11.946	19 588
1600	0.9102	401	4.23	6510	12.080	19 412
1650	1.283	396	4.24	6722	12.210	19 243
1700	1.771	391	4.25	6934	12.336	19 077
1750	2.399	386	4.26	7146	12.460	18 916
1800	3.191	381	4.27	7360	12.581	18 658
1850	4.179	376	4.28	7574	12.698	18 603
1900	5.397	371	4.30	7788	12.812	18 451
1950	6.871	366	4.31	8004	12.924	18 302
2000	8.639	361	4.32	8220	13.033	18 133

Thermodynamic properties of saturated lithium vapor: monatomic molecule fraction x_2, molecular weight M, ρ (kg/m³), c_p, c_v and s (kJ/kg · deg), i (kJ/kg) and u (m/s) [28]

T, °K	x_2	M	ϱ''	c_p''	c_v''	i''	s''	u
800	$7.953 \cdot 10^{-3}$	6.994	$1.006 \cdot 10^{-6}$	5,634	4,123	25 162	36,678	1136
850	$1,134 \cdot 10^{-2}$	7,018	$3.695 \cdot 10^{-6}$	6,291	4,673	25 258	35.181	1158
900	$1.550 \cdot 10^{-2}$	7.047	$1,169 \cdot 10^{-5}$	6.956	5,216	25 341	33,850	1182
950	$2,039 \cdot 10^{-2}$	7,080	$3,266 \cdot 10^{-5}$	7.591	5,719	25 415	32,662	1206
1000	$2.596 \cdot 10^{-2}$	7,119	$8,213 \cdot 10^{-5}$	8,171	6,163	25 477	31.591	1230
1050	$3,218 \cdot 10^{-2}$	7.162	$1,886 \cdot 10^{-4}$	8.685	6.540	25 531	30.625	1254
1100	$3.894 \cdot 10^{-2}$	7,209	$4.010 \cdot 10^{-4}$	9,114	6.836	25 578	29.749	1279
1150	$4.321 \cdot 10^{-2}$	7.260	$7.973 \cdot 10^{-4}$	9,465	7.061	25 618	28.951	1303
1200	$5.383 \cdot 10^{-2}$	7,313	$1.494 \cdot 10^{-3}$	9.723	7.206	25 654	28,225	1327
1250	$6.176 \cdot 10^{-2}$	7,368	$2.658 \cdot 10^{-3}$	9,905	7,286	25 687	27,561	1351
1300	$7,001 \cdot 10^{-2}$	7,425	$4,319 \cdot 10^{-3}$	10,019	7,312	25 717	26,952	1374
1350	$7,837 \cdot 10^{-2}$	7.483	$7.380 \cdot 10^{-3}$	10,066	7.287	25 747	26,394	1397
1400	$8,674 \cdot 10^{-2}$	7,541	$1,162 \cdot 10^{-2}$	10.049	7,214	25 778	25.882	1420
1450	$9.516 \cdot 10^{-2}$	7.599	$1.771 \cdot 10^{-2}$	9,990	7,112	25 811	25,412	1442
1500	0.1035	7,657	$2.620 \cdot 10^{-2}$	9,891	6.984	25 845	24.979	1464
1550	0,1118	7,715	$3.757 \cdot 10^{-2}$	9.752	6.836	25 882	24.580	1486
1600	0.1200	7,771	$5,314 \cdot 10^{-2}$	9,611	6.677	25 921	24,212	1508
1650	0,1280	7,827	$7,316 \cdot 10^{-2}$	9.443	6,511	25 965	23.872	1529
1700	0,1357	7,881	$9,870 \cdot 10^{-2}$	9,259	6,336	26 011	23.558	1550
1750	0,1433	7,933	0.1308	9,076	6,160	26 062	23,289	1571
1800	0,1505	7.983	0,1701	8,871	5,985	26 118	23.002	1592
1850	0,1574	8,081	0.2181	8,676	5,815	26 178	22.754	1613
1900	0,1642	8,078	0,2758	8,481	5.648	26 239	22.523	1633
1950	0,1706	8,123	0.3440	8,287	5.485	26 306	22.310	1654
2000	0,1767	8.165	0,4240	8,098	5,328	26 376	22.111	1674

Saturation pressure of lithium vapor above 10 bar [415]

T, °K	p, bar	T, °K	p, bar	T, °K	p, bar	T, °K	p, bar
2100	12.4	2600	66,1	3100	235.4	3600	668,2
2200	18.3	2700	87,1	3200	295.2	3700	806.7
2300	26,1	2800	113,7	3300	365,8	3800	968,3
2400	33,1	2900	146,5	3400	449,9		
2500	49,1	3000	186,6	3500	550,5		

Thermodynamic properties of lithium vapor at different temperatures and pressures: molar fractions of monatomic, diatomic and electronic components x_1, x_2, and x_e, molecular weight M, ρ (kg/m³), c_p and c_v (kJ/kg · deg), i (kJ/kg), s (kJ/kg · deg) sound velocity (m/s) and adiabatic exponent k [28, 29]

T, °K	x_1	$x_2 \cdot 10^5$	$x_e \cdot 10^6$	M	$\varrho \cdot 10^5$	c_p	c_v	i	s	u	k
					$p = 10^{-5}$ bar						
900	0,99871	128.6	0	6.948	0.0928	3.342	2.122	25 548	37.097	1308	1.589
1000	0.99972	28.49	0	6.941	0.0834	3.060	1.853	25 885	37.440	1407	1.651
1100	0.99992	8.281	0.0005	6.940	0.0758	3.013	1.812	26 188	37.729	1481	1.663
1200	0.99997	2.948	0.0061	6.939	0.0695	3.002	1.802	26 489	37.990	1548	1.665
1300	0.99999	1.229	0.0504	6.939	0.0642	2.999	1.800	26 789	38.230	1611	1.666
1400	0,99999	0.5796	0,3085	6.939	0.0596	2.998	1.799	27 088	38.453	1672	1.666
1500	0.99999	0.3018	1.492	6.939	0.0556	2.999	1.800	27 388	38.660	1731	1.666
1600	0.99999	0.1703	5.955	6.939	0.0521	3.004	1.804	27 689	38.853	1787	1.664
1700	0.99996	0.1026	20.29	6.939	0.0491	3.016	1.816	27 990	39.035	1840	1.661
1800	0.99988	0.0653	60.58	6.938	0.0463	3.047	1.846	28 293	39.208	1888	1.651
1900	0.99967	0.0436	161.8	6.938	0.0439	3.125	1.919	28 601	39.373	1926	1.628
2000	0.99921	0.0302	392.8	6.936	0.0417	3.271	2.056	28 920	39.532	1954	1.591
2100	0.99824	0.0220	879,1	6.933	0.0397	3.556	2.322	29 261	39.691	1964	1.531
2200	0.99634	0.0158	1 832	6.926	0.0378	4.061	2.791	29 640	39.882	1960	1.455

continued

T, °K	x_1	$x_2 \cdot 10^5$	$x_e \cdot 10^6$	M	$\varrho \cdot 10^5$	c_p	c_v	i	s	u	k
2300	0.99283	0.0119	3 587	6.914	0.0361	4.911	3.577	30 086	40.081	1949	1.373
2400	0.98671	0.0091	6 647	6.893	0.0345	6.283	4.838	30 642	40.318	1939	1.299
2500	0.97656	0.0070	11 719	6.858	0.0329	8.392	6.760	31 372	40.617	1940	1.242
2600	0.96050	0.0054	19 750	6.802	0.0314	11.52	9.575	32 363	41.007	1956	1.203
2700	0.93616	0.0042	31 918	6.718	0.0299	16.00	13.55	33 734	41.527	1987	1.181
2800	0.90089	0.0032	49 553	6.595	0.0283	22.21	18.94	35 639	42.223	2035	1.172
2900	0.85201	0.0024	73 994	6.426	0.0266	30.53	25.96	38 272	43.152	2101	1.176
3000	0.78742	0.0017	106 290	6.201	0.0248	41.26	34.68	41 862	44.375	2188	1.190

$p=5 \cdot 10^{-5}$ bar

T, °K	x_1	$x_2 \cdot 10^5$	$x_e \cdot 10^6$	M	$\varrho \cdot 10^5$	c_p	c_v	i	s	u	k
900	0.99364	635.6	0	6.993	0.4663	3.682	3.264	25 487	35.092	1236	1.425
1000	0.99858	142.1	0	6.949	0.4176	3.310	2.068	25 866	35.493	1383	1.598
1100	0.99959	41.38	0.0002	6.942	0.3793	3.073	1.863	26 183	35.795	1474	1.649
1200	0.99985	14.74	0.0027	6.940	0.3476	3.020	1.818	26 487	36.059	1546	1.661
1300	0.99994	6.146	0.0225	6.939	0.3208	3.006	1.805	26 788	36.300	1611	1.655
1400	0.99997	2.898	0.1380	6.939	0.2979	3.001	1.801	27 088	36.523	1672	1.666
1500	0.99998	1.509	0.6672	6.939	0.2780	2.998	1.799	27 388	36.730	1731	1.666
1600	0.99999	0.8513	2.663	6.939	0.2606	3.001	1.802	27 688	36.923	1787	1.666
1700	0.99998	0.5131	9.076	6.939	0.2453	3.006	1.807	27 989	37.106	1841	1.664
1800	0.99994	0.3266	27.09	6.939	0.2317	3.020	1.820	28 291	37.278	1892	1.659
1900	0.99985	0.2177	72.36	6.938	0.2195	3.059	1.857	28 594	37.442	1937	1.647
2000	0.99965	0.1508	175.7	6.938	0.2085	3.124	1.918	28 903	37.601	1976	.1629
2100	0.99921	0.1080	393.3	6.936	0.1985	3.255	2.040	29 222	37.756	2004	1.595
2200	0.99836	0.0795	820.1	6.933	0.1894	3.484	2.253	29 557	37.913	2020	1.546
2300	0.99678	0.0599	1 607	6.928	0.1810	3.867	2.609	29 924	38.076	2023	1.482
2400	0.99403	0.0461	2 983	6.918	0.1732	4.487	3.181	30 340	38.253	2018	1.411
2500	0.98945	0.0359	5 276	6.902	0.1659	5.438	4.053	30 835	38.456	2011	1.342
2600	0.98214	0.0284	8 931	6.877	0.1590	6.844	5.332	31 447	38.696	2009	1.283
2700	0.97093	0.0225	14 537	6.838	0.1522	8.865	7.156	32 230	38.993	2017	1.239
2800	0.95438	0.0179	22 809	6.781	0.1455	11.67	9.658	33 254	39.367	2038	1.208
2900	0.93082	0.0142	34 588	6.699	0.1388	15.47	12.99	34 609	39.844	2071	1.191
3000	0.89845	0.0111	50 775	6.587	0.1320	20.48	17.30	36 406	40.456	2118	1.184

$p=10^{-4}$ bar

T, °K	x_1	$x_2 \cdot 10^5$	$x_e \cdot 10^6$	M	$\varrho \cdot 10^5$	c_p	c_v	i	s	u	k
900	0.98744	1 255	0	7.026	0.9384	6.341	4.606	25 388	34.159	1194	1.339
1000	0.99716	283.4	0	6.959	0.8365	3.617	2.332	25 843	34.641	1360	1.547
1100	0.99917	82.68	0.0002	6.945	0.7589	3.149	1.927	26 176	34.958	1467	1.632
1200	0.99970	29.46	0.0019	6.941	0.6953	3.043	1.837	26 484	35.226	1543	1.656
1300	0.99988	12.29	0.0159	6.940	0.6417	3.014	1.812	26 787	35.469	1610	1.663
1400	0.99994	5.795	0.0976	6.939	0.5958	3.004	1.804	27 087	35.692	1672	1.665
1500	0.99997	3.018	0.4718	6.939	0.5561	3.001	1.802	27 388	35.899	1731	1.666
1600	0.99998	1.703	1.883	6.939	0.5213	3.001	1.802	27 688	36.092	1787	1.666
1700	0.99998	1.026	6.418	6.939	0.4906	3.004	1.805	27 988	36.275	1842	1.664
1800	0.99995	0.6532	19.16	6.939	0.4634	3.014	1.814	28 290	36.447	1893	1.661
1900	0.99989	0.4355	51.16	6.939	0.4390	3.043	1.842	28 592	36.610	1940	1.652
2000	0.99975	0.3017	124.2	6.938	0.4170	3.089	1.885	28 899	36.768	1982	1.639
2100	0.99944	0.2161	278.1	6.937	0.3971	3.183	1.973	29 212	36.920	2015	1.613
2200	0.99884	0.1592	580.0	6.935	0.3789	3.347	2.126	29 538	37.072	2038	1.574
2300	0.99772	0.1201	1 137	6.931	0.3622	3.620	2.379	29 886	37.227	2049	1.521
2400	0.99577	0.0924	2 111	6.924	0.3468	4.062	2.788	30 269	37.390	2050	1.457
2500	0.99253	0.0723	3 736	6.913	0.3324	4.738	3.408	30 708	37.570	2045	1.390
2600	0.98734	0.0573	6 332	6.895	0.3188	5.735	4.319	31 230	37.775	2041	1.328
2700	0.97935	0.0458	10 324	6.867	0.3057	7.170	5.619	31 874	38.018	2043	1.276
2800	0.96752	0.0368	16 239	6.826	0.2930	9.162	7.407	32 688	38.316	2054	1.237
2900	0.95057	0.0296	24 715	6.768	0.2805	11.86	9.802	33 738	38.686	2077	1.210
3000	0.92706	0.0237	36 471	6.686	0.2679	15.43	12.92	35 102	39.150	2112	1.195

$p=5 \cdot 10^{-4}$ bar

T, °K	x_1	$x_2 \cdot 10^5$	$x_e \cdot 10^6$	M	$\varrho \cdot 10^5$	c_p	c_v	i	s	u	k
1000	0.98614	1 386	0	7.035	4.228	5.895	4.269	25 667	32.548	1270	1.363
1100	0.99589	410.7	0.0001	6.967	3.807	3.738	2.427	26 123	32.984	1420	1.534
1200	0.99853	147.0	0.0009	6.949	3.480	3.223	1.986	26 465	33.282	1527	1.623

continued

T, °K	x_1	$x_2 \cdot 10^5$	$x_e \cdot 10^6$	M	$\varrho \cdot 10^5$	c_p	c_v	i	s	u	k
1300	0,99939	61.39	0,0071	6.943	3.210	3,078	1.865	26 779	33.534	1604	1.651
1400	0.99971	28.96	0.0436	6,941	2,980	3,031	1.825	27 084	33.760	1669	1.660
1500	0.99985	15,08	0.2110	6.940	2,781	3.013	1.811	27 386	33,968	1730	1.664
1600	0,99991	8,512	0.8421	6.940	2,607	3,006	1,805	27 687	34,162	1787	1.665
1700	0,99994	5.131	2.870	6,939	2,453	3,004	1.804	27 987	34.344	1842	1.665
1800	0,99995	3,266	8,568	6.939	2,317	3,007	1.807	28 289	34.516	1895	1.664
1900	0,99993	2,178	22.88	6.939	2,195	3,023	1,823	28 590	34,679	1944	1.658
2000	0.99987	1.509	55.56	6.939	2.085	3,043	1.842	28 893	34.835	1990	1.652
2100	0.99974	1.081	124.4	6.938	1,986	3,088	1,884	29 200	34,984	2031	1.639
2200	0.99947	0.7970	259.5	6,937	1,895	3.165	1.956	29 512	35.130	2066	1.618
2300	0.99898	0.6022	508.8	6.935	1,812	3.290	2.072	29 835	35.273	2093	1.587
2400	0.99810	0.4644	945.4	6,932	1.736	3.494	2,262	30 173	35.418	2109	1.545
2500	0.99665	0.3647	1 674	6,927	1.665	3.804	2.547	30 538	35,566	2117	1.493
2600	0,99431	0.2906	2 842	6,919	1.599	4,256	2,962	30 940	35,724	2119	1.437
2700	0.99071	0.2344	4 644	6,907	1,537	4.908	3.557	31 398	35.898	2118	1.380
2800	0,98534	0.1909	7 329	6.888	1.478	5.810	4.374	31 933	36.093	2119	1.328
2900	0,97758	0.1566	11 209	6.861	1,422	7.033	5.474	32 574	36,318	2125	1.285
3000	0,96669	0,1289	16 655	6.823	1,367	8,653	6.918	33 358	36.585	2139	1.251

$p = 10^{-3}$ bar

T, °K	x_1	$x_2 \cdot 10^5$	$x_e \cdot 10^6$	M	$\varrho \cdot 10^5$	c_p	c_v	i	s	u	k
1100	0,99185	814.8	0	6,996	7,644	4.443	3,020	26 057	32.099	1382	1.460
1200	0,99707	293,1	0.0006	6,959	6.971	3.445	2.170	26 441	32.433	1509	1,588
1300	0,99877	122,6	0.0050	6.948	6.424	3.159	1.930	26 769	32.700	1596	1,636
1400	0,99942	57,89	0.0308	6.943	5.961	3,064	1.852	27 079	32,926	1666	1.654
1500	0,99970	30,16	0,1492	6,941	5.562	3.028	1.823	27 383	33.135	1728	1,661
1600	0,99983	17,02	0,5955	6.940	5,214	3.013	1,811	27 685	33,330	1786	1,664
1700	0,99989	10,26	2,029	6,939	4.907	3,007	1.806	27 986	33,513	1842	1.665
1800	0,99992	6.532	6,058	6.939	4.634	3.007	1,807	28 288	33.685	1895	1,664
1900	0,99992	4,355	16,18	6,939	4,390	3.020	1,819	28 589	33.848	1944	1,660
2000	0,99989	3,018	39,29	6,939	4,170	3.033	1,832	28 891	34.003	1992	1.655
2100	0,99980	2.163	87,97	6,938	3,972	3,066	1,864	29 197	34.152	2035	1,645
2200	0,99962	1,594	183,5	6,938	3,791	3,122	1,916	29 506	34,296	2073	1,629
2300	0,99927	1.205	359,9	6,936	3,625	3.212	2,000	29 822	34.437	2105	1,606
2400	0,99865	0,9298	668,7	6,934	3,473	3,360	2,137	30 151	34.576	2127	1,572
2500	0,99762	0,7308	1 184	6,931	3,332	3,582	2,342	30 498	34,718	2142	1,529
2600	0,99597	0,5832	2 011	6,925	3,202	3,906	2,639	30 872	34,865	2150	1,480
2700	0,99342	0,4714	3 288	6,916	3,079	4,372	3,066	31 285	35,021	2152	1,426
2800	0,98961	0,3851	5 194	6.903	2,963	5,015	3,650	31 754	35,192	2153	1,374
2900	0,98409	0,3173	7 952	6.884	2,853	5,887	4,438	32 298	35,384	2156	1,326
3000	0,97633	0.2630	11 836	6,857	2,747	7,042	5,473	32 944	35,603	2164	1,287

$p = 5 \cdot 10^{-3}$ bar

T, °K	x_1	$x_2 \cdot 10^5$	$x_e \cdot 10^6$	M	$\varrho \cdot 10^5$	c_p	c_v	i	s	u	k
1100	0,96170	3 830	0	7,205	39,37	9,029	6,768	25 587	29.779	1280	1,290
1200	0,98568	1 432	0,0003	7,038	35,25	5.089	3,509	26 258	30.365	1434	1,450
1300	0,99393	607.2	0,0022	6,981	32,28	3,781	2,435	26 690	30,711	1551	1,553
1400	0,99712	288,1	0,0138	6,959	29,88	3,323	2,060	27 041	30,972	1643	1,613
1500	0,99850	150.4	0,0667	6,949	27,84	3,147	1,917	27 364	31,194	1717	1,642
1600	0,99915	84,99	0,2662	6,945	26,09	3,072	1,857	27 674	31,395	1781	1,654
1700	0,99948	51,26	0,9074	6,942	24,54	3,038	1,830	27 980	31,580	1839	1,660
1800	0,99967	32,64	2,709	6,941	23,18	3,023	1,818	28 283	31,753	1894	1,663
1900	0,99977	21,77	7,235	6,940	21,95	3,024	1,821	28 585	31,917	1945	1,660
2000	0,99981	15,09	17,57	6,939	20,85	3,025	1,823	28 888	32,072	1974	1,659
2100	0,99981	10,81	39.34	6,939	19,86	3,041	1,838	29 191	32,219	2040	1,654
2200	0,99976	7,974	82,06	6,939	18,96	3,067	1,864	29 496	32,362	2083	1,645
2300	0,99962	6,029	160,9	6,938	18,13	3,110	1,904	29 805	32,499	2122	1,633
2400	0,99935	4,655	299,1	6,937	17,37	3,182	1,972	30 120	32,633	2155	1,614
2500	0,99890	3,663	530,1	6,936	16,67	3,288	2,070	30 444	32,765	2182	1,588

continued

T, °K	x_1	$x_2 \cdot 10^5$	$x_e \cdot 10^6$	M	$\varrho \cdot 10^5$	c_p	c_v	i	s	u	k
2600	0.99817	2.929	900.4	6.933	16.03	3.439	2.210	30 780	32.897	2203	1.556
2700	0.99703	2.374	1 473	6.929	15.42	3.657	2.410	31 135	33.031	2218	1.517
2800	0.99532	1.948	2 329	6.923	14.86	3.954	2.682	31 515	33.170	2227	1.474
2900	0.99284	1.615	3 572	6.914	14.33	4.358	3.049	31 930	33.315	2233	1.429
3000	0.98933	1.350	5 328	6.902	13.83	4.891	3.532	32 392	33.472	2238	1.385
					$p=10^{-2}$ bar						
1200	0.97214	2 786	0.0002	7.132	71.44	6.853	4.908	26 046	29.373	1398	1.396
1300	0.98800	1 200	0.0016	7.022	64.93	4.510	3.019	26 595	29.814	1517	1.494
1400	0.99427	573.0	0.0097	6.979	59.92	3.638	2.311	26 995	30.111	1621	1.574
1500	0.99700	300.0	0.0471	6.960	55.77	3.294	2.036	27 339	30.348	1704	1.620
1600	0.99830	169.7	0.1882	6.951	52.22	3.146	1.914	27 660	30.556	1774	1.643
1700	0.99897	102.4	0.6414	6.946	49.11	3.078	1.860	27 971	30.744	1835	1.654
1800	0.99934	65.24	1.915	6.943	46.37	3.045	1.835	28 278	30.919	1892	1.660
1900	0.99955	43.52	5.116	6.942	43.92	3.036	1.830	28 581	31.084	1944	1.659
2000	0.99967	30.17	12.42	6.941	41.72	3.030	1.826	28 885	31.239	1994	1.659
2100	0.99973	21.62	27.82	6.940	39.73	3.039	1.836	29 188	31.388	2041	1.655
2200	0.99972	15.95	58.03	6.940	37.92	3.057	1.854	29 493	31.529	2085	1.649
2300	0.99965	12.06	113.8	6.939	36.26	3.088	1.883	29 800	31.666	2126	1.640
2400	0.99948	9.313	211.5	6.938	34.75	3.141	1.934	30 112	31.799	2162	1.624
2500	0.99918	7.331	374.9	6.937	33.35	3.219	2.006	30 430	31.928	2193	1.604
2600	0.99867	5.864	636.8	6.935	32.06	3.329	2.108	30 758	32.057	2219	1.579
2700	0.99787	4.756	1 042	6.932	30.86	3.488	2.255	31 098	32.186	2239	1.547
2800	0.99666	3.906	1 648	6.928	29.74	3.703	2.453	31 458	32.316	2253	1.510
2900	0.99491	3.243	2 528	6.922	28.69	3.996	2.720	31 842	32.452	2263	1.469
3000	0.99243	2.717	3 773	6.913	27.67	4.383	3.072	32 262	32.597	2269	1.427
					$p=5 \cdot 10^{-2}$ bar						
1300	0.94510	5 490	0.0007	7.320	338.4	8.838	6.314	25 936	27.431	1438	1.400
1400	0.97259	2 741	0.0043	7.129	306.0	5.808	3.993	26 650	27.962	1541	1.454
1500	0.98535	1 465	0.0209	7.041	282.1	4.378	2.874	27 151	28.308	1643	1.523
1600	0.99162	837.1	0.0839	6.997	262.8	3.711	2.350	27 551	28.566	1733	1.580
1700	0.99492	507.9	0.2863	6.974	246.6	3.388	2.296	27 904	28.781	1810	1.616
1800	0.99675	324.5	0.8555	6.961	232.4	3.223	1.968	28 235	28.969	1877	1.637
1900	0.99783	216.8	2.286	6.954	219.9	3.143	1.908	28 552	29.141	1935	1.647
2000	0.99848	150.5	5.553	6.949	208.8	3.095	1.872	28 864	29.301	1989	1.653
2100	0.99889	107.9	12.43	6.946	198.8	3.075	1.860	29 173	29.451	2039	1.653
2200	0.99915	79.64	25.94	6.944	189.7	3.070	1.859	29 480	29.594	2086	1.652
2300	0.99930	60.26	50.89	6.943	181.4	3.067	1.867	29 787	29.731	2131	1.647
2400	0.99934	46.55	94.60	6.941	173.8	3.100	1.892	30 096	29.863	2171	1.639
2500	0.99930	36.66	167.6	6.940	166.8	3.137	1.927	30 408	29.990	2208	1.627
2600	0.99914	29.34	284.9	6.939	160.4	3.189	1.977	30 724	30.114	2242	1.613
2700	0.99883	23.82	466.2	6.937	154.4	3.268	2.052	31 048	30.236	2271	1.593
2800	0.99833	19.60	737.7	6.935	148.9	3.373	2.149	31 379	30.357	2296	1.570
2900	0.99757	16.30	1 132	6.932	143.7	3.516	2.281	31 724	30.478	2316	1.541
3000	0.99648	13.70	1 691	6.928	138.8	3.704	2.454	32 084	30.600	2332	1.509
					$p=10^{-1}$ bar						
1400	0.94792	5 208	0.0030	7.300	626.8	7.843	5.492	26 276	26.894	1509	1.428
1500	0.97152	2 848	0.0147	7.137	571.9	5.539	3.748	26 933	27.348	1607	1.478
1600	0.98353	1 647	0.0590	7.053	529.9	4.357	2.838	27 421	27.664	1702	1.535
1700	0.98994	1 006	0.2019	7.009	495.6	3.755	2.373	27 823	27.908	1787	1.582
1800	0.99355	644.9	0.6039	6.984	466.4	3.440	2.130	28 182	28.113	1861	1.615
1900	0.99568	431.8	1.614	6.969	440.9	3.275	2.006	28 517	28.294	1924	1.633
2000	0.99699	300.1	3.924	6.960	418.3	3.178	1.932	28 839	28.459	1983	1.644
2100	0.99783	215.4	8.789	6.954	398.0	3.128	1.897	29 154	28.613	2035	1.649
2200	0.99837	159.0	18.34	6.950	379.7	3.103	1.881	29 466	28.758	2084	1.650
2300	0.99872	120.4	35.98	6.947	363.1	3.095	1.878	29 775	28.896	2130	1.648
2400	0.99893	93.03	66.88	6.945	347.8	3.106	1.892	30 086	29.028	2172	1.641
2500	0.99903	73.29	118.5	6.943	333.8	3.128	1.916	30 398	29.155	2211	1.632
2600	0.99901	58.68	201.4	6.942	320.9	3.165	1.952	30 712	29.278	2248	1.621

continued

T, °K	x_1	$x_2 \cdot 10^5$	$x_e \cdot 10^8$	M	$\varrho \cdot 10^5$	c_p	c_v	i	s	u	k
2700	0,99886	47,65	329.7	6,940	309.0	3,223	2,008	31 032	29,399	2279	1,605
2800	0,99856	39,21	521,7	6,938	297.8	3.300	2,080	31 358	29,518	2308	1,586
2900	0,99807	32.64	800.8	6,936	287.5	3,406	2,179	31 693	29,635	2332	1,563
3000	0,99733	27.44	1 196	6,933	277.8	3,547	2,310	32 040	29.753	2351	1,536
				$p=2\cdot10^{-1}$ bar							
1500	0,94599	5 401	0,0103	7.314	1 172	7,356	5,060	26 545	26,291	1575	1,454
1600	0,96809	3 191	0.0414	7.160	1 076	5,476	3,662	27 178	26,700	1667	1,495
1700	0,98028	1 972	0,1421	7,076	1 000	4,427	2,870	27 668	26.997	1756	1,543
1800	0,98726	1 273	0,4257	7,027	938,6	3,848	2,431	28 080	27,232	1837	1,583
1900	0,99143	856,3	1,139	6.998	885,5	3,530	2,192	28 447	27,431	1907	1,610
2000	0,99402	596,6	2,770	6,980	839.1	3,342	2,051	28 790	27,607	1971	1,630
2100	0.99570	428,9	6.208	6.969	797,8	3,236	1,974	29 119	27.767	2027	1.640
2200	0,99680	317,1	12,96	6,961	760,7	3,175	1,931	29 439	27.917	2079	1,644
2300	0,99755	240,2	25,42	6.955	727,0	3,142	1,910	29 755	28,057	2127	1,645
2400	0,99805	185,7	47.27	6,951	696,3	3,134	1.909	30 068	28,191	2172	1,641
2500	0.99837	146,4	83,79	6.948	668,2	3,141	1,920	30 382	28,319	2212	1.635
2600	0,99854	117,2	142,4	6,946	642,4	3,161	1,943	30 698	28,442	2251	1,627
2700	0,99858	95,25	233,1	6,944	618,3	3,201	1,983	31 016	28,562	2285	1,614
2800	0,99848	78,40	368,9	6,942	596,0	3,256	2,036	31 338	28,680	2316	1,599
2900	0,99821	65,30	566,3	6,940	575,3	3,335	2,111	31 668	28.795	2343	1,579
3000	0.99776	54,92	846,0	6.937	555,9	3,440	2,211	32 006	28.910	2366	1,556
				$p=5\cdot10^{-1}$ bar							
1600	0,92686	7 313	0,0256	7.446	2 797	7,828	5,294	26 564	25,270	1626	1,479
1700	0.95336	4 664	0,0886	7.263	2 568	6,036	4,012	27 251	25,689	1712	1,504
1800	0,96931	3 069	0.2668	7,152	2 388	4,906	3,188	27 794	25,997	1795	1,539
1900	0,97912	2 088	0,7160	7,084	2 241	4,223	2,687	28 248	26,243	1872	1,571
2000	0.98534	1 465	1,744	7,041	2 116	3,801	2,377	28 647	26,448	1944	1,599
2100	0,98940	1 059	3,914	7,012	2 007	3,547	2,192	29 014	26,627	2008	1,618
2200	0,99213	785,3	8,175	6,993	1 910	3,388	2,079	29 360	26,788	2065	1,630
2300	0,99400	596,2	16,05	6,980	1 836	3,290	2,010	29 694	26,936	2118	1,637
2400	0,99532	461,8	29,85	6,971	1 746	3,236	1,976	30 019	27,075	2166	1,637
2500	0,99625	364,4	52,94	6,964	1 674	3,209	1,962	30 342	27,207	2210	1,635
2600	0,99690	292,1	89,98	6,959	1 609	3,201	1,963	30 663	27,332	2251	1,630
2700	0,99733	237,5	147,3	6,954	1 548	3,214	1,983	30 984	27,454	2288	1,621
2800	0,99758	195,7	233,2	6,951	1 492	3,243	2,014	31 306	27,571	2323	1,610
2900	0,99765	163,1	358,1	6,948	1 440	3,292	2,064	31 633	27,686	2353	1,595
3000	0,99756	137,2	535,0	6,945	1 391	3,362	2,133	31 965	27,798	2380	1,576
				$p=8\cdot10^{-1}$ bar							
1600	0,89170	10 830	0,0199	7,690	4 622	9,241	6,203	26 077	24,448	1606	1,490
1700	0,92912	7 087	0,0692	7,431	4 203	7,197	4,791	26 893	24,944	1691	1,502
1800	0,95258	4 742	0,2091	7,268	3 883	5,757	3,773	27 537	25,312	1773	1,526
1900	0,96739	3 261	0,5627	7,165	3 626	4,820	3,102	28 062	25,596	1851	1,554
2000	0,97694	2 305	1,373	7,099	3 413	4,215	2,665	28 512	25,827	1925	1,581
2100	0,98326	1 673	3,084	7,055	3 231	3,835	2,392	28 913	26,023	1993	1,603
2200	0,98754	1 245	6,448	7,025	3 071	3,592	2,218	29 284	26,195	2054	1,619
2300	0,99050	947,2	12,67	7,005	2 929	3,435	2,108	29 635	26,351	2110	1,629
2400	0,99260	734,8	23,57	6,990	2 801	3,341	2,046	29 973	26,495	2160	1,633
2500	0,99411	580,5	41,80	6,979	2 684	3,284	2,011	30 305	26,631	2206	1,633
2600	0.99520	465,8	71,08	6,971	2 578	3.253	1,995	30 613	26.759	2249	1,630
2700	0,99598	379,0	116,4	6,964	2 480	3,249	2,001	30 957	26,882	2288	1,623
2800	0,99651	312,4	184,2	6,959	2 390	3,261	2,021	31 282	27,000	2324	1,614
2900	0,99683	260.5	283,0	6,955	2 306	3,294	2,058	31 609	27,115	2356	1,601
3000	0,99696	219,4	422,8	6,951	2 228	3,349	2,114	31 941	27,227	2385	1,584
				$p=1$ bar							
1700	0,91422	8 578	0,0614	7,534	5 327	7,794	5,176	26 682	24,571	1681	1,506
1800	0.94203	5 797	0,1859	7.341	4 902	6,234	4,091	27 379	24,970	1763	1,524
1900	0,95986	4 013	0.5013	7,217	4 566	5.173	3,342	27 946	25.279	1841	1,548

continued

T, °K	x_1	$x_2 \cdot 10^5$	$x_e \cdot 10^8$	M	$\varrho \cdot 10^5$	c_p	c_v	i	s	u	k
2000	0.97150	2 849	1.225	7.137	4 289	4.469	2.839	28 425	25.523	1916	1.574
2100	0.97925	2 075	2.753	7.083	4 054	4.016	2.515	28 848	25.729	1984	1.596
2200	0.98452	1 546	5.758	7.046	3 850	3.721	2.306	29 234	25.909	2047	1.613
2300	0.98819	1 178	11.32	7.021	3 669	3.530	2.171	29 596	26.070	2105	1.625
2400	0.99081	915.2	21.06	7.002	3 507	3.409	2.091	29 942	26.217	2156	1.630
2500	0.99269	723.6	37.36	6.989	3 360	3.334	2.043	30 280	26.355	2204	1.632
2600	0.99406	581.0	63.54	6.979	3 226	3.290	2.018	30 611	26.485	2248	1.630
2700	0.99506	472.9	104.1	6.971	3 104	3.274	2.017	30 939	26.609	2287	1.624
2800	0.99577	389.9	164.7	6.965	2 990	3.278	2.029	31 266	26.728	2324	1.615
2900	0.99624	325.2	253.0	6.960	2 885	3.303	2.060	31 595	26.843	2357	1.603
3000	0.99650	273.9	378.1	6.955	2 787	3.349	2.110	31 928	26.956	2387	1.588

$p=2$ bar

T, °K	x_1	$x_2 \cdot 10^5$	$x_e \cdot 10^8$	M	$\varrho \cdot 10^5$	c_p	c_v	i	s	u	k
1800	0.89528	10 472	0.1282	7.666	10 238	7.871	5.125	26 716	23.831	1732	1.536
1900	0.92555	7 445	0.4212	7.457	9 389	6.526	4.217	27 435	24.222	1810	1.547
2000	0.94597	5 403	0.8546	7.314	8 792	5.513	3.528	28 031	24.527	1885	1.563
2100	0.96011	3 989	1.928	7.216	8 261	4.798	3.036	28 545	24.777	1956	1.581
2200	0.96997	3 002	4.041	7.147	7 810	4.303	2.693	28 998	24.989	2023	1.598
2300	0.97695	2 304	7.956	7.099	7 420	3.961	2.457	29 411	25.172	2084	1.612
2400	0.98199	1 798	14.83	7.063	7 076	3.732	2.303	29 795	25.335	2140	1.621
2500	0.98568	1 427	26.33	7.038	6 768	3.576	2.200	30 160	25.484	2192	1.626
2600	0.98842	1 149	44.80	7.018	6 489	3.472	2.133	30 512	25.622	2239	1.627
2700	0.99048	937.1	73.41	7.003	6 236	3.410	2.099	30 856	25.752	2282	1.624
2800	0.99203	773.9	116.3	6.992	6 003	3.376	2.085	31 195	25.876	2322	1.619
2900	0.99318	646.4	178.6	6.983	5 788	3.370	2.094	31 532	25.994	2358	1.609
3000	0.99401	545.1	267.0	6.975	5 589	3.388	2.122	31 870	26.108	2390	1.596

$p=4$ bar

T, °K	x_1	$x_2 \cdot 10^5$	$x_e \cdot 10^8$	M	$\varrho \cdot 10^5$	c_p	c_v	i	s	u	k
1900	0.86855	13 144	0.2384	7.851	19 868	7.977	5.085	26 653	23.054	1777	1.569
2000	0.90179	9 821	0.5900	7.620	18 320	6.838	4.341	27 393	23.434	1854	1.575
2100	0.92582	7 418	1.338	7.454	17 066	5.912	3.733	28 029	23.744	1927	1.584
2200	0.94321	5 678	2.818	7.333	16 026	5.200	3.261	28 583	24.002	1995	1.595
2300	0.95588	4 411	5.565	7.245	15 146	4.669	2.907	29 075	24.221	2059	1.606
2400	0.96523	3 474	10.39	7.180	14 384	4.286	2.654	29 522	24.411	2119	1.614
2500	0.97220	2 776	18.49	7.131	13 716	4.008	2.472	29 936	24.580	2174	1.621
2600	0.97747	2 247	31.50	7.095	13 120	3.808	2.344	30 326	24.733	2226	1.625
2700	0.98149	1 840	51.67	7.066	12 584	3.672	2.260	30 700	24.875	2272	1.625
2800	0.98459	1 525	81.91	7.044	12 096	3.579	2.207	31 062	25.006	2316	1.622
2900	0.98698	1 278	125.9	7.027	11 650	3.525	2.183	31 417	25.131	2355	1.615
3000	0.98883	1 079	188.4	7.012	11 239	3.503	2.184	31 768	25.250	2389	1.604

$p=6$ bar

T, °K	x_1	$x_2 \cdot 10^5$	$x_e \cdot 10^8$	M	$\varrho \cdot 10^5$	c_p	c_v	i	s	u	k
2000	0.86459	13 541	0.4717	7.878	28 411	7.580	4.762	26 894	22.749	1833	1.592
2100	0.89582	10 417	1.075	7.662	26 314	6.633	4.154	27 604	23.095	1908	1.597
2200	0.91912	8 088	2.271	7.500	24 588	5.843	3.644	28 226	23.385	1978	1.603
2300	0.93649	6 350	4.497	7.380	23 141	5.216	3.237	28 777	23.630	2044	1.611
2400	0.94955	5 043	8.418	7.289	21 904	4.737	2.929	29 274	23.841	2105	1.617
2500	0.95941	4 055	14.99	7.220	20 830	4.375	2.696	29 729	24.027	2162	1.623
2600	0.96697	3 292	25.58	7.168	19 883	4.105	2.524	30 153	24.193	2215	1.626
2700	0.97279	2 712	42.00	7.127	19 037	3.911	2.404	30 553	24.345	2264	1.627
2800	0.97733	2 253	66.63	7.095	18 275	3.771	2.321	30 936	24.484	2309	1.625
2900	0.98088	1 891	102.5	7.069	17 582	3.678	2.272	31 309	24.615	2350	1.619
3000	0.98368	1 601	153.4	7.049	16 946	3.624	2.252	31 673	24.738	2387	1.610

$p=8$ bar

T, °K	x_1	$x_2 \cdot 10^5$	$x_e \cdot 10^8$	M	$\varrho \cdot 10^5$	c_p	c_v	i	s	u	k
2000	0.83258	16 742	0.4009	8.101	38 950	8.006	4.991	26 490	22.247	1815	1.604
2100	0.86923	13 077	0.9171	7.846	35 930	7.111	4.418	27 246	22.616	1893	1.609
2200	0.89723	10 276	1.943	7.652	33 448	6.311	3.910	27 916	22.928	1965	1.614
2300	0.91853	8 146	3.857	7.504	31 375	5.640	3.484	28 512	23.193	2032	1.619
2400	0.93481	6 517	7.233	7.391	29 615	5.107	3.146	29 048	23.422	2094	1.623
2500	0.94726	5 271	12.90	7.305	28 098	4.688	2.881	29 538	23.621	2152	1.627

continued

T, °K	x_1	$x_2 \cdot 10^5$	$x_e \cdot 10^5$	M	$\varrho \cdot 10^5$	c_p	c_v	i	s	u	k
2600	0.95689	4 306	22.04	7.237	26 769	4.366	2.678	29 990	23.798	2207	1.630
2700	0.96439	3 554	36.22	7.185	25 591	4.126	2.531	30 414	23.959	2257	1.630
2800	0.97027	2 961	57.49	7.144	24 536	3.947	2.424	30 817	24.105	2304	1.628
2900	0.97491	2 491	88.49	7.111	23 581	3.823	2.355	31 205	24.241	2347	1.623
3000	0.97860	2 113	132.5	7.085	22 710	3.741	2.317	31 583	24.369	2385	1.614
				$p=10$ bar							
2100	0.84538	15 462	0.8090	8.012	45 860	7.432	4.588	26 938	22.235	1879	1.620
2200	0.87721	12 278	1.719	7.791	42 569	6.656	4.098	27 642	22.563	1953	1.624
2300	0.90184	9 815	3.419	7.620	39 824	5.975	3.670	28 273	22.844	2022	1.628
2400	0.92092	7 907	6.421	7.488	37 502	5.412	3.319	28 841	23.086	2085	1.630
2500	0.93069	6 429	11.47	7.385	35 508	4.956	3.034	29 359	23.297	2145	1.633
2600	0.94721	5 275	19.61	7.305	33 772	4.595	2.810	29 836	23.484	2200	1.635
2700	0.95626	4 367	32.26	7.242	32 241	4.320	2.643	30 281	23.652	2251	1.634
2800	0.96340	3 650	51.24	7.192	30 875	4.110	2.517	30 702	23.805	2299	1.633
2900	0.96907	3 077	78.91	7.152	29 645	3.958	2.432	31 105	23.947	2343	1.627
3000	0.97361	2 615	118.2	7.120	28 527	3.853	2.380	31 495	24.079	2382	1.619

Volume fractions of ionized lithium gas [30]

kg/cm² → T, °K	10^{-8}	10^{-7}	10^{-6}	10^{-5}	10^{-4}	10^{-3}	10^{-2}	10^{-1}	10^{0}	10^{1}	10^{2}
3 000		0.1320	0.4770	0.7872	0.9270	0.9763	0.9924	0.9976	0.9992	0.9998	0.9999
4 000				0.0420	0.2578	0.6322	0.8641	0.9549	0.9855	0.9954	0.9986
5 000					0.0110	0.0940	0.4074	0.7464	0.9114	0.9711	0.9908
6 000						0.0120	0.0840	0.3814	0.7296	0.9048	0.9688
7 000							0.0162	0.1160	0.4650	0.7808	0.9246
8 000							0.0020	0.0380	0.2378	0.6130	0.8555
9 000								0.0130	0.1080	0.4344	0.7630
10 000								0.0058	0.0540	0.2912	0.6620
11 000									0.0260	0.1840	0.5564
12 000									0.0154	0.1200	0.4564
13 000									0.0092	0.0800	0.3678
14 000									0.0058	0.0540	0.2938
15 000										0.0360	0.2344
16 000										0.0260	0.1860
17 000										0.0206	0.1500
18 000										0.0156	0.1200
19 000											0.0980
20 000											0.0800

Volume fractions of z_e and r_{Li^+} of ionized gas [30]

T, °K / p kg/cm² →	10^{-8}	10^{-7}	10^{-6}	10^{-5}	10^{-4}	10^{-3}	10^{-2}	10^{-1}	10^{-0}	10^{1}	10^{2}
3 000	0.5	0.4340	0.2615	0.1064	$0.365 \cdot 10^{-1}$	$0.1185 \cdot 10^{-1}$	$0.378 \cdot 10^{-2}$	$0.120 \cdot 10^{-2}$	$0.379 \cdot 10^{-3}$	$0.120 \cdot 10^{-3}$	$0.379 \cdot 10^{-4}$
4 000	0.5	0.5	0.5	0.4790	0.3711	0.1839	$0.6795 \cdot 10^{-1}$	$0.2255 \cdot 10^{-1}$	$0.725 \cdot 10^{-2}$	$0.230 \cdot 10^{-2}$	$0.730 \cdot 10^{-3}$
5 000	0.5	0.5	0.5	0.5	0.4945	0.4530	0.2963	0.1268	$0.443 \cdot 10^{-1}$	$0.1445 \cdot 10^{-1}$	$0.462 \cdot 10^{-2}$
6 000	0.5	0.5	0.5	0.5	0.5	0.4940	0.4580	0.3093	0.1352	$0.476 \cdot 10^{-1}$	$0.156 \cdot 10^{-1}$
7 000	0.5	0.5	0.5	0.5	0.5	0.5	0.4919	0.4420	0.2675	0.1096	$0.377 \cdot 10^{-1}$
8 000	0.5	0.5	0.5	0.5	0.5	0.5	0.4990	0.4810	0.3811	0.1935	$0.7225 \cdot 10^{-1}$
9 000	0.5	0.5	0.5	0.5	0.5	0.5	0.5	0.4935	0.4460	0.2828	0.1185
10 000	0.5	0.5	0.5	0.5	0.5	0.5	0.5	0.4971	0.4730	0.3544	0.1690
11 000	0.5	0.5	0.5	0.5	0.5	0.5	0.5	0.5	0.4870	0.4080	0.2218
12 000	0.5	0.5	0.5	0.5	0.5	0.5	0.5	0.5	0.4923	0.4400	0.2718
13 000	0.5	0.5	0.5	0.5	0.5	0.5	0.5	0.5	0.4954	0.4600	0.3161
14 000	0.5	0.5	0.5	0.5	0.5	0.5	0.5	0.5	0.4971	0.4730	0.3531
15 000	0.5	0.5	0.5	0.5	0.5	0.5	0.5	0.5	0.5	0.4820	0.3828
16 000	0.5	0.5	0.5	0.5	0.5	0.5	0.5	0.5	0.5	0.4870	0.4070
17 000	0.5	0.5	0.5	0.5	0.5	0.5	0.5	0.5	0.5	0.4897	0.4250
18 000	0.5	0.5	0.5	0.5	0.5	0.5	0.5	0.5	0.5	0.4922	0.4400
19 000	0.5	0.5	0.5	0.5	0.5	0.5	0.5	0.5	0.5	0.5	0.4510
20 000	0.5	0.5	0.5	0.5	0.5	0.5	0.5	0.5	0.5	0.5	0.4600

Molecular weight M of ionized gas [30]

T, °K \ p, kg/cm² →	10^{-8}	10^{-7}	10^{-6}	10^{-5}	10^{-4}	10^{-3}	10^{-2}	10^{-1}	10^{0}	10	100
3 000	3.470	3.928	5.125	6.202	6.687	6.857	6.914	6.932	6.937	6.939	6.940
4 000	3.470	3.470	3.470	3.616	4.365	5.664	6.468	6.783	6.889	6.924	6.935
5 000	3.470	3.470	3.470	3.470	3.508	3.796	4.884	6.060	6.633	6.839	6.908
6 000	3.470	3.470	3.470	3.470	3.470	3.512	3.761	4.793	6.002	6.610	6.832
7 000	3.470	3.470	3.470	3.470	3.470	3.470	3.526	3.873	5.084	6.179	6.678
8 000	3.470	3.470	3.470	3.470	3.470	3.470	3.470	3.602	4.295	5.597	6.438
9 000	3.470	3.470	3.470	3.470	3.470	3.470	3.470	3.515	3.845	4.977	6.118
10 000	3.470	3.470	3.470	3.470	3.470	3.470	3.470	3.490	3.657	4.480	5.767
11 000	3.470	3.470	3.470	3.470	3.470	3.470	3.470	3.470	3.560	4.108	5.401
12 000	3.470	3.470	3.470	3.470	3.470	3.470	3.470	3.470	3.523	3.886	5.054
13 000	3.470	3.470	3.470	3.470	3.470	3.470	3.470	3.470	3.502	3.748	4.746
14 000	3.470	3.470	3.470	3.470	3.470	3.470	3.470	3.470	3.490	3.657	4.489
15 000	3.470	3.470	3.470	3.470	3.470	3.470	3.470	3.470	3.470	3.595	4.283
16 000	3.470	3.470	3.470	3.470	3.470	3.470	3.470	3.470	3.470	3.560	4.115
17 000	3.470	3.470	3.470	3.470	3.470	3.470	3.470	3.470	3.470	3.541	3.991
18 000	3.470	3.470	3.470	3.470	3.470	3.470	3.470	3.470	3.470	3.524	3.886
19 000	3.470	3.470	3.470	3.470	3.470	3.470	3.470	3.470	3.470	3.470	3.810
20 000	3.470	3.470	3.470	3.470	3.470	3.470	3.470	3.470	3.470	3.470	3.748

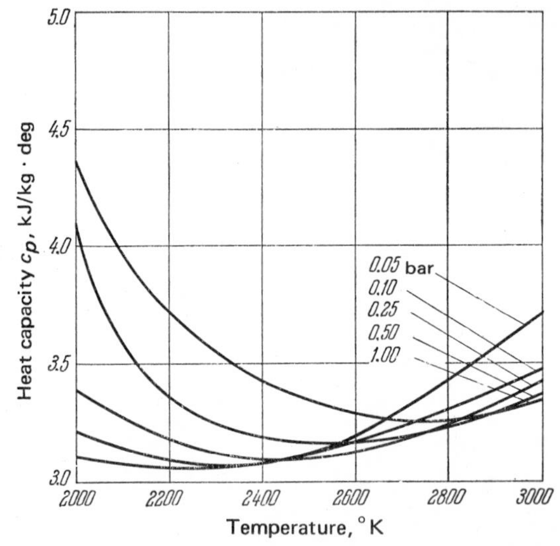

Fig. 9. Heat Capacity c_p of dissociated and partially ionized lithium.

Heat capacity c_p (kcal/kg · deg) for ionized gas [30]

T, °K \ p, kg/cm² →	10^{-7}	10^{-6}	10^{-5}	10^{-4}	10^{-3}	10^{-2}	10^{-1}	10^{0}	10^{1}	10^{2}
3 000	14.60	24.20	9.80	3.73	1.70	1.05	0.85	0.80	0.91	1.30
3 250	6.05	23.50	19.80	7.60	3.06	1.85	1.20	0.92	0.93	1.08
3 500	3.05	11.70	24.40	12.45	5.00	2.90	1.80	1.10	0.95	0.90
3 750	1.70	5.30	16.30	17.60	7.70	4.30	2.30	1.25	1.05	0.86
4 000	1.43	2.50	8.90	18.80	11.15	6.00	2.85	1.40	1.10	0.72
4 250	1.43	1.75	4.40	13.60	14.30	7.80	3.40	1.55	1.25	0.72
4 500	1.43	1.43	2.85	8.3	14.80	9.80	4.05	1.75	1.15	0.95
5 000	1.43	1.43	1.83	3.60	7.8	10.93	5.50	2.00	1.43	1.08
5 500	1.43	1.43	1.55	1.95	4.50	8.80	8.30	3.10	1.78	1.22
6 000	1.43	1.43	1.45	1.57	2.75	5.55	9.00	4.50	2.25	1.40

continued

T, °K \ p, kg/cm² →	10^{-7}	10^{-6}	10^{-5}	10^{-4}	10^{-3}	10^{-2}	10^{-1}	10^{0}	10^{1}	10^{2}
6 500	1.43	1.43	1.43	1.43	1.95	3.80	8.80	5.75	2.78	1.60
7 000	1.43	1.43	1.43	1.43	1.63	2.60	5.25	6.65	3.28	1.83
7 500	1.43	1.43	1.43	1.43	1.48	2.08	3.85	6.85	3.80	2.05
8 000	1.43	1.43	1.43	1.43	1.43	1.75	3.05	6.43	4.40	2.30
8 500	1.43	1.43	1.43	1.43	1.43	1.55	2.50	5.50	4.75	2.50
9 000	1.43	1.43	1.43	1.43	1.43	1.43	2.08	4.35	4.85	2.75
9 500	1.43	1.43	1.43	1.43	1.43	1.43	1.80	3.50	4.80	2.93
10 000	1.43	1.43	1.43	1.43	1.43	1.43	1.60	2.80	4.58	3.06
10 500	1.43	1.43	1.43	1.43	1.43	1.43	1.48	2.50	4.25	3.15
11 000	1.43	1.43	1.43	1.43	1.43	1.43	1.43	2.20	3.88	3.25
11 500	1.43	1.43	1.43	1.43	1.43	1.43	1.43	1.95	3.53	3.30
12 000	1.43	1.43	1.43	1.43	1.43	1.43	1.43	1.78	3.23	3.33
12 500	1.43	1.43	1.43	1.43	1.43	1.43	1.43	1.65	2.90	3.35
13 000	1.43	1.43	1.43	1.43	1.43	1.43	1.43	1.58	2.70	3.30
13 500	1.43	1.43	1.43	1.43	1.43	1.43	1.43	1.55	2.45	3.25
14 000	1.43	1.43	1.43	1.43	1.43	1.43	1.43	1.53	2.30	3.15
14 500	1.43	1.43	1.43	1.43	1.43	1.43	1.43	1.51	2.15	3.08
15 000	1.43	1.43	1.43	1.43	1.43	1.43	1.43	1.505	2.00	3.00
15 500	1.43	1.43	1.43	1.43	1.43	1.43	1.43	1.502	1.85	2.90
16 000	1.43	1.43	1.43	1.43	1.43	1.43	1.43	1.50	1.78	2.80
16 500	1.43	1.43	1.43	1.43	1.43	1.43	1.43	1.499	1.70	2.70
17 000	1.43	1.43	1.43	1.43	1.43	1.43	1.43	1.498	1.67	2.60
17 500	1.43	1.43	1.43	1.43	1.43	1.43	1.43	1.497	1.60	2.54
18 000	1.43	1.43	1.43	1.43	1.43	1.43	1.43	1.43	1.58	2.45
18 500	1.43	1.43	1.43	1.43	1.43	1.43	1.43	1.43	1.57	2.40
19 000	1.43	1.43	1.43	1.43	1.43	1.43	1.43	1.43	1.55	2.33
19 500	1.43	1.43	1.43	1.43	1.43	1.43	1.43	1.43	1.525	2.30
20 000	1.43	1.43	1.43	1.43	1.43	1.43	1.43	1.43	1.50	

Enthalpy i (kcal/kg) for ionized gas [30]

T, °K \ p, kg/cm² →	10^{-8}	10^{-7}	10^{-6}	10^{-5}	10^{-4}	10^{-3}	10^{-2}	10^{-1}	10^{0}	10^{1}	10^{2}
3 000	27 200	22 520	14 260	9 547	7 920	7 403	7 237	7 186	7 169	7 164	7 161
4 000	28 630	28 630	28 430	27 000	20 390	12 740	9 500	8 433	8 107	8 003	7 970
5 000	30 060	30 060	30 060	30 060	29 590	26 420	19 380	11 920	9 819	9 148	8 935
6 000	31 500	31 500	31 500	31 500	31 500	30 980	28 130	19 530	13 220	10 920	10 190
7 000	32 940	32 940	32 940	32 940	32 940	32 940	32 220	28 350	18 960	13 640	11 790
8 000	34 350	34 350	34 350	34 350	34 350	34 350	34 250	32 730	25 800	17 440	13 840
9 000	35 790	35 790	35 790	35 790	35 790	35 790	35 790	35 220	31 420	22 180	16 180
10 000	37 230	37 230	37 230	37 230	37 230	37 230	37 230	36 960	34 890	27 010	19 180
11 000	38 650	38 650	38 650	38 650	38 650	38 650	38 650	38 650	37 500	31 550	22 330
12 000	40 090	40 090	40 090	40 090	40 090	40 090	40 090	40 090	39 400	35 150	25 640
13 000	41 530	41 530	41 530	41 530	41 530	41 530	41 530	41 530	41 090	38 050	28 990
14 000	42 940	42 940	42 940	42 940	42 940	42 940	42 940	42 940	42 660	40 530	32 230
15 000	44 380	44 380	44 380	44 380	44 380	44 380	44 380	44 380	44 380	42 700	35 300
16 000	45 820	45 820	45 820	45 820	45 820	45 820	45 820	45 820	45 820	44 580	38 200
17 000	47 230	47 230	47 230	47 230	47 230	47 230	47 230	47 230	47 230	46 230	40 790
18 000	58 670	48 670	48 670	48 670	48 670	48 670	48 670	48 670	48 670	47 900	43 310
19 000	49 510	49 510	49 510	49 510	49 510	49 510	49 510	49 510	49 510	49 510	45 400
20 000	51 150	51 150	51 150	51 150	51 150	51 150	51 150	51 150	51 150	51 150	47 360

Entropy s (kcal/kg · deg) for ionized gas [30]

T, °K \ p kg/cm² →	10^{-8}	10^{-7}	10^{-6}	10^{-5}	10^{-4}	10^{-3}	10^{-2}	10^{-1}	10^{0}	10^{1}	10^{2}
3 000	19.53	16.74	12.96	10.59	9.34	8.55	7.83	7.00	6.18	5.77	4.85
3 250	—	17.50	15.26	11.82	9.95	9.05	8.08	7.07	6.28	5.83	4.95
4 000	19.95	18.67	17.31	15.60	12.73	10.10	8.39	7.45	6.70	6.01	5.34
5 000	20.27	18.95	17.63	16.31	14.91	13.01	10.21	8.21	7.08	6.27	5.56
6 000	20.54	19.21	17.89	16.57	15.25	13.86	12.11	9.58	7.69	6.58	5.78
7 000	20.75	19.43	18.11	16.79	15.48	14.16	12.75	10.94	8.57	7.02	6.03
8 000	20.94	19.62	18.30	16.98	15.67	14.35	13.02	11.53	9.42	7.51	6.30
9 000	21.11	19.80	18.48	17.16	15.84	14.52	13.20	11.83	10.15	8.07	6.60
10 000	21.26	19.95	18.63	17.31	15.99	14.67	13.35	12.01	10.52	8.58	6.90
11 000	21.40	20.08	18.76	17.44	16.12	14.81	13.49	12.17	10.76	9.01	7.20
12 000	21.52	20.20	18.88	17.57	16.25	14.93	13.61	12.30	10.93	9.30	7.48
13 000	21.63	20.32	19.00	17.68	16.36	15.05	13.73	12.41	11.06	9.55	7.76
14 000	21.74	20.42	19.10	17.79	16.47	15.16	13.84	12.52	11.18	9.74	8.00
15 000	21.84	20.52	19.20	17.89	16.57	15.25	13.93	12.61	11.30	9.89	8.25
16 000	21.93	20.61	19.29	17.98	16.66	15.35	14.03	12.70	11.39	10.01	8.40
17 000	22.02	20.70	19.38	18.07	16.75	15.43	14.11	12.79	11.48	10.11	8.55
18 000	22.10	20.79	19.47	18.15	16.83	15.51	14.19	12.88	11.56	10.20	8.70
19 000	22.18	20.86	19.54	18.24	16.91	15.59	14.27	12.95	11.64	10.32	8.82
20 000	22.25	20.94	19.62	18.30	16.98	15.66	14.34	13.03	11.71	10.39	8.93

Viscosity $\eta \cdot 10^7$ (N · s/m²) for lithium vapor [37]

T, °K	For monatomic vapor	p, bar				At saturation
		0,5	1	2	5	
1000	98					
1100	106					
1200	113					
1300	121					129
1400	129					140
1500	137					150
1600	144	153	159			160
1700	152	158	163			171
1800	159	163	167	174		181
1900	167	170	173	178	189	192
2000	175	177	179	183	193	202

Viscosity of liquid lithium [37]

T, °K	T_{melt}	500	600	700	800	900	1000	1100
$\eta \cdot 10^3$, N · s/m²	0.600	0.531	0.426	0.358	0.310	0.275	0.247	0.225
T, °K	1200	1300	1400	1500	1600	1700	1800	
$\eta \cdot 10^3$, N · s/m²	0.207	0.192	0.180	0.169	0.159	0.151	0.143	

Thermal conductivity $\lambda \cdot 10^3$ (W/m · deg) for lithium vapor [37]

T, °K	For mon-atomic vapor	p, bar									At saturation
		0,005	0,01	0,05	0,1	0,25	0,5	1	2	5	
1000	43.8										
1100	47.6	119									120
1200	50.7	77.3	101								138
1300	54.7	65.4	68.5	138							156
1400	57.9	62.7	64.4	100	133						172
1500	61.4	63.7	64.8	83.3	102	147					183
1600	64.9	66.2	67.5	76.9	88.0	117	152				192
1700	68.3	69.0	69.7	75.2	81.8	99.8	124	160			198
1800	71.4	71.9	72.2	75.6	79.7	91.2	108	135	172		202
1900	75.0	75.2	75.6	77.7	80.4	87.9	99.4	120	150	198	207
2000	78.6	78.9	79.0	80.5	82.2	87.3	95.4	110	134	179	209

Thermal conductivity λ for liquid lithium [37]

T, °K	T_{melt}	500	600	700	800	900	1000	1100	1200	1300
λ, W/m · deg	42.8	43.7	46.1	48.4	50.7	52.9	55.2	57.6	59.8	62.1

Surface tension of lithium [31]

t, °C	179	200	300	400	500	600	700	800	900	1000	1100	1200	1300	1400	1500
σ dyne/cm	398	395	381	367	353	339	325	311	297	283	269	255	241	227	223

SODIUM (Na)

Atomic weight 22.991

$T_{melt} = 371.0$ °K; $T_{boil} = 1151.2$ °K at 760 mm Hg; $T_{cr} = 2500$ °K;
$p_{cr} = 370$ bar; $\rho_{cr} = 180$ kg/m³ Thermodynamic properties of liquid sodium at saturation [28]: ρ (kg/m³), c_p (kJ/kg · deg), i and r (kJ/kg), s (kJ/kg · deg)

T, °K	p, bar	ρ'	c_p'	i'	s'	r
371	$1.61 \cdot 10^{-10}$	928	1.39	212.7	2.815	4536.7
400	$1.844 \cdot 10^{-9}$	921	1.37	252.8	2.918	4526.3
450	$5.902 \cdot 10^{-8}$	909	1.35	320.7	3.079	4503.7
500	$9.363 \cdot 10^{-7}$	897	1.33	387.7	3.219	4469.8
550	$8.880 \cdot 10^{-6}$	886	1.31	453.6	3.345	4438.9
600	$5.749 \cdot 10^{-5}$	874	1.30	518.8	3.459	4404.2
650	$2.781 \cdot 10^{-4}$	862	1.28	583.3	3.562	4366.1
700	$1.071 \cdot 10^{-3}$	850	1.27	647.2	3.657	4324.4
750	$3.432 \cdot 10^{-3}$	838	1.26	710.6	3.744	4280.3
800	$9.493 \cdot 10^{-3}$	826	1.26	773.8	3.826	4233.7
850	$2.328 \cdot 10^{-2}$	814	1.26	836.8	3.902	4185.6
900	$5.154 \cdot 10^{-2}$	802	1.25	899.5	3.974	4136.7
950	0.1049	790	1.25	962.3	4.042	4087.6
1000	0.1986	779	1.26	1025.1	4.106	4038.5
1050	0.3535	767	1.26	1088.1	4.168	3990.1
1100	0.5965	755	1.27	1151.7	4.227	3941.9
1150	0.9607	743	1.28	1213.8	4.282	3896.6
1200	1.504	731	1.29	1279.9	4.338	3848.5
1250	2.244	719	1.30	1344.7	4.391	3803.0

continued

T, °K	p, bar	ϱ'	c_p'	i'	s'	r'
1300	3.216	707	1.31	1409.9	4.445	3761.0
1350	4.563	695	1.32	1475.7	4.492	3715.2
1400	6.256	683	1.33	1542.0	4.540	3672.5
1450	8.383	671	1.34	1608.6	4.587	3631.0
1500	[illegible]	659	1.35	1675.6	4.632	3590.4

Thermodynamic properties of saturated sodium vapor: diatomic fraction X_2, molecular wt M, ρ (kg/m^3), c_p and c_v (kJ/kg · deg), i (kJ/kg), s (kJ/kg · deg) and u (m/s) [28]

T, °K	X_2	M	ϱ''	c''	c_v''	i''	s''	u
400	0	22.990	$1.274 \cdot 10^{-9}$	0.9047	0.5429	4779.1	14.23	481.1
450	0	22.990	$3.625 \cdot 10^{-8}$	0.9047	0.5429	4824.4	13.09	495.0
500	$3.756 \cdot 10^{-3}$	23.078	$5.194 \cdot 10^{-7}$	1.329	0.9208	4857.5	12.16	509.1
550	$6.986 \cdot 10^{-3}$	23.150	$4.493 \cdot 10^{-6}$	1.551	1.111	4892.5	11.42	523.6
600	$1.159 \cdot 10^{-2}$	23.256	$2.679 \cdot 10^{-5}$	1.793	1.311	4923.0	10.80	538.7
650	$1.760 \cdot 10^{-2}$	23.394	$1.203 \cdot 10^{-4}$	2.030	1.501	4949.4	10.28	554.5
700	$2.493 \cdot 10^{-2}$	23.563	$4.334 \cdot 10^{-4}$	2.244	1.664	4971.6	9.834	570.7
750	$3.339 \cdot 10^{-2}$	23.757	$1.307 \cdot 10^{-3}$	2.421	1.790	4990.9	9.451	587.1
800	$4.280 \cdot 10^{-2}$	23.974	$3.419 \cdot 10^{-3}$	2.555	1.877	5007.5	9.118	603.4
850	$5.298 \cdot 10^{-2}$	24.208	$7.968 \cdot 10^{-3}$	2.648	1.928	5022.5	8.826	619.5
900	$6.367 \cdot 10^{-2}$	24.454	$1.683 \cdot 10^{-2}$	2.700	1.945	5036.2	8.570	635.3
950	$7.465 \cdot 10^{-2}$	24.706	$3.278 \cdot 10^{-2}$	2.718	1.937	5049.9	8.345	650.8
1000	$8.580 \cdot 10^{-2}$	24.962	$5.959 \cdot 10^{-2}$	2.709	1.908	5063.7	8.145	666.0
1050	$9.691 \cdot 10^{-2}$	25.218	0.1020	2.679	1.865	5078.3	7.968	680.9
1100	0.1079	25.470	0.1660	2.632	1.812	5093.6	7.810	695.6
1150	0.1185	25.715	0.2624	2.574	1.754	5110.4	7.670	710.0
1200	0.1289	25.953	0.3909	2.508	1.691	5128.4	7.545	724.1
1250	0.1389	26.183	0.5652	2.440	1.629	5147.7	7.434	738.0
1300	0.1474	26.379	0.7844	2.365	1.564	5170.9	7.338	752.2
1350	0.1574	26.608	1.081	2.298	1.507	5190.8	7.244	765.3
1400	0.1658	26.802	1.439	2.228	1.449	5214.5	7.163	778.7
1450	0.1738	26.985	1.875	2.161	1.395	5239.6	7.091	792.0
1500	0.1812	27.157	2.397	2.095	1.342	5266.1	7.026	805.1

Saturated vapor pressure for sodium above 10 bar [416]

T, °K	p, bar	T, °K	p, bar	T, °K	p, bar	T, °K	p, bar	T, °K	p, bar
1550	14.6	1700	29.0	1850	51.6	2000	84.1	2125	120.0
1600	18.6	1750	35.6	1900	61.2	2050	97.5		
1650	23.4	1800	43.0	1950	72.1	2100	112.1		

Thermodynamic properties of sodium vapor at different temperatures and pressures: X_1, X_2, X_e –molar fractions of monatomic, diatomic and electronic components, M–molecular weight, ρ (kg/m^3), c_p and c_v (kJ/kg · deg), i (kJ/kg), s (kJ/kg · deg), speed of sound u (m/s), adiabatic exponent k [28]

T, °K	X_1	$X_2 \cdot 10^4$	$X_e \cdot 10^4$	M	$\varrho \cdot 10^4$	i	s	c	c_v	u	k
$p=10^{-5}$ bar											
700	0.99976	2.446	0	23.004	0.0395	5 048.0	11.617	0.919	0.555	647.3	1.655
800	0.99995	0.4921	0	22.999	0.0346	5 139.1	11.743	0.907	0.545	694.1	1.665
900	0.99999	0.1409	0	22.998	0.0307	5 229.5	11.852	0.905	0.543	736.5	1.666
1000	0.99999	0.0517	0	22.998	0.0276	5 320.0	11.945	0.904	0.543	776.4	1.666
1100	0.99999	0.0227	0	22.998	0.0251	5 410.5	12.030	0.904	0.543	814.3	1.667

continued

T, °K	X_1	$X_2 \cdot 10^4$	$X_e \cdot 10^4$	M	$\varrho \cdot 10^4$	i	s	c_p	c_v	u	k
1200	0.99999	0.0115	0.0002	22.998	0.0230	5 501.0	12.113	0.904	0.543	850.5	1.667
1300	0.99999	0.0068	0.0016	22.998	0.0213	5 591.5	12.185	0.904	0.543	885.3	1.666
1400	0.99999	0.0039	0.0088	22.998	0.0198	5 681.8	12.257	0.905	0.543	918.6	1.666
1500	0.99999	0.0025	0.0396	22.998	0.0184	5 772.4	12.314	0.906	0.544	950.5	1.665
1600	0.99997	0.0017	0.1489	22.997	0.0173	5 863.1	12.373	0.909	0.547	980.8	1.652
1700	0.99990	0.0012	0.4806	22.997	0.0163	5 954.3	12.428	0.917	0.554	1008	1.654
1800	0.99973	0.0009	1.368	22.995	0.0154	6 046.9	12.480	0.936	0.572	1032	1.635
1900	0.99930	0.0007	3.499	22.989	0.0145	6 142.3	12.531	0.978	0.611	1048	1.599
2000	0.99837	0.0005	8.172	22.979	0.0138	6 243.8	12.581	1.060	0.688	1056	1.540
2100	0.99647	0.0004	17.65	22.957	0.0131	6 356.9	12.632	1.214	0.832	1054	1.460
2200	0.99287	0.0003	35.60	22.916	0.0125	6 490.3	12.687	1.477	1.075	1047	1.374
2300	0.98648	0.0003	67.62	22.842	0.0119	6 657.8	12.752	1.910	1.472	1042	1.297
2400	0.97565	0.0002	121.7	22.718	0.0114	6 880.4	12.871	2.590	2.091	1043	1.238
2500	0.95875	0.0002	208.8	22.518	0.0108	7 187.4	12.996	3.612	3.011	1053	1.199
2600	0.93163	0.0001	341.8	22.211	0.0103	7 617.7	13.164	5.088	4.317	1071	1.178
2700	0.89270	0.0001	1 325	21.764	0.0097	8 224.5	13.392	7.154	6.104	1100	1.172
2800	0.83852	0.0001	8 072	21.141	0.0091	9 072.4	13.700	9.936	8.434	1139	1.178
2900	0.76708	0.0001	11 646	20.320	0.0084	10 239	14.108	13.52	11.32	1191	1.195
3000	0.67818	0	16 091	19.297	0.0077	11 801	14.637	17.92	14.69	1256	1.219
					$p=5 \cdot 10^{-5}$ bar						
700	0.99878	12.21	0	23.026	0.1977	5 045.2	11.036	0.976	0.604	645.0	1.614
800	0.99975	2.459	0	23.004	0.1728	5 138.0	11.165	0.916	0.552	692.6	1.658
900	0.99993	0.7042	0	22.999	0.1536	5 229.1	11.268	0.907	0.545	736.2	1.665
1000	0.99997	0.2584	0	22.998	0.1382	5 320.7	11.361	0.905	0.543	776.3	1.666
1100	0.99999	0.1136	0	22.998	0.1256	5 411.4	11.452	0.905	0.543	814.3	1.666
1200	0.99999	0.0584	0.0001	22.998	0.1152	5 501.0	11.530	0.904	0.543	850.5	1.667
1300	0.99999	0.0343	0.0007	22.998	0.1063	5 591.5	11.603	0.904	0.543	885.2	1.667
1400	0.99999	0.0194	0.0039	22.998	0.0987	5 681.8	11.670	0.905	0.543	918.6	1.666
1500	0.99999	0.0125	0.0177	22.998	0.0922	5 772.3	11.732	9.905	0.543	950.8	1.666
1600	0.99999	0.0086	0.0666	22.998	0.0864	5 862.9	11.791	0.906	0.544	981.5	1.664
1700	0.99996	0.0071	0.2150	22.998	0.0813	5 953.7	11.846	0.910	0.548	1011	1.661
1800	0.99988	0.0045	0.6118	22.997	0.0768	6 050.1	11.898	0.918	0.556	1037	1.652
1900	0.99969	0.0034	1.565	22.994	0.0727	6 137.8	11.948	0.937	0.573	1060	1.634
2000	0.99927	0.0027	3.656	22.990	0.0691	6 233.2	11.997	0.974	0.608	1077	1.602
2100	0.99842	0.0021	7.900	22.980	0.0658	6 333.9	12.046	1.044	0.673	1086	1.551
2200	0.99681	0.0017	15.95	22.961	0.0627	6 443.5	12.097	1.162	0.782	1088	1.485
2300	0.99393	0.0014	30.35	22.928	0.0599	6 568.5	12.153	1.355	0.949	1085	1.411
2400	0.98904	0.0012	54.81	22.872	0.0573	6 718.4	12.216	1.660	1.240	1081	1.339
2500	0.98111	0.0010	94.47	22.781	0.0548	6 906.0	12.293	2.119	1.657	1080	1.279
2600	0.96882	0.0008	155.9	22.639	0.0523	7 159.1	12.388	2.782	2.255	1086	1.233
2700	0.95049	0.0007	247.6	22.429	0.0499	7 471.6	12.501	3.716	3.084	1098	1.205
2800	0.92421	0.0006	379.0	22.126	0.0475	7 903.5	12.666	4.988	4.197	1118	1.188
2900	0.88793	0.0005	560.4	21.709	0.0450	8 483.1	12.868	6.674	5.638	1147	1.184
3000	0.83984	0.0004	800.8	21.156	0.0424	9 254.1	13.130	8.914	7.511	1183	1.187
					$p=10^{-4}$ bar						
700	0.99756	24.36	0	23.054	0.3959	5 040.9	10.782	1.048	0.665	639.1	1.572
800	0.99951	4.916	0	23.009	0.3457	5 137.7	10.911	0.927	0.561	690.8	1.650
900	0.99986	1.408	0	23.001	0.3072	5 229.1	11.019	0.910	0.547	735.7	1.663
1000	0.99995	0.5168	0	22.999	0.2765	5 319.9	11.115	0.906	0.544	776.2	1.666
1100	0.99998	0.2272	0	22.998	0.2513	5 410.5	11.200	0.905	0.543	814.2	1.666
1200	0.99999	0.1144	0.0001	22.998	0.2304	5 503.0	11.279	0.904	0.543	850.5	1.667
1300	0.99999	0.0639	0.0005	22.998	0.2126	5 591.5	11.352	0.904	0.543	885.3	1.667
1400	0.99999	0.0388	0.0028	22.998	0.1975	5 681.8	11.419	0.904	0.543	918.6	1.665
1500	0.99999	0.0251	0.0125	22.998	0.1843	5 732.3	11.482	0.905	0.543	950.8	1.666
1600	0.99999	0.0171	0.0471	22.998	0.1728	5 862.9	11.540	0.906	0.544	981.7	1.665
1700	0.99997	0.0122	0.1520	22.998	0.1626	5 953.6	11.595	9.908	0.546	1011	1.662
1800	0.99991	0.0090	0.4325	22.997	0.1536	6 044.7	11.647	0.914	0.552	1038	1.656
1900	0.99978	0.0068	1.107	22.995	0.1455	6 136.8	11.697	0.928	0.564	1063	1.643
2000	0.99948	0.0053	2.586	22.992	0.1382	6 230.7	11.745	0.954	0.589	1083	1.620
2100	0.99888	0.0043	5.588	22.985	0.1316	6 328.5	11.793	1.004	0.636	1096	1.579
2200	0.99774	0.0035	11.28	22.972	0.1255	6 432.5	11.841	1.087	0.713	1102	1.525
2300	0.99570	0.0029	21.48	22.949	0.1199	6 547.5	11.892	1.223	0.839	1103	1.459
2400	0.99224	0.0023	38.82	22.909	0.1147	6 680.0	11.948	1.440	1.037	1100	1.388

continued

T, °K	X_1	$X_2 \cdot 10^4$	$X_e \cdot 10^4$	M	$\varrho \cdot 10^4$	i	s	c_p	c_v	u	k
2500	0.98660	0.0020	66.99	22.844	0.1098	6 839.4	12.013	1.765	1.334	1098	1.323
2600	0.97784	0.0017	110.8	22.743	0.1051	7 037.9	12.091	2.235	1.759	1099	1.270
2700	0.96473	0.0014	176.4	22.592	0.1006	7 292.8	12.187	2.295	2.351	1107	1.232
2800	0.94578	0.0012	271.1	22.374	0.0961	7 625.2	12.308	3.799	3.149	1120	1.206
2900	0.91936	0.0010	403.2	22.071	0.0915	8 062.7	12.460	4.999	4.191	1142	1.193
3000	0.88382	0.0008	580.9	21.662	0.0868	8 636.8	12.655	6.630	5.588	1169	1.186
				$p=5 \cdot 10^{-4}$ bar							
700	0.98805	118.5	0	23.273	1.998	5 010.5	10.160	1.580	1.115	592.2	1.401
800	0.99755	24.48	0	23.054	1.732	5 131.3	10.327	1.015	0.635	678.4	1.594
900	0.99930	7.034	0	23.014	1.537	5 227.3	10.442	0.930	0.564	732.4	1.649
1000	0.99974	2.583	0	23.004	1.383	5 319.2	10.531	0.912	0.549	775.1	1.661
1100	0.99989	1.136	0	23.002	1.257	5 410.2	10.625	0.907	0.545	813.9	1.665
1200	0.99994	0.5717	0	22.999	1.152	5 500.8	10.697	0.906	0.544	850.4	1.666
1300	0.99997	0.3197	0.0002	22.999	1.063	5 591.3	10.770	0.905	0.543	885.2	1.666
1400	0.99998	0.1938	0.0012	22.998	0.9873	5 681.7	10.837	0.905	0.543	918.6	1.666
1500	0.99999	0.1255	0.0056	22.998	0.9215	5 772.2	10.899	0.905	0.543	950.9	1.666
1600	0.99998	0.0856	0.0211	22.998	0.8639	5 862.8	10.958	0.905	0.543	981.9	1.666
1700	0.99998	0.0610	0.0680	22.998	0.8131	5 953.4	11.013	0.906	0.544	1012	1.665
1800	0.99996	0.0450	0.1935	22.998	0.7679	6 044.2	11.065	0.909	0.547	1040	1.662
1900	0.99989	0.0342	0.4950	22.996	0.7275	6 135.3	11.114	0.915	0.552	1067	1.656
2000	0.99977	0.0267	1.156	22.995	0.6911	6 227.4	11.151	0.926	0.563	1091	1.645
2100	0.99950	0.0213	2.500	22.992	0.6582	6 321.2	11.207	0.950	0.581	1110	1.623
2200	0.99898	0.0172	5.051	22.986	0.6280	6 417.7	11.252	0.987	0.620	1126	1.592
2300	0.99807	0.0142	9.620	22.976	0.6004	6 518.3	11.297	1.049	0.676	1136	1.550
2400	0.99652	0.0118	17.40	22.958	0.5749	6 628.8	11.343	1.146	0.766	1140	1.496
2500	0.99393	0.0100	30.07	22.929	0.5512	6 750.3	11.393	1.293	0.900	1141	1.436
2600	0.99003	0.0085	49.84	22.883	0.5290	6 889.6	11.448	1.504	1.092	1140	1.376
2700	0.98403	0.0072	79.66	22.815	0.5079	7 054.1	11.509	1.801	1.361	1141	1.323
2800	0.97537	0.0062	123.1	22.715	0.4876	7 253.4	11.582	2.207	1.726	1145	1.279
2900	0.96309	0.0053	184.6	22.573	0.4678	7 500.2	11.668	2.749	2.207	1154	1.246
3000	0.94624	0.0045	268.8	22.380	0.4484	7 808.7	11.773	3.534	2.905	1165	1.216
				$p=10^{-3}$ bar							
700	0.97665	233.5	0	23.535	4.041	4 974.7	9.862	2.167	1.601	572.5	1.325
800	0.99513	48.73	0	23.110	3.472	5 123.5	10.061	1.123	0.725	666.3	1.542
1900	0.99860	14.05	0	23.030	3.076	5 225.0	10.183	0.955	0.584	728.6	1.633
1000	0.99948	5.163	0	23.010	2.766	5 318.4	10.285	0.920	0.555	773.9	1.656
1100	0.99977	2.271	0	23.003	2.514	5 409.8	10.372	0.910	0.547	813.4	1.665
200	0.99989	1.143	0	23.001	2.304	5 500.6	10.447	0.907	0.544	850.2	1.665
1300	0.99994	0.6393	0.0002	22.999	2.127	5 591.3	10.519	0.906	0.544	885.1	1.666
1400	0.99996	0.3876	0.0009	22.999	1.975	5 681.7	10.586	0.905	0.543	918.6	1.666
1500	0.99997	0.2509	0.0040	22.999	1.843	5 772.2	10.649	0.905	0.543	950.8	1.666
1600	0.99998	0.1712	0.0149	22.998	1.728	5 862.7	10.707	0.905	0.543	982.0	1.666
1700	0.99998	0.1219	0.0481	22.998	1.626	5 953.3	10.762	0.906	0.544	1012	1.665
1800	0.99996	0.0900	0.1368	22.998	1.536	6 044.0	10.814	0.908	0.546	1041	1.663
1900	0.99992	0.0684	0.3500	22.997	1.455	6 134.9	10.863	0.912	0.550	1067	1.659
2000	0.99983	0.0538	0.8178	22.996	1.382	6 226.6	10.910	0.920	0.557	1093	1.651
2100	0.99964	0.0425	1.768	22.994	1.316	6 319.5	10.955	0.937	0.574	1114	1.634
2200	0.99928	0.0345	3.772	22.989	1.256	6 414.2	10.999	0.964	0.598	1132	1.611
2300	0.99864	0.0284	6.804	22.982	1.201	6 512.6	11.043	1.007	0.638	1146	1.578
2400	0.99754	0.0237	12.31	22.970	1.150	6 616.6	11.087	1.077	0.702	1154	1.533
2500	0.99574	0.0200	21.28	22.949	1.103	6 729.3	11.133	1.181	0.798	1158	1.480
2600	0.99293	0.0170	35.29	22.916	1.060	6 854.4	11.182	1.330	0.934	1159	1.424
2700	0.98871	0.0146	56.46	22.868	1.018	6 997.5	11.236	1.541	1.125	1160	1.370
2800	0.98252	0.0126	87.37	22.797	0.9787	7 165.3	11.297	1.830	1.385	1161	1.321
2900	0.97376	0.0108	131.2	22.696	0.9408	7 366.8	11.368	2.214	1.728	1167	1.281
3000	0.96168	0.0093	191.6	22.557	0.9038	7 612.0	11.451	2.795	2.252	1172	1.242
				$p=5 \cdot 10^{-3}$ bar							
800	0.97659	234.6	0	23.538	17.68	5 064.7	9.413	1.881	1.343	622.3	1.370
900	0.99305	69.46	0	23.158	15.46	5 207.1	9.582	1.149	0.742	705.2	1.538
1000	0.99743	25.71	0	23.057	13.86	5 311.7	9.692	0.979	0.603	764.7	1.621
1100	0.99887	11.33	0	23.024	12.58	5 406.8	9.783	0.932	0.564	809.7	1.650

continued

T, °K	X_1	$X_2 \cdot 10^4$	$X_e \cdot 10^4$	M	$\varrho \cdot 10^4$	i	s	c_p	c_v	u	k
1200	0.99943	5.711	0	23.011	11.53	5 499.1	9.863	0.916	0.552	848.9	1.661
1300	0.99968	3.195	0.0001	23.005	10.64	5 590.4	9.936	0.910	0.547	884.5	1.664
1400	0.99981	1.938	0.0004	23.002	9.875	5 681.2	10.000	0.907	0.545	918.3	1.666
1500	0.99987	1.254	0.0018	23.001	9.216	5 771.9	10.066	0.906	0.544	950.7	1.666
1600	0.99991	0.8558	0.0067	23.000	8.640	5 862.5	10.125	0.906	0.544	981.9	1.666
1700	0.99993	0.6096	0.0215	22.999	8.131	5 953.1	10.180	0.906	0.544	1012	1.666
1800	0.99994	0.4502	0.0612	22.999	7.679	6 043.7	10.231	0.906	0.544	1041	1.665
1900	0.99993	0.3422	0.1565	22.999	7.275	6 134.4	10.280	0.908	0.546	1069	1.663
2000	0.99990	0.2670	0.3657	22.998	6.911	6 225.4	10.327	0.912	0.549	1096	1.659
2100	0.99982	0.2127	0.7906	22.997	6.582	6 317.1	10.372	0.921	0.558	1120	1.650
2200	0.99966	0.1727	1.598	22.995	6.282	6 409.5	10.419	0.932	0.569	1142	1.639
2300	0.99938	0.1424	3.044	22.991	6.008	6 503.6	10.457	0.952	0.586	1162	1.622
2400	0.99889	0.1190	5.508	22.986	5.756	6 600.4	10.498	0.984	0.616	1178	1.596
2500	0.99808	0.1007	9.529	22.976	5.524	6 701.1	10.539	1.031	0.660	1189	1.563
2600	0.99683	0.0858	15.81	22.962	5.308	6 807.5	10.580	1.099	0.722	1197	1.522
2700	0.99492	0.0738	25.33	22.939	5.106	6 922.0	10.624	1.194	0.809	1203	1.477
2800	0.99214	0.0640	39.26	22.908	4.917	7 047.0	10.669	1.326	0.928	1205	1.429
2900	0.98817	0.0557	59.11	22.862	4.738	7 188.7	10.719	1.499	1.084	1208	1.383
3000	0.98267	0.0486	86.62	22.799	4.568	7 349.4	10.773	1.808	1.369	1202	1 321

$p=10^{-2}$ bar

T, °K	X_1	$X_2 \cdot 10^4$	$X_e \cdot 10^4$	M	$\varrho \cdot 10^4$	i	s	c_p	c_v	u	k
900	0.98630	137.0	0	23.313	31.14	5 185.5	9.309	1.374	0.923	686.9	1.469
1000	0.99488	51.16	0	23.116	27.79	5 303.4	9.434	1.052	0.661	755.2	1.585
1100	0.99774	22.62	0	23.050	25.19	5 403.2	9.529	0.959	0.586	805.5	1.634
1200	0.99886	11.41	0	23.024	23.06	5 497.3	9.611	0.928	0.560	847.4	1.656
1300	0.99936	6.386	0	23.013	21.28	5 589.4	9.685	0.916	0.551	883.8	1.662
1400	0.99961	3.873	0.0003	23.007	19.75	5 680.5	9.753	0.910	0.547	917.9	1.664
1500	0.99975	2.508	0.0013	23.004	18.43	5 771.4	9.815	0.908	0.545	950.5	1.666
1600	0.99983	1.711	0.0047	23.002	17.28	5 862.2	9.874	0.906	0.544	981.9	1.666
1700	0.99988	1.219	0.0152	23.001	16.26	5 952.9	9.929	0.906	0.544	1012	1.666
1800	0.99990	0.9004	0.0326	22.999	15.36	6 043.5	9.980	0.906	0.544	1041	1.665
1900	0.99991	0.6844	0.1106	22.999	14.55	6 134.2	10.039	0.907	0.545	1069	1.664
2000	0.99989	0.5339	0.2586	22.999	13.82	6 225.1	10.076	0.910	0.548	1096	1.661
2100	0.99985	0.4255	0.5591	22.998	13.16	6 316.5	10.121	0.917	0.554	1121	1.654
2200	0.99974	0.3455	1.129	22.996	12.56	6 408.4	10.163	0.925	0.562	1144	1.646
2300	0.99954	0.2849	2.156	22.994	12.02	6 501.5	10.205	0.938	0.574	1166	1.633
2400	0.99920	0.2382	3.896	22.990	11.51	6 596.5	10.245	0.962	0.596	1184	1.614
2500	0.99863	0.2016	6.740	22.983	11.05	6 694.4	10.285	0.996	0.627	1199	1.587
2600	0.99774	0.1720	11.18	22.972	10.62	6 796.3	10.325	1.044	0.672	1209	1.554
2700	0.99640	0.1480	17.92	22.957	10.22	6 904.1	10.366	1.112	0.734	1218	1.514
2800	0.99443	0.1286	27.80	22.934	9.848	7 019.8	10.394	1.206	0.819	1223	1.473
2900	0.99161	0.1122	41.07	22.902	9.493	7 146.4	10.452	1.330	0.931	1227	1.429
3000	0.98771	0.09995	61.41	22.857	9.158	7 287.2	10.500	1.574	1.158	1218	1.358

$p=5 \cdot 10^{-2}$ bar

T, °K	X_1	$X_2 \cdot 10^4$	$X_e \cdot 10^4$	M	$\varrho \cdot 10^4$	i	s	c_p	c_v	u	k
900	0.93802	619.8	0	24.423	163.1	5 039.3	8.583	2.662	1.918	636.2	1.320
1000	0.97541	245.9	0	23.563	141.6	5 241.7	8.797	1.561	1.059	713.4	1.442
1100	0.98889	111.1	0	23.253	127.0	5 374.6	8.924	1.164	0.745	780.1	1.546
1200	0.99435	56.54	0	23.128	115.8	5 482.6	9.018	1.018	0.628	836.8	1.622
1300	0.99682	31.77	0	23.071	106.7	5 581.1	9.100	0.960	0.583	878.4	1.646
1400	0.99807	19.31	0.0001	23.042	98.92	5 675.4	9.167	0.934	0.564	915.1	1.657
1500	0.99875	12.51	0.0006	23.027	92.26	6 768.1	9.231	0.921	0.554	949.0	1.662
1600	0.99914	8.545	0.0021	23.018	86.46	5 859.9	9.290	0.914	0.550	981.0	1.664
1700	0.99939	6.089	0.0028	23.012	81.36	5 951.2	9.346	0.911	0.547	1012	1.665
1800	0.99954	4.499	0.0193	23.008	76.82	6 042.2	9.398	0.909	0.546	1041	1.665
1900	0.99965	3.420	0.0495	23.006	72.77	6 133.1	9.447	0.908	0.546	1069	1.665
2000	0.99971	2.669	0.1156	23.004	69.13	6 224.0	9.494	0.909	0.546	1097	1.664
2100	0.99973	2.127	0.2500	23.002	65.83	6 315.2	9.538	0.912	0.550	1123	1.660
2200	0.99972	1.727	0.5052	23.000	62.83	6 406.4	9.581	0.916	0.553	1148	1.656
2300	0.99966	1.425	0.9627	22.999	60.10	6 498.3	9.621	0.922	0.559	1172	1.650
2400	0.99953	1.192	1.742	22.996	57.59	6 591.0	9.661	0.933	0.569	1193	1.639
2500	0.99929	1.009	3.015	22.993	55.28	6 685.2	9.699	0.949	0.584	1212	1.625
2600	0.99891	0.8620	5.006	22.988	53.14	6 781.2	9.736	0.972	0.605	1229	1.606
2700	0.99832	0.7429	8.023	22.982	51.16	6 880.0	9.774	1.003	0.634	1244	1.583

continued

T, °K	X_1	$X_2 \cdot 10^4$	$X_e \cdot 10^4$	M	$\varrho \cdot 10^4$	i	s	c_p	c_v	u	k
2800	0.99745	0.6469	12.45	22.971	49.31	6 982.4	9.811	1.047	0.674	1255	1.554
2900	0.99619	0.5660	18.77	22.956	47.58	7 090.0	9.849	1.104	0.726	1264	1.521
3000	0.99444	0.4982	27.56	22.936	45.95	7 203.9	9.888	1.262	0.876	1252	1.440
$p=10^{-1}$ bar											
1000	0.95305	469.5	0	24.078	289.4	5 173.6	8.487	2.052	1.431	690.1	1.378
1100	0.97826	217.4	0	23.498	256.8	5 340.9	8.647	1.391	0.918	760.4	1.485
1200	0.98882	111.8	0	23.255	232.9	5 464.8	8.755	1.124	0.706	826.9	1.593
1300	0.99369	63.13	0	23.143	214.0	5 570.9	8.840	1.013	0.621	872.7	1.630
1400	0.99615	38.47	0.0001	23.086	198.2	5 669.2	8.913	0.962	0.584	911.9	1.648
1500	0.99750	24.97	0.0004	23.055	184.8	5 764.0	8.978	0.937	0.566	947.2	1.657
1600	0.99829	17.06	0.0015	23.037	173.1	5 857.1	9.038	0.924	0.556	979.9	1.662
1700	0.99878	12.16	0.0048	23.026	162.8	5 949.2	9.094	0.917	0.551	1011	1.664
1800	0.99909	8.989	0.0137	23.018	153.7	6 040.7	9.146	0.913	0.548	1041	1.665
1900	0.99931	6.836	0.0350	23.013	145.6	6 131.9	9.196	0.911	0.547	1069	1.665
2000	0.99941	5.334	0.0818	23.010	138.3	6 223.0	9.242	0.910	0.547	1097	1.665
2100	0.99954	4.252	0.1768	23.007	131.7	6 314.3	9.287	0.913	0.550	1123	1.661
2200	0.99958	3.454	0.3572	23.005	125.7	6 405.4	9.329	0.914	0.552	1148	1.658
2300	0.99958	2.849	0.6807	23.003	120.2	6 497.1	9.370	0.918	0.555	1173	1.654
2400	0.99971	2.384	1.232	23.000	115.2	6 589.4	9.409	0.927	0.563	1195	1.646
2500	0.99937	2.019	2.132	22.998	110.6	6 682.7	9.447	0.938	0.574	1216	1.635
2600	0.99912	1.725	3.540	22.993	106.3	6 775.5	9.484	0.955	0.585	1234	1.620
2700	0.99872	1.435	5.675	22.988	102.3	6 874.0	9.521	0.977	0.609	1251	1.602
2800	0.99811	1.296	8.806	22.981	98.66	6 973.3	9.557	1.009	0.639	1265	1.579
2900	0.99723	1.134	13.28	22.970	95.21	7 076.4	9.593	1.051	0.677	1276	1.552
3000	0.99600	0.9995	19.50	22.955	91.98	7 184.1	9.629	1.188	0.809	1263	1.468
$p=2 \cdot 10^{-1}$ bar											
1000	0.91370	864.0	0	24.983	600.6	5 060.5	8.138	2.715	1.913	665.7	1.331
1100	0.95827	417.3	0	23.958	523.6	5 279.4	8.348	1.768	1.199	736.9	1.422
1200	0.97812	218.8	0	23.501	470.8	5 430.8	8.480	1.317	0.848	813.7	1.559
1300	0.98753	124.7	0.00001	23.285	430.6	5 551.0	8.576	1.113	0.693	863.5	1.606
1400	0.99236	76.35	00.0006	23.174	397.9	5 656.8	8.654	1.017	0.622	906.3	1.634
1500	0.99503	49.69	0.0003	23.112	370.4	5 755.9	8.723	0.969	0.588	943.8	1.650
1600	0.99660	34.00	0.0010	23.076	346.7	5 851.4	8.784	0.944	0.569	977.9	1.658
1700	0.99757	24.28	0.0034	23.054	326.0	5 945.1	8.841	0.930	0.559	1010	1.662
1800	0.99820	17.95	0.0097	23.039	307.7	6 037.7	8.894	0.921	0.554	1040	1.664
1900	0.99863	13.65	0.0247	23.029	291.4	6 129.6	8.944	0.916	0.550	1069	1.665
2000	0.99891	11.05	0.0593	23.022	276.5	6 196.9	8.990	0.914	0.544	1095	1.665
2100	0.99913	8.760	0.1320	23.016	263.5	6 297.8	9.034	0.914	0.542	1121	1.663
2200	0.99926	6.904	0.2526	23.013	251.5	6 404.0	9.078	0.915	0.551	1149	1.660
2300	0.99933	5.610	0.4813	23.010	240.5	6 495.6	9.119	0.917	0.553	1174	1.657
2400	0.99935	4.694	0.856	23.007	229.5	6 600.0	9.159	0.923	0.559	1197	1.641
2500	0.99929	4.036	1.507	23.004	221.2	6 680.5	9.196	0.932	0.567	1213	1.642
2600	0.99915	3.450	2.503	23.000	212.7	6 774.3	9.232	0.943	0.578	1238	1.631
2700	0.99890	2.974	4.013	22.996	204.8	6 869.5	9.268	0.960	0.593	1257	1.617
2800	0.99850	2.593	6.228	22.990	197.4	6 966.6	9.304	0.983	0.615	1272	1.598
2900	0.99789	2.272	9.392	22.982	190.5	7 066.5	9.339	1.013	0.643	1286	1.576
3000	0.99704	2.003	13.80	22.971	184.1	7 169.7	9.373	1.136	0.762	1273	1.491
$p=5 \cdot 10^{-1}$ bar											
1100	0.90662	933.8	0	25.145	1 374	5 131.0	7.981	2.485	1.711	702.5	1.356
1200	0.94855	514.5	0	24.181	1 211	5 340.6	8.108	1.768	1.156	794.6	1.529
1300	0.96993	300.7	0	23.690	1 095	5 495.5	8.208	1.374	0.875	846.8	1.571
1400	0.98133	186.7	0	23.427	1 006	5 621.4	8.302	1.168	0.723	893.9	1.607
1500	0.98776	122.4	0.0002	23.280	932.8	5 732.2	8.378	1.060	0.649	935.5	1.633
1600	0.99158	84.16	0.0007	23.191	871.2	5 835.0	8.445	1.000	0.607	972.6	1.648
1700	0.99398	60.23	0.0021	23.137	818.0	5 933.2	8.504	0.966	0.583	1006	1.657
1800	0.99553	44.63	0.0061	23.100	771.3	6 028.7	8.559	0.946	0.569	1038	1.661
1900	0.99659	33.99	0.0156	23.076	729.9	6 122.7	8.609	0.933	0.561	1067	1.664
2000	0.99734	26.56	0.0365	23.059	692.9	6 215.7	8.657	0.926	0.556	1096	1.665
2100	0.99787	21.19	0.0790	23.047	659.6	6 308.2	8.702	0.923	0.555	1123	1.663
2200	0.99824	17.22	0.1596	23.037	629.3	6 400.2	8.745	0.920	0.554	1149	1.662
2300	0.99852	14.21	0.3043	23.030	601.8	6492.2	8.786	0.920	0.554	1175	1.661

continued

T, °K	X_1	$X_2 \cdot 10^4$	$X_e \cdot 10^4$	M	$\varrho \cdot 10^4$	i	s	c_p	c_v	u	k
2400	0.99870	11.90	0.5508	23.024	576.6	6 584.3	8.825	0.923	0.557	1198	1.656
2500	0.99880	10.08	0.9532	23.018	553.4	6 664.4	8.863	0.928	0.563	1221	1.649
2600	0.99882	8.619	1.583	23.014	532.0	6 770.1	8.899	0.935	0.570	1242	1.641
2700	0.99874	7.435	2.006	23.009	512.1	6 861.3	8.931	0.942	0.578	1264	1.631
2800	0.99856	6.484	3.939	23.004	493.8	6 959.6	8.970	0.961	0.594	1280	1.617
2900	0.99824	5.684	5.941	22.997	476.6	7 056.8	9.004	0.983	0.613	1296	1.601
3000	0.99775	5.015	8.728	22.989	460.6	7 156.2	9.038	1.090	0.720	1282	1.514
					$p=8 \cdot 10^{-1}$ bar						
1100	0.86424	1358	0	26.120	2 283	5 019.3	7.647	2.858	1.965	683.3	1.333
1200	0.92219	778.1	0	24.787	1 986	5 264.3	7.860	2.082	1.360	785.1	1.531
1300	0.95350	465.0	0	24.067	1 780	5 445.4	8.006	1.584	1.015	837.4	1.560
1400	0.97077	292.3	0.00003	23.670	1 626	5 588.1	8.112	1.300	0.816	885.7	1.594
1500	0.98069	193.1	0.0001	23.442	1 503	5 709.6	8.196	1.142	0.704	929.2	1.622
1600	0.98667	133.3	0.0005	23.305	1 401	5 819.0	8.266	1.053	0.642	968.2	1.641
1700	0.99043	95.68	0.0017	23.218	1 313	5 921.5	8.329	1.001	0.606	1003	1.653
1800	0.99290	71.03	0.0048	23.169	1 237	6 019.9	8.385	0.970	0.584	1036	1.660
1900	0.99458	54.17	0.0123	23.122	1 170	6 115.9	8.437	0.950	0.571	1066	1.664
2000	0.99563	42.81	0.0275	23.098	1 113	6 210.3	8.489	0.938	0.564	1084	1.666
2100	0.99651	33.09	0.0525	23.076	1 054	6 300.1	8.533	0.931	0.559	1121	1.665
2200	0.99722	27.50	0.1262	23.061	1 008	6 396.5	8.574	0.926	0.557	1149	1.664
2300	0.99768	22.71	0.2404	23.050	963.7	6 489.0	8.615	0.924	0.556	1175	1.662
2400	0.99801	19.01	0.4353	23.041	923.1	6 581.5	8.654	0.925	0.558	1199	1.658
2500	0.99824	16.11	0.7534	23.033	886.0	6 674.3	8.692	0.928	0.562	1222	1.653
2600	0.99837	13.78	1.251	23.027	851.7	6 767.5	8.729	0.934	0.567	1243	1.646
2700	0.99841	11.89	2.006	23.021	819.9	6 861.3	8.764	0.942	0.575	1264	1.637
2800	0.99834	10.37	3.114	23.015	790.4	6 956.1	8.799	0.954	0.587	1282	1.625
2900	0.99815	9.092	4.697	23.008	762.9	7 052.5	8.832	0.971	0.603	1299	1.610
3000	0.99782	8.025	6.901	23.000	737.3	7 150.6	8.866	1.075	0.705	1286	1.524
					$p=1$ bar						
1200	0.90611	938.9	0	25.157	2 520	5 219.5	7.749	2.240	1.511	780.6	1.536
1300	0.94313	568.7	0	24.306	2 247	5 414.6	7.905	1.703	1.120	832.9	1.559
1400	0.96398	360.2	0	23.826	2 046	5 567.1	8.019	1.380	0.884	881.6	1.590
1500	0.97609	239.1	0.0001	23.548	1 887	5 695.0	8.107	1.194	0.738	925.8	1.618
1600	0.98344	165.6	0.0005	23.379	1 756	5 808.6	8.180	1.087	0.664	965.6	1.638
1700	0.98810	119.0	0.0015	23.272	1 646	5 913.9	8.244	1.024	0.620	1002	1.651
1800	0.99115	88.47	0.0043	23.201	1 549	6 014.1	8.302	0.985	0.594	1035	1.659
1900	0.99324	67.53	0.0110	23.153	1 465	6 111.4	8.354	0.961	0.578	1065	1.663
2000	0.99471	52.84	0.0258	23.119	1 390	6 266.7	8.403	0.945	0.567	1095	1.666
2100	0.99577	42.20	0.0558	23.095	1 322	6 300.9	8.449	0.937	0.563	1122	1.664
2200	0.99654	34.33	0.1128	23.077	1 261	6 394.1	8.492	0.931	0.559	1148	1.664
2300	0.99712	28.35	0.2149	23.063	1 205	6 487.0	8.534	0.927	0.557	1175	1.663
2400	0.99755	23.74	0.3892	23.052	1 154	6 579.7	8.573	0.927	0.559	1199	1.659
2500	0.99785	20.12	0.6737	23.043	1 108	6 662.6	8.611	0.929	0.562	1222	1.654
2600	0.99805	17.21	1.119	23.035	1 065	6 765.8	8.647	0.934	0.567	1244	1.647
2700	0.99816	14.85	1.794	23.028	1 025	6 859.7	8.683	0.941	0.574	1265	1.640
2800	0.99815	12.96	2.785	23.021	988.3	6 954.3	8.717	0.952	0.585	1283	1.628
2900	0.99802	11.36	4.201	23.014	953.9	7 050.4	8.751	0.967	0.599	1301	1.615
3000	0.99776	10.03	6.172	23.007	921.8	7 408.0	8.784	1.069	0.700	1287	1.528
					$p=2$ bar						
1300	0.89709	1029	0	25.365	4 691	5 284.7	7.573	2.113	1.344	818.6	1.572
1400	0.93257	674.3	0	24.549	4 216	5 473.4	7.713	1.690	1.064	868.1	1.589
1500	0.95430	457.0	0.0001	24.049	3 854	5 627.6	7.820	1.412	0.877	914.0	1.610
1600	0.96792	320.8	0.0003	23.736	3 566	5 759.3	7.905	1.236	0.759	956.0	1.630
1700	0.97673	232.6	0.0011	23.533	3 328	5 877.1	7.976	1.127	0.685	994.4	1.645
1800	0.98261	173.9	0.0030	23.398	3 125	5 986.1	8.038	1.058	0.639	1029	1.656
1900	0.98667	133.2	0.0078	23.304	2 949	6 089.5	8.094	1.012	0.609	1062	1.663
2000	0.98954	104.6	0.0182	23.238	2 793	6 189.2	8.146	0.983	0.590	1092	1.663
2100	0.99162	83.71	0.0394	23.190	2 654	6 286.7	8.193	0.965	0.579	1120	1.667
2200	0.99316	68.20	0.0796	23.154	2 530	6 382.3	8.237	0.952	0.571	1148	1.667
2300	0.99433	56.38	0.1518	23.127	2 417	6 476.2	8.280	0.942	0.566	1174	1.667
2400	0.99521	47.27	0.2749	23.106	2 314	6 571.1	8.320	0.938	0.564	1199	1.663

continued

T, °K	X_1	$X_2 \cdot 10^4$	$X_e \cdot 10^4$	M	$\varrho \cdot 10^4$	i	s	c_p	c_v	u	k
2500	0.99589	40.09	0.4759	23.089	2 220	6 664.9	8.358	0.937	0.565	1223	1.659
2600	0.99641	34.31	0.7905	23.075	2 134	6 758.8	8.395	0.938	0.567	1245	1.653
2700	0.99678	29.62	1.268	23.063	2 054	6 852.9	8.430	0.942	0.572	1267	1.647
2800	0.99702	25.85	1.968	23.052	1 979	6 947.4	8.465	0.949	0.580	1286	1.637
2900	0.99714	22.68	2.969	23.043	1 910	7 003.1	8.498	0.960	0.590	1305	1.626
3000	0.99712	20.03	4.363	23.034	1 846	7 139.6	8.531	1.056	0.686	1291	1.539
					p=4 bar						
1400	0.87994	1201	0	25.759	8 847	5 328.2	7.380	2.046	1.271	853.0	1.609
1500	0.91582	841.8	0	24.934	7 992	5 515.2	7.509	1.708	1.054	900.6	1.621
1600	0.93955	604.5	0.0002	24.388	7 329	5 673.1	7.611	1.464	0.896	944.4	1.634
1700	0.95548	445.2	0.0007	24.022	6 794	5 810.5	7.694	1.296	0.786	984.7	1.647
1800	0.96635	336.4	0.0021	23.771	6 349	5 934.0	7.765	1.182	0.713	1022	1.658
1900	0.97402	259.7	0.0055	23.595	5 971	6 048.1	7.826	1.104	0.663	1056	1.666
2000	0.97950	204.9	0.0128	23.469	5 642	6 155.9	7.888	1.052	0.629	1088	1.671
2100	0.98353	164.7	0.0277	23.377	5 352	6 259.3	7.932	1.017	0.608	1118	1.672
2200	0.98653	134.6	0.0561	23.307	5 094	6 359.4	7.979	0.991	0.593	1146	1.673
2300	0.98883	111.5	0.1070	23.254	4 861	6 457.6	8.022	0.973	0.582	1173	1.673
2400	0.99059	93.66	0.1939	23.213	4 650	6 554.4	8.064	0.962	0.576	1198	1.670
2500	0.99198	79.55	0.3359	23.180	4 458	6 650.4	8.103	0.955	0.573	1223	1.666
2600	0.99307	68.16	0.5580	23.153	4 282	6 745.8	8.140	0.952	0.573	1245	1.661
2700	0.99393	58.91	0.8951	23.131	4 119	6 841.1	7.176	0.951	0.574	1268	1.656
2800	0.99458	51.46	1.390	23.113	3 969	6 936.4	8.211	0.954	0.580	1288	1.647
2900	0.99506	45.18	2.097	23.097	3 829	7 032.3	8.244	0.960	0.587	1308	1.637
3000	0.99539	39.93	3.082	23.083	3 699	7 128.8	8.277	1.052	0.679	1294	1.550
					p=6 bar						
1400	0.83704	1630	0	26.746	13 778	5 219.6	7.173	2.219	1.365	841.4	1.626
1500	0.88270	1173	0	25.696	12 355	5 424.6	7.315	1.889	1.154	891.4	1.636
1600	0.91416	858.4	0.0002	24.972	11 257	5 599.7	7.428	1.623	0.986	936.6	1.646
1700	0.93592	640.8	0.0006	24.472	10 382	5 751.6	7.520	1.425	0.861	978.1	1.655
1800	0.95111	488.8	0.0017	24.122	9 665	5 886.6	7.597	1.283	0.771	1016	1.664
1900	0.96199	380.1	0.0044	23.872	9 061	6 009.7	7.664	1.183	0.708	1052	1.671
2000	0.96986	301.4	0.0104	23.691	8 543	6 124.4	7.723	1.112	0.663	1085	1.677
2100	0.97568	243.1	0.0256	23.557	8 090	6 233.2	7.776	1.064	0.634	1115	1.678
2200	0.98006	199.2	0.0457	23.456	7 689	6 337.5	7.824	1.028	0.612	1144	1.679
2300	0.98343	165.5	0.0872	23.378	7 331	6 439.0	7.870	1.002	0.597	1172	1.679
2400	0.98605	139.2	0.1580	23.318	7 007	6 538.4	7.912	0.985	0.588	1198	1.676
2500	0.98811	118.4	0.2737	23.270	6 713	6 636.4	7.952	0.974	0.582	1223	1.672
2600	0.98975	101.8	0.4549	23.230	6 444	6 733.5	7.990	0.966	0.579	1246	1.667
2700	0.99106	87.85	0.7298	23.198	6 197	6 830.0	8.026	0.962	0.579	1269	1.662
2800	0.99209	76.80	1.133	23.172	5 969	6 926.2	8.061	0.963	0.582	1289	1.654
2900	0.99291	67.48	1.711	23.149	5 757	7 022.8	8.095	0.966	0.588	1309	1.645
3000	0.99373	59.67	2.514	23.129	5 520	7 119.7	8.128	1.054	0.677	1296	1.557
					p=8 bar						
1500	0.85370	1463	0	26.363	16 901	5 349.7	7.133	2.003	1.215	883.4	1.648
1600	0.89122	1088	0.0002	25.500	15 326	5 536.3	7.294	1.737	1.048	930.2	1.658
1700	0.91783	821.7	0.0005	24.888	14 078	5 699.0	7.392	1.526	0.916	972.8	1.665
1800	0.93677	632.2	0.0015	24.452	13 063	5 843.2	7.475	1.367	0.817	1012	1.672
1900	0.95052	494.8	0.0038	24.135	12 216	5 973.9	7.505	1.251	0.745	1048	1.679
2000	0.96058	394.2	0.0090	23.905	11 493	6 094.7	7.607	1.166	0.693	1082	1.683
2100	0.96808	319.1	0.0195	23.732	10 874	6 208.3	7.663	1.107	0.657	1113	1.684
2200	0.97377	262.2	0.0394	23.601	10 316	6 316.6	7.713	1.062	0.630	1143	1.685
2300	0.97816	218.3	0.0753	23.500	9 825	6 420.9	7.760	1.030	0.611	1171	1.685
2400	0.98158	183.9	0.1365	23.421	9 384	6 522.8	7.803	1.007	0.599	1197	1.682
2500	0.98429	156.6	9.2366	23.358	8 985	6 622.8	7.844	0.991	0.591	1222	1.678
2600	0.98647	134.5	0.3933	23.302	8 620	6 721.4	7.882	0.980	0.586	1246	1.673
2700	0.98823	116.5	0.6311	23.264	8 286	6 819.3	7.919	0.973	0.584	1269	1.668
2800	0.98962	101.9	0.9804	23.230	7 978	6 916.5	7.955	0.972	0.585	1290	1.660
2900	0.99074	89.58	1.479	23.201	7 693	7 013.8	7.989	0.973	0.589	1310	1.650
3000	0.99164	79.26	2.175	23.175	7 429	7 111.2	8.022	1.059	0.677	1297	1.563

continued

$T, °K$	X_1	$X_2 \cdot 10^4$	$X_e \cdot 10^4$	M	$\varrho \cdot 10^4$	i	s	c_p	c_v	u	k
					$p=10$ bar						
1500	0.82798	1720	0	26.954	21 600	5 286.3	7.061	2.075	1.252	875.9	1.657
1600	0.87033	1297	0	25.980	19 518	5 480.8	7.187	1.820	1.091	924.4	1.668
1700	0.90102	989.8	0.0001	25.274	17 871	5 651.7	7.290	1.605	0.958	968.1	1.675
1800	0.92323	767.6	0.0013	24.763	16 537	5 803.4	7.377	1.437	0.855	1008	1.681
1900	0.93956	604.3	0.0034	24.387	15 429	5 940.5	7.451	1.309	0.776	1045	1.686
2000	0.95164	483.6	0.0080	24.110	14 491	6 066.6	7.516	1.214	0.718	1080	1.690
2100	0.96437	356.3	0.0183	23.817	13 686	6 196.3	7.616	1.136	0.676	1112	1.690
2200	0.96762	323.7	0.0352	23.742	12 972	6 296.1	7.625	1.093	0.647	1142	1.691
2300	0.97269	269.9	0.0672	23.619	12 344	6 403.5	7.673	1.055	0.624	1170	1.691
2400	0.97719	227.8	0.1218	23.522	11 781	6 507.6	7.718	1.028	0.609	1197	1.688
2500	0.98053	194.3	0.2112	23.444	11 272	6 609.5	7.759	1.008	0.599	1222	1.684
2600	0.98322	167.0	0.3512	23.381	10 810	6 709.7	7.798	0.994	0.592	1246	1.678
2700	0.98541	144.8	0.5637	23.330	10 386	6 808.8	7.836	0.985	0.588	1269	1.673
2800	0.98715	126.7	0.8758	23.287	9 997	6 907.0	7.872	0.981	0.589	1290	1.664
2900	0.98859	111.5	1.322	23.251	9 638	7 005.2	7.906	0.980	0.592	1311	1.656
3000	0.98974	98.70	1.944	23.220	9 304	7 103.2	7.939	1.064	0.678	1298	1.568

Viscosity $\eta \cdot 10^7$ ($N \cdot s/m^2$) for sodium vapor [37]

$T, °K$	For mon-atomic vapor	p, bar				At saturation
		0,5	1	2	5	
800	183					
900	201					206
1000	221					230
1100	240	252				253
1200	258	265	271			275
1300	276	281	285	293		299
1400	294	297	300	306	320	322
1500	312	314	316	320	331	346

Viscosity η of liquid sodium [37]

$T, °K$	T_{melt}	400	500	600	700	800	900	1000
$\eta \cdot 10^3$, $N \cdot s/m^2$	0.696	0.608	0.424	0.328	0.269	0.230	0.202	0.181
$T, °K$	1100	1200	1300	1400	1500	1600	1700	1800
$\eta \cdot 10^3$, $N \cdot s/m^2$	0.165	0.151	0.141	0.132	0.124	0.118	0.112	0.107

Thermal conductivity $\lambda \cdot 10^3$ (W/m · deg) of sodium vapor [34]

$T, °K$	For mon-atomic vapor	p, bar												At saturation
		0,001	0,005	0,01	0,05	0,1	0,2	0,3	0,5	1	2	6	10	
700	20.1													27.7
800	23.0	23.0	28.8											34.3
900	25.8	25.8	27.1	28.5	39.8									40.6
1000	28.7	28.7	29.2	29.6	33.2	37.7								45.5
1100	31.6	31.6	31.8	32.0	33.4	35.1	38.4	41.8	47.0					49.2
1200	34.6	34.6	34.7	34.8	35.4	36.2	37.8	39.4	42.2	48.1				52.2
1300	37.6	37.6	37.6	37.7	38.0	38.4	39.2	40.1	41.6	45.2	50.9			54.7
1400	40.5	40.5	40.5	40.6	40.8	41.2	41.7	42.2	43.0	45.6	49.2	56.4		57.0
1500	43.5	43.5	43.5	43.6	43.7	44.0	44.4	44.8	45.2	46.4	48.4	54.1	58.5	59.2

Thermal conductivity λ of liquid sodium [37]

T, °K	371	400	500	600	700	800	900	1000	1100
λ, W/m · deg	86.0	84.7	80.0	75.4	70.7	64.9	61.4	56.7	52.1

Surface tension σ (dyne/cm) of sodium [31]

t, °C	σ	t, °C	σ	t, °C	σ	t, °C	σ
98	198	400	167.8	800	127.8	1200	87.8
100	197.8	500	157.8	900	117.8	1300	77.8
200	187.8	600	147.8	1000	107.8	1400	67.8
300	177.8	700	137.8	1100	97.8	1500	57.8

POTASSIUM (K)

Atomic weight 39.100

$T_{melt} = 336.4$ °K; $T_{boil} = 1032.2$ °K at 760 mm Hg; $T_{cr} = 2250$ ° K;
$p_{cr} = 160$ bar; $\rho_{cr} = 160$ kg/m³

Thermodynamic properties of liquid potassium at saturation [28]: ρ (kg/m³), c_p (kJ/kg · deg), i (kJ/kg), s (kJ/kg · deg) and z, (kJ/kg)

T, °K	p, bar	ϱ'	c_p'	i'	s'	ч
336.4	$1.37 \cdot 10^{-9}$	828	0.822	93.75	1.9276	2233
400	$1.837 \cdot 10^{-7}$	814	0.805	145.5	2.0684	2196.4
450	$3.209 \cdot 10^{-6}$	802	0.794	185.6	2.1629	2180.6
500	$3.128 \cdot 10^{-5}$	790	0.785	225.1	2.2458	2164.9
550	$1.992 \cdot 10^{-4}$	778	0.777	264.0	2.3204	2148.1
600	$9.258 \cdot 10^{-4}$	767	0.771	302.7	2.3877	2129.8
650	$3.380 \cdot 10^{-3}$	755	0.766	341.1	2.4493	2110.0
700	$1.022 \cdot 10^{-2}$	743	0.762	379.4	2.5059	2088.6
750	$2.658 \cdot 10^{-2}$	731	0.761	417.5	2.5585	2066.1
800	$6.116 \cdot 10^{-2}$	720	0.761	455.5	2.6076	2042.6
850	0.1274	708	0.762	493.6	2.6538	2018.3
900	0.2441	696	0.769	531.7	2.6973	1993.4
950	0.4357	684	0.780	570.4	2.7392	1968.2
1000	0.7322	672	0.792	609.7	2.7796	1942.3
1050	1.217	659	0.805	649.7	2.8187	1916.1
1100	1.864	647	0.819	690.3	2.8564	1890.0
1150	2.745	635	0.832	731.5	2.8930	1863.3
1200	3.913	623	0.846	773.5	2.9287	1836.9
1250	5.415	612	0.859	816.1	2.9635	1810.3
1300	7.304	598	0.873	859.5	2.9975	1783.6
1350	9.628	586	0.886	903.4	3.0307	1757.3
1400	12.44	574	0.899	948.0	3.0631	1730.8

Thermodynamic properties of saturated potassium vapor [28]: Diatomic molecule fraction X_2, molecular weight M, ρ (kg/m^3), c_p and c_v (kJ/kg · deg), i (kJ/kg), s (kJ/kg · deg) and u (m/s)

T, °K	X_2	M	ϱ''	c_p''	c_v''	i''	s''	u
400	0	39.102	$2{,}159 \cdot 10^{-7}$	0,5319	0.3192	2341.9	7.5594	376.6
450	$1.670 \cdot 10^{-3}$	39.167	$3{,}357 \cdot 10^{-6}$	0.6095	0.3868	2366.2	7.0088	387.7
500	$3.622 \cdot 10^{-3}$	39.244	$2{,}951 \cdot 10^{-5}$	0.6698	0.4376	2390,0	6,5756	402,0
550	$6.728 \cdot 10^{-3}$	39.365	$1.714 \cdot 10^{-4}$	0.7420	0.4966	2412,2	6,2261	415.3
600	$1.110 \cdot 10^{-2}$	39.536	$7.333 \cdot 10^{-4}$	0.8194	0.5576	2432,5	5.9374	428.4
650	$1.677 \cdot 10^{-2}$	39.758	$2{,}485 \cdot 10^{-3}$	0,8953	0,6150	2451.2	5,6956	441.5
700	$2.371 \cdot 10^{-2}$	40.029	$7{,}026 \cdot 10^{-3}$	0.9646	0.6645	2468,0	5,4897	454.5
750	$3.171 \cdot 10^{-2}$	40,342	$1.719 \cdot 10^{-2}$	1.022	0.7030	2483,6	5.3133	467.6
800	$4.048 \cdot 10^{-2}$	40.685	$3{,}739 \cdot 10^{-2}$	1,066	0,7290	2498.1	5.1609	480.6
850	$4.996 \cdot 10^{-2}$	41.055	$7.397 \cdot 10^{-2}$	1.097	0.7444	2511,9	5,0283	493.4
900	$5.979 \cdot 10^{-2}$	41.440	0.1351	1.116	0.7498	2525,2	4.9122	506.0
950	$6.976 \cdot 10^{-2}$	41.830	0.2306	1.123	0.7470	2538.6	4,8109	518,4
1000	$7.965 \cdot 10^{-2}$	42.217	0.3716	1.121	0.7383	2552.0	4.7220	530.6
1050	$8.940 \cdot 10^{-2}$	42.598	0,5933	1.113	0,7255	2565,8	4.6435	542.6
1100	$9.879 \cdot 10^{-2}$	42.965	0.8751	1.100	0.7100	2580.0	4,5743	554,4
1150	0.1077	43.315	1.244	1.083	0.6923	2594.8	4.5133	556.1
1200	0.1161	43,641	1.711	1.064	0.6739	2610.2	4.4593	577.6
1250	0.1238	43.944	2,282	1.043	0.6552	2626.4	4,4118	589.1
1300	0.1310	44,223	2,985	1.022	0,6368	2643.1	4.3695	600,4
1350	0.1374	44,474	3.812	1.001	0,6187	2660.7	4.3324	611.7
1400	0.1431	44.698	4.832	0.9796	0.6013	2678.8	4,2994	623.0

Saturated vapor pressure for potassium above 10 bar [417]

T, °K	p, bar	T, °K	p, bar	T, °K	p, bar	T, °K	p, bar
1450	16,1	1650	35,6	1850	65,4	2050	105,6
1500	20,0	1700	42,0	1900	74,5	2100	117,2
1550	24,6	1750	49,2	1950	84,3	2150	129,4
1600	29,8	1800	57,0	2000	94,7	2170	134,4

Thermodynamic properties of potassium at different temperatures and pressures [28]: Molar fractions of monatomic, diatomic and electronic components X_1, X_2 and X_e, molecular weight M, ρ (kg/m³), c_p and c_v (kJ/kg · deg), i (kJ/kg), s (kJ/kg · deg), u (m/s) and adiabatic exponent k

T, °K	X_1	$X_2 \cdot 10^6$	$X_e \cdot 10^4$	M	$\varrho \cdot 10^4$	c_p	c_v	i	s	u	k
				$p=10^{-5}$ bar							
600	0.99988	122,6	0	39,107	0.0784	0,5352	0.3199	2 448,1	6.926	461.9	1.660
700	0.99998	24,34	0	39,103	0.0702	0,5324	0,3197	2 501.5	7.008	497.8	1.665
800	0.99999	7,190	0	39.102	0,0588	0.5320	0.3194	2 554.7	7.079	532.4	1.666
900	0.999997	2,769	0	39,102	0,0522	0.5319	0.3193	2 607,9	7,142	565.7	1,666
1000	0.999998	1,284	0,0001	39,102	0,0470	0.5319	0,3192	2 661.1	7.197	595.5	1,667
1100	0.999999	0,6808	0,0013	39,102	0,0427	0.5320	0,3192	27 14.3	7,247	624.5	1,666
1200	0.999998	0,3982	0.0099	39,102	0,0392	0.5322	0,3194	2 767.5	7,294	652.2	1,666
1300	0.99999	0,2520	0.0549	39,102	0,0362	0.5329	0.3201	2 820.8	7.336	678.6	1,665
1400	0.99995	0,1690	0.2405	39.101	0.0336	0.5357	0,3328	2 874,2	7,376	703.1	1,660
1500	0.99983	0.1189	0.8698	39,099	0.0313	0.5440	0,3306	2 928.0	7,414	724.7	1,646
1600	0.99946	0,0869	2.694	39,091	0.0294	0.5651	0,3504	2 983,5	7,450	741.1	1,613
1700	0.99853	0,0656	7.328	39.073	0.0276	0.6142	0.3963	3 042,2	7,484	749.0	1.550
1800	0.99642	0,0508	17.91	39,032	0.0261	0.7127	0.4878	3 108,0	7.522	748.7	1,461
1900	0.99201	0.0402	39.93	38.946	0.0246	0.8966	0,6575	3 187,6	7.562	743.9	1.364
2000	0.98356	0.0324	82.22	38,780	0.0233	1,217	0.9510	3 291,8	7.616	741.0	1.280
2100	0.96841	0,0250	157.9	38.484	0.0220	1,745	1.429	3 437.9	7.689	744.6	1.221
2200	0.94302	0.0207	284.9	37.988	0.0208	2.568	2.162	3 650.7	7.788	756.5	1.188
2300	0.90304	0,0152	484.8	37,206	0.0194	3,791	3.225	3 964.8	7.928	777.4	1.175
2400	0.84402	0.0113	779.9	36.052	0.0181	5.520	4,679	4 425.4	8.123	808.3	1.180
2500	0.76262	0,0079	1187	34,461	0.0166	7.834	6.536	5 088.3	8,393	850.5	1,198
2600	0.65874	0,0051	1706	32,430	0.0150	10.68	8.691	6 010.3	8.754	905.4	1.229
2700	0.53752	0,0030	2312	30.060	0.0134	13.72	10.85	7 231.6	9.215	972.2	1.265
2800	0.41023	0,0015	2949	27,571	0.0118	16.16	12.48	8 735.3	9.761	1046	1.294
2900	0.29176	0.0007	3541	25,255	0.0105	16.91	12.97	10 406	10.347	1116	1.304
3000	0,19454	0,0003	4028	23.354	0.0094	15.42	11.96	12 040	10.901	1174	1,289
				$p=5 \cdot 10^{-5}$ bar							
600	0.99939	606.8	0	39.126	0.3921	0,5483	0,3330	2 447,2	6.583	460.1	1.645
700	0.99988	121.7	0	39.107	0.3360	0,5343	0,3212	2 501.4	6.666	497.4	1.663
800	0.99996	35.95	0	39.102	0.2939	0,5325	0.3198	2 554.7	6.737	532,2	1.665
900	0.99999	13,85	0	39.102	0.2611	0,5320	0.3195	2 607.9	6.800	564,9	1.666
1000	0.99999	6,417	0.0001	39.102	0.2350	0.5319	0,3192	2 661.1	6.854	595,5	1.667
1100	0.999996	3,397	0.0006	39.102	0.2136	0,5320	0.3192	2 714,3	6.905	624,5	1.667
1200	0.999997	1,994	0.0044	39.102	0.1958	0.5320	0.3193	2 767,5	6,951	652,3	1.666
1300	0.99999	1,260	0.0246	39.102	0.1807	0,5324	0,3196	2 820.8	6.994	678.8	1.666
1400	0.99998	0.7958	0.1076	39,101	0.1678	0.5336	0.3208	2 874,1	7,033	703,9	1.663

continued

T, °K	X_1	$X_2 \cdot 10^6$	$X_e \cdot 10^4$	M	$\varrho \cdot 10^4$	c_p	c_v	i	s	u	k
1500	0.99992	0.5944	0.3890	39.100	0.1566	0.5374	0.3243	2 927.1	7.070	727.2	1.657
1600	0.99976	0.4343	1.204	39.097	0.1468	0.5468	0.3331	2 981.8	7.105	747.5	1.641
1700	0.99934	0.3274	3.279	39.089	0.1381	0.5694	0.3549	3 037.5	7.139	762.5	1.607
1800	0.99840	0.2531	8.016	39.071	0.1305	0.6141	0.3959	3 096.4	7.173	771.0	1.551
1900	0.99652	0.1997	17.89	39.032	0.1235	0.6969	0.4726	3 161.6	7.208	772.8	1.475
2000	0.99261	0.1599	36.94	38.958	0.1171	0.8409	0.6049	3 237.8	7.247	770.5	1.390
2100	0.98575	0.1293	71.27	38.823	0.1111	1.078	0.8216	3 332.9	7.293	768.5	1.312
2200	0.97410	0.1104	129.5	38.600	0.1054	1.449	1.157	3 457.9	7.351	770.7	1.253
2300	0.95540	0.0851	223.0	38.230	0.0999	2.001	1.649	3 628.7	7.427	779.3	1.213
2400	0.92690	0.0681	365.5	37.673	0.0943	2.791	2.340	3 865.9	7.528	795.0	1.193
2500	0.88560	0.0534	571.9	36.865	0.0862	3.881	3.271	4 196.8	7.663	818.2	1.186
2600	0.8288	0.0405	855.9	35.755	0.0827	5.325	4.460	4 653.9	7.842	849.8	1.194
2700	0.75489	0.0294	1225	34.310	0.0764	7.146	5.896	5 274.3	8.076	890.7	1.212
2800	0.66435	0.0200	1678	32.540	0.0699	9.224	7.502	6 094.2	8.373	941.7	1.239
2900	0.56085	0.0126	2196	30.516	0.0632	11.57	9.105	7 137.3	8.739	1002	1.270
3000	0.45134	0.0073	2743	28.375	0.0569	13.55	10.99	8 397.8	9.166	1069	1.299
				$p=10^{-4}$ bar							
600	0.99879	1 206	0	39.149	0.7847	0.5644	0.3465	2 446.1	6.434	455.3	1.627
700	0.99976	243.0	0	39.112	0.6720	0.5368	0.3233	2 501.1	6.519	496.9	1.659
800	0.99993	69.93	0	39.108	0.5879	0.5330	0.3202	2 554.6	6.590	532.0	1.664
900	0.99997	27.70	0	39.105	0.5222	0.5319	0.3195	2 607.9	6.653	564.9	1.667
1000	0.99999	12.86	0	39.102	0.4700	0.5320	0.3192	2 661.1	6.709	595.5	1.667
1100	0.99999	6.790	0.0004	39.102	0.4273	0.5320	0.3191	2 714.3	6.760	624.5	1.667
1200	0.99999	4.007	0.0031	39.102	0.3916	0.5320	0.3192	2 767.5	6.806	652.3	1.666
1300	0.99999	2.519	0.0174	39.102	0.3616	0.5323	0.3195	2 820.8	6.846	678.8	1.666
1400	0.99998	1.690	0.07606	39.102	0.3357	0.5332	0.3203	2 874.0	6.886	704.1	1.664
1500	0.99994	1.189	0.2751	39.101	0.3133	0.5358	0.3222	2 927.4	6.923	727.8	1.659
1600	0.99983	0.8688	0.8516	39.099	0.2937	0.5425	0.3291	2 981.4	6.957	749.1	1.648
1700	0.99954	0.6550	2.318	39.093	0.2764	0.5588	0.3444	3 036.4	6.991	766.1	1.622
1800	0.99887	0.5066	5.660	39.080	0.2610	0.5907	0.3741	3 093.7	7.024	777.8	1.579
1900	0.99747	0.4002	12.66	39.053	0.2470	0.6496	0.4287	3 155.5	7.057	783.2	1.515
2000	0.99477	0.3212	26.15	39.000	0.2344	0.7517	0.5227	3 225.0	7.092	783.3	1.438
2100	0.98990	0.2608	50.50	38.905	0.2227	0.9202	0.6768	3 308.0	7.133	781.4	1.360
2200	0.98161	0.2243	91.93	38.743	0.2117	1.183	0.9155	3 412.3	7.181	781.4	1.292
2300	0.96825	0.1747	158.8	38.481	0.2011	1.575	1.267	3 549.5	7.242	786.2	1.243
2400	0.94773	0.1424	261.3	38.080	0.1907	2.136	1.763	3 733.2	7.320	797.0	1.212
2500	0.91766	0.1147	411.7	37.492	0.1803	2.913	2.437	3 983.8	7.422	814.3	1.195

continued

T, °K	X_1	$X_2 \cdot 10^6$	$X_e \cdot 10^4$	M	$\varrho \cdot 10^4$	c_p	c_v	i	s	u	k
2600	0.97558	0.0905	622.1	36.670	0.1718	3.951	3.313	4 324.1	7.556	838.7	1.193
2700	0.81943	0.06923	902.8	35.572	0.1584	5.287	4.402	4 783.2	7.729	870.8	1.201
2800	0.74814	0.0507	1259.3	34.178	0.1467	6.931	5.685	5 391.1	7.950	911.5	1.219
2900	0.66250	0.0351	1687.5	32.504	0.1347	8.831	7.094	6 178.0	8.225	961.2	1.245
3000	0.56567	0.0228	2171.6	30.625	0.1226	10.83	8.493	7 150.7	8.558	1019	1.275
				$p=5 \cdot 10^{-4}$ bar							
600	0.99394	6 056	0	39.339	3.941	0.6919	0.4525	2 439.6	6.079	439.2	1.520
700	0.99879	1 214	0	39.149	3.363	0.5562	0.3391	2 499.6	6.172	493.5	1.638
800	0.99964	359.0	0	39.116	2.940	0.5375	0.3237	2 554.2	6.245	531.2	1.659
900	0.99986	138.5	0	39.107	2.612	0.5336	0.3206	2 607.8	6.308	564.3	1.664
1000	0.99986	138.5	0	39.107	2.352	0.5336	0.3206	2 661.1	6.364	596.0	1.667
1100	0.99997	34.04	0.0002	39.103	2.136	0.5322	0.3194	2 714.3	6.415	624.5	1.666
1200	0.99998	19.93	0.0014	39.103	1.958	0.5321	0.3193	2 767.5	6.461	652.3	1.666
1300	0.99999	12.60	0.0078	39.102	1.808	0.5322	0.3194	2 820.7	6.504	678.9	1.666
1400	0.99998	8.449	0.0340	39.102	1.679	0.5325	0.3197	2 873.9	6.543	704.3	1.666
1500	0.99997	5.945	0.1230	39.102	1.567	0.5337	0.3208	2 927.0	6.580	728.6	1.663
1600	0.99992	4.345	0.3808	39.101	1.469	0.5367	0.3236	2 980.8	6.615	751.3	1.658
1700	0.99979	3.277	1.037	39.098	1.382	0.5447	0.3312	3 034.9	6.647	771.3	1.645
1800	0.99949	2.536	2.536	39.092	1.305	0.5595	0.3451	3 090.5	6.679	788.1	1.621
1900	0.99886	2.006	5.666	39.079	1.236	0.5965	0.3701	3 147.7	6.710	800.6	1.585
2000	0.99766	1.615	11.71	39.056	1.174	0.6327	0.4112	3 207.9	6.741	808.1	1.533
2100	0.99547	1.319	22.65	39.020	1.117	0.7093	0.4830	3 274.7	6.774	810.9	1.468
2200	0.99173	1.145	41.32	38.940	1.064	0.8287	0.5921	3 351.3	6.809	811.1	1.400
2300	0.98567	0.9053	71.64	38.822	1.014	1.006	0.7524	3 442.6	6.850	811.7	1.337
2400	0.97628	0.7555	118.6	38.638	0.9676	1.259	0.9793	3 555.4	6.897	815.0	1.285
2500	0.96230	0.6307	188.5	38.365	0.9223	1.611	1.292	3 697.8	6.955	822.3	1.247
2600	0.94228	0.5241	288.6	37.969	0.8778	2.084	1.705	3 881.3	7.027	834.4	1.222
2700	0.91468	0.4313	426.6	37.434	0.8333	2.701	2.234	4 118.9	7.117	851.8	1.209
2800	0.87798	0.3492	610.1	36.716	0.7881	3.487	2.801	4 426.9	7.229	874.8	1.206
2900	0.83096	0.2766	845.2	35.797	0.7489	4.458	3.679	4 822.4	7.368	903.7	1.212
3000	0.77295	0.2129	1135	34.663	0.6944	5.623	4.590	5 324.7	7.538	939.5	1.225
				$p=10^{-3}$ bar							
700	0.99758	2 418	0	39.197	6.735	0.5803	0.3587	2 497.3	6.021	489.5	1.614
800	0.99928	717.0	0	39.130	5.882	0.5430	0.3281	2 553.5	6.096	530.3	1.654
900	0.99972	277.0	0	39.113	5.226	0.5353	0.3219	2 607.5	6.160	564.0	1.662
1000	0.99987	128.4	0	39.107	4.701	0.5332	0.3201	2 660.9	6.216	595.3	1.666

continued

$T, °K$	X_1	$X_2 \cdot 10^6$	$X_e \cdot 10^4$	M	$\varrho \cdot 10^4$	c_p	c_v	i	s	u	k
1100	0.99993	68.07	0.0001	39.105	4.273	0.5325	0.3196	2 714.2	6.267	624.4	1.666
1200	0.99996	39.87	0.0010	39.104	3.917	0.5322	0.3194	2 767.5	6.314	652.2	1.666
1300	0.99997	25.19	0.0055	39.103	3.616	0.5322	0.3194	2 820.7	6.356	678.9	1.666
1400	0.99998	16.90	0.0240	39.103	3.367	0.5324	0.3196	2 873.9	6.396	704.4	1.666
1500	0.99997	11.89	0.0870	39.102	3.133	0.5332	0.3204	2 927.3	6.433	728.8	1.664
1600	0.99994	8.690	0.2693	39.101	2.938	0.5353	0.3223	2 980.7	6.467	751.9	1.661
1700	0.99985	6.555	0.7333	39.099	2.765	0.5414	0.3281	3 034.5	6.500	772.6	1.650
1800	0.99964	5.074	1.794	39.095	2.616	0.5522	0.3382	3 089.0	6.531	790.8	1.633
1900	0.99919	4.016	4.007	39.086	2.471	0.5715	0.3562	3 145.3	6.561	805.5	1.605
2000	0.99834	3.235	8.284	39.070	2.348	0.6045	0.3867	3 204.0	6.591	816.0	1.563
2100	0.99679	2.644	16.04	39.039	2.235	0.6593	0.4370	3 266.9	6.622	821.6	1.509
2200	0.99415	2.300	29.25	38.988	2.130	0.7447	0.5152	3 336.8	6.655	823.8	1.446
2300	0.98986	1.826	50.76	38.904	2.033	0.8708	0.6297	3 417.6	6.690	824.7	1.383
2400	0.98316	1.514	84.17	38.773	1.942	1.051	0.7916	3 513.4	6.731	826.7	1.327
2500	0.97318	1.290	134.1	38.580	1.855	1.301	1.015	3 630.5	6.779	831.2	1.282
2600	0.95083	1.085	205.9	38.297	1.771	1.638	1.312	3 775.8	6.836	839.7	1.248
2700	0.93888	0.9089	305.6	37.907	1.688	2.078	1.694	3 960.6	6.905	852.6	1.227
2800	0.91206	0.7537	439.7	37.383	1.605	2.639	2.172	4 195.4	6.991	870.2	1.215
2900	0.87719	0.6166	614.0	36.701	1.521	3.340	2.755	4 493.0	7.095	892.7	1.212
3000	0.83330	0.4950	833.5	35.843	1.436	4.194	3.445	4 868.1	7.222	920.6	1.217
					$p=5 \cdot 10^{-3}$ bar						
700	0.98812	11 880	0	39.565	33.99	0.7602	0.4600	2 481.8	5.682	468.4	1.492
800	0.99643	3 567	0	39.241	29.50	0.5867	0.3627	2 549.1	5.749	522.8	1.612
900	0.99862	1 381	0	39.156	26.15	0.5489	0.3320	2 605.9	5.816	562.3	1.654
1000	0.99936	641.3	0	39.127	23.52	0.5384	0.3239	2 660.2	5.874	594.5	1.662
1100	0.99966	340.2	0	39.115	21.37	0.5348	0.3212	2 713.8	5.924	624.1	1.665
1200	0.99980	199.3	0.0004	39.109	19.59	0.5334	0.3202	2 767.2	5.971	652.1	1.666
1300	0.99997	125.9	0.0025	39.107	18.08	0.5328	0.3107	2 820.6	6.014	678.8	1.666
1400	0.99992	84.48	0.0108	39.105	16.79	0.5326	0.3196	2 873.8	6.053	704.4	1.666
1500	0.99993	59.44	0.0389	39.104	15.67	0.5328	0.3200	2 927.1	6.090	729.0	1.666
1600	0.99993	43.45	0.1204	39.103	14.69	0.5337	0.3207	2 980.5	6.125	752.6	1.664
1700	0.99990	32.78	0.3280	39.102	13.82	0.5370	0.3239	3 034.0	6.157	774.3	1.658
1800	0.99980	25.38	0.8022	39.100	13.05	0.5424	0.3290	3 087.9	6.188	794.5	1.648
1900	0.99960	20.10	1.792	39.096	12.37	0.5516	0.3377	3 142.7	6.217	812.7	1.634
2000	0.99924	16.20	3.706	39.088	11.74	0.5669	0.3519	3 198.4	6.246	827.5	1.611
2100	0.99855	13.27	4.174	39.074	11.18	0.5926	0.3756	3 256.3	6.274	839.9	1.578
2200	0.99737	11.58	13.10	39.051	10.67	0.6326	0.4124	3 317.5	6.303	847.9	1.534

continued

T, °K	X_1	$X_2 \cdot 10^6$	$X_e \cdot 10^4$	M	$\varrho \cdot 10^4$	c_p	c_v	i	s	u	k
2300	0.99544	9.233	22.76	39.014	10.19	0.6907	0.4655	3 383.0	6.332	853.0	1.484
2400	0.99243	7.808	37.82	38.954	9.755	0.7730	0.5400	3 456.4	6.363	856.5	1.431
2500	0.98791	6.647	60.41	38.870	9.344	0.8882	0.6439	3 539.2	6.397	859.2	1.379
2600	0.98137	5.684	93.14	38.738	8.955	1.042	0.7810	3 635.0	6.434	863.0	1.334
2700	0.97218	4.872	139.1	38.558	8.583	1.242	0.9580	3 749.0	6.477	869.0	1.295
2800	0.95966	4.172	201.7	38.313	8.224	1.504	1.182	3 885.4	6.523	877.8	1.267
2900	0.94305	3.563	284.7	37.988	7.873	1.820	1.460	4 050.8	6.584	889.8	1.247
3000	0.92159	3.027	392.0	37.568	7.527	2.219	1.800	4 251.8	6.653	905.1	1.233
					$p=10^{-2}$ bar						
700	0.97677	23 230	0	40.010	68.74	0.9590	0.6607	2 470.0	5.490	454.6	1.420
800	0.99291	7 090	0	39.380	59.20	0.6950	0.4040	2 543.7	5.596	515.2	1.571
900	0.99724	2 755	0	39.210	52.37	0.5656	0.3445	2 603.9	5.667	559.9	1.642
1000	0.99872	1 280	0	39.152	47.06	0.5449	0.3286	2 659.2	5.726	593.6	1.658
1100	0.99932	679.8	0	39.129	42.76	0.5377	0.3233	2 713.3	5.777	623.7	1.663
1200	0.99960	398.4	0.0003	39.118	39.18	0.5351	0.3212	2 766.9	5.824	651.9	1.665
1300	0.99970	251.8	0.0017	39.112	36.16	0.5336	0.3203	2 820.3	5.866	678.7	1.666
1400	0.99983	168.9	0.0076	39.109	33.58	0.5330	0.3199	2 873.7	5.906	704.4	1.666
1500	0.99988	118.9	0.0275	39.107	31.34	0.5329	0.3199	2 927.3	5.943	729.1	1.666
1600	0.99990	86.89	0.0852	39.105	29.38	0.5334	0.3204	2 980.4	5.977	752.7	1.665
1700	0.99990	65.55	0.2319	39.104	27.65	0.5361	0.3230	3 033.9	6.009	774.7	1.659
1800	0.99980	50.76	0.5672	39.102	26.11	0.5401	0.3269	3 087.6	6.040	795.4	1.652
1900	0.99971	40.29	1.2675	39.099	24.74	0.5469	0.3333	3 142.0	6.070	814.5	1.641
2000	0.99944	32.42	2.621	39.093	23.49	0.5581	0.3437	3 197.2	6.098	831.3	1.624
2100	0.99896	26.56	5.074	39.083	22.37	0.5768	0.3611	3 253.8	6.126	845.1	1.598
2200	0.99812	23.19	9.270	39.067	21.34	0.6060	0.3880	3 312.9	6.153	855.4	1.562
2300	0.99676	18.52	16.11	39.040	20.40	0.6481	0.4265	3 375.4	6.181	863.0	1.520
2400	0.99463	15.68	26.77	38.998	19.53	0.7072	0.4802	3 443.7	6.209	868.3	1.473
2500	0.99143	13.39	42.79	38.935	18.72	0.7902	0.5553	3 518.6	6.240	871.8	1.423
2600	0.98678	11.50	66.04	38.844	17.96	0.9004	0.6542	3 601.1	6.273	875.5	1.376
2700	0.98024	9.907	98.75	38.716	17.24	1.043	0.7814	3 698.8	6.309	880.2	1.335
2800	0.97129	8.547	143.5	38.541	16.54	1.227	0.9428	3 811.9	6.351	886.8	1.301
2900	0.95938	7.375	203.1	38.308	15.88	1.457	1.144	3 945.7	6.398	895.7	1.274
3000	0.94389	6.351	280.5	38.005	15.23	1.744	1.392	4 105.1	6.452	907.3	1.254

continued

T, °K	X_1	$X_2 \cdot 10^6$	$X_e \cdot 10^4$	M	$\varrho \cdot 10^4$	c_p	c_v	i	s	u	k
					$p=5 \cdot 10^{-2}$ bar						
800	0.96642	33 580	0	40.415	303.6	0.9870	0.6602	2 507.5	5.205	496.2	1.495
900	0.98652	1 348	0	39.629	264.6	0.6898	0.4362	2 588.4	5.310	546.6	1.581
1000	0.99366	6 340	0	39.350	237.0	0.5946	0.3645	2 651.8	5.378	587.3	1.631
1100	0.99661	3 381	0	39.234	214.4	0.5603	0.3391	2 709.3	5.433	620.8	1.652
1200	0.99802	1 985	0.0001	39.180	196.0	0.5463	0.3289	2 764.5	5.479	650.5	1.661
1300	0.99874	1 256	0.0008	39.151	181.0	0.5399	0.3244	2 818.8	5.523	678.0	1.664
1400	0.99916	843.5	0.0034	39.135	168.0	0.5367	0.3222	2 872.6	5.563	704.0	1.666
1500	0.99940	593.8	0.0123	39.125	156.8	0.5351	0.3212	2 926.3	5.600	729.1	1.666
1600	0.99956	434.1	0.0381	39.119	146.9	0.5344	0.3208	2 979.7	5.634	752.9	1.666
1700	0.99965	327.6	0.1037	39.114	138.6	0.5357	0.3223	3 033.3	5.667	775.21	1.662
1800	0.99970	253.7	0.2537	39.111	130.6	0.5378	0.3244	3 086.9	5.697	796.7	1.658
1900	0.99969	201.0	0.5668	39.108	123.7	0.5412	0.3277	3 140.9	5.727	816.9	1.651
2000	0.99960	162.1	1.1723	39.104	117.5	0.5466	0.3329	3 195.2	5.754	835.8	1.642
2100	0.99941	132.9	2.269	39.098	111.9	0.5561	0.3418	3 250.3	5.781	852.6	1.627
2200	0.99905	116.2	4.147	39.090	106.8	0.5708	0.3556	3 306.7	5.808	867.0	1.605
2300	0.99347	92.89	7.210	39.077	102.1	0.5913	0.3745	3 365.4	5.833	879.3	1.579
2400	0.99752	78.88	11.99	39.058	97.81	0.6195	0.4003	3 425.1	5.860	889.4	1.547
2500	0.99610	67.58	19.18	39.030	93.83	0.6595	0.4369	3 489.0	5.885	896.9	1.509
2600	0.99401	58.32	29.64	38.988	90.13	0.7117	0.4842	3 557.4	5.912	903.0	1.470
2700	0.99107	50.64	44.40	38.930	86.66	0.7787	0.5444	3 631.7	5.940	908.5	1.430
2800	0.98702	44.13	64.69	38.851	83.39	0.8642	0.6207	3 713.7	5.970	913.6	1.392
2900	0.98159	38.60	91.86	38.744	80.29	0.9792	0.7165	3 805.4	6.002	919.1	1.357
3000	0.97447	33.85	127.5	38.605	77.34	1.109	0.8379	3 908.9	6.037	925.4	1.325
					$p=10^{-1}$ bar						
900	0.97373	26 270	0	40.129	536.0	0.8243	0.5327	2 570.4	5.147	537.3	1.547
1000	0.98748	12 520	0	39.592	475.9	0.6527	0.4058	2 642.8	5.230	581.3	1.608
1100	0.99328	6 716	0	39.365	430.2	0.5875	0.3580	2 704.4	5.280	617.6	1.641
1200	0.99604	3 955	0.0001	39.257	393.2	0.5602	0.3384	2 761.6	5.330	648.9	1.656
1300	0.99750	2 507	0.0005	39.200	362.5	0.5476	0.3295	2 816.9	5.374	677.1	1.662
1400	0.99832	1 684	0.0024	39.168	336.3	0.5413	0.3251	2 871.3	5.415	703.6	1.665
1500	0.99881	1 186	0.0087	39.148	313.7	0.5379	0.3229	2 925.0	5.452	728.7	1.666
1600	0.99913	867.6	0.0269	39.136	294.0	0.5361	0.3218	2 979.0	5.486	752.8	1.666
1700	0.99933	654.8	0.0733	39.127	276.6	0.5367	0.3228	3 032.7	5.519	775.3	1.663
1800	0.99946	507.2	0.1793	39.121	261.3	0.5380	0.3243	3 086.4	5.551	796.9	1.659
1900	0.99518	401.8	0.4008	39.116	247.5	0.5404	0.3267	3 140.4	5.579	817.5	1.654
2000	0.99961	324.2	0.8289	39.111	235.1	0.5443	0.3305	3 195.0	5.607	836.9	1.647

continued

T, °K	X_1	$X_2 \cdot 10^6$	$X_e \cdot 10^4$	M	$\varrho \cdot 10^4$	c_p	c_v	i	s	u	k
2100	0.99941	265.8	1.605	39.106	223.8	0.5515	0.3374	3 249.3	5.633	854.5	1.635
2200	0.99913	220.4	3.206	39.098	213.5	0.5634	0.3471	3 304.1	5.659	870.7	1.620
2300	0.99879	185.9	5.099	39.089	204.3	0.5781	0.3623	3 362.0	5.684	883.8	1.596
2400	0.99815	158.0	8.481	39.075	195.7	0.5989	0.3814	3 420.7	5.709	895.7	1.570
2500	0.99720	153.4	13.57	39.060	187.8	0.6287	0.4088	3 482.1	5.735	904.9	1.538
2600	0.99569	117.0	20.98	39.025	180.4	0.6672	0.4439	3 546.7	5.760	912.7	1.503
2700	0.99361	101.8	31.44	38.983	173.6	0.7160	0.4880	3 615.8	5.787	919.4	1.467
2800	0.99075	88.93	45.83	38.926	167.1	0.7784	0.5440	3 690.4	5.813	925.3	1.431
2900	0.98689	78.04	65.13	38.850	161.0	0.8572	0.6145	3 772.0	5.842	930.8	1.395
3000	0.98184	68.72	90.47	38.751	155.3	0.9578	0.7040	3 862.3	5.873	936.1	1.361
					$p = 2 \cdot 10^{-1}$ bar						
900	0.95000	50 003	0	41.057	1 097	1.038	0.6802	2 538.1	4.967	527.7	1.527
1000	0.97556	24 444	0	40.058	963.0	0.7566	0.4781	2 625.8	5.059	573.3	1.582
1100	0.98674	13 256	0.00001	39.620	865.9	0.6388	0.3932	2 694.8	5.125	612.5	1.624
1200	0.99215	7 849	0.00007	39.409	789.5	0.5872	0.3565	2 755.8	5.178	645.9	1.647
1300	0.99501	4 988	0.0004	39.297	726.7	0.5628	0.3394	2 813.1	5.224	675.5	1.658
1400	0.99664	3 357	0.0016	39.233	673.7	0.5504	0.3309	2 868.8	5.266	702.7	1.663
1500	0.99763	2 367	0.0061	39.194	628.2	0.5437	0.3264	2 923.4	5.303	728.2	1.666
1600	0.99826	1 732	0.0190	39.170	588.5	0.5399	0.3240	2 977.6	5.338	752.5	1.666
1700	0.99868	1 308	0.0518	39.153	553.7	0.5391	0.3241	3 031.6	5.371	775.2	1.664
1800	0.99896	1 013	0.1268	39.141	522.8	0.5393	0.3248	3 085.5	5.402	797.0	1.660
1900	0.99914	803.0	0.2833	39.132	495.1	0.5407	0.3265	3 139.5	5.431	817.9	1.656
2000	0.99923	648.1	0.5860	39.125	470.3	0.5433	0.3292	3 193.7	5.459	837.7	1.650
2100	0.99924	531.4	1.135	39.118	447.8	0.5487	0.3345	3 248.3	5.485	855.9	1.640
2200	0.99914	445.7	1.998	39.111	426.6	0.5555	0.3449	3 300.0	5.509	873.0	1.626
2300	0.99891	371.9	3.606	39.102	408.7	0.5690	0.3538	3 359.8	5.536	887.1	1.608
2400	0.99848	316.1	5.998	39.091	391.6	0.5846	0.3682	3 417.4	5.561	900.5	1.587
2500	0.99781	271.2	9.600	39.075	375.8	0.6071	0.3891	3 477.0	5.585	911.3	1.560
2600	0.99680	234.6	14.84	39.053	361.1	0.6358	0.4154	3 539.0	5.609	920.7	1.530
2700	0.99534	204.3	22.25	39.023	347.5	0.6719	0.4482	3 604.3	5.634	928.9	1.499
2800	0.99333	178.8	32.45	38.982	334.7	0.7178	0.4897	3 673.7	5.659	935.9	1.466
2900	0.99061	157.3	46.14	38.928	322.7	0.7760	0.5420	3 748.3	5.685	941.9	1.432
3000	0.98703	138.9	64.14	38.857	311.4	0.8512	0.6096	3 829.3	5.713	947.0	1.396

continued

T, °K	X_1	$X_2 \cdot 10^6$	$X_e \cdot 10^4$	M	$\varrho \cdot 10^4$	c_p	c_v	i	s	u	k
					$p=5 \cdot 10^{-1}$ bar						
1000	0.94291	57 090	0	41.334	2 484	0.9928	0.6342	2 581.2	4.827	561.3	1.565
1100	0.96810	31 900	0	40.349	2 205	0.7704	0.4808	2 668.1	4.910	602.8	1.602
1200	0.98082	19 180	0	39.830	1 996	0.6609	0.4000	2 739.0	4.972	639.4	1.632
1300	0.98771	12 289	0.0002	39.582	1 849	0.6058	0.3671	2 802.1	5.022	671.5	1.650
1400	0.99170	8 309	0.0011	39.427	1 693	0.5767	0.3474	2 861.1	5.066	700.3	1.660
1500	0.99410	5 875	0.0039	39.332	1 576	0.5605	0.3367	2 917.9	5.105	726.8	1.665
1600	0.99570	4 308	0.0120	39.270	1 475	0.5511	0.3306	2 973.5	5.141	751.7	1.667
1700	0.99674	3 257	0.0327	39.229	1 387	0.5467	0.3283	3 028.41	5.175	774.8	1.665
1800	0.99746	2 526	0.0801	39.200	1 309	0.5445	0.3275	3 082.9	5.206	796.9	1.663
1900	0.99796	2 002	0.1791	39.180	1 236	0.5439	0.3278	3 137.4	5.235	818.1	1.659
2000	0.99831	1 617	0.3705	39.164	1 177	0.5447	0.3292	3 191.7	5.263	838.1	1.654
2100	0.99853	1 327	0.7173	39.151	1 121	0.5480	0.3328	3 246.3	5.290	857.5	1.646
2200	0.99858	1 160	1.3112	39.142	1 069	0.5542	0.3390	3 301.3	5.315	874.3	1.635
2300	0.99860	929.2	2.280	39.129	1 023	0.5621	0.3468	3 357.0	5.340	890.3	1.621
2400	0.99845	790.3	3.793	39.118	979.6	0.5727	0.3569	3 413.9	5.364	905.0	1.605
2500	0.99811	678.5	6.072	39.104	940.1	0.5887	0.3719	3 471.9	5.388	917.5	1.583
2600	0.99753	587.3	9.390	39.088	903.6	0.6086	0.3904	3 5317.0	5.411	928.7	1.559
2700	0.99667	512.1	14.08	39.067	869.6	0.6332	0.4131	3 593.7	5.434	938.8	1.538
2800	0.99544	448.9	20.55	39.039	838.0	0.6645	0.4416	3 658.6	5.458	947.5	1.505
2900	0.99376	395.6	29.23	39.003	808.3	0.7043	0.4778	3 726.9	5.482	954.8	1.474
3000	0.99152	350.4	40.66	38.957	780.5	0.7569	0.5257	3 799.7	5.507	960.4	1.440
					$p=8 \cdot 10^{-1}$ bar						
1100	0.95077	49 230	0	41.027	3 587	0.8754	0.5476	2 644.2	4.792	597.1	1.599
1200	0.96999	30 010	0.00003	40.275	3 227	0.7251	0.4459	2 723.5	4.861	634.9	1.626
1300	0.98062	19 381	0.0002	39.859	2 948	0.6450	0.3918	2 791.6	4.915	668.3	1.646
1400	0.98683	13 165	0.0008	39.617	2 721	0.6014	0.3626	2 853.7	4.962	698.2	1.658
1500	0.99066	9 335	0.0031	39.467	2 530	0.5766	0.3464	2 912.5	5.002	725.5	1.665
1600	0.99314	6 858	0.0094	39.370	2 366	0.5619	0.3369	2 969.4	5.039	750.9	1.668
1700	0.99480	5 191	0.0259	39.305	2 223	0.5542	0.3326	3 025.2	5.073	774.3	1.666
1800	0.99596	4 029	0.0633	39.259	2 097	0.5498	0.3304	3 080.4	5.105	796.7	1.664
1900	0.99677	3 197	0.1415	39.226	1 985	0.5476	0.3297	3 135.3	5.134	818.1	1.661

continued

T, °K	X_1	$X_2 \cdot 10^6$	$X_e \cdot 10^6$	M	$\varrho \cdot 10^6$	c_p	c_v	i	s	u	k
2000	0.99736	2 582	0.2927	39.202	1 885	0.5471	0.3302	3 189.9	5.162	838.6	1.657
2100	0.99777	2 119	0.5669	39.183	1 794	0.5492	0.3330	3 244.7	5.189	857.6	1.649
2200	0.99794	1 854	1.036	39.170	1 712	0.5542	0.3382	3 299.8	5.215	875.1	1.639
2300	0.99815	1 485	1.802	39.153	1 637	0.5605	0.3447	3 355.6	5.240	891.5	1.626
2400	0.99813	1 264	2.999	39.140	1 568	0.5692	0.3531	3 412.0	5.264	906.8	1.612
2500	0.99795	1 085	4.800	39.126	1 505	0.5826	0.3660	3 469.6	5.287	919.9	1.592
2600	0.99758	939.8	7.424	39.110	1 446	0.5993	0.3816	3 528.6	5.310	931.9	1.570
2700	0.99695	819.8	11.13	39.091	1 392	0.6197	0.4005	3 589.5	5.333	942.8	1.547
2800	0.99603	719.0	16.24	39.066	1 342	0.6456	0.4244	3 652.7	5.356	952.4	1.521
2900	0.99474	634.3	23.12	39.036	1 294	0.6788	0.4548	3 718.9	5.379	960.4	1.492
3000	0.99300	562.3	32.17	38.998	1 250	0.7232	0.4955	3 788.7	5.403	966.4	1.459
					$p = 1$ bar						
1100	0.93986	60130	0	41.453	4 530	0.9336	0.5834	2 629.6	4.734	594.4	1.600
1200	0.96308	36 970	0	40.548	4 062	0.7633	0.4698	2 713.6	4.807	632.5	1.625
1300	0.97600	24 000	0.0002	40.040	3 702	0.6694	0.4069	2 784.8	4.864	666.6	1.645
1400	0.98365	16 350	0.0008	39.741	3 412	0.6170	0.3722	2 848.9	4.912	697.0	1.658
1500	0.98838	11 615	0.0027	39.556	3 170	0.5870	0.3526	2 909.0	4.953	724.7	1.665
1600	0.99145	8 543	0.0085	39.436	2 963	0.5698	0.3410	2 966.7	4.991	750.4	1.668
1700	0.99352	6 472	0.0231	39.355	2 783	0.5592	0.3354	3 023.2	5.025	774.0	1.667
1800	0.99496	5 027	0.0566	39.298	2 624	0.5533	0.3323	3 078.7	5.056	796.6	1.665
1900	0.99598	3 990	0.1265	39.258	2 484	0.5501	0.3309	3 133.9	5.086	818.1	1.662
2000	0.99672	3 224	0.2617	39.227	2 358	0.5489	0.3310	3 188.8	5.114	838.6	1.658
2100	0.99725	2 647	0.5069	39.204	2 244	0.5503	0.3333	3 243.7	5.141	857.7	1.651
2200	0.99750	2 316	0.9267	39.189	1 141	0.5547	0.3381	3 298.8	5.167	875.4	1.641
2300	0.99782	1 855	1.6116	39.168	2 047	0.5603	0.3440	3 354.6	5.192	892.0	1.629
2400	0.99788	1 579	2.6816	39.153	1 961	0.5681	0.3518	3 411.0	5.217	907.5	1.615
2500	0.99778	1 356	4.2930	39.138	1 882	0.5805	0.3637	3 468.5	5.239	920.9	1.596
2600	0.99750	1 175	6.6398	39.122	1 809	0.5958	0.3782	3 527.2	5.262	933.2	1.575
2700	0.99698	1 025	9.9590	39.103	1 741	0.6145	0.3956	3 587.7	5.285	944.5	1.553
2800	0.99619	899.1	14.532	39.080	1 678	0.6382	0.4176	3 650.3	5.309	954.4	1.528
2900	0.99507	793.4	20.681	39.052	1 619	0.6687	0.4456	3 715.6	5.331	962.8	1.501
3000	0.99354	703.7	28.780	39.017	1 563	0.7098	0.4835	3 784.2	5.354	969.0	1.468

continued

T, °K	X_1	$X_2 \cdot 10^6$	$X_e \cdot 10^4$	M	$\varrho \cdot 10^4$	c_p	c_v	i	s	u	k
					$p=2$ bar						
1200	0.93090	69 099	0	41.804	8 375	0.9122	0.5584	2 669.8	4.630	624.6	1.634
1300	0.95413	45 869	0.0001	40.896	7 563	0.7723	0.4686	2 753.4	4.697	660.2	1.648
1400	0.96831	31 690	0.0005	40.310	6 927	0.6868	0.4134	2 826.1	4.751	692.3	1.660
1500	0.97729	22 712	0.0019	39.990	6 409	0.6347	0.3805	2 892.0	4.797	721.5	1.668
1600	0.98319	16 802	0.0060	39.759	5 974	0.6022	0.3601	2 953.7	4.837	748.3	1.673
1700	0.98722	12 780	0.0163	39.602	5 600	0.5829	0.3486	3 013.0	4.873	772.7	1.672
1800	0.99004	9 954	0.0399	39.491	5 274	0.5705	0.3416	3 070.5	4.906	795.8	1.670
1900	0.99207	7 917	0.0863	39.411	4 987	0.5627	0.3375	3 127.2	4.936	817.7	1.667
2000	0.99356	6 407	0.1848	39.352	4 730	0.5581	0.3355	3 183.2	4.965	838.7	1.663
2100	0.99466	5 266	0.3580	39.306	4 500	0.5569	0.3361	3 238.9	4.992	858.1	1.657
2200	0.99526	4 611	0.6545	39.280	4 292	0.5592	0.3394	3 294.3	5.018	876.1	1.647
2300	0.99607	3 698	1.1390	39.242	4 102	0.5621	0.3435	3 350.7	5.043	893.2	1.636
2400	0.99647	3 148	1.8950	39.218	3 928	0.5674	0.3493	3 407.1	5.067	909.4	1.624
2500	0.99669	2 706	3.0340	39.196	3 769	0.5768	0.3589	3 464.5	5.090	923.5	1.607
2600	0.99672	2 345	4.6032	39.175	3 622	0.5850	0.3703	3 522.5	5.113	936.7	1.589
2700	0.99654	2 048	7.0405	39.155	3 486	0.6027	0.3839	3 582.0	5.135	949.0	1.570
2800	0.99615	1 708	10.28	39.132	3 360	0.6209	0.4011	3 643.2	5.158	960.0	1.549
2900	0.99549	1 588	14.63	39.107	3 242	0.6446	0.4233	3 706.4	5.180	969.3	1.523
3000	0.99452	1 410	20.36	39.078	3 131	0.6774	0.4540	3 772.2	5.202	976.2	1.492
					$p=4$ bar						
1300	0.91553	84 467	0.0001	42.405	15 684	0.9910	0.5456	2 701.3	4.519	652.6	1.670
1400	0.94024	59 760	0.0004	41.439	14 232	0.7924	0.4728	2 786.0	4.582	686.3	1.676
1500	0.95649	43 511	0.0013	40.803	13 079	0.7126	0.4320	2 861.1	4.633	717.0	1.681
1600	0.96746	32 538	0.0042	40.374	12 129	0.6593	0.3915	2 929.5	4.677	745.1	1.684
1700	0.97506	24 936	0.0115	40.077	11 335	0.6250	0.3714	2 993.7	4.716	770.6	1.683
1800	0.98047	19 530	0.0281	39.865	10 649	0.6020	0.3582	3 054.9	4.751	794.5	1.681
1900	0.98440	15 590	0.0629	39.711	10 049	0.5866	0.3497	3 114.3	4.784	817.1	1.677
2000	0.98732	12 650	0.1303	39.596	9 519	0.5763	0.3445	3 172.4	4.813	838.4	1.673
2100	0.98953	10 420	0.2525	39.509	9 046	0.5707	0.3425	3 229.7	4.841	858.3	1.666
2200	0.99077	9 139	0.4618	39.458	8 624	0.5700	0.3440	3 285.9	4.867	876.7	1.657
2300	0.99254	7 343	0.8037	39.386	8 233	0.5693	0.3459	3 343.5	4.893	894.2	1.646

continued

T, °K	X_1	$X_2 \cdot 10^6$	$X_e \cdot 10^4$	M	$\varrho \cdot 10^4$	c_p	c_v	i	s	u	k
2400	0.99347	6 259	1.338	39.342	7 880	0.5718	0.3497	3 400.5	4.917	910.9	1.635
2500	0.99418	5 385	2.143	39.304	7 559	0.5782	0.3572	3 458.0	4.941	925.8	1.619
2600	0.99467	4 372	3.315	39.272	7 263	0.5867	0.3661	3 516.2	4.964	939.5	1.602
2700	0.99492	4 082	4.974	39.242	6 988	0.5972	0.3768	3 575.3	4.986	952.5	1.585
2800	0.99496	3 587	7.261	39.214	6 734	0.6111	0.3904	3 635.7	5.008	964.3	1.565
2900	0.99476	3 172	10.34	39.186	6 497	0.6296	0.4081	3 697.8	5.030	974.5	1.542
3000	0.99430	2 819	14.400	39.156	6 276	0.6563	0.4337	3 761.8	5.051	982.1	1.513
					$p=6$ bar						
1300	0.88232	117 670	0.0001	43.703	24 246	0.9946	0.5883	2 659.2	4.408	646.8	1.694
1400	0.9151	84 906	0.0003	42.422	21 854	0.8662	0.5112	2 752.0	4.472	682.0	1.695
1500	0.93732	62 678	0.0011	41.552	19 979	0.7745	0.4554	2 833.6	4.533	713.7	1.696
1600	0.95267	47 326	0.0033	40.952	18 460	0.7062	0.4161	2 907.4	4.581	742.7	1.697
1700	0.96348	36 520	0.0093	40.520	17 195	0.6612	0.3902	2 975.7	4.622	769.0	1.695
1800	0.97125	28 740	0.0281	40.226	16 118	0.6299	0.3724	3 040.1	4.659	793.5	1.691
1900	0.97696	23 030	0.0511	40.002	15 185	0.6088	0.3606	3 102.0	4.692	816.5	1.687
2000	0.98123	18 750	0.1060	39.835	14 365	0.5932	0.3527	3 162.0	4.723	838.2	1.682
2100	0.98448	15 470	0.2056	39.706	13 637	0.5840	0.3487	3 220.8	4.752	858.3	1.674
2200	0.98634	13 590	0.3762	39.623	12 992	0.5809	0.3488	3 277.8	4.778	877.0	1.666
2300	0.98893	10 930	0.6550	39.527	12 395	0.5773	0.3491	3 336.7	4.805	894.7	1.654
2400	0.99045	9 332	1.091	39.463	11 859	0.5776	0.3517	3 394.4	4.829	911.6	1.643
2500	0.99161	8 036	1.747	39.409	11 369	0.5821	0.3578	3 452.4	4.853	926.6	1.627
2600	0.99248	6 977	2.704	39.364	10 919	0.5886	0.3654	3 510.9	4.876	940.9	1.611
2700	0.99309	6 101	4.058	39.325	10 504	0.5971	0.3745	3 570.1	4.898	954.3	1.594
2800	0.99345	5 365	5.924	39.289	10 120	0.6087	0.3863	3 630.0	4.920	966.5	1.575
2900	0.99357	4 746	8.436	39.254	9 763	0.6247	0.4022	3 692.0	4.942	977.1	1.553
3000	0.99343	4 221	11.75	39.221	9 429	0.6484	0.4252	3 755.4	4.963	985.1	1.525
					$p=8$ bar						
1400	0.89234	107 600	0.0003	43.311	29 750	0.9186	0.5369	2 722.5	4.400	678.3	1.710
1500	0.91957	80 434	0.0009	42.247	27 084	0.8190	0.4786	2 809.0	4.460	711.0	1.711
1600	0.93873	61 267	0.0029	41.497	24 941	0.7448	0.4354	2 887.0	4.510	740.7	1.710
1700	0.95242	47 580	0.0080	40.962	23 171	0.6924	0.4057	2 958.9	4.553	767.6	1.707

continued

T, °K	X_1	$X_2 \cdot 10^6$	$X_e \cdot 10^4$	M	$\varrho \cdot 10^4$	c_p	c_v	i	s	u	k
1800	0.96237	37 620	0.0197	40.573	21 676	0.6550	0.3847	3 026.0	4.592	792.6	1.702
1900	0.96973	30 260	0.0441	40.285	20 389	0.6280	0.3702	3 090.2	4.627	815.9	1.697
2000	0.97529	24 700	0.0915	40.067	19 265	0.6090	0.3602	3 151.9	4.658	837.9	1.691
2100	0.97954	20 430	0.1776	39.900	18 271	0.5965	0.3545	3 212.2	4.688	858.3	1.683
2200	0.98198	17 960	0.3251	39.803	17 398	0.5913	0.3534	3 270.0	4.715	877.2	1.673
2300	0.98540	14 480	0.5662	39.666	16 584	0.5853	0.3524	3 330.2	4.741	895.1	1.661
2400	0.98740	12 370	0.9431	39.582	15 860	0.5838	0.3539	3 386.5	4.766	912.2	1.650
2500	0.98903	10 660	1.511	39.512	15 199	0.5867	0.3590	3 447.1	4.790	927.4	1.634
2600	0.99027	9 261	2.339	39.455	14 593	0.5917	0 3657	3 506.0	4.813	941.8	1.618
2700	0.99119	8 104	3.511	39.405	14 035	0.5987	0.3738	3 565.4	4.835	955.5	1.602
2800	0.99184	7 130	5.126	39.361	13 517	0.6087	0.3845	3 625.8	4.858	967.9	1.583
2900	0.99223	6 311	7.301	39.320	13 039	0.6230	0.3990	3 687.3	4.879	978.8	1.561
3000	0.99235	5 616	10.17	39.282	12 592	0.6448	0.4206	3 750.4	4.901	987.0	1.533
					$p=10$ bar						
1400	0.87160	128 300	0.0002	44.122	37 883	0.9563	0.5544	2 696.6	4.339	674.8	1.725
1500	0.90304	96 960	0.0008	42.893	34 373	0.8550	0.4959	2 787.0	4.40	708.4	1.725
1600	0.92555	74 450	0.0026	42.013	31 563	0.7769	0.4508	2 868.4	4.45	738.9	1.723
1700	0.94184	58 160	0.0071	41.376	29 256	0.7193	0.4187	2 943.2	4.499	766.3	1.718
1800	0.95380	46 190	0.0175	40.908	27 319	0.6769	0.3953	3 012.8	4.539	791.7	1.712
1900	0.96271	37 280	0.0393	40.559	25 660	0.6460	0.3787	3 078.9	4.575	815.4	1.706
2000	0.96948	30 500	0.0186	40.294	24 218	0.6236	0.3670	3 142.3	4.607	837.7	1.699
2100	0.97469	25 280	0.1585	40.090	22 948	0.6084	0.3599	3 203.9	4.637	858.3	1.690
2200	0.97769	22 250	0.2901	39.971	21 839	0.6013	0.3577	3 262.4	4.664	877.3	1.681
2300	0.98193	17 970	0.5056	39.803	20 802	0.5930	0.3556	3 327.0	4.692	895.4	1.668
2400	0.98447	15 370	0.8423	39.699	19 884	0.5900	0.3562	3 382.8	4.717	912.6	1.656
2500	0.98647	13 260	1.3500	39.615	19 048	0.5915	0.3607	3 441.9	4.741	927.9	1.640
2600	0.98806	11 520	2.0900	39.544	18 282	0.5952	0.3665	3 501.2	4.764	942.5	1.624
2700	0.98928	10 090	3.137	39.484	17 578	0.6009	0.3738	3 560.9	4.787	956.3	1.608
2800	0.99020	8 883	4.581	39.431	16 928	0.6098	0.3837	3 521.6	4.809	969.0	1.589
2900	0.99083	7 866	6.526	39.384	16 325	0.6227	0.3972	3 683.1	4.831	980.0	1.568
3000	0.99118	7 003	9.090	39.340	15 762	0.6431	0.4176	3 746.1	4.852	988.4	1.540

Viscosity $\eta \cdot 10^7$ ($N \cdot s/m^2$) of potassium vapor [351]

T, °K	For monatomic vapor	p, bar				At saturation
		0,5	1	2	5	
800	134					134
900	154					148
1000	173	166				163
1100	192	187	184			178
1200	212	210	207	203		196
1300	232	230	228	226	218	212
1400	251	250	248	246	240	228
1500	270	269	268	266	262	242

Viscosity η ($N \cdot s/m^2$) of liquid potassium [37]

T, °K	$\eta \cdot 10^3$	T, °K	$\eta \cdot 10^3$	T, °K	$\eta \cdot 10^3$	T, °K	$\eta \cdot 10^3$
T_{melt}	0.544						
400	0.413	800	0.171	1200	0.114	1600	0.0875
500	0.301	900	0.151	1300	0.105	1700	0.0830
600	0.238	1000	0.135	1400	0.0984	1800	0.0791
700	0.198	1100	0.123	1500	0.0926	—	—

Thermal conductivity $\lambda \cdot 10^3$ (W/m · deg) of potassium vapor [34]

T, °K	For monatomic vapor	p, bar												At saturation
		0.001	0.005	0,01	0.05	0,1	0,2	0,3	0.5	1	2	6	10	
700	10.7	10.7	12.2	14.2										14.2
800	12.2	12.2	12.6	13.0	16.5									17.5
900	13.8	13.8	13.9	14.0	15.0	16.5	19.3							20.5
1000	15.3	15.3	15.4	15.4	15.8	16.3	17.4	18.5	20.7					22.8
1100	16.9	16.9	17.0	17.0	17.2	17.4	17.9	18.4	19.4	21.8				24.8
1200	18.4	18.4	18.5	18.5	18.6	18.7	18.9	19.2	19.7	21.1	23.7			26.6
1300	20.0	20.0	20.0	20.0	20.1	20.2	20.3	20.5	20.7	21.5	23.2	27.5		28.0
1400	21.8	21.8	21.8	21.8	21.8	21.8	22.0	22.1	22.2	22.6	23.4	26.2	28.0	29.3
1500	23.6	23.6	23.6	23.6	23.6	23.6	23.7	23.9	24.0	24.3	24.8	26.9	28.0	30.3

Thermal conductivity λ of liquid potassium [37]

T, °K	T_{melt}	400	500	600	700	800	900	1000	1100
λ, W/m · deg	49.9	48.0	45.2	42.3	39.4	36.5	33.6	30.7	27.8

Surface tension of potassium [31]

t, °C	64	100	200	300	400	500	600	700
σ, dyne/cm	109	106.6	100	93.4	86.8	80.2	73.6	67.0
t, °C	800	900	1000	1100	1200	1300	1400	1500
σ, dyne/cm	60,4	53.8	47.2	40.6	34,0	27.4	20.8	14.2

RUBIDIUM (Rb)

Atomic weight 85.48

$T_{melt} = 312.7$ °K; $T_{boil} = 959.2$ °K at 760 mm Hg; $T_{cr} = 2100$ ° K;
$p_{cr} = 160$ bar; $\rho_{cr} = 350$ kg/m³

Thermodynamic properties of liquid rubidium at saturation [28]: ρ (kg/m³), c_p (kJ/kg · deg), i and r (kJ/kg), s (kJ/kg · deg)

T, °K	p, bar	ϱ'	c_p'	i'	s'	r
312.7	$2.46 \cdot 10^{-9}$	1481	0.379	118.7	0.99798	917.6
400	$1.690 \cdot 10^{-6}$	1432	0.375	151.6	1.0909	905.5
450	$2.230 \cdot 10^{-5}$	1408	0.372	170.3	1.1349	897.9
500	$1.733 \cdot 10^{-4}$	1386	0.369	188.8	1.1740	889.6
550	$9.194 \cdot 10^{-4}$	1363	0.365	207.2	1.2089	880.6
600	$3.664 \cdot 10^{-3}$	1340	0.362	225.4	1.2406	870.9
650	$1.174 \cdot 10^{-2}$	1323	0.360	243.6	1.2698	860.4
700	$3.174 \cdot 10^{-2}$	1294	0.357	261.3	1.2961	849.7
750	$7.493 \cdot 10^{-2}$	1271	0.355	279.1	1.3206	838.6
800	0.1584	1248	0.353	296.8	1.3434	827.3
850	0.3059	1225	0.352	314.5	1.3648	815.9
900	0.5476	1202	0.353	332.1	1.3849	804.6
950	0.9206	1179	0.355	349.8	1.4040	793.4
1000	1.467	1156	0.360	367.6	1.4223	782.2
1050	2.241	1133	0.366	385.7	1.4399	771.0
1100	3.295	1110	0.373	404.2	1.4571	759.6
1150	4.684	1087	0.379	423.0	1.4738	748.3
1200	6.466	1064	0.385	442.1	1.4901	737.0
1250	8.698	1041	0.392	461.6	1.5060	725.8
1300	11.43	1018	0.399	481.3	1.5215	714.5

Thermodynamic properties of saturated rubidium vapor [28]: Diatomic molecule fraction X_2, molecular weight M, ρ (kg/m³), c_p and c_v (kJ/kg · deg), i (kJ/kg), s (kJ/kg · deg) and u (m/s)

T, °K	X_2	M	ϱ''	c_p''	c_v''	i''	s''	u
400	$1.344 \cdot 10^{-3}$	85.585	$4.347 \cdot 10^{-6}$	0.2731	0.1721	1057.1	3.3548	248.2
450	$3.276 \cdot 10^{-3}$	85.750	$5.109 \cdot 10^{-5}$	0.3006	0.1952	1068.2	3.1302	258.8
500	$6.552 \cdot 10^{-3}$	86.030	$3.585 \cdot 10^{-4}$	0.3353	0.2236	1078.4	2.9532	268.4
550	$1.136 \cdot 10^{-2}$	86.441	$1.737 \cdot 10^{-3}$	0.3733	0.2534	1087.8	2.8100	277.7
600	$1.770 \cdot 10^{-2}$	86.983	$6.386 \cdot 10^{-3}$	0.4100	0.2809	1096.3	2.6921	287.0
650	$2.546 \cdot 10^{-2}$	87.646	$1.904 \cdot 10^{-2}$	0.4423	0.3037	1104.0	2.5935	296.3
700	$3.437 \cdot 10^{-2}$	88.408	$4.819 \cdot 10^{-2}$	0.4679	0.3201	1111.0	2.5100	305.6
750	$4.419 \cdot 10^{-2}$	89.247	0.1072	0.4865	0.3304	1117.7	2.4387	314.8
800	$5.460 \cdot 10^{-2}$	90.137	0.2145	0.4979	0.3349	1124.1	2.3775	323.9
850	$6.534 \cdot 10^{-2}$	91.054	0.3939	0.5034	0.3351	1130.4	2.3247	332.7
900	$7.608 \cdot 10^{-2}$	91.972	0.6726	0.5035	0.3314	1136.7	2.2790	341.5
950	$8.672 \cdot 10^{-2}$	92.882	1.082	0.5002	0.3256	1143.2	2.2392	350.0
1000	$9.701 \cdot 10^{-2}$	93.762	1.654	0.4937	0.3179	1149.8	2.2045	358.4
1050	0.1068	94.603	2.429	0.4857	0.3095	1156.7	2.1742	366.6
1100	0.1162	95.399	3.437	0.4762	0.3005	1163.8	2.1477	374.8
1150	0.1247	96.130	4.709	0.4662	0.2916	1171.3	2.1246	382.7
1200	0.1326	96.803	6.274	0.4558	0.2826	1179.1	2.1043	390.7
1250	0.1397	97.409	8.153	0.4456	0.2742	1187.4	2.0867	398.5
1300	0.1462	97.964	10.36	0.4354	0.2660	1195.8	2.0711	406.2

Saturated vapor pressure for rubidium above 10 bar [350]

T, °K	1350	1400	1450	1500	1550
p, bar	14.7	18.6	23.2	28.5	34.5

Thermodynamic properties of rubidium vapor at different temperatures and pressures [28]: X_1, X_2 and X_e –molar fractions of monatomic, diatomic and electronic components, M, –molecular weight, ρ (kg/m³), c_p and c_v (kJ/kg · deg), i (kJ/kg), s (kJ/kg · deg), speed of sound u (m/s), adiabatic exponent K

T, °K	X_1	$X_2 \cdot 10^5$	$X_e \cdot 10^4$	M	$\varrho \cdot 10^4$	c_p	c_v	i	s	u	k
					$p=10^{-5}$ bar						
600	0.99995	5.004	0	85.474	0.1712	0.2439	0.1464	1106.6	3.282	311.8	1.662
700	0.99999	1.161	0	85.471	0.1468	0.2434	0.1461	1131.0	3.320	336.9	1.666
800	0.999996	0.3857	0	85.470	0.1284	0.2434	0.1460	1155.3	3.352	360.2	1.666
900	0.999998	0.1627	0	85.470	0.1142	0.2434	0.1460	1179.6	3.381	382.1	1.666
1000	0.999999	0.0809	0.0003	85.470	0.1027	0.2434	0.1460	1204.0	3.407	402.8	1.666
1100	0.999999	0.0466	0.0031	85.470	0.0934	0.2434	0.1460	1228.3	3.430	422.4	1.666
1200	0.999995	0.0287	0.0218	85.470	0.0856	0.2436	0.1462	1252.7	3.451	441.1	1.666
1300	0.99998	0.0186	0.1140	85.469	0.0790	0.2442	0.1468	1277.1	3.470	458.8	1.663
1400	0.99990	0.0136	0.4737	85.466	0.0734	0.2464	0.1489	1301.6	3.488	474.8	1.655
1500	0.99967	0.0095	1.637	85.456	0.0685	0.2528	0.1549	1326.5	3.506	488.2	1.632
1600	0.99902	0.0074	4.871	85.428	0.0642	0.2682	0.1693	1352.5	3.522	496.8	1.584
1700	0.99744	0.0055	12.80	85.360	0.0604	0.3025	0.2012	1380.9	3.538	499.1	1.504
1800	0.99394	0.0043	30.30	85.211	0.0569	0.3695	0.2631	1414.3	3.556	496.8	1.404
1900	0.98688	0.0036	65.60	84.909	0.0537	0.4916	0.3749	1457.1	3.576	494.0	1.311
2000	0.97370	0.0028	131.5	84.346	0.0507	0.6990	0.5633	1516.3	3.613	494.8	1.241
2100	0.95082	0.0022	245.9	83.368	0.0477	1.032	0.8614	1602.6	3.655	501.2	1.199
2200	0.91366	0.0017	431.7	81.780	0.0447	1.540	1.305	1731.2	3.716	513.9	1.180
2300	0.85731	0.0013	713.5	79.372	0.0415	2.274	1.926	1922.2	3.801	533.5	1.181
2400	0.77769	0.0009	1112	75.969	0.0380	3.277	2.736	2201.4	3.922	561.0	1.198
2500	0.67391	0.0006	1630	71.535	0.0344	4.541	3.700	2596.0	4.084	597.4	1.227
2600	0.55069	0.0004	2246	66.269	0.0306	5.926	4.688	3126.9	4.295	642.4	1.264
2700	0.41958	0.0002	2902	60.666	0.0270	7.075	5.461	3790.5	4.549	692.6	1.296
2800	0.29663	0.0001	3517	55.412	0.0238	7.472	5.718	4536.8	4.823	741.2	1.307
2900	0.19578	0	4021	51.102	0.0212	6.824	5.280	5270.4	5.084	781.2	1.292
3000	0.12274	0	4386	47.980	0.0192	5.428	4.286	5895.7	5.299	811.6	1.266
					$p=5 \cdot 10^{-5}$ bar						
600	0.99975	25.01	0	85.491	0.8564	0.2459	0.1481	1106.5	3.125	311.3	1.660
700	0.99994	5.806	0	85.475	0.7339	0.2438	0.1464	1130.9	3.163	336.8	1.665
800	0.99998	1.928	0	85.472	0.6421	0.2435	0.1461	1155.3	3.196	360.2	1.666
900	0.99999	0.8137	0	85.469	0.5708	0.2434	0.1460	1179.6	3.224	382.1	1.666
1000	0.999996	0.4062	0.0001	85.470	0.5131	0.2434	0.1460	1204.0	3.250	402.8	1.666
1100	0.999997	0.2290	0.0014	85.470	0.4670	0.2434	0.1460	1228.3	3.273	422.4	1.666
1200	0.999996	0.1409	0.0098	85.470	0.4281	0.2434	0.1461	1252.7	3.294	441.2	1.666
1300	0.99999	0.0927	0.0510	85.469	0.3951	0.2437	0.1464	1277.0	3.314	459.0	1.665
1400	0.99996	0.0645	0.2119	85.468	0.3669	0.2447	0.1473	1301.5	3.332	475.8	1.661
1500	0.99985	0.0469	0.7322	85.464	0.3424	0.2476	0.1500	1326.1	3.349	490.9	1.651
1600	0.99956	0.0353	2.179	85.451	0.3210	0.2545	0.1564	1351.1	3.365	503.4	1.627
1700	0.99885	0.0274	5.728	85.421	0.3020	0.2701	0.1710	1377.3	3.381	511.4	1.579
1800	0.99728	0.0217	13.57	85.354	0.2850	0.3004	0.1990	1405.8	3.397	514.5	1.509
1900	0.99411	0.0175	29.45	85.218	0.2696	0.3551	0.2494	1438.5	3.415	513.9	1.424
2000	0.98815	0.0142	59.23	84.964	0.2553	0.4486	0.3348	1478.5	3.436	512.2	1.340
2100	0.97770	0.0117	111.5	84.517	0.2419	0.5988	0.4708	1530.8	3.461	512.8	1.272
2200	0.96041	0.0096	197.9	83.778	0.2289	0.8277	0.6753	1602.0	3.495	517.5	1.226
2300	0.93341	0.0078	332.9	82.624	0.2159	1.162	0.9684	1701.6	3.539	527.1	1.220
2400	0.89344	0.0062	532.8	80.916	0.2026	1.631	1.370	1841.7	3.600	542.0	1.190
2500	0.83744	0.0048	812.8	78.523	0.1888	2.262	1.892	2037.5	3.680	562.7	1.196
2600	0.76341	0.0035	1183	75.360	0.1742	3.069	2.531	2306.2	3.787	590.0	1.213
2700	0.67140	0.0024	1642	71.436	0.1590	4.034	3.254	2665.2	3.924	624.4	1.240
2800	0.56563	0.0015	2172	66.907	0.1436	5.067	3.983	3126.8	4.094	665.5	1.272
2900	0.45294	0.0009	2735	62.092	0.1287	5.974	4.587	3688.9	4.293	711.3	1.302
3000	0.34360	0.0004	3282	57.418	0.1150	6.474	4.906	4325.1	4.512	757.4	1.320
					$p=10^{-4}$ bar						
600	0.99950	50.00	0	85.513	1.713	0.2484	0.1502	1106.3	3.058	310.6	1.653
700	0.99988	11.61	0	85.480	1.468	0.2442	0.1467	1130.9	3.096	336.7	1.664
800	0.99996	3.856	0	85.473	1.284	0.2436	0.1462	1155.3	3.128	360.2	1.666
900	0.99998	1.627	0	85.469	1.142	0.2434	0.1460	1179.6	3.157	382.1	1.666
1000	0.99999	0.8114	0.0001	85.469	1.027	0.2434	0.1460	1204.0	3.182	402.8	1.666
1100	0.99995	0.4573	0.0010	85.470	0.9340	0.2434	0.1460	1228.3	3.206	422.4	1.666

continued

T, °K	X_1	$X_2 \cdot 10^5$	$X_e \cdot 10^4$	M	$\varrho \cdot 10^4$	c_p	c_v	i	s	u	k
1200	0.99996	0.2820	0.0069	85.470	0.8562	0.2434	0.1461	1252.7	3.227	441.2	1.666
1300	0.99999	0.1855	0.0360	85.470	0.7903	0.2436	0.1463	1277.0	3.246	459.1	1.665
1400	0.99997	0.1291	0.1498	85.469	0.7338	0.2443	0.1470	1301.4	3.264	476.0	1.663
1500	0.99990	0.0939	0.5178	85.466	0.6849	0.2463	0.1488	1326.0	3.281	491.6	1.655
1600	0.99969	0.0707	1.541	85.457	0.6420	0.2512	0.1534	1350.8	3.297	505.1	1.638
1700	0.99919	0.0547	4.051	85.435	0.6041	0.2625	0.1639	1376.5	3.313	514.9	1.602
1800	0.99808	0.0434	9.600	85.388	0.5702	0.2840	0.1838	1403.8	3.329	520.5	1.545
1900	0.99583	0.0350	20.84	85.292	0.5396	0.3229	0.2196	1434.0	3.345	521.9	1.470
2000	0.99161	0.0287	41.96	85.111	0.5115	0.3892	0.2804	1469.5	3.363	520.9	1.388
2100	0.98418	0.0237	79.11	84.794	0.4854	0.4959	0.3772	1513.7	3.385	520.4	1.314
2200	0.97184	0.0196	140.8	84.267	0.4604	0.6583	0.5232	1571.4	3.412	522.8	1.258
2300	0.95244	0.0162	237.8	83.437	0.4361	0.8954	0.7331	1649.1	3.447	529.2	1.221
2400	0.92339	0.0132	383.0	82.196	0.4117	1.229	1.023	1755.7	3.492	540.2	1.201
2500	0.88203	0.0106	589.8	80.428	0.3867	1.682	1.406	1902.0	3.553	556.1	1.196
2600	0.82599	0.0082	870.1	78.034	0.3608	2.272	1.889	2101.2	3.632	577.5	1.203
2700	0.75396	0.0060	1230	74.956	0.3337	3.007	2.464	2367.6	3.733	604.8	1.221
2800	0.66658	0.0042	1667	71.221	0.3058	3.865	3.100	2715.1	3.861	638.6	1.247
2900	0.56715	0.0028	2164	66.972	0.2776	4.769	3.733	3153.0	4.017	678.4	1.278
3000	0.46186	0.0016	2691	62.473	0.2503	5.569	4.262	3679.2	4.197	722.5	1.306
					$p = 5 \cdot 10^{-4}$ bar						
600	0.99751	249.0	0	85.683	8.583	0.2683	0.1665	1105.2	2.899	306.0	1.608
700	0.99942	57.99	0	85.520	7.343	0.2477	0.1495	1130.6	2.938	335.8	1.656
800	0.99981	19.28	0	85.486	6.422	0.2445	0.1469	1155.2	2.971	359.9	1.664
900	0.99992	8.136	0	85.477	5.708	0.2437	0.1463	1179.6	3.000	382.0	1.666
1000	0.99996	4.057	0	85.473	5.137	0.2435	0.1461	1203.9	3.026	402.7	1.666
1100	0.99998	2.283	0.0004	85.472	4.670	0.2434	0.1461	1228.3	3.049	422.4	1.666
1200	0.99998	1.406	0.0031	85.471	4.281	0.2434	0.1461	1252.7	3.070	441.2	1.666
1300	0.99999	0.9273	0.0161	85.471	3.952	0.2435	0.1462	1277.0	3.090	459.1	1.666
1400	0.99998	0.6455	0.0670	85.470	3.669	0.2438	0.1464	1301.4	3.108	476.3	1.665
1500	0.99995	0.4694	0.2316	85.468	3.424	0.2447	0.1473	1325.8	3.125	492.5	1.661
1600	0.99986	0.3536	0.6892	85.464	3.210	0.2469	0.1493	1350.4	3.140	507.4	1.653
1700	0.99963	0.2740	1.812	85.455	3.021	0.2522	0.1543	1375.4	3.156	520.1	1.634
1800	0.99914	0.2175	4.296	85.433	2.853	0.2621	0.1635	1401.1	3.170	530.0	1.603
1900	0.99813	0.1760	9.330	85.390	2.701	0.2798	0.1798	1428.1	3.185	536.6	1.556
2000	0.99624	0.1148	18.81	85.309	2.564	0.3100	0.2076	1457.6	3.200	539.7	1.493
2100	0.99289	0.1206	35.54	85.166	2.437	0.3585	0.2519	1491.0	3.216	540.3	1.423
2200	0.98731	0.1012	63.46	84.928	2.320	0.4320	0.3184	1530.5	3.235	540.7	1.356
2300	0.97844	0.0853	107.8	84.549	2.209	0.5390	0.4145	1579.0	3.257	542.5	1.300
2400	0.96498	0.0726	175.1	83.973	2.103	0.6901	0.5485	1640.6	3.283	546.9	1.258
2500	0.94538	0.0606	273.1	83.136	1.999	0.8961	0.7286	1720.3	3.316	554.7	1.230
2600	0.91796	0.0505	410.2	81.964	1.895	1.168	0.9622	1824.1	3.357	566.1	1.214
2700	0.88105	0.0413	594.7	80.387	1.789	1.519	1.255	1959.4	3.408	581.5	1.210
2800	0.83328	0.0331	833.6	78.345	1.682	1.955	1.609	2134.6	3.473	601.1	1.215
2900	0.77388	0.0257	1131	75.807	1.571	2.479	2.018	2358.5	3.552	625.3	1.229
3000	0.70307	0.0192	1485	72.781	1.458	3.082	2.467	2639.8	3.649	654.5	1.249
					$p = 10^{-3}$ bar						
600	0.99504	495.5	0	85.894	17.21	0.2924	0.1862	1103.7	2.830	301.4	1.563
700	0.99884	115.8	0	85.569	14.69	0.2520	0.1529	1130.3	2.871	334.7	1.646
800	0.99961	38.54	0	85.503	12.85	0.2456	0.1477	1155.1	2.904	359.6	1.662
900	0.99984	16.27	0	85.484	11.42	0.2441	0.1466	1179.5	2.933	381.9	1.665
1000	0.99992	8.113	0	85.477	10.27	0.2437	0.1462	1203.9	2.958	402.7	1.666
1100	0.99995	4.566	0.0003	85.474	9.340	0.2435	0.1461	1228.3	2.982	422.4	1.666
1200	0.99997	2.812	0.0022	85.472	8.562	0.2434	0.1461	1252.6	3.003	441.2	1.666
1300	0.99998	1.855	0.0114	85.471	7.903	0.2435	0.1461	1277.0	3.022	459.2	1.666
1400	0.99998	1.291	0.0474	85.471	7.338	0.2437	0.1463	1301.4	3.040	476.4	1.665
1500	0.99996	0.9388	0.1637	85.469	6.849	0.2443	0.1469	1325.8	3.057	492.7	1.663
1600	0.99990	0.7072	0.4873	85.466	6.421	0.2459	0.1484	1350.3	3.073	508.0	1.657
1700	0.99974	0.5480	1.281	85.460	6.043	0.2498	0.1521	1375.1	3.088	521.4	1.643
1800	0.99939	0.4353	3.038	85.444	5.706	0.2569	0.1587	1400.4	3.102	532.6	1.619
1900	0.99868	0.3524	6.599	85.414	5.404	0.2696	0.1704	1426.7	3.117	541.1	1.582
2000	0.99734	0.2902	13.31	85.356	5.130	0.2912	0.1903	1454.8	3.131	546.1	1.530
2100	0.99497	0.2421	25.15	85.255	4.880	0.3260	0.2221	1485.6	3.146	548.4	1.468

continued

T, °K	X_1	$X_2 \cdot 10^5$	$X_e \cdot 10^4$	M	$\varrho \cdot 10^4$	c_p	c_v	i	s	u	k
2200	0.99101	0.2039	44.96	85.086	4.649	0.3784	0.2697	1520.8	3.162	549.4	1.403
2300	0.98470	0.1729	76.46	84.817	4.433	0.4545	0.3382	1562.4	3.181	550.6	1.344
2400	0.97510	0.1472	124.4	84.406	4.227	0.5619	0.4340	1613.4	3.203	553.4	1.294
2500	0.96106	0.1253	194.7	83.806	4.030	0.7085	0.5632	1677.1	3.229	558.7	1.258
2600	0.94126	0.1061	293.7	82.960	3.835	0.9027	0.7318	1758.1	3.261	567.1	1.233
2700	0.91432	0.0890	428.4	81.808	3.642	1.153	0.9450	1861.5	3.301	578.8	1.220
2800	0.87892	0.0736	605.4	80.296	3.447	1.468	1.206	1993.5	3.349	594.0	1.216
2900	0.83401	0.0597	829.9	78.376	3.249	1.851	1.516	2161.0	3.408	613.1	1.221
3000	0.77900	0.0472	1105	76.025	3.046	2.306	1.869	2371.0	3.480	636.4	1.234

$p = 5 \cdot 10^{-3}$ bar

T, °K	X_1	$X_2 \cdot 10^5$	$X_e \cdot 10^4$	M	$\varrho \cdot 10^4$	c_p	c_v	i	s	u	k
700	0.99426	574.0	0	85.960	73.80	0.2854	0.1794	1127.6	2.710	327.4	1.582
800	0.99808	192.1	0	85.634	64.33	0.2544	0.1545	1154.2	2.746	357.3	1.643
900	0.99919	81.24	0	85.539	57.12	0.2471	0.1488	1179.1	2.776	381.0	1.659
1000	0.99959	40.54	0	85.505	51.39	0.2449	0.1471	1203.7	2.802	402.5	1.665
1100	0.99977	22.82	0.0001	85.490	46.71	0.2441	0.1465	1228.2	2.825	422.3	1.666
1200	0.99986	14.05	0.0010	85.482	42.81	0.2438	0.1463	1252.6	2.846	441.1	1.666
1300	0.99991	9.272	0.0051	85.478	39.52	0.2436	0.1462	1276.9	2.866	459.2	1.666
1400	0.99993	6.454	0.0212	85.475	36.69	0.2436	0.1462	1301.3	2.883	476.4	1.666
1500	0.99994	4.694	0.0732	85.473	34.25	0.2439	0.1465	1325.7	2.900	493.0	1.665
1600	0.99992	3.536	0.2179	85.471	32.11	0.2445	0.1471	1350.1	2.916	508.8	1.662
1700	0.99986	2.741	0.5731	85.467	30.22	0.2466	0.1491	1374.7	2.931	523.2	1.654
1800	0.99971	2.178	1.359	85.462	28.54	0.2501	0.1523	1399.6	2.945	536.3	1.642
1900	0.99939	1.765	2.952	85.446	27.03	0.2560	0.1578	1424.9	2.959	547.8	1.622
2000	0.99879	1.455	5.955	85.420	25.67	0.2662	0.1673	1451.0	2.972	556.8	1.591
2100	0.99773	1.217	11.26	85.375	24.43	0.2825	0.1823	1478.4	2.986	563.2	1.550
2200	0.99596	1.030	20.16	85.299	23.30	0.3068	0.2044	1507.8	2.999	567.4	1.501
2300	0.99312	0.8792	34.34	85.177	22.26	0.3416	0.2360	1540.2	3.014	570.2	1.447
2400	0.98878	0.7566	56.05	84.991	21.28	0.3907	0.2803	1576.9	3.029	572.3	1.394
2500	0.98239	0.6545	88.04	84.718	20.37	0.4578	0.3400	1619.5	3.047	574.9	1.346
2600	0.97328	0.5673	133.6	84.329	19.49	0.5464	0.4185	1669.8	3.067	578.7	1.306
2700	0.96072	0.4915	196.4	83.792	18.65	0.6609	0.5185	1730.5	3.090	584.5	1.274
2800	0.94388	0.4243	280.6	83.072	17.83	0.8058	0.6435	1804.3	3.117	592.6	1.252
2900	0.92195	0.3646	390.2	82.135	17.02	0.9841	0.7946	1894.4	3.149	603.2	1.238
3000	0.89411	0.3109	529 4	80.945	16.22	1.200	0.9738	2004.5	3.187	616.4	1.232

$p = 10^{-2}$ bar

T, °K	X_1	$X_2 \cdot 10^5$	$X_e \cdot 10^4$	M	$\varrho \cdot 10^4$	c_p	c_v	i	s	u	k
700	0.98865	1 135	0	86.440	148.4	0.3246	0.2102	1124.2	2.639	320.8	1.528
800	0.99617	382.7	0	85.797	128.9	0.2652	0.1628	1153.0	2.677	354.7	1.622
900	0.99838	162.2	0	85.609	114 3	0.2508	0.1516	1178.6	2.708	380.1	1.652
1000	0.99919	81.01	0	85.539	102 8	0.2464	0.1482	1203.5	2.734	402.2	1.663
1100	0.99954	45.62	0.0001	85.509	93.44	0.2448	0.1470	1228.0	2.757	422.2	1.665
1200	0.99972	28.10	0.0007	85.494	85.64	0.2441	0.1465	1252.5	2.778	441.1	1.666
1300	0.99981	18.54	0.0036	85.486	79.04	0.2438	0.1463	1276.9	2.798	459.1	1.666
1400	0.99987	12.91	0.0150	85.481	73.39	0.2437	0.1463	1301.3	2.816	476.5	1.666
1500	0.99990	9.387	0.0518	85.478	68.50	0.2438	0.1464	1325.7	2.833	493.1	1.665
1600	0.99990	7.072	0.1541	85.475	64.22	0.2443	0.1468	1350.1	2.849	509.0	1.664
1700	0.99986	5.482	0.4052	85.471	60.44	0.2459	0.1484	1374.6	2.864	523.6	1.657
1800	0.99976	4.356	0.9609	85.466	57.07	0.2484	0.1508	1399.3	2.878	537.3	1.647
1900	0.99955	3.530	2.088	85.455	54.06	0.2528	0.1548	1424.4	2.891	549.5	1.632
2000	0.99913	2.913	4.211	85.436	51.35	0.2603	0.1618	1450.0	2.904	559.7	1.609
2100	0.99838	2.438	7.968	85.404	48.88	0.2722	0.1729	1476.7	2.917	567.6	1.575
2200	0.99713	2.065	14.26	85.350	46.63	0.2898	0.1890	1504.8	2.930	573.5	1.534
2300	0.99512	1.765	24.31	85.264	44.56	0.3149	0.2117	1535.0	2.944	577.7	1.487
2400	0.99204	1.523	39.70	85.131	42.63	0.3502	0.2436	1568.3	2.958	580.6	1.437
2500	0.98750	1.323	62.41	84.938	40.84	0.3983	0.2867	1605.8	2.974	583.2	1.389
2600	0.98102	1.153	94.82	84.660	39.14	0.4619	0.3433	1648.9	2.990	586.3	1.346
2700	0.97205	1.006	139.7	84.277	37.52	0.5439	0.4155	1699.4	3.010	590.7	1.309
2800	0.95998	0.8777	200.1	83.761	35.96	0.6478	0.5060	1759.3	3.032	596.7	1.280
2900	0.94414	0.7648	279.2	83.084	34.44	0.7756	0.6157	1830.9	3.057	604.8	1.260
3000	0.92388	0.6639	380.6	82.218	32.94	0.9306	0.7466	1916.8	3.086	615.1	1.246

continued

$T, °K$	X_1	$X_2 \cdot 10^5$	$X_e \cdot 10^4$	M	$\varrho \cdot 10^4$	c_p	c_v	i	s	u	k
					$p=5 \cdot 10^{-2}$ bar						
800	0,98143	1 857	0	87.058	654.0	0.3432	0,2220	1144,3	2.511	340.8	1,519
900	0,99199	800.8	0	86,154	575,3	0.2792	0,1727	1174,8	2,547	373.3	1.604
1000	0,99598	402.5	0	85.814	515,8	0,2584	0.1565	1201,5	2.576	400.0	1.651
1100	0,99773	227.2	0	85.664	468.0	0,2505	0,1509	1226.9	2.600	421.2	1.661
1200	0.99860	140.2	0,0003	85.590	428.7	0,2472	0.1485	1251.8	2,622	440.6	1.664
1300	0.99907	92.56	0.0016	85,549	395.5	0,2456	0.1474	1276.4	2.641	458.9	1.666
1400	0,99935	64.47	0.0067	85,525	367.2	0,2447	0.1469	1300.9	2,659	476.4	1.666
1500	0.99953	46,90	0,0232	85.510	342.6	0.2444	0.1466	1325.4	2.676	493,1	1.666
1600	0.99963	35.34	0.0689	85,500	321,2	0,2443	0.1467	1349.9	2.692	509.2	1.665
1700	0,99969	27.40	0.1812	85.492	302.2	0.2452	0.1476	1374.3	2.707	524.2	1.661
1800	0,99970	21.78	0.4297	85.485	285.4	0.2465	0.1489	1398.9	2,721	538.5	1.655
1900	0,99964	17,66	0,9337	85.477	270.4	0.2486	0.1509	1423,7	2,734	551,9	1.647
2000	0.99948	14,57	1.884	85.466	256.8	0.2525	0.1546	1448.8	2.747	563.9	1,634
2100	0.99916	12.21	3.565	85.450	244.6	0.2586	0.1603	1474.4	2.760	574.3	1.613
2200	0.99862	10,35	6.382	85.424	233.4	0,2673	0.1683	1500.6	2.772	583.3	1,588
2300	0.99773	8.874	10.88	85.384	223,1	0,2793	0,1793	1527.9	2.784	590.8	1.558
2400	0.99636	7.682	17.79	85.324	213.7	0,2961	0.1947	1556.7	2.796	596.6	1,521
2500	0,99433	6.705	28.01	85,236	204.9	0,3190	0.2154	1587,5	2.809	601.2	1.481
2600	0.99142	5.887	42.63	85,111	196.7	0.3490	0.2424	1621.0	2,822	604.9	1,440
2700	0.98736	5.191	62.96	84.936	189.1	0.3876	0.2768	1657.9	2.836	608.5	1.400
2800	0.98186	4.591	90.49	84.700	181,8	0.4366	0.3202	1699.2	2,851	612.3	1.363
2900	0,97458	4,075	126.9	84.389	174.9	0.4963	0.3726	1746.1	2.868	617,0	1.332
3000	0,96517	3,623	173,9	83.986	168.2	0.5686	0,4355	1799.6	2,886	622.9	1.306
					$p=10^{-1}$ bar						
800	0.96415	3 585	0	88,534	1 330	0.4233	0,2812	1134,5	2.433	331,1	1.458
900	0.98423	1 576	0	86,818	1 160	0,3118	0,1967	1170,2	2.476	367.0	1,562
1000	0.99201	798.6	0	86.152	1 036	0,2727	0.1664	1199.1	2.506	397.8	1,638
1100	0.99548	452,5	0	85.857	938.2	0,2575	0.1555	1225.5	2,531	420.1	1,656
1200	0,99720	279.6	0.0002	85.709	858.5	0.2509	0,1509	1250,9	2,553	440,0	1.662
1300	0.99815	184,8	0,0011	85,628	791.8	0,2477	0,1488	1275,8	2.573	458,6	1,665
1400	0,99871	128,8	0.0047	85,580	734.8	0,2461	0.1477	1300,5	2.592	476.2	1.666
1500	0.99906	93.71	0,0164	85,550	685.6	0,2452	0,1471	1325,1	2.608	493,0	1,666
1600	0,99928	70.63	0.0487	85.530	642,6	0,2448	0.1469	1349,6	2.624	509.2	1.666
1700	0.99943	54.77	0.1281	85.516	604.7	0,2454	0,1476	1374,1	2.639	524.3	1,662
1800	0.99950	43.54	0.3038	85.505	571.0	0.2463	0,1486	1398,7	2.653	538,8	1,658
1900	0,99951	35.30	0.6602	85.494	540.9	0.2478	0,1501	1423.5	2.667	552.5	1,651
2000	0.99944	29.14	1.332	85.484	513.8	0.2508	0.1529	1448.4	2.679	565.0	1,640
2100	0.99925	24.42	2.521	85.469	489.2	0,2555	0.1574	1473.7	2.692	576.1	1,623
2200	0,99889	20.72	4.514	85.449	466.9	0,2620	0,1634	1499,6	2.704	586.0	1,603
2300	0,99828	17.77	7.699	85.419	446.4	0,2709	0,1716	1526.2	2.716	594.6	1,578
2400	0,99733	15,39	12.59	85.376	427,6	0.2834	0.1831	1553.9	2.727	601.6	1,548
2500	0,99590	13,45	19.82	85.312	410.2	0,3002	0.1984	1583.2	2.739	607.3	1,513
2600	0,99384	11,83	30.18	85.222	394,0	0,3223	0.2184	1614.3	2.752	612.0	1.476
2700	0,99098	10.46	44 60	85.098	378.8	0,3506	0.2438	1648.0	2.764	616,1	1.438
2800	0.98728	9,280	64.15	84.930	364,6	0,3865	0,2759	1685.0	2,778	619,9	1.401
2900	0,98191	8,273	90.05	84.707	351.1	0.4300	0.3144	1725,9	2.792	624,2	1.368
3000	0.97520	7.397	123.6	84.420	338,2	0.4827	0.3605	1771.7	2.808	629,2	1.339
					$p=2 \cdot 10^{-1}$ bar						
900	0,96941	3 059	0	88,084	2 353	0.3685	0,2376	1161.6	2,400	358.1	1.509
1000	0,98428	1 572	0	86.814	2 087	0.2993	0,1846	1194.5	2.435	394.2	1.622
1100	0,99103	896.9	0	86.236	1 845	0.2709	0,1644	1222.8	2.462	418.1	1.647
1200	0,99444	556.1	0.0002	85.945	1 722	0.2582	0,1556	1249,2	2,485	439,0	1.659
1300	0,99632	368,2	0,0008	85.785	1 586	0,2520	0.1514	1274.7	2,505	458.0	1.664
1400	0,99743	256.9	0,0033	85,690	1 471	0.2487	0,1492	1299.7	2,524	475.9	1,666
1500	0,99813	187.1	0.0116	85,630	1 372	0.2469	0.1481	1324.5	2.541	492.9	1,667
1600	0,99858	141,1	0,0344	85,590	1 286	0.2459	0.1475	1349,1	2,557	509.2	1.667
1700	0,99889	109,4	0,0906	85,563	1 210	0,2460	0,1479	1373.7	2.572	524.4	1,664
1800	0,99909	87,00	0,2148	85.542	1 142	0.2465	0.1485	1398.4	2,586	539,0	1,660
1900	0,99920	70.56	0.4668	85,526	1 082	0,2476	0.1496	1423.1	2,599	552.9	1,654
2000	0,99923	58,27	0,9418	85.512	1 028	0.2498	0.1518	1448.0	2,612	565.8	1,645
2100	0,99916	48.83	1,782	85,496	978,8	0.2535	0,1554	1473.2	2.624	577.3	1,631

continued

T, °K	X_1	$X_2 \cdot 10^5$	$X_e \cdot 10^4$	M	$\varrho \cdot 10^4$	c_p	c_v	i	s	u	k
2200	0,99895	41.44	3,192	85.478	934,1	0,2584	0,1601	1498.7	2.636	587.9	1,614
2300	0,99856	35.55	5,445	85.454	893.2	0.2651	0.1663	1524.9	2.648	597.5	1.594
2400	0,99791	30.82	8,904	85.420	855,6	0,2744	0.1749	1551.9	2.659	605.6	1.569
2500	0,99692	26.96	14,02	85.373	821.0	0,2871	0.1865	1580,0	2.671	612.4	1.539
2600	0.99549	23.74	21.36	85.308	788.8	0.3035	0.2015	1609.5	2.682	618.0	1.506
2700	0.99347	21.02	31.58	85.218	758.8	0,3245	0.2204	1641,0	2.694	622.9	1,472
2800	0.99072	18.70	45.45	85.098	730.6	0.3512	0.2444	1674.8	2.706	627.1	1.437
2900	0.98706	16.72	63.84	84.939	704.1	0,3832	0.2730	1711.6	2.719	631.4	1.404
3000	0.98230	15.01	87.74	84.733	679.0	0.4219	0,3072	1752.0	2.733	636.0	1.373

$p = 5 \cdot 10^{-1}$ bar

T, °K	X_1	$X_2 \cdot 10^5$	$X_e \cdot 10^4$	M	$\varrho \cdot 10^4$	c_p	c_v	i	s	u	k
900	0.92967	7 033	0	91,481	6 109	0.4893	0.3218	1139.7	2,291	343.1	1,438
1000	0,96242	3 758	0	88,682	5 330	0.3660	0,2283	1181,8	2.335	387,8	1,603
1100	0.97816	2 184	0	87.337	4 772	0.3070	0.1879	1215.1	2,367	413.8	1.634
1200	0,98632	1 368	0.0001	86,639	4 339	0.2786	0.1686	1244.2	2,392	436.4	1,653
1300	0.99089	910.5	0,0005	86,248	3 987	0.2641	0.1589	1271.3	2.414	456.6	1,662
1400	0.99363	637.3	0.0021	86,015	3 693	0.2563	0.1538	1297.3	2,433	475.1	1,667
1500	0.99535	465.1	0.0073	85,867	3 440	0,2519	0.1510	1322.7	2,451	492.4	1,668
1600	0.99648	351.2	0,0218	85,770	3 222	0,2493	0.1494	1347.7	2,467	508.9	1,669
1700	0.99726	272.7	0,0572	85.702	3 040	0.2483	0.1490	1372.6	2.482	524.3	1,666
1800	0.99780	217.0	0.1358	85,654	2 860	0,2480	0,1492	1397.4	2,496	539.1	1.662
1900	0,99818	176.0	0.2951	85.618	2 708	0,2483	0.1497	1422.3	2.509	553.3	1,658
2000	0,99843	145.4	0.5954	85.589	2 572	0,2496	0.1512	1447.2	2,522	566.4	1,650
2100	0,99856	121.9	1,126	85,565	2 449	0,2522	0.1539	1472.3	2.534	578,5	1,639
2200	0.99856	103.5	2.018	85,541	2 337	0.2557	0.1573	1497.7	2,546	589.8	1,626
2300	0.99842	88.86	3.443	85.516	2 235	0.2603	0.1616	1523.4	2,558	600.2	1.610
2400	0.99810	77.09	5.632	85.488	2 141	0.2668	0.1678	1549.8	2,569	609.4	1,590
2500	0.99755	67.09	8.871	85.452	2 054	0.2756	0.1760	1578.0	2,580	617.4	1.566
2600	0.99670	59.50	13.52	85.405	1 974	0.2870	0.1865	1605.1	2.591	624.3	1.539
2700	0.99547	52.77	19.99	85.344	1 900	0.3015	0.1997	1634,5	2.602	630.3	1.510
2800	0.99377	47.03	28,79	85.264	1 830	0.3199	0.2165	1665.7	2.614	635.4	1,478
2900	0.99148	42,17	40.47	85.160	1 765	0.3418	0.2362	1698.8	2.625	640.2	1.447
3000	0.98849	38.00	55.67	85.027	1 703	0,3680	0,2597	1734,3	2.637	645.0	1.417

$p = 8 \cdot 10^{-1}$ bar

T, °K	X_1	$X_2 \cdot 10^5$	$X_e \cdot 10^4$	M	$\varrho \cdot 10^4$	c_p	c_v	i	s	u	k
1000	0.94235	5 765	0	90.397	8 693	0.4170	0,2601	1170.6	2.280	384.1	1,603
1100	0.96592	3 408	0	88.383	7 726	0.3379	0.2072	1207.9	2.316	410.8	1.630
1200	0.97846	2 154	0.0001	87.311	6 997	0,2971	0.1800	1239,4	2.343	434.4	1,650
1300	0.98559	1 441	0,0004	86.702	6 413	0,2755	0,1658	1268,0	2.336	455.3	1.662
1400	0.98988	1 012	0.0017	86.335	5 930	0.2636	0.1581	1294,9	2.386	474,3	1,668
1500	0.99260	740.0	0.0058	86.102	5 520	0,2567	0.1537	1320.9	2.404	492.0	1,670
1600	0.99440	559,5	0,0172	85,948	5 165	0,2526	0.1521	1346.3	2.420	508.7	1.671
1700	0.99564	434.8	0,0452	85.841	4 856	0,2506	0.1503	1371,5	2.436	524,2	1.668
1800	0.99652	346.2	0,1072	85.765	4 582	0.2496	0.1499	1396.6	2.450	539.1	1.665
1900	0.99714	281.1	0.2331	85.708	4 338	0.2494	0.1502	1421,5	2.463	553.4	1.661
2000	0.99758	232.3	0.4705	85.664	4 119	0.2502	0,1513	1446.5	2.476	566.7	1,653
2100	0,99787	194.8	0,8906	85,629	3 921	0,2523	0.1536	1471.6	2.488	579,0	1.643
2200	0.99803	165,5	1.595	85.598	3 742	0,2551	0.1564	1497.0	2.500	590.5	1.631
2300	0.99804	142.1	2,722	85.568	3 578	0,2589	0,1601	1522,7	2.512	601,3	1.617
2400	0.99788	123.3	4,452	85.537	3 427	0,2643	0.1653	1548,8	2.523	610.9	1,599
2500	0.99752	108.0	7.013	85.502	3 289	0.2717	0.1722	1575.7	2.534	619.4	1.577
2600	0.99691	95.24	10,69	85.460	3 161	0.2813	0.1812	1603.3	2,545	626.9	1.553
2700	0,99599	84.52	15.81	85,407	3 042	0,2934	0,1923	1632,1	2,556	633,4	1.525
2800	0,99469	75,39	22.77	85,340	2 931	0,3088	0.2065	1662,2	2,566	638.9	1,495
2900	0,99292	67,67	32.02	85.254	2 827	0,3270	0.2230	1694,0	2,578	644,2	1,466
3000	0,99058	61.05	44,06	85,146	2 729	0,3487	0.2426	1727.8	2,589	649,1	1.438

$p = 1$ bar

T, °K	X_1	$X_2 \cdot 10^5$	$X_e \cdot 10^4$	M	$\varrho \cdot 10^4$	c_p	c_v	i	s	u	k
1000	0,92984	7 016	0	91.466	10 995	0.4445	0,2767	1163.8	2.253	382.3	1.607
1100	0.95809	4 191	0	89.052	9 731	0.3560	0,2184	1203,4	2,291	409.3	1.630
1200	0.97336	2 664	0,0001	87.747	8 790	0,3085	0,1869	1236.4	2,319	433.3	1.650

continued

T, °K	X_1	$X_2 \cdot 10^4$	$X_e \cdot 10^5$	M	$\varrho \cdot 10^4$	c_p	c_v	i	s	u	k
1300	0.98211	1 789	0.0004	86.999	8 044	0.2827	0.1701	1265.8	2.343	454.6	1.662
1400	0.98741	1 259	0.0015	86.546	7 431	0.2683	0.1608	1293.3	2.363	473.8	1.668
1500	0.99078	921.6	0.0052	86.258	6 912	0.2599	0.1555	1319.7	2.382	491.7	1.671
1600	0.99302	697.5	0.0154	86.066	6 466	0.2548	0.1524	1345.4	2.398	508.5	1.672
1700	0.99457	542.4	0.0404	85.933	6 076	0.2522	0.1511	1370.8	2.414	524.1	1.669
1800	0.99566	432.0	0.0959	85.838	5 732	0.2507	0.1505	1396.0	2.428	539.1	1.666
1900	0.99645	350.8	0.2084	85.768	5 426	0.2501	0.1505	1421.0	2.442	553.4	1.662
2000	0.99702	290.0	0.4207	85.714	5 152	0.2507	0.1515	1446.0	2.454	566.8	1.655
2100	0.99741	243.3	0.7964	85.671	4 904	0.2525	0.1535	1471.2	2.467	579.1	1.645
2200	0.99765	206.7	1.426	85.634	4 679	0.2550	0.1562	1496.6	2.478	590.8	1.633
2300	0.99774	177.5	2.434	85.601	4 474	0.2585	0.1596	1522.2	2.490	601.7	1.620
2400	0.99766	154.0	3.981	85.568	4 286	0.2635	0.1644	1548.4	2.501	611.5	1.603
2500	0.99740	134.9	6.272	85.532	4 112	0.2702	0.1708	1575.1	2.512	620.2	1.582
2600	0.99690	119.0	9.558	85.490	3 952	0.2791	0.1791	1602.5	2.523	627.9	1.558
2700	0.99612	105.7	14.14	85.439	3 804	0.2902	0.1894	1631.0	2.533	634.7	1.532
2800	0.99498	94.29	20.37	85.376	3 665	0.3044	0.2025	1660.8	2.544	640.4	1.503
2900	0.99342	84.68	28.64	85.298	3 536	0.3211	0.2177	1692.1	2.555	645.9	1.475
3000	0.99135	76.44	39.42	85.198	3 414	0.3410	0.2357	1725.2	2.566	651.0	1.447
					p=2 bar						
1100	0.92232	7 768	0	92.110	20 131	0.4245	0.2582	1183.7	2.209	404.1	1.644
1200	0.94932	5 068	0	89.802	17 991	0.3558	0.2147	1222.4	2.243	429.2	1.657
1300	0.96543	3 457	0.0002	88.425	16 352	0.3144	0.1885	1255.7	2.269	451.7	1.668
1400	0.97543	2 457	0.0010	87.570	15 038	0.2897	0.1730	1285.8	2.292	471.9	1.674
1500	0.98190	1 810	0.0036	87.017	13 946	0.2746	0.1637	1314.0	2.311	490.5	1.678
1600	0.98624	1 376	0.0108	86.646	13 019	0.2652	0.1580	1341.0	2.329	507.8	1.679
1700	0.98926	1 073	0.0285	86.387	12 216	0.2597	0.1550	1367.2	2.344	523.8	1.676
1800	0.99142	856.8	0.0676	86.202	11 513	0.2562	0.1532	1393.0	2.359	539.0	1.672
1900	0.99300	696.9	0.1471	86.064	10 890	0.2541	0.1523	1418.6	2.373	553.5	1.668
2000	0.99417	576.8	0.2970	85.960	10 333	0.2536	0.1526	1444.0	2.386	567.0	1.661
2100	0.99504	484.3	0.5625	85.879	9 831	0.2543	0.1540	1469.4	2.398	579.6	1.652
2200	0.99568	411.7	1.008	85.813	9 377	0.2559	0.1560	1494.9	2.410	591.6	1.641
2300	0.99612	353.8	1.720	85.758	8 964	0.2582	0.1585	1520.6	2.422	602.8	1.629
2400	0.99636	307.3	2.813	85.709	8 585	0.2620	0.1623	1546.6	2.433	613.1	1.614
2500	0.99642	259.3	4.433	85.662	8 238	0.2672	0.1674	1573.0	2.444	622.4	1.596
2600	0.99627	237.8	6.757	85.615	7 916	0.2740	0.1740	1600.1	2.454	630.7	1.575
2700	0.99589	211.2	9.997	85.565	7 619	0.2827	0.1822	1627.9	2.465	638.1	1.551
2800	0.99523	188.7	14.40	85.508	7 342	0.2939	0.1928	1656.8	2.475	644.5	1.525
2900	0.99425	169.6	20.26	85.442	7 083	0.3069	0.2047	1686.9	2.486	650.6	1.499
3000	0.99289	153.3	27.90	85.363	6 841	0.3223	0.2189	1718.3	2.496	656.1	1.472
					p=4 bar						
1200	0.90740	9 260	0	93.385	37 418	0.4171	0.2479	1199.5	2.160	424.1	1.682
1300	0.93513	6 487	0.0002	91.015	33 663	0.3613	0.2141	1238.2	2.192	447.8	1.688
1400	0.95309	4 691	0.0007	89.480	30 731	0.3241	0.1916	1272.4	2.217	469.2	1.691
1500	0.96502	3 497	0.0025	88.459	28 365	0.2996	0.1770	1303.5	2.238	488.6	1.692
1600	0.97320	2 680	0.0076	87.750	26 373	0.2835	0.1676	1332.6	2.257	506.6	1.692
1700	0.97898	2 102	0.0200	87.266	24 682	0.2733	0.1619	1360.5	2.274	523.1	1.688
1800	0.98314	1 685	0.0476	86.910	23 215	0.2664	0.1582	1387.4	2.290	538.7	1.684
1900	0.98623	1 375	0.1037	86.644	21 926	0.2619	0.1560	1413.9	2.304	553.5	1.679
2000	0.98855	1 140	0.2094	86.443	20 782	0.2595	0.1552	1439.9	2.317	567.2	1.672
2100	0.99032	959.5	0.3968	86.287	19 756	0.2587	0.1557	1465.9	2.330	580.0	1.662
2200	0.99169	816.8	0.7111	86.162	18 831	0.2590	0.1569	1491.7	2.342	592.2	1.651
2300	0.99273	702.8	1.214	86.060	17 991	0.2602	0.1587	1517.7	2.353	603.8	1.640
2400	0.99349	611.0	1.986	85.975	17 224	0.2626	0.1616	1543.8	2.364	614.4	1.626
2500	0.99401	536.1	3.131	85.901	16 521	0.2664	0.1656	1570.3	2.375	624.1	1.609
2600	0.99431	473.7	4.773	85.834	15 873	0.2717	0.1709	1597.2	2.386	632.9	1.590
2700	0.99438	421.2	7.064	85.770	15 274	0.2785	0.1776	1624.7	2.396	640.9	1.568
2800	0.99420	376.6	10.18	85.705	14 717	0.2874	0.1862	1653.0	2.407	647.8	1.544
2900	0.99374	338.9	14.32	85.637	14 198	0.2976	0.1958	1682.3	2.417	654.3	1.420
3000	0.99299	306.8	19.73	85.564	13 713	0.3097	0.2071	1712.6	2.427	660.3	1.495

continued

T, °K	X_1	$X_2 \cdot 10^5$	$X_e \cdot 10^4$	M	$\varrho \cdot 10^4$	c_p	c_v	i	s	u	k
					p=6 bar						
1200	0,87178	12 822	0	96,429	57 956	0,4523	0,2655	1181,4	2,110	420,0	1,704
1300	0,90821	9 179	0,0001	93,315	51 770	0,3931	0,2302	1223,5	2,144	444,9	1,708
1400	0,93262	6 738	0,0006	91,229	46 998	0,3500	0,2049	1260,6	2,171	467,0	1,708
1500	0,94924	5 076	0,0021	89,808	43 181	0,3199	0,1873	1294,0	2,194	487,1	1,708
1600	0,96082	3 918	0,0062	88,818	40 036	0,2991	0,1753	1324,9	2,214	505,6	1,706
1700	0,96910	3 090	0,0163	88,111	37 381	0,2853	0,1677	1354,1	2,232	522,4	1,701
1800	0,97513	2 486	0,0387	87,595	35 098	0,2757	0,1626	1382,1	2,248	538,4	1,695
1900	0,97964	2 035	0,0844	87,208	33 104	0,2691	0,1593	1409,4	2,263	553,4	1,690
2000	0,98305	1 692	0,1705	86,914	31 342	0,2651	0,1577	1436,1	2,276	567,3	1,681
2100	0,98568	1 426	0,3232	86,686	29 771	0,2631	0,1575	1462,5	2,289	580,3	1,671
2200	0,98773	1 216	0,5794	86,504	28 358	0,2624	0,1581	1488,8	2,301	592,6	1,660
2300	0,98933	1 047	0,9895	86,356	27 079	0,2626	0,1594	1515,0	2,313	604,3	1,648
2400	0,99056	911,2	1,620	86,235	25 914	0,2643	0,1617	1541,4	2,324	615,1	1,634
2500	0,99149	800,1	2,553	86,132	24 848	0,2673	0,1652	1568,0	2,336	625,0	1,618
2600	0,99215	707,5	3,893	86,041	23 867	0,2716	0,1699	1594,9	2,346	634,0	1,599
2700	0,99255	629,5	5,762	85,959	22 961	0,2774	0,1758	1622,3	2,356	642,2	1,578
2800	0,99271	563,2	8,306	85,880	22 121	0,2852	0,1835	1650,5	2,366	649,4	1,555
2900	0,99259	507,2	11,69	85,804	21 339	0,2941	0,1920	1679,5	2,376	656,2	1,531
3000	0,99219	459,4	16,10	85,725	20 609	0,3047	0,2021	1709,4	2,387	662,5	1,508
					p=8 bar						
1300	0,88404	11 596	0,0001	95,381	70 555	0,4152	0,2408	1210,9	2,108	442,2	1,724
1400	0,91376	8 624	0,0005	92,841	63 771	0,3698	0,2144	1250,0	2,138	465,1	1,724
1500	0,93442	6 558	0,0018	91,075	58 387	0,3364	0,1953	1285,3	2,162	485,8	1,722
1600	0,94904	5 096	0,0053	89,826	53 987	0,3124	0,1817	1317,6	2,183	504,7	1,719
1700	0,95960	4 039	0,0140	88,922	50 300	0,2958	0,1727	1348,1	2,201	521,9	1,713
1800	0,96736	3 263	0,0334	88,258	47 151	0,2840	0,1665	1377,0	2,218	538,1	1,706
1900	0,97321	2 677	0,0728	87,758	44 416	0,2758	0,1623	1405,0	2,233	553,2	1,699
2000	0,97766	2 231	0,1473	87,376	42 012	0,2704	0,1600	1432,3	2,247	567,4	1,690
2100	0,98111	1 883	0,2793	87,077	39 874	0,2673	0,1592	1459,3	2,260	580,4	1,679
2200	0,98382	1 608	0,5008	86,840	37 958	0,2657	0,1593	1485,9	2,272	592,8	1,668
2300	0,98596	1 386	0,8554	86,648	36 228	0,2653	0,1602	1512,4	2,284	604,6	1,655
2400	0,98764	1 208	1,400	86,490	34 655	0,2662	0,1622	1539,0	2,296	615,5	1,641
2500	0,98894	1 061	2,208	86,358	33 218	0,2686	0,1653	1565,8	2,307	625,5	1,625
2600	0,98994	939,1	3,368	86,244	31 898	0,2723	0,1695	1592,8	2,317	634,7	1,606
2700	0,99064	836,1	4,986	86,142	30 680	0,2774	0,1749	1620,3	2,328	643,1	1,586
2800	0,99108	748,4	7,187	86,048	29 552	0,2844	0,1820	1648,4	2,338	650,4	1,563
2900	0,99123	674,4	10,12	85,960	28 504	0,2925	0,1899	1677,2	2,348	657,4	1,540
3000	0,99110	611,2	13,94	85,873	27 526	0,3021	0,1992	1706,9	2,358	663,9	1,516
					p=10 bar						
1300	0,86214	13 786	0,0001	97,253	89 924	0,4305	0,2478	1199,9	2,081	439,6	1,738
1400	0,89628	10 372	0,0004	94,334	80 996	0,3851	0,2215	1240,6	2,111	463,3	1,738
1500	0,92046	7 954	0,0016	92,269	73 940	0,3499	0,2016	1277,3	2,135	484,5	1,736
1600	0,93779	6 220	0,0047	90,786	68 206	0,3238	0,1870	1310,9	2,158	503,8	1,731
1700	0,95046	4 953	0,0125	89,704	63 428	0,3052	0,1770	1342,4	2,177	521,4	1,724
1800	0,95984	4 015	0,0298	88,902	59 368	0,2916	0,1699	1372,2	2,194	537,7	1,717
1900	0,96695	3 304	0,0649	88,293	55 859	0,2819	0,1650	1400,9	2,210	553,1	1,709
2000	0,97238	2 759	0,1314	87,827	52 786	0,2754	0,1621	1428,7	2,224	567,3	1,699
2100	0,97662	2 333	0,2492	87,462	50 063	0,2713	0,1608	1456,1	2,237	580,6	1,687
2200	0,97997	1 994	0,4471	87,170	47 628	0,2689	0,1606	1483,1	2,250	593,0	1,675
2300	0,98263	1 721	0,7638	86,935	45 434	0,2678	0,1611	1509,9	2,262	604,9	1,662
2400	0,98474	1 501	1,251	86,742	43 445	0,2682	0,1628	1536,7	2,273	615,9	1,648
2500	0,98641	1 320	1,972	86,581	41 630	0,2701	0,1656	1563,7	2,284	626,0	1,631
2600	0,98771	1 168	3,009	86,443	39 965	0,2733	0,1695	1590,9	2,295	635,2	1,613
2700	0,98870	1 041	4,455	86,322	38 430	0,2778	0,1745	1618,4	2,305	643,7	1,592
2800	0,98939	932,4	6,423	86,212	37 011	0,2843	0,1812	1646,5	2,316	651,1	1,569
2900	0,98978	840,6	9,041	86,111	35 693	0,2917	0,1886	1675,3	2,326	658,3	1,547
3000	0,98989	762,1	12,46	86,015	34 464	0,3006	0,1973	1704,9	2,336	664,8	1,523

Viscosity $\eta \cdot 10^7$ (N · s/m²) for rubidium vapor [351]

T, °K	Monatomic vapor	p, bar				At saturation
		0.5	1	2	5	
700	152					135
800	182					158
900	212					183
1000	241	230	219			208
1100	273	268	262	253		244
1200	302	299	296	289	270	268
1300	332	329	326	322	307	289
1400	362	360	358	354	344	314
1500	392	390	389	386	376	336

Viscosity η of liquid rubidium [37]

T, °K	T_{melt} (312.7)	400	500	600	700	800	900	1000	1100	1200	1300	1400	1500
$\eta \cdot 10^3$, N · s/m²	0.643	0.437	0.323	0.258	0.218	0.189	0.169	0.153	0.140	0.130	0.121	0.114	0.108

Thermal conductivity $\lambda \cdot 10^3$ (W/m · deg) of rubidium vapor [419]

T, °K	Mon-atomic vapor	p, bar												At saturation
		0.001	0.005	0.01	0.05	0.1	0.2	0.3	0.5	1	2	6	10	
600	6.06	6.41												7.30
700	6.90	6.97	7.24	7.56										8.86
800	7.75	7.77	7.85	7.95	8.68	9.48								10.3
900	8.59	8.60	8.63	8.66	8.95	9.28	9.89	10.4	11.3					11.5
1000	9.44	9.44	9.45	9.47	9.60	9.76	10.1	10.3	10.8	11.8				12.5
1100	10.3	10.3	10.3	10.3	10.4	10.5	10.6	10.8	11.1	11.7	12.6			13.3
1200	11.1	11.1	11.1	11.1	11.1	11.2	11.3	11.4	11.6	12.0	12.7	14.0		14.1
1300	12.0	12.0	12.0	12.0	12.0	12.1	12.1	12.1	12.3	12.5	13.0	14.2	14.8	14.9
1400	12.8	12.8	12.8	12.8	12.8	12.8	12.9	13.0	13.2	13.2	13.5	14.4	15.0	15.6
1500	13.7	13.7	13.7	13.7	13.7	13.7	13.8	14.0	14.1	14.1	14.2	14.9	15.5	16.0

Thermal conductivity λ of liquid rubidium [32, 33, 37]

T, °K	315	400	500	600	700	800	900	1000	1100
λ, W/m · deg	33.3	31.6	29.8	27.8	25.9	24.1	22.2	20.3	18.5

Surface tension σ of rubidium [31]

t, °C	39	100	200	300	400	500	600	700
σ, dyne/cm	87.5	84.0	78.2	72.4	66.4	60.8	55.0	49.2
t, °C	800	900	1000	1100	1200	1300	1400	
σ, dyne/cm	43.4	37.6	31.8	26.0	20.2	14.4	8.6	

CESIUM (Cs)

Atomic weight 132.91
$T_{melt} = 301.6$ °K; $T_{boil} = 943$ °K at 760 mm Hg; $T_{cr} = 2050$ °K;
$P_{cr} = 117$ bar; $\rho_{cr} = 430$ kg/m³

Thermodynamic properties of saturated liquid cesium [28]: ρ (kg/m³), c_p (kJ/kg · deg), i and u (kJ/kg), s (kJ/kg · deg)

T, °K	p, bar	ϱ'	c_p'	i'	s'	r
301.6	$2.661 \cdot 10^{-9}$	1.837	0.245	74.59	0.6958	563.0
400	$3.825 \cdot 10^{-6}$	1.781	0.240	98.51	0.7645	553.4
450	$4.435 \cdot 10^{-5}$	1.753	0.236	110.4	0.7925	548.8
500	$3.110 \cdot 10^{-4}$	1.724	0.232	122.0	0.8172	544.0
550	$1.517 \cdot 10^{-3}$	1.695	0.228	133.6	0.8391	538.9
600	$5.646 \cdot 10^{-3}$	1.667	0.224	144.9	0.8587	533.4
650	$1.708 \cdot 10^{-2}$	1.638	0.221	156.0	0.8765	527.8
700	$4.395 \cdot 10^{-2}$	1.609	0.219	167.0	0.8928	521.9
750	$9.954 \cdot 10^{-2}$	1.580	0.217	177.9	0.9078	515.8
800	0.2029	1.552	0.217	188.7	0.9219	509.6
850	0.3798	1.524	0.219	199.6	0.9351	503.2
900	0.6622	1.495	0.222	210.6	0.9476	496.7
950	1.086	1.467	0.226	221.8	0.9598	490.0
1000	1.693	1.438	0.231	233.2	0.9715	483.1
1050	2.527	1.408	0.235	244.9	0.9829	476.2
1100	3.629	1.378	0.239	256.7	0.9939	469.2
1150	5.038	1.345	0.243	268.8	1.005	462.2
1200	6.790	1.311	0.248	281.1	1.015	455.1
1250	8.889	1.277	0.252	293.5	1.025	448.1
1300	11.41	1.244	0.256	306.2	1.035	440.9

Thermodynamic properties of saturated cesium vapor [28]: Diatomic fraction X_2 molecular weight M, ρ (kg/m³), c_p and c_v (kJ/kg · deg), i (kJ/kg), s (kJ/kg · deg) and u (m/s)

T, °K	X_2	M	ϱ''	c_p''	c_v''	i''	s''	u
400	$1.146 \cdot 10^{-3}$	133.06	$1.529 \cdot 10^{-5}$	0.1702	0.1057	651.9	2.1480	200.5
450	$2.747 \cdot 10^{-3}$	133.27	$1.579 \cdot 10^{-4}$	0.1823	0.1158	659.2	2.0121	210.0
500	$5.508 \cdot 10^{-3}$	133.64	$9.991 \cdot 10^{-4}$	0.1982	0.1286	666.1	1.9051	218.4
550	$9.665 \cdot 10^{-3}$	134.19	$4.448 \cdot 10^{-3}$	0.2162	0.1426	672.5	1.8188	226.4
600	$1.526 \cdot 10^{-2}$	134.93	$1.526 \cdot 10^{-2}$	0.2344	0.1560	678.4	1.7478	234.1
650	$2.222 \cdot 10^{-2}$	135.86	$4.292 \cdot 10^{-2}$	0.2510	0.1675	683.8	1.6886	241.9
700	$3.029 \cdot 10^{-2}$	136.93	0.1034	0.2645	0.1762	688.9	1.6384	249.3
750	$3.934 \cdot 10^{-2}$	138.13	0.2204	0.2751	0.1822	693.7	1.5956	256.7
800	$4.908 \cdot 10^{-2}$	139.43	0.4250	0.2821	0.1853	698.3	1.5589	264.0
850	$5.924 \cdot 10^{-2}$	140.78	0.7562	0.2864	0.1864	702.8	1.5271	271.2
900	$6.954 \cdot 10^{-2}$	142.15	1.257	0.2878	0.1854	707.3	1.4995	278.2
950	$7.977 \cdot 10^{-2}$	143.51	1.972	0.2873	0.1832	711.8	1.4756	285.0
1000	$8.980 \cdot 10^{-2}$	144.84	2.985	0.2850	0.1800	716.4	1.4547	291.7
1050	$9.945 \cdot 10^{-2}$	146.12	4.283	0.2818	0.1763	721.1	1.4364	298.3
1100	0.1086	147.34	5.922	0.2776	0.1721	725.9	1.4204	304.7
1150	0.1171	148.47	7.924	0.2732	0.1680	730.9	1.4065	311.1
1200	0.1250	149.52	10.31	0.2681	0.1636	736.1	1.3943	317.4
1250	0.1319	150.43	13.03	0.2632	0.1595	741.6	1.3838	323.6
1300	0.1385	151.31	16.18	0.2582	0.1555	747.1	1.3744	329.7

Saturation pressure of cesium vapor above 10 bar [404, 414]

T, °K	p, bar	T, °K	p, bar	T, °K	p, bar	T, °K	p, bar
1350	15.0	1550	33.0	1750	60.0	1950	96.0
1400	18.7	1600	38.9	1800	68.2	2000	106.3
1450	22.9	1650	45.4	1850	77.0	2050	117.0
1500	27.6	1700	52.4	1900	86.2		

Thermodynamic properties of cesium vapor [28]: Molar fractions of monatomic, diatomic and electronic components X_1, X_2 and X_e, molecular weight M, ρ (kg/m^3), c_p and c_v (kJ/kg · deg), i (kJ/kg), s (kJ/kg · deg), u (m/s), adiabatic exponent k

T, °K	X_1	$X_2 \cdot 10^5$	$X_e \cdot 10^4$	M	$\varrho \cdot 10^3$	c_p	c_v	i	s	u	k
					$p=10^{-5}$ bar						
600	0.99997	2.787	0	132.91	0.0266	0.1566	0.0940	683.62	2.152	250.1	1.666
700	0.99999	0.7331	0	132.91	0.0228	0.1565	0.0940	699.28	2.176	270.2	1.666
800	0.999997	0.2674	0	132.90	0.0200	0.1565	0.0939	714.94	2.197	288.9	1.666
900	0.999999	0.1213	0	132.90	0.0178	0.1565	0.0939	730.57	2.216	306.4	1.666
1000	0.999999	0.0641	0.0016	132.90	0.0160	0.1565	0.0939	746.22	2.232	323.0	1.666
1100	0.999996	0.0377	0.0139	132.90	0.0145	0.1566	0.0940	761.88	2.247	338.7	1.666
1200	0.99998	0.0242	0.0858	132.90	0.0133	0.1569	0.0943	777.56	2.261	353.5	1.664
1300	0.99992	0.0165	0.4035	132.90	0.0123	0.1582	0.0955	793.31	2.273	367.1	1.656
1400	0.99969	0.0117	1.532	132.88	0.0114	0.1621	0.0992	809.31	2.285	378.5	1.634
1500	0.99902	0.0087	4.895	132.84	0.0106	0.1727	0.1091	826.02	2.296	385.6	1.583
1600	0.99728	0.0068	13.59	132.72	0.0100	0.1963	0.1311	844.38	2.308	387.6	1.498
1700	0.99328	0.0048	33.57	132.46	0.0094	0.2443	0.1753	866.28	2.320	385.7	1.393
1800	0.98497	0.0041	75.13	131.91	0.0088	0.3342	0.2576	894.98	2.338	383.7	1.297
1900	0.96913	0.0033	154.3	130.85	0.0083	0.4898	0.3984	935.96	2.361	385.4	1.229
2000	0.94123	0.0026	293.9	129.00	0.0078	0.7421	0.6225	997.37	2.393	392.1	1.192
2100	0.89566	0.0020	521.7	125.97	0.0072	1.129	0.9569	1091.0	2.439	404.5	1.180
2200	0.82678	0.0015	866.1	121.39	0.0066	1.688	1.422	1232.4	2.505	423.1	1.187
2300	0.73102	0.0010	1345	115.03	0.0060	2.439	2.013	1440.5	2.599	448.9	1.212
2400	0.61000	0.0006	1950	106.99	0.0054	3.340	2.676	1733.4	2.725	482.6	1.248
2500	0.47343	0.0003	2633	97.913	0.0047	4.209	3.273	2118.7	2.884	522.6	1.286
2600	0.33853	0.0001	3307	88.948	0.0041	4.698	3.594	2576.2	3.066	563.8	1.307
2700	0.22348	0.00006	3882	81.304	0.0036	4.491	3.453	3049.6	3.248	599.4	1.301
2800	0.13843	0.00002	4308	75.652	0.0032	3.662	2.872	3467.9	3.402	626.5	1.275
2900	0.08266	0.000006	4587	71.945	0.0030	2.641	2.110	3787.7	3.516	647.9	1.252
3000	0.04873	0.000002	4756	69.691	0.0028	1.788	1.434	4010.3	3.592	668.3	1.247
					$p=5 \cdot 10^{-5}$ bar						
600	0.99986	13.93	0	132.92	0.1331	0.1572	0.0945	683.58	2.051	249.9	1.664
700	0.99996	3.665	0	132.91	0.1141	0.1566	0.0940	699.27	2.076	270.2	1.666
800	0.999987	1.337	0	132.91	0.1000	0.1565	0.0939	714.94	2.096	288.9	1.666
900	0.999994	0.6066	0	132.91	0.0888	0.1565	0.0939	730.57	2.115	306.4	1.666
1000	0.999997	0.3204	0.0007	132.90	0.0799	0.1565	0.0939	746.22	2.131	323.0	1.666
1100	0.999997	0.1887	0.0062	132.90	0.0726	0.1565	0.0939	761.88	2.146	338.7	1.666
1200	0.99992	0.1207	0.0384	132.90	0.0666	0.1567	0.0941	777.55	2.160	353.7	1.665
1300	0.99996	0.0821	0.1805	132.90	0.0614	0.1573	0.0946	793.25	2.173	367.8	1.662
1400	0.99986	0.0587	0.6850	132.90	0.0570	0.1590	0.0963	809.06	2.184	380.5	1.652
1500	0.99956	0.0437	2.190	132.88	0.0532	0.1640	0.1009	825.20	2.195	390.6	1.625
1600	0.99678	0.0335	6.083	132.82	0.0499	0.1747	0.1109	842.10	2.206	397.3	1.575
1700	0.99699	0.0263	15.04	132.70	0.0469	0.1963	0.1309	860.60	2.218	399.8	1.500
1800	0.99326	0.0211	33.74	132.46	0.0442	0.2371	0.1684	882.16	2.230	399.0	1.408
1900	0.98607	0.0171	69.63	131.98	0.0417	0.3074	0.2325	909.29	2.245	397.9	1.322
2000	0.97327	0.0139	133.6	131.13	0.0394	0.4211	0.3351	945.61	2.263	399.3	1.257
2100	0.95190	0.0113	240.5	129.71	0.0371	0.5962	0.4906	996.49	2.288	404.6	1.215
2200	0.91836	0.0090	408.2	127.48	0.0348	0.8530	0.7138	1069.1	2.323	414.2	1.195
2300	0.86886	0.0070	655.7	124.19	0.0324	1.213	1.017	1173.0	2.369	428.6	1.193
2400	0.80023	0.0052	998.8	119.63	0.0300	1.692	1.405	1319.5	2.432	448.3	1.204
2500	0.71135	0.0036	1443	113.72	0.0273	2.292	1.865	1521.0	2.516	474.0	1.229
2600	0.60465	0.0023	1977	106.63	0.0246	2.970	2.354	1787.9	2.622	505.9	1.262
2700	0.48724	0.0013	2564	98.831	0.0220	3.614	2.790	2123.5	2.750	542.6	1.295
2800	0.37004	0.0007	3150	91.043	0.0195	4.035	3.060	2515.3	2.894	580.8	1.319
2900	0.26518	0.0003	3674	84.074	0.0174	4.042	3.058	2929.5	3.042	615.9	1.322
3000	0.18072	0.0001	4096	78.462	0.0157	3.604	2.759	3321.3	3.176	644.6	1.306
					$p=10^{-4}$ bar						
600	0.99972	27.86	0	132.94	0.2663	0.1580	0.0951	683.53	2.008	249.7	1.661
700	0.99993	7.330	0	132.91	0.2282	0.1568	0.0941	699.26	2.032	270.1	1.665
800	0.99997	2.674	0	132.91	0.1997	0.1566	0.0940	714.94	2.053	288.8	1.666
900	0.99988	1.213	0	132.91	0.1775	0.1665	0.0939	730.57	2.072	306.4	1.666
1000	0.999993	0.6407	0.0005	132.90	0.1598	0.1565	0.0939	746.22	2.088	323.0	1.666
1100	0.999995	0.3774	0.0044	132.90	0.1452	0.1565	0.0939	761.88	2.103	338.7	1.666
1200	0.99999	0.2412	0.0271	132.90	0.1331	0.1566	0.0940	777.54	2.117	353.7	1.667

continued

T, °K	X_1	$X_2 \cdot 10^5$	$X_e \cdot 10^4$	M	$\varrho \cdot 10^3$	c_p	c_v	i	s	u	k
1300	0.99997	0.1642	0.1276	132.90	0,1229	0,1570	0.0944	793.23	2,129	367.9	1,663
1400	0.99990	0.1174	0.4844	132.90	0,1141	0,1583	0.0956	809.00	2.141	381.0	1,656
1500	0.99969	0.0873	1,548	132.88	0,1065	0,1619	0,0990	825,00	2.152	391.9	1,636
1600	0,99914	0.0670	4,302	132,85	0.0998	0,1696	0.1061	841,56	2.163	400.1	1.598
1700	0,99787	0.0527	10.64	132.76	0,0939	0,1849	0.1204	859,26	2.173	404.6	1.536
1800	0.99522	0.0423	23.88	132.59	0,0885	0,2140	0,1472	879.12	2.185	405.3	1,454
1900	0.99013	0.0344	49.33	132,25	0.0837	0,2641	0,1930	902.96	2.198	404.5	1.369
2000	0.98102	0,0282	94.87	131.64	0.0791	0,3450	0.2661	933,34	2,213	404.8	1.296
2100	0.96574	0.0232	171.3	130.63	0,0748	0.4693	0,3773	974,05	2.233	407.8	1,244
2200	0.94154	0.0189	292.3	129,02	0.0705	0.6520	0.5379	1030.2	2.260	414.7	1.212
2300	0.90534	0.0151	473.3	126.61	0,0662	0.9093	0.7589	1108.7	2,295	425.5	1,198
2400	0.85407	0.0118	729.6	123,21	0,0617	1.256	1.048	1217.8	2.342	440.9	1.199
2500	0.78551	0.0088	1072	118.65	0,0571	1.703	1.404	1367.2	2.404	461.2	1.213
2600	0,69935	0.0062	1503	112.93	0.0522	2,245	1.813	1566.9	2.483	486.9	1.238
2700	0,59824	0.0040	2009	106.21	0,0473	2.840	2.238	1825.1	2.582	518.1	1.269
2800	0.48830	0.0024	2558	98.901	0,0425	3.399	2,612	2143.2	2.699	553,6	1,301
2900	0,37890	0.0013	3105	91.631	0,0380	3.772	2,849	2509.7	2.829	590.5	1,324
3000	0.27952	0.0007	3602	85.027	0.0341	3.818	2.871	2898.6	2.963	624.8	1.330

$p=5 \cdot 10^{-4}$ bar

T, °K	X_1	$X_2 \cdot 10^5$	$X_e \cdot 10^4$	M	$\varrho \cdot 10^3$	c_p	c_v	i	s	u	k
600	0.99861	139.0	0	133.09	1.333	0.1640	0.1000	683,14	1.907	247.9	1.638
700	0.99963	36.63	0	132.95	1.142	0.1580	0.0951	699.16	1.931	269,7	1.661
800	0.99987	13.37	0	132.92	0.9986	0.1569	0.0942	714.90	1.952	288.7	1.665
900	0,99994	6.065	0	132,91	0,8876	0.1566	0.0940	730.57	1.971	306.4	1.666
1000	0.99997	3.203	0.0002	132.91	0.7988	0.1566	0.0940	746,21	1.987	323.0	1.666
1100	0.99998	1.887	0.0020	132.91	0,7262	0.1565	0.0939	761.87	2.002	338,7	1.666
1200	0.99998	1.206	0.0121	132.91	0,6657	0.1566	0.0940	777,54	2.016	353.8	1.666
1300	0.99998	0.8210	0.0571	132.90	0,6144	0.1568	0.0941	793,21	2.028	368.1	1.665
1400	0.99995	0.5872	0.2166	132.90	0.5706	0.1573	0.0947	808.91	2.040	381.6	1.662
1500	0.99985	0.4369	0.6925	132,90	0.5325	0.1591	0.0964	824.75	2.051	393.7	1.651
1600	0.99961	0,3354	1.924	132.88	0.4991	0.1627	0.0998	840.84	2.061	404.2	1.631
1700	0.99904	0.2643	4.762	132.84	0.4696	0.1698	0.1063	857.46	2.071	412.4	1.597
1800	0.99786	0,2128	10.69	132.76	0.4433	0.1833	0.1188	875.07	2.082	417.1	1.543
1900	0.99557	0.1741	22.12	132.61	0.4195	0.2064	0.1401	894.53	2.092	419.1	1.474
2000	0.99147	0.1443	42.65	132.34	0.3977	0.2433	0.1736	916.96	2.104	419.7	1.401
2100	0.98453	0,1205	77.35	131.88	0.3774	0.2998	0.2247	944.10	2.117	420.4	1.334
2200	0.97342	0.1010	132.9	131.14	0.3583	0.3827	0.2988	978.26	2.133	422.8	1.281
2300	0.95649	0.0845	217.6	130.01	0.3397	0.4999	0.4021	1022.6	2.153	427.7	1.243
2400	0.93183	0.0702	340.8	128.83	0.3215	0.6594	0.5402	1080.8	2.178	435.7	1.221
2500	0.89747	0.0575	512.6	126,09	0.3031	0.8694	0.7178	1157.9	2.210	446.9	1.211
2600	0.85163	0.0460	741.9	123.04	0.2844	1.137	0.9374	1259.0	2.250	461.8	1.213
2700	0.79312	0,0357	1034	119.16	0,2652	1.466	1,197	1390.7	2.300	480.4	1.224
2800	0.72178	0.0267	1391	114.42	0.2456	1.852	1.488	1558.8	2,362	503.3	1.244
2900	0.63922	0.0189	1804	108.93	0.2258	2.275	1.791	1768.0	2.436	530.4	1.270
3000	0.54860	0,0126	2257	102.91	0,2062	2,697	2.076	2020.9	2.523	561,3	1.299

$p=10^{-3}$ bar

T, °K	X_1	$X_2 \cdot 10^5$	$X_e \cdot 10^4$	M	$\varrho \cdot 10^3$	c_p	c_v	i	s	u	k
600	0.99723	277.2	0	133.27	2.670	0,1714	0.1059	682.66	1,862	245.9	1.614
700	0.99927	73.20	0	133.00	2.284	0,1594	0.0962	699.03	1.888	269.3	1.656
800	0.99973	26.73	0	132.94	1.998	0.1573	0.0945	714.85	1.909	288.6	1.664
900	0.99988	12.13	0	132.92	1.775	0.1568	0.0941	730.52	1.927	306.3	1.666
1000	0.99994	6.406	0,0002	132.91	1.598	0.1566	0.0940	746.20	1.944	322.9	1.666
1100	0.99996	3.774	0,0014	132.91	1.452	0.1566	0,0940	761.87	1.959	338.7	1.666
1200	0.99997	2,412	0,0086	132.91	1.331	0.1566	0.0940	777.53	1.972	353.8	1.666
1300	0.99998	1.642	0.0404	132,91	1.229	0.1567	0.0941	793.20	1.985	368.1	1.666
1400	0.99996	1,174	0,1532	132.90	1.141	0,1571	0.0944	808.89	1.997	381.8	1.663
1500	0.99989	0.8738	0.4897	132.90	1.065	0.1585	0.0958	824.68	2.008	394.2	1.655
1600	0,99972	0.6709	1.361	132.89	0.9984	0.1611	0.0982	840.67	2.018	405.3	1.640
1700	0.99932	0.5288	3,368	132.86	0,9394	0.1662	0.1030	857.03	2.028	414.5	1.614
1800	0.99848	0,4261	7.564	132,80	0.8869	0.1760	0.1121	874.11	2.038	420.8	1.570
1900	0.99687	0.3492	15.65	132.70	0.8395	0.1927	0.1275	892.53	2.048	424,4	1.512
2000	0.99396	0.2900	30.20	132.50	0.7964	0,2192	0.1516	913.07	2.058	426.0	1.445
2100	0,98903	0.2432	54,82	132.18	0.7566	0.2596	0.1883	937.00	2.070	426.9	1.379
2200	0,98113	0,2052	94,35	131.65	0,7193	0.3188	0.2414	965.94	2.083	428.5	1.321

continued

T, °K	X_1	$X_2 \cdot 10^5$	$X_e \cdot 10^4$	M	$\varrho \cdot 10^3$	c_p	c_v	i	s	u	k
2300	0.96903	0.1736	154.8	130.85	0.6838	0.4025	0.3157	1002.1	2.100	431.8	1.275
2400	0.95130	0.1464	243.5	129.67	0.6494	0.5163	0.4153	1048.3	2.119	437.5	1.243
2500	0.92634	0.1225	368.3	128.01	0.6155	0.6664	0.5443	1107.8	2.144	446.0	1.224
2600	0.89259	0.1011	537.0	125.77	0.5814	0.8590	0.7059	1184.6	2.174	457.5	1.217
2700	0.84868	0.0817	756.6	122.85	0.5469	1.098	0.9009	1283.6	2.212	472.2	1.219
2800	0.79370	0.0646	1031	119.20	0.5117	1.387	1.127	1409.4	2.258	490.3	1.230
2900	0.72779	0.0490	1361	114.82	0.4759	1.720	1.377	1566.6	2.314	512.2	1.249
3000	0.65202	0.0357	1740	109.78	0.4399	2.083	1.637	1759.6	2.380	537.9	1.273

$p = 5 \cdot 10^{-3}$ bar

T, °K	X_1	$X_2 \cdot 10^5$	$X_e \cdot 10^4$	M	$\varrho \cdot 10^3$	c_p	c_v	i	s	u	k
600	0.98644	1 356	0	134.71	13.49	0.2262	0.1495	678.9	1.756	235.2	1.493
700	0.99636	363.9	0	133.39	11.45	0.1709	0.1051	698.01	1.786	265.9	1.620
800	0.99867	133.4	0	133.08	9.998	0.1606	0.0970	714.47	1.808	287.6	1.653
900	0.99939	60.59	0	132.98	8.881	0.1580	0.0950	730.35	1.826	306.1	1.662
1000	0.99968	32.02	0.0001	132.95	7.990	0.1572	0.0944	746.11	1.843	322.8	1.666
1100	0.99981	18.86	0.0006	132.93	7.263	0.1568	0.0941	761.81	1.858	338.7	1.666
1200	0.99988	12.06	0.0038	132.92	6.657	0.1567	0.0940	777.49	1.872	353.8	1.666
1300	0.99991	8.209	0.0180	132.92	6.145	0.1567	0.0940	793.17	1.884	368.2	1.666
1400	0.99993	5.872	0.0685	132.91	5.706	0.1568	0.0942	808.85	1.896	382.0	1.665
1500	0.99991	4.369	0.2190	132.91	5.325	0.1576	0.0950	824.59	1.907	394.8	1.660
1600	0.99984	3.355	0.6086	132.90	4.992	0.1590	0.0962	840.43	1.917	406.7	1.652
1700	0.99967	2.646	1.506	132.89	4.698	0.1614	0.0985	856.46	1.927	417.6	1.638
1800	0.99930	2.134	3.384	132.86	4.436	0.1663	0.1031	872.82	1.936	426.3	1.613
1900	0.99858	1.752	7.007	132.81	4.201	0.1745	0.1107	889.85	1.945	433.1	1.576
2000	0.99728	1.460	13.53	132.73	3.988	0.1870	0.1222	907.89	1.954	438.0	1.530
2100	0.99507	1.231	24.59	132.58	3.794	0.2060	0.1395	927.52	1.964	441.1	1.476
2200	0.99151	1.048	42.42	132.34	3.615	0.2334	0.1644	949.48	1.974	443.1	1.420
2300	0.98602	0.8984	69.85	131.98	3.449	0.2723	0.1994	974.83	1.986	445.0	1.366
2400	0.97791	0.7734	110.4	131.44	3.292	0.3249	0.2461	1004.8	1.998	447.8	1.320
2500	0.96635	0.6664	168.2	130.67	3.141	0.3940	0.3069	1041.0	2.013	452.0	1.284
2600	0.95043	0.5730	247.8	129.61	2.996	0.4830	0.3841	1084.9	2.031	458.1	1.258
2700	0.92918	0.4895	354.0	128.20	2.854	0.5947	0.4794	1139.3	2.051	466.2	1.241
2800	0.90166	0.4171	491.7	126.37	2.713	0.7118	0.5969	1206.3	2.076	476.6	1.232
2900	0.86712	0.3475	664.4	124.08	2.571	0.8958	0.7274	1288.5	2.105	489.3	1.231
3000	0.82495	0.2859	875.2	121.27	2.430	1.088	0.8790	1388.8	2.140	504.6	1.237

$p = 10^{-2}$ bar

T, °K	X_1	$X_2 \cdot 10^5$	$X_e \cdot 10^4$	M	$\varrho \cdot 10^3$	c_p	c_v	i	s	u	k
700	0.99277	722.5	0	133.86	22.99	0.1847	0.1158	696.76	1.741	262.5	1.584
800	0.99734	266.0	0	133.26	20.02	0.1647	0.1000	714.00	1.764	286.3	1.641
900	0.99879	121.0	0	133.06	17.77	0.1595	0.0961	730.13	1.783	305.4	1.658
1000	0.99936	63.99	0	132.99	15.99	0.1578	0.0948	745.99	1.800	322.7	1.665
1100	0.99962	37.71	0.0004	132.96	14.53	0.1572	0.0943	761.74	1.815	338.6	1.666
1200	0.99976	24.11	0.0027	132.94	13.32	0.1569	0.0941	777.45	1.828	353.7	1.666
1300	0.99983	16.42	0.0128	132.93	12.29	0.1568	0.0941	793.14	1.841	368.2	1.666
1400	0.99987	11.74	0.0484	132.92	11.41	0.1568	0.0942	808.82	1.852	382.0	1.666
1500	0.99988	8.738	0.1548	132.91	10.65	0.1575	0.0948	824.55	1.863	394.9	1.661
1600	0.99985	6.711	0.4303	132.91	9.985	0.1585	0.0958	840.36	1.874	407.1	1.655
1700	0.99973	5.293	1.065	132.90	9.397	0.1603	0.0975	856.31	1.883	418.3	1.644
1800	0.99948	4.269	2.393	132.88	8.874	0.1640	0.1010	872.51	1.892	427.8	1.624
1900	0.99897	3.506	4.955	132.84	8.404	0.1702	0.1067	889.21	1.902	435.6	1.594
2000	0.99806	2.924	9.569	132.78	7.980	0.1794	0.1152	906.65	1.910	441.6	1.557
2100	0.99650	2.469	17.40	132.68	7.594	0.1932	0.1279	925.27	1.920	446.0	1.510
2200	0.99397	2.106	30.03	132.51	7.240	0.2133	0.1461	945.58	1.929	449.0	1.459
2300	0.99008	1.812	49.50	132.25	6.912	0.2415	0.1716	968.36	1.939	451.2	1.407
2400	0.98432	1.567	78.33	131.87	6.604	0.2795	0.2056	994.46	1.950	453.6	1.359
2500	0.97608	1.360	119.5	131.32	6.314	0.3293	0.2498	1025.0	1.963	457.0	1.318
2600	0.96468	1.180	176.6	130.56	6.036	0.3934	0.3059	1061.2	1.977	461.6	1.286
2700	0.94938	1.022	253.0	129.54	5.767	0.4739	0.3754	1105.0	1.994	467.8	1.262
2800	0.92940	0.8863	353.0	128.22	5.504	0.5728	0.4594	1157.8	2.013	475.9	1.247
2900	0.90405	0.7556	479.7	126.53	5.245	0.6915	0.5583	1221.6	2.036	486.0	1.238
3000	0.87269	0.6400	636.5	124.45	4.986	0.8315	0.6722	1298.5	2.062	498.1	1.237

continued

T, °K	X_1	$X_2 \cdot 10^5$	$X_e \cdot 10^4$	M	$\varrho \cdot 10^3$	c_p	c_v	i	s	u	k
					$p=5 \cdot 10^{-2}$ bar						
800	0.98697	1 303	0	134.64	101.1	0.1950	0.1226	710.38	1.659	278.6	1.570
900	0.99401	599.4	0	133.70	89.29	0.1711	0.1045	728.43	1.681	301.9	1.643
1000	0.99682	318.3	0	133.33	80.13	0.1629	0.0984	745.08	1.698	320.7	1.658
1100	0.99812	188.0	0.0002	133.15	72.75	0.1597	0.0960	761.19	1.713	337.6	1.666
1200	0.99880	120.3	0.0012	133.06	66.64	0.1583	0.0951	777.09	1.727	353.2	1.666
1300	0.99918	81.97	0.0057	133.01	61.50	0.1576	0.0946	792.88	1.740	368.1	1.666
1400	0.99941	58.66	0.0217	132.98	57.09	0.1572	0.0944	808.63	1.752	382.0	1.666
1500	0.99955	43.66	0.0692	132.96	53.28	0.1575	0.0947	824.39	1.762	395.1	1.663
1600	0.99963	33.54	0.1924	132.95	49.94	0.1581	0.0953	840.18	1.773	407.5	1.659
1700	0.99964	26.46	0.4763	132.93	47.00	0.1590	0.0962	856.05	1.782	419.4	1.653
1800	0.99957	21.35	1.070	132.92	44.38	0.1611	0.0982	872.03	1.791	429.8	1.640
1900	0.99938	17.55	2.216	132.90	42.04	0.1645	0.1015	888.31	1.800	439.1	1.621
2000	0.99900	14.65	4.282	132.87	39.43	0.1693	0.1060	904.96	1.809	447.3	1.598
2100	0.99832	12.39	7.789	132.82	38.01	0.1764	0.1125	922.23	1.817	454.1	1.567
2200	0.99720	10.60	13.45	132.74	36.26	0.1863	0.1217	940.34	1.826	459.5	1.531
2300	0.99547	9.158	22.20	132.62	34.66	0.2003	0.1345	959.69	1.834	463.6	1.489
2400	0.99288	7.972	35.18	132.45	33.17	0.2189	0.1513	980.67	1.843	466.9	1.446
2500	0.98917	6.983	53.82	132.20	31.78	0.2429	0.1729	1003.8	1.853	470.0	1.405
2600	0.98399	6.141	79.74	131.85	30.48	0.2737	0.2004	1029.6	1.863	473.3	1.366
2700	0.97698	5.412	114.8	131.39	29.25	0.3122	0.2344	1059.2	1.874	477.2	1.332
2800	0.96774	4.804	161.1	130.77	28.07	0.3594	0.2756	1092.9	1.886	481.9	1.304
2900	0.95584	4.223	220.6	129.98	26.94	0.4160	0.3246	1131.9	1.900	487.7	1.282
3000	0.94085	3.719	295.6	128.98	25.84	0.4829	0.3816	1177.2	1.916	494.9	1.266
					$p=10^{-1}$ bar						
800	0.97460	2 540	0	136.28	204.8	0.2279	0.1467	706.15	1.611	272.2	1.518
900	0.98815	1 185	0	134.48	179.6	0.1846	0.1134	726.38	1.635	298.2	1.627
1000	0.99367	632.6	0	133.75	160.8	0.1691	0.1028	743.95	1.654	318.9	1.652
1100	0.99625	374.6	0.0001	133.40	145.8	0.1629	0.0982	760.51	1.670	336.6	1.662
1200	0.99760	240.0	0.0009	133.22	133.4	0.1600	0.0962	776.64	1.684	352.6	1.665
1300	0.99836	163.7	0.0040	133.12	123.1	0.1586	0.0952	792.58	1.696	368.0	1.667
1400	0.99882	117.2	0.0153	133.06	114.2	0.1579	0.0947	808.40	1.708	382.0	1.667
1500	0.99912	87.24	0.0490	133.02	106.6	0.1579	0.0949	824.21	1.719	395.1	1.664
1600	0.99930	67.04	0.1360	133.00	99.91	0.1582	0.0953	840.03	1.729	407.6	1.660
1700	0.99940	52.89	0.3368	132.97	94.02	0.1588	0.0959	855.90	1.739	419.6	1.655
1800	0.99942	42.69	0.7568	132.95	88.78	0.1605	0.0976	871.85	1.748	430.3	1.644
1900	0.99934	35.09	1.567	132.93	84.10	0.1633	0.1003	888.03	1.757	440.0	1.628
2000	0.99910	29.30	3.028	132.90	79.88	0.1670	0.1038	904.51	1.765	448.8	1.609
2100	0.99865	24.80	5.509	132.86	76.05	0.1724	0.1089	921.47	1.773	456.3	1.584
2200	0.99788	21.23	9.515	132.81	72.56	0.1800	0.1159	939.06	1.782	462.6	1.553
2300	0.99668	18.36	15.70	132.72	69.36	0.1906	0.1257	957.60	1.790	467.6	1.516
2400	0.99486	16.01	24.90	132.60	66.41	0.2046	0.1384	977.37	1.798	471.7	1.478
2500	0.99224	14.05	38.12	132.42	63.67	0.2225	0.1546	998.76	1.807	475.3	1.438
2600	0.98857	12.40	56.52	132.17	61.11	0.2453	0.1752	1022.1	1.816	478.7	1.400
2700	0.98360	10.97	81.45	131.84	58.69	0.2738	0.2006	1048.3	1.826	482.2	1.365
2800	0.97701	9.794	114.4	131.40	56.41	0.3087	0.2314	1077.5	1.837	486.3	1.334
2900	0.96851	8.672	157.0	130.83	54.23	0.3504	0.2679	1110.6	1.849	491.1	1.308
3000	0.95775	7.708	210.9	130.11	52.13	0.3997	0.3105	1148.4	1.861	496.9	1.287
					$p=2 \cdot 10^{-1}$ bar						
900	0.97685	2 315	0	135.98	363.2	0.2090	0.1299	722.47	1.588	292.6	1.609
1000	0.98750	1 250	0	134.57	323.5	0.1808	0.1101	741.76	1.609	315.5	1.642
1100	0.99256	743.6	0.0001	133.89	292.6	0.1689	0.1024	759.17	1.625	334.6	1.658
1200	0.99522	477.8	0.0006	133.54	267.5	0.1634	0.0985	775.77	1.640	351.4	1.664
1300	0.99674	326.3	0.0028	133.34	246.6	0.1607	0.0964	791.96	1.653	367.7	1.667
1400	0.99766	233.8	0.0108	133.22	228.8	0.1592	0.0954	807.95	1.664	381.8	1.668
1500	0.99825	174.2	0.0346	133.14	213.4	0.1588	0.0954	823.87	1.675	395.0	1.665
1600	0.99864	133.9	0.0962	133.08	200.0	0.1587	0.0955	839.75	1.686	407.7	1.662
1700	0.99890	105.7	0.2381	133.04	188.1	0.1590	0.0959	855.65	1.695	419.8	1.658
1800	0.99904	85.31	0.5350	133.01	177.6	0.1604	0.0973	871.60	1.704	430.7	1.648
1900	0.99908	70.14	1.108	132.98	168.3	0.1625	0.0995	887.74	1.713	440.7	1.634
2000	0.99899	58.60	2.141	132.95	159.8	0.1655	0.1023	904.11	1.722	449.9	1.617
2100	0.99872	49.60	3.895	132.92	152.2	0.1697	0.1063	920.86	1.730	458.0	1.596
2200	0.99823	42.48	6.729	132.87	145.2	0.1756	0.1118	938.09	1.738	465.0	1.570

continued

T, °K	X_1	$X_2 \cdot 10^5$	$X_e \cdot 10^4$	M	$\varrho \cdot 10^3$	c_p	c_v	i	s	u	k
2300	0.99741	36.77	11.11	132.81	138.8	0.1838	0.1195	956.07	1.746	470.8	1.538
2400	0.99615	32.10	17.62	132.71	132.9	0.1945	0.1293	974.99	1.754	475.6	1.504
2500	0.99432	28.22	26.98	132.58	127.5	0.2081	0.1417	995.14	1.762	479.9	1.468
2600	0.99174	24.95	40.03	132.41	122.4	0.2253	0.1574	1016.7	1.771	483.6	1.432
2700	0.98823	22.15	57.73	132.17	117.7	0.2467	0.1767	1040.5	1.780	487.2	1.397
2800	0.98356	19.85	81.19	131.85	113.2	0.2729	0.2000	1066.6	1.789	491.0	1.364
2900	0.97752	17.67	111.5	131.45	109.0	0.3040	0.2276	1095.5	1.799	495.2	1.336
3000	0.96983	15.81	150.0	130.93	104.9	0.3407	0.2597	1128.0	1.810	500.1	1.312
				$p=5 \cdot 10^{-1}$ bar							
900	0.94574	5 426	0	140.12	935.7	0.2653	0.1660	712.14	1.521	292.2	1.598
1000	0.96986	3 013	0	136.91	822.9	0.2112	0.1317	735.63	1.546	314.8	1.631
1100	0.98181	1 819	0.0001	135.32	739.4	0.1856	0.1136	755.32	1.565	334.3	1.652
1200	0.98822	1 178	0.0004	134.47	673.5	0.1731	0.1048	773.20	1.581	351.4	1.663
1300	0.99192	807.9	0.0018	133.98	619.4	0.1666	0.1004	790.16	1.594	367.0	1.668
1400	0.99419	580.5	0.0068	133.68	573.9	0.1630	0.0976	806.63	1.606	381.5	1.670
1500	0.99566	433.2	0.0218	133.48	534.8	0.1613	0.0967	822.85	1.618	394.9	1.668
1600	0.99665	333.4	0.0608	133.35	500.9	0.1604	0.0963	838.95	1.628	407.7	1.665
1700	0.99734	263.4	0.1504	133.25	471.1	0.1601	0.0964	854.98	1.638	419.9	1.661
1800	0.99780	212.7	0.3382	133.18	444.7	0.1609	0.0974	871.01	1.647	431.0	1.652
1900	0.99811	175.0	0.7005	133.13	421.1	0.1624	0.0990	887.18	1.656	441.3	1.640
2000	0.99827	146.3	1.353	133.08	399.9	0.1645	0.1012	903.49	1.664	450.9	1.626
2100	0.99827	123.9	2.463	133.04	380.8	0.1676	0.1042	920.08	1.672	459.6	1.608
2200	0 99809	106.2	4.256	132.99	363.3	0.1720	0.1084	937.03	1.680	467.3	1.587
2300	0.99767	91.98	7.026	132.93	347.4	0.1780	0.1141	954.54	1.688	473.9	1.560
2400	0.99697	80.38	11.15	132.86	332.7	0.1857	0.1213	972.72	1.695	479.6	1.531
2500	0.99588	70.78	17.08	132.77	319.2	0.1954	0.1303	991.79	1.703	484.7	1.500
2600	0.99430	62.71	25.35	132.65	306.6	0.2077	0.1416	1011.8	1.711	489.1	1.467
2700	0.99212	55.81	36.58	132.49	294.9	0.2228	0.1554	1033.5	1.719	493.9	1.434
2800	0.98920	50.20	51.50	132.29	284.0	0.2412	0.1720	1056.8	1.728	496.8	1.402
2900	0.98539	44.88	70.82	132.02	273.6	0.2629	0.1916	1082.0	1.737	500.8	1.372
3000	0.98051	40.39	95.42	131.69	263.8	0.2885	0.2143	1109.7	1.746	505.0	1.346
				$p=8 \cdot 10^{-1}$ bar							
1000	0.95341	4 659	0	139.10	1 338	0.2356	0.1445	730.10	1.512	312.3	1.631
1100	0.97150	2 850	0	136.69	1 195	0.2003	0.1213	751.71	1.533	332.5	1.652
1200	0.98141	1 858	0.0003	135.38	1 085	0.1820	0.1094	770.74	1.550	350.3	1.664
1300	0.98720	1 280	0.0014	134.61	995.7	0.1722	0.1039	788.41	1.564	366.3	1.670
1400	0.99077	922.4	0.0054	134.13	921.3	0.1666	0.0996	805.33	1.576	381.1	1.673
1500	0.99310	689.6	0.0172	133.82	857.9	0.1638	0.0980	821.85	1.588	394.7	1.670
1600	0.99468	531.3	0.0480	133.61	803.0	0.1621	0.0972	838.16	1.598	407.6	1.668
1700	0.99578	420.1	0.1188	133.46	754.9	0.1613	0.0969	854.34	1.608	419.9	1.664
1800	0.99655	339.5	0.2672	133.35	712.4	0.1616	0.0977	870.47	1.617	431.1	1.655
1900	0.99709	279.4	0.5535	133.27	674.5	0.1628	0.0991	886.69	1.626	441.5	1.643
2000	0.99745	233.7	1.070	133.20	640.4	0.1646	0.1009	903.03	1.634	451.3	1.630
2100	0.99763	198.0	1.947	133.14	609.7	0.1672	0.1036	919.60	1.642	460.2	1.614
2200	0.99763	169.7	3.364	133.09	581.7	0.1709	0.1072	936.47	1.650	468.2	1.594
2300	0.99742	147.1	5.554	133.03	556.2	0.1761	0.1122	953.82	1.658	475.1	1.569
2400	0.99695	128.6	8.814	132.96	532.7	0.1827	0.1185	971.75	1.666	481.2	1.542
2500	0.99617	113.3	13.50	132.88	511.1	0.1910	0.1262	990.45	1.673	486.7	1.513
2600	0.99499	100.5	20.05	132.77	491.1	0.2014	0.1359	1010.0	1.681	491.4	1.482
2700	0.99332	89.51	28.94	132.64	472.4	0.2143	0.1477	1030.9	1.689	495.6	1.450
2800	0.99104	80.62	40.75	132.47	455.0	0.2298	0.1619	1053.2	1.697	499.5	1.419
2900	0.98806	72.20	56.07	132.26	438.6	0.2482	0.1786	1077.1	1.705	503.5	1.390
3000	0.98423	65.12	75.58	131.99	423.1	0.2697	0.1979	1103.1	1.714	507.6	1.362
				$p=1$ bar							
1000	0.94302	5 698	0	140.48	1 689	0.2494	0.1571	726.71	1.496	311.1	1.634
1100	0.96486	3 514	0	137.57	1 503	0.2090	0.1290	749.42	1.517	331.6	1.653
1200	0.97698	2 302	0.0003	135.96	1 362	0.1875	0.1126	769.15	1.534	349.7	1.666
1300	0.98410	1 590	0.0013	135.02	1 248	0.1757	0.1051	787.26	1.549	365.9	1.672
1400	0.98852	1 148	0.0048	134.43	1 154	0.1690	0.1009	804.48	1.562	380.9	1.674
1500	0.99141	859.0	0.0154	134.05	1 074	0.1654	0.0989	821.20	1.573	394.6	1.672
1600	0.99337	662.4	0.0429	133.78	1 005	0.1632	0.0978	837.64	1.584	407.5	1.669
1700	0.99474	524.0	0.1062	133.60	944.7	0.1621	0.0973	853.92	1.594	419.9	1.666

continued

T, °K	X_1	$X_2 \cdot 10^5$	$X_e \cdot 10^4$	M	$\varrho \cdot 10^3$	c_p	c_v	i	s	u	k
1800	0.99572	423.7	0.2389	133.46	891.3	0.1622	0.0979	870.11	1.603	431.2	1.657
1900	0.99641	348.8	0.4949	133.36	843.7	0.1632	0.0992	886.38	1.612	441.6	1.645
2000	0.99689	291.8	0.9564	133.28	801.0	0.1647	0.1009	902.74	1.620	451.4	1.633
2100	0.99718	247.3	1.741	133.21	762.5	0.1671	0.1034	919.32	1.628	460.4	1.617
2200	0.99728	212.0	3.008	133.15	727.5	0.1705	0.1068	936.17	1.636	468.6	1.597
2300	0.99717	183.8	4.967	133.08	695.5	0.1754	0.1115	953.47	1.644	475.6	1.573
2400	0.99682	160.7	7.883	133.01	666.2	0.1816	0.1174	971.31	1.652	481.9	1.547
2500	0.99617	141.6	12.08	132.93	639.2	0.1893	0.1246	989.86	1.659	487.5	1.519
2600	0.99516	125.6	17.93	132.83	614.1	0.1990	0.1336	1009.2	1.667	492.4	1.489
2700	0.99370	112.0	25.89	132.71	590.8	0.2109	0.1447	1029.8	1.674	496.7	1.458
2800	0.99170	100.9	36.46	132.55	569.1	0.2253	0.1579	1051.7	1.682	500.7	1.427
2900	0.98906	90.43	50.17	132.36	548.6	0.2423	0.1734	1075.1	1.691	504.7	1.397
3000	0.98565	81.64	67.65	132.11	529.4	0.2622	0.1914	1100.4	1.699	508.7	1.370
				p=2 bar							
1100	0.93413	6 587	0	141.66	3 096	0.2436	0.1511	739.20	1.467	328.2	1.668
1200	0.95592	4 408	0.0002	138.76	2 780	0.2110	0.1290	761.81	1.486	347.3	1.676
1300	0.96915	3 085	0.0009	137.00	2 534	0.1916	0.1160	781.86	1.502	364.4	1.682
1400	0.97755	2 245	0.0034	135.89	2 333	0.1798	0.1068	800.39	1.516	379.9	1.684
1500	0.98310	1 689	0.0109	135.15	2 166	0.1730	0.1029	818.02	1.528	394.0	1.682
1600	0.98692	1 308	0.0302	134.64	2 023	0.1687	0.1005	835.10	1.539	407.3	1.678
1700	0.98961	1 037	0.0749	134.28	1 899	0.1660	0.0992	851.85	1.550	419.9	1.674
1800	0.99156	840.4	0.1686	134.02	1 790	0.1651	0.0992	868.38	1.559	431.3	1.665
1900	0.99300	692.9	0.3494	133.82	1 693	0.1652	0.1000	884.89	1.568	441.9	1.653
2000	0.99406	580.2	0.6753	133.67	1 607	0.1660	0.1012	901.42	1.576	451.9	1.641
2100	0.99483	492.2	1.229	133.54	1 529	0.1677	0.1032	918.09	1.584	461.1	1.626
2200	0.99535	422.4	2.125	133.44	1 458	0.1703	0.1059	934.96	1.592	469.6	1.608
2300	0.99563	366.4	3.510	133.34	1 394	0.1742	0.1099	952.18	1.600	477.0	1.585
2400	0.99568	320.7	5.571	133.26	1 335	0.1792	0.1148	969.84	1.608	483.6	1.561
2500	0.99546	282.9	8.537	133.17	1 281	0.1854	0.1207	988.07	1.615	489.7	1.535
2600	0.99495	251.2	12.68	133.07	1 230	0.1932	0.1282	1006.9	1.622	495.0	1.507
2700	0.99410	224.1	18.31	132.96	1 184	0.2028	0.1372	1026.8	1.630	499.7	1.478
2800	0.99282	202.3	25.80	132.83	1 140	0.2144	0.1480	1047.7	1.638	504.0	1.448
2900	0.99108	181.6	35.51	132.67	1 100	0.2280	0.1606	1069.8	1.645	508.1	1.420
3000	0.98878	164.3	47.91	132.49	1 062	0.2438	0.1751	1093.5	1.653	512.1	1.392
				p=4 bar							
1200	0.91859	8 141	0.0001	143.72	5 759	0.2431	0.1487	749.49	1.435	344.0	1.704
1300	0.94174	5 826	0.0006	140.65	5 202	0.2157	0.1265	772.34	1.454	362.1	1.705
1400	0.95697	4 303	0.0024	138.62	4 761	0.1976	0.1159	792.95	1.469	378.4	1.704
1500	0.96729	3 271	0.0076	137.25	4 400	0.1860	0.1094	812.10	1.482	393.1	1.700
1600	0.97450	2 550	0.0212	136.29	4 096	0.1783	0.1052	830.32	1.494	406.8	1.695
1700	0.97966	2 033	0.0527	135.61	3 835	0.1733	0.1026	847.90	1.504	419.6	1.689
1800	0.98344	1 653	0.1187	135.10	3 609	0.1706	0.1016	865.07	1.514	431.3	1.679
1900	0.98628	1 367	0.2462	134.72	3 409	0.1694	0.1017	882.06	1.523	442.1	1.666
2000	0.98843	1 147	0.4762	134.42	3 232	0.1691	0.1022	898.95	1.532	452.3	1.653
2100	0.99008	975.0	0.8673	134.19	3 072	0.1698	0.1037	915.88	1.540	461.8	1.638
2200	0.99132	837.9	1.499	134.00	2 929	0.1715	0.1059	932.92	1.548	470.4	1.620
2300	0.99223	727.8	2.477	133.84	2 798	0.1745	0.1092	950.22	1.556	478.1	1.599
2400	0.99284	637.7	3.933	133.70	2 678	0.1785	0.1133	967.85	1.564	485.1	1.576
2500	0.99316	563.1	6.029	133.57	2 569	0.1834	0.1182	985.95	1.571	491.4	1.551
2600	0.99320	500.6	8.957	133.45	2 468	0.1898	0.1245	1004.5	1.578	497.1	1.524
2700	0.99294	447.2	12.94	133.33	2 374	0.1977	0.1321	1024.0	1.586	502.1	1.496
2800	0.99231	404.1	18.24	133.20	2 287	0.2072	0.1411	1044.3	1.593	506.7	1.468
2900	0.99134	363.4	25.12	133.05	2 206	0.2183	0.1516	1065.5	1.600	510.9	1.440
3000	0.98993	329.4	33.90	132.89	2 130	0.2312	0.1637	1088.0	1.608	515.0	1.412
				p=6 bar							
1200	0.88632	11 368	0.0001	148.01	8 896	0.2627	0.1604	739.51	1.404	341.3	1.727
1300	0.91712	8 287	0.0005	143.92	7 984	0.2327	0.1347	764.20	1.424	360.2	1.727
1400	0.93799	6 201	0.0019	141.14	7 271	0.2112	0.1225	786.34	1.440	377.2	1.724
1500	0.95243	4 757	0.0062	139.23	6 694	0.1967	0.1145	806.71	1.454	392.4	1.718
1600	0.96267	3 733	0.0172	137.86	6 214	0.1866	0.1091	825.86	1.466	406.4	1.711
1700	0.97009	2 990	0.0428	136.88	5 807	0.1797	0.1055	844.18	1.478	419.5	1.703

continued

T, °K	X_1	$X_2 \cdot 10^5$	$X_e \cdot 10$	M	$\varrho \cdot 10^3$	c_p	c_v	i	s	u	k
1800	0.97558	2 440	0.0965	136.15	5 455	0.1756	0.1038	861.92	1.488	431.3	1.692
1900	0.97972	2 023	0.2003	135.59	5 147	0.1733	0.1033	879.35	1.497	442.2	1.678
2000	0.98290	1 702	0.3877	135.16	4 874	0.1721	0.1034	896.59	1.506	452.6	1.664
2100	0.98537	1 449	0.7064	134.82	4 630	0.1721	0.1045	913.79	1.514	462.1	1.648
2200	0.98729	1 247	1.222	134.55	4 411	0.1732	0.1063	931.03	1.522	470.9	1.630
2300	0.98875	1 084	2.019	134.32	4 212	0.1756	0.1092	948.47	1.530	478.6	1.608
2400	0.98985	950.9	3.207	134.13	4 031	0.1790	0.1129	966.18	1.537	485.8	1.585
2500	0.99061	840.4	4.917	133.96	3 864	0.1833	0.1174	984.30	1.545	492.3	1.561
2600	0.99106	747.6	7.306	133.80	3 712	0.1889	0.1231	1002.8	1.552	498.1	1.535
2700	0.99120	668.5	10.56	133.65	3 570	0.1959	0.1300	1022.2	1.560	503.3	1.507
2800	0.99098	604.6	14.88	133.51	3 439	0.2044	0.1382	1042.2	1.567	508.0	1.479
2900	0.99046	544.1	20.50	133.36	3 316	0.2144	0.1478	1063.1	1.574	512.4	1.451
3000	0.98953	493.7	27.67	133.19	3 202	0.2260	0.1587	1085.1	1.582	516.5	1.424
					p=8 bar						
1300	0.89481	10 519	0.0004	146.88	10 865	0.2449	0.1478	757.14	1.402	358.5	1.745
1400	0.92040	7 960	0.0016	143.48	9 856	0.2219	0.1274	780.42	1.419	376.0	1.742
1500	0.93842	6 157	0.0053	141.09	9 045	0.2054	0.1185	801.76	1.434	391.6	1.734
1600	0.95139	4 861	0.0148	139.36	8 376	0.1937	0.1122	821.71	1.446	406.0	1.726
1700	0.96088	3 911	0.0369	138.10	7 812	0.1854	0.1080	840.67	1.458	419.3	1.717
1800	0.96795	3 203	0.0833	137.16	7 328	0.1801	0.1057	858.91	1.468	431.3	1.704
1900	0.97334	2 663	0.1729	136.44	6 906	0.1769	0.1047	876.75	1.478	442.3	1.689
2000	0.97749	2 244	0.3348	135.88	6 533	0.1750	0.1045	894.32	1.487	452.8	1.674
2100	0.98074	1 913	0.6104	135.44	6 202	0.1744	0.1052	911.78	1.496	462.4	1.657
2200	0.98330	1 649	1.056	135.08	5 904	0.1750	0.1068	929.23	1.504	471.2	1.639
2300	0.98530	1 435	1.746	134.79	5 636	0.1769	0.1094	946.82	1.512	479.1	1.617
2400	0.98684	1 260	2.773	134.54	5 391	0.1798	0.1128	964.64	1.519	486.3	1.593
2500	0.98800	1 115	4.252	134.33	5 167	0.1836	0.1170	982.80	1.527	492.9	1.569
2600	0.98881	992.3	6.320	134.14	4 961	0.1888	0.1223	1001.3	1.534	498.8	1.543
2700	0.98929	887.9	9.133	133.96	4 771	0.1952	0.1288	1020.6	1.541	504.1	1.516
2800	0.98939	803.6	12.88	133.80	4 595	0.2031	0.1365	1040.5	1.548	508.9	1.487
2900	0.98921	723.7	17.74	133.63	4 431	0.2123	0.1455	1061.3	1.556	513.3	1.459
3000	0.98864	657.1	23.95	133.46	4 278	0.2231	0.1558	1083.1	1.563	517.5	1.432
					p=10 bar						
1300	0.87444	12 556	0.0004	149.59	13 832	0.2536	0.1528	750.93	1.384	356.7	1.760
1400	0.90401	9 599	0.0015	145.66	12 507	0.2302	0.1310	775.08	1.402	374.8	1.757
1500	0.92519	7 481	0.0047	142.85	11 447	0.2127	0.1216	797.21	1.418	390.8	1.749
1600	0.94060	5 939	0.0132	140.80	10 578	0.1998	0.1149	817.83	1.431	405.5	1.739
1700	0.95200	4 799	0.0329	139.28	9 848	0.1904	0.1101	837.34	1.443	419.0	1.729
1800	0.96055	3 943	0.0742	138.14	9 225	0.1842	0.1074	856.04	1.453	431.2	1.715
1900	0.96711	3 286	0.1542	137.27	8 684	0.1803	0.1061	874.26	1.463	442.4	1.699
2000	0.97219	2 775	0.2987	136.59	8 209	0.1777	0.1055	892.13	1.472	452.9	1.684
2100	0.97620	2 370	0.5446	136.05	7 787	0.1766	0.1060	909.84	1.481	462.6	1.666
2200	0.97937	2 045	0.9426	135.61	7 409	0.1768	0.1073	927.48	1.489	471.4	1.647
2300	0.98187	1 782	1.559	135.25	7 069	0.1783	0.1098	945.22	1.497	479.4	1.624
2400	0.98385	1 566	2.476	134.95	6 759	0.1808	0.1129	963.16	1.505	486.6	1.601
2500	0.98538	1 386	3.798	134.70	6 476	0.1842	0.1169	981.40	1.512	493.4	1.576
2600	0.98652	1 235	5.646	134.47	6 217	0.1890	0.1219	999.93	1.520	499.3	1.550
2700	0.98731	1 105	8.151	134.26	5 978	0.1950	0.1281	1019.3	1.527	504.7	1.522
2800	0.98769	1 001	11.54	134.08	5 756	0.2024	0.1355	1039.1	1.534	509.5	1.494
2900	0.98781	902.0	15.86	133.89	5 550	0.2111	0.1440	1059.8	1.541	514.0	1.466
3000	0.98752	819.5	21.41	133.71	5 357	0.2213	0.1538	1081.4	1.549	518.2	1.439

Viscosity $\eta \cdot 10^7$ $(N \cdot s/m^2)$ of cesium vapor [424]

T. °K	For monatomic vapor	p, bar				At saturation
		0.5	1	2	3	
900	232	215				210
950	242	228	217			215
1000	252	241	232			220
1050	261	253	245	231	226	225
1100	271	264	258	246	236	230
1150	280	275	269	260	251	235
1200	290	285	281	272	264	240
1250	300	296	292	284	278	245
1300	309	306	302	296	290	250

Viscosity $\eta \cdot 10^7 (N \cdot s/m^2)$ of ionized cesium vapor at high temperatures [39]

140 T. °K / p, atm →	10^{-5}	10^{-4}	10^{-3}	10^{-2}	10^{-1}	10^{0}	10^{1}
2000	317	386	406	413	412	412	418
3000	6.85	3.88	398	480	561	583	592
4000	3.34	6.64	19.6	49.5	224	488	663
5000	5.58	7.93	11.7	18.8	66.8	226	482
7000	11.6	15.0	19.4	25.4	37.7	80.5	221
10 000	26.0	31.4	38.2	48.1	63.2	91.0	188

Viscosity of liquid cesium [37]

T. °K	T_{melt}(301.6)	400	500	600	700	800	900	1000	1100	1200	1300	1400
$\eta \cdot 10^3$. $N \cdot s/m^2$	0.697	0.425	0.318	0.254	0.215	0.186	0.171	0.151	0.142	0.132	0.124	0.117

Thermal conductivity $\lambda \cdot 10^3$ $(W/m \cdot deg)$ of cesium vapor [418]

T. °K	For monatomic vapor	p, bar												At saturation
		0.001	0.005	0.01	0.05	0.1	0.2	0.3	0.5	1	2	6	10	
600	4.57	4.71	5.22											5.30
700	5.16	5.20	5.32	5.46										6.31
800	5.75	5.77	5.81	5.85	6.21	6.60	7.22							7.24
900	6.36	6.37	6.38	6.40	6.55	6.73	7.05	7.32	7.78					8.07
1000	6.95	6.96	6.98	6.98	7.05	7.14	7.30	7.46	7.73	8.28				8.78
1100	7.55	7.55	7.55	7.56	7.60	7.65	7.74	7.83	8.00	8.36	8.90			9.42
1200	8.14	8.14	8.14	8.15	8.17	8.20	8.25	8.31	8.42	8.66	9.05	9.91		10.0
1300	8.75	8.75	8.75	8.75	8.77	8.78	8.82	8.86	8.93	9.09	9.38	10.1	10.5	10.6
1400	9.34	9.34	9.34	9.34	9.35	9.36	9.38	9.41	9.46	9.57	9.79	10.4	10.8	11.1
1500	9.93	9.93	9.93	9.93	9.93	9.95	9.97	9.98	10.0	10.1	10.3	10.7	11.1	11.5

Thermal conductivity λ of liquid cesium [37]

T, °K	T_{melt}(301.6)	400	500	600	700	800	900	1000	1100	1200	1300	1400
λ, $W/m \cdot deg$	19.0	19.3	19.5	19.4	19.2	18.5	17.7	16.5	15.2	13.5	11.7	9.4

Surface tension σ of cesium [31]

t, °C	29	100	200	300	400	500	600	700	800	900	1000	1100	1200	1300
σ, dyne/cm	71.3	67.9	63.1	58.3	53.5	48.7	43.9	39.1	34.3	29.5	24.7	19.9	15.1	10.3

MERCURY (Hg)

Atomic weight 200.61

$t_{melt} = -38.83$ °C; $t_{boil} = 356.95$ °C; at 760 mm Hg; $t_{cr} = 1490$ °C;
$p_{cr} = 1510$ bar; $\rho_{cr} = 5500$ kg/m³

Thermodynamic properties of mercury at saturation [40]:

ρ (kg/m³), ν (m³/kg), $\alpha = \frac{1}{v}\left(\frac{\partial v}{\partial T}\right)_p$ (deg⁻¹); $\beta = -\frac{1}{v}\left(\frac{\partial v}{\partial p}\right)_T$ (bar⁻¹)

t, °C	p, bar	ϱ'	$v' \cdot 10^5$	v''	$\alpha' \cdot 10^4$	$\beta' \cdot 10^6$
0	$2.728 \cdot 10^{-7}$	13 595.03	7.35563	$4.150 \cdot 10^5$	1.81445	3.918
10	$7.101 \cdot 10^{-7}$	13 570.39	7.36898	$1.653 \cdot 10^5$	1.81265	3.966
20	$1.729 \cdot 10^{-6}$	13 545.83	7.38234	$7.026 \cdot 10^4$	1.81103	4.013
30	$3.68 \cdot 10^{-6}$	13 521.33	7.39572	$3.167 \cdot 10^4$	1.80960	4.061
40	$8.626 \cdot 10^{-6}$	13 496.89	7.40911	$1.505 \cdot 10^4$	1.80836	4.109
50	$1.786 \cdot 10^{-5}$	13 472.51	7.42252	$7.501 \cdot 10^3$	1.80731	4.158
60	$3.536 \cdot 10^{-5}$	13 448.19	7.43594	$3.905 \cdot 10^3$	1.80647	4.208
70	$6.724 \cdot 10^{-5}$	13 423.93	7.44938	$2.115 \cdot 10^3$	1.80583	4.257
80	$1.232 \cdot 10^{-4}$	13 399.71	7.46285	$1.188 \cdot 10^3$	1.80540	4.308
90	$2.182 \cdot 10^{-4}$	13 375.54	7.47633	$6.899 \cdot 10^2$	1.80518	4.359
100	$3.745 \cdot 10^{-4}$	13 351.42	7.48984	413.0	1.80518	4.410
110	$6.247 \cdot 10^{-4}$	13 327.34	7.50337	254.2	1.80541	4.462
120	$1.015 \cdot 10^{-3}$	13 303.30	7.51693	169.6	1.80587	4.515
130	$1.608 \cdot 10^{-3}$	13 279.29	7.53052	103.9	1.80656	4.568
140	$2.491 \cdot 10^{-3}$	13 255.31	7.54415	68.75	1.80748	4.622
150	$3.778 \cdot 10^{-3}$	13 231.37	7.55780	46.43	1.80865	4.676
160	$5.618 \cdot 10^{-3}$	13 207.45	7.57148	31.96	1.81007	4.731
170	$8.204 \cdot 10^{-3}$	13 183.56	7.58520	22.39	1.81173	4.787
180	$1.178 \cdot 10^{-2}$	13 159.68	7.59897	15.95	1.81365	4.844
190	$1.664 \cdot 10^{-2}$	13 135.82	7.61277	11.54	1.81583	4.901
200	$2.315 \cdot 10^{-2}$	13 111.97	7.62662	8.469	1.81827	4.960
210	$3.177 \cdot 10^{-2}$	13 088.14	7.64051	6.301	1.82097	5.019
220	$4.304 \cdot 10^{-2}$	13 064.31	7.65444	4.748	1.82395	5.078
230	$5.758 \cdot 10^{-2}$	13 040.48	7.66843	3.621	1.82720	5.139
240	$7.614 \cdot 10^{-2}$	13 016.65	7.68247	2.793	1.83073	5.201
250	$9.959 \cdot 10^{-2}$	12 992.82	7.69656	2.176	1.83454	5.263
260	0.12892	12 968.98	7.71071	1.7132	1.83864	5.327
270	0.16527	12 945.14	7.72491	1.3613	1.84303	5.391
280	0.20993	12 921.27	7.73918	1.0912	1.84771	5.454
290	0.26435	12 897.39	7.75351	0.88213	1.85268	5.523
300	0.33015	12 873.5	7.7679	0.71874	1.85796	5.590
310	0.40910	12 849.6	7.7823	0.59002	1.86354	5.659
320	0.50320	12 825.6	7.7969	0.48779	1.86943	5.728
330	0.61460	12 801.6	7.8115	0.40600	1.87563	5.799
340	0.74567	12 777.6	7.8262	0.34008	1.88213	5.871
350	0.89896	12 753.6	7.8409	0.28660	1.88896	5.944
360	1.0772	12 729.4	7.8558	0.24291	1.8961	6.02
370	1.2834	12 705.3	7.8707	0.20702	1.9036	6.10
380	1.5207	12 681.1	7.8858	0.17735	1.9114	6.17
390	1.7925	12 656.9	7.9008	0.15269	1.9195	6.25
400	2.1024	12 632.6	7.9160	0.13207	1.9279	6.33
410	2.454	12 608.2	7.9313	0.11476	1.9367	6.41
420	2.852	12 583.8	7.9467	0.10014	1.9458	6.49
430	3.299	12 559.3	7.9622	0.08775	1.9553	6.58
440	3.801	12 534.8	7.9778	0.07719	1.9651	6.66
450	4.362	12 510.1	7.9935	0.06815	1.9752	6.75
460	4.986	12 485.4	8.0094	0.06039	1.9856	6.84
470	5.679	12 460.7	8.0252	0.05369	1.9964	6.93
480	6.446	12 435.8	8.0413	0.04789	2.0076	7.02

continued

t, °C	p, bar	ϱ'	$v' \cdot 10^5$	v''	$\alpha' \cdot 10^4$	$\beta' \cdot 10^6$
490	7.292	12 410.9	8.0574	0.04285	2.0191	7.12
500	8.222	12 386	8.074	0.03846	2.031	7.2
510	9.242	12 361	8.090	0.03462	2.043	7.3
520	10.358	12 336	8.106	0.03124	2.056	7.4
530	11.576	12 310	8.123	0.02827	2.069	7.5
540	12.901	12 285	8.140	0.02565	2.082	7.6
550	14.340	12 259	8.157	0.02333	2.097	7.7
560	15.899	12 234	8.174	0.02126	2.109	7.8
570	17.584	12 208	8.191	0.019426	2.124	7.9
580	19.403	12 182	8.209	0.017785	2.138	8.0
590	21.36	12 156	8.226	0.016317	2.153	8.2
600	23.46	12 130	8.244	0.015000	2.168	8.3
610	25.72	12 104	8.262	0.013815	2.184	8.4
620	28.14	12 078	8.280	0.012748	2.200	8.5
630	30.72	12 051	8.298	0.011784	2.217	8.6
640	33.47	12 025	8.316	0.010911	2.233	8.8
650	36.41	11 998	8.335	0.010120	2.25	8.9
660	39.53	11 972	8.353	0.009401	2.27	9.0
670	42.85	11 945	8.372	0.008746	2.29	9.2
680	46.36	11 918	8.391	0.008150	2.30	9.3
690	50.09	11 891	8.410	0.007604	2.32	9.4
700	54.03	11 863	8.430	0.007105	2.34	9.6
710	58.20	11 836	8.450	0.006648	2.36	9.7
720	62.59	11 809	8.468	0.006228	2.38	9.9
730	67.22	11 781	8.488	0.005842	2.40	10.0
740	72.10	11 753	8.508	0.005487	2.42	10.2
750	77.22	11 725	8.529	0.005159	2.44	10.3
760	82.60	11 697	8.550	0.004856	2.46	10.5
770	88.25	11 669	8.570	0.004576	2.48	10.6
780	94.17	11 641	8.590	0.004317	2.50	10.8
790	100.37	11 612	8.612	0.004077	2.52	11.0
800	106.85	11 584	8.632	0.003854	2.54	11.3

Thermodynamic properties of mercury at saturation [40] : i and r (kJ/kg), s, c_p and c_v (kJ/kg · deg)

t, °C	p, mm Hg	i'	i''	r	s'	s''	c_p'	c_v'
0	$2.05 \cdot 10^{-4}$	43.074	349.891	306.817	0.36642	1.48967	0.1404	0.1235
10	$5.33 \cdot 10^{-4}$	44.476	350.927	306.451	0.37146	1.45375	0.1400	0.1227
20	$1.30 \cdot 10^{-3}$	45.874	351.964	306.090	0.37631	1.42045	0.1396	0.1219
30	$2.98 \cdot 10^{-3}$	47.268	353.000	305.732	0.38099	1.38951	0.1392	0.1211
40	$6.47 \cdot 10^{-3}$	48.659	354.036	305.377	0.38550	1.36068	0.1389	0.1204
50	$1.34 \cdot 10^{-2}$	50.046	355.072	305.026	0.38986	1.33378	0.1385	0.1197
60	$2.65 \cdot 10^{-2}$	51.430	356.108	304.678	0.39408	1.30862	0.1382	0.1190
70	$5.04 \cdot 10^{-2}$	52.810	357.145	304.335	0.39816	1.28505	0.1379	0.1183
80	$9.24 \cdot 10^{-2}$	54.188	358.181	303.993	0.40212	1.26292	0.1376	0.1177
90	0.164	55.563	359.217	303.654	0.40596	1.24213	0.1374	0.1171
100	0.281	56.936	360.253	303.317	0.40969	1.22255	0.1371	0.1165
110	0.468	58.306	361.289	302.983	0.41331	1.20408	0.1369	0.1159
120	0.761	59.674	362.326	302.652	0.41684	1.18665	0.1367	0.1153
130	1.21	61.039	363.362	302.323	0.42027	1.17017	0.1365	0.1148
140	1.87	62.403	364.397	301.994	0.42361	1.15456	0.1363	0.1143
150	2.83	63.765	365.433	301.668	0.42687	1.13978	0.1361	0.1137
160	4.21	65.125	366.469	301.344	0.43004	1.12575	0.1360	0.1132
170	6.15	66.484	367.504	301.020	0.43314	1.11242	0.1358	0.1128
180	8.83	67.842	368.539	300.697	0.43647	1.09971	0.1357	0.1123
190	12.48	69.198	369.574	300.376	0.43913	1.08768	0.1356	0.1119
200	17.37	70.553	370.609	300.056	0.44203	1.07619	0.1355	0.1114
210	23.83	71.908	371.642	299.734	0.44486	1.06524	0.1354	0.1110

continued

t, °C	p, mm Hg	i'	i''	r	s'	s''	c_p'	c_v'
220	32.28	73.261	372.676	299.415	0.44763	1.05478	0.1353	0.1106
230	43.19	74.614	373.708	299.094	0.45035	1.04479	0.1353	0.1102
240	57.11	75.967	374.740	298.773	0.45301	1.03521	0.1352	0.1098
250	74.70	77.319	375.771	298.452	0.45562	1.02610	0.1352	0.1094
260	96.70	78.671	376.800	298.129	0.45818	1.01737	0.1352	0.1091
270	124.0	80.023	377.829	297.806	0.46069	1.00899	0.1352	0.1087
280	157.5	81.375	378.855	297.480	0.46316	1.00095	0.1352	0.1084
290	198.3	82.728	379.880	297.152	0.46558	0.99324	0.1352	0.1081
300	247.6	84.080	380.904	296.824	0.46796	0.98584	0.1353	0.1078
310	306.9	85.434	381.925	296.491	0.47030	0.97873	0.1353	0.1075
320	377.4	86.788	382.944	296.156	0.47260	0.97190	0.1354	0.1072
330	461.0	88.143	383.960	295.817	0.47487	0.96532	0.1355	0.1069
340	559.3	89.499	384.973	295.474	0.47709	0.95899	0.1356	0.1066
350	674.3	90.856	385.984	295.128	0.47929	0.95289	0.1357	0.1063
360	807.9	92.215	386.991	294.776	0.48145	0.94702	0.1358	0.1061
370	962.7	93.575	387.994	294.419	0.48358	0.94135	0.1359	0.1058
380	1140.6	94.937	388.994	294.057	0.48568	0.93589	0.1361	0.1056
390	1344.4	96.300	389.989	293.689	0.48774	0.93061	0.1362	0.1054
400	1576.9	97.666	390.980	293.314	0.48978	0.92552	0.1364	0.1051
410	2.454 bar	99.033	391.966	292.933	0.49180	0.92059	0.1366	0.1049
420	2.852	100.403	392.947	292.544	0.49378	0.91583	0.1368	0.1047
430	3.299	101.775	393.923	292.148	0.49574	0.91123	0.1370	0.1045
440	3.801	103.150	394.893	291.743	0.49768	0.90677	0.1373	0.1043
450	4.362	104.528	395.858	291.330	0.49959	0.90245	0.1375	0.1041
460	4.986	105.908	395.816	290.908	0.50148	0.89827	0.1378	0.1039
470	5.679	107.292	397.767	290.475	0.50335	0.89422	0.1380	0.1037
480	6.446	108.679	398.711	290.032	0.50519	0.89029	0.1383	0.1036
490	7.292	110.069	399.649	289.580	0.50702	0.88647	0.1386	0.1034
500	8.222	111.463	400.579	289.116	0.50882	0.88277	0.1389	0.1032
510	9.242	112.861	401.501	288.640	0.51061	0.87917	0.1392	0.1031
520	10.358	114.262	402.415	288.153	0.51238	0.87568	0.1396	0.1029
530	11.576	115.668	403.321	287.653	0.51412	0.87228	0.1399	0.1028
540	12.901	117.078	404.218	287.140	0.51586	0.86898	0.1403	0.1026
550	14.340	118.492	405.106	286.614	0.51757	0.86576	0.1407	0.1024
560	15.899	119.911	405.985	286.074	0.51927	0.86263	0.1410	0.1023
570	17.584	121.335	406.855	285.520	0.52095	0.85959	0.1414	0.1022
580	19.403	122.763	407.715	284.952	0.52262	0.85662	0.1418	0.1021
590	21.36	124.197	408.565	284.368	0.52427	0.85372	0.1423	0.1019
600	23.46	125.636	409.405	283.769	0.52591	0.85090	0.1427	0.1018
610	25.72	127.080	410.235	283.155	0.52753	0.84815	0.1432	0.1017
620	28.14	128.530	411.054	282.524	0.52914	0.84546	0.1436	0.1016
630	30.72	129.986	411.861	281.875	0.53074	0.84284	0.1441	0.1015
640	33.47	131.448	412.210	281.210	0.53232	0.84028	0.1446	0.1014
650	36.41	132.915	413.444	280.529	0.53389	0.83777	0.1451	0.1013
660	39.53	134.389	414.218	279.829	0.53545	0.83533	0.1456	0.1012
670	42.85	135.869	414.980	279.111	0.53700	0.83294	0.1461	0.1011
680	46,36	137.356	415.731	278.375	0.53854	0.83060	0.1466	0.1010
690	50.09	138.850	416.619	277.619	0.54006	0.82831	0.1472	0.1009
700	54.03	140.350	417.195	276.845	0.54158	0.8260	0.1478	0.1008
710	58.20	141.858	417.909	276.051	0.54308	0.82387	0.1483	0.1007
720	62.59	143.372	418.610	275.238	0.54458	0.82172	0.1489	0.1006
730	67.22	144.894	419.298	274.404	0.54607	0.81961	0.1495	0.1006
740	72.10	146.424	419.974	273.550	0.54754	0.81754	0.1501	0.1005
750	77.22	147.961	420.636	272.675	0.54901	0.81552	0.1507	0.1004
760	82.60	149.506	421.286	271.780	0.55047	0.81353	0.1514	0.1004
770	88.25	151.059	421.923	270.864	0.55192	0.81158	0.1520	0.1003
780	94.17	152.619	422.546	269.927	0.55336	0.80966	0.1527	0.1002
790	100.37	154.288	423.156	268.968	0.55479	0.80778	0.1533	0.1002
800	106.85	155.766	423.752	267.986	0.55621	0.80593	0.1540	0.1001

Thermodynamic properties of mercury vapor at different temperatures and pressures [40]: v (m^3/kg), i (kJ/kg), and s (kJ/kg · deg)

t, °C	v	i	s	v	i	s
		$p=10^{-2}$ bar			$p=5\cdot10^{-2}$ bar	
180	18.782	368.540	1.10652			
200	19.611	370.613	1.11100			
220	20.440	372.685	1.11529			
240	21.269	374.758	1.11941	4.2529	374.747	1.05268
260	22.098	376.831	1.12337	4.4188	376.820	1.05665
280	22.927	378.903	1.12719	4.5847	378.894	1.06047
300	23.756	380.976	1.13087	4.7506	380.967	1.06415
320	24.585	383.049	1.13442	4.9164	383.040	1.06770
340	25.414	385.121	1.13786	5.0822	385.113	1.07114
360	26.243	387.194	1.14118	5.2480	387.186	1.07446
380	27.072	389.266	1.14441	5.4139	389.259	1.07769
400	27.901	391.339	1.14753	5.5797	391.332	1.08082
420	28.730	393.411	1.15057	5.7455	393.405	1.08385
440	29.559	395.484	1.15352	5.9114	395.478	1.08680
460	30.388	397.556	1.15638	6.0772	397.551	1.08967
480	31.217	399.629	1.15917	6.2430	399.623	1.09246
500	32.046	401.702	1.16189	6.4088	401.696	1.09517
520	32.875	403.774	1.16453	6.5746	403.769	1.09782
540	33.704	405.847	1.16711	6.7405	405.842	1.10040
560	34.533	407.919	1.16963	6.9063	407.914	1.10292
580	35.362	409.992	1.17209	7.0721	409.987	1.10538
600	36.191	412.064	1.17449	7.2379	412.060	1.10778
620	37.020	414.137	1.17684	7.4037	414.132	1.11012
640	37.849	416.209	1.17913	7.5695	416.205	1.11242
660	38.678	418.282	1.18138	7.7353	418.278	1.11466
680	39.507	420.354	1.18357	7.9011	420.350	1.11685
700	40.336	422.427	1.18573	8.0670	422.423	1.11901
800	44.481	432.789	1.19586	8.8960	432.786	1.12915
900	48.926	443.152	1.20510	9.7250	443.149	1.13838
1000	52.771	453.514	1.21357	10.554	453.512	1.14686
1200	61.061	474.238	1.22869	12.212	474.237	1.16198
1400	69.351	494.963	1.24188	13.870	494.962	1.17517
1600	77.641	515.688	1.25358	15.528	515.687	1.18687
1800	85.931	536.413	1.26410	17.186	536.412	1.19739
2000	94.221	557.138	1.27364	18.844	557.137	1.20693
		$p=10^{-1}$ bar			$p=2\cdot10^{-1}$ bar	
260	2.2089	376.808	1.02790			
280	2.2919	378.882	1.03172	1.1455	378.858	1.00296
300	2.3748	380.956	1.03540	1.1870	380.933	1.00665
320	2.4578	383.029	1.03896	1.2285	383.008	1.01021
340	2.5407	385.103	1.04240	1.2700	385.083	1.01365
360	2.6237	387.177	1.04573	1.3115	387.158	1.01698
380	2.7066	389.250	1.04895	1.3530	389.232	1.02020
400	2.7895	391.323	1.05208	1.3944	391.306	1.02333
420	2.8725	393.397	1.05511	1.4359	393.381	1.02637
440	2.9554	395.470	1.05806	1.4774	395.454	1.02932
460	3.0383	397.543	1.06093	1.5188	397.528	1.03219
480	3.1212	399.616	1.06372	1.5603	399.602	1.03498
500	3.2042	401.689	1.06644	1.6018	401.676	1.03769
520	3.2871	403.762	1.06908	1.6433	403.750	1.04034
540	3.3700	405.835	1.07166	1.6878	405.823	1.04292
560	3.4529	407.908	1.07418	1.7262	407.896	1.04544
580	3.5358	409.981	1.07664	1.7677	409.970	1.04790
600	3.6187	412.054	1.07904	1.8092	412.043	1.05030
620	3.7017	414.127	1.08139	1.8506	414.116	1.05265
640	3.7846	416.200	1.08369	1.8921	416.190	1.05495
660	3.8675	418.273	1.08593	1.9336	418.263	1.05719
680	3.9504	420.346	1.08813	1.9750	420.336	1.05939
700	4.0333	422.418	1.09028	2.0165	422.409	1.06154
800	4.4479	432.782	1.10042	2.2238	432.774	1.07168
900	4.8624	443.145	1.10965	2.4311	443.139	1.08092

continued

t, °C	v	i	s	v	i	s
1000	5.2769	453.508	1.11813	2.6383	453.503	1.08939
1200	6.1060	474.234	1.13325	3.0529	474.229	1.10452
1400	6.9350	494.960	1.14644	3.4674	494.956	1.11771
1600	7.7640	515.686	1.15814	3.8819	515.682	1.12941
1800	8.5930	536.411	1.16865	4.2965	536.408	1.13992
2000	9.4220	557.136	1.17820	4.7110	557.133	1.14945
	$p = 3 \cdot 10^{-1}$ bar			$p = 4 \cdot 10^{-1}$ bar		
300	0.79105	380.910	0.98982			
320	0.81873	382.987	0.99338	0.61385	382.966	0.98143
340	0.84641	385.063	0.99682	0.63462	385.043	0.98488
360	0.87408	387.139	1.00015	0.65538	387.120	0.98821
380	0.90175	389.214	1.00338	0.67614	389.196	0.99144
400	0.92942	391.289	1.00651	0.69690	391.272	0.99457
420	0.95708	393.364	1.00955	0.71766	393.348	0.99761
440	0.98474	395.439	1.01250	0.73841	395.424	1.00056
460	1.0124	397.514	1.01537	0.75916	397.499	1.00343
480	1.0401	399.588	1.01816	0.77991	399.574	1.00622
500	1.0677	401.662	1.02088	0.80066	401.649	1.00894
520	1.0954	403.737	1.02353	0.82140	403.724	1.01159
540	1.1230	405.811	1.02611	0.84215	405.798	1.01417
560	1.1507	407.885	1.02863	0.86289	407.873	1.01669
580	1.1783	409.958	1.03109	0.88363	409.947	1.01915
600	1.2060	412.032	1.03349	0.90437	412.021	1.02156
620	1.2336	414.106	1.03584	0.92511	414.095	1.02391
640	1.2613	416.179	1.03813	0.94585	416.169	1.02620
660	1.2889	418.253	1.04038	0.96659	418.243	1.02845
680	1.3161	420.326	1.04258	0.98733	420.317	1.03065
700	1.3442	422.400	1.04473	1.0081	422.391	1.03280
800	1.4824	432.766	1.05487	1.1117	432.758	1.04294
900	1.6206	443.132	1.06411	1.2154	443.125	1.05218
1000	1.7588	453.496	1.07259	1.3191	453.490	1.06066
1200	2.0352	474.224	1.08771	1.5264	474.220	1.07578
1400	2.3116	494.952	1.10090	1.7336	494.948	1.08898
1600	2.5879	515.679	1.11260	1.9409	515.676	1.10068
1800	2.8643	536.405	1.12312	2.1482	536.402	1.11119
2000	3.14063	557.131	1.13266	2.3554	557.129	1.12073
	$p = 5 \cdot 10^{-1}$ bar			$p = 6 \cdot 10^{-1}$ bar		
320	0.49092	382.944	0.97216			
340	0.50755	385.023	0.97561	0.42283	385.003	0.96803
360	0.52417	387.101	0.97894	0.43669	387.082	0.97137
380	0.54078	389.178	0.98217	0.45054	389.160	0.97460
400	0.55739	391.255	0.98530	0.46439	391.238	0.97773
420	0.57400	393.332	0.98834	0.47824	393.316	0.98077
440	0.59061	395.408	0.99130	0.49208	395.393	0.98373
460	0.60722	397.484	0.99417	0.50592	397.469	0.98660
480	0.62382	399.560	0.99696	0.51976	399.546	0.98939
500	0.64042	401.635	0.99968	0.53360	401.622	0.99211
520	0.65703	403.711	1.00233	0.54744	403.698	0.99476
540	0.67362	405.786	1.00492	0.56128	405.773	0.99735
560	0.69022	407.861	1.00744	0.57511	407.849	0.99987
580	0.70682	409.935	1.00990	0.58894	409.924	1.00233
600	0.72342	412.010	1.01230	0.60278	411.999	1.00474
620	0.74001	414.085	1.01465	0.61661	414.074	1.00709
640	0.75661	416.159	1.01695	0.63044	416.149	1.00938
660	0.77320	418.233	1.01919	0.64427	418.223	1.01163
680	0.78979	420.307	1.02139	0.65810	420.298	1.01383
700	0.80638	422.381	1.02355	0.67193	422.372	1.01598
800	0.88933	432.750	1.03369	0.74106	432.742	1.02613
900	0.97228	443.118	1.04293	0.81019	443.111	1.03537
1000	1.0552	453.484	1.05141	0.87930	453.478	1.04385
1200	1.2210	474.215	1.06653	1.0175	474.210	1.05897
1400	1.3869	494.944	1.07973	1.1557	494.940	1.07217

continued

t, °C	v	i	s	v	i	s
1600	1.5527	515.672	1.09143	1.2939	515.669	1.08387
1800	1.7185	536.400	1.10194	1.4321	536.397	1.09438
2000	1.8843	557.126	1.11149	1.5703	557.124	1.10393
	$p=7\cdot10^{-1}$ bar			$p=8\cdot10^{-1}$ bar		
340	0.36232	384.983	0.96162			
360	0.37420	387.063	0.96496	0.32734	387.044	0.95940
380	0.38608	389.142	0.96819	0.33774	389.124	0.96264
400	0.39796	391.221	0.97133	0.34813	391.204	0.96578
420	0.40983	393.299	0.97437	0.35852	393.283	0.96882
440	0.42170	395.377	0.97732	0.36891	395.362	0.97178
460	0.43357	397.455	0.98020	0.37930	397.440	0.97465
480	0.44544	399.532	0.98299	0.38969	399.518	0.97745
500	0.45730	401.608	0.98571	0.40007	401.595	0.98017
520	0.46916	403.685	0.98836	0.41046	403.672	0.98282
540	0.48103	405.761	0.99095	0.42084	405.749	0.98541
560	0.49289	407.837	0.99347	0.43122	407.825	0.98793
580	0.50475	409.913	0.99593	0.44160	409.901	0.99039
600	0.51661	411.988	0.99834	0.45198	411.977	0.99280
620	0.52846	414.063	1.00070	0.46236	414.053	0.99515
640	0.54032	416.138	1.00299	0.47273	416.128	0.99744
660	0.55218	418.213	1.00523	0.48311	418.203	0.99969
680	0.56403	420.288	1.00743	0.49348	420.278	1.00190
700	0.57589	422.363	1.00959	0.50386	422.353	1.00405
800	0.63516	432.734	1.01973	0.55572	432.727	1.01419
900	0.69441	443.104	1.02897	0.60758	443.097	1.02343
1000	0.75366	453.472	1.03745	0.65942	453.466	1.03193
1200	0.87214	474.205	1.05258	0.76310	474.200	1.04704
1400	0.99060	494.936	1.06578	0.86676	494.932	1.06024
1600	1.1090	515.666	1.07748	0.97041	515.662	1.07194
1800	1.2275	536.394	1.08799	1.0740	536.391	1.08246
2000	1.3459	557.122	1.09754	1.1777	557.119	1.09200
	$p=9\cdot10^{-1}$ bar			$p=1$ bar		
360	0.29089	387.025	0.95450	0.26173	387.005	0.95012
380	0.30013	389.106	0.95774	0.27005	389.088	0.95336
400	0.30938	391.187	0.96088	0.27838	391.170	0.95649
420	0.31862	393.267	0.96392	0.28670	393.251	0.95954
440	0.32786	395.347	0.96688	0.29501	395.331	0.96250
460	0.33710	397.425	0.96975	0.30333	397.410	0.96538
480	0.34633	399.503	0.97255	0.31164	399.489	0.96817
500	0.35557	401.581	0.97527	0.31996	401.568	0.97090
520	0.36480	403.659	0.97793	0.32827	403.646	0.97355
540	0.37403	405.736	0.98051	0.33658	405.724	0.97614
560	0.38326	407.813	0.98303	0.34489	407.801	0.97866
580	0.39249	409.890	0.98550	0.35319	409.878	0.98112
600	0.40171	411.966	0.98791	0.36150	411.955	0.98353
620	0.41094	414.042	0.99026	0.36980	414.031	0.98588
640	0.42016	416.118	0.99256	0.37811	416.108	0.98818
660	0.42939	418.193	0.99480	0.38641	418.184	0.99043
680	0.43861	420.269	0.99700	0.39472	420.259	0.99263
700	0.44784	422.344	0.99916	0.40302	422.335	0.99479
800	0.49394	432.719	1.00931	0.44452	432.711	1.00494
900	0.54004	443.090	1.01855	0.48601	443.083	1.01418
1000	0.58612	453.460	1.02703	0.52749	453.454	1.02266
1200	0.67829	474.196	1.04216	0.61044	474.191	1.03779
1400	0.77044	494.928	1.05536	0.69338	494.925	1.05099
1600	0.86257	515.659	1.06706	0.77631	515.656	1.06269
1800	0.95470	536.388	1.07757	0.85923	536.386	1.07320
2000	1.0468	557.117	1.08712	0.94214	557.114	1.08275

continued

t, °C	v	i	s	v	i	s
	$p=1.2$ bar			$p=1.4$ bar		
380	0.22493	389.052	0.94576	0.19270	389.016	0.93934
400	0.23187	391.135	0.94891	0.19866	391.101	0.94248
420	0.23881	393.218	0.95195	0.20461	393.185	0.94554
440	0.24575	395.300	0.95491	0.21056	395.269	0.94850
460	0.25268	397.381	0.95779	0.21651	397.351	0.95138
480	0.25962	399.461	0.96059	0.22245	399.433	0.95418
500	0.26655	401.541	0.96332	0.22840	401.514	0.95691
520	0.27348	403.620	0.96597	0.23434	403.594	0.95956
540	0.28040	405.699	0.96856	0.24028	405.674	0.96215
560	0.28733	407.777	0.97109	0.24622	407.753	0.96468
580	0.29426	409.855	0.97355	0.25216	409.832	0.96714
600	0.30118	411.933	0.97596	0.25810	411.911	0.96955
620	0.30810	414.010	0.97831	0.26403	413.989	0.97191
640	0.31503	416.087	0.98061	0.26997	416.066	0.97421
660	0.32195	418.164	0.98286	0.27590	418.144	0.97646
680	0.32887	420.240	0.98506	0.28184	420.221	0.97866
700	0.33579	422.316	0.98722	0.28777	422.298	0.98082
800	0.37038	432.695	0.99737	0.31743	432.679	0.99097
900	0.40497	443.070	1.00661	0.34708	443.056	1.00022
1000	0.43954	453.442	1.01510	0.37672	453.430	1.00870
1200	0.50868	474.181	1.03023	0.43598	474.172	1.02383
1400	0.57779	494.917	1.04343	0.49523	494.908	1.03703
1600	0.64690	515.649	1.05513	0.55447	515.643	1.04874
1800	0.71601	536.380	1.06565	0.61371	536.374	1.05926
2000	0.78511	557.110	1.07519	0.67294	557.105	1.06880
	$p=1.6$ bar			$p=1.8$ bar		
400	0.17374	391.067	0.93692	0.15437	391.032	0.93200
420	0.17896	393.153	0.93997	0.15900	393.120	0.93506
440	0.18417	395.237	0.94294	0.16364	395.206	0.93803
460	0.18937	397.321	0.94582	0.16827	397.292	0.94091
480	0.19458	399.404	0.94862	0.17290	399.376	0.94372
500	0.19978	401.487	0.95135	0.17753	401.460	0.94645
520	0.20498	403.568	0.95401	0.18215	403.542	0.94911
540	0.21019	405.649	0.95660	0.18678	405.624	0.95170
560	0.21539	407.729	0.95913	0.19140	407.705	0.95423
580	0.22058	409.809	0.96159	0.19603	409.786	0.95669
600	0.22578	411.888	0.96400	0.20065	411.866	0.95910
620	0.23098	413.967	0.96636	0.20527	413.946	0.96146
640	0.23617	416.046	0.96866	0.20989	416.025	0.96376
660	0.24137	418.124	0.97091	0.21451	418.104	0.96601
680	0.24656	420.202	0.97311	0.21913	420.183	0.96822
700	0.25176	422.279	0.97527	0.22374	422.261	0.97038
800	0.27771	432.663	0.98543	0.24682	432.647	0.98053
900	0.30366	443.042	0.99467	0.26989	443.028	0.98978
1000	0.32960	453.418	1.00317	0.29295	453.406	0.99827
1200	0.38146	474.162	1.01829	0.33906	474.152	1.01340
1400	0.43331	494.901	1.03150	0.38515	494.893	1.02661
1600	0.48515	515.636	1.04320	0.43123	515.630	1.03832
1800	0.53698	536.369	1.05372	0.47731	536.363	1.04883
2000	0.58881	557.100	1.06326	0.52338	557.095	1.05838
	$p=2$ bar			$p=2.2$ bar		
400	0.13887	390.998	0.92760			
420	0.14304	393.087	0.93066	0.12998	393.054	0.92668
440	0.14722	395.175	0.93363	0.13378	395.144	0.92965
460	0.15139	397.262	0.93652	0.13757	397.232	0.93254
480	0.15556	399.348	0.93933	0.14137	399.319	0.93535
500	0.15972	401.432	0.94206	0.14516	401.405	0.93808
520	0.16389	403.516	0.94472	0.14895	403.490	0.94075
540	0.16805	405.599	0.94731	0.15273	405.574	0.94334
560	0.17222	407.681	0.94984	0.15652	407.658	0.94587
580	0.17338	409.763	0.95231	0.16031	409.740	0.94834

continued

t, °C	v	i	s	v	i	s
600	0.18054	411.844	0.95472	0.16409	411.822	0.95075
620	0.18470	413.925	0.95708	0.16787	413.903	0.95311
640	0.18886	416.005	0.95938	0.17166	415.984	0.95542
660	0.19302	418.084	0.96163	0.17544	418.064	0.95767
680	0.19718	420.163	0.96384	0.17922	420.144	0.95987
700	0.20134	422.242	0.96600	0.18300	422.224	0.96203
800	0.22211	432.631	0.97616	0.20189	432.615	0.97220
900	0.24288	443.014	0.98541	0.22078	443.001	0.98146
1000	0.26364	453.393	0.99390	0.23965	453.381	0.98994
1200	0.30514	474.142	1.00904	0.27738	474.133	1.00508
1400	0.34662	494.885	1.02224	0.31510	494.877	1.01829
1600	0.38810	515.623	1.03395	0.35281	515.616	1.02999
1800	0.42957	536.358	1.04446	0.39051	536.352	1.04051
2000	0.47104	557.090	1.05401	0.42821	557.086	1.05006
		p=2.4 bar			p=2.6 bar	
420	0.11910	393.022	0.92305	0.10989	392.989	0.91970
440	0.12258	395.113	0.92602	0.11311	395.082	0.92268
460	0.12606	397.203	0.92891	0.11632	397.173	0.92557
480	0.12954	399.291	0.93172	0.11954	399.262	0.92838
500	0.13302	401.378	0.93446	0.12275	401.351	0.93112
520	0.13649	403.464	0.93712	0.12596	403.438	0.93378
540	0.13997	405.549	0.93972	0.12916	405.524	0.93638
560	0.14344	407.634	0.94225	0.13237	407.610	0.93891
580	0.14691	409.717	0.94472	0.13558	409.694	0.94138
600	0.15038	411.800	0.94713	0.13878	411.778	0.94380
620	0.15385	413.882	0.94949	0.14199	413.861	0.94616
640	0.15732	415.963	0.95179	0.14519	415.943	0.94846
660	0.16079	418.044	0.95405	0.14839	418.025	0.95072
680	0.16426	420.125	0.95626	0.15159	420.106	0.95293
700	0.16772	422.205	0.95842	0.15479	422.186	0.95510
800	0.18504	432.599	0.96858	0.17079	432.584	0.96526
900	0.20236	442.987	0.97784	0.18677	442.973	0.94751
1000	0.21966	453.369	0.98633	0.20275	453.357	0.98301
1200	0.25425	474.123	1.00147	0.23468	474.113	0.99815
1400	0.28883	494.869	1.01468	0.26660	494.862	1.01136
1600	0.32340	515.610	1.02639	0.29852	515.603	1.02307
1800	0.35796	536.347	1.03690	0.33042	536.341	1.03358
2000	0.39252	557.081	1.04645	0.36232	557.076	1.04313
		p=2,8 bar			p=3 bar	
420	0.10200	392.956	0.91660			
440	0.10499	395.050	0.91958	0.097948	395.019	0.91669
460	0.10797	397.143	0.92247	0.10074	397.113	0.91958
480	0.11096	399.234	0.92528	0.10353	399.206	0.92240
500	0.11394	401.324	0.92802	0.10631	401.296	0.92514
520	0.11692	403.412	0.93069	0.10910	403.386	0.92781
540	0.11990	405.499	0.93329	0.11188	405.474	0.93041
560	0.12288	407.586	0.93582	0.11466	407.562	0.93294
580	0.12586	409.671	0.93830	0.11744	409.648	0.93542
600	0.12884	411.755	0.94071	0.12022	411.733	0.93784
620	0.13182	413.839	0.94307	0.12300	413.818	0.94020
640	0.13479	415.922	0.94538	0.12578	415.902	0.94250
660	0.13776	418.005	0.94763	0.12856	417.985	0.94476
680	0.14074	420.086	0.94984	0.13133	420.067	0.94697
700	0.14371	422.168	0.95200	0.13411	422.149	0.94913
800	0.15857	432.568	0.96217	0.14798	432.552	0.95931
900	0.17341	442.959	0.97143	0.16184	442.945	0.96857
1000	0.18825	453.345	0.97993	0.17569	453.333	0.97706
1200	0.21791	474.104	0.99507	0.20337	474.094	0.99221
1400	0.24755	494.854	1.00828	0.23104	494.846	1.00542
1600	0.27718	515.597	1.01999	0.25870	515.590	1.01713
1800	0.30681	536.336	1.03051	0.28635	536.330	1.02765
2000	0.33644	557.071	1.40060	0.31400	557.067	1.03720

continued

t, °C	v	i	s	v	i	s
		$p=4$ bar			$p=6$ bar	
460	0.075413	396.964	0.90753			
480	0.077510	399.063	0.91036	0.051494	398.776	0.89331
500	0.079606	401.160	0.91311	0.052899	400.886	0.89608
520	0.081700	403.255	0.91578	0.054302	402.993	0.89877
540	0.083792	405.349	0.91839	0.055704	405.098	0.90139
560	0.085883	407.441	0.92093	0.057104	407.200	0.90394
580	0.087973	409.532	0.92341	0.058503	409.300	0.90643
600	0.090062	411.622	0.92583	0.059902	411.399	0.90887
620	0.092150	413.711	0.92820	0.061299	413.496	0.91124
640	0.094237	415.798	0.93051	0.062695	415.591	0.91356
660	0.096323	417.885	0.93277	0.064091	417.685	0.91583
680	0.098409	419.971	0.93498	0.065485	419.778	0.91805
700	0.10049	422.056	0.93715	0.066879	421.869	0.92022
800	0.11091	432.472	0.94733	0.073841	432.313	0.93043
900	0.12131	442.876	0.95660	0.080791	442.738	0.93972
1000	0.13171	453.272	0.96511	0.087733	453.150	0.94824
1200	0.15248	474.046	0.98026	0.10160	473.949	0.96341
1400	0.17325	494.806	0.99348	0.11545	494.727	0.97664
1600	0.19400	515.557	1.00519	0.12930	515.491	0.98836
1800	0.21474	536.302	1.01572	0.14314	536.246	0.99889
2000	0.23549	557.043	1.02527	0.15697	556.995	1.00845
		$p=8$ bar			$p=10$ bar	
500	0.039544	400.609	0.88393			
520	0.040602	402.729	0.88663	0.032382	402.463	0.87717
540	0.041659	404.845	0.88927	0.033232	404.590	0.87982
560	0.042714	406.957	0.89184	0.034080	406.713	0.88240
580	0.043768	409.067	0.89434	0.034926	408.833	0.88492
600	0.044821	411.175	0.89678	0.035772	410.950	0.88737
620	0.045873	413.280	0.89916	0.036617	413.063	0.88976
640	0.046924	415.383	0.90149	0.037461	415.174	0.89210
660	0.047974	417.485	0.90377	0.038304	417.283	0.89438
680	0.049023	419.584	0.90600	0.039146	419.390	0.89662
700	0.050072	421.682	0.90818	0.039987	421.494	0.89880
800	0.055307	432.153	0.91842	0.044186	431.993	0.90907
900	0.060530	442.599	0.92772	0.048373	442.461	0.91840
1000	0.065745	453.029	0.93626	0.052552	452.907	0.92694
1200	0.076158	473.853	0.95145	0.060893	473.757	0.94216
1400	0.086558	494.649	0.96468	0.069220	494.570	0.95540
1600	0.096947	515.426	0.97641	0.077537	515.360	0.96714
1800	0.10733	635.191	0.98695	0.085848	536.135	0.97768
2000	0.11771	556.947	0.99651	0.094155	556.900	0.98724
		$p=12$ bar			$p=14$ bar	
540	0.027613	404.334	0.87207			
560	0.028323	406.468	0.87466	0.024211	406.221	0.86808
580	0.029032	408.597	0.87719	0.024821	408.361	0.87062
600	0.029739	410.723	0.87965	0.025430	410.496	0.87310
620	0.030446	412.846	0.88205	0.026038	412.627	0.87551
640	0.031152	414.965	0.88440	0.026645	414.754	0.87786
660	0.031857	417.081	0.88669	0.027252	416.878	0.88016
680	0.032561	419.195	0.88893	0.027857	418.999	0.88241
700	0.033264	421.306	0.89112	0.028462	421.117	0.88461
800	0.036772	431.832	0.90142	0.031476	431.672	0.89494
900	0.040268	442.322	0.91077	0.034479	442.182	0.90430
1000	0.043757	452.785	0.91933	0.037474	452.663	0.91288
1200	0.050716	473.660	0.93455	0.043447	473.563	0.92813
1400	0.057661	494.491	0.94782	0.049405	494.412	0.94139
1600	0.064597	515.294	0.95956	0.055354	515.228	0.95315
1800	0.071526	536.079	0.97010	0.061297	536.024	0.96370
2000	0.078452	556.852	0.97967	0.067235	556.804	0.97326

continued

t, °C	v	i	s	v	i	s
	$p=16$ bar			$p=18$ bar		
580	0.021663	408.123	0.86491	0.019206	407.884	0.85985
600	0.022198	410.268	0.86740	0.019683	410.038	0.86235
620	0.022732	412.407	0.86982	0.020160	412.187	0.86478
640	0.023265	414.543	0.87218	0.020636	414.331	0.86715
660	0.023798	416.674	0.87449	0.021111	416.470	0.86947
680	0.024329	418.802	0.87675	0.021585	418.605	0.87174
700	0.024860	420.927	0.87896	0.022058	420.737	0.87395
800	0.027505	431.510	0.88931	0.024415	431.349	0.88433
900	0.030138	442.043	0.89869	0.026761	441.903	0.89373
1000	0.032762	452.541	0.90728	0.029098	452.418	0.90234
1200	0.037995	473.466	0.92255	0.033755	473.369	0.91762
1400	0.043213	494.333	0.93583	0.038397	494.254	0.93091
1600	0.048422	515.162	0.94759	0.043030	515.096	0.94268
1800	0.053624	535.968	0.95814	0.047657	535.912	0.95324
2000	0.058822	556.756	0.96771	0.052279	556.709	0.96282
	$p=20$ bar			$p=30$ bar		
600	0.017672	409.807	0.85781			
620	0.018103	411.965	0.86026			
640	0.018533	414.118	0.86264	0.012221	413.038	0.84508
660	0.018962	416.265	0.86497	0.012512	415.227	0.84745
680	0.019390	418.408	0.86724	0.012802	417.408	0.84976
700	0.019817	520.546	0.86946	0.013092	419.582	0.85202
800	0.021944	431.187	0.87987	0.014529	430.371	0.86258
900	0.024059	441.763	0.88930	0.015954	441.060	0.87210
1000	0.026166	452.296	0.89791	0.017370	451.681	0.88079
1200	0.030362	473.272	0.91321	0.021085	472.786	0.89619
1400	0.034544	494.174	0.92652	0.022986	493.779	0.90955
1600	0.038717	515.031	0.93829	0.025777	514.701	0.92137
1800	0.042883	535.856	0.94885	0.028561	535.578	0.93195
2000	0.047045	556.661	0.95843	0.031342	556.423	0.94155
	$p=40$ bar			$p=50$ bar		
680	0.0095073	416.389	0.83716			
700	0.0097279	418.601	0.83946	0.0077086	417.603	0.82955
800	0.010821	429.546	0.85016	0.0085954	428.711	0.84042
900	0.011901	440.351	0.85980	0.0094689	439.636	0.85015
1000	0.012972	451.062	0.86855	0.010333	450.439	0.85899
1200	0.015096	472.299	0.88405	0.012044	471.810	0.87458
1400	0.017206	493.382	0.89747	0.013739	492.985	0.88806
1600	0.019307	514.372	0.90932	0.015425	514.042	0.89995
1800	0.021400	535.300	0.91994	0.017104	535.021	0.91059
2000	0.023490	556.184	0.92955	0.018779	555.946	0.92023
	$p=60$ bar			$p=80$ bar		
800	0.0071113	427.865	0.83235	0.0052550	426.141	0.81939
900	0.0078473	438.914	0.84220	0.0058196	437.452	0.82947
1000	0.0085738	449.812	0.85111	0.0063742	448.547	0.83854
1200	0.010008	471.319	0.86682	0.0074640	470.333	0.85444
1400	0.011428	492.588	0.88034	0.0085380	491.791	0.86811
1600	0.012837	513.712	0.89227	0.0096021	513.052	0.88010
1800	0.014240	534.743	0.90294	0.010660	534.186	0.89082
2000	0.015639	555.709	0.91259	0.011713	555.233	0.90052
	$p=100$ bar			$p=120$ bar		
820	0.0042335	426.718	0.81123			
840	0.0043264	429.051	0.81334			
860	0.0044189	431.368	0.81540	0.0036339	429.742	0.80690
880	0.0045108	433.671	0.81742	0.0037123	432.102	0.80897
900	0.0046023	435.963	0.81939	0.0037902	434.445	0.81098
1000	0.0050540	447.265	0.82864	0.0041737	445.967	0.82041
1200	0.0059374	469.340	0.84475	0.0049196	468.341	0.83674
1400	0.0068044	490.991	0.85853	0.0056487	490.189	0.85065

continued

t, °C	v	i	s	v	i	s
1600	0,0076614	512.391	0.87061	0.0063676	511.730	0.86281
1800	0.0085118	533.630	0.88139	0.0070800	533.074	0.87364
2000	0.0093579	554,759	0,89112	0.0077878	554,285	0.88341
		p=140 bar			p=160 bar	
860	0.0030725	428.078	0.79954	0.0026508	426.375	0.79300
880	0,0031413	430.498	0.80166	0,0027125	428.859	0.79518
900	0.0032096	432,898	0.80372	0.0027737	431.319	0.79729
1000	0.0035446	444,651	0.81334	0,0030726	443.317	0.80711
1200	0.0041926	467.336	0.82990	0.0036474	466.323	0.82390
1400	0,0048233	489.385	0.84393	0.0042043	488.578	0.83807
1600	0,0054436	511,068	0.85618	0.0047407	510.405	0.85040
1800	0,0060573	532.518	0.86706	0.0052903	531.963	0.86133
2000	0.0066664	553,812	0.87687	0,0058255	553.339	0.87118
		p=180 bar			p=200 bar	
920	0.0024893	432.204	0.79360			
940	0.0025439	434.676	0.79565			
960	0,0025981	437,126	0.79765			
980	0.0026518	439.555	0.79961			
1000	0,0027052	441.965	0.80152	0,0024112	440.593	0.79643
1200	0.0032233	465.304	0.81856	0.0028240	464.272	0.81972
1400	0.0037229	487.769	0.83286	0.0033378	486.958	0,82818
1600	0.0042118	509.742	0.84527	0.0037808	509.079	0.84066
1800	0.0046940	531.408	0.85626	0.0042169	530.854	0,85170
2000	0,0051715	552.668	0,86614	0,0046484	552.397	0.86162

Thermodynamic properties of mercury vapor at different temperatures and pressures [40]: c_p, c_v (kJ/kg · deg) and u (m/s)

t, °C	c_p	c_v	u	c_p	c_v	u	c_p	c_v	u
		p=0.1 bar			p=1 bar			p=10 bar	
300	0.1037	0.06219	199.0						
400	0.1037	0.06219	215.6	0.1041	0.06229	215.4			
500	0.1037	0.06218	231.1	0.1039	0.06225	230.9			
600	0.1036	0.06218	245.6	0.1038	0.06222	245.5	0.1058	0.06267	244.3
700	0.1036	0.06218	259.3	0.1038	0.06221	259.2	0.1052	0.06251	258.3
800	0.1036	0.06218	272.3	0.1037	0.06220	272.2	0.1048	0.06242	271.5
900	0.1036	0.06218	284.7	0.1037	0.06219	284.6	0.1046	0.06235	284.1
1000	0.1036	0.06218	296.6	0.1037	0.06219	296.5	0.1044	0.06231	296.1
1100	0.1036	0.06218	308.0	0.1037	0.06219	308.0	1.1042	0.06228	307.6
1200	0.1036	0.06218	319.0	0.1037	0.06218	319.0	0.1041	0.06226	318.7
1300	0.1036	0.06217	329.7	0.1037	0.06218	329.7	0.1041	0.06225	329.4
1400	0.1036	0.06217	340.0	0.1037	0.06218	340.0	0.1040	0.06224	339.8
1500	0.1036	0.06217	350.0	0.1037	0.06218	350.0	0.1040	0.06223	349.8
1600	0.1036	0.06217	359.7	0.1037	0.06218	359.7	0.1039	0.06222	359.6
1700	0.1036	0.06217	369.2	0.1037	0.06218	369.2	0.1039	0.06221	369.1
1800	0.1036	0.06217	378.4	0.1037	0.06218	378.4	0.1039	0.06221	378.4
1900	0.1036	0.06217	387.5	0.1036	0.06218	387.5	0.1038	0.06220	387.4
2000	0.1036	0.06217	396.3	0.1036	0.06218	396.3	0.1038	0.06220	396.3
		p=20 bar			p=40 bar			p=80 bar	
600	0.1081	0.06319	242.9		0.06434				
700	0.1068	0.06286	257.2	0.1104	0.06360	255.1			
800	0.1060	0.06266	270.7	0.1086	0.06318	269.1	0.1145	0.06428	265.8
900	0.1055	0.06254	283.4	0.1075	0.06291	282.2	0.1119	0.06370	279.7
1000	0.1051	0.06245	295.6	0.1067	0.06274	294.6	0.1101	0.06332	292.7
1100	0.1049	0.06239	307.2	0.1062	0.06262	306.4	0.1089	0.06307	304.7
1200	0.1047	0.06235	318.4	0.1057	0.06253	317.8	0.1080	0.06289	316.6
1300	0.1045	0.06232	329.2	0.1054	0.06247	328.7	0.1073	0.06276	327.8
1400	0.1044	0.06230	339.6	0.1051	0.06242	339.2	0.1067	0.06266	338.5

continued

t, °C	c_p	c_v	u	c_p	c_v	u	c_p	c_v	u
1500	0.1043	0.06228	349.7	0.1049	0.06238	349.4	0.1063	0.06259	348.9
1600	0.1042	0.06226	359.5	0.1048	0.06235	359.3	0.1060	0.06253	358.9
1700	0.1041	0.06225	369.0	0.1046	0.06233	368.9	0.1057	0.06248	368.6
1800	0.1041	0.06224	378.3	0.1045	0.06231	378.2	0.1054	0.06244	378.0
1900	0.1040	0.06223	387.6	0.1044	0.06229	387.3	0.1052	0.06241	387.2
2000	0.1040	0.06223	396.2	0.1043	0.06228	396.2	0.1051	0.06238	396.2
	p=120 bar			p=160 bar			p=200 bar		
900	0.1168	0.06454	277.1	0.1224	0.06545	274.6	0.1291	0.06639	272.0
1000	0.1138	0.06394	290.7	0.1179	0.06458	238.8	0.1224	0.06526	287.0
1100	0.1118	0.06354	303.4	0.1149	0.06402	302.0	0.1182	0.06452	300.6
1200	0.1103	0.06326	315.4	0.1128	0.06364	314.4	0.1154	0.06403	313.3
1300	0.1092	0.06306	326.9	0.1112	0.06337	326.0	0.1133	0.06367	325.3
1400	0.1083	0.06291	337.8	0.1100	0.06316	337.2	0.1108	0.06341	336.6
1500	0.1077	0.06280	348.3	0.1091	0.06301	347.9	0.1106	0.06322	347.5
1600	0.1071	0.06271	358.5	0.1084	0.06288	358.2	0.1096	0.06306	357.9
1700	0.1067	0.06263	368.4	0.1078	0.06279	368.1	0.1089	0.06293	368.0
1800	0.1064	0.06257	377.9	0.1073	0.06271	377.8	0.1082	0.06284	377.7
1900	0.1061	0.06253	387.2	0.1069	0.06264	387.1	0.1077	0.06276	387.2
2000	0.1058	0.06249	396.2	0.1065	0.06259	396.2	0.1073	0.06269	396.3

Viscosity η of mercury vapor above 1 bar [40, 125]

t, °C	200	220	240	260	280	300	320	340	360	380	400
$\eta \cdot 10^7$, N · s/m²	464	483	502	522	542	562	582	602	622	642	662
t, °C	420	440	460	480	500	550	600	650	700	800	
$\eta \cdot 10^7$, N · s/m²	682	702	722	742	762	812	862	911	961	1057	

Thermal conductivity λ of mercury vapor above 1 bar [44]

t, °C	200	300	400	500	600	700	800	900
$\lambda \cdot 10^3$, W/m · deg	7.7	9.4	11.2	13.1	14.9	16.8	18.5	20.1

Transfer coefficients of liquid mercury [40]:
R_{spec} (μohm · m), λ (W/m · deg), η (N · s/m²), ν (m²/s),
a (m² · s) and Pr

t, °C	R_{spec}	λ	$\eta \cdot 10^3$	$\nu \cdot 10^7$	$a \cdot 10^6$	Pr · 10²
—38.87	0.91013	7.639	2.055	1.502	3.919	3.833
—20	0.91775	7.903	1.847	1.354	4.100	3.302
0	0.94120	8.178	1.687	1.241	4.285	2.8096
20	0.95830	8.447	1.556	1.152	4.467	2.579
40	0.97616	8.712	1.457	1.080	4.648	2.324
60	0.99478	8.971	1.372	1.020	4.826	2.114
80	1.01414	9.225	1.301	0.971	5.002	1.941
100	1.03425	9.475	1.241	0.929	5.175	1.796
120	1.0551	9.719	1.189	0.894	5.346	1.672
140	1.0768	9.958	1.144	0.863	5.513	1.565
160	1.0992	10.19	1.104	0.836	5.675	1.473
180	1.1224	10.42	1.070	0.813	5.836	1.393
200	1.1464	10.64	1.039	0.793	5.990	1.323
250	1.2101	11.18	0.975	0.751	6.365	1.179
300	1.2796	11.69	0.926	0.719	6.71	1.07
350	1.3556	12.16	0.886	0.695	7.03	0.99

continued

t, °C	R_{spec}	λ	$\eta \cdot 10^3$	$\nu \cdot 10^7$	$a \cdot 10^6$	$Pr \cdot 10^2$
400	1.439	12.60	0.853	0.676	7.31	0.92
450	1.538	13.01	0.826	0.661	7.56	0.87
500	1.635	13.39	0.804	0.648	7.78	0.83
550	1.752	13.73	0.784	0.640	7.96	0.80
600	1.884	14.04	0.767	0.630	8.11	0.78
650	2.034	14.33	0.752	0.627	8.23	0.76
700	2.208	14.58	0.739	0.623	8.32	0.75
750	2.408	14.79	0.728	0.621	8.37	0.74
800	2.640	14.98	0.717	0.619	8.40	0.74

Note: The values of resistivity R_{spec} are given above in *absolute ohms*.

Chapter 3

CARBON COMPOUNDS

CARBON MONOXIDE (CO)

Molecular weight 28.011
$t_{boil} = -191.5$ °C at 760 mm Hg; $t_{melt} = -205$ °C; $t_{cr} = -140$ °C;
$p_{cr} = 34.98$ bar; $\rho_{cr} = 301$ kg/m³

Thermodynamic properties of saturated carbon monoxide [51]:
ρ (kg/m³), i (kJ/kg) and s (kJ/kg · deg)

t, °C	p, bar	ϱ'	ϱ''	i'	i''	s'	s''
−205.01	0.1535	846	0.7826	121.5	357.02	2.6207	6.0766
−203.38	0.203	839	1.024	124.8	358.20	2.6700	6.0143
−200.73	0.304	829	1.468	130.5	360.03	2.7500	5.9185
−198.77	0.405	819	1.895	134.8	361.35	2.8075	5.8536
−197.14	0.506	812	2.314	138.3	362.48	2.8544	5.8042
−195.75	0.608	807	2.743	141.3	363.35	2.8932	5.7623
−193.43	0.810	798	3.581	146.2	364.73	2.9569	5.6970
−191.52	1.013	789	4.404	150.40	366.04	3.0080	5.6505
−187.79	1.520	776	6.498	158.68	367.96	3.1072	5.5588
−184.90	2.026	765	8.552	164.90	369.15	3.1788	5.4935
−182.55	2.532	753	10.49	169.83	369.84	3.2ɛ40	5.4416
−180.53	3.039	741	12.57	174.35	370.48	3.2833	5.4001
−177.04	4.052	722	16.72	182.31	371.50	3.3678	5.3361
−174.17	5.065	707	20.84	189.54	372.46	3.4420	5.2896
−171.69	6.078	695	24.74	196.27	373.58	3.5090	5.2565
−169.49	7.091	685	28.55	201.86	374.16	3.5636	5.2255
−167.46	8.104	673	32.26	206.14	374.44	3.6024	5.1950
−163.98	10.13	651	40.41	214.28	374.56	3.6802	5.1485
−161.02	12.16	632	48.29	220.87	374.59	3.7398	5.1108
−158.32	14.18	614	56.58	226.67	374.14	3.7908	5.0748
−155.94	16.21	597	65.13	232.31	373.28	3.8393	5.0422
−153.65	18.23	579	74.89	237.84	371.42	3.8863	5.0041
−151.70	20.26	561	85.13	243.54	369.26	3.9334	4.9685
−147.18	25.32	516	171.1	262.10	362.13	4.0667	4.8604
−143.30	30.39	451	163.8	277.61	348.66	4.1876	4.7353
−140.23	34.98	301	301	314.33	314.33	4.4661	4.4661

Thermodynamic properties of carbon monoxide at different temperatures and pressures [50]:
ρ (kg/m³), i (kJ/kg), s and c_p (kJ/kg · deg), u (m/s)

T, °K	ϱ	i	s	c_p	u
		$p = 10^{-2}$ bar			
200	0.016845	207.67	8.0141	1.040	288.4
210	0.016036	218.06	8.0644	1.040	295.1
220	0.015312	228.47	8.1129	1.040	302.2
230	0.014648	238.87	8.1594	1.040	309.0
240	0.014036	249.27	8.2034	1.040	315.7

continued

T, °K	ϱ	i	s	c_p	u
250	0.013475	259.68	8.2461	1.040	322.4
260	0.012957	270.08	8.2867	1.040	328.8
270	0.012476	280.49	8.3261	1.040	334.9
280	0.012032	290.89	8.3642	1.040	341.3
290	0.011617	301.30	8.4006	1.041	347.4
300	0.011229	311.71	8.4357	1.041	353.1
310	0.010868	322.12	8.4701	1.041	359.2
320	0.010528	332.54	8.5027	1.042	364.9
330	0.010209	342.95	8.5350	1.042	370.3
340	0.009909	353.38	8.5664	1.043	376.0
350	0.009625	363.82	8.5961	1.043	381.4
360	0.009359	374.26	8.6258	1.044	386.8
370	0.009105	384.70	8.6543	1.045	391.8
380	0.008867	395.16	8.6823	1.046	397.2
390	0.008639	405.63	8.7096	1.047	402.3
400	0.008422	416.10	8.7359	1.048	407.3
410	0.008217	426.59	8.7619	1.049	412.4
420	0.008021	437.10	8.7874	1.050	417.1
430	0.007835	447.61	8.8117	1.052	421.8
440	0.007658	458.12	8.8364	1.053	426.5
450	0.007485	468.67	8.8599	1.055	431.3
460	0.007322	478.97	8.8834	1.057	436.0
470	0.007168	489.81	8.9060	1.058	440.7
480	0.007014	500.41	8.9282	1.060	445.1
490	0.006876	511.00	8.9494	1.063	449.5
500	0.006737	521.63	8.9712	1.064	453.8
510	0.006606	532.31	8.9926	1.066	458.2
520	0.006479	542.99	9.0135	1.068	462.6
530	0.006536	553.66	9.0336	1.070	467.0
540	0.006237	564.42	9.0537	1.073	471.0
550	0.006124	575.14	9.0734	1.075	475.4
560	0.006017	585.90	9.0831	1.078	479.4
570	0.0059103	596.70	9.1119	1.080	483.5
580	0.0058077	607.50	9.1308	1.082	487.5
590	0.0057100	618.35	9.1492	1.085	491.2
600	0.0056153	629.19	9.1676	1.087	495.3
610	0.0055229	640.08	9.1856	1.090	499.3
620	0.0054330	651.00	9.2032	1.092	503.0
630	0.0053471	661.93	9.2208	1.095	506.7
640	0.0052633	672.90	9.2379	1.097	510.8
650	0.0051836	683.91	9.2551	1.100	514.5
660	0.0051050	694.92	9.2719	1.103	518.2
670	0.0050290	705.98	9.2882	1.105	521.6
680	0.0049542	717.03	9.3049	1.108	525.3
690	0.0048829	728.17	9.3208	1.111	529.0
700	0.0048135	739.26	9.3372	1.114	532.7
710	0.0047457	750.40	9.3527	1.116	536.4
720	0.0046786	761.16	9.3686	1.119	539.8
730	0.0046145	772.80	9.3841	1.122	543.1
740	0.0043500	784.02	9.3991	1.124	546.8
750	0.0044923	795.28	9.4142	1.126	550.2
760	0.0044329	806.55	9.4293	1.129	553.6
770	0.0043749	817.85	9.4440	1.132	556.9
780	0.0043193	829.24	9.4590	1.135	560.3
790	0.0042638	840.58	9.4732	1.137	563.7
800	0.0042108	851.93	9.4875	1.140	567.0
850	0.0039628	909.20	9.5570	1.152	583.2
900	0.0037429	967.15	9.6231	1.164	599.1
950	0.0035454	1025.6	9.6863	1.175	614.6
1000	0.0033691	1084.6	9.7471	1.185	629.7
1100	0.0030631	1204.1	9.8609	1.204	658.4
1200	0.0028076	1325.4	9.9660	1.221	686.3
1300	0.0025917	1448.2	10.064	1.235	712.9
1400	0.0024064	1572.3	10.157	1.247	738.4

continued

T, °K	ϱ	i	s	c_p	u
1500	0.0022563	1697.7	10.243	1.258	763.5
1600	0.0021053	1823.9	10.324	1.267	787.7
1700	0.0019821	1951.0	10.401	1.275	811.0
1800	0.0018720	2079.0	10.475	1.283	833.9
1900	0.0017733	2207.6	10.544	1.289	856.1
2000	0.0016847	2336.9	10.610	1.295	878.0
2100	0.0016044	2466.7	10.674	1.299	898.9
2200	0.0015315	2596.9	10.734	1.304	919.8
2300	0.0014648	2727.5	10.792	1.308	940.0
2400	0.0014032	2858.7	10.848	1.312	959.6
2500	0.0013477	2990.0	10.902	1.315	979.1
2600	0.0012958	3121.8	10.954	1.319	998.0
2700	0.0012518	3253.9	11.002	1.322	1017
2800	0.0012033	3386.2	11.052	1.324	1035
2900	0.0011614	3518.8		1.327	1053
3000	0.0011230	3651.6		1.329	1071
			$p=1$ bar		
200	1.6888	207.11	6.6443	1.045	288.4
210	1.6076	217.55	6.6949	1.044	295.1
220	1.5341	227.99	6.7435	1.044	302.2
230	1.4668	238.43	6.7900	1.043	309.0
240	1.4055	248.86	6.8344	1.043	315.7
250	1.3490	259.30	6.8771	1.043	322.4
260	1.2967	269.72	6.9177	1.043	328.8
270	1.2485	280.15	6.9574	1.043	334.9
280	1.2038	290.58	6.9951	1.042	341.3
290	1.1622	301.01	7.0320	1.043	347.4
300	1.1233	311.43	7.0671	1.043	353.1
310	1.0870	321.86	7.1015	1.043	359.2
320	1.0529	332.31	7.1345	1.043	364.9
330	1.0210	342.73	7.1674	1.044	370.3
340	0.9909	353.17	7.1984	1.044	376.0
350	0.9524	363.62	7.2285	1.045	381.4
360	0.9357	374.07	7.2578	1.045	386.8
370	0.9103	384.53	7.2867	1.046	391.8
380	0.8864	395.00	7.3148	1.047	397.2
390	0.8637	405.48	7.3420	1.048	402.3
400	0.8421	415.96	7.3683	1.049	407.3
410	0.8214	426.47	7.3943	1.050	412.4
420	0.8019	436.98	7.4198	1.051	417.1
430	0.7832	447.48	7.4445	1.053	421.8
440	0.7654	458.03	7.4688	1.054	426.5
450	0.7483	468.59	7.4923	1.055	431.3
460	0.73210	479.14	7.5157	1.057	436.0
470	0.71655	489.73	7.5383	1.060	440.7
480	0.70157	500.32	7.5605	1.061	445.1
490	0.68725	510.96	7.5823	1.063	449.5
500	0.67352	521.59	7.6041	1.065	453.8
510	0.66028	532.27	7.6250	1.067	458.2
520	0.64861	542.90	7.6459	1.069	462.6
530	0.63537	553.62	7.6660	1.071	467.0
540	0.62360	564.38	7.6861	1.073	471.0
550	0.61226	575.10	7.7058	1.076	475.4
560	0.60133	585.86	7.7255	1.078	479.4
570	0.59079	596.66	7.7443	1.080	483.5
580	0.58060	607.46	7.7632	1.083	487.5
590	0.57075	618.31	7.7820	1.085	491.2
600	0.56126	629.19	7.8000	1.088	495.3
610	0.55204	640.08	7.8180	1.091	499.3
620	0.54304	651.00	7.8360	1.093	503.0
630	0.53453	661.93	7.8536	1.095	506.7
640	0.52617	672.90	7.8708	1.098	510.8
650	0.51806	683.91	7.8879	1.101	514.5

continued

T, °K	ρ	i	s	c_p	u
660	0.51021	694.92	7.9048	1.104	518.2
670	0.50259	705.98	7.9210	1.107	521.6
680	0.49520	717.03	7.9378	1.109	525.3
690	0.48854	728.17	7.9537	1.111	529.0
700	0.48102	739.26	7.9700	1.114	532.7
710	0.47431	750.40	7.9855	1.116	536.4
720	0.46768	761.62	8.0014	1.119	539.8
730	0.46129	772.80	8.0169	1.122	543.1
740	0.45503	784.06	8.0320	1.125	546.8
750	0.44899	795.28	8.0470	1.127	550.2
760	0.44308	806.59	8.0008	1.130	553.6
770	0.43732	817.85	8.0768	1.133	556.9
780	0.43171	829.24	8.0918	1.135	560.3
790	0.42624	840.58	8.1061	1.137	563.7
800	0.42095	851.93	8.1203	1.140	567.0
850	0.39617	909.20	8.1898	1.152	583.2
900	0.37417	967.15	8.2560	1.164	599.1
950	0.35447	1025.6	8.3192	1.175	614.6
1000	0.33677	1084.6	8.3799	1.185	629.7
1100	0.30616	1204.1	8.4933	1.204	658.4
1200	0.28064	1325.4	8.5988	1.221	686.3
1300	0.25906	1448.2	8.6972	1.235	712.9
1400	0.24055	1572.3	8.7893	1.247	738.9
1500	0.22452	1697.7	8.8760	1.258	763.5
1600	0.21053	1823.9	8.9572	1.267	787.7
1700	0.19812	1951.0	9.0343	1.275	811.0
1800	0.18712	2079.0	9.1075	1.283	833.9
1900	0.17727	2207.6	9.1770	1.289	856.1
2000	0.16841	2336.9	9.2432	1.295	878.0
2100	0.16039	2466.7	9.3064	1.299	898.9
2200	0.15310	2596.9	9.3671	1.304	919.8
2300	0.14669	2727.5	9.4253	1.308	940.0
2400	0.14034	2858.7	9.4810	1.312	959.6
2500	0.13473	2990.0	9.5346	1.315	979.1
2600	0.12954	3121.8	9.5865	1.319	998.0
2700	0.12476	3253.9	8.6363	1.322	1017
2800	0.12029	3386.2	9.6845	1.324	1035
2900	0.11614	3598.8		1.327	1053
3000	0.11227	3651.6		1.329	1071
		$p=10$ bar			
200	17.299	201.99	5.9419	1.088	286.4
210	16.402	212.86	5.9951	1.082	293.8
220	15.597	223.67	6.0449	1.078	301.2
230	14.873	234.44	6.0931	1.073	308.6
240	14.215	245.17	6.1391	1.070	315.7
250	13.620	255.87	6.1826	1.068	322.8
260	13.067	266.54	6.2241	1.065	329.2
270	12.563	277.19	6.2643	1,063	335.9
280	12.097	287.82	6.3032	1.061	342.3
290	11.666	298.43	6.3405	1.060	348.4
300	11.264	309.04	6.3765	1.060	354.4
310	10.891	319.62	6.4108	1.058	360.5
320	10.542	330.20	6.4447	1.057	366.2
330	10.215	340.77	6.4774	1.057	372.0
340	9.909	351.33	6.5092	1.056	377.7
350	9.621	361.90	6.5394	1.056	383.4
360	9.348	372.47	6.5691	1.056	388.8
370	9.092	383.03	6.5980	1.057	393.9
380	8.849	393.59	6.6264	1.057	399.3
390	8.629	404.16	6.6537	1.057	404.3
400	8.402	414.74	6.6805	1.058	409.7
410	8.195	425.29	6.7068	1.058	414.8
420	7.997	435.89	6.7320	1.060	419.5

continued

T, °K	ϱ	i	s	c_p	u
430	7.810	446.48	6.7571	1.060	424.5
440	7.630	457.11	6.7818	1.061	429.2
450	7.460	467.11	6.8052	1.063	434.0
460	7.296	478.34	6.8291	1.064	438.7
470	7.140	488.98	6.8517	1.065	443.1
480	6.991	499.65	6.8743	1.067	447.8
490	6.847	510.33	6.8957	1.068	452.2
500	6.710	521.00	6.9178	1.070	456.5
510	6.578	531.72	6.9388	1.072	460.9
520	6.452	542.44	6.9601	1.074	465.3
530	6.329	553.20	6.9802	1.076	469.3
540	6.212	564.00	7.0003	1.078	473.7
550	6.098	574.76	7.0200	1.080	478.1
560	5.990	585.57	7.0397	1.082	482.1
570	5.884	596.41	7.0589	1.084	486.2
580	5.7825	607.25	7.0774	1.087	490.2
590	5.6844	618.14	7.0962	1.089	494.3
600	5.5895	629.02	7.1146	1.091	498.3
610	5.4980	639.95	7.1326	1.093	502.0
620	5.4092	650.92	7.1506	1.096	505.7
630	5.3232	661.89	7.1678	1.099	509.4
640	5.2402	672.90	7.1854	1.101	513.1
650	5.1591	683.91	7.2021	1.103	516.8
660	5.0815	694.96	7.2197	1.106	520.5
670	5.0045	706.06	7.2360	1.109	524.2
680	4.9321	717.16	7.2524	1.111	528.0
690	4.8605	728.29	7.2687	1.114	531.7
700	4.7910	739.43	7.2846	1.116	535.0
710	4.7236	750.61	7.3005	1.119	538.7
720	4.6570	761.79	7.3160	1.122	542.4
730	4.5942	773.05	7.3319	1.124	545.8
740	4.5324	784.27	7.3470	1.127	549.2
750	4.4719	795.53	7.3621	1.130	552.6
760	4.4132	806.84	7.3771	1.132	556.3
770	4.3561	818.18	7.3918	1.134	559.6
780	4.3002	829.57	7.4069	1.137	562.7
790	4.2460	841.00	7.4211	1.140	566.0
800	4.1929	852.31	7.4353	1.142	569.4
850	3.9469	909.71	7.5048	1.153	586.9
900	3.7280	967.74	7.5714	1.165	601.7
950	3.5322	1026.2	7.6346	1.176	616.9
1000	3.3558	1085.4	7.6949	1.186	631.7
1100	3.0515	1204.9	7.8092	1.205	661.0
1200	2.7978	1326.3	7.9147	1.222	688.3
1300	2.5832	1449.2	8.0131	1.235	715.0
1400	2.3990	1573.4	8.1052	1.248	740.9
1500	2.2394	1698.8	8.1919	1.259	765.8
1600	2.1000	1825.0	8.2731	1.268	789.8
1700	1.9766	1952.2	8.3506	1.276	813.3
1800	1.8669	2080.2	8.4276	1.283	835.6
1900	1.7690	2208.8	8.4929	1.291	857.8
2000	1.6807	2338.0	8.5591	1.295	879.7
2100	1.6008	2467.8	8.6223	1.300	900.9
2200	1.5283	2598.0	8.6830	1.305	921.5
2300	1.4618	2728.7	8.7412	1.308	941.7
2400	1.4016	2859.8	8.7973	1.312	961.3
2500	1.3452	2991.1	8.8505	1.315	980.8
2600	1.2934	3122.8	8.9024	1.319	999.7
2700	1.2456	3255.0	8.9522	1.322	1018
2800	1.2012	3387.4	9.0004	1.325	1037
2900	1.1599	3520.0		1.327	1054
3000	1.1213	3652.8		1.329	1072

continued

T, °K	ϱ	i	s	c_p	u
		$p=40$ bar			
250	58.90	244.78	5.7351	1.144	327.0
260	53.50	256.29	5.7803	1.134	334.1
270	51.09	267.69	5.8234	1.126	341.2
280	49.00	279.00	5.8645	1.120	347.9
290	47.10	290.23	5.9042	1.114	354.7
300	45.34	301.40	5.9419	1.109	361.1
310	43.72	312.50	5.9783	1.104	367.1
320	42.23	323.56	6.0135	1.101	373.2
330	40.84	334.57	6.0474	1.097	379.3
340	39.56	345.54	6.0801	1.095	385.0
350	38.35	356.49	6.1119	1.092	390.7
360	37.21	367.42	6.1425	1.090	396.5
370	36.16	378.31	6.1726	1.089	402.2
380	35.15	391.19	6.2019	1.087	407.6
390	34.20	400.06	6.2295	1.086	418.0
400	33.31	410.91	6.2572	1.085	418.0
410	32.47	421.74	6.2844	1.084	423.1
420	31.67	432.58	6.3103	1.083	428.1
430	30.90	443.42	6.3359	1.083	433.2
440	30.19	454.27	6.3602	1.083	437.9
450	29.50	465.11	6.3849	1.083	442.6
460	28.84	475.95	6.4092	1.083	447.3
470	28.21	486.76	6.4322	1.084	452.0
480	27.62	497.64	6.4548	1.085	456.7
490	27.05	508.49	6.4770	1.086	461.0
500	26.50	519.37	6.4992	1.087	465.4
510	25.97	530.22	6.5209	1.088	469.8
520	25.47	541.10	6.5423	1.089	474.2
530	24.00	551.99	6.5628	1.090	478.2
540	24.51	562.91	6.5833	1.092	482.6
550	24.07	573.80	6.6030	1.093	487.0
560	23.64	584.77	6.6231	1.095	491.0
570	23.22	595.70	6.6424	1.097	495.1
580	22.81	606.71	6.6604	1.098	499.1
590	22.43	617.68	6.6805	1.100	502.8
600	22.06	628.69	6.6989	1.102	506.9
610	21.43	639.74	6.7169	1.105	510.6
620	21.34	650.80	6.7349	1.107	514.6
630	20.90	661.85	6.7525	1.109	518.3
640	20.67	672.94	6.7701	1.111	522.0
650	20.35	684.08	6.7876	1.113	525.7
660	20.05	695.22	6.8044	1.115	529.4
670	19.75	706.40	6.8211	1.117	533.2
680	19.47	717.58	6.8379	1.119	536.5
690	19.18	728.80	6.8542	1.121	540.2
700	18.91	740.02	6.8701	1.124	543.9
710	18.64	751.24	6.8860	1.127	547.3
720	18.38	762.54	6.9019	1.129	550.7
730	18.13	773.85	6.9174	1.131	554.4
740	17.89	785.15	6.9329	1.133	557.7
750	17.65	796.50	6.9480	1.136	561.1
760	17.41	807.88	6.9635	1.138	564.5
770	17.19	819.23	6.9777	1.140	567.8
780	16.99	830.70	6.9932	1.143	571.2
790	16.76	842.13	7.0074	1.145	574.6
800	16.55	853.56	7.0736	1.148	578.0
850	15.59	911.26	7.0916	1.158	594.2
900	14.73	969.49	7.1582	1.170	609.7
950	13.96	1028.1	7.2218	1.176	625.2
1000	13.27	1087.4	7.2825	1.190	640.1
1100	12.08	1207.4	7.3968	1.208	668.4
1200	11.08	1329.0	7.5023	1.224	695.7
1300	10.24	1452.1	7.6011	1.238	722.3

continued

T, °K	ϱ	i	s	c_p	u
1400	9.511	1576.4	7.6932	1.249	747.9
1500	8.884	1701.9	7.7799	1.260	772.5
1600	8.333	1828.4	7.8616	1.273	796.4
1700	7.846	1955.6	7.9386	1.277	819.3
1800	7.415	2083.7	8.0119	1.284	842.2
1900	7.028	2212.4	8.0814	1.290	864.1
2000	6.679	2341.6	8.1475	1.296	885.3
2100	6.364	2471.5	8.2112	1.300	906.2
2200	6.076	2601.8	8.2719	1.305	926.9
2300	5.815	2732.5	8.3301	1.309	947.0
2400	5.574	2863.6	8.3857	1.313	966.5
2500	5.353	2995.0	8.4393	1.316	985.7
2600	5.149	3126.8	8.4908	1.319	1005
2700	4.959	3258.9	8.5411	1.322	1023
2800	4.783	3391.3	8.5888	1.325	1041
2900	4.618	3523.9		1.327	1060
3000	4.465	3656.6		1.330	1077
		$p=70$ bar			
270		258.75	5.6275	1.181	350.8
280	83.32	270.74	5.6714	1.170	357.5
290	82.75	282.59	5.7129	1.160	364.2
300	79.43	294.31	5.7531	1.153	370.6
310	76.44	305.90	5.7912	1.145	376.7
320	73.70	317.42	5.8276	1.140	382.8
330	71.17	328.86	5.8628	1.135	388.8
340	68.83	340.22	5.8967	1.130	394.6
350	66.64	351.54	5.9293	1.126	400.6
360	64.61	362.81	5.9612	1.122	406.4
370	62.71	374.01	5.9921	1.119	411.8
380	60.93	385.19	6.0219	1.117	417.1
390	59.25	396.35	6.0508	1.113	422.5
400	57.67	407.46	6.0788	1.111	427.6
410	56.18	418.57	6.1064	1.109	432.6
420	54.77	429.61	6.1332	1.107	437.7
430	53.44	442.29	6.1592	1.105	442.8
440	52.19	451.76	6.1847	1.104	447.5
450	50.97	462.81	6.2090	1.103	452.5
460	49.83	473.86	6.2337	1.103	456.9
470	48.74	484.83	6.2572	1.103	461.6
480	47.40	495.88	6.2806	1.102	466.3
490	46.69	506.89	6.3032	1.102	470.4
500	45.74	517.91	6.3258	1.102	475.1
510	44.83	528.96	6.3472	1.103	479.5
520	43.95	539.97	6.3694	1.103	483.9
530	43.08	551.07	6.3903	1.104	487.9
540	42.30	562.04	6.4104	1.105	492.3
550	41.53	573.09	6.4309	1.106	496.3
560	40.78	584.18	6.4510	1.107	500.4
570	40.06	595.24	6.4703	1.108	504.1
580	39.37	606.33	6.4895	1.110	508.1
590	38.70	617.43	6.5088	1.111	512.5
600	38.05	628.56	6.5272	1.112	516.2
610	37.42	639.70	6.5456	1.114	
620	36.82	650.84	6.5641	1.116	523.6
630	36.24	662.02	6.5816	1.117	
640	35.68	673.20	6.5997	1.119	531.0
650	35.14	684.42	6.6168	1.121	
660	34.60	695.64	6.6340	1.123	538.4
670	34.08	706.90	6.6507	1.125	
680	33.59	718.16	6.6675	1.127	545.5
690	33.11	729.42	6.6838	1.129	
700	32.64	740.73	6.7001	1.132	552.9
710	32.18	752.07	6.7160	1.134	

continued

$T, °K$	ϱ	i	s	c_p	u
720	31.74	763.38	6.7324	1.136	559.7
730	31.31	774.72	6.7479	1.138	
740	30.89	786.11	6.7634	1.140	566.4
750	30.47	797.54	6.7784	1.142	
760	30.08	808.97	6.7939	1.144	573.1
770	29.71	820.40	6.8086	1.146	
780	29.33	831.96	6.8236	1.148	579.9
790	28.97	843.47	6.8383	1.150	
800	28.60	854.90	6.8530	1.153	586.3
850	26.95	912.85	6.9229	1.163	602.5
900	25.47	971.34	6.9899	1.174	618.0
950	24.15	1030.1	7.0535	1.184	632.8
1000	22.96	1089.7	7.1146	1.193	647.6
1100	20.91	1209.8	7.2293	1.210	675.9
1200	19.19	1331.7	7.3349	1.226	703.3
1300	17.74	1455.0	7.4337	1.239	729.6
1400	16.51	1579.6	7.5258	1.250	754.5
1500	15.42	1705.2	7.6129	1.261	778.8
1600	14.46	1831.7	7.6945	1.270	802.7
1700	13.63	1959.1	7.7715	1.278	825.6
1800	12.88	2087.2	7.8448	1.285	848.2
1900	12.22	2216.0	7.9143	1.291	870.1
2000	11.61	2345.3	7.9809	1.296	891.3
2100	11.07	2475.2	8.0441	1.300	912.2
2200	10.57	2605.5	8.1048	1.305	932.4
2300	10.12	2736.3	8.1630	1.309	952.3
2400	9.702	2867.6	8.2191	1.313	971.8
2500	9.314	2999.0	8.2723	1.317	990.8
2600	8.964	3130.8	8.3242	1.319	1010
2700	8.636	3262.8	8.3740	1.322	1029
2800	8.330	3395.2	8.4222	1.325	1046
2900	8.047	3527.7		1.328	1064
3000	7.781	3660.4		1.330	1082
		$p=100$ bar			
280	123.4	263.06	5.5416	1.213	372.0
290	118.0	275.51	5.5701	1.200	378.1
300	113.0	287.77	5.6271	1.196	383.8
310	108.6	299.85	5.6664	1.182	388.6
320	104.5	311.81	5.7045	1.174	395.3
330	100.9	323.65	5.7414	1.168	401.1
340	97.42	335.38	5.7761	1.162	406.8
350	94.24	347.03	5.8096	1.156	412.2
360	91.30	358.63	5.8423	1.151	417.6
370	88.56	370.13	5.8628	1.147	423.0
380	86.08	381.60	5.9042	1.143	428.1
390	83.64	393.02	5.9340	1.139	433.5
400	81.33	404.38	5.9628	1.135	438.5
410	79.20	415.73	5.9913	1.132	443.6
420	77.19	427.01	6.0181	1.129	448.6
430	75.29	438.36	6.0449	1.127	453.3
440	73.49	449.54	6.0709	1.125	458.1
450	71.78	460.80	6.0960	1.123	462.8
460	70.16	472.02	6.1211	1.121	467.5
470	68.61	483.24	6.1445	1.119	472.2
480	67.14	494.46	6.1680	1.119	476.6
490	65.73	505.60	6.1910	1.118	481.0
500	64.39	516.78	6.2140	1.117	485.1
510	63.10	527.95	6.2362	1.117	489.1
520	61.86	539.13	6.2580	1.117	493.9
530	60.68	550.31	6.2794	1.117	497.9
540	59.55	561.49	6.2999	1.117	502.0
550	58.45	572.63	6.3204	1.118	506.0
560	57.40	583.81	6.3409	1.118	510.0

continued

T,°K	ϱ	i	s	c_p	u
570	56.39	594.99	6.3606	1.119	514.1
580	55.40	606.21	6.3798	1.120	517.8
590	54.48	617.43	6.3991	1.121	521.8
600	53.58	628.65	6.4175	1.122	525.9
610	52.70	639.87	6.4364	1.123	529.6
620	51.86	651.09	6.4548	1.125	533.3
630	51.04	662.35	6.4724	1.126	537.0
640	50.24	673.66	6.4904	1.128	540.7
650	49.49	684.92	6.5080	1.129	544.1
660	48.75	696.18	6.5251	1.131	547.8
670	48.02	707.48	6.5419	1.133	551.5
680	47.32	718.83	6.5590	1.135	554.9
690	46.64	730.22	6.5754	1.137	558.6
700	45.99	741.57	6.5917	1.138	561.9
710	45.35	752.95	6.6080	1.140	565.3
720	44.73	764.38	6.6239	1.142	568.7
730	44.22	775.81	6.6398	1.144	572.0
740	43.54	787.29	6.6553	1.146	575.4
750	42.97	798.76	6.6708	1.148	578.8
760	42.40	810.23	6.6859	1.150	582.1
770	41.86	821.70	6.7010	1.152	585.5
780	41.35	833.34	6.7156	1.154	588.9
790	40.83	844.81	6.7303	1.156	591.9
800	40.33	856.33	6.7454	1.158	595.3
850	38.01	914.48	6.8153	1.168	610.8
900	35.94	973.18	6.8827	1.178	625.9
950	34.10	1032.2	6.9467	1.187	641.1
1000	32.43	1092.0	7.0079	1.197	655.5
1100	29.56	1212.4	7.1222	1.213	683.7
1200	27.15	1334.4	7.2285	1.228	710.6
1300	25.11	1458.0	7.3273	1.241	736.6
1400	23.36	1582.6	7.4198	1.252	761.5
1500	21.84	1708.4	7.5069	1.262	785.4
1600	20.50	1835.0	7.5886	1.271	808.7
1700	19.33	1962.5	7.6656	1.279	831.9
1800	18.27	2090.8	7.7389	1.285	854.1
1900	17.33	2219.6	7.8084	1.292	875.7
2000	16.48	2349.0	7.8750	1.297	896.6
2100	15.71	2478.9	7.9382	1.301	917.5
2200	15.01	2609.3	7.9989	1.306	937.7
2300	14.36	2740.1	8.0571	1.310	958.0
2400	13.79	2871.4	8.1132	1.313	976.9
2500	13.25	3002.8	8.1668	1.317	996.1
2600	12.74	3134.7	8.2187	1.320	1015
2700	12.28	3266.8	8.2685	1.323	1033
2800	11.84	3399.2	8.3196	1.325	1051
2900	11.44	3531.6		1.328	1069
3000	11.07	3664.2		1.330	1087

Thermodynamic properties of carbon monoxide at high pressures [51]:
ρ (kg/m^3), i (kJ/kg), s and c_p (kJ/kg · deg)

t, °C	ϱ	i	s	c_p	ϱ	i	s	c_p
		p=0.1 bar				p=1 bar		
—200	0.4674	364.17	6.283	1.08				
—190	0.4088	374.90	6.421	1.07	4.267	367.80	5.676	1.29
—180	0.3639	385.53	6.541	1.06	3.762	380.28	5.817	1.16
—170	0.3303	396.06	6.648	1.05	3.370	392.08	5.937	1.12
—160	0.2987	406.55	6.729	1.05	3.048	403.43	6.042	1.10
—150	0.2742	417.00	6.834	1.05	2.787	414.53	6.136	1.08
—140	0.2535	427.44	6.915	1.04	2.567	425.40	6.221	1.07

continued

t, °C	ϱ	i	s	c_p	ϱ	i	s	c_p
−130	0.2357	437.87	6.991	1.04	2.382	436.15	6.299	1.07
−120	0.2202	448.29	7.061	1.04	2.221	446.84	6.371	1.06
−110	0.2067	458.71	7.127	1.04	2.081	457.46	6.438	1.06
−100	0.1947	469.13	7.189	1.04	1.957	468.01	6.501	1.05
− 90	0.1841	479.54	7.247	1.04	1.847	478.55	6.560	1.05
− 80	0.1745	489.94	7.303	1.04	1.750	489.06	6.616	1.05
− 70	0.1657	500.35	7.355	1.04	1.663	499.58	6.669	1.05
− 60	0.1581	510.75	7.405	1.04	1.584	510.11	6.720	1.04
− 50	0.1510	521.16	7.453	1.04	1.511	520.62	6.768	1.04
− 25	0.1358	547.17	7.563	1.04	1.359	546.77	6.879	1.04
0	0.1234	573.17	7.663	1.04	1.234	572.85	6.979	1.04
25	0.1130	599.18	7.754	1.04	1.131	598.93	7.070	1.04
50	0.1043	625.21	7.838	1.04	1.043	624.98	7.154	1.04
100	0.09030	677.37	7.988	1.05	0.9029	677.20	7.304	1.05
150	0.07963	729.74	8.120	1.05	0.7961	729.62	7.436	1.05
200	0.07122	780.94	8.237	1.06	0.7119	782.35	7.553	1.06
300	0.05879	889.33	8.442	1.08	0.5877	889.29	7.758	1.08
400	0.05006	998.69	8.617	1.11	0.5004	998.69	7.933	1.11
		p=2 bar				p=4 bar		
−180	7.772	374.89	5.570	1.29				
−170	6.937	387.83	5.702	1.20	14.634	380.04	5.443	1.36
−160	6.242	400.21	5.815	1.15	12.932	393.72	5.570	1.27
−150	5.677	411.81	5.914	1.13	11.666	406.64	5.679	1.22
−140	5.208	423.17	6.003	1.11	10.642	418.90	5.774	1.18
−130	4.814	434.33	6.084	1.09	9.797	430.72	5.860	1.15
−120	4.478	445.27	6.158	1.08	9.082	442.21	5.937	1.13
−110	4.187	456.09	6.226	1.07	8.470	453.43	6.008	1.11
−100	3.933	466.81	6.290	1.07	7.939	464.47	6.074	1.09
− 90	3.709	477.49	6.350	1.06	7.473	475.44	6.136	1.08
− 80	3.511	488.15	6.406	1.06	7.061	486.35	6.194	1.07
− 70	3.334	498.79	6.460	1.05	6.699	497.22	6.249	1.07
− 60	3.175	509.41	6.511	1.05	6.375	508.06	6.301	1.06
− 50	3.031	520.01	6.560	1.05	6.081	518.84	6.351	1.06
− 25	2.722	546.29	6.671	1.04	5.455	545.41	6.464	1.05
0	2.471	572.51	6.772	1.04	4.948	571.79	6.565	1.05
25	2.262	598.64	6.864	1.04	4.527	598.06	6.657	1.05
50	2.091	624.73	6.948	1.05	4.173	624.24	6.741	1.05
100	1.805	677.01	7.098	1.05	3.610	676.62	6.892	1.05
150	1.592	729.48	7.230	1.05	3.181	729.22	7.024	1.05
200	1.423	782.26	7.348	1.06	2.844	782.06	7.142	1.06
300	1.175	889.23	7.552	1.08	2.347	889.11	7.346	1.08
400	1.000	998.69	7.728	1.11	1.998	998.69	7.522	1.11
		p=6 bar				p=8 bar		
−170	23.538	373.23	5.277	1.54				
−160	20.282	388.00	5.413	1.39	28.151	382.62	5.295	1.51
−150	18.059	401.84	5.530	1.31	24.766	397.22	5.419	1.40
−140	16.361	414.86	5.632	1.25	22.230	410.93	5.526	1.32
−130	14.987	427.80	5.722	1.21	20.238	423.94	5.620	1.26
−120	13.839	439.28	5.803	1.17	18.624	436.36	5.704	1.22
−110	12.866	450.89	5.876	1.14	17.269	448.38	5.780	1.18
−100	12.032	462.24	5.944	1.12	16.126	460.07	5.850	1.15
− 90	11.294	473.50	6.007	1.10	15.132	471.63	5.915	1.13
− 80	10.658	484.66	6.067	1.09	14.276	483.03	5.976	1.11
− 70	10.105	495.77	6.123	1.08	13.526	494.35	6.033	1.10
− 60	9.602	506.79	6.176	1.07	12.849	505.56	6.087	1.09
− 50	9.154	517.75	6.226	1.07	12.247	516.67	6.138	1.08
− 25	8.200	544.55	6.340	1.06	10.954	543.73	6.252	1.06
0	7.430	571.12	6.442	1.05	9.918	570.48	6.356	1.06
25	6.794	597.52	6.535	1.05	9.068	596.98	6.448	1.05
50	6.186	623.77	6.619	1.05	8.346	623.32	6.533	1.05
100	5.411	676.26	6.770	1.05	7.213	675.92	6.684	1.05
150	4.768	728.96	6.902	1.06	6.354	728.69	6.816	1.06

continued

t, °C	ϱ	i	s	c_p	ϱ	i	s	c_p
200	4.263	781.88	7.020	1.06	5.680	781.68	6.934	1.06
300	3.517	889.00	7.225	1.08	4.686	888.90	7.139	1.08
400	2.994	998.69	7.401	1.11	3.988	998.69	7.316	1.11
		p=10 bar				p=15 bar		
−160	36.758	377.68	5.125	1.64				
−150	31.938	392.95	5.328	1.50	53.556	383.38	5.158	1.76
−140	28.465	407.22	5.439	1.40	46.221	398.87	5.277	1.60
−130	25.768	420.72	5.537	1.33	40.890	413.46	5.382	1.49
−120	23.637	433.58	5.624	1.27	36.855	427.35	5.476	1.39
−110	21.866	445.99	5.702	1.22	33.747	440.65	5.560	1.32
−100	20.356	458.05	5.774	1.18	31.192	453.51	5.637	1.26
−90	19.067	469.89	5.840	1.15	29.086	466.01	5.706	1.21
−80	17.955	481.55	5.903	1.13	27.300	478.19	5.771	1.17
−70	16.986	493.07	5.961	1.11	25.768	490.12	5.831	1.15
−60	16.126	504.43	6.016	1.10	24.420	501.83	5.888	1.13
−50	15.356	515.67	6.067	1.08	23.226	513.34	5.940	1.11
−25	13.724	542.97	6.183	1.07	20.687	541.28	6.058	1.08
0	12.410	569.85	6.287	1.06	18.673	568.46	6.163	1.07
25	11.340	596.46	6.380	1.06	17.027	595.25	6.257	1.06
50	10.440	622.88	6.465	1.06	15.666	621.83	6.342	1.06
100	9.012	675.58	6.616	1.06	13.505	674.75	6.494	1.06
150	7.937	728.44	6.749	1.06	11.884	727.80	6.627	1.06
200	7.093	781.50	6.867	1.06	10.614	781.03	6.746	1.07
300	5.851	888.79	7.072	1.09	8.780	888.52	6.952	1.09
400	4.980	9998.69	7.249	1.11	7.451	998.69	7.128	1.11
		p=20 bar				p=25 bar		
−150	81.424	375.95	5.034	2.05				
−140	67.332	392.63	5.160	1.83	92.442	377.77	5.003	2.13
−130	57.992	408.08	5.271	1.66	76.950	400.24	5.152	1.88
−120	51.300	422.64	5.369	1.53	60.010	417.64	5.278	1.68
−110	46.298	436.50	5.456	1.43	59.723	432.40	5.372	1.53
−100	42.504	449.86	5.536	1.34	54.283	446.45	5.455	1.42
−90	39.451	462.85	5.609	1.27	50.197	459.92	5.530	1.33
−80	36.909	475.45	5.675	1.22	46.816	472.90	5.599	1.27
−70	34.786	487.70	5.737	1.18	43.979	485.47	5.662	1.23
−60	32.879	499.64	5.794	1.16	41.496	497.66	5.734	1.19
−50	31.202	511.32	5.848	1.13	39.301	509.48	5.775	1.16
−25	27.711	539.70	5.968	1.10	34.799	538.18	5.896	1.12
0	24.964	567.16	6.074	1.08	31.296	565.87	6.003	1.09
25	22.735	594.10	6.168	1.07	28.454	592.98	6.098	1.08
50	20.887	620.83	6.254	1.07	26.226	619.84	6.184	1.07
100	17.990	673.98	6.406	1.06	22.462	673.26	6.337	1.07
150	15.816	727.18	6.540	1.07	19.739	726.58	6.470	1.07
200	14.125	780.57	6.659	1.07	17.616	780.15	6.591	1.07
300	11.642	888.30	6.865	1.09	14.513	888.09	6.797	1.09
400	9.912	998.69	7.042	1.12	12.356	998.69	6.974	1.12
		p=50 bar				p=75 bar		
−140	508.348	274.33	4.150		559.082	269.47	4.059	
−130	250.089	349.04	4.681		410.102	311.90	4.375	
−120	173.975	382.57	4.905	2.88	319.749	348.42	4.620	
−110	140.754	406.82	5.057	2.16	247.002	378.03	4.806	2.68
−100	122.154	425.98	5.170	1.83	204.751	402.10	4.949	2.22
−90	109.714	443.15	5.265	1.64	178.408	422.90	5.063	1.94
−80	100.322	458.73	5.348	1.51	159.874	441.19	5.161	1.74
−70	92.810	473.08	5.420	1.41	145.809	457.78	5.244	1.59
−60	86.638	486.59	5.485	1.34	134.534	473.11	5.318	1.48
−50	81.377	499.45	5.544	1.27	125.380	487.30	5.382	1.38
−25	70.965	529.87	5.673	1.19	107.855	520.01	5.521	1.26
0	63.185	558.82	5.784	1.14	95.240	550.32	5.637	1.19
25	57.105	587.00	5.882	1.13	85.657	579.73	5.740	1.17
50	52.189	614.65	5.971	1.11	78.001	608.60	5.833	1.15

continued

t, °C	ϱ	i	s	c_p	ϱ	i	s	c_p
100	44.645	669.30	6.128	1.10	66.437	665.23	5.995	1.12
150	39.104	723.67	6.265	1.09	58.064	721.01	6.135	1.11
200	34.843	778.03	6.386	1.09	51.669	776.16	6.258	1.10
300	28.675	887.18	6.594	1.10	42.472	886.49	6.469	1.11
400	24.399	998.75	6.774	1.13	36.147	998.88	6.649	1.14
		$p=100$ bar				$p=150$ bar		
−140	590.928	266.00	4.007		639.498	263.31	3.921	2.55
−130	512.066	296.23	4.230		585.983	288.52	4.106	2.52
−120	431.587	326.36	4.436		529.490	313.31	4.274	2.48
−110	358.643	355.54	4.620	2.82	473.142	337.62	4.429	2.43
−100	298.933	382.39	4.779	2.51	419.311	361.45	4.572	2.37
− 90	254.174	405.95	4.911	2.17	371.485	384.53	4.702	2.28
− 80	222.655	426.30	5.018	1.92	330.697	407.09	4.821	2.16
− 70	200.358	444.67	5.110	1.74	299.252	427.99	4.926	2.00
− 60	183.432	461.52	5.191	1.60	274.070	446.86	5.016	1.80
− 50	169.758	477.02	5.262	1.49	253.026	463.69	5.093	1.59
− 25	144.530	511.51	5.408	1.31	214.472	499.94	5.246	1.39
0	126.972	543.13	5.529	1.24	187.609	533.15	5.374	1.32
25	113.769	573.68	5.636	1.20	167.524	565.11	5.486	1.27
50	103.282	603.56	5.732	1.18	151.733	596.31	5.586	1.23
100	87.751	661.82	5.899	1.14	128.604	656.53	5.758	1.18
150	76.572	718.66	6.041	1.13	112.040	714.85	5.905	1.15
200	68.068	774.54	6.166	1.12	99.573	771.96	6.032	1.14
300	55.930	885.95	6.379	1.12	81.805	885.26	6.248	1.14
400	47.596	999.12	6.560	1.14	69.968	999.89	6.432	1.16
		$p=200$ bar				$p=300$ bar		
−140	673.317	263.10	3.856	2.38				
−130	619.690	287.08	4.030	2.37				
−120	569.309	310.57	4.189	2.36				
−110	518.704	333.52	4.334	2.34				
−100	472.344	355.88	4.468	2.30				
− 90	432.921	377.56	4.590	2.26				
− 80	399.002	399.87	4.701	2.20				
− 70	369.525	418.09	4.801	2.11	466.057	406.21	4.624	2.03
− 60	344.103	436.40	4.889	1.90	441.102	425.90	4.718	1.89
− 50	321.584	453.37	4.966	1.66	417.437	444.06	4.802	1.73
− 25	275.689	490.76	5.125	1.44	369.038	483.12	4.967	1.48
0	242.092	525.63	5.258	1.36	330.697	518.79	5.104	1.39
25	216.796	558.94	5.375	1.30	299.252	552.76	5.223	1.33
50	196.699	590.93	5.478	1.26	273.802	585.47	5.328	1.29
100	166.925	652.24	6.654	1.20	234.590	647.98	5.507	1.23
150	145.431	711.78	5.803	1.17	205.653	708.73	5.660	1.20
200	129.257	770.13	5.933	1.16	183.552	768.34	5.793	1.18
300	106.340	885.08	6.153	1.16	151.651	885.91	6.017	1.17
400	90.677	1000.98	6.338	1.17	129.916	1003.98	6.207	1.19
		$p=400$ bar				$p=500$ bar		
−70	523.551	407.30	4.528	1.91	565.859	410.78	4.454	1.86
−60	501.971	425.79	4.617	1.79	546.004	428.87	4.541	1.76
−50	481.271	443.01	4.697	1.67	525.516	445.85	4.619	1.65
−25	434.938	481.54	4.860	1.48	482.100	484.17	4.781	1.47
0	395.063	517.21	4.997	1.39	444.603	519.66	4.918	1.39
25	362.820	551.33	5.116	1.34	412.518	553.45	5.036	1.34
50	335.440	584.25	5.222	1.30	384.753	586.22	5.141	1.29
100	291.164	647.51	5.404	1.24	338.285	649.44	5.323	1.24
150	257.445	708.76	5.558	1.21	301.832	710.96	5.477	1.22
200	231.106	769.00	5.692	1.20	272.736	771.67	5.613	1.21
300	192.641	888.24	5.920	1.19	229.214	891.86	5.843	1.20
400	165.642	1007.93	6.112	1.20	198.371	1012.82	6.066	1.22

continued

t,°C	ϱ	i	s	c_p	ϱ	i	s	c_p
	p=600 bar				p=700 bar			
−70	598.504	415.77	4.392	1.85	625.223	421.84	4.341	1.84
−60	579.917	433.74	4.478	1.74	607.592	439.69	4.426	1.74
−50	562.450	450.65	4.556	1.64	589.684	456.56	4.504	1.63
−25	520.632	488.80	4.718	1.46	551.378	494.58	4.665	1.46
0	485.442	524.13	4.854	1.38	516.790	529.89	4.801	1.38
25	453.971	557.80	4.971	1.33	487.130	563.46	4.918	1.32
50	426.332	590.44	5.076	1.29	459.180	595.94	5.023	1.28
100	379.026	653.40	5.257	1.24	412.518	658.76	5.203	1.24
150	340.754	714.92	5.412	1.22	374.966	720.19	5.357	1.22
200	309.503	775.83	5.548	1.21	342.840	780.99	5.493	1.21
300	262.512	896.61	5.779	1.21	292.685	902.26	5.725	1.22
400	228.280	1018.59	5.974	1.23	256.033	1025.17	5.922	1.24
	p=800 bar				p=900 bar			
−70	648.380	428.72	4.297	1.84	668.496	436.21	4.258	1.83
−60	630.856	446.54	4.382	1.73	652.914	454.04	4.344	1.73
−50	615.604	463.36	4.459	1.63	636.591	470.82	4.421	1.62
−25	578.719	501.30	4.620	1.46	602.366	508.60	4.582	1.45
0	546.004	536.53	4.756	1.37	570.468	543.81	4.717	1.37
25	515.838	570.00	4.873	1.32	541.779	577.19	4.833	1.31
50	489.685	602.40	4.977	1.28	515.838	609.48	4.937	1.27
100	443.196	665.01	5.157	1.24	469.966	671.94	5.117	1.23
150	404.185	726.23	5.311	1.22	452.504	732.95	5.270	1.22
200	371.485	786.95	5.447	1.21	397.869	793.65	5.406	1.22
300	320.114	908.65	5.679	1.23	345.376	915.64	5.639	1.23
400	281.508	1032.40	5.878	1.25	305.453	1040.15	5.838	1.26

t,°C	ϱ	i	s	c_p	t,°C	ϱ	i	s	c_p
	p=1000 bar					p=1000 bar			
−70	686.520	444.33	4.225	1.83	50	538.654	617.03	4.902	1.27
−60	671.703	462.13	4.310	1.73	100	494.004	679.30	5.080	1.23
−50	657.512	478.89	4.387	1.62	150	455.447	740.23	5.234	1.22
−25	622.444	516.55	4.547	1.45	200	422.474	800.92	5.369	1.22
0	592.178	551.60	4.682	1.36	300	368.553	923.15	5.603	1.24
25	564.718	584.87	4.798	1.31	400	327.602	1048.26	5.803	1.27

Viscosity η (N · s/m²) of gaseous carbon monoxide at $p \leqslant 1$ bar [42, 50]

t, °C	$\eta \cdot 10^7$	t, °C	$\eta \cdot 10^7$	t, °C	$\eta \cdot 10^7$	t, °C	$\eta \cdot 10^7$
−200	48.0	−100	113	200	245	700	387
−180	61.5	−75	127	300	279	800	410
−160	74.5	−50	140	400	309	900	433
−140	88.0	0	166	500	337	1000	453
−120	102	100	207	600	363		

Viscosity $\eta \cdot 10^8$ (N · s/m²) of carbon monoxide at different temperatures and pressures [52]

p, atm \ t, °C →	0	25	50	100	150	200	250
1	1660	1765	1870	2075	2270	2450	2625
20	1690	1795	1900	2105	2290	2470	2645
50	1750	1850	1945	2145	2320	2500	2670
100	1895	1990	2050	2225	2385	2560	2715
150	2080	2140	2175	2320	2465	2630	2770
200	2300	2305	2315	2430	2550	2710	2830
300	2740	2680	2640	2680	2765	2870	2970
400	3175	3065	2985	2950	2970	3035	
500	3600	3450	3330	3225	3185	3200	
600	—	3825	3660	3490	3405	3400	
800	—	4550	4300	4010	3820	3760	

Thermal conductivity λ (W/m · deg) of gaseous carbon monoxide at $p \leqslant 1$ bar [42, 50]

t, °C	λ · 10⁴	t, °C	λ · 10⁴	t, °C	λ · 10⁴	t, °C	λ · 10⁴
−200	60.3	−100	151.2	200	365.2	700	650.1
−180	80.9	−75	169.8	300	425.7	800	701.3
−160	90.0	−50	193.0	400	485.0	900	754.8
−140	116.3	0	232.6	500	540.8	1000	805.9
−120	134.9	100	301.2	600	596.6		

CARBON DIOXIDE (CO_2)

Molecular weight 44.011

$T_{subl} = 194.65$ °K at 760 mm Hg; $T_{melt} = 216.55$ °K; $T_{cr} = 304.19$ °K, $p_{cr} = 73.82$ bar, $\rho_{cr} = 468$ kg/m³

Thermodynamic properties of saturated carbon dioxide [53, 58]: v (dm³/kg), i (kJ/kg), s (kJ/kg · deg) and r (kJ/kg)

T, °K	p, bar	v′	v″	i′	i″	r	s′	s″
216.55	5.18	0.848	72.464	−206.2	141.1	347.3	2.671	4.275
220	6.00	0.857	63.291	−200.0	142.7	342.7	2.702	4.260
225	7.34	0.871	50.943	−190.9	145.8	336.7	2.741	4.237
230	8.91	0.885	48.103	−181.5	148.5	330.0	2.780	4.214
235	10.75	0.901	36.232	−172.0	150.5	322.5	2.819	4.191
240	12.82	0.918	30.581	−162.5	151.7	314.2	2.859	4.168
245	15.18	0.936	25.773	−152.6	151.6	304.2	2.899	4.141
250	17.87	0.956	21.787	−142.6	151.1	293.7	2.939	4.114
255	20.85	0.978	18.450	−132.4	149.9	282.3	2.979	4.086
260	24.21	1.002	15.723	−121.9	148.6	270.5	3.019	4.059
265	27.87	1.029	13.387	−111.0	146.4	257.4	3.059	4.030
270	32.03	1.059	11.287	−99.6	142.9	242.5	3.100	3.998
273.15	34.839	1.078	10.31	−92.5	140.0	232.5	3.1259	3.9772
274	35.633	1.084	10.04	−90.3	139.5	229.8	3.1327	3.9716
275	36.576	1.092	9.728	−88.1	138.9	227.0	3.1406	3.9653
276	37.543	1.099	9.416	−85.7	138.2	225.9	3.1487	3.9591
277	38.521	1.107	9.116	−83.2	137.4	220.6	3.1589	3.9531
278	39.520	1.115	8.818	−80.7	136.6	217.3	3.1654	3.9471
279	40.547	1.123	8.525	−78.2	135.8	214.0	3.1749	3.9409
280	41.588	1.132	8.244	−75.7	134.9	210.6	3.1828	3.9346
281	42.654	1.141	7.968	−73.1	134.0	207.1	3.1917	3.9282
282	43.732	1.150	7.704	−70.5	133.0	203.5	3.2006	3.9217
283	44.831	1.160	7.452	−67.8	132.0	199.8	3.2096	3.9157
284	45.956	1.170	7.210	−65.1	130.9	196.0	3.2187	3.9084

continued

T, °K	p, bar	v'	v''	i'	i''	r	s'	s''
285	47.096	1.181	6.974	−62.3	129.8	192.1	3.2279	3.9015
286	48.261	1.193	6.738	−59.5	128.6	188.1	3.2373	3.8943
287	49.450	1.204	6.502	−56.6	127.3	183.9	3.2468	3.8869
288	50.666	1.217	6.262	−53.6	125.9	179.5	3.2565	3.8793
289	51.895	1.229	6.035	−50.6	124.4	175.0	3.2664	3.8714
290	53.148	1.243	5.817	−47.6	122.8	170.4	3.2765	3.8633
291	54.432	1.258	5.605	−44.5	121.1	165.6	3.2867	3.8550
292	55.732	1.273	5.397	−41.5	119.2	160.5	3.2971	3.8462
293	57.066	1.290	5.187	−38.0	117.2	155.2	3.3076	3.8368
294	58.421	1.309	4.980	−34.6	115.0	149.6	3.3184	3.8268
295	59.802	1.329	4.778	−31.1	112.6	143.7	3.3297	3.8164
296	61.205	1.350	4.574	−27.4	109.9	137.3	3.3415	3.8053
297	62.639	1.374	4.372	−23.5	107.0	130.5	3.3539	3.7932
298	64.098	1.401	4.168	−19.5	103.9	123.4	3.3669	3.7861
299	65.598	1.433	3.964	−15.4	100.4	115.8	3.3804	3.7662
300	67.115	1.479	3.733	−10.8	96.3	107.1	3.3945	3.7513
301	68.661	1.515	3.504	−5.7	91.5	97.2	3.4108	3.7337
302	70.246	1.573	3.259	0.5	85.4	84.9	3.4304	3.7121
303	71.858	1.656	2.978	8.4	77.4	69.0	3.4560	3.6833
304.19	73.815	2.136	2.136	42.8	42.8	0	3.5666	3.5666

Heat capacity c_p (kJ/kg · deg) of saturated carbon dioxide [53, 58]

T, °K	c_p'	c_p''	T, °K	c_p'	c_p''	T, °K	c_p'	c_p''
273.15	2.47	1.61	283	2.95	2.17	293	4.14	3.75
274	2.50	1.64	284	3.02	2.26	294	4.38	4.08
275	2.53	1.68	285	3.10	2.35	295	4.65	4.48
276	2.57	1.73	286	3.19	2.46	296	4.99	4.98
277	2.61	1.78	287	3.28	2.58	297	5.42	5.60
278	2.66	1.83	288	3.38	2.71	298	5.96	6.45
279	2.71	1.88	289	3.50	2.88	299	6.67	7.57
280	2.76	1.94	290	3.63	3.03	300	7.69	9.25
281	2.82	2.01	291	3.77	3.23	301	9.20	11.72
282	2.88	2.09	292	3.94	3.47			

The following tables of thermodynamic properties of carbon dioxide at different temperatures and pressures have been compiled by Kesselman and Kotlyarovsky. The properties of CO_2 were calculated in the temperature range 273–800 °K from the equation of state. The coefficients in the equation were determined on the basis of experimental P, V, T data. This equation describes both the liquid and the gas phases and includes two neighboring boundary curves [56, 57]. The accuracy of the calculated empirical data for different properties does not exceed the limits of experimental error. In the range 770–4000 °K, the equation of state contains two virial coefficients $B(T)$ and $C(T)$, both of which were calculated using the method of Kesselman [344, 345].

In calculating the thermodynamic properties of dissociated CO_2, the following reactions were taken into account:

$$CO_2 \rightleftarrows CO + \frac{1}{2} O_2 \qquad (1)$$

$$O_2 \rightleftarrows 2\,O \qquad (2)$$

These are the basic reactions describing the composition of the dissociated mixture at temperatures of 1800–4000 °K and pressures of 1–600 bar. The properties of the components within the indicated range of the parameters were calculated taking into account the real properties. The second and third virial coefficients were calculated using the method of Kesselman for CO_2 as well as for the components CO and O_2.

The properties of atomic oxygen were calculated taking into account only the second virial coefficient. The equilibrium composition was calculated using the law of mass action for reactions (1) and (2).

The thermodynamic functions for each component in the ideal state and the reaction constants for (1) and (2) were taken from Refs [346].

Thermodynamic properties of carbon dioxide at different temperatures and pressures [56–58] : v (dm³/kg), i (kJ/kg) and s (kJ/kg · deg)

T, °K	v	i	s	v	i	s
		p=1 bar			p=2 bar	
273.15	512.6	191.1	4.7858	254.6	190.1	4.6522
280	525.7	196.8	4.8061	261.2	195.7	4.6727
290	544.9	205.1	4.8352	270.9	204.1	4.7019
300	564.0	213.6	4.8638	280.6	212.7	4.7307
310	583.1	222.1	4.8920	290.2	221.3	4.7591
320	602.1	230.8	4.9194	299.9	230.0	4.7867
330	621.2	239.6	4.9464	309.5	238.8	4.8138
340	640.3	248.4	4.9729	319.1	247.7	4.8405
350	659.3	257.4	4.9990	328.7	256.7	4.8667
360	678.3	266.4	5.0242	338.2	265.8	4.8920
370	697.3	275.6	5.0494	347.8	275.0	4.9173
380	716.3	284.8	5.0742	357.4	284.2	4.9422
390	735.3	294.1	5.0982	366.9	293.5	4.9662
400	754.3	303.5	5.1221	376.5	303.0	4.9902
410	773.3	312.9	5.1452	386.0	312.4	5.0134
420	792.2	322.4	5.1682	395.5	322.0	5.0365
430	811.2	332.1	5.1909	405.0	331.6	5.0592
440	830.2	341.8	5.2131	414.6	341.4	5.0815
450	849.2	351.5	5.2349	424.1	351.1	5.1033
460	868.1	361.4	5.2568	433.6	361.0	5.1252
470	887.1	371.3	5.2781	443.1	370.9	5.1466
480	906.0	381.3	5.2991	452.6	380.9	5.1676
490	925.0	391.3	5.3201	462.1	391.0	5.1886
500	943.9	401.5	5.3402	471.6	401.1	5.2087
510	962.9	411.7	5.3603	481.1	411.3	5.2288
520	981.8	421.9	5.3804	490.6	421.6	5.2490
530	1001	432.2	5.4001	500.1	431.9	5.2687
540	1020	442.6	5.4194	509.6	442.3	5.2880
550	1039	453.1	5.4387	519.1	452.8	5.3073
560	1058	463.6	5.4575	528.6	463.3	5.3262
570	1076	474.2	5.4764	538.1	473.9	5.3451
580	1095	484.8	5.4948	547.5	484.5	5.3635
590	1114	495.4	5.5133	557.0	495.2	5.3820
600	1133	506.2	5.5313	566.5	506.0	5.4000
620	1171	527.8	5.5665	585.5	527.6	5.4352
640	1209	549.7	5.6013	604.4	549.5	5.4701
660	1247	571.8	5.6352	623.4	571.6	5.5040
680	1285	594.0	5.6683	648.3	593.9	5.5371
700	1322	616.5	5.7010	661.2	616.3	5.5698
720	1360	639.2	5.7328	680.2	639.0	5.6017
740	1398	662.0	5.7642	699.1	661.9	5.6331
760	1436	684.9	5.7948	718.0	684.8	5.6637
780	1474	708.1	5.8249	736.9	708.0	5.6938
800	1512	731.4	5.8543	755.9	731.3	5.7232
850	1606	790.4	5.9259	803.7	790.3	5.7946
900	1682	850.2	5.9945	850.4	850.2	5.8635
950	1795	910.9	6.0599	897.7	910.8	5.9289
1000	1890	972.3	6.1227	945.0	972.3	5.9917
1050	1984	1034.4	6.1835	992.2	1034.3	6.0524
1100	2079	1097.4	6.2421	1039	1097.3	6.1111
1150	2173	1160.6	6.2982	1087	1160.6	6.1672
1200	2268	1224.2	6.3522	1134	1224.2	6.2212
1250	2362	1288.5	6.4050	1181	1288.5	6.2740
1300	2456	1353.2	6.4556	1228	1353.2	6.3246
1350	2551	1418.3	6.5050	1276	1418.3	6.3740
1400	2645	1483.9	6.5528	1323	1483.9	6.4218
1450	2740	1549.8	6.5988	1370	1549.8	6.4678
1500	2834	1616.0	6.6440	1418	1616.0	6.5131
1600	3023	1749.3	6.7299	1512	1749.4	6.5989
1700	3212	1883.8	6.8111	1607	1883.8	6.6801
1800	3401	2019.1	6.8886	1701	2019.1	6.7576

continued

T, °K	v	i	s	v	i	s
		p=4 bar			p=6 bar	
273.15	125.5	187.9	4.5158	82.49	185.6	4.4336
280	129.0	193.6	4.5366	84.84	191.5	4.4547
290	133.9	202.2	4.5662	88.25	200.2	4.4848
300	138.9	210.8	4.5955	91.63	208.9	4.5144
310	143.8	219.5	4.6242	94.99	217.8	4.5436
320	148.7	228.4	4.6522	98.43	226.7	4.5719
330	153.6	237.3	4.6796	101.7	235.8	4.5997
340	158.5	246.3	4.7066	105.0	244.9	4.6270
350	163.4	255.4	4.7330	108.3	254.0	4.6537
360	168.2	264.6	4.7586	111.5	263.3	4.6795
370	173.1	273.8	4.7841	114.8	272.6	4.7052
380	177.9	283.1	4.8092	118.1	282.0	4.7304
390	182.7	292.5	4.8333	121.3	291.4	4.7547
400	187.5	301.9	4.8574	124.6	300.9	4.7790
410	192.4	311.5	4.8807	127.8	310.5	4.8024
420	197.2	321.1	4.9039	131.0	320.1	4.8257
430	202.0	330.7	4.9267	134.3	329.9	4.8486
440	206.8	340.5	4.9491	137.5	339.6	4.8710
450	211.6	350.3	4.9710	140.7	349.5	4.8930
460	216.3	360.2	4.9929	143.9	359.4	4.9150
470	221.1	370.2	5.0144	147.1	369.4	4.9365
480	225.9	380.2	5.0354	150.3	379.4	4.9576
490	230.7	390.3	5.0565	153.6	389.6	4.9788
500	235.5	400.4	5.0767	156.8	399.8	4.9990
510	240.2	410.7	5.0969	160.0	410.0	5.0192
520	245.0	421.0	5.1171	163.2	420.4	5.0395
530	249.8	431.3	5.1368	166.4	430.7	5.0593
540	254.6	441.8	5.1562	169.5	441.2	5.0787
550	259.3	452.2	5.1755	172.7	451.7	5.0981
560	264.1	462.8	5.1944	175.9	462.3	5.1170
570	268.8	473.4	5.2133	179.1	472.9	5.1360
580	273.6	484.0	5.2318	182.3	483.5	5.1545
590	278.4	494.7	5.2503	185.5	494.3	5.1730
600	283.1	505.5	5.2684	188.7	505.1	5.1911
620	292.6	527.2	5.3037	195.0	526.8	5.2265
640	302.1	549.1	5.3386	201.4	548.8	5.2614
660	311.6	571.3	5.3726	207.7	570.9	5.2955
680	321.1	593.6	5.4057	214.1	593.2	5.3287
700	330.6	616.0	5.4385	220.4	615.8	5.3615
720	340.1	638.8	5.4704	226.8	638.5	5.3934
740	349.6	661.6	5.5018	233.1	661.4	5.4249
760	359.0	684.6	5.5324	239.4	684.4	5.4555
780	368.5	707.8	5.5626	245.8	707.6	5.4856
800	378.0	731.2	5.5920	252.1	731.0	5.5151
850	401.7	790.2	5.6637	267.8	790.0	5.5868
900	425.3	850.0	5.7323	283.6	849.9	5.6555
950	449.0	910.7	5.7978	299.4	910.6	5.7210
1000	472.7	972.2	5.8605	315.2	972.1	5.7838
1050	496.3	1034.2	5.9213	331.0	1034.2	5.8446
1100	520.0	1097.3	5.9800	346.8	1097.2	5.9032
1150	543.6	1160.6	6.0362	362.6	1160.5	5.9595
1200	567.3	1224.1	6.0901	378.3	1224.1	6.0134
1250	590.9	1288.4	6.1429	394.1	1288.4	6.0662
1300	614.5	1353.2	6.1936	409.9	1353.2	6.1169
1350	638.2	1418.3	6.2430	425.6	1418.3	6.1663
1400	661.8	1483.9	6.2908	441.4	1483.9	6.2141
1450	685.4	1549.8	6.3368	457.2	1549.8	6.2602
1500	709.1	1616.0	6.3821	472.9	1616.1	6.3054
1600	756.3	1749.4	6.4679	504.4	1749.4	6.3913
1700	803.6	1883.9	6.5491	536.0	1883.9	6.4725
1800	850.8	2019.2	6.6266	567.5	2019.2	6.5500

continued

T, °K	v	i	s	v	i	s
		p=8 bar			p=10 bar	
273.15	60.95	183.3	4.3733	48.00	180.9	4.3250
280	62.71	189.3	4.3948	49.51	187.0	4.3470
290	65.39	198.1	4.4254	51.67	196.0	4.3781
300	68.00	207.0	4.4556	53.81	205.0	4.4088
310	70.58	216.0	4.4852	55.92	214.2	4.4389
320	73.13	225.1	4.5139	58.01	223.4	4.4680
330	75.67	234.2	4.5420	60.08	232.6	4.4965
340	78.19	243.4	4.5696	62.13	242.0	4.5243
350	80.70	252.7	4.5966	64.16	251.3	4.5516
360	83.20	262.0	4.6226	66.19	260.7	4.5779
370	85.68	271.4	4.6485	68.20	270.2	4.6040
380	88.15	280.8	4.6739	70.20	279.7	4.6296
390	90.62	290.3	4.6984	72.20	289.2	4.6542
400	93.08	299.9	4.7228	74.18	298.9	4.6787
410	95.53	309.5	4.7463	76.17	308.5	4.7023
420	97.98	319.2	4.7697	78.14	318.3	4.7259
430	100.4	329.0	4.7927	80.11	328.1	4.7490
440	102.9	338.8	4.8152	82.07	337.9	4.7716
450	105.3	348.7	4.8373	84.04	347.8	4.7937
460	107.7	358.6	4.8593	85.99	357.8	4.8158
470	110.1	368.6	4.8809	87.94	367.9	4.8375
480	112.6	378.7	4.9021	89.90	378.0	4.8588
490	115.0	388.9	4.9233	91.84	388.2	4.8800
500	117.4	399.1	4.9436	93.79	398.4	4.9004
510	119.8	409.4	4.9639	95.73	408.8	4.9207
520	122.2	419.8	4.9842	97.67	419.1	4.9410
530	124.6	430.1	5.0040	99.60	429.5	4.9610
540	127.0	440.6	5.0235	101.5	440.0	4.9804
550	129.4	451.8	5.0429	103.5	450.6	4.9999
560	131.8	461.7	5.0619	105.4	461.2	5.0189
570	134.2	472.4	5.0809	107.3	471.9	5.0380
580	136.6	483.0	5.0994	109.2	482.6	5.0566
590	139.0	493.8	5.1180	111.2	493.3	5.0752
600	141.4	504.6	5.1361	113.1	504.2	5.0933
620	146.2	526.4	5.1715	116.9	526.0	5.1288
640	151.0	548.4	5.2065	120.8	548.0	5.1638
660	155.8	570.6	5.2406	124.6	570.2	5.1980
680	160.6	592.9	5.2739	128.4	592.6	5.2313
700	165.3	615.5	5.3067	132.3	615.2	5.2641
720	170.1	638.2	5.3386	136.1	638.0	5.2961
740	174.8	661.1	5.3701	139.9	660.9	5.3277
760	179.7	684.2	5.4009	143.7	683.9	5.3584
780	184.4	707.4	5.4230	147.5	707.2	5.3886
800	189.1	730.8	5.4605	151.3	730.6	5.4181
850	200.9	789.8	5.5322	160.8	789.7	5.4898
900	212.8	849.8	5.6009	170.3	849.6	5.5586
950	224.7	910.5	5.6664	179.8	910.4	5.6241
1000	236.5	972.0	5.7293	189.3	971.9	5.6870
1050	248.4	1034.1	5.7901	198.8	1034.0	5.7478
1100	260.0	1097.1	5.8488	208.3	1097.1	5.8065
1150	272.0	1160.5	5.9052	217.7	1160.4	5.8622
1200	283.9	1224.0	5.9590	227.2	1224.0	5.9167
1250	295.7	1288.4	6.0118	236.7	1288.4	5.9695
1300	307.5	1353.2	6.0625	246.1	1353.2	6.0202
1350	319.4	1418.3	6.1119	255.6	1418.3	6.0697
1400	331.2	1483.9	6.1597	265.1	1483.9	6.1174
1450	343.0	1549.9	6.2057	274.5	1549.9	6.1635
1500	354.9	1616.1	6.2510	284.0	1616.1	6.2088
1600	378.5	1749.5	6.3368	302.9	1749.5	6.2946
1700	402.1	1884.0	6.4181	321.9	1884.0	6.3759
1800	425.8	2019.3	6.4956	340.8	2019.4	6.4534

continued

T, °K	v	i	s	v	i	s
		$p=15$ bar			$p=20$ bar	
273.15	30.82	174.5	4.2320	21.94	167.5	4.1584
280	31.93	180.9	4.2554	22.85	174.5	4.1837
290	33.50	190.4	4.2883	24.13	184.6	4.2189
300	35.03	199.7	4.3205	25.36	194.6	4.2529
310	36.53	209.4	4.3507	26.55	204.6	4.2858
320	38.00	219.0	4.3821	27.72	214.6	4.3173
330	39.71	228.6	4.4116	28.86	224.5	4.3479
340	40.89	238.2	4.4403	29.97	234.4	4.3775
350	42.30	247.8	4.4683	31.07	244.3	4.4062
360	43.71	257.1	4.4952	32.00	254.2	4.4338
370	45.10	267.1	4.5219	33.23	264.0	4.4610
380	46.48	276.8	4.5479	34.30	273.9	4.4875
390	47.85	286.5	4.5729	35.35	283.7	4.5130
400	49.21	296.3	4.5978	36.40	293.6	4.5382
410	50.57	306.1	4.6217	37.44	303.6	4.5624
420	51.92	316.4	4.6455	38.47	313.5	4.5866
430	53.27	325.8	4.6789	39.49	323.6	4.6101
440	54.61	335.8	4.6916	40.52	333.6	4.6332
450	55.95	345.8	4.7139	41.53	343.7	4.6558
460	57.28	355.8	4.7303	42.55	353.9	4.6783
470	58.61	366.0	4.7582	43.56	364.1	4.7003
480	59.94	376.4	4.7796	44.56	374.4	4.7219
490	61.26	386.4	4.7801	45.56	384.7	4.7434
500	62.58	396.7	4.8214	46.56	395.1	4.7640
510	63.90	407.1	4.8410	47.56	405.5	4.7847
520	65.21	417.6	4.8624	48.55	416.0	4.8053
530	66.53	428.1	4.8824	49.55	426.6	4.8254
540	67.83	438.6	4.9020	50.54	437.2	4.8451
550	68.53	449.2	4.9216	51.52	447.9	4.8648
560	70.45	454.9	4.9408	52.51	458.6	4.8840
570	71.75	470.7	4.9599	53.49	469.4	4.9032
580	73.06	481.3	4.9786	54.47	480.2	4.9220
590	74.35	492.2	4.9972	55.45	491.0	4.9408
600	75.66	503.1	5.0155	56.43	502.0	4.9591
620	78.25	525.0	5.0504	58.38	524.0	4.9949
640	80.83	547.0	5.0863	60.32	546.1	5.0302
660	83.41	569.3	5.1205	62.27	568.5	5.0645
680	85.99	591.8	5.1374	64.20	591.0	5.0980
700	88.57	614.4	5.1869	66.13	613.7	5.1311
720	91.14	637.3	5.2190	68.06	636.6	5.1632
740	93.71	660.2	5.2506	69.99	659.7	5.1949
760	96.28	683.4	5.2814	71.91	682.8	5.2258
780	98.83	706.7	5.3166	73.84	706.1	5.2560
800	101.4	730.1	5.3411	75.76	729.6	5.2857
850	109.0	789.3	5.4130	80.51	788.9	5.3577
900	114.1	849.3	5.4818	85.29	849.0	5.4266
950	120.5	910.1	5.5474	90.06	909.8	5.4922
1000	126.8	971.6	5.6104	94.83	971.4	5.5552
1050	133.2	1033.8	5.6590	99.59	1033.6	5.6161
1100	139.6	1096.6	5.7299	104.3	1096.8	5.6748
1150	151.0	1160.0	5.7862	109.1	1160.2	5.7311
1200	152.3	1224.0	5.8402	113.9	1223.8	5.7852
1250	158.6	1288.3	5.8931	118.6	1288.3	5.8381
1300	165.0	1353.2	5.9438	123.4	1353.1	5.8888
1350	171.3	1418.3	5.9932	128.1	1418.3	5.9383
1400	177.7	1484.0	6.0410	132.8	1484.0	5.9861
1450	184.0	1549.9	6.0871	137.6	1550.0	6.0322
1500	190.3	1616.2	6.1324	142.3	1616.2	6.0775
1600	203.1	1749.7	6.2183	151.8	1749.7	6.1634
1700	215.7	1884.1	6.2996	161.3	1884.3	6.2447
1800	228.4	2019.5	6.3771	170.7	2019.7	6.3222

continued

T, °K	v	i	s	v	i	s
		$p=25$ bar			$p=30$ bar	
273.15	16.62	159.6	4.0946	12.97	150.5	4.0344
280	17.43	167.3	4.1224	13.75	159.3	4.0661
290	18.56	178.2	4.1606	14.80	171.4	4.1083
300	19.63	189.0	4.1969	15.78	182.9	4.1475
310	20.65	199.5	4.2316	16.69	194.2	4.1844
320	21.64	210.0	4.2646	17.57	205.1	4.2191
330	22.60	220.3	4.2964	18.41	215.9	4.2522
340	23.53	230.5	4.3270	19.23	226.5	4.2839
350	24.45	240.7	4.3566	20.02	236.9	4.3144
360	25.35	250.8	4.3848	20.80	247.3	4.3434
370	26.24	260.8	4.4126	21.57	257.6	4.3718
380	27.11	270.9	4.4396	22.32	267.9	4.3994
390	27.98	280.9	4.4655	23.06	278.1	4.4257
400	28.84	291.0	4.4911	23.80	288.3	4.4517
410	29.69	301.0	4.5157	24.53	298.5	4.4766
420	30.53	311.1	4.5401	25.24	308.7	4.5014
430	31.37	321.3	4.5640	25.96	319.0	4.5255
440	32.21	331.4	4.5873	26.67	329.2	4.5490
450	33.04	341.6	4.6101	27.37	339.5	4.5721
460	33.86	351.9	4.6328	28.07	349.9	4.5950
470	34.68	362.2	4.6550	28.76	360.3	4.6174
480	35.50	372.6	4.6767	29.46	370.7	4.6393
490	36 31	383.0	4.6984	30.14	381.2	4.6612
500	37.12	393.4	4.7192	30.83	391.8	4.6821
510	37.93	403.9	4.7400	31.51	402.3	4.7030
520	38.73	414.5	4.7607	32.19	413.0	4.7239
530	39.54	425.1	4.7810	32.86	423.7	4.7443
540	40.34	435.8	4.8008	33.54	434.4	4.7642
550	41.13	446.5	4.8206	34.21	445.2	4.7841
560	41.93	457.3	4.8399	34.88	456.0	4.8035
570	42.72	468.1	4.8592	35.55	466.9	4.8229
580	43.52	479.0	4.8781	36.21	477.8	4.8419
590	44.31	489.9	4.8969	36.88	488.8	4.8608
600	45.09	500.9	4.9153	37.54	500.0	4.8793
620	46.67	523.0	4.9513	38.86	522.0	4.9154
640	48.23	545.2	4.9866	40.17	544.3	4.9509
660	49.80	567.7	5.0212	41.48	566.8	4.9855
680	51.35	590.2	5.0547	42.79	589.5	5.0192
700	52.91	613.0	5.0879	44.09	612.3	5.0524
720	54.46	635.9	5.1201	45.39	635.3	5.0847
740	56.01	659.0	5.1519	46.69	658.4	5.1165
760	57.56	682.2	5.1829	47.98	681.6	5.1476
780	59.10	705.6	5.2130	49.28	705.1	5.1779
800	60.64	729.1	5.2428	50.57	728.6	5.2077
850	64.45	788.5	5.3150	53.75	788.1	5.2799
900	68.29	848.6	5.3839	56.96	848.3	5.3489
950	72.12	909.5	5.4496	60.15	909.3	5.4147
1000	75.94	971.2	5.5126	63.35	970.9	5.4778
1050	79.76	1033.4	5.5736	66.53	1033.2	5.5387
1100	83.57	1096.3	5.6323	69.72	1096.5	5.5976
1150	87.38	1160.1	5.6887	72.90	1160.0	5.6539
1200	91.19	1223.8	5.7428	76.07	1223.7	5.7080
1250	94.99	1288.2	5.7956	79.25	1288.2	5.7610
1300	98.79	1353.1	5.8464	82.42	1353.1	5.8118
1350	102.6	1418.3	5.8959	85.59	1418.3	5.8613
1400	106.4	1484.0	5.9437	88.76	1484.0	5.9091
1450	110.2	1550.0	5.9899	91.93	1550.1	5.9553
1500	114.0	1616.3	6.0352	95.09	1616.4	6.0006
1600	121.6	1749.9	6.1211	101.4	1750.0	6.0865
1700	129.2	1884.4	6.2024	107.7	1884.6	6.1679
1800	136.7	2019.9	6.2800	114.1	2020.0	6.2454

continued

T, °K	v	i	s	v	i	s
		p=35 bar			p=40 bar	
273.15	1.078	−92.5	3.1243	1.073	−93.1	3.1205
280	11.04	150.1	4.0113	8.887	139.0	3.9541
290	12.07	163.8	4.0590	9.961	155.2	4.0106
300	12.99	176.4	4.1020	10.87	169.4	4.0586
310	13.85	188.5	4.1416	11.69	182.4	4.1015
320	14.65	200.1	4.1783	12.44	194.8	4.1406
330	15.41	211.3	4.2129	13.15	206.6	4.1770
340	16.15	222.3	4.2458	13.83	218.0	4.1212
350	16.86	233.1	4.2773	14.48	229.2	4.2438
360	17.55	243.8	4.3070	15.11	240.2	4.2744
370	18.23	254.3	4.3361	15.73	251.0	4.3042
380	18.90	264.8	4.3643	16.33	261.7	4.3229
390	19.55	275.2	4.3911	16.92	272.3	4.3603
400	20.20	285.6	4.4175	17.50	282.8	4.3872
410	20.84	295.9	4.4428	18.07	293.3	4.4122
420	21.47	306.3	4.4679	18.64	303.8	4.4382
430	22.09	316.7	4.4923	19.19	314.3	4.4629
440	22.71	327.0	4.5161	19.75	324.8	4.4870
450	23.35	337.4	4.5394	20.29	335.3	4.5105
460	23.94	347.9	4.5625	20.84	345.9	4.5339
470	24.54	358.4	4.5851	21.37	356.5	4.5567
480	25.14	368.9	4.6071	21.91	367.1	4.5790
490	25.74	379.5	4.6292	22.44	377.8	4.6012
500	26.33	390.1	4.6503	22.96	388.4	4.6224
510	26.93	400.8	4.6714	23.49	399.2	4.6436
520	27.51	411.5	4.6924	24.01	410.0	4.6648
530	28.10	422.2	4.7129	24.53	420.8	4.6854
540	28.68	433.0	4.7329	25.04	431.6	4.7056
550	29.27	443.9	4.7529	25.56	442.5	4.7257
560	29.84	454.8	4.7725	26.07	453.5	4.7454
570	30.42	465.7	4.7920	26.58	464.5	4.7650
580	31.00	476.6	4.8110	27.08	475.5	4.7841
590	31.57	487.7	4.8300	27.59	486.6	4.8032
600	32.14	498.8	4.8486	28.10	497.7	4.8218
620	33.28	521.0	4.8848	29.10	520.0	4.8582
640	34.42	543.4	4.9380	30.10	542.5	4.8939
660	35.55	566.0	4.9552	31.09	565.1	4.9287
680	36.67	588.7	4.9889	32.08	587.9	4.9626
700	37.79	611.6	5.0222	33.07	610.8	4.9960
720	38.91	634.6	5.0546	34.06	622.4	5.0284
740	40.03	657.9	5.0865	35.04	657.1	5.0604
760	41.15	681.0	5.1176	36.02	680.5	5.0915
780	42.26	704.5	5.1480	37.00	703.9	5.1221
800	43.37	728.1	5.1779	37.97	727.7	5.1517
850	46.11	787.7	5.2502	40.37	787.3	5.2244
900	48.86	848.0	5.3193	42.79	847.6	5.2936
950	51.61	909.0	5.3857	45.20	908.7	5.3594
1000	54.35	970.7	5.4482	47.61	970.5	5.4226
1050	57.09	1033.1	5.5092	50.01	1032.9	5.4836
1100	59.82	1096.3	5.5681	52.40	1096.2	5.5426
1150	62.55	1159.9	5.6245	54.80	1159.7	5.5990
1200	65.83	1223.4	5.6787	57.19	1223.5	5.6532
1250	68.01	1288.1	5.7316	59.57	1288.1	5.7061
1300	70.73	1353.1	5.7824	61.96	1353.1	5.7570
1350	73.45	1418.4	5.8319	64.34	1418.4	5.8065
1400	76.17	1484.1	5.8798	66.72	1484.2	5.8544
1450	78.88	1550.1	5.9260	69.10	1550.2	5.9006
1500	81.60	1616.5	5.9713	71.48	1616.6	5.9459
1600	87.03	1750.1	6.0573	76.23	1750.2	6.0319
1700	92.45	1884.7	6.1386	80.98	1884.9	6.1133
1800	97.87	2020.2	6.2162	85.73	2020.4	6.1909

continued

T, °K	v	i	s	v	i	s
		$p=45$ bar			$p=50$ bar	
273.15	1.068	−93.5	3.1168	1.063	−94.0	3.1133
280	1.126	−76.3	3.1792	1.118	−77.1	3.1744
290	8.244	145.2	3.9605	6.757	132.9	3.9050
300	9.182	161.5	4.0158	7.783	152.7	3.9721
310	9.988	175.9	4.0631	8.602	168.8	4.0252
320	10.71	189.2	4.1050	9.315	183.0	4.0707
330	11.39	201.6	4.1434	9.964	196.5	4.1116
340	12.02	213.6	4.1792	10.57	209.0	4.1491
350	12.63	225.2	4.2130	11.14	221.0	4.1842
360	13.21	236.5	4.2445	11.69	232.7	4.2168
370	13.78	247.6	4.2751	12.22	244.1	4.2482
380	14.33	258.5	2.3045	12.73	255.3	4.2782
390	14.87	269.5	4.3323	13.23	266.3	4.3067
400	15.40	280.0	4.3597	13.72	277.5	4.3345
410	15.92	290.7	4.3858	14.20	288.1	4.3610
420	16.45	301.4	4.4115	14.67	298.9	4.3871
430	16.94	312.0	4.4365	15.14	309.6	4.4124
440	17.44	322.6	4.4609	15.60	320.4	4.4371
450	17.93	332.2	4.4846	16.05	331.1	4.4611
460	18.42	343.9	4.5082	16.50	341.9	4.4849
470	18.91	354.6	4.5312	16.94	352.7	4.5082
480	19.39	365.3	4.5537	17.38	363.6	4.5309
490	19.87	376.0	4.5761	17.82	374.3	4.5534
500	20.34	386.8	4.5975	18.25	385.1	4.5750
510	20.82	397.6	4.6189	18.68	396.0	4.5965
520	21.28	408.5	4.6401	19.11	407.0	4.6179
530	21.75	419.3	4.6609	19.53	417.9	4.6388
540	22.21	430.2	4.6812	19.95	428.9	4.6592
550	22.67	441.2	4.7014	20.37	439.9	4.6796
560	23.13	452.2	4.7212	20.78	451.0	4.6994
570	23.59	463.3	4.7409	21.20	462.1	4.7192
580	24.04	474.3	4.7601	21.61	473.2	4.7385
590	24.50	485.5	4.7793	22.02	484.4	4.7578
600	24.95	496.6	4.7980	22.43	495.6	4.7766
620	25.85	519.0	4.8345	23.25	518.1	4.8132
640	26.74	541.6	4.8704	24.06	540.7	4.8492
660	27.63	564.3	4.9053	24.86	563.5	4.8842
680	28.52	587.1	4.9392	25.66	586.4	4.9182
700	29.40	610.6	4.9727	26.46	609.4	4.9517
720	30.28	621.7	5.0052	27.26	632.6	4.9843
740	31.16	656.5	5.0372	28.05	655.9	5.0164
760	32.03	679.9	5.0683	28.84	679.3	5.0476
780	32.90	703.4	5.0992	29.63	702.8	5.0782
800	33.78	727.1	5.1289	30.41	726.4	5.1082
850	35.92	786.9	5.2016	32.35	786.5	5.1811
900	38.07	847.3	5.2708	34.29	847.0	5.2504
950	40.22	908.4	5.3367	36.23	908.2	5.3163
1000	42.36	970.3	5.3999	38.16	970.0	5.3796
1050	44.50	1032.7	5.4610	40.09	1032.5	5.4408
1100	46.63	1096.1	5.5200	42.02	1095.9	5.4997
1150	48.76	1159.6	5.5764	43.94	1159.5	5.5562
1200	50.89	1223.5	5.6306	45.85	1223.4	5.6105
1250	53.01	1288.0	5.6836	47.47	1288.0	5.6635
1300	55.14	1353.1	5.7345	49.68	1353.0	5.7144
1350	57.26	1418.4	5.7841	51.59	1418.4	5.7639
1400	59.38	1484.2	5.8319	53.50	1484.2	5.8119
1450	61.49	1550.2	5.8781	55.41	1550.3	5.8581
1500	63.61	1616.6	5.9235	57.31	1616.7	5.9034
1600	67.84	1750.3	6.0095	61.12	1750.4	5.9895
1700	72.06	1885.0	6.0909	64.92	1885.1	6.0709
1800	76.28	2020.6	6.1685	68.72	2020.7	6.1485

continued

T, °K	v	i	s	v	i	s
		$p=55$ bar			$p=60$ bar	
273.15	1.059	−94.4	3.1098	1.054	−94.7	3.1066
280	1.111	−77.8	3.1698	1.105	−78.4	3.1654
290	1.236	−48.4	3.2726	1.218	−50.2	3.2642
300	6.574	142.2	3.9254	5.469	129.2	3.8719
310	7.438	161.0	3.9870	6.434	152.1	3.9474
320	8.155	176.8	4.0371	7.172	169.9	4.0035
330	8.791	191.0	4.0809	7.804	185.2	4.0508
340	9.374	204.2	4.1204	8.374	199.2	4.0927
350	9.921	216.8	4.1369	8.901	212.4	4.1309
360	10.44	228.8	4.1907	9.399	224.9	4.1659
370	10.94	240.5	4.2230	9.873	236.9	4.1991
380	11.42	252.0	4.2537	10.33	248.7	4.2307
390	11.89	263.3	4.2828	10.77	260.2	4.2603
400	12.34	274.4	4.3111	11.20	271.5	4.2892
410	12.79	285.4	4.3380	11.62	282.7	4.3166
420	13.23	296.4	4.3645	12.03	293.8	4.3435
430	13.66	307.2	4.3902	12.44	304.9	4.3695
440	14.09	318.1	4.4152	12.83	315.9	4.3948
450	14.51	329.0	4.4394	13.22	326.9	4.4193
460	14.92	339.9	4.4635	13.61	337.8	4.4436
470	15.33	350.8	4.4868	13.99	348.8	4.4673
480	15.74	361.6	4.5098	14.37	359.8	4.4904
490	16.14	372.6	4.5326	14.74	370.8	4.5133
500	16.54	383.5	4.5543	15.11	381.9	4.5352
510	16.93	394.5	4.5760	15.48	392.9	4.5571
520	17.32	405.5	4.5975	15.84	404.0	4.5788
530	17.71	416.5	4.6186	16.20	415.1	4.5999
540	18.10	427.6	4.6391	16.56	426.2	4.6206
550	18.48	438.6	4.6596	16.91	437.4	4.6412
560	18.86	449.8	4.6795	17.27	448.5	4.6612
570	19.24	460.9	4.6994	17.62	459.7	4.6812
580	19.62	472.1	4.7188	17.96	471.0	4.7007
590	20.00	483.3	4.7382	18.31	482.2	4.7202
600	20.37	494.6	4.7570	18.66	493.5	4.7391
620	20.75	517.1	4.7938	19.34	516.2	4.7760
640	21.86	539.8	4.8299	20.03	539.0	4.8122
660	22.59	562.7	4.8650	20.71	561.9	4.8474
680	23.33	585.6	4.8991	21.38	584.8	4.8816
700	24.06	608.7	4.9327	22.05	608.0	4.9152
720	24.78	631.9	4.9653	22.72	631.2	4.9479
740	25.51	655.2	4.9974	23.39	654.6	4.9801
760	26.23	678.7	5.0287	24.05	678.1	5.0113
780	26.96	702.2	5.0593	24.72	701.7	5.0433
800	27.67	725.9	5.0896	25.38	725.4	5.0725
850	29.43	786.2	5.1625	26.68	785.8	5.1455
900	31.20	846.7	5.2319	28.65	846.4	5.2149
950	32.97	907.9	5.2979	30.25	907.7	5.2810
1000	34.73	969.8	5.3612	31.87	969.2	5.3444
1050	36.49	1032.4	5.4224	33.48	1032.2	5.4056
1100	38.24	1095.8	5.4814	35.09	1095.7	5.4646
1150	39.99	1159.4	5.5379	36.70	1159.3	5.5212
1200	41.73	1223.3	5.5922	38.30	1223.3	5.5755
1250	43.48	1288.0	5.6452	39.90	1287.9	5.6285
1300	45.22	1353.0	5.6961	41.50	1353.0	5.6795
1350	46.95	1418.4	5.7457	43.09	1418.4	5.7291
1400	48.69	1484.2	5.7937	44.69	1484.3	5.7770
1450	50.43	1550.4	5.8399	46.28	1550.4	5.8233
1500	52.16	1616.8	5.8853	47.87	1616.9	5.8687
1600	55.63	1750.5	5.9713	51.05	1750.6	5.9548
1700	59.09	1885.3	6.0528	54.22	1885.4	6.0362
1800	62.54	2020.9	6.1304	57.39	2021.1	6.1139

continued

T, °K	v	i	s	v	i	s
		p=65 bar			p=70 bar	
273.15	1.050	−95.1	3.1034	1.047	−95.4	3.1003
280	1.099	−79.0	3.1613	1.093	−79.6	3.1574
290	1.203	−51.7	3.2569	1.191	−53.0	3.2502
300	4.338	110.1	3.8001	1.412	−15.2	3.3790
310	5.539	141.9	3.9047	4.712	129.4	3.8563
320	6.320	162.3	3.9694	5.569	153.9	3.9339
330	6.959	179.1	4.0211	6.225	172.6	3.9913
340	7.522	194.0	4.0657	6.786	188.6	4.0392
350	8.036	207.8	4.1058	7.291	203.1	4.0813
360	8.515	220.8	4.1421	7.757	216.6	4.1192
370	8.970	233.2	4.1764	8.196	229.4	4.1547
380	9.405	245.3	4.2088	8.614	241.8	4.1879
390	9.825	257.0	4.2391	9.015	253.9	4.2120
400	10.23	268.6	4.2686	9.404	265.7	4.2490
410	10.63	280.0	4.2964	9.781	277.2	4.2773
420	11.02	291.3	4.3237	10.15	288.7	4.3050
430	11.40	302.5	4.3501	10.51	300.1	4.3318
440	11.77	313.6	4.3757	10.86	311.4	4.3577
450	12.14	324.7	4.4005	11.21	322.6	4.3828
460	12.50	335.8	4.4257	11.55	335.8	4.4076
470	12.86	346.9	4.4490	11.89	345.0	4.4318
480	13.21	358.0	4.4723	12.22	356.2	4.4553
490	13.56	369.1	4.4954	12.55	367.4	4.4786
500	13.90	380.2	4.5175	12.87	378.6	4.5009
510	14.25	391.4	4.5395	13.19	389.8	4.5230
520	14.58	402.5	4.5613	13.51	401.0	4.5450
530	14.92	413.7	4.5826	13.82	412.3	4.5664
540	15.25	424.9	4.6034	14.14	423.5	4.5874
550	15.58	436.1	4.6241	14.45	434.8	4.6082
560	15.91	447.3	4.6443	14.75	446.1	4.6284
570	16.24	458.6	4.6644	15.06	457.4	4.6486
580	16.56	469.8	4.6840	15.36	468.7	4.6683
590	16.89	481.2	4.7035	15.66	480.1	4.6879
600	17.21	492.5	4.7225	15.96	491.5	4.7070
620	17.85	515.2	4.7595	16.56	514.3	4.7441
640	18.48	538.1	4.7958	17.15	537.2	4.7806
660	19.11	561.1	4.8311	17.74	560.3	4.8160
680	19.73	584.1	4.8654	18.32	583.3	4.8503
700	20.35	607.3	4.8991	18.91	606.6	4.8841
720	20.98	630.6	4.9318	19.49	629.9	4.9169
740	21.60	654.0	4.9640	20.06	653.3	4.9491
760	22.21	677.4	4.9953	20.64	676.8	4.9804
780	22.83	701.1	5.0261	21.21	700.5	5.0112
800	23.45	724.9	5.0566	21.80	724.4	5.0417
850	24.95	785.5	5.1298	23.19	785.2	5.1152
900	26.45	846.1	5.1993	24.59	845.8	5.1848
950	27.95	907.4	5.2654	25.98	907.2	5.2510
1000	29.45	969.4	5.3289	27.38	969.2	5.3145
1050	30.94	1032.0	5.3902	28.76	1031.9	5.3757
1100	32.43	1095.5	5.4492	30.15	1095.4	5.4349
1150	33.91	1159.2	5.5058	31.53	1159.2	5.4915
1200	35.39	1223.2	5.5601	32.90	1223.2	5.5458
1250	36.87	1287.9	5.6132	34.28	1287.9	5.5989
1300	38.35	1353.0	5.6641	35.65	1353.0	5.6499
1350	39.82	1418.4	5.7138	37.02	1418.5	5.6996
1400	41.30	1484.3	5.7617	38.39	1484.4	5.7475
1450	42.77	1550.5	5.8080	39.76	1550.6	5.7938
1500	44.24	1617.0	5.8534	41.12	1617.0	5.8392
1600	47.17	1750.8	5.9395	43.85	1750.9	5.9254
1700	50.10	1885.6	6.0210	46.57	1885.7	6.0069
1800	53.03	2021.3	6.0986	49.29	2021.4	6.0845

continued

T, °K	v	i	s	v	i	s
		p=75 bar			p=80 bar	
273.15	1.043	−95.7	3.0973	1.039	−96.0	3.0944
280	1.088	−80.1	3.1536	1.083	−80.6	3.1500
290	1.180	−54.2	3.2442	1.170	−55.3	3.2385
300	1.360	−19.8	3.3606	1.326	−23.2	3.3472
310	3.900	113.1	3.7967	3.006	87.8	3.7094
320	4.894	144.5	3.8963	4.276	133.7	3.8554
330	5.579	165.5	3.9610	5.103	157.9	3.9300
340	6.144	182.8	4.0128	5.577	176.8	3.9864
350	6.643	198.2	4.0574	6.073	193.1	4.0338
360	7.098	212.3	4.0970	6.521	207.9	4.0752
370	7.524	225.6	4.1336	6.936	221.7	4.1133
380	7.927	238.3	4.1678	7.327	234.8	4.1485
390	8.313	250.7	4.1996	7.700	247.4	4.1811
400	8.685	262.7	4.2303	8.058	259.7	4.2124
410	9.046	274.5	4.2592	8.404	271.7	4.2418
420	9.397	286.1	4.2873	8.739	283.6	4.2704
430	9.739	297.7	4.3144	9.067	295.2	4.2979
440	10.07	309.1	4.3407	9.387	306.8	4.3244
450	10.40	320.5	4.3661	9.700	318.3	4.3502
460	10.73	331.8	4.3912	10.01	329.8	4.3755
470	11.04	343.1	4.4155	10.31	341.2	4.4001
480	11.36	354.4	4.4392	10.61	352.6	4.4241
490	11.67	365.7	4.4627	10.90	364.0	4.4477
500	11.98	377.0	4.4852	11.19	375.4	4.4704
510	12.28	388.3	4.5075	11.48	386.7	4.4928
520	12.58	399.6	4.5296	11.76	398.1	4.5152
530	12.87	410.9	4.5512	12.04	409.5	4.5369
540	13.17	422.2	4.5723	12.32	420.9	4.5580
550	13.46	433.6	4.5932	12.60	432.3	4.5791
560	13.75	444.9	4.6136	12.87	443.7	4.5996
570	14.04	456.3	4.6339	13.14	455.2	4.6200
580	14.32	467.6	4.6536	13.41	466.6	4.6398
590	14.61	479.1	4.6733	13.68	478.0	4.6596
600	14.89	490.5	4.6925	13.95	489.5	4.6788
620	15.45	513.4	4.7297	14.47	512.5	4.7162
640	16.00	536.4	4.7663	15.00	535.5	4.7529
660	16.55	559.5	4.8018	15.52	558.7	4.7884
680	17.10	582.6	4.8362	16.03	581.9	4.8229
700	17.65	605.8	4.8700	16.55	605.2	4.8568
720	18.19	629.2	4.9029	17.06	628.6	4.8897
740	18.75	652.7	4.9352	17.57	652.1	4.9221
760	19.27	676.5	4.9665	18.08	675.6	4.9534
780	19.81	699.9	4.9973	18.58	699.4	4.9842
800	20.35	723.9	5.0276	19.09	723.4	5.0143
850	21.66	784.7	5.1020	20.32	784.3	5.0883
900	22.97	845.5	5.1715	21.56	845.2	5.1586
950	24.28	906.9	5.2375	22.78	906.7	5.2249
1000	25.58	969.0	5.3010	24.01	968.8	5.2884
1050	26.87	1031.7	5.3624	25.22	1031.5	5.3498
1100	28.17	1095.3	5.4215	26.44	1095.2	5.4090
1150	29.46	1159.1	5.4782	27.65	1159.0	5.4657
1200	30.75	1223.1	5.5325	28.86	1223.0	5.5201
1250	32.03	1287.8	5.5857	30.06	1287.8	5.5732
1300	33.31	1353.0	5.6366	31.27	1353.0	5.6242
1350	34.59	1418.5	5.6863	32.47	1418.5	5.6739
1400	35.87	1484.4	5.7343	33.67	1484.5	5.7220
1450	37.15	1550.6	5.7806	34.87	1550.7	5.7683
1500	38.42	1617.1	5.8260	36.06	1617.2	5.8137
1600	40.97	1751.0	5.9122	38.45	1751.1	5.8999
1700	43.52	1885.9	5.9937	40.84	1886.0	5.9814
1800	46.06	2021.6	6.0714	43.22	2021.8	6.0591

continued

T, °K	v	i	s	v	i	s
		p=90 bar			p=100 bar	
273.15	1.032	−96.4	3.0888	1.026	−96.9	3.0835
280	1.074	−81.4	3.1431	1.065	−82.2	3.1367
290	1.153	−57.0	3.2284	1.138	−58.5	3.2193
300	1.280	−27.9	3.3271	1.247	−31.3	3.3117
310	1.629	18.5	3.4792	1.458	4.4	3.4285
320	3.155	106.0	3.7572	2.237	69.9	3.6362
330	4.015	140.7	3.8641	3.199	120.3	3.7914
340	4.621	163.7	3.9331	3.846	149.2	3.8780
350	5.120	182.4	3.9873	4.354	170.9	3.9409
360	5.558	198.7	4.0330	4.787	189.0	3.9919
370	5.957	213.6	4.0740	5.175	205.2	4.0363
380	6.328	227.5	4.1115	5.531	220.1	4.0763
390	6.679	240.8	4.1458	5.865	234.1	4.1125
400	7.013	253.7	4.1784	6.181	247.5	4.1467
410	7.335	266.1	4.2090	6.483	260.5	4.1784
420	7.646	278.4	4.2385	6.775	273.1	4.2089
430	7.948	290.4	4.2668	7.056	285.5	4.2381
440	8.243	302.3	4.2941	7.330	297.7	4.2661
450	8.530	314.0	4.3204	7.597	309.8	4.2931
460	8.812	325.8	4.3463	7.858	321.7	4.3195
470	9.089	337.4	4.3714	8.113	333.6	4.3451
480	9.360	349.0	4.3958	8.364	345.4	4.3700
490	9.628	360.6	4.4199	8.610	357.2	4.3945
500	9.892	372.1	4.4429	8.853	368.9	4.4178
510	10.15	383.7	4.4657	9.091	380.7	4.4410
520	10.41	395.2	4.4883	9.327	392.4	4.4639
530	10.66	406.8	4.5103	9.560	404.0	4.4862
540	10.91	418.3	4.5318	9.790	415.7	4.5078
550	11.16	429.8	4.5530	10.02	427.4	4.5294
560	11.41	441.4	4.5737	10.24	439.0	4.5503
570	11.65	452.9	4.5943	10.47	450.7	4.5710
580	11.90	464.4	4.6143	10.69	462.3	4.5913
590	12.14	476.0	4.6343	10.91	474.0	4.6113
600	12.38	487.6	4.6537	11.13	485.6	4.6309
620	12.85	510.7	4.6913	11.56	508.9	4.6688
640	13.32	533.9	4.7282	11.98	532.2	4.7059
660	13.79	557.1	4.7639	12.41	555.6	4.7418
680	14.25	580.4	4.7986	12.83	579.0	4.7766
700	14.71	603.8	4.8326	13.25	602.4	4.8107
720	15.17	627.2	4.8656	13.66	625.9	4.8437
740	15.63	650.8	4.8980	14.08	649.6	4.8762
760	16.09	674.4	4.9294	14.49	673.2	4.9078
780	16.54	698.2	4.9603	14.91	697.0	4.9384
800	16.99	722.5	4.9906	15.32	721.5	4.9688
850	18.10	783.7	5.0646	16.32	782.9	5.0432
900	19.20	844.6	5.1354	17.32	844.1	5.1145
950	20.30	906.2	5.2018	18.31	905.7	5.1810
1000	21.39	968.4	5.2654	19.29	968.0	5.2447
1050	22.47	1031.2	5.3269	20.27	1030.9	5.3063
1100	23.56	1094.9	5.3861	21.25	1094.7	5.3656
1150	24.63	1158.8	5.4428	22.22	1158.4	5.4224
1200	25.71	1222.9	5.4973	23.20	1222.8	5.4769
1250	26.79	1287.8	5.5505	24.16	1287.7	5.5306
1300	28.86	1353.0	5.6016	25.13	1353.0	5.5812
1350	28.93	1418.6	5.6513	26.10	1418.6	5.6310
1400	30.00	1484.6	5.6993	27.06	1484.7	5.6791
1450	31.06	1550.8	5.7457	28.02	1551.0	5.7254
1500	32.13	1617.4	5.7911	28.98	1617.6	5.7709
1600	34.26	1751.4	5.8774	30.90	1751.6	5.8572
1700	36.38	1886.4	5.9589	32.81	1886.7	5.9388
1800	38.50	2022.1	6.0367	34.72	2022.5	6.0166

continued

T, °K	v	i	s	v	i	s
		p=120 bar			p=140 bar	
273.15	1.015	−97.5	3.0736	1.004	−98.0	3.0645
280	1.050	−83.3	3.1249	1.037	−84.2	3.1143
290	1.114	−60.9	3.2034	1.094	−62.7	3.1897
300	1.201	−36.0	3.2879	1.168	−39.2	3.2692
310	1.332	−7.2	3.3821	1.268	−13.4	3.3538
320	1.581	29.2	3.4977	1.420	15.7	3.4462
330	2.099	76.6	3.6434	1.671	50.1	3.5519
340	2.709	116.9	3.7639	2.051	87.5	3.6636
350	3.217	145.9	3.8480	2.474	120.6	3.7597
360	3.642	168.5	3.9117	2.864	147.3	3.8351
370	4.013	187.7	3.9644	3.211	169.7	3.8965
380	4.347	204.7	4.0101	3.524	189.1	3.9483
390	4.655	220.4	4.0505	3.810	206.5	3.9933
400	4.943	235.1	4.0879	4.076	222.6	4.0342
410	5.216	249.1	4.1222	4.326	237.7	4.0713
420	5.477	262.6	4.1549	4.564	252.1	4.1062
430	5.728	275.8	4.1859	4.792	266.1	4.1390
440	5.971	288.6	4.2154	5.011	279.6	4.1701
450	6.206	301.3	4.2437	5.223	292.9	4.1997
460	6.435	313.8	4.2713	5.420	305.9	4.2285
470	6.658	326.1	4.2979	5.629	318.7	4.2562
480	6.877	338.4	4.3237	5.823	331.4	4.2829
490	7.091	350.6	4.3490	6.014	344.0	4.3090
500	7.301	362.6	4.3731	6.201	356.5	4.3339
510	7.508	374.7	4.3969	6.384	368.9	4.3584
520	7.711	386.7	4.4205	6.564	381.2	4.3826
530	7.911	398.7	4.4433	6.741	393.5	4.4060
540	8.109	410.7	4.4655	6.915	405.7	4.4287
550	8.304	422.6	4.4875	7.087	417.9	4.4511
560	8.498	434.5	4.5088	7.257	430.0	4.4729
570	8.688	446.3	4.5300	7.425	442.1	4.4944
580	8.878	458.2	4.5506	7.591	454.1	4.5154
590	9.065	470.0	4.5710	7.755	466.2	4.5361
600	9.251	481.8	4.5908	7.918	478.2	4.5562
620	9.619	505.4	4.6292	8.240	502.0	4.5951
640	9.982	529.0	4.6667	8.557	525.9	4.6330
660	10.34	552.6	4.7029	8.871	549.7	4.6695
680	10.70	576.1	4.7380	9.182	573.4	4.7048
700	11.05	599.7	4.7723	9.490	597.1	4.7393
720	11.41	623.4	4.8055	9.798	620.9	4.7727
740	11.76	648.0	4.8382	10.10	644.7	4.8055
760	12.11	670.8	4.8698	10.41	668.5	4.8372
780	12.46	694.7	4.9007	10.71	692.4	4.8681
800	12.82	719.6	4.9311	11.02	717.7	4.8986
850	13.65	781.4	5.0072	11.75	780.3	4.9741
900	14.49	843.0	5.0776	12.47	841.9	5.0471
950	15.32	904.8	5.1448	13.19	904.0	5.1141
1000	16.14	967.3	5.2088	13.91	966.6	5.1781
1050	16.97	1030.4	5.2704	14.62	1029.8	5.2400
1100	17.79	1094.3	5.3299	15.32	1093.9	5.2996
1150	18.61	1158.4	5.3868	16.03	1158.1	5.3566
1200	19.42	1222.7	5.4414	16.73	1222.5	5.4113
1250	20.23	1287.7	5.4948	17.43	1287.7	5.4647
1300	21.04	1353.1	5.5459	18.12	1353.2	5.5160
1350	21.85	1418.8	5.5958	18.82	1418.9	5.5659
1400	22.65	1484.9	5.6439	19.51	1485.1	5.6141
1450	23.46	1551.3	5.6903	20.20	1551.6	5.6606
1500	24.26	1618.0	5.7359	20.89	1618.4	5.7062
1600	25.86	1752.2	5.8222	22.27	1752.7	5.7226
1700	27.47	1887.3	5.9039	23.64	1887.9	5.8744
1800	29.06	2023.2	5.9817	25.01	2024.0	5.9522

continued

T, °K	v	i	s	v	i	s
	$p=160$ bar			$p=180$ bar		
273.15	0.9953	−98.3	3.0560	0.9869	−98.5	3.0480
280	1.025	−84.9	3.1045	1.015	−85.4	3.0954
290	1.077	−64.0	3.1775	1.063	−65.4	3.1665
300	1.142	−41.6	3.2536	1.121	−43.4	3.2399
310	1.225	−17.6	3.3324	1.193	−20.6	3.3149
320	1.338	8.4	3.4146	1.284	3.5	3.3912
330	1.499	37.0	3.5025	1.405	29.1	3.4698
340	1.731	68.1	3.5956	1.567	56.3	3.5511
350	2.028	99.5	3.6866	1.774	84.4	3.6328
360	2.346	127.8	3.7664	2.016	111.8	3.7097
370	2.653	152.4	3.8339	2.269	137.0	3.7789
380	2.937	173.8	3.8911	2.517	159.6	3.8395
390	3.200	192.8	3.9405	2.754	179.9	3.8921
400	3.445	210.3	3.9847	2.977	198.5	3.9393
410	3.676	226.5	4.0245	3.188	215.7	3.9816
420	3.894	241.9	4.0617	3.389	231.9	4.0207
430	4.103	256.6	4.0963	3.581	247.4	4.0571
440	4.303	270.8	4.1290	3.765	262.3	4.0913
450	4.496	284.6	4.1600	3.943	276.7	4.1236
460	4.684	298.2	4.1899	4.114	290.8	4.1546
470	4.865	311.6	4.2186	4.281	304.5	4.1843
480	5.042	324.7	4.2462	4.442	318.1	4.2128
490	5.215	337.6	4.2732	4.600	331.4	4.2406
500	5.383	350.5	4.2988	4.754	344.6	4.2669
510	5.548	363.2	4.3240	4.905	357.7	4.2927
520	5.711	375.9	4.3487	5.053	370.7	4.3181
530	5.870	388.4	4.3727	5.198	383.5	4.3426
540	6.026	400.9	4.3959	5.341	396.3	4.3663
550	6.181	413.3	4.4188	5.481	408.9	4.3896
560	6.333	425.7	4.4410	5.619	421.5	4.4122
570	6.483	438.0	4.4629	5.755	434.0	4.4345
580	6.631	450.2	4.4842	5.890	446.4	4.4561
590	6.778	462.4	4.5052	6.023	458.8	4.4774
600	6.923	474.6	4.5256	6.154	471.2	4.4981
620	7.290	498.8	4.5650	6.414	495.6	4.5380
640	7.492	522.9	4.6033	6.668	519.9	4.5766
660	7.771	546.8	4.6401	6.920	544.1	4.6138
680	8.048	570.7	4.6756	7.169	568.1	4.6495
700	8.322	594.6	4.7104	7.416	592.1	4.6844
720	8.594	618.4	4.7439	7.662	616.1	4.7181
740	8.866	642.3	4.7767	7.906	640.0	4.7510
760	9.136	666.2	4.8086	8.149	664.0	4.7830
780	9.406	690.5	4.8400	8.392	688.9	4.8146
800	9.669	715.8	4.8711	8.639	714.0	4.8460
850	10.33	778.7	4.9471	9.221	777.4	4.9227
900	10.96	841.1	5.0201	9.793	840.0	4.9962
950	11.60	903.2	5.0872	10.36	902.4	5.0634
1000	12.23	966.0	5.1515	10.92	965.4	5.1278
1050	12.85	1029.4	5.2134	11.48	1028.9	5.1899
1100	13.47	1093.5	5.2732	12.04	1093.2	5.2497
1150	14.09	1157.9	5.3303	12.59	1157.7	5.3070
1200	14.71	1222.4	5.3851	13.14	1222.4	5.3619
1250	15.32	1287.7	5.4386	13.68	1287.7	5.4155
1300	15.93	1353.3	5.4899	14.23	1353.4	5.4669
1350	16.54	1419.1	5.5399	14.77	1419.3	5.5169
1400	17.15	1485.4	5.5882	15.32	1485.7	5.5653
1450	17.76	1552.0	5.6347	15.86	1552.4	5.6118
1500	18.36	1618.8	5.6804	16.40	1619.2	5.6575
1600	19.57	1753.2	5.7669	17.47	1753.8	5.7441
1700	20.77	1888.6	5.8487	18.54	1889.3	5.8260
1800	21.98	2024.8	5.9266	19.61	2025.5	5.9040

continued

T, °K	v	i	s	v	i	s
		$p=200$ bar			$p=250$ bar	
273.15	0.9791	−98.6	3.0404	0.9621	−98.5	3.0231
280	1.006	−85.8	3.0870	0.9856	−86.1	3.0678
290	1.050	−65.9	3.1564	1.024	−67.2	3.1341
300	1.103	−44.8	3.2277	1.068	−47.2	3.2017
310	1.167	−22.9	3.2999	1.119	−26.7	3.2692
320	1.245	− 0.1	3.3722	1.178	− 5.8	3.3554
330	1.343	23.7	3.4451	1.246	15.4	3.4006
340	1.467	48.4	3.5192	1.326	36.9	3.4649
350	1.622	74.0	3.5934	1.420	58.8	3.5283
360	1.806	99.6	3.6653	1.529	80.8	3.5902
370	2.009	124.2	3.7329	1.652	102.8	3.6507
380	2.218	147.1	3.7942	1.786	124.4	3.7085
390	2.425	168.2	3.8487	1.928	145.2	3.7624
400	2.625	187.6	3.8980	2.073	165.2	3.8130
410	2.817	205.6	3.9422	2.218	184.1	3.8595
420	3.001	222.5	3.9832	2.361	202.1	3.9030
430	3.177	238.6	4.0211	2.501	219.3	3.9435
440	3.346	254.1	4.0566	2.638	235.8	3.9875
450	3.510	269.0	4.0901	2.771	251.8	4.0172
460	3.668	283.6	4.1222	2.901	267.3	4.0514
470	3.822	297.8	4.1528	3.028	282.4	4.0840
480	3.971	311.8	4.1821	3.151	297.2	4.1151
490	4.116	325.5	4.2107	3.272	311.7	4.1452
500	4.258	339.0	4.2377	3.390	326.0	4.1737
510	4.397	352.4	4.2641	3.505	340.0	4.2015
520	4.533	365.6	4.2900	3.618	353.9	4.2287
530	4.666	378.8	4.3150	3.729	367.6	4.2548
540	4.798	391.8	4.3393	3.838	381.2	4.2801
550	4.926	404.6	4.3630	3.945	394.6	4.3048
560	5.053	417.4	4.3860	4.050	408.0	4.3287
570	5.178	430.2	4.4086	4.154	421.1	4.3522
580	5.301	442.8	4.4305	4.257	434.2	4.3749
590	5.423	455.3	4.4522	4.358	447.1	4.3972
600	5.543	467.8	4.4731	4.457	460.0	4.4188
620	5.780	492.6	4.5134	4.653	485.4	4.4602
640	6.013	517.1	4.5524	4.846	510.5	4.5001
660	6.243	541.5	4.5899	5.035	545.3	4.5382
680	6.470	565.7	4.6259	5.222	559.9	4.5748
700	6.695	589.8	4.6609	5.407	584.3	4.6102
720	6.807	613.8	4.6948	5.591	608.6	4.6444
740	7.141	637.9	4.7278	5.773	632.6	4.6777
760	7.363	662.1	4.7598	5.955	657.4	4.7098
780	7.584	687.0	4.7915	6.140	682.9	4.7420
800	7.810	712.3	4.8230	6.320	708.3	4.7738
850	8.338	776.3	4.9004	6.753	773.3	4.8516
900	8.856	839.2	4.9737	7.175	837.2	4.9268
950	9.369	901.8	5.0419	7.591	900.2	4.9960
1000	9.980	964.9	5.1065	8.004	963.7	5.0609
1050	10.38	1028.5	5.1687	8.413	1027.7	5.1235
1100	10.89	1093.0	5.2287	8.820	1092.4	5.1838
1150	11.39	1157.6	5.2860	9.225	1157.3	5.2414
1200	11.88	1222.3	5.3410	9.625	1222.3	5.2966
1250	12.38	1287.7	5.3947	10.03	1288.0	5.3505
1300	12.87	1353.5	5.4462	10.42	1354.0	5.4021
1350	13.36	1419.6	5.4963	10.82	1420.0	5.4524
1400	13.85	1486.0	5.5447	11.21	1486.9	5.5009
1450	14.34	1552.7	5.5913	11.60	1553.8	5.5477
1500	14.83	1619.7	5.6370	12.00	1620.9	5.5935
1600	15.80	1754.4	5.7237	12.78	1755.9	5.6804
1700	16.76	1890.0	5.8057	13.55	1891.8	5.7625
1800	17.73	2026.3	5.8837	14.33	2028.3	5.8407

continued

T, °K	v	i	s	v	i	s
		p=300 bar			p=400 bar	
273.15	0.9475	−98.0	3.0075	0.9235	−96.2	2.9799
280	0.9687	−86.0	3.0509	0.9416	−84.7	3.0214
290	1.003	−67.7	3.1149	0.9699	−67.3	3.0823
300	1.041	−48.5	3.1799	1.001	−49.1	3.1439
310	1.084	−28.8	3.2444	1.034	−30.6	3.2048
320	1.132	− 9.0	3.3072	1.071	−12.0	3.2637
330	1.186	10.8	3.3682	1.110	6.4	3.3203
340	1.247	30.7	3.4277	1.152	24.7	3.3749
350	1.315	50.7	3.4857	1.198	42.8	3.4274
360	1.392	70.7	3.5419	1.248	60.8	3.4779
370	1.478	90.7	3.5970	1.302	78.7	3.5272
380	1.571	110.7	3.6505	1.359	96.6	3.5751
390	1.672	130.4	3.7014	1.421	114.4	3.6213
400	1.777	149.7	3.7504	1.486	132.2	3.6664
410	1.886	168.4	3.7963	1.553	149.8	3.7097
420	1.996	186.6	3.8403	1.623	167.3	3.7518
430	2.106	204.1	3.8816	1.695	184.5	3.7923
440	2.216	221.2	3.9207	1.768	201.4	3.8312
450	2.324	237.6	3.9576	1.842	218.1	3.8685
460	2.431	253.7	3.9931	1.916	234.4	3.9046
470	2.536	269.4	4.0269	1.989	250.5	3.9393
480	2.639	284.8	4.0592	2.063	266.4	3.9726
490	2.740	299.8	4.0905	2.136	282.0	4.0050
500	2.839	314.6	4.1201	2.208	297.4	4.0358
510	2.937	329.2	4.1489	2.279	312.5	4.0658
520	3.033	343.6	4.1771	2.350	327.5	4.0950
530	3.127	357.8	4.2042	2.421	342.3	4.1233
540	3.220	371.9	4.2302	2.490	356.9	4.1504
550	3.311	385.8	4.2558	2.559	371.4	4.1770
560	3.401	399.4	4.2804	2.627	385.6	4.2027
570	3.490	413.0	4.3046	2.694	399.7	4.2278
580	3.577	426.4	4.3279	2.761	413.7	4.2521
590	3.663	439.7	4.3508	2.827	427.5	4.2758
600	3.749	452.9	4.3730	2.893	441.2	4.2988
620	3.916	478.9	4.4153	3.022	468.1	4.3426
640	4.081	504.5	4.4560	3.149	494.5	4.3846
660	4.242	529.8	4.4948	3.274	520.4	4.4244
680	4.402	554.7	4.5319	3.397	545.9	4.4624
700	4.559	579.4	4.5678	3.519	571.1	4.4990
720	4.716	603.9	4.6022	3.640	596.0	4.5340
740	4.871	628.2	4.6358	3.760	620.9	4.5680
760	5.025	653.5	4.6681	3.879	646.9	4.6013
780	5.179	678.8	4.7002	3.997	672.5	4.6347
800	5.333	704.7	4.7314	4.115	699.0	4.6683
850	5.703	770.6	4.8107	4.399	766.2	4.7483
900	6.059	835.5	4.8872	4.673	833.0	4.8259
950	6.410	898.9	4.9579	4.942	897.0	4.8970
1000	6.758	962.7	5.0232	5.208	961.5	4.9629
1050	7.103	1027.0	5.0861	5.472	1026.3	5.0263
1100	7.445	1092.1	5.1467	5.733	1091.9	5.0874
1150	7.785	1157.2	5.2045	5.992	1157.5	5.1456
1200	8.122	1222.5	5.2600	6.248	1223.3	5.2015
1250	8.458	1288.4	5.3140	6.504	1289.6	5.2559
1300	8.791	1354.6	5.3658	6.757	1356.2	5.3090
1350	9.123	1421.1	5.4163	7.009	1423.0	5.3587
1400	9.454	1487.9	5.4649	7.260	1490.2	5.4076
1450	9.784	1555.0	5.5118	7.510	1557.6	5.4547
1500	10.11	1622.2	5.5577	7.759	1625.2	5.5009
1600	10.77	1757.5	5.6448	8.254	1761.0	5.5883
1700	11.42	1893.6	5.7271	8.746	1897.5	5.6708
1800	12.07	2030.4	5.8054	9.236	2034.7	5.7493

continued

T, °K	v	i	s	v	i	s
		$p=500$ bar			$p=600$ bar	
273.15	0.9040	−93.7	2.9556	0.8875	−90.8	2.9333
280	0.9200	−82.5	2.9961	0.9022	−79.7	2.9734
290	0.9447	−65.6	3.0549	0.9242	−63.2	3.0310
300	0.9710	−48.1	3.1143	0.9474	−46.2	3.0889
310	0.9992	−30.2	3.1731	0.9719	−28.7	3.1461
320	1.029	−12.4	3.2297	0.9976	−11.3	3.2013
330	1.061	5.3	3.2840	1.024	5.9	3.2541
340	1.094	22.7	3.3360	1.053	22.7	3.3046
350	1.130	39.8	3.3659	1.082	39.3	3.3529
360	1.167	56.8	3.4334	1.113	55.7	3.3987
370	1.207	73.6	3.4798	1.145	71.9	3.4433
380	1.249	90.4	3.5247	1.178	88.0	3.4864
390	1.295	107.2	3.5680	1.213	104.0	3.5278
400	1.340	123.9	3.6105	1.250	120.0	3.5686
410	1.389	140.6	3.6515	1.288	136.1	3.6080
420	1.439	157.3	3.6918	1.327	152.2	3.6468
430	1.491	173.8	3.7309	1.367	168.2	3.6847
440	1.544	190.4	3.7688	1.409	184.3	3.7216
450	1.597	206.8	3.8054	1.451	200.4	3.7575
460	1.652	223.0	3.8413	1.494	216.4	3.7929
470	1.707	239.1	3.8759	1.537	232.3	3.8272
480	1.762	255.0	3.9093	1.580	248.1	3.8604
490	1.817	270.7	3.9419	1.624	263.8	3.8930
500	1.872	286.2	3.9730	1.668	279.4	3.9242
510	1.926	301.6	4.0034	1.711	294.9	3.9547
520	1.981	316.8	4.0331	1.755	310.2	3.9846
530	2.035	331.8	4.0618	1.798	325.3	4.0134
540	2.089	346.7	4.0895	1.842	340.3	4.0413
550	2.142	361.4	4.1166	1.885	355.1	4.0686
560	2.196	376.0	4.1427	1.928	369.8	4.0950
570	2.249	390.4	4.1683	1.971	384.3	4.1208
580	2.301	404.6	4.1930	2.013	398.6	4.1458
590	2.354	418.6	4.2173	2.056	412.8	4.1702
600	2.406	432.6	4.2407	2.098	426.9	4.1938
620	2.509	460.0	4.2853	2.183	454.5	4.2389
640	2.611	486.9	4.3281	2.267	481.6	4.2819
660	2.712	513.3	4.3686	2.350	508.2	4.3228
680	2.812	539.2	4.4071	2.434	534.3	4.3617
700	2.911	564.7	4.4443	2.517	560.5	4.3991
720	3.010	590.4	4.4798	2.599	587.0	4.4353
740	3.107	616.0	4.5150	2.682	613.0	4.4713
760	3.204	641.7	4.5493	2.764	639.0	4.5072
780	3.301	668.0	4.5833	2.845	664.9	4.5412
800	3.400	694.3	4.6175	2.925	691.5	4.5750
850	3.626	762.6	4.6995	3.115	760.1	4.6578
900	3.848	830.6	4.7768	3.303	828.9	4.7378
950	4.067	896.0	4.8488	3.488	895.6	4.8088
1000	4.284	960.9	4.9153	3.671	961.0	4.8758
1050	4.498	1026.3	4.9792	3.851	1026.8	4.9401
1100	4.710	1092.3	5.0406	4.030	1093.3	5.0020
1150	4.919	1158.4	5.0993	4.207	1159.8	5.0610
1200	5.128	1224.6	5.1555	4.382	1226.3	5.1175
1250	5.334	1291.3	5.2102	4.556	1293.4	5.1725
1300	5.539	1358.3	5.2626	4.729	1360.6	5.2252
1350	5.743	1425.4	5.3136	4.901	1428.1	5.2764
1400	5.946	1492.9	5.3627	5.071	1495.8	5.3257
1450	6.148	1560.5	5.4100	5.241	1563.8	5.3732
1500	6.349	1628.4	5.4563	5.410	1631.9	5.4197
1600	6.748	1764.7	5.5441	5.745	1768.6	5.5077
1700	7.145	1901.6	5.6269	6.077	1906.0	5.5907
1800	7.539	2039.2	5.7056	6.408	2043.9	5.6697

Heat capacity c_p (kJ/kg · deg) of carbon dioxide at different temperatures and pressures [57, 58]

T, °K \ p, bar →	1	10	20	40	60	80	100	120	140	160	180	200	250	300	350	400	450	500	550	600
273.15	0.822	0.891	1.04	2.42	2.28	2.17	2.09	2.02	1.97	1.93	1.89	1.85	1.79	1.74	1.70	1.67	1.65	1.64	1.64	1.64
280	0.830	0.892	1.02	1.78	2.51	2.34	2.22	2.14	2.07	2.01	1.96	1.92	1.84	1.78	1.74	1.70	1.67	1.65	1.63	1.62
290	0.841	0.900	1.01	1.49	3.28	2.76	2.51	2.36	2.25	2.17	2.10	2.05	1.95	1.88	1.83	1.78	1.75	1.72	1.70	1.68
300	0.851	0.910	1.00	1.35	2.83	3.93	3.00	2.65	2.45	2.32	2.23	2.15	2.03	1.95	1.89	1.84	1.81	1.78	1.75	1.73
310	0.862	0.917	1.00	1.27	1.95	9.21	4.47	3.16	2.72	2.49	2.34	2.24	2.07	1.98	1.91	1.86	1.82	1.79	1.77	1.75
320	0.872	0.924	0.995	1.21	1.63	2.91	7.20	4.28	3.15	2.71	2.48	2.32	2.10	1.98	1.91	1.85	1.81	1.78	1.75	1.73
330	0.881	0.929	0.992	1.16	1.46	2.08	3.55	4.71	3.70	3.00	2.64	2.42	2.14	1.99	1.90	1.83	1.79	1.75	1.73	1.70
340	0.891	0.934	0.989	1.13	1.35	1.73	2.43	3.37	3.62	3.19	2.79	2.52	2.17	1.99	1.89	1.82	1.76	1.73	1.70	1.67
350	0.900	0.939	0.987	1.11	1.28	1.54	1.96	2.52	2.98	3.02	2.81	2.57	2.20	2.00	1.89	1.80	1.75	1.70	1.67	1.65
360	0.908	0.943	0.986	1.09	1.23	1.42	1.70	2.06	2.43	2.64	2.64	2.53	2.21	2.01	1.88	1.80	1.73	1.69	1.65	1.63
370	0.917	0.948	0.986	1.07	1.19	1.34	1.54	1.79	2.06	2.28	2.39	2.38	2.18	2.00	1.88	1.79	1.73	1.68	1.64	1.61
380	0.926	0.953	0.986	1.06	1.16	1.28	1.44	1.62	1.82	2.01	2.14	2.20	2.13	1.99	1.87	1.79	1.72	1.68	1.64	1.60
390	0.934	0.959	0.988	1.06	1.14	1.24	1.37	1.51	1.67	1.81	1.94	2.02	2.04	1.95	1.86	1.78	1.72	1.67	1.63	1.60
400	0.942	0.964	0.991	1.05	1.13	1.21	1.32	1.43	1.55	1.68	1.78	1.86	1.94	1.90	1.83	1.77	1.72	1.67	1.63	1.60
410	0.950	0.970	0.995	1.05	1.11	1.19	1.28	1.37	1.47	1.58	1.67	1.74	1.85	1.84	1.80	1.75	1.71	1.67	1.64	1.61
420	0.958	0.976	0.999	1.05	1.11	1.17	1.25	1.33	1.42	1.50	1.58	1.65	1.76	1.78	1.77	1.73	1.70	1.66	1.63	1.61
430	0.966	0.983	1.00	1.05	1.10	1.16	1.23	1.30	1.37	1.44	1.51	1.58	1.68	1.73	1.73	1.71	1.68	1.66	1.63	1.61
440	0.973	0.989	1.01	1.05	1.10	1.15	1.21	1.28	1.34	1.40	1.46	1.52	1.62	1.68	1.69	1.68	1.66	1.64	1.63	1.61
450	0.981	0.996	1.01	1.05	1.10	1.15	1.20	1.26	1.31	1.37	1.42	1.47	1.57	1.63	1.65	1.65	1.64	1.63	1.62	1.60
460	0.988	1.00	1.02	1.06	1.10	1.14	1.19	1.24	1.29	1.34	1.39	1.44	1.53	1.59	1.61	1.62	1.62	1.61	1.61	1.60
470	0.995	1.01	1.02	1.06	1.10	1.14	1.18	1.23	1.28	1.32	1.37	1.41	1.49	1.55	1.58	1.60	1.60	1.60	1.59	1.59
480	1.00	1.01	1.03	1.06	1.10	1.14	1.18	1.22	1.26	1.30	1.34	1.38	1.46	1.52	1.56	1.57	1.58	1.58	1.58	1.58
490	1.01	1.02	1.04	1.07	1.10	1.14	1.18	1.21	1.25	1.29	1.33	1.36	1.42	1.49	1.53	1.55	1.56	1.56	1.56	1.56
500	1.02	1.03	1.04	1.07	1.10	1.14	1.17	1.21	1.24	1.28	1.31	1.34	1.40	1.47	1.51	1.53	1.54	1.55	1.55	1.55

continued

T, °K \ p, bar →	1	10	20	40	60	80	100	120	140	160	180	200	250	300	350	400	450	500	550	600
550	1.05	1.06	1.07	1.09	1.12	1.14	1.17	1.19	1.21	1.24	1.26	1.28	1.34	1.38	1.41	1.44	1.45	1.46	1.47	1.48
600	1.08	1.08	1.09	1.11	1.13	1.15	1.16	1.18	1.20	1.21	1.23	1.24	1.28	1.31	1.34	1.36	1.37	1.38	1.39	1.40
650	1.10	1.11	1.12	1.13	1.14	1.16	1.17	1.18	1.19	1.20	1.21	1.22	1.24	1.26	1.28	1.30	1.31	1.31	1.32	1.33
700	1.13	1.13	1.14	1.15	1.15	1.17	1.17	1.18	1.19	1.19	1.20	1.20	1.22	1.23	1.24	1.25	1.26	1.27	1.28	1.28
750	1.15	1.15	1.16	1.17	1.17	1.18	1.18	1.19	1.19	1.20	1.20	1.21	1.22	1.23	1.23	1.24	1.24	1.25	1.25	1.26
800	1.17	1.17	1.18	1.18	1.19	1.20	1.20	1.20	1.21	1.21	1.21	1.22	1.23	1.24	1.24	1.25	1.26	1.26	1.27	1.27
850	1.19	1.19	1.19	1.20	1.20	1.21	1.21	1.22	1.22	1.23	1.23	1.24	1.24	1.25	1.26	1.26	1.26	1.28	1.28	1.28
900	1.20	1.21	1.21	1.21	1.22	1.22	1.23	1.23	1.24	1.24	1.24	1.25	1.25	1.26	1.27	1.28	1.28	1.28	1.29	1.29
950	1.22	1.22	1.22	1.23	1.23	1.23	1.24	1.24	1.25	1.25	1.25	1.26	1.26	1.27	1.28	1.28	1.29	1.30	1.30	1.30
1000	1.23	1.24	1.24	1.24	1.24	1.25	1.25	1.26	1.26	1.26	1.26	1.27	1.27	1.28	1.29	1.29	1.30	1.30	1.31	1.31
1050	1.25	1.25	1.25	1.25	1.26	1.26	1.26	1.27	1.27	1.27	1.28	1.28	1.28	1.29	1.30	1.30	1.31	1.31	1.32	1.32
1100	1.26	1.26	1.26	1.27	1.27	1.27	1.27	1.28	1.28	1.28	1.28	1.29	1.29	1.30	1.30	1.31	1.31	1.32	1.32	1.33
1150	1.27	1.27	1.27	1.28	1.28	1.28	1.28	1.29	1.29	1.29	1.29	1.30	1.30	1.31	1.31	1.32	1.32	1.32	1.33	1.33
1200	1.28	1.28	1.28	1.29	1.29	1.29	1.29	1.30	1.30	1.30	1.30	1.31	1.31	1.32	1.32	1.32	1.33	1.33	1.34	1.34
1250	1.29	1.29	1.29	1.30	1.30	1.30	1.30	1.30	1.31	1.31	1.31	1.31	1.32	1.32	1.32	1.33	1.33	1.34	1.34	1.34
1300	1.30	1.30	1.30	1.30	1.31	1.31	1.31	1.31	1.31	1.32	1.32	1.32	1.32	1.33	1.33	1.34	1.34	1.34	1.34	1.35
1400	1.31	1.31	1.32	1.32	1.32	1.32	1.32	1.32	1.33	1.33	1.33	1.33	1.33	1.34	1.34	1.34	1.35	1.35	1.35	1.36
1500	1.33	1.33	1.33	1.33	1.33	1.33	1.33	1.34	1.34	1.34	1.34	1.34	1.34	1.35	1.35	1.35	1.36	1.36	1.36	1.36
1600	1.34	1.34	1.34	1.34	1.34	1.34	1.34	1.35	1.35	1.35	1.35	1.35	1.35	1.36	1.36	1.36	1.36	1.37	1.37	1.37
1700	1.35	1.35	1.35	1.35	1.35	1.35	1.35	1.36	1.36	1.36	1.36	1.36	1.36	1.36	1.37	1.37	1.37	1.37	1.37	1.38
1800	1.36	1.36	1.36	1.36	1.36	1.36	1.36	1.36	1.36	1.36	1.37	1.37	1.37	1.37	1.37	1.38	1.38	1.38	1.38	1.38

Sound velocity u (m/s) and adiabatic exponent k for carbon dioxide at different temperatures and pressures [57, 58]

p, bar →	1		10		20		40		60	
T, °K	u	k	u	k	u	k	u	k	u	k
300	269.4	1.287	262.9	1.284	254.9	1.281	233.9	1.280	210.5	1.350
350	289.0	1.267	284.7	1.263	279.9	1.261	270.4	1.263	261.5	1.281
400	307.3	1.252	304.7	1.252	302.1	1.254	297.3	1.263	293.4	1.281
450	324.4	1.239	323.0	1.242	321.7	1.246	319.3	1.256	317.5	1.271
500	340.6	1.229	340.0	1.233	339.4	1.237	338.3	1.246	337.7	1.258
550	356.0	1.221	355.9	1.224	355.8	1.228	355.6	1.237	355.6	1.246
600	370.8	1.213	371.0	1.217	371.2	1.221	371.7	1.229	372.3	1.238
650	385.0	1.207	385.4	1.211	385.9	1.215	386.9	1.223	388.0	1.232
700	398.7	1.202	399.3	1.206	400.0	1.210	401.5	1.218	403.1	1.228
750	411.9	1.197	412.6	1.201	413.5	1.205	415.3	1.214	417.3	1.224
800	424.6	1.193	425.5	1.197	426.4	1.201	428.7	1.209	430.9	1.221
850	437.1	1.190	438.0	1.193	439.0	1.197	441.2	1.206	443.8	1.216
900	449.1	1.186	450.1	1.190	451.3	1.194	453.7	1.203	456.2	1.212
950	460.9	1.184	462.0	1.187	463.2	1.191	465.7	1.200	468.3	1.208
1000	472.4	1.181	473.5	1.184	474.8	1.188	477.4	1.197	480.1	1.205
1050	483.6	1.179	484.8	1.182	486.1	1.186	488.7	1.194	491.5	1.202
1100	494.6	1.177	495.7	1.180	497.1	1.184	499.8	1.192	502.6	1.200
1150	505.3	1.175	506.5	1.178	507.8	1.182	510.6	1.190	513.5	1.197
1200	515.8	1.173	517.0	1.176	518.4	1.180	521.2	1.188	524.1	1.195
1300	536.2	1.170	537.5	1.174	538.9	1.177	541.7	1.184	544.6	1.191
1400	555.9	1.168	557.2	1.171	558.6	1.174	561.5	1.181	564.4	1.188
1500	574.9	1.166	576.2	1.169	577.6	1.172	580.5	1.179	583.4	1.185
1600	593.4	1.164	594.6	1.167	596.1	1.170	598.9	1.176	601.8	1.183
1700	611.3	1.163	612.5	1.166	614.0	1.169	616.8	1.174	619.7	1.180
1800	628.6	1.162	629.9	1.164	631.3	1.167	634.4	1.173	637.0	1.178

p, bar →	80		100		120		140		160	
T, °K	u	k	u	k	u	k	u	k	u	k
300	347.1	11.35	411.1	13.56	457.9	14.55	496.0	15.05	528.7	15.30
350	254.2	1.330	249.6	1.431	250.3	1.623	260.9	1.965	285.0	2.503
400	290.5	1.309	289.0	1.351	289.1	1.409	291.2	1.487	295.9	1.588
450	316.4	1.290	316.1	1.315	316.7	1.347	318.3	1.386	321.0	1.433
500	337.5	1.272	337.8	1.289	338.7	1.310	340.3	1.334	342.7	1.364
550	356.0	1.257	356.8	1.271	358.1	1.287	359.9	1.306	362.3	1.327
600	373.1	1.248	374.4	1.260	376.1	1.274	378.2	1.290	380.8	1.309
650	389.4	1.242	391.1	1.254	393.2	1.268	395.7	1.284	398.6	1.301
700	405.0	1.239	407.2	1.252	409.7	1.265	412.6	1.281	415.7	1.298
750	419.9	1.236	422.4	1.248	425.2	1.262	428.1	1.276	431.3	1.291
800	433.6	1.232	436.4	1.245	439.2	1.257	442.2	1.271	445.4	1.285
850	446.6	1.227	449.6	1.239	452.5	1.250	455.4	1.262	458.6	1.276
900	458.9	1.221	461.7	1.232	464.6	1.243	467.6	1.253	470.7	1.265
950	471.1	1.218	473.9	1.227	476.9	1.237	479.9	1.247	483.1	1.258
1000	482.9	1.214	485.8	1.223	488.8	1.233	491.8	1.242	495.0	1.252
1050	494.4	1.211	497.3	1.220	500.3	1.229	503.4	1.238	506.5	1.248
1100	505.5	1.208	508.5	1.217	511.5	1.225	514.6	1.234	517.7	1.243
1150	516.4	1.206	519.3	1.214	522.4	1.222	525.4	1.231	528.6	1.239
1200	527.0	1.203	530.0	1.211	533.0	1.219	536.1	1.227	539.2	1.236
1300	547.6	1.199	550.6	1.206	553.6	1.214	556.6	1.220	559.7	1.229
1400	567.3	1.195	570.3	1.202	573.3	1.209	576.3	1.216	579.4	1.223
1500	586.4	1.192	589.3	1.198	592.3	1.205	595.3	1.212	598.3	1.218
1600	604.7	1.189	607.7	1.195	610.6	1.201	613.6	1.208	616.6	1.214
1700	622.6	1.186	625.5	1.192	628.4	1.198	631.3	1.204	634.3	1.210
1800	639.9	1.184	642.7	1.190	645.6	1.195	648.5	1.201	651.4	1.207

p, bar →	180		200		250		300		350	
T, °K	u	k	u	k	u	k	u	k	u	k
300	557.5	15.40	585.6	15.43	639.7	15.32	687.0	15.11	728.4	14.88
350	318.2	3.170	353.0	3.843	430.9	5.229	494.0	6.184	546.7	6.845
400	303.4	1.717	314.0	1.877	351.7	2.387	397.4	2.962	441.2	3.505

continued

T, °K ↓ / p, bar →	180		200		250		300		350	
	u	k	u	k	u	k	u	k	u	k
450	325.0	1.489	330.3	1.554	349.2	1.760	374.9	2.016	404.9	2.299
500	345.8	1.397	349.6	1.435	362.5	1.551	379.6	1.691	399.9	1.851
550	365.2	1.352	368.7	1.380	379.5	1.460	392.9	1.554	408.5	1.659
600	383.8	1.330	387.2	1.353	397.4	1.417	409.4	1.490	422.9	1.570
650	401.8	1.320	405.3	1.340	415.5	1.397	426.9	1.460	439.2	1.526
700	419.2	1.316	422.7	1.336	432.8	1.388	443.8	1.444	454.8	1.502
750	434.8	1.306	438.4	1.325	447.8	1.370	458.3	1.418	469.2	1.468
800	448.8	1.301	452.5	1.317	461.7	1.357	471.8	1.398	482.0	1.441
850	461.8	1.290	465.4	1.303	474.2	1.339	483.8	1.374	493.5	1.411
900	473.9	1.277	477.2	1.288	486.0	1.320	495.2	1.355	504.8	1.386
950	486.3	1.268	489.6	1.279	498.1	1.307	506.9	1.336	516.0	1.366
1000	498.2	1.262	501.4	1.273	509.9	1.299	518.6	1.326	527.5	1.354
1050	509.7	1.257	513.0	1.267	521.3	1.292	529.9	1.318	538.7	1.344
1100	520.9	1.252	524.1	1.262	532.4	1.285	540.9	1.310	549.5	1.334
1150	531.7	1.248	535.0	1.257	543.1	1.279	551.5	1.302	560.0	1.326
1200	542.4	1.244	545.6	1.252	553.7	1.274	562.0	1.296	570.3	1.318
1300	562.8	1.237	566.0	1.245	574.0	1.264	582.1	1.285	590.2	1.304
1400	582.5	1.231	585.6	1.238	593.4	1.256	601.4	1.275	609.3	1.294
1500	601.4	1.225	604.4	1.232	612.1	1.249	619.9	1.267	627.7	1.284
1600	619.6	1.221	622.6	1.227	630.2	1.243	637.8	1.260	645.5	1.276
1700	637.2	1.216	640.2	1.222	647.6	1.238	665.1	1.253	662.6	1.268
1800	654.3	1.213	657.2	1.218	664.6	1.233	671.9	1.247	679.3	1.262

T, °K ↓ / p, bar →	400		450		500		550		600	
	u	k	u	k	u	k	u	k	u	k
300	765.5	14.64	799.3	14.42	830.5	14.21	859.6	14.01	886.9	13.84
350	592.2	7.315	632.5	7.660	668.8	7.919	702.1	8.119	732.9	8.275
400	486.5	3.983	526.5	4.391	563.5	4.740	597.9	5.038	630.1	5.295
450	436.6	2.588	458.6	2.868	500.1	3.132	530.6	3.377	560.1	3.604
500	422.6	2.023	446.9	2.201	471.9	2.380	497.2	2.566	522.4	2.728
550	426.0	1.773	444.9	1.894	465.1	2.019	486.0	2.148	507.5	2.278
600	437.5	1.654	453.3	1.744	470.2	1.838	488.0	1.936	506.5	2.038
650	452.1	1.595	466.3	1.667	481.4	1.743	497.0	1.823	513.5	1.906
700	467.0	1.562	479.7	1.624	493.4	1.688	507.6	1.751	522.4	1.814
750	480.6	1.521	492.2	1.574	504.6	1.626	517.3	1.679	530.0	1.735
800	493.3	1.484	504.0	1.530	515.3	1.574	526.9	1.619	538.4	1.665
850	503.6	1.448	514.5	1.486	525.5	1.524	536.6	1.563	547.5	1.604
900	514.8	1.418	524.8	1.451	535.0	1.484	545.4	1.517	556.0	1.553
950	525.4	1.396	534.8	1.427	544.4	1.457	554.0	1.488	564.3	1.518
1000	536.7	1.382	545.9	1.411	555.2	1.439	564.0	1.468	573.9	1.496
1050	547.6	1.370	556.6	1.397	565.8	1.423	574.9	1.450	584.0	1.476
1100	558.3	1.359	567.1	1.384	576.0	1.409	585.0	1.434	593.9	1.459
1150	568.7	1.349	577.4	1.373	586.1	1.396	594.8	1.420	603.6	1.443
1200	578.8	1.340	587.4	1.363	596.0	1.385	604.5	1.408	613.1	1.430
1300	598.5	1.325	606.8	1.346	615.1	1.366	623.4	1.386	631.7	1.406
1400	617.4	1.312	625.4	1.331	633.5	1.350	641.6	1.369	649.6	1.387
1500	635.6	1.302	643.4	1.319	651.3	1.336	659.2	1.354	667.0	1.371
1600	653.1	1.292	660.8	1.308	668.5	1.324	676.2	1.341	683.8	1.357
1700	670.2	1.284	677.7	1.299	685.2	1.314	692.7	1.329	700.1	1.344
1800	686.6	1.276	694.0	1.291	701.4	1.305	708.7	1.319	716.0	1.333

Thermodynamic properties of liquid carbon dioxide at different temperatures and pressures [53, 54]: v (dm³/kg), i (kJ/kg), s and c_p (kJ/kg · deg)

T, °K	v	i	s	c_p	v	i	s	c_p
	$p=10$ bar				$p=20$ bar			
220	0.8566	−199.9	2.701	1.82	0.8550	−199.6	2.698	1.82
225	0.8702	−190.8	2.740	1.85	0.8684	−190.6	2.737	1.84
230	0.8850	−181.5	2.780	1.83	0.8829	−181.3	2.777	1.87

continued

T, °K	v	i	s	c_p	v	i	s	c_p
235					0.8985	−171.9	2.816	1.91
240					0.9156	−162.5	2.856	1.95
245					0.9343	−152.6	2.897	2.00
250					0.9551	−142.6	2.938	2.06
	p=30 bar				p=40 bar			
220	0.8534	−199.3	2.696	1.81	0.8519	−199.1	2.693	1.80
225	0.8666	−190.4	2.735	1.83	0.8649	−190.1	2.732	1.82
230	0.8808	−181.1	2.774	1.86	0.8789	−181.0	2.771	1.85
235	0.8962	−171.7	2.813	1.90	0.8939	−171.6	2.810	1.88
240	0.9129	−162.4	2.853	1.94	0.9102	−162.3	2.849	1.92
245	0.9311	−152.7	2.893	1.98	0.9279	−152.6	2.889	1.96
250	0.9511	−142.8	2.934	2.03	0.9474	−142.8	2.930	2.01
255	0.9734	−132.6	2.975	2.10	0.9690	−132.8	2.970	2.07
260	0.9985	−122.1	3.016	2.18	0.9930	−122.4	3.011	2.14
265	1.0271	−111.1	3.058	2.28	1.0202	−111.6	3.052	2.23
270					1.0516	−100.3	3.094	2.35
275					1.0887	−88.5	3.138	2.51
	p=50 bar				p=60 bar			
220	0.8504	−198.7	2.691	1.79	0.8490	−198.4	2.688	1.79
225	0.8632	−189.8	2.729	1.82	0.8616	−189.6	2.727	1.81
230	0.8769	−180.7	2.768	1.84	0.8750	−180.4	2.765	1.83
235	0.8917	−171.4	2.806	1.87	0.8895	−171.3	2.803	1.86
240	0.9076	−162.2	2.846	1.91	0.9051	−162.1	2.843	1.89
245	0.9249	−152.6	2.886	1.95	0.9220	−152.5	2.882	1.93
250	0.9439	−142.9	2.926	1.99	0.9405	−142.9	2.922	1.97
255	0.9647	−133.0	2.966	2.05	0.9606	−133.1	1.961	2.02
260	0.9878	−122.8	3.006	2.11	0.9830	−123.1	3.001	2.08
265	1.0138	−112.2	3.046	2.19	1.0078	−112.6	3.041	2.16
270	1.0434	−101.0	3.088	2.29	1.0359	−101.6	3.082	2.25
275	1.0779	−89.6	3.130	2.43	1.0683	−90.5	3.123	2.36
280	1.1193	−77.0	3.175	2.62	1.1063	−78.4	3.166	2.52
285	1.1715	−63.0	3.224	2.93	1.1528	−65.0	3.213	2.75
	p=70 bar				p=80 bar			
220	0.8475	−198.1	2.686	1.78	0.8461	−197.8	2.683	1.77
225	0.8599	−189.3	2.724	1.80	0.8584	−189.0	2.722	1.79
230	0.8732	−180.2	1.762	1.82	0.8714	−180.0	2.760	1.82
235	0.8874	−171.1	2.800	1.85	0.8854	−170.9	2.798	1.84
240	0.9027	−162.0	2.840	1.88	0.9004	−161.8	2.836	1.87
245	0.9192	−152.5	2.879	1.92	0.9165	−152.4	2.875	1.90
250	0.9372	−142.9	2.918	1.96	0.9340	−142.9	2.914	1.94
255	0.9568	−133.2	2.957	2.00	0.9531	−133.3	2.953	1.98
260	0.9783	−123.3	2.996	2.06	0.9740	−123.5	2.992	2.04
265	1.0022	−113.0	3.036	2.12	0.9970	−113.3	3.031	2.09
270	1.0290	−102.2	3.076	2.20	1.0226	−102.6	3.070	2.17
275	1.0595	−91.3	3.116	2.30	1.0514	−92.0	3.110	2.25
280	1.0948	−79.5	3.158	2.43	1.0845	−80.5	3.151	2.36
285	1.1370	−66.7	3.203	2.61	1.1232	−68.1	3.195	2.51
	p=90 bar				p=100 bar			
220	0.8448	−197.4	2.681	1.77	0.8434	−197.1	2.679	1.76
225	0.8568	−188.7	2.719	1.78	0.8553	−188.4	2.717	1.78
230	0.8697	−179.8	2.757	1.81	0.8680	−179.4	2.754	1.80
235	0.8834	−170.7	2.795	1.83	0.8815	−170.4	2.792	1.82
240	0.8981	−161.7	2.833	1.86	0.8959	−161.5	2.830	1.85
245	0.9139	−152.3	2.872	1.89	0.9114	−152.2	2.869	1.88
250	0.9310	−142.9	2.911	1.93	0.9281	−142.9	2.907	1.91
255	0.9496	−133.4	2.949	1.97	0.9462	−133.4	2.945	1.95
260	0.9698	−123.6	2.987	2.01	0.9658	−123.7	2.983	2.00
265	0.9920	−113.5	3.026	2.07	0.9873	−113.8	3.021	2.04
270	1.0166	−103.2	3.065	2.13	1.0109	−103.4	3.060	2.10
275	1.0440	−92.6	3.104	2.21	1.0372	−93.1	3.098	2.17

continued

T, °K	v	i	s	c_p	v	i	s	c_p
280	1.0752	−81.3	3.144	2.31	1.0662	−82.1	3.137	2.26
285	1.1111	−69.3	3.186	2.43	1.1002	−70.3	3.179	2.36
290	1.1537	−56.6	3.230	2.60	1.1394	−58.0	3.221	2.50
		$p=125$ bar				$p=150$ bar		
220	0.8402	−196.3	2.673	1.75	0.8371	−195.4	2.668	1.73
225	0.8517	−187.6	2.711	1.76	0.8482	−186.8	2.705	1.75
230	0.8639	−178.8	2.749	1.78	0.8600	−178.0	2.742	1.76
235	0.8768	−169.8	2.785	1.80	0.8725	−169.2	2.778	1.78
240	0.8907	−161.0	2.823	1.82	0.8858	−160.4	2.816	1.80
245	0.9054	−151.8	2.861	1.85	0.8999	−151.4	2.853	1.83
250	0.9213	−142.6	2.899	1.88	0.9149	−142.3	2.891	1.85
255	0.9385	−133.3	2.938	1.92	0.9310	−133.2	2.928	1.88
260	0.9574	−123.9	2.973	1.95	0.9483	−123.9	2.964	1.92
265	0.9765	−114.1	3.010	1.99	0.9668	−114.4	3.000	1.95
270	0.9981	−104.1	3.048	2.04	0.9869	−104.5	3.037	1.99
275	1.0218	−94.1	3.085	2.10	1.0086	−94.8	3.073	2.04
280	1.0480	−83.5	3.123	2.16	1.0323	−84.6	3.110	2.08
285	1.0771	−72.3	3.162	2.23	1.0582	−73.8	3.148	2.14
290	1.1101	−60.8	3.202	2.32	1.0870	−62.8	3.185	2.20
295	1.1479	−49.4	3.241	2.43	1.1191	−52.0	3.222	2.27
300					1.1556	−40.5	3.261	2.37
		$p=175$ bar				$p=200$ bar		
225	0.8449	−186.0	2.699	1.73	0.8418	−185.1	2.694	1.72
230	0.8563	−177.2	2.736	1.75	0.8528	−176.4	2.730	1.74
235	0.8684	−168.5	2.772	1.77	0.8645	−167.8	2.766	1.75
240	0.8811	−159.8	2.809	1.78	0.8768	−159.2	2.803	1.77
245	0.8947	−150.9	2.846	1.80	0.8898	−150.3	2.840	1.78
250	0.9090	−142.0	2.883	1.83	0.9036	−141.5	2.876	1.81
255	0.9246	−133.0	2.919	1.86	0.9182	−132.6	2.912	1.83
260	0.9410	−123.6	2.955	1.88	0.9337	−123.6	2.947	1.86
265	0.9581	−114.4	2.991	1.92	0.9502	−114.4	2.982	1.88
270	0.9768	−104.8	3.027	1.95	0.9678	−104.9	3.018	1.92
275	0.9969	−95.3	3.062	1.99	0.9865	−95.6	3.052	1.95
280	1.0186	−85.3	3.098	2.03	1.0066	−85.8	3.087	1.98
285	1.0422	−74.8	3.135	2.07	1.0283	−75.6	3.123	2.02
290	1.0679	−64.2	3.171	2.12	1.0516	−65.3	3.158	2.05
295	1.0961	−53.9	3.207	2.17	1.0769	−55.5	3.193	2.09
300	1.1273	−43.0	3.243	2.23	1.1045	−44.8	3.228	2.14
305	1.1625	−31.6	3.280	2.31	1.1349	−34.0	3.263	2.19
		$p=250$ bar				$p=300$ bar		
225	0.8358	−183.3	2.673	1.70	0.8304	−181.3	2.673	1.68
230	0.8463	−174.7	2.719	1.71	0.8403	−172.9	2.709	1.69
235	0.8572	−166.2	2.754	1.72	0.8506	−164.5	2.744	1.70
240	0.8687	−157.8	2.791	1.74	0.8615	−156.2	2.779	1.71
245	0.8809	−149.1	2.827	1.75	0.8728	−147.6	2.815	1.72
250	0.8936	−140.4	2.862	1.77	0.8847	−139.1	2.850	1.74
255	0.9070	−131.7	2.897	1.79	0.8971	−130.6	2.884	1.75
260	0.9212	−122.9	2.932	1.81	0.9102	−122.0	2.918	1.77
265	0.9361	−113.9	2.966	1.83	0.9239	−113.2	2.952	1.79
270	0.9519	−104.7	3.001	1.86	0.9383	−104.2	2.985	1.82
275	0.9686	−95.7	3.034	1.88	0.9534	−95.4	3.018	1.84
280	0.9863	−86.9	3.068	1.91	0.9693	−86.2	3.050	1.86
285	1.0050	−76.4	3.102	1.94	0.9860	−76.6	3.084	1.88
290	1.0249	−66.5	3.136	1.96	1.0036	−67.0	3.117	1.90
295	1.0462	−57.1	3.169	1.98	1.0221	−58.0	3.148	1.91
300	1.0689	−47.2	3.202	2.01	1.0416	−48.4	3.180	1.93
305	1.0932	−37.1	3.235	2.04	1.0622	−38.7	3.213	1.94
310	1.1195	−26.9	3.269	2.07	1.0841	−29.1	3.244	1.96
315	1.1480	−16.4	3.302	2.11	1.1074	−19.1	3.275	1.98
320					1.1322	−9.2	3.306	2.00

continued

T, °K	v	i	s	c_p	v	i	s	c_p
	p=350 bar				p=400 bar			
225	0.8253	−179.3	2.664	1.66				
230	0.8347	−171.0	2.699	1.67	0.8295	−169.0	2.689	1.65
235	0.8445	−162.7	2.733	1.68	0.8389	−160.8	2.723	1.66
240	0.8548	−154.5	2.769	1.69	0.8487	−152.7	2.758	1.67
245	0.8655	−146.0	2.803	1.70	0.8588	−144.3	2.793	1.68
250	0.8767	−137.7	2.838	1.71	0.8693	−136.1	2.827	1.69
255	0.8883	−129.3	2.872	1.73	0.8803	−127.8	2.860	1.70
260	0.9005	−120.8	2.905	1.74	0.8917	−119.4	2.893	1.72
265	0.9132	−112.2	2.938	1.76	0.9036	−110.9	2.926	1.73
270	0.9264	−103.3	2.971	1.78	0.9159	−102.2	2.958	1.75
275	0.9403	−94.8	3.003	1.80	0.9288	−93.8	2.990	1.77
280	0.9548	−85.7	3.035	1.82	0.9421	−85.0	3.021	1.78
285	0.9699	−76.4	3.068	1.83	0.9560	−75.8	3.053	1.80
290	0.9857	−67.0	3.100	1.85	0.9704	−66.6	3.084	1.81
295	1.0022	−58.2	3.130	1.86	0.9854	−58.0	3.114	1.82
300	1.0195	−48.9	3.161	1.87	1.0010	−48.9	3.144	1.83
305	1.0376	−39.5	3.192	1.88	1.0173	−39.7	3.175	1.84
310	1.0566	−30.2	3.223	1.89	1.0341	−30.5	3.205	1.84
315	1.0765	−20.6	3.253	1.90	1.0517	−21.3	3.234	1.85
320	1.0974	−11.2	3.283	1.91	1.0700	−12.1	3.263	1.85
	p=450 bar				p=500 bar			
230	0.8247	−166.9	2.680	1.64	0.8202	−164.8	2.672	1.62
235	0.8337	−158.8	2.714	1.64	0.8287	−156.7	2.705	1.63
240	0.8430	−150.8	2.749	1.65	0.8376	−148.8	2.739	1.63
245	0.8526	−142.5	2.783	1.66	0.8468	−140.6	2.773	1.64
250	0.8626	−134.4	2.816	1.67	0.8564	−132.5	2.806	1.65
255	0.8730	−126.2	2.849	1.68	0.8662	−124.5	2.839	1.66
260	0.8837	−117.9	2.882	1.69	0.8764	−116.3	2.871	1.68
265	0.8948	−109.6	2.914	1.71	0.8870	−108.0	2.903	1.69
270	0.9065	−101.0	2.946	1.73	0.8979	−99.6	2.934	1.71
275	0.9185	−92.7	2.977	1.74	0.9092	−91.4	2.965	1.72
280	0.9309	−84.0	3.008	1.76	0.9208	−82.8	2.995	1.73
285	0.9438	−74.9	3.040	1.77	0.9328	−73.8	3.027	1.75
290	0.9571	−65.9	3.070	1.78	0.9452	−64.9	3.057	1.76
295	0.9709	−57.4	3.100	1.79	0.9580	−56.5	3.086	1.76
300	0.9851	−48.5	3.129	1.80	0.9712	−47.8	3.115	1.77
305	0.9999	−39.5	3.159	1.80	0.9848	−38.9	3.144	1.77
310	1.0152	−30.6	3.188	1.81	0.9988	−30.1	3.174	1.78
315	1.0310	−21.4	3.217	1.81	0.0133	−21.2	3.202	1.78
320	1.0473	−12.5	3.245	1.81	1.0281	−12.4	3.229	1.78
	p=550 bar				p=600 bar			
230	0.8159	−162.6	2.663	1.61	0.8118	−160.4	2.655	1.60
235	0.8241	−154.6	2.697	1.62	0.8198	−152.4	2.688	1.60
240	0.8327	−148.7	2.731	1.62	0.8280	−144.6	2.722	1.61
245	0.8415	−138.6	2.764	1.63	0.8364	−136.6	2.755	1.61
250	0.8506	−130.6	2.797	1.63	0.8452	−128.7	2.788	1.62
255	0.8600	−122.6	2.829	1.64	0.8541	−120.7	2.820	1.63
260	0.8697	−114.6	2.861	1.66	0.8634	−112.7	2.852	1.64
265	0.8797	−106.4	2.892	1.67	0.8730	−104.6	2.882	1.66
270	0.8900	−98.0	2.924	1.69	0.8828	−96.3	2.913	1.67
275	0.9007	−89.9	2.954	1.70	0.8930	−88.3	2.943	1.68
280	0.9117	−81.4	2.984	1.71	0.9033	−79.9	2.973	1.70
285	0.9230	−72.5	3.015	1.73	0.9140	−71.1	3.004	1.71
290	0.9346	−63.7	3.045	1.74	0.9249	−62.4	3.034	1.72
295	0.9466	−55.5	3.074	1.74	0.9362	−54.2	3.062	1.72
300	0.9589	−46.8	3.102	1.75	0.9477	−45.7	3.090	1.73
305	0.9715	−38.2	3.131	1.75	0.9596	−37.0	3.119	1.73
310	0.9845	−29.4	3.160	1.75	0.9717	−28.5	3.147	1.73
315	0.9978	−20.6	3.187	1.75	0.9841	−19.7	3.174	1.73
320	1.0115	−11.9	3.215	1.75	0.9968	−11.1	3.202	1.73

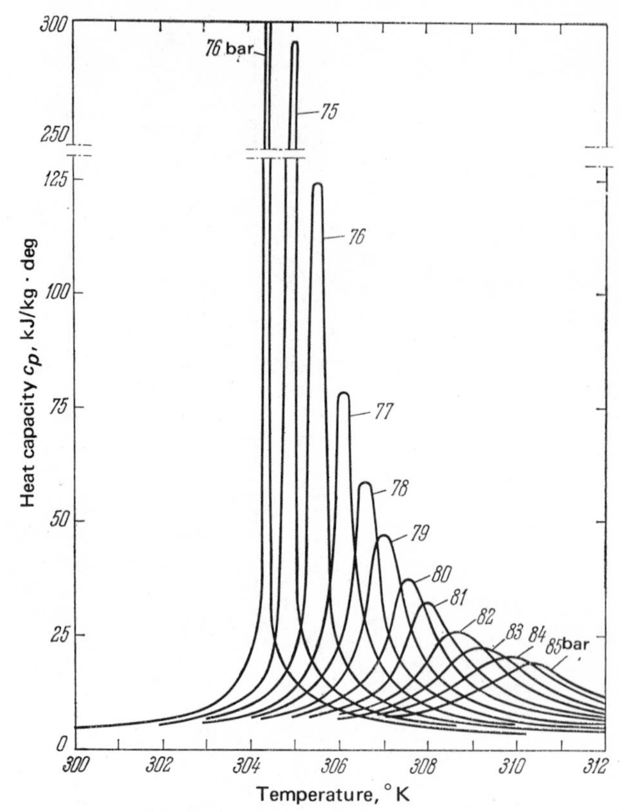

Fig. 10. Heat capacity of carbon dioxide near the critical state (p_{cr} = 73.815 bar, T_{cr} = 304.19°K). Temperatures at which the heat capacity of carbon dioxide reaches a maximum value at different pressures are given in the table below:

Pressure, bar	75	76	77	78	79	80	85	90	95	100
Temperature, °K	304.9	305.5	306.0	306.5	307.0	307.5	310.6	313.0	315.6	318.0

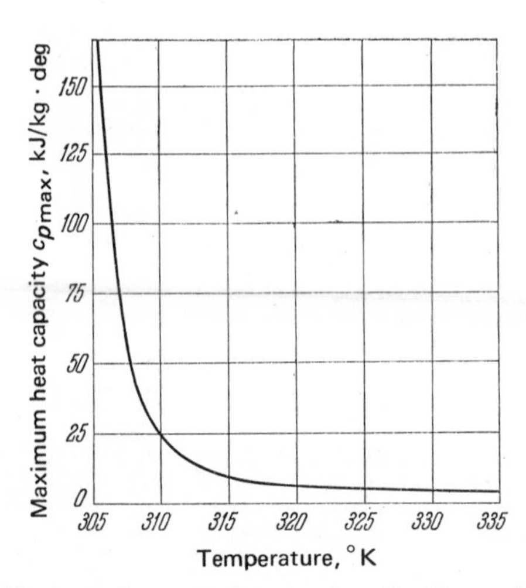

Fig. 11. Maximum heat capacity of carbon dioxide as a function of temperature.

Thermodynamic properties of carbon dioxide in the critical region [57, 58]:
v (dm^3/kg), i (kJ/kg) s and c_p (kJ/kg · deg)

T, °K	v	i	s	c_p	v	i	s	c_p
	$p=60$ bar				$p=61$ bar			
300	5.469	129.2	3.8719	2.83	5.252	126.1	3.8597	3.06
301	5.585	131.9	3.8812	2.67	5.374	129.2	3.8697	2.86
302	5.694	134.6	3.8898	2.54	5.488	131.8	3.8789	2.70
303	5.799	137.0	3.8980	2.43	5.597	134.4	3.8876	2.57
304.19	5.912	139.8	3.9073	2.32	5.718	137.4	3.8973	2.44
305	5.995	141.7	3.9134	2.25	5.800	139.4	3.9039	2.36
306	6.088	143.9	3.9206	2.18	5.895	141.6	3.9114	2.27
307	6.178	146.0	3.9277	2.11	5.987	143.9	3.9187	2.20
308	6.266	148.1	3.9344	2.05	6.077	146.0	3.9257	2.13
309	6.351	150.2	3.9410	2.00	6.163	148.2	3.9325	2.07
310	6.434	152.1	3.9474	1.95	6.247	150.2	3.9391	2.01
311	6.514	154.0	3.9536	1.91	6.329	152.2	3.9456	1.97
312	6.593	155.9	3.9597	1.87	6.409	154.1	3.9518	1.92
313	6.670	157.8	3.9656	1.83	6.487	156.1	3.9579	1.88
314	6.746	159.6	3.9713	1.79	6.563	157.9	3.9638	1.84
315	6.820	161.4	3.9774	1.76	6.638	159.7	3.9700	1.81
316	6.893	163.1	3.9825	1.73	6.712	161.5	3.9752	1.77
317	6.964	164.9	3.9879	1.70	6.783	163.3	3.9808	1.74
318	7.034	166.6	3.9933	1.68	6.854	165.0	3.9863	1.72
319	7.103	168.2	3.9985	1.65	6.924	166.7	3.9916	1.69
320	7.171	169.8	4.0035	1.63	6.992	168.4	3.9968	1.66
	$p=62$ bar				$p=63$ bar			
300	5.033	122.7	3.8467	3.36	4.809	119.0	3.8327	3.74
301	5.162	125.9	3.8575	3.10	4.949	122.5	3.8447	3.39
302	5.283	128.9	3.8675	2.90	5.077	125.8	3.8555	3.14
303	5.396	131.7	3.8767	2.74	5.197	128.8	3.8654	2.93
304.19	5.524	134.9	3.8872	2.58	5.330	132.2	3.8765	2.73
305	5.607	136.9	3.8940	2.48	5.416	134.4	3.8838	2.62
306	5.705	139.3	3.9019	2.38	5.518	136.9	3.8921	2.51
307	5.800	141.7	3.9095	2.30	5.615	139.4	3.8991	2.40
308	5.891	143.9	3.9169	2.22	5.709	141.7	3.9078	2.31
309	5.980	146.1	3.9239	2.15	5.800	144.0	3.9151	2.24
310	6.065	148.2	3.9308	2.09	5.886	146.2	3.9223	2.17
311	6.148	150.3	3.9375	2.03	5.971	148.3	3.9292	2.10
312	6.229	152.2	3.9439	1.98	6.054	150.3	3.9358	2.05
313	6.308	154.3	3.9502	1.94	6.134	152.4	3.9423	1.99
314	6.386	156.2	3.9562	1.89	6.212	154.4	3.9487	1.94
315	6.461	158.0	3.9626	1.85	6.288	156.3	3.9550	1.91
316	6.535	159.9	3.9679	1.82	6.363	158.2	3.9606	1.87
317	6.607	161.7	3.9737	1.79	6.436	160.0	3.9665	1.83
318	6.679	163.5	3.9793	1.76	6.508	161.9	3.9722	1.80
319	6.748	165.2	3.9847	1.73	6.578	163.7	3.9778	1.76
320	6.817	166.9	3.9900	1.70	6.647	165.4	3.9831	1.74
	$p=64$ bar				$p=65$ bar			
300	4.579	114.8	3.8174	4.26	4.338	110.1	3.8001	5.01
301	4.732	118.8	3.8308	3.77	4.509	114.7	3.8156	4.29
302	4.870	122.4	3.8427	3.43	4.660	118.8	3.8290	3.80
303	4.997	125.7	3.8535	3.16	4.796	122.4	3.8409	3.45
304.19	5.137	129.3	3.8655	2.92	4.944	126.3	3.8538	3.14
305	5.227	131.7	3.8732	2.79	5.038	128.8	3.8621	2.98
306	5.322	134.3	3.8820	2.65	5.148	131.6	3.8715	2.81
307	5.433	136.9	3.8905	2.53	5.253	134.4	3.8804	2.67
308	5.529	139.4	3.8984	2.42	5.352	137.0	3.8889	2.54
309	5.622	141.8	3.9062	2.33	5.448	139.5	3.8970	2.44
310	5.711	144.1	3.9136	2.25	5.539	141.9	3.9047	2.35
311	5.798	146.3	3.9207	2.18	5.628	144.2	3.9121	2.27
312	5.882	148.4	3.9276	2.12	5.713	146.4	3.9193	2.20
313	5.963	150.5	3.9344	2.06	5.796	148.6	3.9263	2.13
314	6.042	152.6	3.9407	2.00	5.876	150.7	3.9329	2.07

continued

T, °K	v	i	s	c_p	v	i	s	c_p
315	6.119	154.5	3.9474	1.96	5.955	152.7	3.9398	2.02
316	6.195	156.5	3.9532	1.92	6.031	154.7	3.9457	1.97
317	6.269	158.4	3.9592	1.88	6.106	156.7	3.9519	1.93
318	6.341	160.3	3.9651	1.84	6.179	158.6	3.9579	1.89
319	6.412	162.1	3.9708	1.81	6.250	160.5	3.9638	1.85
320	6.481	163.9	3.9763	1.77	6.320	162.3	3.9694	1.82
		$p=66$ bar				$p=67$ bar		
300	4.076	104.5	3.7800	6.25	3.775	97.3	3.7547	8.77
301	4.275	110.1	3.7987	5.02	4.024	104.6	3.7790	6.19
302	4.444	114.7	3.8141	4.30	4.218	110.1	3.7974	5.01
303	4.592	118.8	3.8274	3.82	4.383	114.8	3.8127	4.31
304.19	4.751	123.0	3.8415	3.42	4.555	119.5	3.8284	3.76
305	4.850	125.8	3.8505	3.20	4.661	122.5	3.8382	3.49
306	4.966	128.8	3.8605	3.00	4.783	125.8	3.8491	3.22
307	5.074	131.7	3.8701	2.83	4.897	128.9	3.8593	3.01
308	5.177	134.5	3.8789	2.68	5.004	131.8	3.8687	2.84
309	5.276	137.1	3.8875	2.56	5.106	134.6	3.8777	2.70
310	5.370	139.6	3.8956	2.45	5.203	137.2	3.8862	2.57
311	5.460	142.0	3.9034	2.36	5.296	139.7	3.8943	2.47
312	5.548	144.3	3.9108	2.28	5.385	142.1	3.9021	2.37
313	5.632	146.6	3.9180	2.21	5.471	144.5	3.9096	2.29
314	5.714	148.7	3.9248	2.14	5.554	146.8	3.9167	2.22
315	5.793	150.8	3.9320	2.08	5.635	148.9	3.9241	2.15
316	5.871	152.9	3.9381	2.03	5.714	151.0	3.9304	2.09
317	5.947	154.9	3.9444	1.98	5.790	153.1	3.9369	2.04
318	6.020	156.9	3.9506	1.94	5.865	155.2	3.9432	1.99
319	6.092	158.8	3.9566	1.90	5.938	157.1	3.9495	1.95
320	6.163	160.7	3.9624	1.86	6.009	159.0	3.9554	1.91
		$p=68$ bar				$p=69$ bar		
300	1.447	−12.2	3.3892	6.90	1.428	−12.7	3.3838	6.27
301	3.739	97.6	3.7547	8.43	1.496	−6.5	3.4080	8.63
302	3.977	104.8	3.7783	6.11	3.708	98.2	3.7552	8.07
303	4.165	110.2	3.7964	4.98	3.934	105.0	3.7778	5.99
304.19	4.355	115.7	3.8143	4.20	4.149	111.4	3.7968	4.79
305	4.469	118.9	3.8257	3.84	4.274	115.1	3.8109	4.29
306	4.599	122.5	3.8370	3.50	4.414	119.0	3.8241	3.83
307	4.719	125.9	3.8470	3.23	4.542	122.7	3.8361	3.50
308	4.831	129.0	3.8580	3.02	4.660	126.1	3.8470	3.24
309	4.937	132.0	3.8676	2.85	4.770	129.2	3.8571	3.03
310	5.038	134.8	3.8766	2.71	4.874	132.2	3.8666	2.86
311	5.133	137.4	3.8851	2.58	4.973	134.9	3.8759	2.71
312	5.225	139.9	3.8933	2.48	5.067	137.5	3.8842	2.59
313	5.313	142.4	3.9011	2.38	5.158	140.1	3.8923	2.49
314	5.398	144.7	3.9084	2.30	5.245	142.6	3.9000	2.39
315	5.480	146.9	3.9160	2.23	5.329	144.9	3.9078	2.31
316	5.560	149.1	3.9226	2.16	5.410	147.2	3.9146	2.24
317	5.638	151.3	3.9293	2.10	5.489	149.4	3.9216	2.17
318	5.714	153.4	3.9359	2.05	5.565	151.6	3.9284	2.11
319	5.787	155.4	3.9422	2.00	5.640	153.7	3.9349	2.06
320	5.859	157.4	3.9483	1.96	5.712	155.7	3.9412	2.01
		$p=70$ bar				$p=71$ bar		
300	1.412	−15.2	3.3790	5.81	1.398	−16.2	3.3747	5.44
301	1.466	−8.5	3.4007	7.43	1.446	−10.2	3.3947	6.65
302	3.370	89.0	3.7236	13.1	1.524	−2.0	3.4217	9.58
303	3.680	98.7	3.7558	7.71	3.381	90.4	3.7271	11.4
304.19	3.932	106.5	3.7814	5.64	3.698	100.8	3.7613	6.96
305	4.073	110.8	3.7954	4.89	3.862	105.9	3.7781	5.73

continued

T, °K	v	i	s	c_p	v	i	s	c_p
306	4.226	115.2	3.8103	4.26	4.032	111.0	3.7952	4.82
307	4.362	119.3	3.8235	3.82	4.181	115.6	3.8100	4.23
308	4.487	122.9	3.8353	3.49	4.314	119.6	3.8229	3.80
309	4.603	126.3	3.8462	3.24	4.437	132.2	3.8347	3.48
310	4.712	129.4	3.8563	3.03	4.550	126.6	3.8456	3.23
311	4.814	132.4	3.8658	2.86	4.657	129.7	3.8556	3.03
312	4.911	135.1	3.8748	2.72	4.757	132.6	3.8652	2.86
313	5.004	137.9	3.8833	2.60	4.853	135.5	3.8741	2.72
314	5.093	140.4	3.8913	2.49	4.944	138.1	3.8825	2.60
315	5.179	142.8	3.8995	2.40	5.032	140.6	3.8906	2.50
316	5.262	145.2	3.9066	2.32	5.117	143.1	3.8983	2.40
317	5.342	147.5	3.9138	2.24	5.198	145.5	3.9058	2.32
318	5.420	149.7	3.9208	2.18	5.277	147.8	3.9130	2.25
319	5.497	151.9	3.9275	2.12	5.354	150.0	3.9200	2.18
320	5.569	153.9	3.9339	2.06	5.429	152.1	3.9266	2.12
	$p=72$ bar				$p=73$ bar			
300	1.387	−17.2	3.3707	5.15	1.377	−18.2	3.3671	4.91
301	1.430	−11.6	3.3894	6.10	1.416	−12.9	3.3847	5.67
302	1.491	−4.6	3.4124	8.02	1.469	−6.6	3.4056	7.06
303	1.625	7.5	3.4530	15.4	1.554	2.8	3.4356	10.7
304.19	3.438	93.6	3.7364	9.34	3.116	83.7	3.7029	15.3
305	3.636	100.2	3.7582	7.03	3.385	93.2	3.7341	9.29
306	3.831	106.3	3.7785	5.59	3.617	100.9	3.7596	6.71
307	3.995	111.5	3.7953	4.75	3.803	107.0	3.7793	5.44
308	4.139	115.9	3.8098	4.18	3.960	112.0	3.7956	4.67
309	4.269	119.9	3.8226	3.78	4.100	116.4	3.8098	4.14
310	4.389	123.5	3.8343	3.47	4.227	120.3	3.8225	3.75
311	4.500	126.8	3.8451	3.23	4.344	123.9	3.8341	3.45
312	4.605	130.0	3.8552	3.03	4.605	127.2	3.8448	3.22
313	4.703	133.0	3.8645	2.86	4.703	130.4	3.8548	3.02
314	4.797	135.7	3.8734	2.72	4.797	133.3	3.8641	2.86
315	4.887	138.4	3.8823	2.60	4.887	136.0	3.8734	2.72
316	4.974	140.9	3.8899	2.50	4.974	138.7	3.8814	2.60
317	5.057	143.4	3.8977	2.41	5.057	141.3	3.8895	2.50
318	5.138	145.8	3.9052	2.33	5.138	143.8	3.8972	2.41
319	5.216	148.1	3.9124	2.25	5.216	146.1	3.9045	2.33
320	5.291	150.3	3.9192	2.19	5.291	148.4	3.9118	2.26
	$p=74$ bar				$p=75$ bar			
300	1.368	−19.0	3.3637	4.70	1.360	−19.8	3.3606	4.53
301	1.404	−14.0	3.3805	5.34	1.393	−15.0	3.3767	5.07
302	1.451	−8.2	3.3999	6.41	1.436	−9.6	3.3948	5.92
303	1.517	−0.4	3.4245	8.66	1.492	−2.8	3.4166	7.49
304.19	1.699	15.3	3.4774	27.8	1.611	8.6	3.4548	13.7
305	3.082	83.7	3.7019	14.4	2.615	66.2	3.6438	44.0
306	3.385	94.5	3.7362	8.52	3.120	86.2	3.7093	11.9
307	3.601	101.8	3.7613	6.42	3.385	95.8	3.7405	7.89
308	3.777	107.6	3.7801	5.29	3.586	102.7	3.7630	6.14
309	3.929	112.5	3.7960	4.58	3.754	108.3	3.7812	5.15
310	4.064	116.8	3.8100	4.09	3.900	113.1	3.7970	4.50
311	4.188	120.7	3.8226	3.72	4.031	117.3	3.8104	4.03
312	4.302	124.3	3.8341	3.43	4.151	121.2	3.8228	3.68
313	4.408	127.6	3.8447	3.20	4.262	124.8	3.8341	3.41
314	4.509	130.7	3.8545	3.01	4.366	128.0	3.8445	3.18
315	4.604	133.6	3.8642	2.85	4.464	131.1	3.8548	3.00
316	4.695	136.4	3.8726	2.72	4.558	134.0	3.8636	2.85
317	4.782	139.1	3.8810	2.60	4.647	136.8	3.8724	2.71
318	4.865	141.7	3.8891	2.50	4.733	139.5	3.8808	2.60
319	4.946	144.1	3.8968	2.41	4.815	142.1	3.8888	2.50
320	5.024	146.5	3.9041	2.33	4.894	144.5	3.8963	2.41

continued

T, °K	v	i	s	c_p	v	i	s	c_p
	$p=76$ bar				$p=77$ bar			
300	1.352	−20.6	3.3576	4.38	1.345	−21.3	3.3548	4.25
301	1.384	−16.0	3.3731	4.85	1.375	−16.8	3.3697	4.65
302	1.422	−10.8	3.3902	5.54	1.410	−11.9	3.3861	5.24
303	1.472	−4.7	3.4102	6.72	1.455	−6.2	3.4047	6.16
304.19	1.565	4.9	3.4420	10.2	1.532	2.2	3.4327	8.45
305	1.696	16.3	3.4795	21.3	1.620	10.6	3.4600	12.8
306	2.783	74.3	3.6693	21.0	2.141	45.3	3.5739	
307	3.147	88.5	3.7156	10.3	2.870	78.9	3.6835	15.2
308	3.385	97.1	3.7436	7.35	3.169	90.5	3.7211	9.19
309	3.573	103.7	3.7649	5.89	3.385	98.4	3.7468	6.90
310	3.732	109.1	3.7824	5.01	3.561	104.6	3.7669	5.66
311	3.873	113.7	3.7975	4.41	3.713	109.8	3.7838	4.87
312	4.000	117.9	3.8110	3.97	3.848	114.4	3.7985	4.32
313	4.116	121.7	3.8232	3.64	3.970	118.6	3.8117	3.64
314	4.224	125.2	3.8342	3.38	4.084	122.3	3.8235	3.38
315	4.326	128.5	3.8456	3.16	4.189	125.7	3.8350	3.16
316	4.423	131.6	3.8543	2.99	4.289	129.0	3.8448	2.99
317	4.514	134.5	3.8637	2.84	4.383	132.1	3.8549	2.84
318	4.602	137.3	3.8723	2.71	4.473	135.0	3.8636	2.71
319	4.686	139.9	3.8806	2.59	4.559	137.7	3.8723	2.59
320	4.767	142.5	3.8885	2.49	4.641	140.4	3.8804	2.49
	$p=78$ bar				$p=79$ bar			
300	1.338	−21.9	3.3522	4.13	1.332	−22.6	3.3496	4.03
301	1.367	−17.7	3.3666	4.49	1.359	−18.4	3.3637	4.35
302	1.400	−12.9	3.3823	4.99	1.390	−13.8	3.3788	4.78
303	1.441	−7.6	3.3998	5.74	1.428	−8.8	3.3954	5.40
304.19	1.507	0.1	3.4251	7.39	1.487	−1.7	3.4188	6.67
305	1.575	7.0	3.4478	9.88	1.543	4.3	3.4386	8.31
306	1.743	21.0	3.4939	22.4	1.665	14.7	3.4726	13.5
307	2.512	64.5	3.6360	28.1	2.023	40.0	3.5552	47.6
308	2.928	82.4	3.6938	12.2	2.650	71.8	3.6586	18.0
309	3.186	92.4	3.7262	8.33	2.972	85.3	3.7022	10.5
310	3.384	99.7	3.7498	5.51	3.200	94.1	3.7309	7.64
311	3.550	105.6	3.7690	5.44	3.383	100.9	3.7529	6.16
312	3.694	110.7	3.7853	4.74	3.539	106.6	3.7711	5.24
313	3.824	115.2	3.7996	4.23	3.678	111.6	3.7869	4.61
314	3.943	119.2	3.8124	3.85	3.803	115.9	3.8007	4.15
315	4.053	122.9	3.8245	3.56	3.918	119.9	3.8137	3.79
316	4.156	126.3	3.8350	3.32	4.024	123.5	3.8248	3.51
317	4.253	129.5	3.8452	3.12	4.125	126.9	3.8356	3.28
318	4.346	132.6	3.8547	2.95	4.220	130.1	3.8456	3.09
319	4.433	135.5	3.8638	2.81	4.310	133.1	3.8551	2.93
320	4.517	138.2	3.8723	2.69	4.396	136.0	3.8639	2.80

$p=80$ bar

T, °K	v	i	s	c_p	T, °K	v	i	s	c_p
300	1.326	−23.2	3.3472	3.93	311	3.211	95.8	3.7353	7.09
301	1.352	−19.1	3.3609	4.22	312	3.382	102.2	3.7560	5.86
302	1.381	−14.7	3.3755	4.60	313	3.530	107.6	3.7733	5.05
303	1.416	−9.8	3.3914	5.13	314	3.662	112.4	3.7884	4.49
304.19	1.470	−3.2	3.4133	6.13	315	3.783	116.7	3.8024	4.06
305	1.518	2.2	3.4311	7.32	316	3.894	120.6	3.8143	3.73
306	1.604	10.8	3.4592	10.3	317	3.997	124.2	3.8260	3.47
307	1.781	25.2	3.5062	21.3	318	4.095	127.6	3.8363	3.25
308	2.317	57.1	3.6099	28.8	319	4.188	130.7	3.8462	3.07
309	2.738	76.6	3.6733	13.8	320	4.276	133.7	3.8554	2.91
310	3.006	87.8	3.7094	9.21					

Heat capacity c_p (kJ/kg · deg) of carbon dioxide at supercritical pressures near the critical region [57, 58]

T, °K \ p, bar →	81	82	83	84	85	86	87	88	89	90	95	100	105	110
300	3.84	3.76	3.69	3.62	3.56	3.51	3.45	3.41	3.36	3.32	3.13	3.00	2.88	2.79
301	4.10	4.00	3.90	3.82	3.74	3.68	3.61	3.55	3.50	3.44	3.23	3.07	2.94	2.84
302	4.43	4.29	4.17	4.07	3.97	3.88	3.80	3.72	3.66	3.59	3.34	3.15	3.01	2.89
303	4.89	4.69	4.52	4.38	4.25	4.13	4.03	3.94	3.85	3.77	3.46	3.25	3.08	2.95
304	5.71	5.38	5.11	4.89	4.70	4.53	4.38	4.25	4.14	4.03	3.64	3.37	3.18	3.03
305	6.61	6.10	5.70	5.38	5.11	4.89	4.70	4.53	4.39	4.26	3.78	3.47	3.25	3.09
306	8.61	7.55	6.81	6.26	5.83	5.49	5.21	4.97	4.77	4.60	3.99	3.61	3.36	3.17
307	13.7	10.6	8.84	7.73	6.96	6.39	5.94	5.59	5.29	5.05	4.24	3.78	3.47	3.25
308	30.3	19.0	13.4	10.6	8.94	7.84	7.06	6.48	6.03	5.66	4.55	3.97	3.60	3.35
309	18.9	24.3	22.7	16.8	12.8	10.4	8.91	7.87	7.11	6.53	4.94	4.19	3.75	3.46
310	11.41	14.42	17.93	19.9	18.1	14.8	12.0	10.1	8.78	7.82	5.44	4.47	3.93	3.58
311	8.29	9.86	11.85	14.2	16.1	16.6	15.3	13.1	11.2	9.69	6.01	4.80	4.13	3.72
312	6.63	7.58	8.76	10.2	11.8	13.3	14.3	14.2	13.2	11.8	6.94	5.20	4.36	3.87
313	5.59	6.23	7.01	7.93	8.10	10.2	11.3	12.3	12.7	12.5	7.97	5.68	4.63	4.04
314	4.88	5.35	5.90	6.53	7.27	8.11	9.01	9.92	10.7	11.2	8.10	6.25	4.95	4.24
315	4.37	4.73	5.13	5.60	6.14	6.74	7.41	8.13	8.85	9.50	9.58	6.87	5.30	4.46
316	3.98	4.21	4.58	4.94	5.34	5.80	6.30	6.85	7.43	8.02	9.43	7.44	5.69	4.71
317	3.67	3.90	4.15	4.44	4.76	5.11	5.51	5.93	6.39	6.87	8.73	7.82	6.09	4.97
318	3.42	3.61	3.82	4.05	4.31	4.60	4.91	5.25	5.61	6.00	7.85	7.89	6.44	4.24
319	3.21	3.38	3.55	3.75	3.96	4.19	4.45	4.72	5.02	5.34	7.00	7.63	6.69	5.50
320	3.04	3.18	3.32	3.49	3.67	3.87	4.08	4.31	4.55	4.82	6.27	7.20	6.78	5.73
325	2.46	2.54	2.62	2.70	2.80	2.89	2.99	3.11	3.22	3.34	4.05	4.85	5.48	5.66
330	2.13	2.18	2.23	2.28	2.34	2.40	2.46	2.53	2.60	2.67	3.07	3.55	4.04	4.47
335	1.91	1.95	1.98	2.02	2.06	2.10	2.15	2.19	2.24	2.28	2.55	2.85	3.18	3.52
340	1.76	1.79	1.81	1.84	1.87	1.90	1.93	1.97	1.99	2.03	2.22	2.43	2.66	2.91
345	1.65	1.67	1.69	1.71	1.73	1.76	1.78	1.81	1.83	1.86	2.00	2.15	2.32	2.50
350	1.56	1.58	1.59	1.61	1.63	1.65	1.67	1.69	1.71	1.73	1.84	1.96	2.09	2.23

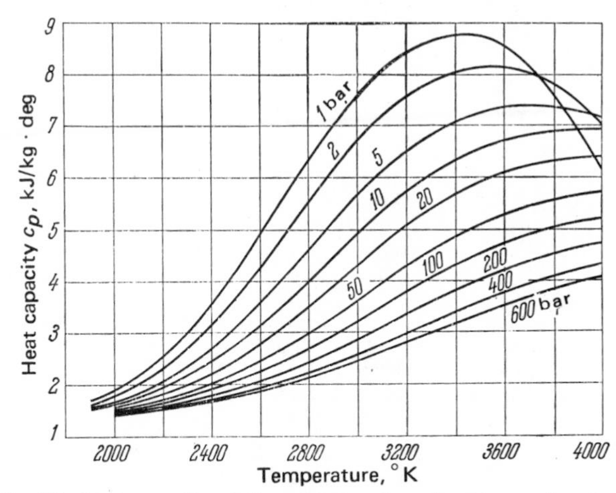

Fig. 12. Heat capacity of dissociated carbon dioxide as a function of temperature at different pressures.

Thermodynamic properties of dissociated carbon dioxide [56–58]: v (dm³/kg), i (kJ/kg), s and c_p (kJ/kg · deg)

p, bar	v	i	s	c_p	v	i	s	c_p
	T=1900 °K				T=2000 °K			
1	3 605	2 208.6	6.9922	1.69	3 808	2 387.8	7.0839	1.91
2	1 801	2 197.7	6.8550	1.61	1 901	2 368.2	6.9423	1.79
3	1 201	2 192.4	6.7753	1.58	1 267	2 358.6	6.8605	1.75

continued

p, bar	v	i	s	c_p	v	i	s	c_p
4	900.4	2 189.1	6.7190	1.56	949.8	2 352.7	6.8028	1.71
5	720.4	2 186.7	6.6755	1.55	759.7	2 348.4	6.7583	1.68
6	600.3	2 184.9	6.6400	1.54	633.1	2 345.1	6.7221	1.67
7	514.6	2 183.5	6.6099	1.53	542.6	2 342.5	6.6913	1.65
8	450.3	2 182.3	6.5840	1.52	474.8	2 340.4	6.6651	1.64
9	400.4	2 181.3	6.5612	1.52	422.1	2 338.6	6.6418	1.63
10	360.4	2 180.4	6.5408	1.52	379.9	2 337.1	6.6210	1.62
12	300.4	2 179.4	6.5055	1.51	316.6	2 334.5	6.5852	1.60
14	257.6	2 178.0	6.4756	1.50	271.5	2 332.5	6.5549	1.59
16	225.4	2 177.1	6.4498	1.50	237.6	2 330.9	6.5287	1.58
18	200.5	2 176.3	6.4271	1.49	211.2	2 329.5	6.5056	1.57
20	180.5	2 175.7	6.4067	1.49	190.2	2 328.4	6.4850	1.56
25	144.5	2 174.5	6.3637	1.49	152.3	2 326.0	6.4414	1.55
30	120.5	2 173.6	6.3285	1.48	127.0	2 324.3	6.4058	1.54
40	90.58	2 172.4	6.2731	1.46	95.42	2 321.9	6.3498	1.54
50	72.60	2 171.7	6.2302	1.45	76.47	2 320.3	6.3064	1.52
60	60.62	2 171.2	6.1950	1.45	63.84	2 319.2	6.2709	1.51
70	52.06	2 170.9	6.1653	1.45	54.82	2 318.4	6.2410	1.50
80	45.64	2 170.7	6.1396	1.45	48.06	2 317.8	6.2150	1.50
90	40.65	2 170.6	6.1169	1.45	42.80	2 317.8	6.1922	1.50
100	36.66	2 170.6	6.0966	1.44	38.60	2 317.1	6.1717	1.48
150	24.69	2 170.9	6.0183	1.44	25.98	2 316.5	6.0929	1.48
200	18.70	2 171.8	5.9625	1.43	19.67	2 316.9	6.0369	1.47
300	12.72	2 174.2	5.8835	1.43	13.37	2 318.7	5.9576	1.47
400	9.728	2 176.8	5.8270	1.43	10.22	2 321.2	5.9010	1.46
500	7.935	2 179.7	5.7829	1.43	8.329	2 324.0	5.8569	1.46
600	6.750	2 182.5	5.7466	1.42	7.070	2 326.9	5.8206	1.45
	T=2100 °K				T=2200 °K			
1	4 019	2 591.4	7.1831	2.19	4 242	2 827.8	7.2927	2.56
2	2 004	2 558.3	7.0349	2.02	2 113	2 774.6	7.1353	2.32
3	1 335	2 542.2	6.9499	1.94	1 406	2 748.7	7.0458	2.20
4	1 000	2 532.0	6.8902	1.89	1 053	2 732.4	6.9832	2.13
5	800.1	2 524.7	6.8442	1.85	842.0	2 720.7	6.9352	2.08
6	666.6	2 519.2	6.8069	1.83	701.3	2 711.8	6.8963	2.04
7	571.3	2 514.8	6.7754	1.81	600.9	2 704.7	6.8636	2.01
8	499.8	2 511.2	6.7483	1.79	525.7	2 698.8	6.8355	1.98
9	444.3	2 508.1	6.7244	1.78	467.2	2 693.9	6.8107	1.96
10	399.8	2 505.5	6.7031	1.76	420.4	2 689.6	6.7886	1.94
12	333.2	2 501.1	6.6663	1.73	350.2	2 682.6	6.7506	1.90
14	285.6	2 497.7	6.6354	1.71	300.2	2 677.0	6.7186	1.88
16	250.0	2 494.9	6.6086	1.69	262.7	2 672.4	6.6911	1.85
18	222.2	2 492.5	6.5850	1.68	233.5	2 668.5	6.6668	1.83
20	200.1	2 490.4	6.5640	1.67	210.2	2 665.2	6.6452	1.82
25	160.1	2 486.4	6.5195	1.65	168.2	2 658.6	6.5995	1.80
30	133.6	2 483.4	6.4833	1.64	140.2	2 653.5	6.5624	1.77
40	103.3	2 479.1	6.4264	1.63	105.3	2 646.4	6.5041	1.73
50	80.38	2 476.1	6.3823	1.60	84.37	2 641.4	6.4591	1.71
60	67.10	2 474.0	6.3464	1.60	70.41	2 637.7	6.4225	1.68
70	57.62	2 472.4	6.3160	1.58	60.45	2 634.9	6.3916	1.67
80	50.50	2 471.1	6.2898	1.57	52.98	2 632.6	6.3648	1.67
90	44.97	2 470.1	6.2667	1.57	47.17	2 630.8	6.3413	1.66
100	40.55	2 469.3	6.2460	1.56	42.53	2 629.2	6.3203	1.65
150	27.28	2 467.2	6.1664	1.54	28.60	2 624.6	6.2395	1.61
200	20.65	2 466.6	6.1099	1.53	21.64	2 622.4	6.1824	1.59
300	14.02	2 467.4	6.0301	1.51	14.68	2 621.5	6.1017	1.58
400	10.71	2 469.4	5.9733	1.50	11.21	2 622.4	6.0444	1.57
500	8.724	2 471.9	5.9290	1.50	9.122	2 624.3	5.9998	1.56
600	7.400	2 474.6	5.8926	1.50	7.732	2 626.6	5.9632	1.55

continued

p, bar	v	i	s	c_p	v	i	s	c_p
	T=2300 °K				T=2400 °K			
1	4 484	3 106.2	7.4161	3.03	4 748	3 436.1	7.5560	3.60
2	2 228	3 024.8	7.2462	2.70	2 353	3 316.7	7.3700	3.16
3	1 481	2 985.0	7.1506	2.54	1 562	3 258.2	7.2664	2.94
4	1 109	2 959.9	7.0841	2.44	1 168	3 221.1	7.1950	2.80
5	886.0	2 941.9	7.0334	2.36	932.8	3 194.6	7.1406	2.71
6	737.7	2 928.2	6.9923	2.30	776.2	3 174.4	7.0968	2.63
7	631.9	2 917.3	6.9580	2.26	664.6	3 158.2	7.0602	2.57
8	552.6	2 908.3	6.9284	2.23	581.0	3 144.8	7.0288	2.53
9	491.0	2 900.6	6.9024	2.19	516.1	3 133.5	7.0013	2.48
10	441.7	2 894.0	6.8793	2.17	464.4	3 123.8	6.9769	2.44
12	367.9	2 883.2	6.8396	2.13	386.5	3 107.7	6.9350	2.39
14	315.3	2 874.5	6.8063	2.08	331.0	3 094.8	6.8998	2.34
16	275.8	2 867.4	6.7776	2.05	289.5	3 084.2	6.8697	2.30
18	245.1	2 861.4	6.7524	2.03	257.3	3 075.3	6.8432	2.26
20	220.6	2 856.2	6.7300	2.00	231.5	3 067.6	6.8197	2.22
25	176.5	2 845.9	6.6827	1.96	185.2	3 052.1	6.7703	2.18
30	147.1	2 838.0	6.6443	1.93	154.2	3 040.4	6.7303	2.13
40	110.4	2 826.8	6.5842	1.88	115.7	3 023.4	6.6678	2.07
50	88.45	2 818.9	6.5379	1.85	92.66	3 011.5	6.6198	2.02
60	73.80	2 812.9	6.5003	1.82	77.29	3 002.5	6.5808	1.98
70	63.35	2 808.3	6.4686	1.80	66.32	2 995.4	6.5481	1.95
80	55.51	2 804.6	6.4412	1.78	58.16	2 989.7	6.5199	1.92
90	49.42	2 801.5	6.4171	1.77	51.72	2 984.9	6.4950	1.91
100	44.54	2 798.9	6.3956	1.76	46.61	2 980.8	6.4729	1.89
150	29.94	2 790.6	6.3132	1.71	31.30	2 967.3	6.3884	1.83
200	22.64	2 786.2	6.2550	1.68	23.66	2 959.7	6.3288	1.79
300	15.35	2 782.4	6.1732	1.66	16.03	2 952.0	6.2453	1.75
400	11.71	2 781.8	6.1152	1.63	12.21	2 948.9	6.1862	1.72
500	9.522	2 782.6	6.0701	1.62	9.928	2 948.1	6.1404	1.70
600	8.066	2 784.5	6.0331	1.61	8.405	2 948.5	6.1030	1.69
	T=2500 °K				T=2600 °K			
1	5 041	3 826.6	7.7148	4.24	5 368	4 285.0	7.8937	4.94
2	2 489	3 658.1	7.5089	3.69	2 639	4 055.8	7.6642	4.28
3	1 649	3 575.2	7.3954	3.41	1 745	3 942.5	7.5389	3.95
4	1 232	3 522.5	7.3176	3.24	1 302	3 870.3	7.4535	3.73
5	983.0	3 484.9	7.2587	3.11	1 038	3 818.6	7.3892	3.58
6	817.5	3 456.1	7.2115	3.02	862.2	3 779.0	7.3377	3.46
7	699.6	3 433.0	7.1721	2.94	737.4	3 747.2	7.2949	3.36
8	611.3	3 414.0	7.1383	2.88	644.0	3 720.9	7.2583	3.28
9	542.8	3 397.8	7.1089	2.82	571.6	3 698.6	7.2265	3.21
10	488.1	3 383.9	7.0828	2.77	513.7	3 679.4	7.1983	3.14
12	406.2	3 360.9	7.0380	2.70	427.2	3 647.6	7.1502	3.05
14	347.8	3 342.5	7.0007	2.63	365.6	3 622.2	7.1100	2.98
16	304.0	3 327.3	6.9687	2.58	319.5	3 601.2	7.0757	2.92
18	270.1	3 314.5	6.9406	2.53	283.7	3 583.4	7.0458	2.85
20	242.9	3 303.4	6.9158	2.48	255.1	3 568.0	7.0192	2.80
25	194.2	3 281.3	6.8636	2.42	203.7	3 537.2	6.9637	2.71
30	161.7	3 264.4	6.8215	2.36	169.6	3 513.7	6.9190	2.63
40	121.3	3 239.9	6.7559	2.28	127.1	3 479.5	6.8497	2.53
50	97.04	3 222.6	6.7057	2.22	101.6	3 455.3	6.7968	2.45
60	80.91	3 209.4	6.6651	2.17	84.70	3 436.8	6.7541	2.38
70	69.41	3 199.1	6.6311	2.13	72.63	3 422.2	6.7184	2.34
80	60.79	3 190.6	6.6017	2.10	63.60	3 410.3	6.6877	2.31
90	54.10	3 183.5	6.5760	2.07	56.57	3 400.2	6.6608	2.26
100	48.74	3 177.5	6.5531	2.05	50.96	3 391.6	6.6369	2.25
150	32.71	3 157.0	6.4657	1.97	34.16	3 362.1	6.5459	2.13
200	24.71	3 145.0	6.4043	1.92	25.79	3 344.4	6.4824	2.07
300	16.72	3 132.0	6.3186	1.86	17.43	3 324.3	6.3939	1.99
400	12.73	3 125.6	6.2582	1.82	13.26	3 313.6	6.3318	1.94
500	10.34	3 122.5	6.2115	1.79	10.76	3 307.4	6.2838	1.19
600	8.749	3 121.2	6.1734	1.77	9.101	3 303.8	6.2448	1.88

continued

p, bar	v	i	s	c_p	v	i	s	c_p
		T=2700 °K				T=2800 °K		
1	5 736	4 815.8	8.0932	5.68	6 147	5 420.0	8.3118	6.40
2	2 807	4 515.0	7.8368	4.91	2 992	5 038.2	8.0262	5.55
3	1 851	4 365.3	7.6978	4.52	1 968	4 846.5	7.8720	5.11
4	1 378	4 269.5	7.6036	4.26	1 463	4 723.4	7.7679	4.82
5	1 097	4 200.7	7.5328	4.08	1 163	4 634.6	7.6899	4.60
6	911.0	4 147.9	7.4764	3.93	964.6	4 566.3	7.6279	4.44
7	778.5	4 105.5	7.4296	3.82	823.5	4 511.4	7.5766	4.30
8	679.5	4 070.4	7.3897	3.72	718.3	4 465.8	7.5329	4.19
9	602.7	4 040.6	7.3550	3.64	636.7	4 427.1	7.4950	4.09
10	541.5	4 014.8	7.3244	3.56	571.7	4 393.6	7.4616	4.01
12	449.9	3 972.2	7.2722	3.45	474.6	4 338.1	7.4048	3.88
14	384.8	3 938.1	7.2288	3.35	405.6	4 293.6	7.3576	3.76
16	336.0	3 909.8	7.1918	3.28	354.0	4 256.7	7.3175	3.67
18	298.3	3 885.8	7.1596	3.20	314.0	4 225.3	7.2826	3.58
20	268.1	3 865.2	7.1310	3.15	282.1	4 198.3	7.2517	3.52
25	214.0	3 823.7	7.0715	3.02	224.9	4 143.9	7.1875	3.38
30	178.0	3 792.0	7.0237	2.94	187.0	4 102.2	7.1362	3.27
40	133.2	3 745.7	6.9498	2.81	139.8	4 041.3	7.0570	3.12
50	106.5	3 712.8	6.8937	2.71	111.6	3 997.9	6.9970	3.00
60	88.69	3 687.7	6.8485	2.63	92.93	3 964.8	6.9490	2.91
70	76.02	3 667.8	6.8108	2.57	79.61	3 938.3	6.9089	2.83
80	66.54	3 651.4	6.7784	2.53	69.64	3 916.6	6.8746	2.77
90	59.17	3 637.6	6.7502	2.49	61.91	3 898.2	6.8447	2.73
100	53.28	3 625.8	6.7250	2.45	55.73	3 882.5	6.8181	2.67
150	35.68	3 584.8	6.6298	2.32	37.27	3 827.5	6.7178	2.53
200	26.91	3 560.0	6.5635	2.24	28.08	3 793.8	6.6483	2.43
300	18.17	3 530.9	6.4717	2.14	18.93	3 773.6	6.5524	2.31
400	13.81	3 514.5	6.4074	2.08	14.38	3 730.1	6.4856	2.24
500	11.20	3 504.4	6.3580	2.03	11.65	3 715.1	6.4344	2.18
600	9.462	3 497.8	6.3178	2.00	9.834	3 704.8	6.3929	2.13
		T=2900 °K				T=3000 °K		
1	6 605	6 094.0	8.5472	7.06	7 110	6 830.3	8.7956	7.63
2	3 199	5 624.7	8.2710	6.15	3 426	6 270.4	8.4486	6.74
3	2 098	5 386.7	8.0607	5.69	2 240	5 983.5	8.2620	6.23
4	1 556	5 233.0	7.9459	5.37	1 659	5 796.8	8.1362	5.90
5	1 235	5 121.8	7.8601	5.14	1 315	5 661.3	8.0421	5.65
6	1 023	5 035.9	7.7919	4.96	1 088	5 556.3	7.9676	5.45
7	872.9	4 966.8	7.7357	4.80	927.0	5 471.5	7.9060	5.29
8	760.7	4 909.2	7.6879	4.68	807.1	5 400.8	7.8538	5.15
9	673.9	4 860.3	7.6464	4.57	714.5	5 340.6	7.8085	5.03
10	604.7	4 817.9	7.6099	4.48	640.7	5 288.4	7.7687	4.93
12	501.3	4 747.6	7.5479	4.32	530.8	5 201.5	7.7011	4.76
14	428.2	4 691.0	7.4966	4.19	452.8	5 131.5	7.6452	4.62
16	373.4	4 644.1	7.4529	4.08	394.6	5 073.3	7.5978	4.50
18	331.1	4 604.2	7.4150	3.99	349.6	5 023.8	7.5566	4.40
20	297.3	4 569.8	7.3816	3.91	313.7	4 980.9	7.5203	4.31
25	236.8	4 500.3	7.3121	3.75	249.6	4 894.3	7.4451	4.13
30	196.7	4 447.0	7.2567	3.63	207.1	4 827.7	7.3852	3.99
40	146.8	4 368.8	7.1715	3.44	154.4	4 729.9	7.2934	3.78
50	117.1	4 313.0	7.1072	3.30	123.0	4 659.8	7.2243	3.63
60	97.44	4 270.3	7.0558	3.20	102.3	4 606.0	7.1692	3.51
70	83.42	4 236.2	7.0130	3.12	87.50	4 563.0	7.1234	3.42
80	72.94	4 208.0	6.9765	3.04	76.46	4 527.4	7.0844	3.32
90	64.81	4 184.2	6.9447	2.99	67.90	4 497.3	7.0504	3.27
100	58.32	4 163.8	6.9165	2.93	61.08	4 471.4	7.0204	3.21
150	38.94	4 092.0	6.8104	2.76	40.71	4 380.1	6.9077	3.00
200	29.31	4 047.7	6.7372	2.64	30.61	4 323.2	6.8302	2.86
300	19.73	3 993.9	6.6366	2.50	20.57	4 253.6	6.7243	2.70
400	14.97	3 962.1	6.5668	2.40	15.58	4 211.7	6.6511	2.58
500	12.12	3 941.0	6.5134	2.34	12.60	4 183.4	6.5954	2.51
600	10.22	3 926.1	6.4703	2.29	10.62	4 163.1	6.5504	2.45

continued

p, bar	v	i	s	c_p	v	i	s	c_p
	T=3100 °K				T=3200 °K			
1	7 659	7 618.6	9.0529	8.10	8 251	8 447.3	9.3148	8.45
2	3 674	6 968.5	8.6766	7.21	3 942	7 710.0	8.9109	7.59
3	2 396	6 631.5	8.4735	6.71	2 565	7 323.6	8.6922	7.11
4	1 771	6 410.9	8.3366	6.39	1 892	7 069.0	8.5445	6.77
5	1 402	6 250.0	8.2342	6.11	1 496	6 882.3	8.4340	6.51
6	1 158	6 124.8	8.1531	5.90	1 234	6 736.7	8.3464	6.31
7	985.9	6 023.4	8.0861	5.74	1 050	6 618.3	8.2741	6.14
8	857.8	5 938.7	8.0293	5.59	912.6	6 519.1	8.2127	6.00
9	758.7	5 866.4	7.9801	5.47	806.7	6 434.3	8.1596	5.87
10	679.9	5 803.6	7.9368	5.36	722.4	6 360.4	8.1128	5.76
12	562.6	5,698.9	7.8634	5.18	597.1	6 237.1	8.0335	5.57
14	479.5	5 614.3	7.8028	5.03	508.4	6 137.1	7.9680	5.41
16	417.6	5 543.8	7,7514	4.91	442.4	6 053.7	7.9125	5.28
18	369.7	5 483.7	7.7068	4.79	391.4	5 982.4	7.8643	5.17
20	331.6	5 431.6	7.6675	4.70	350.8	5 920.5	7.8220	5.08
25	263.4	5 326.2	7.5861	4.51	278.4	5 794.9	7.7342	4.86
30	218.4	5 244.9	7.5214	4.36	230.5	5 697.8	7.6646	4.70
40	162.6	5 125.1	7.4225	4.13	171.3	5 554.2	7.5581	4.46
50	129.4	5 039.0	7.3482	3.95	136.2	5 450.6	7.4783	4.28
60	107.4	4 972.8	7.2890	3.82	113.0	5 370.8	7.4148	4.13
70	91.86	4 919.7	7.2399	3.72	96.54	5 306.6	7.3623	4.02
80	80.22	4 875.7	7.1982	3.62	84.25	5 253.4	7.3176	3.92
90	71.20	4 838.5	7.1619	3.56	74.73	5 208.2	7.2788	3.84
100	64.02	4 806.3	7.1298	3.49	67.15	5 169.2	7.2445	3.77
150	42.59	4 692.8	7.0098	3.25	44.59	5 030.7	7.1167	3.50
200	31.98	4 621.5	6.9277	3.10	33.44	4 943.4	7.0295	3.34
300	21.46	4 533.7	6.8158	2.91	22.39	4 834.9	6.9110	3.12
400	16.23	4 480.1	6.7388	2.78	16.91	4 768.1	6.8299	2.98
500	13.11	4 443.5	6.6803	2.69	13.65	4 722.0	6.7684	2.87
600	11.04	4 416.8	6.6332	2.62	11.48	4 688.1	6.7190	2.80
	T=3300 °K				T=3400 °K			
1	8 881	9 305.0	9.5777	8.68	9 546	10 180.6	9.8380	8.79
2	4 230	8 485.2	9.1484	7.88	4 534	9 284.8	9.3861	8.09
3	2 746	8 051.3	8.9151	7.42	2 938	8 806.0	9.1394	7.66
4	2 031	7 763.5	8.7572	7.10	2 161	8 486.6	8.9720	7.34
5	1 596	7 551.6	8.6390	6.84	1 704	8 250.3	8.8466	7.10
6	1 316	7 385.7	8.5451	6.65	1 404	8 064.7	8.7469	6.91
7	1 119	7 250.3	8.4676	6.48	1 192	7 912.9	8.6645	6.75
8	971.7	7 136.7	8.4018	6.34	1 035	7 785.1	8.5945	6.61
9	858.3	7 039.3	8.3448	6.21	913.4	7 675.3	8.5338	6.49
10	768.2	6 954.3	8.2946	6.09	817.1	7 579.4	8.4803	6.38
12	634.3	6 812.0	8.2095	5.90	674.0	7 418.3	8.3896	6.19
14	539.6	6 696.3	8.1393	5.75	572.9	7 287.0	8.3148	6.04
16	469.2	6 599.5	8.0796	5.62	497.8	7 176.9	8.2512	5.91
18	414.8	6 516.7	8.0280	5.51	439.8	7 082.5	8.1961	5.79
20	371.6	6 444.6	7.9825	5.40	393.8	7 000.1	8.1475	5.69
25	294.4	6 298.0	7.8864	5.19	311.6	6 832.3	8.0471	5.48
30	243.6	6 184.3	7.8136	5.03	257.6	6 701.7	7.9673	5.31
40	180.8	6 015.7	7.6994	4.77	190.8	6 507.1	7.8454	5.05
50	143.5	5 893.5	7.6140	4.58	151.4	6 365.7	7.7542	4.86
60	119.0	5 799.1	7.5460	4.43	125.3	6 256.1	7.6818	4.70
70	101.5	5 723.1	7.4898	4.30	106.9	6 167.5	7.6219	4.57
80	88.55	5 659.8	7.4421	4.20	93.14	6 093.7	7.5710	4.47
90	78.50	5 606.1	7.4006	4.12	82.52	6 030.9	7.5269	4.38
100	70.50	5 559.5	7.3641	4.04	74.06	5 976.4	7.4880	4.30
150	46.72	5 393.9	7.2280	3.76	48.98	5 781.8	7.3432	4.00
200	34.98	5 288.9	7.1354	3.58	36.62	5 657.8	7.2450	3.80
300	23.37	5 157.6	7.0099	3.34	24.42	5 501.8	7.1122	3.55
400	17.63	5 076.1	6.9243	3.18	18.39	5 404.2	7.0218	3.88
500	14.21	5 019.4	6.8595	3.06	14.80	5 335.9	6.9535	3.25
600	11.94	4 977.3	6.8076	2.98	12.43	5 284.8	6.8990	3.17

continued

p, bar	v	i	s	c_p	v	i	s	c_p
	T=3500 °K				T=3600 °K			
1	10 239	11 062.2	10.0928	8.89	10 954	11 936.3	10.3383	8.64
2	4 854	10 100.0	9.6215	8.19	5 188	10 922.0	9.8522	8.22
3	3 141	9 579.6	9.3627	7.80	3 353	10 364.6	9.5830	7.88
4	2 308	9 230.4	9.1867	7.53	2 462	9 981.1	9.3993	7.63
5	1 818	8 971.2	9.0546	7.31	1 938	9 707.3	9.2612	7.41
6	1 497	8 766.8	8.9495	7.12	1 594	9 485.3	9.1510	7.25
7	1 270	8 599.2	8.8625	6.96	1 352	9 302.8	9.0598	7.10
8	1 102	8 457.8	8.7886	6.83	1 172	9 148.6	8.9823	6.97
9	972.0	8 336.1	8.7244	6.71	1 034	9 015.5	8.9150	6.86
10	869.1	8 229.5	8.6679	6.60	923.8	8 898.8	8.8556	6.77
12	716.2	8 050.3	8.5720	6.42	760.8	8 702.1	8.7548	6.59
14	608.3	7 903.8	8.4927	6.27	645.7	8 541.0	8.6713	6.45
16	528.2	7 780.6	8.4253	6.14	560.4	8 405.1	8.6004	6.33
18	466.4	7 674.7	8.3669	6.03	494.6	8 288.3	8.5389	6.22
20	417.4	7 582.3	8.3154	5.93	442.3	8 186.0	8.4847	6.12
25	330.0	7 393.3	8.2089	5.73	349.3	7 976.4	8.3724	5.93
30	272.4	7 245.7	8.1242	5.56	288.2	7 812.3	8.2830	5.76
40	201.6	7 025.1	7.9949	5.30	212.9	7 566.0	8.1465	5.51
50	159.7	6 864.2	7.8972	5.10	168.5	7 385.6	8.0442	5.31
60	132.1	6 739.0	7.8211	4.95	139.2	7 244.9	7.9629	5.16
70	112.6	6 637.6	7.7575	4.82	118.6	7 130.5	7.8957	5.03
80	98.02	6 553.0	7.7035	4.71	103.2	7 034.9	7.8386	4.93
90	86.79	6 480.7	7.6567	4.62	91.31	6 953.2	7.7891	4.83
100	77.86	6 418.0	7.6154	4.53	81.87	6 882.1	7.7455	4.75
150	51.38	6 193.2	7.4619	4.22	53.92	6 626.2	7.5833	4.43
200	38.35	6 049.0	7.3579	4.02	40.19	6 461.2	7.4734	4.22
300	25.52	5 866.8	7.2175	3.75	26.68	6 251.5	7.3254	3.94
400	19.19	5 752.0	7.1221	3.57	20.04	6 118.6	7.2248	3.76
500	15.43	5 671.1	7.0502	3.43	16.09	6 024.4	7.1492	3.62
600	12.94	5 610.3	6.9928	3.35	13.48	5 953.2	7.0890	3.52
	T=3700 °K				T=3800 °K			
1	11 679	12 785.7	10.5704	8.29	12 402	13 591.3	10.7848	7.74
2	5 533	11 740.8	10.0759	8.13	5 884	12 544.7	10.2897	7.92
3	3 574	11 153.4	9.7984	7.87	3 801	11 937.4	10.0068	7.77
4	2 622	10 752.9	9.6081	7.66	2 788	11 517.7	9.8114	7.62
5	2 063	10 452.6	9.4646	7.47	2 192	11 200.8	9.6634	7.47
6	1 696	10 214.3	9.3500	7.33	1 802	10 948.2	9.5450	7.34
7	1 437	10 018.0	9.2550	7.19	1 526	10 739.2	9.4466	7.23
8	1 246	9 851.6	9.1741	7.07	1 322	10 561.9	9.3628	7.13
9	1 098	9 707.9	9.1039	6.97	1 165	10 408.2	9.2899	7.03
10	981.1	9 581.6	9.0419	6.87	1 041	10 273.1	9.2255	6.95
12	807.4	9 368.4	8.9365	6.71	856.1	10 044.4	9.1160	6.80
14	685.0	9 193.3	8.8493	6.58	725.9	9 856.2	9.0253	6.66
16	594.1	9 045.5	8.7751	6.46	629.3	9 697.0	8.9481	6.56
18	524.1	8 918.0	8.7107	6.36	554.9	9 559.5	8.8810	6.46
20	468.5	8 806.3	8.6339	6.27	495.9	9 438.8	8.8218	6.37
25	369.7	5 877.0	8.5361	6.08	391.0	9 190.5	8.6990	6.18
30	304.8	8 396.8	8.4424	5.92	322.1	8 995.0	8.6012	6.04
40	224.9	8 125.6	8.2991	5.67	237.4	8 699.7	8.4515	5.79
50	177.8	7 926.1	8.1916	5.48	187.5	8 481.9	8.3383	5.62
60	146.8	7 770.0	8.1061	5.34	154.7	8 311.0	8.2480	5.47
70	124.9	7 643.0	8.0354	5.20	131.6	8 171.5	8.1756	5.35
80	108.6	7 536.5	7.9754	5.10	114.4	8 054.2	8.1128	5.25
90	96.09	7 445.3	7.9233	5.01	101.1	7 953.8	8.0582	5.15
100	86.11	7 365.8	7.8774	4.93	90.56	7 866.1	8.0101	5.07
150	56.57	7 078.6	7.7066	4.62	59.40	7 547.9	7.8312	4.77
200	42.12	6 892.6	7.5910	4.40	44.15	7 340.7	7.7099	4.55
300	27.91	6 654.6	7.4352	4.12	29.19	7 074.3	7.5466	4.27
400	20.92	6 502.9	7.3296	3.93	21.85	6 903.4	7.4358	4.08
500	16.78	6 394.9	7.2502	3.78	17.50	6 781.2	7.3527	3.94
600	14.04	6 312.9	7.1870	3.68	14.63	6 688.0	7.2864	3.83

continued

p, bar	v	i	s	c_p	v	i	s	c_p
	T=3900 °K				T=4000 °K			
1	13 107	14 333.4	10.9774	7.05	13 784	14 999.2	11.1456	6.24
2	6 238	13 319.5	10.4905	7.54	6 588	14 050.0	10.6751	7.07
3	4 032	12 706.6	10.2059	7.57	4 264	13 447.5	10.3932	7.20
4	2 957	12 274.4	10.0074	7.49	3 129	13 013.1	10.1939	7.26
5	2 325	11 945.0	9.8561	7.39	2 461	12 677.0	10.0409	7.24
6	1 910	11 680.7	9.7346	7.29	2 022	12 404.9	9.9174	7.18
7	1 618	11 461.1	9.6335	7.20	1 712	12 177.4	9.8143	7.12
8	1 402	11 274.1	9.5471	7.11	1 483	11 982.7	9.7260	7.06
9	1 235	11 111.7	9.4720	7.03	1 306	11 813.1	9.6489	7.00
10	1 103	10 968.5	9.4055	6.95	1 166	11 663.1	9.5807	6.94
12	906.6	10 725.7	9.2923	6.82	958.6	11 407.8	9.4644	6.83
14	768.4	10 525.2	9.1984	6.70	812.2	11 196.5	9.3677	6.73
16	665.9	10 355.4	9.1184	6.61	703.7	11 016.9	9.2852	6.63
18	587.0	10 208.5	9.0489	6.51	620.2	10 861.3	9.2135	6.54
20	524.4	10 079.4	8.9875	6.43	553.9	10 674.4	9.1501	6.46
25	413.2	9 813.2	8.8600	6.25	436.2	10 441.4	9.0184	6.29
30	340.2	9 603.0	8.7584	6.14	356.9	10 217.5	8.9134	6.16
40	250.5	9 284.9	8.6028	5.89	264.1	9 877.5	8.7521	5.95
50	197.7	9 049.3	8.4858	5.72	208.2	9 625.1	8.6309	5.79
60	163.0	8 864.1	8.3926	5.58	171.6	9 426.3	8.5343	5.66
70	138.5	8 712.7	8.3155	5.46	145.8	9 263.3	8.4543	5.55
80	120.4	8 585.2	8.2500	5.36	126.6	9 125.9	8.3862	5.45
90	106.3	8 475.6	8.1931	5.27	111.8	9 007.6	8.3271	5.35
100	95.20	8 379.9	8.1429	5.19	100.0	8 904.2	8.2750	5.27
150	62.35	8 031.4	7.9561	4.89	65.41	8 526.3	8.0808	5.00
200	46.28	7 803.3	7.8294	4.68	48.50	8 277.8	7.9490	4.78
300	30.54	7 508.5	7.6588	4.41	31.95	7 955.2	7.7713	4.52
400	22.83	7 318.4	7.5430	4.22	23.84	7 745.9	7.6507	4.34
500	18.26	7 181.8	7.4562	4.07	19.05	7 594.9	7.5602	4.18
600	15.25	7 077.2	7.3870	3.96	15.90	7 479.0	7.4881	4.07

Volume fractions of O, O_2, CO and CO_2 and molecular weight M of dissociated carbon dioxide [56–58]

p, bar	M	x_O	x_{O_2}	x_{CO}	x_{CO_2}	M	x_O	x_{O_2}	x_{CO}	x_{CO_2}
	T=1900 °K					T=2000 °K				
1	43.827		0.0042	0.0084	0.9874	43.682		0.0075	0.0150	0.9775
2	43.865		0.0034	0.0066	0.9900	43.749		0.0059	0.0119	0.9822
4	43.895		0.0026	0.0053	0.9921	43.803		0.0047	0.0095	0.9858
6	43.909		0.0023	0.0046	0.9931	43.829		0.0041	0.0083	0.9876
8	43.919		0.0021	0.0042	0.9937	43.846		0.0038	0.0075	0.9887
10	43.925		0.0020	0.0039	0.9941	43.857		0.0035	0.0070	0.9895
12	43.930		0.0018	0.0037	0.9945	43.865		0.0033	0.0066	0.9901
14	43.934		0.0017	0.0035	0.9948	43.874		0.0031	0.0063	0.9906
16	43.938		0.0016	0.0034	0.9950	43.880		0.0030	0.0060	0.9910
18	43.941		0.0016	0.0032	0.9952	43.885		0.0029	0.0057	0.9914
20	43.943		0.0016	0.0031	0.9953	43.889		0.0028	0.0056	0.9916
30	43.952		0.0014	0.0027	0.9959	43.904		0.0024	0.0049	0.9927
40	43.957		0.0012	0.0025	0.9963	43.914		0.0022	0.0044	0.9934
60	43.964		0.0010	0.0022	0.9968	43.927		0.0019	0.0039	0.9942
80	43.968		0.0010	0.0019	0.9971	43.934		0.0018	0.0035	0.9947
100	43.971		0.0009	0.0018	0.9973	43.940		0.0016	0.0033	0.9951
200	43.979		0.0007	0.0014	0.9979	43.954		0.0013	0.0026	0.9961
400	43.986		0.0006	0.0011	0.9983	43.966		0.0010	0.0021	0.9969
600	43.989		0.0005	0.0010	0.9985	43.972		0.0009	0.0018	0.9973
	T=2100 °K					T=2200 °K				
1	43.456	0.0001	0.0125	0.0252	0.9622	43.123	0.0004	0.0199	0.0401	0.9396
2	43.569		0.0100	0.0201	0.9699	43.302	0.0002	0.0159	0.0321	0.9518
4	43.659		0.0080	0.0160	0.9760	43.445	0.0002	0.0128	0.0256	0.9614

continued

p, bar	M	x_O	x_{O_2}	x_{CO}	x_{CO_2}	M	x_O	x_{O_2}	x_{CO}	x_{CO_2}
6	43.703		0.0070	0.0140	0.9790	43.516	0.0001	0.0112	0.0225	0.9662
8	43.731		0.0064	0.0127	0.9809	43.561		0.0102	0.0205	0.9693
10	43.751		0.0059	0.0118	0.9823	43.593		0.0095	0.0190	0.9715
12	43.766		0.0055	0.0112	0.9833	43.617		0.0089	0.0179	0.9732
14	43.778		0.0053	0.0106	0.9841	43.636		0.0085	0.0170	0.9745
16	43.788		0.0051	0.0101	0.9848	43.652		0.0081	0.0163	0.9756
18	43.797		0.0049	0.0097	0.9854	53.666		0.0078	0.0157	0.9765
20	43.804		0.0047	0.0094	0.9859	43.678		0.0075	0.0152	0.9773
30	43.830		0.0041	0.0082	0.9877	43.720		0.0066	0.0133	0.9801
40	43.847		0.0037	0.0075	0.9888	43.746		0.0060	0.0121	0.9819
60	43.867		0.0033	0.0065	0.9902	43.779		0.0053	0.0105	0.9842
80	43.880		0.0030	0.0059	0.9911	43.800		0.0048	0.0096	0.9856
100	43.890		0.0028	0.0055	0.9917	43.816		0.0044	0.0089	0.9867
200	43.915		0.0022	0.0044	0.9934	43.856		0.0035	0.0071	0.9894
400	43.934		0.0017	0.0035	0.9948	43.886		0.0028	0.0056	0.9916
600	43.944		0.0015	0.0030	0.9955	43.903		0.0025	0.0049	0.9926
			T=2300 °K					T=2400 °K		
1	42.658	0.0009	0.0300	0.0609	0.9082	42.036	0.0018	0.0433	0.0883	0.8666
2	42.927	0.0006	0.0242	0.0489	0.9263	42.422	0.0011	0.0351	0.0714	0.8924
4	43.144	0.0004	0.0194	0.0392	0.9410	42.735	0.0007	0.0284	0.0575	0.9134
6	43.251	0.0003	0.0171	0.0344	0.9482	42.891	0.0006	0.0250	0.0506	0.9238
8	43.319	0.0002	0.0156	0.0314	0.9528	42.990	0.0005	0.0228	0.0462	0.9305
10	43.367	0.0002	0.0145	0.0292	0.9561	43.060	0.0004	0.0213	0.0430	0.9353
12	43.405	0.0002	0.0137	0.0275	0.9586	43.115	0.0004	0.0201	0.0405	0.9390
14	43.434	0.0001	0.0130	0.0262	0.9607	43.158	0.0003	0.0192	0.0386	0.9419
16	43.459	0.0001	0.0125	0.0250	0.9624	43.194	0.0003	0.0183	0.0370	0.9444
18	43.480	0.0001	0.0120	0.0241	0.9638	43.225	0.0003	0.0177	0.0356	0.9464
20	43.498	0.0001	0.0116	0.0233	0.9650	43.251	0.0003	0.0171	0.0344	0.9482
30	43.562		0.0102	0.0204	0.9694	43.345	0.0002	0.0150	0.0302	0.9546
40	43.602		0.0093	0.0186	0.9721	43.405	0.0002	0.0137	0.0275	0.9586
60	43.653		0.0081	0.0163	0.9756	43.480	0.0001	0.0120	0.0241	0.9638
80	43.686		0.0074	0.0148	0.9778	43.528	0.0001	0.0109	0.0219	0.9671
100	43.709		0.0068	0.0138	0.9794	43.562		0.0102	0.0204	0.9694
200	43.771		0.0055	0.0109	0.9836	43.654		0.0081	0.0163	0.9756
400	43.820		0.0044	0.0087	0.9869	43.727		0.0065	0.0129	0.9806
600	43.903		0.0038	0.0076	0.9886	43.762		0.0056	0.0113	0.9831
			T=2500 °K					T=2600 °K		
1	41.242	0.0035	0.0596	0.1229	0.8140	40.275	0.0065	0.0787	0.1640	0.7508
2	41.770	0.0023	0.0489	0.1000	0.8488	40.963	0.0042	0.0653	0.1349	0.7956
4	42.204	0.0014	0.0398	0.0811	0.8777	41.538	0.0027	0.0537	0.1102	0.8334
6	42.420	0.0011	0.0352	0.0715	0.8922	41.827	0.0021	0.0478	0.0976	0.8525
8	42.558	0.0009	0.0322	0.0654	0.9015	42.013	0.0017	0.0439	0.0895	0.8649
10	42.657	0.0008	0.0301	0.0610	0.9081	42.147	0.0015	0.0411	0.0836	0.8738
12	42.734	0.0007	0.0285	0.0576	0.9132	42.250	0.0013	0.0389	0.0790	0.8808
14	42.796	0.0006	0.0271	0.0549	0.9174	42.333	0.0012	0.0371	0.0754	0.8863
16	42.846	0.0006	0.0260	0.0526	0.9208	42.402	0.0011	0.0356	0.0723	0.8910
18	42.889	0.0005	0.0251	0.0507	0.9237	42.461	0.0010	0.0344	0.0697	0.8949
20	42.926	0.0005	0.0243	0.0490	0.9262	42.511	0.0009	0.0333	0.0675	0.8983
30	43.059	0.0004	0.0213	0.0431	0.9352	42.692	0.0007	0.0294	0.0595	0.9104
40	43.143	0.0003	0.0195	0.0393	0.9409	42.808	0.0006	0.0269	0.0543	0.9182
60	43.250	0.0002	0.0171	0.0345	0.9482	42.954	0.0005	0.0236	0.0478	0.9281
80	43.318	0.0002	0.0156	0.0314	0.9528	43.048	0.0004	0.0216	0.0436	0.9344
100	43.367	0.0002	0.0145	0.0292	0.9561	43.115	0.0003	0.0201	0.0406	0.9390
200	43.497	0.0001	0.0116	0.0233	0.9650	43.295	0.0002	0.0161	0.0325	0.9512
400	43.602		0.0093	0.0186	0.9721	43.440	0.0001	0.0129	0.0259	0.9611
600	43.653		0.0081	0.0163	0.9756	43.511	0.0001	0.0113	0.0227	0.9659
			T=2700 °K					T=2800 °K		
1	39.144	0.0114	0.0997	0.2107	0.6782	37.876	0.0189	0.1211	0.2611	0.5989
2	40.005	0.0074	0.0840	0.1755	0.7331	38.908	0.0124	0.1041	0.2205	0.6630
4	40.735	0.0048	0.0700	0.1447	0.7805	39.802	0.0080	0.0880	0.1841	0.7199
6	41.107	0.0037	0.0626	0.1289	0.8048	40.262	0.0062	0.0793	0.1649	0.7496

continued

p, bar	M	X_O	X_{O_2}	X_{CO}	X_{CO_2}	M	X_O	X_{O_2}	X_{CO}	X_{CO_2}
8	41.348	0.0031	0.0577	0.1185	0.8207	40.563	0.0052	0.0735	0.1522	0.7691
10	41.522	0.0027	0.0542	0.1109	0.8322	40.781	0.0045	0.0692	0.1429	0.7834
12	41.656	0.0024	0.0514	0.1051	0.8411	40.951	0.0040	0.0658	0.1356	0.7946
14	41.765	0.0021	0.0491	0.1004	0.8484	41.088	0.0036	0.0631	0.1297	0.8036
16	41.855	0.0020	0.0472	0.0964	0.8544	41.203	0.0033	0.0607	0.1248	0.8112
18	41.932	0.0018	0.0456	0.0931	0.8595	41.301	0.0031	0.0588	0.1206	0.8175
20	41.999	0.0017	0.0442	0.0901	0.8640	41.385	0.0029	0.0570	0.1169	0.8232
30	42.238	0.0013	0.0392	0.0796	0.8799	41.690	0.0022	0.0507	0.1037	0.8434
40	42.391	0.0011	0.0359	0.0729	0.8901	41.886	0.0019	0.0466	0.0951	0.8564
60	42.585	0.0008	0.0317	0.0642	0.9033	42.137	0.0014	0.0413	0.0841	0.8732
80	42.710	0.0007	0.0290	0.0587	0.9116	42.298	0.0012	0.0379	0.0770	0.8839
100	42.799	0.0006	0.0271	0.0547	0.9176	42.414	0.0010	0.0354	0.0719	0.8917
200	43.041	0.0004	0.0218	0.0439	0.9339	42.729	0.0006	0.0286	0.0579	0.9129
400	43.235	0.0003	0.0175	0.0351	0.9471	42.984	0.0004	0.0230	0.0465	0.9301
600	43.331	0.0002	0.0153	0.0309	0.9536	43.109	0.0003	0.0203	0.0408	0.9386
	T=2900 °K					T=3000 °K				
1	36.509	0.0298	0.1413	0.3125	0.5164	35.088	0.0451	0.1585	0.3620	0.4344
2	37.700	0.0198	0.1242	0.2682	0.5878	36.413	0.0303	0.1431	0.3164	0.5102
4	38.752	0.0130	0.1070	0.2270	0.6530	37.610	0.0201	0.1260	0.2720	0.5819
6	39.303	0.0101	0.0973	0.2048	0.6878	38.248	0.0157	0.1158	0.2473	0.6212
8	39.666	0.0084	0.0907	0.1899	0.7110	38.671	0.0132	0.1086	0.2305	0.6477
10	39.931	0.0073	0.0858	0.1788	0.7281	38.984	0.0115	0.1032	0.2179	0.6674
12	40.138	0.0065	0.0818	0.1702	0.7415	39.228	0.0103	0.0989	0.2080	0.6828
14	40.306	0.0059	0.0766	0.1631	0.7524	39.428	0.0093	0.0953	0.1998	0.6956
16	40.447	0.0055	0.0759	0.1572	0.7614	39.595	0.0086	0.0922	0.1929	0.7063
18	40.567	0.0051	0.0735	0.1521	0.7693	39.738	0.0080	0.0895	0.1870	0.7155
20	40.671	0.0047	0.0715	0.1477	0.7761	39.864	0.0075	0.0872	0.1818	0.7235
30	41.049	0.0037	0.0639	0.1315	0.8009	40.318	0.0058	0.0785	0.1627	0.7530
40	41.293	0.0030	0.0590	0.1210	0.8170	40.614	0.0048	0.0727	0.1502	0.7723
60	41.607	0.0023	0.0525	0.1074	0.8378	40.996	0.0037	0.0651	0.1339	0.7973
80	41.810	0.0019	0.0483	0.0985	0.8513	41.244	0.0031	0.0600	0.1231	0.8138
100	41.956	0.0017	0.0452	0.0921	0.8610	41.424	0.0027	0.0563	0.1154	0.8256
200	42.355	0.0011	0.0367	0.0745	0.8877	41.917	0.0017	0.0461	0.0938	0.8584
400	42.680	0.0007	0.0297	0.0600	0.9096	42.323	0.0011	0.0374	0.0759	0.8856
600	42.842	0.0005	0.0262	0.0528	0.9205	42.525	0.0008	0.0331	0.0670	0.8991
	T=3200 °K					T=3400 °K				
1	32.251	0.0907	0.1775	0.4457	0.2861	29.617	0.1581	0.1710	0.4992	0.1717
2	33.753	0.0630	0.1710	0.4050	0.3610	31.181	0.1163	0.1789	0.4715	0.2333
4	35.169	0.0429	0.1588	0.3605	0.4378	32.712	0.0796	0.1778	0.4353	0.3073
6	35.950	0.0340	0.1499	0.3338	0.4823	33.580	0.0648	0.1733	0.4112	0.3507
8	36.479	0.0288	0.1430	0.3149	0.5133	34.180	0.0554	0.1690	0.3983	0.3823
10	36.875	0.0252	0.1376	0.3004	0.5368	34.635	0.0489	0.1650	0.3789	0.4072
12	37.188	0.0227	0.1330	0.2887	0.5556	35.000	0.0435	0.1614	0.3671	0.4280
14	37.446	0.0207	0.1291	0.2789	0.5713	35.302	0.0406	0.1583	0.3569	0.4442
16	37.664	0.0191	0.1257	0.2705	0.5847	35.560	0.0375	0.1553	0.4381	0.4591
18	37.852	0.0178	0.1227	0.2633	0.5962	35.784	0.0349	0.1527	0.3404	0.4720
20	38.017	0.0167	0.1201	0.2568	0.6064	35.982	0.0328	0.1502	0.3334	0.4836
30	38.623	0.0130	0.1099	0.2329	0.6442	36.717	0.0261	0.1404	0.3068	0.5267
40	39.025	0.0109	0.1028	0.2166	0.6697	37.213	0.0221	0.1331	0.2883	0.5566
60	39.551	0.0085	0.0933	0.1951	0.7031	37.873	0.0174	0.1228	0.2628	0.5970
80	39.897	0.0071	0.0868	0.1807	0.7254	38.314	0.0145	0.1156	0.2455	0.6244
100	40.150	0.0062	0.0820	0.1700	0.7418	38.640	0.0127	0.1100	0.2325	0.6448
200	40.854	0.0040	0.0681	0.1401	0.7878	39.563	0.0081	0.0933	0.1948	0.7038
400	41.444	0.0025	0.0560	0.1146	0.8269	40.356	0.0053	0.0781	0.1615	0.7551
600	41.742	0.0020	0.0498	0.1016	0.8466	40.762	0.0040	0.0700	0.1442	0.7818
	T=3600 °K					T=3800 °K				
1	27.328	0.2378	0.1425	0.5227	0.0970	25.478	0.3187	0.1036	0.5259	0.0518
2	28.852	0.1808	0.1648	0.5103	0.1441	26.851	0.2567	0.1344	0.5255	0.0834
4	30.407	0.1327	0.1775	0.4878	0.2020	28.345	0.1977	0.1594	0.5165	0.1264
6	31.312	0.1092	0.1804	0.4700	0.2404	29.245	0.1667	0.1700	0.5066	0.1567
8	31.948	0.0946	0.1805	0.4556	0.2693	29.887	0.1466	0.1754	0.4975	0.1805

continued

p, bar	M	x_O	x_{O_2}	x_{CO}	x_{CO}	M	x_O	x_{O_2}	x_{CO}	x_{CO_2}
10	32.435	0.0844	0.1796	0.4436	0.2924	30.385	0.1323	0.1784	0.4892	0.2001
12	32.829	0.0768	0.1782	0.4333	0.3117	30.790	0.1213	0.1801	0.4817	0.2169
14	33.159	0.0708	0.1767	0.4243	0.3282	31.132	0.1126	0.1811	0.4748	0.2365
16	33.442	0.0659	0.1752	0.4162	0.3427	31.427	0.1055	0.1815	0.4685	0.2445
18	33.689	0.0619	0.1736	0.4090	0.3555	31.686	0.0994	0.1816	0.4625	0.2565
20	33.909	0.0584	0.1720	0.4024	0.3672	31.917	0.0943	0.1815	0.4573	0.2669
30	34.735	0.0467	0.1649	0.3765	0.4119	32.795	0.0765	0.1793	0.4351	0.3091
40	35.301	0.0397	0.1590	0.3577	0.4436	33.405	0.0657	0.1762	0.4181	0.3400
60	36.068	0.0315	0.1498	0.3309	0.4878	34.245	0.0527	0.1701	0.3929	0.3843
80	36.589	0.0266	0.1427	0.3121	0.5186	34.823	0.0449	0.1647	0.3743	0.4161
100	36.978	0.0233	0.1371	0.2977	0.5419	35.260	0.0396	0.1600	0.3597	0.4407
200	38.103	0.0154	0.1194	0.2542	0.6110	36.547	0.0265	0.1437	0.3142	0.5156
400	39.095	0.0101	0.1021	0.2143	0.6735	37.715	0.0176	0.1261	0.2697	0.5866
600	39.613	0.0078	0.0925	0.1929	0. 7068	38.339	0.0138	0.1157	0.2451	0.6254

p, bar	M	x_O	x_{O_2}	x_{CO}	x_{CO_2}	p, bar	M	x_O	x_{O_2}	x_{CO}	x_{CO_2}
					T=4000 °K						
1	24.130	0.3857	0.0672	0.5201	0.0270	20	30.076	0.1402	0.1776	0.4952	0.1870
2	25.243	0.3295	0.0981	0.5257	0.0467	30	30.977	0.1157	0.1817	0.4788	0.2238
4	26.579	0.2677	0.1295	0.5268	0.0760	40	31.606	0.1005	0.1824	0.4653	0.2518
6	27.429	0.2320	0.1459	0.5239	0.0982	60	32.486	0.0817	0.1811	0.4440	0.2932
8	28.051	0.2078	0.1560	0.5198	0.1164	80	33.100	0.0703	0.1786	0.4275	0.3236
10	28.539	0.1898	0.1628	0.5155	0.1319	100	33.568	0.0624	0.1758	0.4141	0.3477
12	28.942	0.1759	0.1677	0.5122	0.1442	200	34.971	0.0425	0.1637	0.3699	0.4239
14	29.284	0.1645	0.1712	0.5070	0.1573	400	36.279	0.0286	0.1478	0.3242	0.4994
16	29.580	0.1551	0.1739	0.5029	0.1681	600	36.991	0.0225	0.1376	0.2978	0.5421
18	29.842	0.1471	0.1759	0.4991	0.1779						

Viscosity η ($N \cdot s/m^2$) of gaseous carbon dioxide at $p = 1$ bar [60]

T, °K	$\eta \cdot 10^7$	T, °K	$\eta \cdot 10^7$	T, °K	$\eta \cdot 10^7$
500	236.8	1200	446.2	1750	565.8
600	273.3	1250	458.2	1800	576.2
700	306.9	1300	470.1	1900	595.4
800	338.2	1400	492.9	2000	614.3
900	367.5	1500	514.8	2500	700.4
1000	395.1	1600	535.9		
1100	421.3	1700	556.4		

Viscosity $\eta \cdot 10^7$ ($N \cdot s/m^2$) of carbon dioxide at different temperatures and pressures [59]

p, bar \ t, °C →	—15	—10	0	10	20	30	40	50	60
1	129.5	131.5	136.5	141.3	146.0	150.6	155.3	159.9	164.4
5	133.0	134.9	139.2	143.6	148.2	152.6	156.8	161.4	165.4
10	137.5	138.6	142.0	146.1	150.5	154.6	157.7	162.6	167.2
20	153.1	150.4	149.3	152.0	155.7	159.0	162.0	165.9	170.2
30			161.0	159.8	162.1	164.6	167.2	170.2	173.3
40				172.6	170.9	171.7	173.0	175.0	177.3
50					183.8	181.6	180.9	181.5	182.8
60					200.4	196.2	192.2	190.0	189.7
70					734.2	227.2	210.2	202.7	199.4
80					771.2	529.1	242.1	222.4	214.0
90					803.4	592.7	320.5	258.7	235.6
100					833.6	644.9	453.9	315.9	271.9
110					860.5	685.5	529.4	373.0	315.2

continued

t, °C → / p, bar	—12	—10	0	10	20	30	40	50	60
120					885.6	720.3	580.3	427.2	355.2
130					909.4	751.7	619.4	474.9	390.5
140					931.9	779.6	652.4	510.4	425.2
150					951.4	804.8	681.0	553.0	459.1
200					1039.4	907.6	792.3	692.9	600.0
250					1112.6	987.1	881.1	787.5	696.7
300					1177.2	1055.8	954.4	863.2	777.0
350					1236.0	1116.7	1018.8	928.1	845.6
400					1291.6	1173.6	1075.9	987.5	907.6
450					1345.6	1228.6	1130.7	1042.5	963.8
500					1398.6	1280.8	1182.2	1095.2	1016.5
550					1448.0	1330.0	1231.0	1145.0	1067.0
600					1495.6	1378.1	1279.2	1191.8	1114.0

t, °C → / p, bar	80	100	150	200	300	400	600	800	1000
1	173.4	182.3	203.8	224.3	262.7	297.9	360.4	415.0	464.3
5	174.4	183.0	204.3	224.9	263.2	298.4	360.7	415.3	464.5
10	175.4	184.0	205.0	225.7	263.8	298.9	361.1	415.6	464.7
20	177.6	186.0	206.9	227.5	264.9	299.9	361.8	416.1	465.2
30	180.4	188.2	208.8	229.0	266.2	300.9	362.5	416.7	465.7
40	183.4	191.1	210.3	230.8	267.6	302.9	363.3	417.3	466.2
50	187.8	194.7	213.8	233.1	269.1	303.1	364.1	417.9	466.7
60	193.4	199.1	216.5	235.5	270.7	304.3	364.9	418.6	467.3
70	200.3	204.4	219.4	237.9	272.5	305.6	366.0	419.3	467.8
80	209.1	210.3	222.8	240.6	274.4	307.0	366.9	420.0	468.4
90	221.3	217.2	226.1	243.1	276.4	308.5	367.9	420.7	469.0
100	236.6	224.3	229.8	246.2	278.5	310.2	369.0	421.5	469.6
110	255.3	233.2	234.4	249.4	280.7	311.8	370.0	422.3	470.2
120	276.7	243.3	238.9	254.8	283.1	313.7	370.9	423.2	470.9
130	298.7	255.0	243.9	256.6	285.4	315.2	372.2	424.1	471.6
140	322.8	268.1	249.4	260.7	287.9	317.5	373.6	424.9	472.3
150	345.7	281.9	255.1	264.7	290.4	319.1	374.7	425.8	473.0
200	461.8	371.8	296.5	291.7	304.7	329.3	381.1	430.6	476.7
250	560.9	463.5	345.5	319.8	321.7	341.1	388.5	435.8	480.7
300	642.5	542.2	396.5	351.6	339.6	353.3	396.1	441.3	485.1
350	713.6	611.4	445.0	385.5	359.1	366.7	404.4	447.2	489.6
400	777.8	674.2	493.0	421.0	379.0	380.9	413.0	453.4	494.4
450	835.0	730.1	540.6	456.9	400.5	395.2	421.8	459.7	499.3
500	889.0	784.4	585.9	490.7	422.0	410.2	430.9	466.2	504.3
550	942.3	835.0	629.3	523.7	443.1	425.4	440.3	472.9	509.5
600	986.7	880.4	668.0	556.5	465.0	440.8	449.8	479.8	514.8

Viscosity $\eta \cdot 10^7$ ($N \cdot s/m^2$) of carbon dioxide in the critical region [352]

T, °K → / p, bar	300	302	304.19	306	308	310	315	320
60	193.9	192.4	191.2	190.5	189.9	189.4	188.9	188.8
62	199.1	196.8	195.0	193.9	192.9	192.3	191.2	190.9
64	205.9	202.1	199.4	197.8	196.4	195.4	193.8	193.0
66	215.8	209.0	204.7	202.3	200.4	198.9	196.6	195.4
68	556.4	218.9	211.5	207.9	205.0	202.9	199.6	197.9
70	580.2	237.3	220.8	214.8	210.5	207.6	203.0	200.6
72	598.7	529.8	235.8	224.2	217.4	213.1	206.8	203.6
74	613.7	554.0	436.8	238.4	226.4	219.8	211.1	206.8
76	627.1	573.4	491.4	268.9	239.1	228.4	216.1	210.5
78	639.3	589.1	521.0	422.5	260.5	239.9	221.8	214.4
80	650.1	603.5	542.4	474.0	311.1	256.9	228.7	218.9

Viscosity $\eta \cdot 10^7$ ($N \cdot s/m^2$) of dissociated carbon dioxide at high temperatures [353]

T, °K \ p, bar →	0.01	1	100	T, °K \ p, bar →	0.01	1	100
1600	564	564	564	3000	1007	948	899
1800	615	614	614	3200	1061	1020	952
2000	667	663	662	3400	1113	1092	1008
2200	743	712	709	3600	1164	1161	1069
2400	790	762	755	3800	1215	1222	1133
2600	866	817	802	3900	1241	1249	1165
2800	942	879	849	4000	1266	1275	1199

Thermal conductivity $\lambda \cdot 10^3$ (W/m · deg) of carbon dioxide at different temperatures and pressures [15]

T, °K \ p, bar →	1	10	20	30	40	50	60	70	80	90
220	10.70	177	178	179	180	181	182	183	184	185
230	11.47	162	163	164	165	166	167	168	169	171
240	12.20		149.8	151	152	153	154	155	156	157
250	12.95		136	137	138	139	141	142	143	144
260	13.65			125	126	127	129	130	131	132
270	14.45	15.4	16.3	18.0	115	117	118	119	120	122
280	15.20	16.1	17.3	18.6	21.0	104	106	108	110	111
290	15,95	16.7	17.7	19.0	21.1	22.0	92	95	98	100
300	16.55	17.4	18.4	19.4	21.4	23.0	26.4			
310	17.40	18.2	19.0	20.2	21.6	23.4	25.6	29.1	34.6	93.8
320	18.05	18.8	19.6	20.8	21.9	23.8	25.4	27.9	31.4	36.4
330	18.95	19.7	20.5	21.5	22.7	24.2	25.7	27.5	30.2	33.6
340	19.70	20.4	21.2	22.1	23.2	24.7	25.8	27.4	29.6	32.2
350	20.4	21.1	21.9	22.7	23.8	25.0	26.1	27.6	29.4	31.4
360	21.2	21.8	22.6	23.3	24.4	25.4	26.6	28.2	29.5	31.2
370	21.95	22.6	23.3	24.1	25.0	26.0	27.1	28.3	29.7	31.3
380	22.75	23.4	24.1	24.8	25.6	26.6	27.6	28.7	30.0	31.4
390	23.5	24.1	24.8	25.5	26.3	27.2	28.2	29.1	30.3	31.5
400	24.3	24.8	25.5	26.2	27.0	27.8	28.7	29.7	30.7	31.6
450	28.3	28.8	29.3	30.0	30.6	31.3	32.0	32.8	33.6	34.4
500	32.5	33.0	33.5	34.0	34.5	35.1	35.8	36.4	36.9	37.7
550	36.6	37.1	37.6	38.0	38.5	39.0	39.6	40.1	40.7	41.2
600	40.7	41.1	41.5	41.9	42.4	42.8	43.3	43.8	44.3	44.8
650	44.5	45.0	45.2	45.6	46.0	46.4	46.8	47.3	47.7	48.2
700	48.1	48.4	48.8	49.2	49.5	49.8	50.3	50.7	51.1	51.4
750	51.7	52.1	52.4	52.7	53.0	53.4	53.7	54.1	54.4	54.8
800	55.1	55.4	55.7	56.0	56.3	56.6	57.0	57.3	57.6	58.0
850	58.5	58.8	59.1	59.3	59.6	59.8	60.1	60.4	60.7	61.0
900	61.8	62.0	62.2	62.5	62.8	63.0	63.3	63.5	63.8	64.1
950	65.0	65.2	65.4	65.6	65.8	66.0	66.3	66.6	66.9	67.2
1000	68.1	68.3	68.5	68.6	68.8	68.9	69.2	69.4	69.7	70.0
1100	74.4	74.6	74.8	75.0	75.2	75.3	75.5	75.8	76.0	76.2
1200	80.3	80.5	80.7	80.8	81.0	81.2	81.4	81.6	81.8	82.0
1300	86.2	86.4	86.6	86.7	86.9	87.0	87.2	87.4	87.5	87.7
1400	92.1	92.3	92.5	92.6	92.8	92.9	93.0	93.2	93.4	93.5

T, °K \ p, bar →	100	110	120	130	140	150	160	170	180	190
220	186	187	188	189	190	191	192	193	194	195
230	171	172	173	174	175	176	177	178	179	180
240	158	159	160	161	162	163	164	165	166	167
250	145	147	148	149	150	151	152	153	154	155

continued

T, °K ↓ / p, bar →	100	110	120	130	140	150	160	170	180	190
260	133	134	135	136	137	138	139	140	142	143
270	123	124	125	126	127	128	130	131	132	133
280	113	114	116	117	118	119	120	121	123	124
290	101	103	104	105	107	109	110	112	113	114
300	90	93	95	97	99	101	102	103	105	107
310	67.2	74.4				91	93	95	97	99
320	44.6	54.9	63.5	69.0	73.5					
330	37.7	43.2	49.6	56.0	61.2	66.2	70.4	73.4	76.2	
340	35.3	38.7	42.9	47.4	52.3	56.7	64.5	68.1	70.9	75.9
350	33.9	36.8	39.6	43.0	46.7	50.3	54.2	57.0	60.4	63.6
360	33.4	35.5	38.0	40.7	43.4	46.4	49.6	52.6	55.6	58.4
370	32.9	35.0	37.2	39.3	41.4	44.0	46.6	48.4	51.8	54.4
380	31.1	34.7	36.6	38.0	40.4	42.4	44.6	46.9	49.3	51.5
390	33.0	34.5	36.2	37.8	39.8	41.6	43.4	45.6	47.4	49.2
400	33.2	34.4	36.1	37.2	38.6	40.9	42.5	44.2	46.0	48.3
450	35.3	36.3	37.1	38.2	39.4	40.5	41.3	42.5	43.4	45.3
500	38.3	38.4	39.8	40.6	41.4	42.2	43.2	44.3	45.1	46.0
550	41.7	42.3	43.1	43.6	44.3	45.0	45.6	46.4	47.1	47.9
600	45.4	45.9	46.3	46.9	47.4	48.1	48.5	49.2	49.7	50.4
650	48.6	49.1	49.5	49.9	50.5	50.9	51.4	52.0	52.4	53.1
700	51.7	52.3	52.7	53.2	53.7	54.0	54.5	55.0	55.4	55.8
750	55.2	55.5	55.9	56.4	56.7	57.2	57.6	58.0	58.4	58.8
800	58.2	58.6	59.1	59.3	59.8	60.2	60.5	60.9	61.2	61.9
850	61.4	61.7	62.1	62.4	62.8	63.2	63.6	63.9	64.2	64.6
900	64.2	64.4	64.9	65.3	65.8	66.0	66.4	66.8	67.2	67.6
950	67.4	67.8	68.1	68.4	68.7	69.0	69.3	69.6	69.9	70.2
1000	70.2	70.5	70.9	71.2	71.5	71.9	72.2	72.4	72.7	73.0
1100	76.5	76.7	76.9	77.2	77.4	77.7	78.0	78.2	78.5	78.8
1200	82.2	82.4	82.6	82.8	83.0	83.3	83.5	83.7	84.0	84.2
1300	87.9	88.1	88.3	88.5	88.7	88.9	89.2	89.4	89.6	89.8
1400	93.7	93.9	94.1	94.4	94.6	94.8	95.0	95.2	95.4	95.7

T, °K ↓ / p, bar →	200	250	300	350	400	450	500	550	600
220	196	198	203	206	208	211	215	218	221
230	182	186	189	193	196	200	203	206	209
240	168	172	176	181	185	189	192	196	200
250	156	160	164	169	173	177	181	185	189
260	144	149	154	158	162	166	170	174	178
270	134	139	144	148	152	156	160	164	168
280	125	129	134	139	143	147	151	155	159
290	115	120	125	130	134	138	142	146	150
300	108	114	119	123	128	132	136	139	143
310	100	106	111	116	120	124	128	132	136
320	92	99	106	110	114	118	122	126	130
330									
340									
350	66.6	77.6							
360	60.6	72.4							
370	56.9	67.6	76.2						
380	53.6	63.7	72.4	79.0					
390	51.3	60.1	74.7	75.6	81.5				
400	49.5	58.1	65.4	62.9	78.5				
450	46.2	52.2	57.9	63.3	68.3	72.9	77.7	80.9	85.1
500	46.9	51.3	55.9	60.2	64.5	68.3	71.8	75.1	78.7
550	48.6	52.5	56.3	59.7	63.2	66.5	69.8	72.9	75.6
600	51.1	54.3	57.7	60.7	63.6	66.6	69.4	72.1	74.7
650	53.8	56.4	59.4	62.1	64.7	67.3	69.8	72.3	73.5
700	56.3	58.4	61.4	64.0	66.4	68.7	71.0	73.3	75.4
750	59.2	61.4	63.8	66.1	68.5	70.6	72.8	74.4	76.6
800	62.3	64.0	66.0	68.2	70.4	72.2	74.2	76.0	77.9

continued

T, °K \ p, bar →	200	250	300	350	400	450	500	550	600
850	64.9	66.7	69.6	70.6	72.6	74.5	76.7	77.8	79.5
900	67.9	68.4	71.2	72.9	74.7	76.6	78.5	79.8	81.4
950	70.5	72.0	73.6	75.3	77.0	78.7	80.4	81.8	83.4
1000	73.3	74.9	76.4	77.9	79.3	80.8	82.6	83.8	85.5
1100	79.1	80.1	81.2	83.1	84.3	85.8	87.3	88.7	90.0
1200	84.5	85.8	86.8	88.1	89.3	90.6	91.9	93.0	94.4
1300	90.1	91.2	92.3	93.3	94.3	95.4	96.3	97.4	98.3
1400	95.9	96.8	97.9	99.1	100	101	102	103	104

Thermal conductivity $\lambda \cdot 10^3$ (W/m·deg) of carbon dioxide in the critical region*

t, °C \ p, bar →	62	64	66	68	70	71	72	73	74	74.5	75	75.5	76	77	78	79	80
30	30.6	32.7	35.6	39.8	47.3	52.8											
30.5	30.5	32.4	34.6	38.1	44.4	48.6											
31	30.3	32.3	33.9	36.8	42.3	46.1											
31.2	30.2	32.2	33.5	36.0	41.9	45.2	51.1	60.3	79.8	105	339	109	94.2	82.1	79.6	79.2	78.3
31.5	30.1	31.9	33.1	35.6	40.6	44.0	48.6	56.5	67.0	86.3	209	159	117	85.8	80.0	79.1	78.3
32	30.1	31.7	32.7	34.8	39.4	41.9	46.1	51.9	59.5	67.0	80.4	102	136	88.8	80.4	79.1	79.0
33	30.0	31.4	31.8	33.9	37.3	39.4	42.3	45.6	50.2	53.6	58.6	69.5	75.4	80.4	78.3	77.4	78.7
34	29.8	30.6	31.0	33.1	35.6	37.7	39.8	42.3	45.2	47.3	50.2	53.6	56.9	62.4	70.3	74.5	77.0
35	29.7	30.1	30.6	32.6	34.8	36.0	37.7	39.8	41.9	43.1	45.2	46.9	49.4	54.4	59.0	68.2	73.7
40								34.3	35.2	35.6	36.0	36.4	37.3	38.9	40.6	42.3	44.0
45													33.1	33.9	34.8	35.6	36.4
50													31.4	31.8	32.2	32.6	33.5

*This table is based on experimental data [354]. Values of $\lambda = f(p, t)$ were computed graphically from $\lambda = \varphi(p, t)$ using the values of ρ, given on pp. 193-196 on the present book.

Thermal conductivity $\lambda \cdot 10^3$ (W/m · deg) of dissociated carbon dioxide at high temperatures [353]

T, °K \ p, bar →	10^{-2}	10^{-1}	10^0	10^1	10^2
1600	128	115	109	107	105
1800	211	160	136	125	120
2000	406	259	189	156	140
2200	774	446	285	207	170
2400	1226	731	440	288	214
2600	1664	1071	652	405	277
2800	1895	1389	892	553	359

T, °K \ p, bar →	10^{-2}	10^{-1}	10^0	10^1	10^2
3000	1643	1621	1122	719	459
3200	1009	1670	1313	882	569
3400	548	1419	1447	1027	681
3600	352	984	1483	1148	787
3800	285	672	1365	1243	881
3900	272	515	1250	1277	923
4000	266	435	1113	1299	962

Thermal conductivity λ of saturated liquid carbon dioxide [15]

T, °K	218	223	228	233	238	243	248	253	258	263	268	273	278	283	288	293
$\lambda \cdot 10^3$, W/m · deg	179	172	163	156	149	142	137	131	125	120	115	109	104	99.2	93.3	86.2

Chapter 4

HYDROCARBONS AND ORGANIC COMPOUNDS

ALKANES

Methane (CH_4)

Molecular weight 16.042
T_{boil} = 111.42 °K at 760 mm Hg; T_{melt} = 90.66 °K; T_{cr} = 190.55 °K;
p_{cr} = 46.41 bar; ρ_{cr} = 162 kg/m³

Thermodynamic properties of saturated methane [61]: v (m³/kg), i (kJ/kg), s (kJ/kg · deg) and r (kJ/kg)

T, °K	p, bar	v'	v''	i'	i''	r	s'	s''
91	0,1219	0.002208	3,841	646,8	1190,2	543,4	4.257	10.228
95	0,1969	0.002236	2,475	659,4	1197.6	538,2	4,397	10.062
100	0.3400	0.002271	1,501	676,5	1207,5	531,0	4,569	9,879
105	0,5600	0,002306	0.9506	693,8	1216,8	523,0	4.735	9.716
110	0,8789	0,002345	0.6287	711,0	1225.5	514,5	4,892	9,569
115	1.324	0.002385	0,4316	728,6	1233.9	505,3	5.045	9,439
120	1,920	0,002427	0,3065	747,0	1241.8	494.8	5,200	9.323
125	2,691	0,002472	0,2243	765,5	1249,1	483.6	5,351	9.220
130	3.671	0,002521	0,1681	784,1	1255,7	471,6	5,499	9,127
135	4.895	0,002575	0,1282	802,9	1261,7	458,8	5,639	9.037
140	6,375	0,002633	0,09971	821,9	1267.2	445.3	5,770	8,951
145	8,136	0,002697	0.07878	840,7	1271,6	430,9	5.898	8,870
150	10.33	0,002770	0.06223	860,0	1274.9	414,9	6,024	8.790
155	12,88	0,002851	0,04977	880,2	1277,1	396,9	6,151	8.712
160	15,88	0,002947	0,03996	901,4	1277,6	376,2	6,279	8,630
165	19,38	0,003061	0,03214	924,1	1276,4	352,3	6.411	8,546
170	23.38	0,003202	0,02593	948,4	1273,3	324,9	6,547	8,458
175	27.88	0,003394	0.02093	976,3	1267,6	291,3	6,700	8,365
180	32,88	0,003678	0,01691	1011,1	1258,9	247,8	6,889	8.266
181	33.95	0,003752	0,01613	1019,0	1256,7	[illegible]7.7	6,930	8,243
182	35,05	0.003835	0.01539	1027,4	1254,3	[illegible]6,9	6.972	8,218
183	36.18	0,003930	0,01464	1036,6	1251,7	[illegible]15,1	7,016	8,191
184	37,34	0,004040	0,01388	1046,4	1248,6	202,2	7,062	8,161
185	38,54	0,004167	0,01311	1057,0	1245,0	188.0	7.110	8.127
186	39,80	0,004316	0.01232	1068,4	1240,8	172,4	7,160	8,088
187	41,10	0,004494	0,01148	1080.6	1235.6	155,0	7,214	8,044
188	42.47	0.004710	0.01059	1094,0	1229,0	135,0	7,272	7,990
189	43,95	0,005012	0,009625	1110,9	1220,1	109,2	7,345	7,923
190	45,52	0,005494	0,008273	1133,4	1203,2	69,8	7,452	7,819
190.55	46,41	0.006161		1156,9		0	7,600	

Thermodynamic properties of methane at different temperatures and pressures [61]:
v (m^3 kg), i (kJ/kg), s and c_p (kJ/kg · deg)

T, °K	v	i	s	c_p	v	i	s	c_p
	p=0,2 bar				p=0.5 bar			
95	0.002236	659,3	4.398		0,002236	659.3	4.397	
100	2.568	1208,5	10.160	2.101	0,002271	676,6	4,570	
110	2.831	1229,4	10.361	2,094	1.121	1227,8	9.875	2.126
120	3,093	1250,4	10,541	2.089	1.227	1248.9	10,060	2.113
130	3.354	1271,2	10,709	2.086	1,333	1270,0	10,228	2.104
140	3,615	1292,1	10.863	2.083	1.439	1291.0	10,383	2.097
150	3.876	1312,9	11,007	2,082	1.544	1312.0	10.528	2.093
160	4,136	1333,7	11,142	2,082	1.648	1332,9	10,664	2,089
170	4,396	1354,6	11.269	2.082	1,753	1353.8	10.791	2,090
180	4.656	1375,4	11,387	2,084	1.858	1374,8	10.910	2.091
190	4.916	1396,2	11.500	2,087	1.962	1395.6	11.023	2,093
200	5,176	1417,1	11.607	2,091	2,067	1416,6	11,130	2,096
220	5,695	1459,1	11,807	2.104	2.275	1458.6	11.331	2.108
240	6,215	1501,3	11,991	2,123	2.483	1500.9	11,515	2.126
260	6,733	1544,0	12,162	2,150	2.691	1543.7	11.686	2.153
280	7,252	1587.4	12.323	2,187	2.899	1587,1	11.847	2.189
300	7,771	1631.6	12,475	2,235	3,107	1631,3	12,000	2.236
320	8.289	1676,8	12,621	2,290	3,315	1676.6	12,146	2,291
340	8,808	1723,2	12,762	2.347	3.522	1723.0	12,286	2.348
360	9,327	1770,8	12,898	2,406	3.730	1770.5	12,422	2.408
380	9,846	1819,5	13.030	2,469	3,937	1819.3	12,554	2,469
400	10.36	1869,6	13,157	2,533	4.145	1869.4	12.682	2.533
450	11,66	2000.4	13,465	2.702	4,664	2000.3	12,990	2.702
500	12,96	2140,1	13,759	2,883	5.183	2140,0	13,284	2.883
550	14.25	2289.2	14.043	3,075	5.701	2289.1	13.568	3,075
600	15.55	2448,1	14,319	3,275	6,220	2448.0	13,844	3,276
700	18,14	2797.2	14.856	3,700	7.257	2797,2	14.381	3.700
800	20,73	3190.3	15,379	4,146	8,293	3190.2	14.904	4.146
900	23,32	3629.0	15,893	4.604	9,330	3628.9	15.418	4,604
1000	25.91	4114,0	16,402	5,062	10.37	4114.1	15.927	5.062
	p=1 bar				p=1.5 bar			
95	0,002235	659.5	4.396		0.002235	659,5	4.396	
100	0,002271	676.7	4,570		0.002271	676.7	4.569	
110	0.002345	711.0	4.892		0.002345	711,2	4.891	
120	0,6050	1246.5	9.686	2,155	0.3992	1243,9	9.464	2.200
130	0,6592	1268.0	9,859	2.136	0.4364	1265,8	9,636	2.171
140	0.7129	1289.2	10.017	2.122	0,4731	1487,4	9.795	2.149
150	0,7662	1310,4	10.163	2.113	0,5093	1308.8	9.945	2.133
160	0,8193	1331,5	10.299	2.107	0.5453	1330.1	10.085	2,123
170	0,8722	1352.5	10.426	2.103	0,5811	1351,3	10,212	2,116
180	0,9249	1373.6	10.547	2.102	0,6167	1372,4	10,333	2.113
190	0.9775	1394.6	10.660	2.102	0.6522	1393,5	10.447	2,111
200	1,030	1415,6	10,768	2.104	0.6876	1414.7	10,556	2.112
220	1,135	1457.8	10.969	2.114	0,7581	1456.9	10,758	2.120
240	1,239	1500,2	11,154	2.131	0,8284	1499,5	10,943	2.135
260	1.344	1543,1	11.325	2.156	0.8985	1542,4	11,100	2.160
280	1,448	1586.5	11,486	2,192	0.9684	1586.0	11,476	2.185
300	1,552	1630,8	11,639	2.240	1,038	1630.3	11,429	2,241
320	1,656	1676.1	11,785	2,293	1.108	1675,7	11,575	2.295
340	1,760	1722,6	11,926	2,350	1,178	1722,2	11,716	2.352
360	1.864	1770,2	12,062	2.409	1.248	1769.8	11,852	2,411
380	1.968	1819.0	12.194	2,471	1.317	1818,6	11,984	2,472
400	2,072	1869.0	12.322	2.535	1,387	1868,7	12,113	2.536
450	2,332	2000.0	12,631	2,704	1,561	1999.8	12.421	2,704
500	2,591	2139,8	12,925	2.884	1,735	2139,6	12.715	2,885
550	2,851	2288.9	13.208	3,076	1,909	2288.7	12,999	3,076
600	3,110	2447 9	13 485	3.276	2,083	2447,7	13,275	3,277
700	3,629	2797,1	14.021	3.701	2.430	2797.0	13,812	3.701

continued

T, °K	v	i	s	c_p	v	i	s	c_p
800	4.147	3190.2	14.544	4.146	2.778	3190.1	14.335	4.147
900	4.666	3628.9	15.059	4.604	3.125	3628.9	14.849	4.604
1000	5.184	4114.1	15.568	5.063	3.472	4114.1	15.358	5.063
		$p=2$ bar				$p=2.5$ bar		
95	0.002235	659.6	4.396		0.002235	659.6	4.396	
100	0.002270	676.8	4.569		0.002270	676.9	4.568	
110	0.002345	711.4	4.891		0.002344	711.4	4.891	
120	0.002427	747.0	5.200		0.002427	747.1	5.200	
130	0.3220	1263.6	9.476	2.206	0.2548	1261.3	9.352	2.241
140	0.3499	1285.5	9.637	2.176	0.2776	1283.6	9.518	2.204
150	0.3774	1307.2	9.791	2.155	0.3001	1305.5	9.668	2.177
160	0.4046	1328.6	9.932	2.140	0.3222	1327.2	9.807	2.158
170	0.4316	1350.0	10.059	2.130	0.3441	1348.7	9.936	2.144
180	0.4585	1371.3	10.180	2.125	0.3657	1370.1	10.058	2.136
190	0.4852	1392.5	10.294	2.121	0.3873	1391.4	10.174	2.131
200	0.5118	1413.7	10.402	2.120	0.4087	1412.7	10.284	2.129
220	0.5647	1456.2	10.605	2.126	0.4514	1455.3	10.487	2.132
240	0.6174	1498.8	10.791	2.140	0.4938	1498.1	10.673	2.145
260	0.6700	1541.8	10.963	2.164	0.5361	1541.2	10.846	2.168
280	0.7224	1585.4	11.124	2.199	0.5782	1584.9	11.008	2.202
300	0.7747	1629.8	11.278	2.245	0.6202	1629.3	11.161	2.247
320	0.8270	1675.3	11.424	2.298	0.6622	1674.8	11.308	2.299
340	0.8792	1721.8	11.565	2.354	0.7041	1721.4	11.449	2.355
360	0.9313	1769.5	11.701	2.413	0.7460	1769.1	11.586	2.414
380	0.9834	1818.4	11.834	2.474	0.7877	1818.0	11.718	2.475
400	1.036	1868.5	11.962	2.537	0.8295	1868.2	11.846	2.538
450	1.166	1999.6	12.270	2.706	0.9339	1999.3	12.155	2.706
500	1.296	2139.4	12.565	2.886	1.038	2139.2	12.449	2.887
550	1.426	2288.6	12.849	3.077	1.142	2288.4	12.733	3.077
600	1.555	2447.6	13.125	3.277	1.246	2447.5	13.009	3.278
700	1.815	2796.9	13.662	3.701	1.454	2796.8	13.546	3.702
800	2.074	3190.1	14.185	4.147	1.662	3190.0	14.069	4.147
900	2.334	3628.9	14.700	4.604	1.870	3628.9	14.584	4.605
1000	2.593	4114.1	15.208	5.063	2.078	4114.1	15.093	5.063
		$p=3$ bar				$p=3.5$ bar		
95	0.002235	659.7	4.395		0.002234	659.8	4.395	
100	0.002270	677.0	4.568		0.002270	677.0	4.568	
110	0.002344	711.5	4.891		0.002344	711.6	4.891	
120	0.002427	747.2	5.200		0.002426	747.3	5.199	
130	0.2092	1259.0	9.247	2.275	0.1770	1256.6	9.156	2.310
140	0.2287	1281.7	9.414	2.233	0.1940	1279.7	9.325	2.263
150	0.2477	1303.8	9.565	2.200	0.2106	1302.1	9.478	2.224
160	0.2664	1325.7	9.705	2.176	0.2268	1324.2	9.621	2.195
170	0.2847	1347.4	9.836	2.159	0.2427	1346.1	9.752	2.175
180	0.3029	1368.9	9.960	2.148	0.2584	1367.7	9.876	2.161
190	0.3210	1390.4	10.076	7.141	0.2741	1389.3	9.993	2.152
200	0.3990	1411.8	10.186	2.138	0.2896	1410.8	10.103	2.146
220	0.3747	1454.5	10.390	2.138	0.3204	1453.7	10.307	2.145
240	0.4101	1497.4	10.576	2.150	0.3509	1496.7	10.494	2.155
260	0.4454	1540.6	10.749	2.172	0.3812	1540.0	10.668	2.176
280	0.4805	1584.4	10.912	2.205	0.4114	1583.8	10.830	2.208
300	0.5156	1628.8	11.065	2.250	0.4416	1628.3	10.984	2.253
320	0.5506	1674.4	11.212	2.302	0.4716	1674.0	11.131	2.304
340	0.5855	1721.0	11.353	2.358	0.5016	1720.6	11.272	2.360
360	0.6204	1768.7	11.490	2.416	0.5315	1768.4	11.409	2.418
380	0.6552	1817.7	11.622	2.477	0.5614	1817.4	11.542	2.478
400	0.6900	1867.9	11.751	2.540	0.5913	1867.6	11.670	2.541
450	0.7769	1999.1	12.059	2.708	0.6659	1998.9	11.979	2.709
500	0.8637	2139.1	12.354	2.887	0.7404	2138.9	12.274	2.888
550	0.9505	2288.3	12.638	3.078	0.8147	2288.2	12.558	3.079
600	1.037	2447.4	12.914	3.279	0.8891	2447.3	12.834	3.279
700	1.210	2796.8	13.451	3.702	1.038	2796.7	13.371	3.702

continued

T, °K	v	i	s	c_p	v	i	s	c_p
800	1.383	3190.0	13.974	4.148	1.186	3190.0	13.894	4.148
900	1.556	3628.8	14.489	4.605	1.334	3628.8	14.409	4.605
1000	1.729	4114.1	14.998	5.063	1.483	4114.1	14.918	5.064
		$p=4$ bar				$p=5$ bar		
95	0.002234	659.9	4.394		0.002234	660.0	4.394	
100	0.002270	677.1	4.567		0.002269	677.3	4.567	
110	0.002344	711.6	4.890		0.002343	711.8	4.890	
120	0.002426	747.3	5.199		0.002425	747.4	5.198	
130	0.002521	784.2	5.498		0.002520	784.3	5.497	
140	0.1679	1277.6	9.241	2.296	0.1314	1273.4	9.111	2.374
150	0.1827	1300.4	9.398	2.250	0.1437	1296.8	9.272	2.305
160	0.1971	1322.8	9.546	2.215	0.1556	1319.7	9.420	2.257
170	0.2112	1344.7	9.680	1.191	0.1671	1342.0	9.554	2.225
180	0.2251	1366.7	9.804	2.174	0.1784	1364.2	9.678	2.200
190	0.2389	1388.4	9.920	2.162	0.1896	1386.1	9.796	2.184
200	0.2526	1409.8	10.030	2.155	0.2007	1407.9	9.908	2.174
220	0.2796	1452.9	10.236	2.152	0.2226	1451.2	10.115	2.166
240	0.3064	1496.0	10.423	2.160	0.2443	1494.5	10.303	2.171
260	0.3331	1539.4	10.597	2.180	0.2657	1538.1	10.478	2.189
280	0.3596	1583.2	10.760	2.212	0.2871	1582.2	10.642	2.219
300	0.3860	1627.9	10.914	2.255	0.3083	1626.9	10.796	2.261
320	0.4124	1673.5	11.061	2.307	0.3295	1672.7	10.943	2.312
340	0.4387	1720.2	11.202	2.362	0.3506	1719.4	11.085	2.366
360	0.4649	1768.1	11.339	2.420	0.3716	1767.3	11.222	2.423
380	0.4911	1817.1	11.472	2.480	0.3926	1816.4	11.355	2.483
400	0.5173	1867.3	11.600	2.543	0.4136	1866.7	11.483	2.545
450	0.5826	1998.7	11.909	2.710	0.4660	1998.2	11.793	2.711
500	0.6478	2138.7	12.204	2.889	0.5183	2138.3	12.088	2.891
550	0.7129	2288.0	12.488	3.080	0.5704	2287.7	12.372	3.081
600	0.7780	2447.2	12.765	3.280	0.6225	2446.9	12.648	3.281
700	0.9080	2796.6	13.302	3.703	0.7266	2796.5	13.186	3.704
800	1.038	3189.9	13.825	4.148	0.8306	3189.8	13.709	4.149
900	1.168	3628.8	14.340	4.605	0.9345	3628.8	14.224	4.606
1000	1.297	4114.1	14.849	5.064	1.038	4114.1	14.733	5.064
		$p=6$ bar				$p=7$ bar		
95	0.002334	660.2	4.393		0.002233	660.4	4.392	
100	0.002269	677.4	4.566		0.002268	677.6	4.565	
110	0.002343	711.9	4.889		0.002343	712.1	4.888	
120	0.002425	747.6	5.197		0.002424	747.8	5.196	
130	0.002520	784.4	5.496		0.002519	784.5	5.495	
140	0.1070	1269.0	8.990	2.465	0.002632	822.0	5.770	
150	0.1176	1293.1	9.158	2.366	0.09884	1289.3	9.060	2.436
160	0.1277	1316.5	9.312	2.303	0.1079	1313.2	9.215	2.352
170	0.1376	1339.2	9.452	2.260	0.1166	1336.3	9.360	2.298
180	0.1472	1361.7	9.578	2.228	0.1250	1359.2	9.490	2.258
190	0.1568	1383.9	9.695	2.206	0.1333	1381.7	9.606	2.232
200	0.1662	1405.9	9.807	2.193	0.1414	1403.8	9.720	2.213
220	0.1846	1449.5	10.015	2.180	0.1574	1447.9	9.930	2.194
240	0.2028	1493.1	10.205	2.182	0.1732	1491.6	10.121	2.192
260	0.2208	1536.9	10.380	2.197	0.1887	1535.6	10.297	2.206
280	0.2387	1581.1	10.544	2.225	0.2041	1580.0	10.461	2.232
300	0.2565	1625.9	10.699	2.267	0.2195	1625.0	10.617	2.272
320	0.2742	1671.8	10.847	2.317	0.2347	1670.9	10.765	2.321
340	0.2918	1718.6	10.988	2.370	0.2499	1717.9	10.907	2.374
360	0.3094	1766.6	11.126	2.427	0.2650	1766.0	11.044	2.430
380	0.3270	1815.8	11.259	2.486	0.2801	1815.1	11.177	2.489
400	0.3445	1866.1	11.388	2.548	0.2952	1865.6	11.307	2.551
450	0.3883	1997.7	11.697	2.714	0.3327	1997.2	11.616	2.716
500	0.4319	2137.9	11.992	2.892	0.3702	2137.5	11.912	2.894
550	0.4754	2287.4	12.277	3.082	0.4075	2287.1	12.196	3.083
600	0.5189	2446.7	12.553	3.282	0.4448	2446.4	12.473	3.283
700	0.6057	2796.3	13.091	3.704	0.5193	2796.2	13.010	3.705

continued

T, °K	v	i	s	c_p	v	i	s	c_p
800	0.6924	3189.7	13.614	4.149	0.5937	3189.6	13.534	4.150
900	0.7790	3628.7	14.129	4.606	0.6680	3628.7	14.049	4.607
1000	10.8656	4114.1	14.638	5.064	0.7422	4114.1	14.558	5.065
		p=8 bar				p=9 bar		
95	0.002233	660.5	4.391		0.002233	660.7	4.391	
100	0.002268	677.8	4.564		0.002268	677.9	4.564	
110	0.002342	712.2	4.888		0.002341	712.4	4.887	
120	0.002424	747.9	5.195		0.002423	748.0	4.194	
130	0.002518	784.6	5.494		0.002518	784.7	5.493	
140	0.002631	822.1	5.768		0.002630	822.1	5.767	
150	0.08473	1285.3	8.967	2.515	0.07367	1281.0	8.887	2.605
160	0.09293	1309.8	9.129	2.407	0.08125	1306.2	9.051	2.467
170	0.1007	1333.5	9.273	2.338	0.08835	1330.6	9.196	2.381
180	0.1083	1356.6	9.409	2.290	0.09529	1354.0	9.332	2.324
190	0.1156	1379.4	9.529	2.257	0.1019	1377.0	9.460	2.284
200	0.1229	1401.8	9.644	2.234	0.1085	1399.7	9.576	2.255
220	0.1371	1446.1	9.856	2.209	0.1212	1444.4	9.789	2.224
240	0.1509	1490.2	10.048	2.203	0.1337	1488.8	9.983	2.214
260	0.1647	1534.4	10.224	2.214	0.1459	1533.1	10.160	2.223
280	0.1782	1578.9	10.389	2.239	0.1581	1577.8	10.325	2.246
300	0.1917	1624.0	10.545	2.278	0.1701	1623.0	10.482	2.283
320	0.2051	1670.0	10.694	2.326	0.1821	1669.2	10.631	2.331
340	0.2184	1717.1	10.836	2.378	0.1940	1716.3	10.773	2.382
360	0.2317	1765.2	10.974	2.434	0.2058	1764.5	10.911	2.437
380	0.2450	1814.5	11.107	2.492	0.2176	1813.9	11 044	2.495
400	0.2582	1865.0	11.236	2.554	0.2294	1864.4	11.174	2.556
450	0.2911	1996.8	11.546	2.718	0.2587	1996.3	11.484	2.720
500	0.3239	2137.1	11.842	2.895	0.2879	2136.8	11.780	2.897
550	0.3566	2286.8	12.126	3.085	0.3171	2286.5	12.065	3.086
600	0.3893	2446.2	12.403	3.284	0.3461	2445.9	12.342	3.285
700	0.4545	2796.0	12.941	3.706	0.4041	2795.8	12.879	3.707
800	0.5196	3189.6	13.465	4.151	0.4621	3189.5	13.403	4.151
900	0.5847	3628.7	13.980	4.607	0.5199	3628.6	13.918	4.608
1000	0.6497	4114.1	14.489	5.065	0.5777	4114.1	14.428	5.066
		p=10 bar				p=12 bar		
95	0.002232	660.8	4.390		0.002232	671.2	4.389	
100	0.002267	678.1	4.563		0.002267	678.4	4.561	
110	0.002341	712.5	4.886		0.002340	712.8	4.884	
120	0.002422	748.1	5.193		0.002421	748.4	5.191	
130	0.002517	784.9	5.492		0.002515	785.1	5.490	
140	0.002629	822.2	5.766		0.002627	822.4	5.763	
150	0.06478	1276.5	8.815	2.705	0.002767	860.1	6.023	
160	0.07186	1302.6	8.979	2.533	0.05772	1294.9	8.853	2.690
170	0.07846	1327.5	9.130	2.428	0.06357	1321.0	9.009	2.535
180	0.08485	1351.5	9.268	2.359	0.06914	1346.0	9.151	2.438
190	0.09094	1374.7	9.396	2.311	0.07443	1369.8	9.285	2.372
200	0.09691	1397.6	9.514	2.278	0.07956	1393.3	9.405	2.326
220	0.1085	1442.7	9.730	2.239	0.08949	1439.2	9.624	2.272
240	0.1198	1487.3	9.924	2.226	0.09910	1484.4	9.821	2.250
260	0 1310	1531.9	10.102	2.231	0.1085	1529.3	10.001	2.250
280	0.1419	1576.7	10.268	2.253	0.1178	1574.5	10.168	2.267
300	0.1528	1622.0	10.425	2.289	0.1269	1620.1	10.326	2.301
320	0.1636	1668.3	10.574	2.336	0.1360	1666.6	10.475	2.345
340	0.1744	1715.5	10.717	2.386	0.1450	1714.0	10.619	2.394
360	0.1851	1763.8	10.855	2.441	0.1540	1762.4	10.757	2.448
380	0.1957	1813.2	10.988	2.498	0.1629	1811.9	10.891	2.504
400	0.2064	1863.8	11.118	2.559	0.1718	1862.6	11.021	2.564
450	0.2330	1995.8	11.429	2.722	0.1939	1994.9	11.332	2.726
500	0.2591	2136.4	11.725	2.899	0.2159	2135.7	11.629	2.902
550	0.2854	2286.2	12.010	3.087	0.2379	2285.6	11.914	3.090
600	0.3116	2445.7	12.287	3.286	0.2598	2445.2	12.191	3.288
700	0.3638	2795.7	12.824	3.707	0.3034	2795.4	12.729	3.709

continued

T, °K	v	i	s	c_p	v	i	s	c_p
800	0.4160	3189.4	13.348	4,152	0.3469	3189.2	13.253	4.153
900	0.4681	3628,6	13,864	4.608	0,3903	3628.5	13,769	4.609
1000	0,5201	4114,1	14.373	5,066	0,4337	4114.1	14.278	5.067
		p=14 bar				p=16 bar		
95	0,002231	661,6	4.387		0,002230	661.9	4.386	
100	0.002266	678.7	4.560		0,002265	679.0	4.559	
110	0,002339	713,1	4.882		0,002338	713.4	4,880	
120	0,002420	748,7	5,190		0.002419	749.0	5.188	
130	0.002513	785,3	5,488		0,002512	785.6	5,486	
140	0,002624	822,6	5.761		0,002622	822.7	5,758	
150	0,002763	860.2	6,019		0,002760	860,3	6.015	
160	0.04744	1286.5	8.737	2.894	0.002947	901,5	6.278	
170	0,05288	1314.1	8.904	2,665	0,04472	1306.7	8.800	2.818
180	0.05786	1340.1	9.051	2.527	0.04936	1334.3	8.959	2.630
190	0.06260	1364.8	9.186	2,438	0.05370	1359.6	9,098	2.513
200	0,06716	1388.9	9.310	2,378	0,05783	1384.3	9,225	2.434
220	0.07588	1435,6	9,533	2,306	0.06567	1432.0	9,452	2.343
240	0,08428	1481.4	9.732	2,274	0,07316	1478.4	9,654	2.301
260	0.09246	1526.9	9.914	2.268	0.08043	1524.2	9.837	2.288
280	0,1004	1572,2	10.083	2,282	0,08754	1570.0	10,007	2.297
300	0.1084	1618.1	10.241	2,313	0,09454	1616.2	10,167	2.325
320	0,1163	1664,8	10,391	2,355	0,1015	1663,1	10.318	2,365
340	0.1240	1712.4	10,536	2.402	0,1083	1710.8	10.463	2,411
360	0.1318	1761,0	10,674	2,455	0,1151	1759,6	10.602	2.462
380	0,1395	1810,7	10,808	2.511	0,1219	1809,4	10.737	2.517
400	0.1471	1861,5	10.939	2,570	0.1286	1860,3	10.867	2,575
450	0,1662	1994.0	11,251	2.730	0,1454	1993,1	11,180	2,734
500	0.1851	2134.9	11.547	2.095	0.1620	2134.2	11,476	2.908
550	0.2039	2285,0	11.833	3.092	0.1785	2284,4	11.762	3,095
600	0,2227	2444.7	12,110	3.290	0.1950	2444,2	12.040	3.292
700	0.2602	2795.1	12.649	3,711	0.2278	2794.8	12.579	3.712
800	0,2975	3189.0	13.173	4,154	0.2605	3188.8	13,103	4.155
900	0.3348	3628.4	13.688	4,610	0.2932	3628.4	13.619	4.611
1000	0.3720	4114.1	14.178	5.067	0.3257	4114,1	14.128	5,068
		p=18 bar				p=20 bar		
95	0,002229	662,2	4.385		0.002229	662,6	4.383	
100	0,002264	679,3	4.557		0.002264	679.6	4.555	
110	0,002337	713.7	4.879		0,002336	714,1	4.877	
120	0,002418	749,3	5.186		0.002417	749,6	5.184	
130	0,002510	785,9	5,484		0,002509	786,1	5.480	
140	0,002620	822,9	5,756		0,002618	823,0	5,753	
150	0,002756	860.3	6.012		0,002753	860,5	6.009	
160	0,002941	901,3	6,273		0,002935	901,2	6,270	
170	0,03829	1299.0	8,706	3,013	0.03303	1290.2	8.616	3,260
180	0,04266	1327.6	8,873	2,750	0,03733	1320,7	8.791	2,892
190	0,04675	1354,2	9,017	2.593	0.04116	1348,6	8,941	2,687
200	0,05056	1379,7	9.147	2,496	0.04472	1374.8	9.076	2.564
220	0,05772	1428,3	9,380	2,382	0.05136	1424,5	9,313	2,423
240	0,06451	1475,3	9,584	2,327	0.05759	1472.2	9,521	2,355
260	0.07107	1521,6	9,770	2,307	0,06358	1519,0	9,708	2.328
280	0.07746	1567.7	9.941	2,312	0,06940	1565,5	9,881	2,328
300	0,08375	1614.2	10,101	2.337	0,07512	1612,2	10,042	2,350
320	0.08995	1661,3	10.253	2.375	0,08074	1659.6	10.194	2,385
340	0.09609	1709,3	10,398	2,420	0,08631	1707,7	10.340	2.428
360	0,1022	1758,2	10,538	2,469	0.09182	1756,8	10.480	2.476
380	0,1082	1808,1	10,673	2,523	0,09729	1806,9	10,616	2.529
400	0,1142	1859,2	10,804	2,581	0.1027	1858.0	10.746	2,586
450	0,1292	1992,2	11,117	2,738	0.1162	1991.2	11,060	2,742
500	0,1440	2133,4	11,414	2,911	0.1296	2132.7	11,358	2,915
550	0,1587	2283,8	11,700	3,098	0.1429	2283.2	11,644	3,100
600	0.1734	2443,7	11.978	3,294	0.1561	2443.2	11.922	3.297
700	0.2026	2794.6	12,517	3,714	0.1825	2794,2	12.462	3.715

continued

T, °K	v	i	s	c_p	v	i	s	c_p
800	0.2317	3188.7	13.041	4.156	0.2087	3188.5	12.986	4.157
900	0.2608	3628.3	13.557	4.612	0.2348	3628.2	13.502	4.612
1000	0.2898	4114.1	14.067	5.069	0.2610	4114.1	14.012	5.070
	p=22 bar				p=24 bar			
95	0.002228	663.0	4.382		0.002227	663.4	4.381	
100	0.002263	680.0	4.553		0.002262	680.3	4.551	
110	0.002335	714.4	4.875		0.002334	714.7	4.873	
120	0.002416	749.9	5.183		0.002314	750.2	5.181	
130	0.002507	786.4	5.478		0.002505	786.7	5.476	
140	0.002616	823.2	5.751		0.002614	823.4	5.749	
150	0.002750	860.5	6.006		0.002747	860.6	6.003	
160	0.002929	901.1	6.266		0.002924	901.0	6.262	
170	0.02863	1280.6	8.523	3.598	0.003202	948.3	6.545	
180	0.03288	1313.5	8.712	3.064	0.02909	1305.8	8.635	3.272
190	0.03655	1342.7	8.869	2.795	0.03269	1336.6	8.800	2.918
200	0.03993	1369.9	9.009	2.639	0.03592	1364.7	8.945	2.722
220	0.04614	1420.7	9.251	2.467	0.04179	1416.8	9.194	2.513
240	0.05192	1469.1	9.462	2.384	0.04720	1465.9	9.407	2.415
260	0.05745	1516.4	9.651	2.349	0.05235	1513.7	9.599	2.371
280	0.06281	1563.2	9.825	2.344	0.05731	1561.0	9.774	2.360
300	0.06806	1610.3	9.987	2.362	0.06217	1608.2	9.937	2.375
320	0.07321	1657.8	10.141	2.396	0.06694	1656.1	10.092	2.406
340	0.07831	1706.2	10.287	2.437	0.07164	1704.6	10.239	2.445
360	0.08335	1755.4	10.428	2.484	0.07629	1754.0	10.380	2.491
380	0.08835	1806.6	10.563	2.537	0.08089	1804.3	10.516	2.542
400	0.09331	1856.9	10.695	2.592	0.08547	1855.7	10.647	2.597
450	0.1056	1990.3	11.009	2.746	0.09679	1989.4	10.962	2.750
500	0.1178	2132.0	11.307	2.918	0.1080	2131.2	11.260	2.921
550	0.1299	2282.6	11.594	3.103	0.1191	2282.0	11.547	3.105
600	0.1420	2442.8	11.872	3.299	0.1302	2442.3	11.826	3.301
700	0.1660	2793.9	12.411	3.716	0.1522	2793.5	12.366	3.718
800	0.1898	3188.3	12.936	4.159	0.1741	3188.2	12.891	4.160
900	0.2136	3628.1	13.452	4.613	0.1960	3628.1	13.407	4.614
1000	0.2374	4114.1	13.962	5.070	0.2178	4114.1	13.917	5.071
	p=26 bar				p=28 bar			
95	0.002227	663.8	4.378		0.002226	664.1	4.377	
100	0.002261	680.6	4.550		0.002261	680.9	4.549	
110	0.002334	715.0	4.871		0.002333	715.3	4.870	
120	0.002413	750.4	5.179		0.002412	750.7	5.177	
130	0.002504	786.9	5.474		0.002503	787.1	5.472	
140	0.002612	823.6	5.747		0.002609	823.7	5.744	
150	0.002743	860.7	6.000		0.002740	860.7	5.997	
160	0.002918	900.9	6.258		0.002913	900.8	6.254	
170	0.003188	947.7	6.537		0.003176	947.1	6.530	
180	0.02583	1297.4	8.557	3.544	0.02295	1288.1	8.479	3.898
190	0.02938	1330.1	8.734	3.061	0.02651	1323.2	8.668	3.229
200	0.03251	1359.4	8.884	2.815	0.02957	1353.8	8.825	2.918
220	0.03810	1412.8	9.139	2.563	0.03493	1408.7	9.088	2.616
240	0.04320	1462.8	9.357	2.446	0.03977	1459.5	9.309	2.479
260	0.04802	1511.0	9.550	2.393	0.04432	1508.4	9.504	2.416
280	0.05267	1558.7	9.727	2.377	0.04869	1556.4	9.682	2.394
300	0.05719	1606.3	9.891	2.388	0.05293	1604.3	9.848	2.402
320	0.06163	1654.4	10.046	2.417	0.05708	1652.6	10.003	2.427
340	0.06600	1703.0	10.193	2.454	0.06116	1701.5	10.152	2.463
360	0.07031	1752.6	10.335	2.498	0.06519	1751.2	10.294	2.506
380	0.07459	1803.1	10.471	2.548	0.06918	1801.8	10.430	2.555
400	0.07883	1854.6	10.604	2.603	0.07314	1853.5	10.563	2.608
450	0.08932	1988.5	10.919	2.754	0.08292	1987.6	10.878	2.758
500	0.09969	2130.5	11.217	2.924	0.09258	2129.8	11.178	2.927
550	0.1100	2281.4	11.505	3.108	0.1022	2280.8	11.465	3.110
600	0.1202	2441.8	11.783	3.303	0.1117	2441.4	11.744	3.305
700	0.1406	2793.3	12.323	3.719	0.1306	2793.0	12.284	3.721

continued

T, °K	v	i	s	c_p	v	i	s	c_p
800	0,1608	3188.0	12.849	4.161	0.1495	3187.8	12.810	4.162
900	0.1810	3628.0	13.365	4.615	0.1682	3627.9	13.326	4.616
1000	0.2012	4114.1	13.875	5,072	0,1869	4114.1	13.836	5.072
		p=30 bar				p=40 bar		
95	0.002225	664.4	4.375		0.002222	666.0	4.367	
100	0,002260	681,2	4.548		0.002256	682.8	4.541	
110	0.002332	715.6	4.869		0.002327	717.1	4.862	
120	0,002411	751.0	5.175		0.002405	752.4	5.168	
130	0.002501	787.3	5.471		0.002494	788.5	5.462	
140	0.002607	823.9	5.742		0.002597	824.9	5.731	
150	0.002737	860.9	5.994		0.002722	861.6	5.980	
160	0.002908	900.7	6.249		0.002883	900.5	6.229	
170	0,003164	946.5	6,524		0.003112	944.4	6.494	
180	0.02035	1277.5	8.398	4.390	0.003534	1002.6	6.805	
190	0,02399	1315.9	8.604	3.431	0.01450	1268.7	8.256	5.735
200	0,02700	1348.1	8.768	3.034	0.01777	1314.9	8.493	3,929
220	0,03218	1404.6	9.038	2.672	0.02249	1382.4	8.815	3,019
240	0,03680	1456,2	9.263	2,514	0.02638	1439.3	9.063	2.710
260	0.04111	1505.7	9.461	2.440	0.02988	1491.9	9.273	2.569
280	0,04524	1554,2	9.640	2.412	0.03316	1542.5	9.461	2.504
300	0.04923	1602.3	9.807	2,415	0.03631	1592.4	9.633	2,487
320	0.05314	1650.8	9.964	2.438	0.03935	1642.1	9.794	2.494
340	0,05697	1699.9	10.112	2.472	0,04233	1692.2	9.946	2.517
360	0,06076	1749.8	10.255	2.513	0,04525	1742.9	10.090	2.551
380	0.06450	1800,6	10.392	2.561	0.04812	1794.3	10.229	2.593
400	0.06821	1852,3	10.525	2.614	0.05096	1846.7	10.364	2.641
450	0.07737	1986.7	10.841	2.762	0.05796	1982.3	10.683	2.783
500	0.08641	2129.1	11.140	2.930	0,06484	2125.5	10.984	2.946
550	0.09538	2280.2	11.428	3.113	0,07164	2277.4	11.273	3.125
600	0.1043	2440.9	11.707	3.307	0.07838	2438.6	11.553	3.317
700	0.1220	2792.7	12.248	3.722	0.09175	2791.2	12.095	3.730
800	0.1396	3187.6	12.773	4.163	0,1050	3186.8	12,621	4.168
900	0,1571	3627.8	13.290	4.617	0,1182	3627.5	13.139	4.621
1000	0.1746	4114.1	13.800	5.073	0,1314	4114.2	13.649	5.077
		p=50 bar				p=60 bar		
95	0.002218	667.3	4.361		0.002215	668.7	4.356	
100	0.002252	684.3	4.534		0,002249	685.9	4.528	
110	0.002323	718.6	4.855		0,002318	720.1	4.847	
120	0.002400	753.7	5.160		0.002394	755.3	5.151	
130	0.002487	789.8	5.453		0.002480	791.1	5.444	
140	0.002587	826.0	5.719		0.002578	826.9	5.709	
150	0,002708	862.4	5.966		0,002692	862.9	5.953	
160	0.002860	900.5	6.212		0.002839	900.7	6.193	
170	0,003068	942.9	6.466		0.003031	941.9	6.441	
180	0.003408	993.5	6.744		0.003322	990.3	6.700	
190	0.004340	1062.5	7.136	11,084	0.003850	1048.0	7.024	7.515
200	0.01169	1269.2	8.191	6.324	0.006487	1181.2	7.706	20.664
220	0,01659	1357.5	8.614	3.519	0,01259	1329.3	8.420	4.256
240	0,02011	1421.3	8.892	2,950	0,01593	1402.3	8.738	3,243
260	0,02315	1477.6	9.118	2.715	0.01867	1463.0	8.981	2.882
280	0,02594	1530.7	9.315	2,606	0.02113	1518.7	9.188	2.716
300	0.02857	1582.2	9.493	2.561	0,02343	1572.2	9.373	2.640
320	0,03110	1633.4	9.657	2.552	0,02562	1624.7	9.542	2.613
340	0,03356	1684.5	9.812	2,564	0.02773	1676.9	9.700	2.612
360	0,03596	1736.0	9.960	2,590	0,02978	1729.3	9.850	2.629
380	0,03831	1788.2	10.101	2.626	0.03178	1782.2	9.993	2.658
400	0,04063	1841.2	10.236	2.669	0.03376	1835.7	10.130	2.697
450	0,04632	1977.9	10.558	2.803	0.03857	1973.7	10.455	2.822
500	0.05190	2122.0	10.861	2.961	0,04328	2118.6	10.760	2.976
550	0,05740	2274.6	11,152	3.137	0.04791	2271.8	11,052	3.149
600	0,06284	2436.3	11.433	3.327	0.05249	2434.1	11.333	3.337
700	0,07362	2789.8	11.976	3.737	0.06153	2788.4	11.878	3.744

continued

T, °K	v	i	s	c_p	v	i	s	c_p
800	0.08429	3186.0	12.503	4.174	0,07047	3185.2	12.406	4.179
900	0.09490	3627.2	13.021	4.625	0.07934	3626.9	12,924	4.629
1000	0.1055	4114.2	13.532	5.080	0,08817	4114,3	13.435	5.083
		p=70 bar				p=80 bar		
95	0.002212	670.3	4.350		0.002208	671.9	4.343	
100	0.002245	687.4	4.521		0.002241	689.0	4.514	
110	0.002314	721.6	4.840		0.002310	723.1	4.833	
120	0,002389	756.7	5.143		0.002384	758.1	5.135	
130	0.002473	792.4	5.435		0.002467	793.8	5.426	
140	0.002569	828.1	5.698		0.002560	829.2	5.688	
150	0.002682	863.7	5.940		0.002670	864.6	5.928	
160	0,002819	900.9	6.177		0,002801	901,3	6,162	
170	0.002998	940.9	6.418		0,002969	940,6	6,399	
180	0.003254	987.0	6.666		0.003199	984.9	6.640	
190	0.003666	1040.0	6.959	6.364	0,003544	1034,6	6.912	5.755
200	0,004595	1116.8	7.358	10.162	0.004169	1097.7	7.240	7.386
220	0.009710	1297.4	8.225	5,307	0,007632	1263,1	8,030	6,463
240	0,01295	1382.2	8.595	3.591	0.01075	1361,5	8.460	3.980
260	0.01549	1448.0	8.859	3,066	0,01313	1432.8	8.745	3.264
280	0.01772	1506.7	9.076	2.833	0.01518	1494.6	8.975	2.956
300	0,01978	1562.1	9.267	2.723	0,01705	1552.1	9.173	2.808
320	0.02172	1616.0	9.441	2.675	0.01881	1607.4	9.351	2.738
340	0,02358	1669.3	9.603	2.661	0,02048	1661.9	9.517	2.710
360	0.02538	1722.6	9.755	2.669	0,02209	1716,1	9.671	2,708
380	0.02713	1776,2	9.900	2.691	0.02366	1770.4	9.818	2,724
400	0.02866	1830.4	10.039	2.725	0,02519	1825.2	9.959	2.753
450	0.03305	1969.5	10.366	2.842	0.02891	1965.4	10.289	2,862
500	0.03713	2115.3	10.673	2.991	0.03253	2112.1	10.597	3,005
550	0.04114	2269.2	10.966	3.161	0.03607	2266.5	10.891	3,172
600	0.04509	2432.0	11.249	3.346	0.03955	2429.9	11,175	3,355
700	0.05289	2787,1	11.795	3.750	0.04642	2785.8	11.722	3.757
800	0,06059	3184.5	12.323	4.184	0,05319	3183.8	12.252	4,189
900	0.06823	3626.6	12.842	4.633	0.05990	3626.3	12.771	4,637
1000	0,07582	4114.4	13.354	5.087	0,06656	4114.4	13.283	5,090
		p=90 bar				p=100 bar		
95	0,002205	673.5	4.377		0.002202	675,0	4.330	
100	0,002238	690.6	4.507		0,002235	692.1	4.504	
110	0.002306	724.4	4.826		0,002302	726.3	4.822	
120	0,002379	759.5	5.125		0.002374	761.0	5,121	
130	0,002460	795.1	5.418		0,002454	796.4	5.407	
140	0,002552	830.5	5.679		0.002544	831.8	5.668	
150	0.002658	865.5	5.917		0,002647	866.5	5.907	
160	0,002785	901.9	6.149		0,002768	902.5	6.137	
170	0.002942	940.5	6.380		0,002918	941,6	6,363	
180	0,003153	983.5	6.617		0,003113	982.5	6.595	
190	0.003452	1030.7	6,874	5.365	0,003380	1027.2	6.842	5,085
200	0.003943	1087.1	7,167	6.297	0.003791	1080.0	7.112	5.696
220	0.006253	1231,5	7.855	6.948	0.005422	1207.3	7,719	6.609
240	0,009091	1340.7	8.331	4.372	0.007840	1320.5	8,212	4.697
260	0.01133	1417.6	8.640	3.468	0.009916	1402.6	8,541	3,665
280	0,01323	1482.6	8.881	3,082	0.01169	1470.7	8.794	3.207
300	0,01495	1542.1	9.087	2.895	0.01329	1532.3	9,007	2.981
320	0.01656	1599,0	9.270	2,802	0.01478	1590,7	9,195	2,866
340	0.01808	1654.6	9.439	2.760	0.01618	1647.4	9,367	2,809
360	0.01955	1709.6	9.596	2,748	0,01752	1703.3	9,527	2,787
380	0.02097	1764.7	9.744	2.757	0.01882	1759,0	9,678	2.789
400	0,02235	1820.1	9,886	2.780	0,02009	1815,1	9,821	2.808
450	0,02570	1961.5	10.219	2,881	0.02314	1957.6	10.156	2,900
500	0,02895	2109.0	10.530	3,020	0.02609	2105.9	10.468	3,034
550	0,03212	2264.1	10.825	3,183	0,02897	2261.7	10.765	3,194
600	0.03525	2427.9	11.110	3.364	0.03180	2426.0	11.051	3,373
700	0.04139	2784.6	11,658	3.763	0.03736	2783,4	11.600	3,770

continued

T, °K	v	i	s	c_p	v	i	s	c_p
800	0.04743	3183.1	12.188	4.194	0.04283	3182.4	12.131	4.199
900	0.05342	3626.0	12.708	4.641	0.04823	3625.8	12.651	4.645
1000	0.05936	4114.5	13.220	5.093	0.05360	4114.6	13.164	5.096
		p=150 bar				p=200 bar		
95	0.002186	682.9	4.297		0.002172	690.8	4.266	
100	0.002218	700.1	4.469		0.002202	707.9	4.438	
110	0.002282	733.9	4.785		0.002264	741.9	4.753	
120	0.002350	768.5	5.084		0.002329	776.0	5.050	
130	0.002425	803.3	5.369		0.002398	810.4	5.331	
140	0.002506	838.1	5.623		0.002474	844.5	5.583	
150	0.002597	871.8	5.853		0.002555	878.1	5.808	
160	0.002701	906.6	6.075		0.002645	911.6	6.023	
170	0.002821	942.4	6.290		0.002748	946.6	6.229	
180	0.002966	980.0	6.503		0.002867	982.7	6.433	
190	0.003148	1020.4	6.720	4.364	0.003010	1020.1	6.625	4.025
200	0.003373	1063.9	6.943	4.518	0.003186	1059.6	6.839	4.089
220	0.004039	1156.9	7.386	4.754	0.003615	1142.0	7.232	4.141
240	0.005007	1251.7	7.799	4.643	0.004173	1224.5	7.591	4.094
260	0.006191	1339.9	8.152	4.148	0.004863	1305.1	7.914	3.944
280	0.007391	1417.8	8.441	3.666	0.005637	1381.7	8.198	3.718
300	0.008528	1487.6	8.682	3.344	0.006437	1453.8	8.447	3.494
320	0.009595	1552.4	8.891	3.149	0.007227	1521.8	8.666	3.316
340	0.01061	1614.2	9.078	3.034	0.007994	1586.8	8.863	3.190
360	0.01156	1674.2	9.250	2.970	0.008734	1649.7	9.043	3.108
380	0.01249	1733.2	9.409	2.940	0.009450	1711.4	9.210	3.061
400	0.01339	1792.0	9.560	2.935	0.01014	1772.4	9.366	3.040
450	0.01553	1939.8	9.908	2.988	0.01181	1924.7	9.725	3.064
500	0.01758	2091.9	10.228	3.099	0.01339	2080.1	10.052	3.157
550	0.01957	2250.6	10.530	3.246	0.01492	2241.4	10.359	3.291
600	0.02151	2417.2	10.820	3.415	0.01641	2410.0	10.652	3.451
700	0.02531	2778.1	11.374	3.799	0.01931	2773.9	11.211	3.825
800	0.02902	3179.7	11.909	4.221	0.02214	3177.8	11.749	4.241
900	0.03269	3625.0	12.431	4.663	0.02492	3624.9	12.273	4.678
1000	0.03631	4115.5	12.946	5.110	0.02767	4116.8	12.789	5.123
		p=300 bar				p=400 bar		
95	0.002145	706.8	4.206		0.002121	722.6	4.149	
100	0.002174	723.8	4.379		0.002148	740.0	4.323	
110	0.002232	757.7	4.693		0.002202	773.7	4.636	
120	0.002291	791.6	4.986		0.002257	803.3	4.927	
130	0.002353	825.5	5.263		0.002314	840.9	5.202	
140	0.002418	859.0	5.510		0.002372	874.1	5.446	
150	0.002488	891.4	5.729		0.002433	906.0	5.663	
160	0.002562	923.9	5.937		0.002497	937.4	5.865	
170	0.002642	957.1	6.134		0.002565	969.5	6.055	
180	0.002733	991.2	6.325		0.002641	1003.0	6.241	
190	0.002838	1026.2	6.513	3.668	0.002727	1036.9	6.422	
200	0.002959	1062.2	6.698	3.689	0.002823	1071.2	6.599	3.476
220	0.003227	1135.9	7.050	3.666	0.003022	1140.6	6.930	3.451
240	0.003537	1208.6	7.366	3.597	0.003243	1209.0	7.227	3.383
260	0.003896	1279.7	7.651	3.522	0.003489	1275.9	7.495	3.313
280	0.004299	1349.5	7.909	3.455	0.003758	1341.6	7.739	3.263
300	0.004737	1417.9	8.146	3.394	0.004049	1406.5	7.963	3.236
320	0.005199	1485.2	8.363	3.333	0.004356	1471.1	8.171	3.222
340	0.005672	1551.3	8.563	3.274	0.004678	1535.5	8.366	3.213
360	0.006148	1616.3	8.749	3.224	0.005009	1600.0	8.550	3.206
380	0.006621	1680.4	8.922	3.188	0.005345	1663.8	8.723	3.201
400	0.007088	1743.9	9.085	3.167	0.005684	1727.8	8.887	3.202
450	0.008222	1902.2	9.458	3.174	0.006527	1888.6	9.266	3.232
500	0.009311	2062.6	9.795	3.248	0.007351	2051.9	9.609	3.305
550	0.01036	2227.9	10.110	3.364	0.008153	2220.0	9.929	3.417
600	0.01139	2399.9	10.409	3.512	0.008936	2394.5	10.233	3.559
700	0.01337	2769.0	10.976	3.869	0.01045	2767.7	10.806	3.904

continued

T, °K	v	i	s	c_p	v	i	s	c_p
800	0.01530	3176.7	11.519	4.274	0.01192	3178.5	11.353	4.301
900	0.01719	3626.7	12.047	4.705	0.01336	3631.0	11.884	4.727
1000	0.01906	4121.0	12.566	5.145	0.01477	4127.2	12.405	5.163
		$p=500$ bar				$p=600$ bar		
95	0.002098	738.6	4.094					
100	0.002124	756.1	4.270					
110	0.002176	789.8	4.584					
120	0.002228	823.2	4.875					
130	0.002280	856.7	5.149					
140	0.002334	889.8	5.390					
150	0.002388	921.3	5.605					
160	0.002445	952.0	5.805					
170	0.002505	983.5	5.993					
180	0.002570	1016.2	6.175					
190	0.002645	1049.8	6.351					
200	0.002725	1083.2	6.520	3.332	0.002654	1097.0	6.454	3.221
220	0.002886	1149.8	6.838	3.319	0.002785	1161.5	6.762	3.225
240	0.003060	1215.7	7.124	3.261	0.002931	1225.7	7.041	3.180
260	0.003251	1280.3	7.383	3.197	0.003088	1288.7	7.293	3.124
280	0.003455	1343.7	7.618	3.150	0.003255	1350.6	7.523	3.079
300	0.003673	1406.4	7.834	3.128	0.003430	1412.0	7.735	3.057
320	0.003901	1468.9	8.036	3.125	0.003612	1473.1	7.932	3.056
340	0.004140	1531.5	8.225	3.133	0.003802	1534.3	8.117	3.068
360	0.004388	1594.3	8.405	3.148	0.003998	1595.9	8.293	3.090
380	0.004642	1657.5	8.576	3.166	0.004200	1658.0	8.461	3.119
400	0.004901	1721.0	8.739	3.186	0.004407	1720.7	8.622	3.152
450	0.005558	1881.9	9.117	3.250	0.004938	1880.7	8.998	3.244
500	0.006214	2046.6	9.464	3.338	0.005477	2045.6	9.346	3.351
550	0.006860	2216.4	9.787	3.454	0.006015	2216.3	9.671	3.476
600	0.007493	2392.7	10.094	3.594	0.006545	2393.8	9.979	3.619
700	0.008723	2769.1	10.672	3.933	0.007581	2772.7	10.562	3.958
800	0.009914	3182.6	11.223	4.325	0.008586	3188.4	11.115	4.346
900	0.01108	3637.2	11.756	4.746	0.009566	3645.0	11.651	4.763
1000	0.01222	4135.2	12.279	5.179	0.01053	4144.5	12.175	5.193
		$p=700$ bar				$p=800$ bar		
200	0.002591	1111.8	6.397	3.130	0.002539	1127.4	6.347	3.051
220	0.002706	1174.7	6.697	3.151	0.002641	1188.9	6.640	3.090
240	0.002832	1237.5	6.970	3.121	0.002753	1250.6	6.909	3.074
260	0.002968	1299.4	7.218	3.073	0.002872	1311.7	7.153	3.035
280	0.003109	1360.5	7.445	3.032	0.002997	1372.0	7.377	2.999
300	0.003257	1420.9	7.653	3.010	0.003126	1431.7	7.583	2.979
320	0.003410	1481.0	7.847	3.008	0.003258	1491.3	7.775	2.976
340	0.003568	1541.3	8.030	3.021	0.003394	1550.8	7.956	2.986
360	0.003730	1601.9	8.203	3.044	0.003533	1610.8	8.127	3.009
380	0.003897	1663.1	8.368	3.076	0.003675	1671.3	8.290	3.042
400	0.004068	1725.1	8.527	3.115	0.003821	1732.6	8.447	3.082
450	0.004510	1883.6	8.900	3.225	0.004197	1889.7	8.817	3.202
500	0.004964	2048.0	9.246	3.349	0.004587	2053.3	9.162	3.339
550	0.005421	2219.0	9.572	3.486	0.004982	2224.0	9.487	3.487
600	0.005876	2397.2	9.881	3.636	0.005380	2402.5	9.797	3.644
700	0.006771	2777.9	10.467	3.977	0.006166	2784.5	10.384	3.992
800	0.007642	3195.6	11.023	4.364	0.006935	3203.7	10.942	4.380
900	0.008491	3653.8	11.560	4.779	0.007685	3663.4	11.482	4.793
1000	0.009323	4154.8	12.086	5.207	0.008421	4165.8	12.009	5.219
		$p=900$ bar				$p=1000$ bar		
200	0.002493	1143.5	6.301	2.981	0.002454	1159.9	6.260	2.916
220	0.002586	1203.7	6.589	3.036	0.002538	1219.1	6.542	2.989
240	0.002687	1264.5	6.853	3.035	0.002631	1279.1	6.803	3.001
260	0.002794	1325.0	7.095	3.006	0.002730	1338.9	7.043	2.982
280	0.002906	1384.8	7.316	2.974	0.002831	1398.3	7.263	2.956
300	0.003021	1444.0	7.521	2.956	0.002936	1457.2	7.466	2.940

continued

T, °K	v	i	s	c_p	v	i	s	c_p
320	0.003139	1503.1	7.712	2.953	0.003041	1516.0	7.655	2.937
340	0.003259	1562.2	7.891	2.963	0.003149	1574.8	7.834	2.946
360	0.003381	1621.7	8.061	2.984	0.003258	1633.9	8.003	2.966
380	0.003505	1681.7	8.223	3.015	0.003369	1693.5	8.164	2.995
400	0.003632	1742.4	8.379	3.055	0.003482	1753.8	8.319	3.034
450	0.003959	1898.2	8.746	3.179	0.003772	1908.6	8.682	3.159
500	0.004299	2060.9	9.088	3.325	0.004072	2070.3	9.023	3.309
550	0.004646	2231.1	9.412	3.481	0.004380	2239.9	9.346	3.472
600	0.004997	2409.5	9.722	3.647	0.004693	2418.0	9.656	3.644
700	0.005697	2792.3	10.310	4.003	0.005322	2801.1	10.244	4.010
800	0.006385	3212.7	10.870	4.393	0.005945	3222.5	10.805	4.404
900	0.007059	3673.8	11.411	4.806	0.006557	3684.7	11.348	4.818
1000	0.007719	4177.4	11.940	5.231	0.007156	4189.4	11.877	5.242

Viscosity η (N · s/m^2) of saturated methane [61]

T_S, °K	$\eta' \cdot 10^6$	$\eta'' \cdot 10^6$	p_S, bar	$\eta' \cdot 10^6$	$\eta'' \cdot 10^6$	p_S, bar	$\eta' \cdot 10^6$	$\eta'' \cdot 10^6$
100	144.3	4.073	0.5	125.8	4.206	20	40.45	7.335
110	106.5	4.430	1	102.8	4.492	22	38.75	7.544
120	86.05	4.836	2	85.05	4.860	24	37.25	7.760
130	71.65	5.278	3	75.76	5.129	26	35.79	7.983
140	61.26	5.744	4	70.00	5.343	28	34.39	8.216
150	52.24	6.270	5	65.79	5.519	30	33.00	8.478
160	44.54	6.889	6	62.44	5.683	32	31.60	8.764
170	37.69	7.692	7	59.50	5.836	34	30.20	9.062
180	30.98	8.894	8	56.94	5.974	36	28.81	9.368
182	29.46	9.220	9	54.70	6.102	38	27.38	9.700
184	27.85	9.584	10	52.83	6.229	40	25.82	10.14
186	25.98	10.09	12	49.49	6.470	42	24.13	10.80
188	23.65	10.99	14	46.66	6.691	44	21.96	11.68
190	19.34	12.96	16	44.42	6.903	46	18.06	13.91
190.55	15.8	15.8	18	42.35	7.120	46.41	15.8	15.8

Viscosity $\eta \cdot 10^6$ (N · s/m^2) of methane liquid and gas at different temperatures and pressures [61]

p, bar → / T, °K	1	2	4	6	8	10	15
100	144.5	144.8	145.1	145.5	146.1	146.5	147.7
110	106.6	106.8	107.1	107.5	107.8	108.2	109.3
120	4.78	86.08	86.29	86.53	86.75	87.00	87.65
130	5.17	5.18	71.69	71.92	72.12	72.35	72.86
140	5.54	5.56	5.64	5.73	61.32	61.51	61.95
150	5.92	5.93	5.98	6.04	6.13	6.25	52.64
160	6.29	6.32	6.36	6.40	6.48	6.56	6.83
170	6.66	6.67	6.72	6.78	6.80	6.87	7.05
180	7.03	7.05	7.09	7.14	7.16	7.23	7.38
190	7.40	7.42	7.45	7.49	7.53	7.58	7.71
200	7.75	7.78	7.82	7.86	7.91	7.95	8.08
220	8.48	8.49	8.52	8.58	8.59	8.65	8.74
240	9.18	9.20	9.23	9.27	9.30	9.34	9.42
260	9.85	9.87	9.90	9.93	9.96	9.99	10.07
280	10.50	10.52	10.54	10.57	10.60	10.62	10.70
300	11.14	11.15	11.17	11.19	11.23	11.23	11.30
320	11.76	11.76	11.78	11.79	11.82	11.84	11.91
340	12.36	12.37	12.39	12.41	12.43	12.45	12.50

continued

p, bar → / T, °K	1	2	4	6	8	10	15
360	12.94	12.95	12.96	12.98	13.00	13.01	13.06
380	13.52	13.53	13.54	13.55	13.57	13.57	13.62
400	14.08	14.08	14.09	14.11	14.12	14.14	14.18
420	14.64	14.64	14.65	14.66	14.68	14.69	14.72
440	15.18	15.19	15.20	15.21	15.21	15.23	15.27
460	15.71	15.71	15.72	15.73	15.74	15.76	15.79
480	16.21	16.22	16.23	16.25	16.26	16.27	16.30
500	16.70	16.71	16.72	16.73	16.75	16.76	16.79
520	17.18	17.19	17.20	17.22	17.23	17.24	17.28
540	17.66	17.67	17.68	17.70	17.71	17.73	17.78
560	18.17	18.18	18.19	18.21	18.22	18.23	18.26

p, bar → / T, °K	20	30	40	60	80	100	120
100	149.1	152.1	155.3	161.9	168.9	176.1	183.2
110	110.4	112.7	115.0	120.3	125.8	131.4	137.2
120	88.28	89.65	91.00	94.20	97.50	101.03	104.65
130	73.45	74.58	75.78	78.27	80.70	83.15	85.55
140	62.40	63.32	64.24	66.30	68.30	70.25	72.17
150	53.08	54.04	55.01	57.00	58.90	60.70	62.45
160	44.85	46.02	47.14	49.26	51.20	53.00	54.72
170	7.36	38.60	39.94	42.35	44.49	46.45	48.27
180	7.58	8.40	32.40	35.75	38.34	40.49	42.40
190	7.89	8.70	10.00	27.70	31.70	34.58	36.94
200	8.22	8.56	9.05	18.80	24.70	28.84	31.70
220	8.86	9.15	9.52	10.68	14.56	18.86	22.60
240	9.51	9.72	9.98	10.81	12.61	14.92	17.37
260	10.15	10.34	10.56	11.24	12.40	13.75	15.35
280	10.77	10.94	11.15	11.70	12.46	13.48	14.66
300	11.38	11.54	11.72	12.16	12.78	13.58	14.50
320	11.98	12.12	12.27	12.68	13.22	13.86	14.60
340	12.56	12.68	12.82	13.22	13.73	14.28	14.85
360	13.12	13.24	13.38	13.75	14.20	14.69	15.18
380	13.67	13.78	13.91	14.25	14.66	15.09	15.55
400	14.22	14.32	14.44	14.76	15.14	15.54	15.95
420	14.76	14.82	14.93	15.22	15.56	15.92	16.31
440	15.31	15.38	15.48	15.74	16.04	16.36	16.70
460	15.83	15.90	16.00	16.23	16.50	16.80	17.12
480	16.34	16.41	16.50	16.69	16.92	17.22	17.53
500	16.83	16.91	16.99	17.17	17.40	17.67	17.96
520	17.31	17.39	17.48	17.67	17.89	18.12	18.38
540	17.81	17.88	17.96	18.14	18.34	18.56	18.81
560	18.29	18.35	18.43	18.58	18.77	18.99	19.24

p, bar → / T, °K	140	160	180	200	300	400	500
100	190.4	197.5	204.6	211.5	248.9	283.9	319.7
110	143.1	149.0	154.9	160.6	188.8	217.9	253.1
120	108.43	112.45	116.67	120.95	143.42	167.68	195.40
130	87.95	90.30	92.70	95.10	108.20	126.45	150.20
140	74.10	76.00	72.90	79.80	89.75	102.10	118.43
150	64.20	65.90	67.58	69.28	77.55	86.97	97.50
160	56.34	57.94	59.46	60.94	68.50	76.35	84.10
170	49.94	51.52	53.40	54.50	61.25	68.11	74.90
180	44.14	45.67	47.15	48.56	55.30	61.63	67.62
190	38.90	40.60	42.10	43.50	50.13	56.14	61.59
200	34.00	35.88	37.54	39.06	45.71	51.34	56.64
220	25.60	28.10	30.17	31.97	38.70	43.95	49.18

continued

T, °K \ p, bar →	140	160	180	200	300	400	500
240	19.93	22.27	24.30	26.19	33.55	39.00	43.65
260	17.17	19.10	20.97	22.70	29.68	34.98	39.54
280	15.91	17.33	18.89	20.40	26.60	31.74	36.13
300	15.48	16.54	17.66	18.83	24.41	29.22	33.36
320	15.36	16.16	17.04	18.03	22.98	27.28	31.16
340	15.48	16.16	16.91	17.69	21.96	25.89	29.49
360	15.72	16.30	16.92	17.57	21.25	24.89	28.23
380	16.01	16.51	17.05	17.61	20.81	24.13	27.25
400	16.37	16.80	17.26	17.75	20.56	23.60	26.52
420	16.71	17.12	17.55	17.99	20.49	23.25	25.97
440	17.08	17.45	17.85	18.26	20.50	23.05	25.51
460	17.46	17.81	18.17	18.54	20.60	22.90	25.20
480	17.80	18.20	18.54	18.87	20.75	22.83	24.94
500	18.25	18.56	18.87	19.19	20.94	22.83	24.81
520	18.66	18.94	19.23	19.52	21.16	22.90	24.69
540	19.07	19.34	19.60	19.88	21.40	23.07	24.68
560	19.50	19.76	20.03	20.30	21.66	23.21	24.80

Thermal conductivity $\lambda \cdot 10^3$ (W/m · deg) of methane liquid and gas at different temperatures and pressures [15]

t, °C \ p, bar →	1	10	20	30	40	50	60	80	100
−170	208	209	210	211	212	213	214	216	218
−160	12.2	193	194	195	196	197	198	200	202
−150	13.3	178	180	181	183	184	185	187	189
−140	14.4	162	164	166	167	169	170	173	175
−130	15.5	146	147	149	150	152	154	157	160
−120	16.6	18.5	130	132	134	136	138	141	144
−110	17.6	19.4	114	116	119	122	124	128	131
−100	18.7	20.2	22.2	99	102	105	108	113	117
−90	19.8	21.2	22.9	25.0			89	97	103
−80	20.9	22.0	23.6	25.5	28.7	34.1			88
−60	23.2	24.3	25.6	27.1	29.3	32.2	36.0		
−40	25.5	26.5	27.6	28.9	30.5	32.4	34.7	40.9	50.7
−20	27.9	28.9	29.9	30.9	32.2	33.7	36.0	39.4	44.6
0	30.4	31.3	32.3	33.2	34.2	35.4	36.7	39.8	43.8
20	33.2	34.0	34.8	35.7	36.6	37.6	38.7	41.4	44.4
40	36.0	36.7	37.5	38.3	39.1	40.0	41.0	43.2	45.5
60	38.9	39.6	40.3	41.1	41.8	42.5	43.4	45.4	47.5
80	41.9	42.5	43.2	43.9	44.6	45.3	46.1	48.0	50.0
100	50.0	45.6	46.2	46.9	47.6	48.2	48.9	50.4	52.0
150	53.2	53.7	54.2	54.8	55.4	56.0	56.6	57.9	59.2
200	62.0	62.5	63.0	63.5	64.0	64.5	65.0	66.0	67.1
250	70.9	71.4	71.8	72.2	72.6	73.0	73.4	74.4	75.4
300	80.1	80.5	80.9	81.3	81.7	82.1	82.5	83.2	84.0

t, °C \ p, bar →	150	200	250	300	350	400	450	500	550	600
−170	222	225	229	233	236	240	243	246	249	252
−160	206	209	213	217	220	224	228	232	236	240
−150	193	197	201	205	209	213	217	221	225	229
−140	180	184	189	193	198	203	207	212	216	220
−130	166	171	176	181	186	191	196	201	206	211
−120	151	158	164	169	175	180	185	190	195	200
−110	138	145	152	159	165	171	176	181	186	191
−100	125	134	141	148	154	160	166	171	176	181
−90	113	123	130	137	143	149	155	161	166	171

continued

t, °C \ p, bar →	150	200	250	300	350	400	450	500	550	600
−80	101	112	120	128	134	140	146	151	157	162
−60	80	93	103	111	117	123	129	134	140	146
−40	65.2	78.0	87.8	96.6	104	111	117	122	127	132
−20	57.6	68.6	77.5	86.3	93.8	101	107	112	117	121
0	54.3	63.8	72.2	80.0	86.7	93.0	98.5	104	109	113
20	52.6	61.0	68.5	75.0	81.2	87.1	92.4	97.6	103	107
40	52.3	59.3	66.2	72.8	78.8	84.3	89.1	93.9	98.5	103
60	53.2	59.0	64.8	70.9	76.5	81.9	87.0	91.6	95.9	100
80	55.0	60.1	65.4	71.0	76.0	81.0	85.5	89.9	94.1	98.1
100	56.7	61.4	66.2	71.0	75.6	80.1	83.7	88.3	92.4	96.3
150	62.8	66.4	70.2	74.0	77.8	81.6	85.2	88.8	92.3	95.7
200	70.0	73.0	76.1	79.3	82.6	86.0	89.3	92.6	95.4	98.2
250	78.0	80.7	83.5	86.3	89.1	91.9	94.6	97.2	99.8	102
300	86.3	88.5	90.8	93.2	95.5	98.7	101	103	105	107

Thermal conductivity λ (W/m · deg) of methane gas at a pressure of 1 bar [15]

t, °C	$\lambda \cdot 10^3$	t, °C	$\lambda \cdot 10^3$	t, °C	$\lambda \cdot 10^3$	t, °C	$\lambda \cdot 10^3$
−180	10.0	−40	25.5	100	45.0	240	69.1
−160	12.2	−20	27.9	120	48.2	260	72.7
−140	14.4	0	30.4	140	51.5	280	76.3
−120	16.6	20	33.2	160	54.9	300	80.1
−100	18.7	40	36.0	180	58.4	320	83.9
−80	20.9	60	38.9	200	62.0	350	89.5
−60	23.2	80	41.9	220	65.5	400	99.2

Surface tension of methane [42, 84]

t, °C	−180	−170	−160
$\sigma \cdot 10^3$, N/m	18.0	15.8	13.7

ETHANE (C_2H_6)

CH_3—CH_3

Molecular weight 30.068

$T_{boil} = 184.52$ °K at 760 mm Hg; $T_{melt} = 89.88$ °K; $p_{cr} = 49.13$ bar, $\rho_{cr} = 212$ kg/m³; $T_{cr} = 305.5$ °K

Thermodynamic properties of saturated ethane [51]: v (m³ kg), i (kJ/kg) and s (kJ/kg · deg)

T, °K	p, bar	v'	v''	i'	i''	s'	s''
89.88		0.001518		179.01	780.20	2.571	9.260
90		0.001525		179.29	780.06	2.574	9.250
100	0.00007	0.001556		202.02	790.55	2.814	8.699
110	0.00077	0.001587		224.80	801.24	3.031	8.272
120	0.00350	0.001618		247.65	812.24	3.230	7.935
130	0.01288	0.001649		270.61	823.64	3.414	7.669
140	0.03834	0.001682		293.73	835.59	3.585	7.456
150	0.09680	0.001713	4.2653	317.05	847.77	3.747	7.284
160	0.2147	0.001746	2.0419	340.61	860.10	3.898	7.145
170	0.4291	0.001779	1.0776	364.42	872.23	4.042	7.030
180	0.7879	0.001813	0.6143	388.49	883.76	4.178	6.929

continued

T, °K	p, bar	v'	v''	i'	i''	s'	s''
184.52	1.013	0.001830	0.4899	399.52	889.19	4.237	6.890
190	1.347	0.001850	0.3795	412.84	894.37	4.309	6.842
200	2.174	0.001890	0.2446	437.50	903.74	4.450	6.767
210	3.340	0.001935	0.1611	462.53	912.82	4.558	6.701
220	4.921	0.001985	0.1058	488.10	921.35	4.675	6.645
230	7.002	0.002042	0.07842	514.34	929.18	4.794	6.597
240	9.675	0.002107	0.05694	541.41	935.72	4.909	6.552
250	13.02	0.002182	0.04217	569.45	940.22	5.023	6.508
260	17.12	0.002272	0.03160	598.79	943.27	5.137	6.463
270	22.08	0.002382	0.02379	629.79	943.23	5.254	6.417
280	28.01	0.002523	0.01787	663.10	941.14	5.376	6.368
290	35.10	0.002743	0.01297	700.28	930.10	5.505	6.297
300	43.65	0.003162	0.008391	753.08	892.31	5.696	6.151
305.5	49.13	0.004713	0.004713	835.87	835.87	5.939	5.939

Thermodynamic properties of ethane at different temperatures and pressures [51]:
v (m³/kg), i (kJ/kg), s and c_p (kJ/kg · deg)

T, °K	v	i	s	c_p	v	i	s	c_p
	p=1 bar				p=2 bar			
200	0.53875	911.62	7.0047	1.431	0.26134	905.76	6.7913	1.502
210	0.56751	926.08	7.0753	1.460	0.27661	920.95	6.8655	1.524
220	0.59618	940.83	7.1440	1.491	0.29167	936.32	6.9371	1.548
230	0.62478	955.90	7.2110	1.523	0.30664	951.93	7.0064	1.574
240	0.65332	971.28	7.2765	1.555	0.32147	967.79	7.0738	1.604
250	0.68179	987.02	7.3407	1.588	0.33617	983.90	7.1395	1.629
260	0.71019	1003.10	7.4037	1.623	0.35074	1000.26	7.2037	1.658
270	0.73849	1019.52	7.4656	1.659	0.36524	1016.91	7.2667	1.688
280	0.76673	1036.31	7.5268	1.697	0.38443	1033.90	7.3285	1.722
290	0.79493	1053.48	7.5870	1.736	0.39401	1051.22	7.3893	1.757
300	0.82304	1071.03	7.6466	1.775	0.40831	1068.92	7.4495	1.775
310	0.95114	1088.98	7.7055	1.815	0.42261	1086.99	7.5089	1.815
320	0.87921	1107.33	7.7639	1.856	0.43684	1105.45	7.5677	1.856
330	0.90724	1126.09	7.8217	1.896	0.45108	1124.32	7.6259	1.896
340	0.93521	1145.24	7.8789	1.936	0.46525	1143.59	7.6834	1.936
350	0.96315	1164.81	7.9356	1.978	0.47938	1163.25	7.7404	1.978
360	0.99102	1184.81	7.9918	2.018	0.49345	1183.33	7.7969	2.018
370	1.01896	1205.22	8.0476	2.060	0.50755	1203.84	7.8530	2.060
380	1.04686	1226.04	8.1032	2.103	0.52158	1224.73	7.9087	2.103
390	1.07473	1247.27	8.1584	2.145	0.53565	1246.03	7.9640	2.145
400	1.10254	1268.94	8.2132	2.188	0.54965	1267.77	8.0190	2.188
410	1.13037	1291.02	8.2678	2.230	0.56366	1289.88	8.0737	2.230
420	1.15821	1313.52	8.3221	2.272	0.57766	1312.42	8.1281	2.272
430	1.18601	1336.44	8.3760	2.314	0.59166	1335.38	8.1822	2.314
440	1.21382	1359.78	8.4296	2.354	0.60566	1358.76	8.2359	2.354
450	1.24162	1383.53	8.4829	2.396	0.61963	1382.56	8.2894	2.396
460	1.26942	1407.69	8.5360	2.436	0.63356	1406.76	8.3426	2.436
470	1.29716	1432.26	8.5889	2.476	0.64757	1431.37	8.3955	2.476
480	1.32496	1457.24	8.6415	2.517	0.66150	1456.39	8.4481	2.517
490	1.35274	1482.63	8.6939	2.557	0.67547	1481.82	8.5006	2.557
500	1.38051	1508.43	8.7459	2.597	0.68937	1507.68	8.5528	2.597
	p=3 bar				p=4 bar			
210	0.18042	915.60	6.7353	1.592				
220	0.19014	931.70	6.8102	1.608	0.13872	926.86	6.7144	1.672
230	0.20045	947.86	6.8822	1.627	0.14703	943.66	6.7895	1.684
240	0.21066	964.18	6.9517	1.650	0.15512	960.48	6.8610	1.697
250	0.22077	980.68	7.0191	1.672	0.16304	977.38	6.9298	1.712
260	0.23081	997.36	7.0847	1.694	0.17081	994.40	6.9964	1.730
270	0.24075	1014.25	7.1486	1.719	0.17847	1011.55	7.0611	1.750
280	0.25063	1031.43	7.2112	1.746	0.18602	1028.94	7.1245	1.771

continued

T, °K	v	i	s	c_p	v	i	s	c_p
290	0.26041	1048.94	7.2728	1.775	0.19351	1046.64	7.1867	1.796
300	0.27015	1066.80	7.3335	1.808	0.20093	1064.66	7.2480	1.825
310	0.27983	1085.01	7.3934	1.844	0.20832	1083.02	7.3084	1.858
320	0.28944	1103.63	7.4525	1.882	0.21565	1101.79	7.3682	1.894
330	0.29902	1122.62	7.5112	1.921	0.22295	1120.90	7.4272	1.933
340	0.30857	1141.99	7.5691	1.958	0.23021	1140.38	7.4854	1.970
350	0.31808	1161.72	7.6264	1.998	0.23744	1160.22	7.5430	2.007
360	0.32756	1181.88	7.6831	2.036	0.24464	1180.46	7.6000	2.045
370	0.33704	1202.45	7.7394	2.077	0.25182	1201.10	7.6564	2.085
380	0.34652	1223.42	7.7952	2.117	0.25897	1222.14	7.7125	2.124
390	0.35593	1244.79	7.8506	2.158	0.26611	1243.58	7.7682	2.165
400	0.36537	1266.60	7.9058	2.199	0.27323	1265.41	7.8236	2.206
410	0.37478	1288.75	7.9606	2.241	0.28034	1287.64	7.8786	2.247
420	0.38416	1311.33	8.0151	2.281	0.28744	1310.28	7.9332	2.287
430	0.39354	1334.34	8.0692	2.322	0.29452	1333.33	7.9875	2.327
440	0.40292	1357.76	8.1231	2.362	0.30159	1356.80	8.0415	2.366
450	0.41230	1381.61	8.1767	2.404	0.30865	1380.66	8.0953	2.408
460	0.42164	1405.85	8.2299	2.443	0.31570	1404.95	8.1486	2.447
470	0.43099	1430.48	8.2830	2.483	0.32275	1429.63	8.2016	2.488
480	0.44034	1455.54	8.3357	2.524	0.32978	1454.74	8.2546	2.528
490	0.44965	1481.04	8.3882	2.564	0.33680	1480.27	8.3072	2.568
500	0.45899	1506.95	8.4404	2.604	0.34381	1506.21	8.3596	2.607
		$p=5$ bar				$p=6$ bar		
230	0.11495	939.48	6.7148	1.747	0.09302	934.77	6.6501	1.817
240	0.12175	956.66	6.7888	1.750	0.09940	952.72	6.7265	1.807
250	0.12835	974.00	6.8591	1.755	0.10522	970.52	6.7985	1.797
260	0.13479	991.35	6.9268	1.764	0.11074	988.23	6.8675	1.797
270	0.14110	1008.79	6.9925	1.776	0.11612	1005.98	6.9343	1.804
280	0.14730	1026.44	7.0567	1.794	0.12140	1023.87	6.9995	1.818
290	0.15341	1044.31	7.1196	1.817	0.12662	1041.95	7.0632	1.839
300	0.15946	1062.51	7.1816	1.843	0.13177	1060.34	7.1259	1.862
310	0.16545	1081.06	7.2426	1.874	0.13687	1079.11	7.1619	1.890
320	0.17141	1099.97	7.3027	1.907	0.14192	1098.13	7.2480	1.921
330	0.17733	1119.20	7.3620	1.945	0.14693	1117.50	7.3077	1.953
340	0.18321	1138.77	7.4207	1.979	0.15189	1137.20	7.3666	1.988
350	0.18906	1158.73	7.4786	2.016	0.15682	1157.25	7.4248	2.024
360	0.19489	1179.06	7.5358	2.055	0.16172	1177.64	7.4825	2.063
370	0.20068	1199.75	7.5925	2.094	0.16652	1198.41	7.5394	2.102
380	0.20646	1220.86	7.6487	2.131	0.17144	1219.58	7.5960	2.140
390	0.21220	1242.35	7.7046	2.172	0.17626	1241.14	7.6521	2.178
400	0.21793	1264.24	7.7601	2.212	0.18108	1263.09	7.7078	2.217
410	0.22365	1286.55	7.8153	2.251	0.18587	1285.48	7.7630	2.256
420	0.22936	1309.26	7.8700	2.291	0.19066	1308.24	7.8179	2.295
430	0.23505	1332.36	7.9243	2.332	0.19544	1331.38	7.8724	2.336
440	0.24074	1355.85	7.9783	2.371	0.20020	1354.93	7.9265	2.375
450	0.24642	1379.76	8.0321	2.411	0.20496	1378.88	7.9804	2.415
460	0.25209	1404.08	8.0855	2.451	0.20971	1403.23	8.0339	2.455
470	0.25775	1428.81	8.1387	2.490	0.21411	1428.00	8.0871	2.494
480	0.26340	1453.96	8.1916	2.531	0.21917	1453.16	8.1402	2.535
490	0.26905	1479.51	8.2443	2.571	0.22389	1478.76	8.1929	2.574
500	0.27468	1505.48	8.2966	2.610	0.22861	1504.75	8.2451	2.613
		$p=7$ bar				$p=8$ bar		
240	0.08346	948.67	6.6718	1.868	0.07145	944.48	6.6211	1.936
250	0.08859	966.91	6.7458	1.842	0.07612	963.16	6.6976	1.885
260	0.09352	985.00	6.8161	1.833	0.08059	981.70	6.7696	1.868
270	0.09829	1003.10	6.8842	1.833	0.08489	1000.13	6.8390	1.864
280	0.10296	1019.85	6.9504	1.843	0.08908	1018.58	6.9064	1.868
290	0.10753	1039.58	7.0152	1.860	0.09316	1037.16	6.9720	1.879
300	0.11203	1058.17	7.0785	1.881	0.09717	1055.98	7.0361	1.899
310	0.11646	1077.15	7.1406	1.906	0.10111	1075.14	7.0987	1.922
320	0.12085	1096.29	7.2016	1.933	0.10501	1094.44	7.1601	1.947
330	0.12519	1115.77	7.2616	1.964	0.10887	1114.04	7.2206	1.977

continued

T, °K	v	i	s	c_p	v	i	s	c_p
340	0.12950	1135.60	7.3208	1.998	0.11268	1133.97	7.2802	2.009
350	0.13376	1155.78	7.3793	2.034	0.11647	1154.26	7.3389	2.043
360	0.13800	1176.23	7.4372	2.070	0.12022	1171.81	7.3970	2.078
370	0.14222	1197.07	7.4944	2.107	0.12395	1195.74	7.4545	2.116
380	0.14642	1218.31	7.5511	2.146	0.12766	1217.06	7.5114	2.152
390	0.15035	1239.95	7.6074	2.185	0.13134	1238.75	7.5680	2.192
400	0.15475	1261.95	7.6632	2.224	0.13501	1260.82	7.6239	2.230
410	0.15889	1284.40	7.7185	2.262	0.13866	1283.33	7.6794	2.268
420	0.16302	1307.24	7.7734	2.301	0.14229	1306.22	7.7345	2.305
430	0.16713	1330.44	7.8279	2.340	0.14591	1329.48	7.7892	2.344
440	0.17124	1354.04	7.8822	2.379	0.14952	1353.12	7.8437	2.383
450	0.17533	1378.02	7.9363	2.419	0.15313	1377.14	7.8978	2.423
460	0.17942	1402.38	7.9899	2.458	0.15672	1401.56	7.9516	2.462
470	0.18350	1427.18	8.0432	2.497	0.16030	1426.39	8.0050	2.501
480	0.18756	1452.40	8.0962	2.538	0.16388	1451.62	8.0582	2.540
490	0.19163	1478.02	8.1490	2.577	0.16745	1477.27	8.1110	2.579
500	0.19570	1504.03	8.2015	2.616	0.17102	1503.29	8.1635	2.618
		p=9 bar				p=10 bar		
240	0.06206	940.12	6.5753	2.010				
250	0.06632	959.27	6.6537	1.928	0.05853	955.20	6.6120	1.972
260	0.07043	978.30	6.7279	1.906	0.06251	974.80	6.6890	1.940
270	0.07439	997.11	6.7989	1.893	0.06612	994.01	6.7616	1.922
280	0.07824	1015.87	6.8675	1.893	0.06961	1013.11	6.8314	1.918
290	0.08198	1034.72	6.9339	1.901	0.07289	1032.26	6.8988	1.922
300	0.08564	1053.77	6.9986	1.917	0.07616	1051.54	6.9642	1.935
310	0.08922	1073.11	7.0618	1.936	0.07973	1071.01	7.0280	1.953
320	0.09274	1092.56	7.1237	1.961	0.08291	1090.64	7.0904	1.975
330	0.09621	1112.29	7.1845	1.989	0.08606	1110.54	7.1516	2.003
340	0.09963	1132.33	7.2445	2.020	0.08918	1130.67	7.2119	2.032
350	0.10303	1152.70	7.3037	2.053	0.09227	1151.10	7.2714	2.063
360	0.10639	1173.33	7.3620	2.087	0.09533	1171.86	7.3300	2.095
370	0.10973	1194.37	7.4197	2.123	0.09837	1192.98	7.3879	2.130
380	0.11306	1215.77	7.4769	2.159	0.10138	1214.48	7.4453	2.166
390	0.11636	1237.55	7.5336	2.197	0.10438	1236.35	7.5021	2.204
400	0.11965	1259.70	7.5897	2.236	0.10736	1258.59	7.5584	2.240
410	0.12291	1282.28	7.6452	2.273	0.11032	1281.22	7.6142	2.277
420	0.12684	1305.21	7.7005	2.311	0.11327	1304.19	7.6695	2.315
430	0.12940	1328.50	7.7554	2.348	0.11620	1327.56	7.7243	2.352
440	0.13263	1352.20	7.8098	2.387	0.11912	1351.30	7.7789	2.391
450	0.13584	1376.26	7.8640	2.426	0.12203	1375.40	7.8332	2.430
460	0.13904	1400.73	7.9179	2.465	0.12497	1399.90	7.8871	2.469
470	0.14225	1425.59	7.9715	2.504	0.12783	1424.79	7.9407	2.508
480	0.14544	1450.84	8.0247	2.543	0.13071	1450.07	7.9939	2.547
490	0.14863	1476.50	8.0774	2.582	0.13359	1475.75	8.0468	2.585
500	0.15182	1502.55	8.1299	2.621	0.13646	1501.83	8.0994	2.624
		p=15 bar				p=20 bar		
260	0.03834	955.13	6.5228	2.227				
270	0.04097	977.14	6.6042	2.146	0.02748	954.94	6.4685	
280	0.04340	998.42	6.6806	2.094	0.03001	981.73	6.5558	2.357
290	0.04602	1019.24	6.7534	2.063	0.03230	1004.77	6.6362	2.254
300	0.04853	1039.82	6.8233	2.050	0.03444	1026.90	6.7115	2.199
310	0.05094	1060.26	6.8907	2.049	0.03645	1048.69	6.7834	2.171
320	0.05328	1080.85	6.9562	2.059	0.03837	1070.39	6.8523	2.160
330	0.05555	1101.49	7.0198	2.075	0.04023	1091.95	6.9188	2.163
340	0.05778	1122.29	7.0820	2.095	0.04202	1113.54	6.9834	2.169
350	0.05997	1143.30	7.1432	2.119	0.04377	1135.24	7.0467	2.181
360	0.06212	1164.56	7.2033	2.146	0.04548	1157.11	7.1086	2.202
370	0.06425	1186.14	7.2625	2.174	0.04715	1179.17	7.1693	2.223
380	0.06634	1208.06	7.3210	2.205	0.04880	1201.52	7.2289	2.247
390	0.06842	1230.34	7.3787	2.237	0.05043	1224.17	7.2877	2.273
400	0.07048	1252.98	7.4358	2.270	0.05204	1247.21	7.3457	2.304
410	0.07253	1275.87	7.4924	2.306	0.05362	1270.41	7.4031	2.337

continued

T, °K	v	i	s	c_p	v	i	s	c_p
420	0.07456	1299.11	7.5485	2.341	0.05520	1293.93	7.4598	2.369
430	0.07658	1322.72	7.6040	2.376	0.05676	1317.81	7.5160	2.401
440	0.07858	1346.72	7.6592	2.412	0.05830	1342.08	7.5717	2.436
450	0.08057	1371.08	7.7139	2.450	0.05984	1366.68	7.6270	2.472
460	0.08255	1395.78	7.7682	2.488	0.06136	1391.61	7.6819	2.508
470	0.08452	1420.86	7.8221	2.525	0.06288	1416.88	7.7362	2.545
480	0.08649	1446.30	7.8757	2.564	0.06438	1442.50	7.7902	2.581
490	0.08845	1472.11	7.9290	2.602	0.06588	1468.44	7.8438	2.616
500	0.09040	1198.26	7.9821	2.639	0.06738	1494.70	7.8971	2.652
		$p=25$ bar				$p=30$ bar		
280	0.02156	961.48	6.4353					
290	0.02385	987.98	6.5292	2.571	0.01786	967.68	6.4216	
300	0.02586	1012.64	6.6133	2.408	0.01986	996.14	6.5192	2.714
310	0.02767	1036.13	6.6909	2.325	0.02164	1022.22	6.6055	2.539
320	0.02935	1059.17	6.7641	2.283	0.02327	1046.78	6.6846	2.437
330	0.03096	1081.81	6.8340	2.263	0.02476	1071.01	6.7587	2.380
340	0.03252	1104.34	6.9014	2.254	0.02617	1094.65	6.8294	2.347
350	0.03402	1126.86	6.9670	2.252	0.02750	1118.06	6.8975	2.330
360	0.03548	1149.37	7.0309	2.261	0.02878	1141.31	6.9634	2.326
370	0.03690	1171.97	7.0933	2.274	0.03003	1164.52	7.0274	2.332
380	0.03829	1194.79	7.1543	2.293	0.03124	1187.88	7.0900	2.343
390	0.03965	1217.88	7.2142	2.315	0.03209	1211.58	7.1512	2.358
400	0.04098	1241.30	7.2731	2.339	0.03358	1235.23	7.2114	2.379
410	0.04230	1264.86	7.3311	2.369	0.03539	1259.16	7.2707	2.403
420	0.04359	1288.68	7.3886	2.398	0.03584	1283.36	7.3290	2.429
430	0.04488	1312.84	7.4456	2.429	0.03695	1307.81	7.3865	2.457
440	0.04615	1337.36	7.5020	2.461	0.03804	1332.58	7.4434	2.486
450	0.04741	1362.20	7.5578	2.494	0.03912	1357.67	7.4997	2.518
460	0.04866	1387.37	7.6131	2.529	0.04019	1383.07	7.5556	2.550
470	0.04990	1412.85	7.6679	2.564	0.04125	1408.77	7.6109	2.584
480	0.05113	1438.64	7.7224	2.597	0.04229	1434.76	7.6657	2.616
490	0.05235	1464.74	7.7764	2.632	0.04334	1461.03	7.7202	2.649
500	0.05357	1491.15	7.8299	2.666	0.04437	1487.58	7.7740	2.681
		$p=35$ bar				$p=40$ bar		
300	0.01540	976.42	6.4219		0.01157	951.47	6.3060	
310	0.01724	1006.30	6.5217	2.854	0.01374	989.17	6.4344	3.480
320	0.01884	1033.49	6.6093	2.645	0.01541	1019.84	6.5344	2.948
330	0.02027	1059.34	6.6891	2.526	0.01649	1047.88	6.6217	2.745
340	0.02158	1084.30	6.7639	2.458	0.01807	1074.35	6.7016	2.602
350	0.02282	1108.75	6.8347	2.421	0.01925	1099.91	6.7762	2.528
360	0.02399	1132.86	6.9028	2.401	0.02035	1124.91	6.8473	2.493
370	0.02512	1156.78	6.9688	2.394	0.02140	1149.55	6.9155	2.471
380	0.02618	1180.76	7.0330	2.398	0.02241	1174.16	6.9815	2.461
390	0.02724	1204.82	7.0957	2.407	0.02339	1198.73	7.0457	2.460
400	0.02828	1229.03	7.1571	2.422	0.02434	1223.35	7.1082	2.469
410	0.02930	1253.37	7.2174	2.440	0.02527	1248.09	7.1695	2.482
420	0.03030	1277.93	7.2765	2.462	0.02617	1272.85	7.2296	2.497
430	0.03128	1302.70	7.3349	2.486	0.02705	1298.08	7.2888	2.518
440	0.03225	1327.75	7.3925	2.518	0.02792	1323.38	7.3471	2.542
450	0.03320	1353.08	7.4495	2.542	0.02877	1348.93	7.4046	2.568
460	0.03415	1378.73	7.5059	2.574	0.02961	1374.80	7.4616	2.596
470	0.03509	1404.65	7.5616	2.604	0.03044	1400.94	7.5178	2.625
480	0.03599	1430.84	7.6168	2.635	0.03126	1427.31	7.5735	2.654
490	0.03690	1457.30	7.6716	2.667	0.03208	1453.94	7.6287	2.687
500	0.03780	1484.02	7.7259	2.698	0.03289	1480.83	7.6833	2.716
		$p=45$ bar				$p=50$ bar		
310	0.01076	963.36	6.3337		0.00767	925.01	6.1868	
320	0.01262	1001.25	6.4568	3.430	0.01025	980.33	6.3712	4.594
330	0.01408	1032.73	6.5551	3.000	0.01181	1017.04	6.4866	3.396
340	0.01533	1061.40	6.6415	2.784	0.01311	1048.56	6.5819	3.021
350	0.01646	1088.77	6.7207	2.663	0.01425	1077.52	6.6667	2.828

continued

T, °K	v	i	s	c_p	v	i	s	c_p
360	0.01751	1114.76	6.7950	2.593	0.01528	1105.09	6.7449	2.717
370	0.01851	1140.42	6.8658	2.553	0.01623	1131.94	6.8186	2.648
380	0.01948	1165.81	6.9337	2.531	0.01712	1158.00	6.8888	2.607
390	0.02038	1191.07	6.9994	2.520	0.01797	1183.92	6.9563	2.585
400	0.02126	1216.25	7.0635	2.518	0.01879	1209.69	7.0217	2.574
410	0.02212	1241.49	7.1260	2.525	0.01959	1235.43	7.0854	2.572
420	0.02294	1266.83	7.1870	2.535	0.02036	1261.18	7.1475	2.577
430	0.02376	1292.30	7.2469	2.552	0.02111	1287.00	7.2084	2.588
440	0.02455	1317.95	7.3059	2.571	0.02185	1312.96	7.2683	2.604
450	0.02533	1343.79	7.3641	2.596	0.02257	1339.11	7.3272	2.624
460	0.02609	1369.93	7.4216	2.621	0.02328	1365.48	7.3853	2.645
470	0.02685	1396.31	7.4784	2.648	0.02397	1392.09	7.4425	2.670
480	0.02759	1422.92	7.5347	2.675	0.02465	1418.94	7.4990	2.696
490	0.02833	1449.79	7.5902	2.705	0.02533	1446.02	7.5550	2.724
500	0.02906	1476.90	7.6452	2.734	0.02600	1473.35	7.6104	2.752
		$p=55$ bar				$p=60$ bar		
310	0.00409	838.22	5.8692		0.00354	803.19	5.7812	
320	0.00806	953.46	6.2680		0.00605	915.99	6.1337	
330	0.00991	999.00	6.4149	4.037	0.00823	978.06	6.3343	5.178
340	0.01125	1034.46	6.5214	3.341	0.00967	1019.01	6.4593	3.758
350	0.01238	1065.83	6.6133	3.021	0.01084	1053.27	6.5602	3.263
360	0.01340	1094.96	6.6963	2.861	0.01184	1084.32	6.6486	3.025
370	0.01433	1122.84	6.7732	2.752	0.01274	1113.52	6.7292	2.870
380	0.01519	1149.94	6.8459	2.687	0.01358	1141.67	6.8048	2.777
390	0.01600	1176.45	6.9154	2.650	0.01436	1169.13	6.8765	2.726
400	0.01678	1203.01	6.9825	2.629	0.01510	1196.18	6.9452	2.689
410	0.01753	1229.24	7.0475	2.621	0.01582	1222.94	7.0114	2.671
420	0.01825	1255.43	7.1107	2.620	0.01651	1249.60	7.0758	2.663
430	0.01895	1281.65	7.1725	2.624	0.01717	1276.23	7.1386	2.662
440	0.01964	1307.95	7.2331	2.636	0.01782	1302.90	7.2001	2.670
450	0.02031	1334.41	7.2927	2.653	0.01845	1329.67	7.2605	2.684
460	0.02098	1361.03	7.3513	2.673	0.01907	1356.57	7.3200	2.700
470	0.02162	1387.87	7.4091	2.694	0.01967	1383.66	7.3785	2.720
480	0.02226	1414.94	7.4662	2.719	0.02026	1410.96	7.4361	2.742
490	0.02288	1442.25	7.5226	2.744	0.02085	1438.49	7.4928	2.764
500	0.02351	1469.80	7.5784	2.771	0.02143	1466.24	7.5488	2.790
		$p=65$ bar				$p=70$ bar		
310	0.00335	789.89	5.7413		0.00321	782.39	5.7145	
320	0.00465	876.64	6.0010		0.00401	849.86	5.9171	
330	0.00712	953.78	6.2464	6.320	0.00562	927.88	6.1569	6.71
340	0.00833	1002.04	6.3947	4.315	0.00716	983.66	6.3279	4.90
350	0.00950	1039.89	6.5065	3.550	0.00836	1025.71	6.4524	3.90
360	0.01051	1073.21	6.6015	3.207	0.00937	1061.55	6.5546	3.415
370	0.01140	1103.87	6.6863	3.000	0.01024	1093.86	6.6442	3.160
380	0.01222	1133.18	6.7650	2.877	0.01104	1124.40	6.7263	2.989
390	0.01297	1161.51	6.8390	2.801	0.01178	1153.70	6.8028	2.886
400	0.01369	1189.22	6.9095	2.756	0.01247	1182.13	6.8752	2.822
410	0.01437	1216.57	6.9773	2.724	0.01313	1210.09	6.9446	2.780
420	0.01503	1243.72	7.0429	2.706	0.01376	1237.77	7.0114	2.775
430	0.01566	1270.77	7.1067	2.699	0.01436	1265.27	7.0763	2.744
440	0.01627	1297.80	7.1690	2.706	0.01495	1292.69	7.1395	2.742
450	0.01687	1324.91	7.2302	2.714	0.01551	1320.11	7.2014	2.748
460	0.01745	1352.12	7.2902	2.728	0.01607	1347.63	7.2619	2.758
470	0.01802	1379.46	7.3492	2.744	0.01661	1375.26	7.3215	2.770
480	0.01858	1407.10	7.4073	2.763	0.01714	1403.02	7.3801	2.787
490	0.01913	1434.72	7.4645	2.784	0.01766	1430.97	7.4379	2.805
500	0.01968	1462.69	7.5210	2.809	0.01800	1459.12	7.4949	2.827
		$p=75$ bar				$p=80$ bar		
310	0.00314	777.29	5.6939		0.00307	773.52	5.6772	
320	0.00361	833.71	5.8662	6.26	0.00351	823.42	5.8314	5.61
330	0.00485	904.59	6.0794	6.58	0.00433	886.00	6.0185	6.15

continued

T, °K	v	i	s	c_p	v	i	s	c_p
340	0.00620	964.81	6.2616	6.36	0.00548	947.71	6.1997	5.51
350	0.00741	1010.99	6.3982	4.255	0.00658	996.11	6.3450	4.55
360	0.00840	1049.51	6.5082	3.637	0.00756	1037.24	6.4623	3.856
370	0.00926	1083.59	6.6028	3.302	0.00841	1073.44	6.5624	3.460
380	0.01004	1115.47	6.6884	3.104	0.00918	1106.39	6.6516	3.227
390	0.01075	1145.76	6.7676	2.973	0.00988	1137.72	6.7335	3.068
400	0.01143	1174.99	6.8421	2.891	0.01053	1167.76	6.8101	2.965
410	0.01206	1203.56	6.9131	2.837	0.01114	1196.99	6.8828	2.898
420	0.01267	1231.77	6.9814	2.803	0.01172	1225.74	6.9522	2.856
430	0.01325	1259.73	7.0472	2.785	0.01227	1254.16	7.0192	2.830
440	0.01381	1287.54	7.1113	2.778	0.01281	1282.37	7.0842	2.816
450	0.01435	1315.30	7.1739	2.778	0.01333	1310.48	7.1477	2.812
460	0.01488	1343.18	7.2352	2.785	0.01384	1338.64	7.2097	2.816
470	0.01540	1371.05	7.2953	2.795	0.01433	1366.84	7.2704	2.822
480	0.01590	1399.06	7.3545	2.809	0.01481	1395.07	7.3300	2.831
490	0.01639	1427.22	7.4127	2.826	0.01528	1423.49	7.3886	2.847
500	0.01688	1455.45	7.4701	2.847	0.01575	1452.02	7.4466	2.863
		$p=85$ bar				$p=90$ bar		
310	0.00301	770.47	5.6629		0.00295	767.95	5.6501	
320	0.00337	816.22	5.8052	5.08	0.00326	810.78	5.7839	4.65
330	0.00399	872.09	5.9727	5.71	0.00377	861.63	5.9369	5.26
340	0.00493	930.29	6.1444	5.47	0.00451	916.77	6.0993	5.32
350	0.00593	981.57	6.2943	4.73	0.00539	968.08	6.2480	4.809
360	0.00684	1024.95	6.4178	4.070	0.00625	1012.92	6.3751	4.220
370	0.00767	1062.64	6.5226	3.623	0.00703	1052.24	6.4841	3.763
380	0.00841	1097.35	6.6156	3.341	0.00776	1088.06	6.5806	3.459
390	0.00909	1129.58	6.7001	3.163	0.00841	1121.45	6.6678	3.250
400	0.00972	1160.48	6.7789	3.040	0.00903	1153.19	6.7487	3.112
410	0.01032	1190.38	6.8532	2.961	0.00960	1183.79	6.8247	3.021
420	0.01088	1219.70	6.9241	2.909	0.01014	1213.67	6.8971	2.954
430	0.01142	1248.58	6.9924	2.874	0.01067	1243.02	6.9665	2.918
440	0.01194	1277.19	7.0584	2.854	0.01117	1272.04	7.0334	2.891
450	0.01244	1305.65	7.1225	2.845	0.01165	1300.85	7.0983	2.879
460	0.01293	1333.82	7.1852	2.845	0.01212	1329.64	7.1617	2.873
470	0.01340	1362.60	7.2466	2.848	0.01257	1358.41	7.2236	2.873
480	0.01386	1391.13	7.3068	2.856	0.01302	1387.19	7.2843	2.879
490	0.01431	1419.75	7.3658	2.869	0.01345	1416.02	7.3439	2.888
500	0.01475	1448.47	7.4240	2.883	0.01387	1444.94	7.4026	2.899
		$p=95$ bar				$p=100$ bar		
310	0.00292	765.81	5.6387		0.00291	763.93	5.6284	
320	0.00318	806.51	5.7662	4.38	0.00312	803.07	5.7510	4.16
330	0.00360	854.21	5.9084	4.94	0.00347	847.50	5.8850	4.65
340	0.00420	905.70	6.0606	5.12	0.00397	896.29	6.0285	4.89
350	0.00496	955.91	6.2063	4.802	0.00462	945.15	6.1696	4.73
360	0.00575	1001.52	6.3353	4.343	0.00533	990.94	6.2984	4.381
370	0.00650	1042.07	6.4474	3.884	0.00603	1032.28	6.4126	4.009
380	0.00719	1079.03	6.5468	3.564	0.00668	1070.13	6.5142	3.703
390	0.00782	1113.39	6.6366	3.341	0.00730	1105.38	6.6064	3.462
400	0.00841	1145.93	6.7334	3.184	0.00788	1138.76	6.6912	3.323
410	0.00897	1177.23	6.7971	3.079	0.00842	1170.73	6.7704	3.172
420	0.00950	1207.66	6.8709	3.011	0.00893	1201.71	6.8455	3.087
430	0.01000	1237.47	6.9415	2.962	0.00942	1231.98	6.9170	3.029
440	0.01049	1266.90	7.0095	2.930	0.00988	1261.82	6.9859	2.991
450	0.01095	1296.07	7.0752	2.912	0.01033	1291.37	7.0526	2.962
460	0.01140	1325.19	7.1391	2.902	0.01076	1320.79	7.1174	2.945
470	0.01184	1354.25	7.2016	2.898	0.01118	1350.13	7.1805	2.938
480	0.01227	1383.28	7.2629	2.902	0.01159	1379.42	7.2422	2.938
490	0.01268	1412.35	7.3229	2.911	0.01199	1408.69	7.3027	2.943
500	0.01309	1441.43	7.3819	2.923	0.01238	1437.94	7.3622	2.954

continued

T, °K	v	i	s	c_p	v	i	s	c_p
	$p=125$ bar				$p=150$ bar			
310	0.00274	757.97	5.5867		0.00264	754.79	5.5553	
320	0.00290	792.46	5.6950	3.545	0.00277	786.80	5.6562	3.260
330	0.00311	829.22	5.8069	3.800	0.00291	820.23	5.7584	3.417
340	0.00338	868.83	5.9231	4.037	0.00310	855.30	5.8620	3.589
350	0.00371	907.64	6.0419	4.176	0.00332	891.40	5.9674	3.717
360	0.00412	950.93	6.1593	4.144	0.00358	929.30	6.0728	3.789
370	0.00457	993.12	6.2714	4.012	0.00387	967.63	6.1767	3.814
380	0.00502	1032.51	6.3762	3.842	0.00419	1005.65	6.2775	3.749
390	0.00549	1069.91	6.4728	3.678	0.00453	1042.95	6.3738	3.665
400	0.00595	1105.70	6.5629	3.513	0.00488	1079.28	6.4650	3.577
410	0.00640	1140.06	6.6479	3.382	0.00522	1114.66	6.5519	3.490
420	0.00682	1173.25	6.7286	3.278	0.00557	1149.08	6.6349	3.406
430	0.00757	1205.64	6.8058	3.195	0.00591	1182.62	6.7144	3.332
440	0.00797	1237.40	6.8796	3.135	0.00623	1215.45	6.7907	3.273
450	0.00835	1268.60	6.9504	3.097	0.00656	1247.76	6.8641	3.229
460	0.00872	1299.35	7.0187	3.074	0.00687	1279.73	6.9348	3.202
470	0.00907	1329.94	7.0847	3.058	0.00718	1311.40	7.0032	3.178
480	0.00942	1360.42	7.1490	3.048	0.00748	1342.86	7.0695	3.158
490	0.00976	1390.78	7.2118	3.043	0.00777	1374.01	7.1341	3.143
500	0.01009	1421.07	7.2732	3.039	0.00805	1405.31	7.1972	3.132
	$p=175$ bar				$p=200$ bar			
310	0.00256	753.12	5.5292		0.00250	752.41	5.5068	
320	0.00266	783.66	5.6257	3.094	0.00258	781.87	5.6002	2.993
330	0.00278	815.19	5.7222	3.204	0.00268	812.10	5.6931	3.069
340	0.00292	847.80	5.8190	3.323	0.00280	843.17	5.7856	3.151
350	0.00308	881.65	5.9164	3.424	0.00292	875.10	5.8779	3.241
360	0.00327	916.58	6.0140	3.508	0.00307	907.89	5.9699	3.324
370	0.00348	952.18	6.1108	3.566	0.00323	941.44	6.0615	3.394
380	0.00372	988.09	6.2062	3.596	0.00341	975.60	6.1525	3.440
390	0.00397	1024.01	6.2992	3.575	0.00361	1010.12	6.2420	3.459
400	0.00423	1059.67	6.3893	3.529	0.00382	1044.68	6.3296	3.452
410	0.00450	1094.77	6.4760	3.479	0.00404	1079.15	6.4146	3.437
420	0.00478	1129.32	6.5593	3.423	0.00426	1113.42	6.4969	3.412
430	0.00505	1164.74	6.6394	3.373	0.00449	1147.38	6.5767	3.381
440	0.00533	1196.86	6.7165	3.324	0.00471	1181.02	6.6540	3.346
450	0.00560	1229.95	6.7910	3.289	0.00494	1214.35	6.7289	3.314
460	0.00587	1262.60	6.8630	3.260	0.00517	1247.37	6.8017	3.289
470	0.00613	1295.02	6.9329	3.236	0.00539	1280.21	6.8725	3.273
480	0.00639	1327.22	7.0008	3.217	0.00562	1312.91	6.9412	3.257
490	0.00664	1359.20	7.0670	3.200	0.00584	1345.43	7.0084	3.243
500	0.00688	1391.09	7.1313	3.186	0.00605	1377.84	7.0739	3.231
	$p=250$ bar				$p=300$ bar			
310	0.00242	752.97	5.4693		0.00235	755.06	5.4380	
320	0.00249	781.22	5.5587	2.849	0.00242	782.54	5.5250	2.762
330	0.00256	809.94	5.6469	2.897	0.00248	810.31	5.6104	2.799
340	0.00265	839.23	5.7339	2.959	0.00255	838.45	5.6944	2.844
350	0.00274	869.15	5.8202	3.018	0.00262	867.08	5.7771	2.893
360	0.00285	899.74	5.9060	3.087	0.00270	896.26	5.8589	2.945
370	0.00296	930.82	5.9911	3.150	0.00279	926.03	5.9400	3.000
380	0.00308	962.75	6.0755	3.209	0.00288	956.36	6.0205	3.055
390	0.00321	995.05	6.1590	3.256	0.00298	987.21	6.1004	3.107
400	0.00335	1027.83	6.2417	3.286	0.00309	1018.55	6.1795	3.151
410	0.00350	1060.86	5.3232	3.302	0.00320	1050.32	6.2576	3.185
420	0.00365	1093.98	6.4030	3.306	0.00331	1082.35	6.3346	3.213
430	0.00382	1127.12	6.4808	3.310	0.00343	1114.62	6.4103	3.232
440	0.00398	1160.29	6.5568	3.309	0.00356	1147.04	6.4847	3.248
450	0.00415	1193.43	6.6312	3.306	0.00368	1179.57	6.5576	3.259
460	0.00432	1226.51	6.7038	3.303	0.00381	1212.15	6.6294	3.267
470	0.00449	1259.55	6.7749	3.296	0.00394	1244.82	6.6998	3.273

continued

T, °K	v	i	s	c_p	v	i	s	c_p
480	0.00465	1292.54	6.8443	3.286	0.00408	1277.62	6.7690	3.278
490	0.00482	1325.43	6.9123	3.278	0.00421	1310.60	6.8370	3.280
500	0.00499	1358.26	6.9787	3.270	0.00435	1343.72	6.9035	3.281
		$p=350$ bar				$p=400$ bar		
310	0.00231	758.18	5.4107		0.00227	762.02	5.3866	
320	0.00236	785.12	5.4964	2.702	0.00231	788.57	5.4709	2.659
330	0.00241	812.24	5.5798	2.730	0.00236	815.25	5.5528	2.681
340	0.00247	839.63	5.6612	2.773	0.00241	843.53	5.6330	2.710
350	0.00254	867.41	5.7418	2.805	0.00247	869.37	5.7118	2.746
360	0.00260	895.68	5.8215	2.849	0.00252	896.97	5.7895	2.787
370	0.00267	924.40	5.9052	2.902	0.00258	924.94	5.8663	2.831
380	0.00275	953.50	5.9780	2.952	0.00265	953.36	5.9425	2.879
390	0.00283	983.37	6.0551	3.002	0.00272	982.31	6.0180	2.930
400	0.00291	1013.75	6.1316	3.051	0.00278	1011.86	6.0927	2.980
410	0.00300	1044.59	6.2073	3.096	0.00286	1041.99	6.1668	3.032
420	0.00309	1075.82	6.2822	3.131	0.00293	1072.58	6.2400	3.075
430	0.00318	1107.33	6.3560	3.160	0.00301	1103.53	6.3123	3.110
440	0.00328	1139.08	6.4287	3.188	0.00309	1134.76	6.3836	3.139
450	0.00338	1171.05	6.5003	3.207	0.00317	1166.22	6.4539	3.157
460	0.00348	1203.19	6.5709	3.225	0.00326	1197.87	6.5232	3.178
470	0.00359	1235.49	6.6405	3.241	0.00334	1229.75	6.5918	3.200
480	0.00370	1267.99	6.7090	3.254	0.00343	1261.89	6.6594	3.220
490	0.00381	1300.70	6.7762	3.266	0.00352	1294.26	6.7261	3.241
500	0.00392	1333.60	6.8425	3.274	0.00362	1326.93	6.7921	3.261
		$p=450$ bar				$p=500$ bar		
310	0.00223	766.36	5.3649		0.00220	771.11	5.3447	
320	0.00227	792.60	5.4479	2.627	0.00224	797.06	5.4270	2.599
330	0.00232	818.93	5.5288	2.643	0.00228	823.13	5.5072	2.614
340	0.00236	845.45	5.6079	2.668	0.00232	849.36	5.5858	2.638
350	0.00241	872.28	5.6854	2.699	0.00237	875.86	5.6629	2.666
360	0.00246	899.42	5.7620	2.735	0.00241	902.64	5.7389	2.699
370	0.00252	926.92	5.8378	2.780	0.00246	929.78	5.8140	2.739
380	0.00257	954.85	5.9127	2.827	0.00251	957.39	5.8880	2.787
390	0.00263	983.27	5.9868	2.879	0.00256	985.53	5.9611	2.840
400	0.00269	1012.27	6.0601	2.929	0.00261	1014.22	6.0334	2.890
410	0.00275	1041.84	6.1328	2.975	0.00267	1043.39	6.1048	2.936
420	0.00282	1071.90	6.2047	3.018	0.00272	1073.01	6.1754	2.975
430	0.00288	1102.31	6.2757	3.051	0.00278	1102.96	6.2452	3.008
440	0.00295	1133.02	6.3459	3.082	0.00284	1133.20	6.3141	3.039
450	0.00302	1164.02	6.4152	3.110	0.00290	1163.74	6.3823	3.068
460	0.00309	1195.25	6.4836	3.135	0.00296	1194.54	6.4499	3.094
470	0.00316	1126.73	6.5511	3.161	0.00302	1225.66	6.5167	3.124
480	0.00324	1258.49	6.6179	3.188	0.00308	1257.09	6.5835	3.154
490	0.00331	1290.50	6.6841	3.214	0.00315	1288.83	6.6482	3.188
500	0.00339	1322.90	6.7494	3.243	0.00321	1320.90	6.7128	3.222

Viscosity η of ethane gas at a pressure of 1 bar [52]

t, °C	−100	−75	−50	−25	0	25	50	75
$\eta \cdot 10^7$, N · s/m²	55.2	62.3	70.3	78.0	85.5	92.9	102.0	107.0
t, °C	100	150	200	250	300	400	500	600
$\eta \cdot 10^7$, N · s/m²	115.0	128.0	141.0	152.5	164.0	190.0	214.0	238.0

Viscosity $\eta \cdot 10^8$ ($N \cdot s/m^2$) of ethane gas and liquid at different temperatures and pressures [52]

p, atm \ t, °C →	−15	0	21	31,5	39,5	60	100	150	200	250
1	806	855	914	945	969	1030	1145	1278	1410	1530
20	6 830	1 067	1 020	1 006	1 016	1070	1170	1295	1417	1540
30	6 970	5 525	1 168	1 108	1 071	1105	1201	1318	1422	1550
40	7 110	5 740	4 090	1 340	1 229	1165	1239	1349	1437	1555
50	7 250	5 940	4 409	3 090	1 560	1270	1305	1385	1460	1565
60	7 380	6 090	4 650	3 709		1480	1385	1429	1485	1575
70	7 500	6 250	4 852	4 078		1860	1500	1487	1508	1585
80	7 630	6 400	5 035	4 360	3 800	2320	1640	1553	1547	1615
100	7 880	6 675	5 371	4 785	4 245	3190	1980	1714	1660	1680
125	8 170	6 978	5 711	5 165	4 690	3775	2451	1955	1775	1770
150	8 460	7 290	6 025	5 487	5 060	4170	2916	2250	1930	1863
200	9 000	7 870	6 617	6 049	5 670	4810	3674	2815	2288	2080
300	10 060	8 890	7 609	7 020	6 665	5840	4690	3725	3025	2575
400	11 050	9 820	8 487	7 903	7 560	6700	5488	4470	3660	3100
500	12 000	10 700	9 310	8 720	8 390	7480	6190	5165	4270	3610
600	12 900	11 530	10 070	9 470	9 110	8150	6800	5735	4849	4090
700	13 720	12 300	10 790	10 195	9 790	8840	7400	6280	5335	4515
800	14 500	13 060	11 496	10 835	10 400	9400	8020	6790	5794	5010

Viscosity η ($N \cdot s/m^2$) of liquid ethane at low temperatures [63]

T, °K	$\eta \cdot 10^7$	T, °K	$\eta \cdot 10^7$	T, °K	$\eta \cdot 10^7$	T, °K	$\eta \cdot 10^7$
101.2	8780	111.1	6240	172.3	1750	130.0	900
103.3	7870	150.3	2710	186.0	1370	243.4	820
105.7	7290	159.8	2360	201.2	1140	270.0	670
108.0	6750	166.8	2070	115.4	970	288.0	550

Heat capacity c_p of liquid ethane [63]

T, °K	96.8	150	180	240	270
c_p, kJ/kg · deg	2.28	2.80	2.98	3.30	3.48

Thermal conductivity λ of ethane gas at a pressure of 1 bar [15]

t, °C	−40	−20	0	20	40	60	80	100	120
$\lambda \cdot 10^3$, W/m · deg	13.8	15.7	18.0	20.6	23.2	25.9	28.8	31.7	34.7
t, °C	140	160	180	200	220	240	260	280	300
$\lambda \cdot 10^3$, W/m · deg	37.8	41.0	44.3	47.7	51.1	54.7	58.4	62.1	65.9

Thermal conductivity $\lambda \cdot 10^3$ (W/m · deg) of ethane liquid and gas [15]

p, bar \ t, °C →	20	40	60	80	100	125	150	175	200
1	20.6	23.2	25.9	28.8	31.7	35.5	39.4	43.5	47.7
25	24.1	26.2	28.6	31.4	34.2	37.7	41.4	45.3	49.4
50		33.2	33.0	34.7	36.9	40.1	43.6	47.3	51.3
75			44.4	40.6	41.1	43.4	46.2	49.4	53.2
100	89	79	61.6	50.0	47.0	47.3	49.3	52.2	55.5
125	93	84	70.9	58.6	52.8	51.7	52.3	55.1	57.9
150	97	89	78.5	68.6	61.3	57.2	56.9	58.2	60.5
200	103	95	87.6	79.8	72.4	66.8	64.8	64.8	66.1
250	108	101	94.0	87.0	81.2	75.1	72.0	71.0	71.4
300	112	106	100	94.0	88.0	81.8	77.5	76.5	76.5
350	116	111	105	99.0	93.5	87.4	82.8	81.6	81.1

Surface tension σ of ethane [64]

t, °C	−160	−150	−140	−130	−120	−110	−100	−90
$\sigma \cdot 10^3$, N/m	28.08	26.34	24.62	22.91	21.23	19.57	17.93	16.31

PROPANE (C_3H_8)

$CH_3—CH_2—CH_3$

Molecular weight 44.094

$T_{boil} = -42.07$ °C at 760 mm Hg; $t_{melt} = -187.69$ °C; $t_{cr} = 96.84$ °C;
$p_{cr} = 42.64$ bar; $\rho_{cr} = 225$kg/m³

Thermodynamic properties of saturated propane [51]: ρ (kg/m³), i (kJ/kg), s (kJ/kg · deg) aand r (kJ/kg)

p, bar	T, °K	ϱ′	ϱ″	i′	i″	r	s′	s″
0.1	189.50	630	0.285	324.5	790.0	465.5	3.410	5.866
0.5	216.54	599	1.27	389.4	830.2	440.8	3.731	5.769
1.013	231.10	582	2.42	421.2	847.4	426.2	3.875	5.719
2.026	248.06	562	4.63	459.7	866.7	407.0	4.033	5.673
3.039	259.83	549	6.77	485.2	879.2	394.0	4.134	5.652
4.056	268.05	538	8.89	505.8	888.4	382.6	4.212	5.640
5.065	275.24	528	11.0	522.5	895.6	373.1	4.275	5.627
6.078	281.44	519	13.2	537.6	901.8	364.2	4.325	5.619
7.091	286.90	511	15.3	551.0	906.9	355.9	4.375	5.614
8.104	291.83	504	17.5	563.1	911.0	347.9	4.417	5.606
9.117	296.30	497	19.8	574.8	914.8	340.0	4.455	5.602
10.13	300.44	490	22.0	585.7	918.2	332.5	4.492	5.598
15.20	317.42	460	33.9	631.8	929.5	297.7	4.639	5.577
20.26	330.70	434	47.1	672.8	937.4	264.6	4.760	5.560
25.33	341.71	409	62.2	710.1	942.0	231.9	4.865	5.543
30.39	351.23	381	80.4	745.7	942.4	196.7	4.965	5.522
35.45	359.61	347	104	781.7	934.9	153.2	5.066	5.493
40.52	367.18	300	150	829.0	915.6	86.6	5.196	5.443
42.65	370.0	225	225	875.9	875.9	0	5.330	5.330

Thermodynamic properties of propane at different temperatures and pressures [51]: ρ (kg/m^3), i (kJ/kg) and s (kJ/kg · deg)

T, °K	ϱ	i	s	ϱ	i	s
		$p=0.1$ bar			$p=0.5$ bar	
230	0.2313	821.26	6.1609	1.172	848.92	5.8544
240	0.2216	864.62	6.2199	1.120	862.61	5.9134
250	0.2126	878.52	6.2777	1.074	876.72	5.9712
260	0.2044	892.84	6.3355	1.032	891.37	6.0290
270	0.1968	907.53	6.3924	0.9920	906.27	6.0859
280	0.1897	923.02	6.4485	0.9554	921.85	6.1420
290	0.1832	938.97	6.5046	0.9219	937.76	6.1981
300	0.1771	955.22	6.5595	0.8906	954.09	6.2530
310	0.1714	972.01	6.6147	0.8603	970.96	6.3082
320	0.1659	989.22	6.6700	0.8337	988.25	6.3635
330	0.1609	1006.88	6.7240	0.8081	1006.00	6.4184
340	0.1562	1025.10	6.7788	0.7840	1024.34	6.4736
350	0.1517	1043.81	6.8333	0.7613	1043.06	6.5276
360	0.1475	1063.07	6.8864	0.7399	1062.32	6.5808
370	0.1434	1082.75	6.9405	0.7197	1081.99	6.6348
380	0.1397	1102.89	6.9936	0.7005	1102.09	6.6888
390	0.1361	1123.49	7.0476	0.6823	1122.82	6.7428
400	0.1327	1144.55	7.1008	0.6651	1143.88	6.7964
420	0.1262	1188.13	7.2072	0.6332	1187.59	6.9028
440	0.1206	1233.60	7.3127	0.6042	1233.14	7.0079
460	0.1154	1280.91	7.4182	0.5775	1280.53	7.1134
480	0.1106	1330.10	7.5224	0.5535	1329.60	7.2180
500	0.1061	1381.10	7.6258	0.5312	1380.60	7.3215
520	0.1021	1433.69	7.7284	0.5106	1433.31	7.4240
540	0.09824	1487.61	7.8302	0.4916	1487.32	7.5254
560	0.09473	1542.96	7.9306	0.4741	1542.67	7.6263
580	0.09147	1599.65	8.0303	0.4576	1599.36	7.7267
600	0.08841	1657.39	8.1303	0.4424	1657.09	7.8264
		$p=1$ bar			$p=2$ bar	
230	584	418.93	3.8665	583	419.01	3.8655
240	2.279	859.97	5.7757	571	441.33	3.9605
250	2.179	874.46	5.8343	4.500	869.89	5.6873
260	2.089	889.36	5.8933	4.288	885.26	5.7481
270	2.005	904.56	5.9511	4.102	900.87	5.8079
280	1.929	920.30	6.0081	3.935	917.03	5.8665
290	1.859	936.38	6.0642	3.784	933.36	5.9247
300	1.793	952.79	6.1203	3.645	950.07	5.9817
310	1.734	969.79	6.1755	3.518	967.28	6.0378
320	1.678	987.16	6.2304	3.400	984.78	6.0935
330	1.626	1005.00	6.2856	3.290	1002.74	6.1496
340	1.570	1023.42	6.3405	3.186	1021.33	6.2048
350	1.530	1042.14	6.3945	3.091	1040.25	6.2597
360	1.487	1061.40	6.4489	3.000	1059.60	6.3141
370	1.445	1081.12	6.5029	2.915	1079.44	6.3690
380	1.407	1101.34	6.5569	2.834	1099.79	6.4230
390	1.369	1122.02	6.6110	2.758	1120.47	6.4774
400	1.335	1143.12	6.6641	2.687	1141.66	6.5314
420	1.270	1186.92	6.7705	2.554	1185.62	6.6378
440	1.211	1232.47	6.8760	2.434	1231.30	6.7554
460	1.158	1279.95	6.9815	2.324	1278.86	6.8496
480	1.108	1329.06	7.0857	2.226	1328.05	6.9513
500	1.064	1380.05	7.1896	2.134	1379.13	7.0573
520	1.023	1432.72	7.2921	2.050	1431.84	7.1598
540	0.9845	1486.86	7.3935	1.973	1486.02	7.2616
560	0.9490	1542.21	7.4944	1.901	1541.45	7.4579
580	0.9162	1598.90	7.5949	1.836	1598.14	7.4638
600	0.8854	1656.72	7.6945	1.774	1655.96	7.5634

continued

T, °K	ϱ	i	s	ϱ	i	s
		p=3 bar			p=4 bar	
230	584	419.10	3.8655	584	419.22	3.8644
240	572	441.41	3.9605	572	441.54	3.9595
250	560	464.11	4.0516	560	464.23	4.0516
260	6.656	880,74	5.6568	548	487.09	4.1407
270	6,330	896.90	5.7196	8.690	892.12	5.6513
280	6.045	913.48	5.7803	8.267	909.46	5.7158
290	5,792	930.18	5.8402	7.897	926,71	5.7774
300	5.566	947.18	5.8979	7.565	944.08	5.8364
310	5,359	964.60	5.9549	7.266	961.88	5.8942
320	5.170	982.35	6,0118	6.995	979.92	5.9524
330	4.995	1000.60	6.0679	6,748	998.34	6.0093
340	4.833	1019.32	6.1240	6.519	1017.27	6.0650
350	4.681	1038.28	6.1789	6,308	1036.40	6,1211
360	4.540	1057.84	6.2341	6.112	1055.95	6.1764
370	4,408	1077.77	6.2894	5.930	1074.97	6.2312
380	4,284	1098.16	6.3434	5,758	1096.48	6.2865
390	4,164	1118.88	6.3974	5.596	1117.29	6,3405
400	4,056	1140.11	6.4514	5.445	1138.56	6,3945
420	3,851	1184.19	6,5590	5.166	1182,81	6.5021
440	3,670	1230.04	6.6654	4.915	1228.74	6.6084
460	3.501	1277.73	6.7705	4,689	1276.51	6.7135
480	3,350	1326,92	6,8751	4.484	1325,88	6.8182
500	3,212	1378.08	6.9786	4.297	1377.12	6.9170
520	3.084	1430,80	7,0811	4.121	1429,92	7,0242
540	2.967	1485.18	7.1829	3.964	1484.35	7.1268
560	2.857	1540.74	7.2842	3.818	1539.86	7.2285
580	2,758	1597.43	7,3851	3,686	1596.68	7.3290
600	2,665	1655.34	7.4847	3.558	1654.58	7.4203
		p=5 bar			p=6 bar	
230	584	419.31	3.8644	584	419,39	3.8644
240	573	441.62	3.9595	573	441,71	3.9595
250	560	464.32	4.0516	561	464.40	4.0516
260	548	487.18	4.1407	549	487.30	4.1407
270	535	510.45	4.2282	535	510.54	4.2282
280	10,61	904.81	5,6618	521	534.19	4.3137
290	10.10	922.98	5.7263	12.40	918.79	5.6530
300	9.643	940.82	5.7870	11.81	937.30	5.7460
310	9,240	959.07	5.8460	11.28	956,14	5.8071
320	8.878	977.41	5.9038	10.82	974.81	5.8657
330	8.550	996.16	5.9616	10.42	993.82	5.9239
340	8.248	1015.17	6.0185	10.02	1013.04	5.9808
350	7.971	1034.43	6.0746	9.676	1032.51	6.0378
360	7.715	1054.11	6.1307	9.353	1052.27	6.0935
370	7.478	1074.21	6.1856	9.055	1072.41	6.1496
380	7,256	1094.85	6.2408	8.777	1093.13	6.2048
390	7,048	1115.66	6.2961	8.521	1114.11	6.2597
400	6,853	1137.05	6,3501	8.280	1135,54	6,3141
420	6,506	1181.39	6.4581	7.840	1180.01	6.4221
440	6.176	1227.44	6.5645	7.450	1226.15	6.5293
460	5,887	1275,30	6.6700	7,094	1274.17	6.6348
480	5,624	1324.74	6.7747	6.773	1323.62	6.7395
500	5,385	1376.12	6.8781	6.483	1375.07	6,8429
520	5,166	1428.95	6.9815	6.217	1428.08	6.9463
540	4,966	1483.38	7.0937	5.973	1482,55	7,0464
560	4,782	1539.03	7.1858	5.750	1538.19	7.1506
580	4,612	1595.92	7.2863	5.544	1595,04	7.2511
600	4.455	1653.83	7.3859	5.354	1653.07	7.3508

continued

T, °K	ϱ	i	s	ϱ	i	s
		p=7 bar			p=8 bar	
230	585	419,48	3.8636	585	419.60	3.8636
240	573	441.79	3.9586	574	441.92	3.9586
250	561	464,48	4.0507	562	464.61	4.0507
260	549	487.38	4.1399	549	487,47	4.1399
270	536	510.66	4.2274	536	510.75	4.2274
280	521	534.28	4.3128	522	534.28	4,3124
290	14.86	913,56	5.6371	506	558.90	4.3999
300	14.10	933,36	5,7054	16.51	928.88	5.6681
310	13.83	953.29	5,7682	15.64	949.11	5.7338
320	12.83	971.88	5.8289	14.94	968.83	5.7966
330	12.32	991,31	5,8875	14.30	988.71	5,8573
340	11,85	1010,78	5.9457	13.72	1008.56	5.9159
350	11.41	1030.50	6,0034	13.20	1028,45	5.9741
360	11.02	1050,43	6,0604	12.73	1048.58	6,0311
370	10.65	1070,65	6,1165	12.30	1068.85	6,0880
380	10.33	1091.46	6,1726	11.90	1089.74	6.1441
390	10.02	1112.47	6,2274	11.53	1110.93	6,1998
400	9,729	1134,04	6,2823	11.19	1132.57	6.2551
420	8,201	1178,58	6,3907	10.57	1177.16	6,3635
440	8,732	1224,81	6,4983	10.03	1223.51	6.4707
460	8,312	1272,95	6,6047	9.540	1271,74	6.5770
480	7,932	1322,57	6,7089	9,096	1321.48	6.6826
500	7,587	1374,02	6.8123	8,697	1373,02	6,7860
520	7,272	1427,11	6,9158	8,332	1426.15	6,8894
540	6,985	1481,62	7,0183	8.000	1480.79	6,9920
560	6,722	1537,35	7,1201	7.696	1536,51	7.0937
580	6,480	1594.33	7,2206	7,417	1593,41	7,1942
600	6.256	1652,36	7,3215	7,161	1651.57	7.2947

T, °K	ϱ	i	s	ϱ	i	s
		p=9 bar			p=10 bar	
230	585	419,68	3.8636	586	419.77	3.8636
240	574	442.00	3.9586	574	442,08	3.9586
250	562	464.69	4.0507	562	464,78	4.0507
260	549	487,59	4.1399	550	487,68	4.1399
270	536	510,83	4.2262	537	510,83	4.2262
280	522	534.40	4.3116	523	534.49	4.3116
290	507	558.98	4.3991	507	558.98	4.3991
300	19.08	923.73	5,6333	491	584.52	4.4874
310	18.02	944.46	5.7024	20,51	940.44	5.6748
320	17.13	965,48	5.7669	19.42	961,96	5.7422
330	16,34	985,95	5.8289	18,48	983,02	5.8050
340	15,65	1006.21	5.8887	17.66	1003,83	5.8649
350	15,04	1026,48	5.9473	16.93	1024.38	5.9239
360	14.48	1046,66	6.0055	16.28	1044.73	5.9817
370	13.98	1067.09	6.0625	15.68	1065,29	6.0386
380	13.50	1088,07	6.1194	15.14	1086,35	6,0956
390	13,08	1109.29	6,1755	14.65	1107.74	6.1517
400	12.68	1131,06	6,2304	14,20	1129.47	6,2065
420	11.97	1175,78	6.3396	13,38	1174.36	6,3158
440	11,34	1222.21	6.4468	12.66	1220.87	6,4242
460	10,78	1270.48	6.5532	12,02	1269,31	6,5306
480	10.27	1320.35	6.6587	11,45	1319.22	6,6357
500	9.815	1372,01	6.7629	10.94	1370.97	6,7403
520	9.399	1425,23	6.8668	10.46	1424,22	6,8437
540	9,021	1479.82	6,9689	10,05	1478.99	6,9463
560	8,696	1535,76	7,0707	9,662	1534,92	7,0481
580	8.359	1592.70	7,1716	9,308	1591,95	7,1494
600	8.070	1650.81	7,2720	8.982	1650.14	7,2503

continued

T, °K	ϱ	i	s	ϱ	i	s
		$p=15$ bar			$p=20$ bar	
230	587	420.27	3,8627	588	420.73	3.8608
240	575	442.54	3.9577	577	443.17	3.9558
250	564	465.15	4.0498	565	465.66	4.0478
260	551	488.06	4,1381	553	488.43	4.1362
270	539	511.21	4,2245	541	511,58	4.2216
280	524	534.78	4.3090	526	535.07	4.3061
290	510	559.06	4,3953	511	559,19	4.3924
300	423	584.44	4.4836	494	584.35	4.4799
310	475	611.19	4,5737	477	611.02	4.5695
320	32.77	938.60	5,6057	457	639.41	4.6607
330	30.60	966.15	5.6903	436	670.26	4.7545
340	28.82	990.47	5.7602	42.91	973.22	5,6626
350	27.30	1012.54	5,8251	39.82	999.14	5.7384
360	26.00	1034.18	5.8858	37.35	1022.67	5,8050
370	24.86	1055.58	5.9444	35.33	1045.11	5.8678
380	23.86	1077.31	6.0026	33.58	1067.68	5.9285
390	22.95	1099.41	6.0596	32.07	1090.33	5.9871
400	22,13	1121.52	6,1157	30.73	1113.10	6,0453
420	20.73	1167.15	6.2274	28.55	1159.53	6.1592
440	18.92	1214.30	6,3376	26.73	1207.47	6,2714
460	18.45	1263.12	6.4460	25.15	1256,84	6.3815
480	17.50	1313.48	6.5523	23,78	1307.70	6.4895
500	16.66	1365.61	6,6578	22.57	1360.21	6.5959
520	15.91	1419.37	6,7621	21.50	1414.38	6.7014
540	15.24	1474.38	6.8655	20.54	1469.73	6,8048
560	14.63	1530.61	6.9681	19.69	1526.30	6.9074
580	14,08	1588.05	7.0698	18,92	1583.99	7,0091
600	13.57	1648.46	7,1703	18,23	1642,69	7.1096
		$p=25$ bar			$p=30$ bar	
230	589	421.15	3.8599	589	421.65	3.8581
240	577	443.47	3.9549	579	443.97	3.9530
250	566	465.99	4,0470	567	466.45	4,0451
260	553	488.85	4,0799	555	489.23	4,1325
270	541	511.92	4,2195	543	512.30	4.2174
280	528	535.32	4.3036	529	535.58	4.3007
290	513	559,27	4.3890	514	559.40	4.3852
300	497	584,35	4.4757	498	584.31	4,4715
310	479	610.81	4,5636	481	610.69	4.5590
320	460	639,03	4,6540	462	638.70	4.6482
330	439	669,51	4,7470	442	668,80	4.7403
340	414	703.59	4.8479	418	702.21	4.8391
350	55.96	977.53	5.6484	387	740.77	4.9505
360	51.21	1007.01	5,7271	69.74	985.40	5.6417
370	47,59	1032.92	5.7975	62.71	1017.85	5.7300
380	44,68	1056.75	5.8628	57.68	1043.81	5,8012
390	42.29	1080.28	5.9256	53.87	1068.76	5,8678
400	40.26	1103.72	5.9863	50.77	1093.26	5.9314
420	37.00	1151.45	6.1039	46.06	1142.70	6.0528
440	34.37	1200.36	6.2182	42.45	1192.82	6.1697
460	32.19	1250.47	6.3292	39.52	1243.81	6.2835
480	30.30	1301.80	6.4385	37.06	1295.81	6.3945
500	28,66	1354.72	6.5456	34.95	1349.32	6.5038
520	27.23	1409.40	6.6520	33,11	1404.34	6.6110
540	25.96	1465.13	6.7562	31.51	1460.44	6.7165
560	24.85	1521.99	6.8588	30.11	1517.59	6.8199
580	23.86	1579.89	6.9606	28.87	1575.87	6.9216
600	22.96	1638.92	7.0610	27.76	1635.07	7.0221

continued

T, °K	ϱ	i	s	ϱ	i	s
		p=35 bar			p=40 bar	
230	591	422.11	3.8561	592	422.70	3.8552
240	580	444.43	3.9510	581	444.89	3,9501
250	562	466,91	4.0432	569	467.41	4,0414
260	556	489.60	4.1306	557	490,19	4,1279
270	544	512.59	4.2144	545	512.97	4,2115
280	530	535.91	4.2969	531	536.20	4,2940
290	515	559.65	4.3815	516	559.82	4.3786
300	499	584.44	4.4677	501	584.52	4.4640
310	482	610.64	4.5552	485	610.52	4.5506
320	465	638.44	4.6436	467	638.15	4.6390
330	445	668.26	4.7348	447	667.71	4,7298
340	423	701.12	4.8316	426	700.16	4.8257
350	395	738.34	4.9400	340	736.16	4,9304
360	101.8	946.13	5.5228	361	777.87	5,0480
370	83.12	997.00	5.6559	120.5	959.53	5.5383
380	73.65	1027,82	5,7405	95.21	1007.72	5.6681
390	67.37	1055,03	5,8134	83.98	1037.78	5,7556
400	62.72	1081,45	5.8799	76,62	1068.26	5,8297
420	56.04	1133,20	6.0072	67.06	1122.86	5.9628
440	51.14	1184.78	6,1270	60,34	1176.28	6.0872
460	47.29	1236.82	6,2425	55.43	1229.54	6,2057
480	44.14	1289.62	6.3556	51.45	1283.30	6.3208
500	41.45	1343,80	6,4657	48,16	1338.18	6.4326
520	39.17	1399,31	6.5741	45.35	1394.16	6.5419
540	37.92	1455,75	6.6805	42,96	1451.10	6,6482
560	35.52	1513.19	6.7839	40.94	1508,76	6,7525
580	33.99	1571,72	6.8856	39,14	1567.62	6.8550
600	32 62	1631.22	6.9861	37.55	1627.70	6,9559
		p=50 bar			p=60 bar	
230	592	423.70	3,8547	593	424,71	3.8519
240	583	445,89	3,9487	585	446,90	3.9459
250	571	468,34	4.0389	573	469.26	4.0352
260	559	490,94	4,1253	561	491,74	4.1215
270	547	513,76	4,2090	549	514,39	4.2052
280	534	536,62	4.2915	536	537,08	4,2869
290	519	560,15	4.3752	522	560,57	4,3693
300	504	584,73	4.4594	507	584,98	4.4531
310	488	610,44	4.5452	491	610.52	4.5372
320	471	637,69	4,6323	474	637.40	4.6239
330	452	666,71	4,7227	456	665,95	4.7122
340	432.2	698,40	4.8165	438	696,60	4,8031
350	409.4	732,61	4,9153	417	729,80	4,8990
360	382,0	771,12	5,0216	393	766,35	5,0016
370	340.2	823,21	5.1678	361	809.31	5,1175
380	247.9	912,47	5,4127	310	861,64	5.2569
390	134.0	983.94	5,5969	228,7	928,21	5,4282
400	115,0	1034.18	5,7167	175,3	988,29	5,5818
420	93.81	1100.12	5.8770	113,3	1074,25	5,7945
440	81,91	1158.15	6,0110	104,8	1138,89	5,9465
460	73.93	1214,26	6,1353	92,45	1198.30	6,0784
480	67.79	1270,07	6,2551	83,64	1256,25	6.2019
500	62.91	1326.50	6.3710	76,94	1314,40	6,3196
520	58.94	1383.70	6.4828	71,61	1372,89	6,4334
540	55.61	1441.43	6.5913	67.26	1431,89	6.5435
560	52,78	1499.96	6.6968	63.59	1491.21	6,6512
580	50,32	1559.37	6.8002	60.46	1551,29	6,7554
600	48.16	1619,70	6,9015	57,75	1612.29	6.8580
		p=70 bar			p=80 bar	
280	539	537.58	4.2831	541	538.05	4.2781
290	526	560.95	4.3647	526	561.32	4.3597

continued

T, °K	ϱ	i	s	ϱ	i	s
300	510	585.23	4,4481	512	585.52	4.4426
310	494	610.64	4,5326	497	610.73	4,5259
320	478	637.23	4,6180	481	637,15	4.6113
330	461	665.37	4,7055	465	665,07	4.6980
340	443	695.34	4,7947	448	694,67	4,7863
350	423	727.54	4,8877	429	725,99	4.8772
360	401	762.42	4,9856	410	759,19	4,9706
370	377	801.27	5,0899	388	794.65	5.0664
380	343	844.56	5,2029	360	832.54	5.1661
390	296,6	892,54	5,3264	325.5	873.24	5,2695
400	246,0	943,79	5,4659	289.1	917.16	5,3775
420	166,3	1045.23	5.7062	211.7	1012.62	5.6103
440	132,5	1118,34	5,8783	163.1	1096,02	5,8079
460	113,6	1181,51	6,0177	137.4	1163,47	5,9570
480	101,6	1242,06	6,1479	121,0	1223.30	6,0947
500	92,60	1302,35	6,2714	109.3	1290.33	6,2237
520	85,66	1364,27	6,3891	100.3	1352,29	6,3451
540	80,06	1422.63	6,5021	93.20	1413,80	6,4611
560	75,41	1483,05	6,6110	87.44	1475,18	6.5724
580	71,48	1543,76	6,7173	82.65	1536.68	6.6805
600	68,10	1605,22	6,8211	78.59	1598.48	6,7847
		$p=90$ bar			$p=100$ bar	
280	543	538,51	4,2735	544	539.01	4.2689
290	529	561.70	4.3551	531	562,08	4.3505
300	515	585.73	4.4368	516	585,98	4,4321
310	499	610,81	4,5192	502	610,98	4,5146
320	484	637,15	4,6038	487	637.23	4,5984
330	469	664,78	4,6905	472	664,65	4,6825
340	452	693,88	4.7776	456	693,38	4,7679
350	435	724,57	4,8667	440	723,48	4,8546
360	415	756,76	4,9580	422	754.92	4,9425
370	395	790.64	5,0501	403	787,58	5,0321
380	372	826,35	5,1443	383	822,08	5,1234
390	349	864.03	5.2402	362	857.88	5.2163
400	315	903,76	5,3378	337	895,26	5,3101
420	250	987,92	5,5370	277,9	973,47	5,4994
440	198,1	1069,94	5,7338	224,1	1047,83	5,6806
460	162,0	1144,29	5,9046	186.6	1127,13	5,8477
480	141,1	1212,83	6.0520	161,3	1198,81	6,0005
500	126,4	1278,69	6,1826	143,6	1267,39	6,1412
520	115,3	1342,54	6,3062	130,4	1333,12	6,2714
540	106,7	1405,34	6.4242	120,1	1397,09	6,3928
560	99,60	1467,47	6,5373	111,9	1459,94	6,5075
580	93,91	1529,65	6,6461	105,1	1522,74	6,6177
600	89,11	1591.90	6.7525	99.60	1585.50	6.7240
		$p=150$ bar			$p=200$ bar	
280	551	541,31	4.2458	556	546.29	4,2299
290	539	564,30	4,3275	545	569,15	4.3103
300	526	588,24	4.4091	533	592.81	4.3911
310	513	613,11	4.9908	522	617,34	4.4719
320	500	638.86	4.5724	510	642,63	4,5515
330	487	665,49	4.6540	499	668.59	4,6314
340	467	692,87	4,7348	487	695,09	4.7110
350	459	721,05	4,8165	474	722,31	4,7901
360	445	749,94	4.8973	462	750,11	4.8680
370	432	779,58	4.9781	450	778,45	4.9446
380	416	809,94	5.0585	439	807,42	5,0216
390	402	841,09	5.1393	421	836,94	5.0987
400	386	873.07	5.2201	415	867,00	5,1745
420	352	939.52	5.3805	388	928,84	5.3244
440	313,1	1008,35	5.5400	359	992,82	5,4738
460	278,7	1078.64	5.6957	330	1058.67	5,6199

continued

T, °K	ϱ	i	s	ϱ	i	s
480	248,5	1149,61	5,8469	304	1125,87	5,7623
500	223,5	1220,16	5,9913	281	1189,85	5,9009
520	202,9	1289,53	6,1265	260	1262,45	6,0348
540	186,1	1357,49	6,2551	241	1331,07	6,1630
560	171,9	1424,85	6,3778	223	1398,98	6,2865
580	160,1	1490,67	6,4941	208	1466,38	6,4050
600	149,7	1556,65	6,6064	194,5	1533,46	6,5188
		$p=250$ bar			$p=300$ bar	
310	529	621,91	4,4577	536	627,64	4,4443
320	519	646,99	4,5364	526	652,18	4,5222
330	508	672,57	4,6143	516	677,21	4,5992
340	497	698,61	4,6921	506	702,80	4,6750
350	486	725,24	4,7692	496	728,84	4,7512
360	476	752,33	4,8450	486	755,30	4,8261
370	465	779,96	4,9212	476	782,22	4,9002
380	454	808,01	4,9961	466	809,64	4,9731
390	444	836,52	5,0702	456	837,49	5,0455
400	433	865,58	5,1431	446	865,83	5,1167
420	411	924,91	5,2875	426	923,78	5,2569
440	387	986,20	5,4299	405	983,44	5,3959
460	362	1049,13	5,5697	380,7	1044,73	5,5316
480	339	1109,50	5,7062	365	1107,72	5,6656
500	315,6	1179,55	5,8402	346	1171,97	5,7966
520	296,2	1246,28	5,9712			
540	280	1313,48	6,0977			
560	264	1380,47	6,2191			
580	248	1446,92	6,3359			
600	235	1512,77	6,4468			
		$p=350$ bar			$p=400$ bar	
310	543	632,96	4,4321	548	638,44	4,4196
320	533	657,08	4,5088	540	662,39	4,4945
330	523	681,82	4,5850	530	686,80	4,5695
340	514	707,02	4,6599	522	711,21	4,6436
350	505	732,73	4,7340	512	736,92	4,7168
360	495	758,73	4,8069	504	762,63	4,7889
370	485	785,23	4,8793	495	788,75	4,8600
380	476	812,16	4,9513	485	815,30	4,9316
390	467	839,54	5,0225	476	842,30	5,0016
400	457	867,34	5,0928	467	869,68	5,0710
420	439	924,32	5,2314	449	925,78	5,2080
440	420	982,98	5,3675	433	983,77	5,3428
460	402	1043,27	5,5010	416	1043,39	5,4747
480	384	1105,06	5,6333	400	1104,60	5,6044
500	367	1168,37	5,7631	383	1167,40	5,7330
		$p=500$ bar			$p=600$ bar	
310	559	649,67	4,3957	568	660,93	4,3731
320	550	673,07	4,4698	561	684,00	4,4464
330	542	696,93	4,5439	553	707,61	4,5192
340	534	721,30	4,6164	546	731,64	4,5917
350	526	746,13	4,6884	538	756,18	4,6628
360	518	771,38	4,7596	530	781,09	4,7332
370	509	797,04	4,8299	522	806,42	4,8023
380	501	823,21	4,8990	515	832,21	4,8705
390	493	849,29	4,9685	507	858,42	4,9392
400	486	876,72	5,0367	500	885,13	5,0066
420	471	932,02	5,1715	486	939,98	5,1406
440	455	987,05	5,3038	473	996,42	5,2712
460	440	1047,79	5,4336	458	1054,65	5,4006
480	423	1108,20	5,5617	445	1114,53	5,5278
500	412	1170,25	5,6882	429	1176,07	5,6530

Specific volume $v \cdot 10^3$ (m^3/kg) of liquid propane at different temperatures and pressures [66]

p, bar \ t, °C →	20	30	40	50	60	70	80	90	100
20	1.958	2.023	2.097	2.188					
30	1.950	2.012	2.082	2.167	2.272	2.414			
40	1.941	2.001	2.069	2.148	2.243	2.368	2.541	2.794	
50	1.939	1.992	2.055	2.128	2.217	2.328	2.477	2.683	2.975
60	1.927	1.982	2.042	2.111	2.193	2.294	2.423	2.594	2.877
70	1.919	1.973	2.031	2.095	2.171	2.263	2.377	2.522	2.712
80	1.912	1.964	2.019	2.080	2.152	2.236	2.338	2.464	2.623
90	1.905	1.955	2.009	2.067	2.133	2.211	2.304	2.416	2.552
100	1.898	1.947	1.998	2.054	2.117	2.189	2.274	2.373	2.493
110	1.892	1.939	1.989	2.042	2.101	2.169	2.247	2.338	2.446
120	1.886	1.932	1.980	2.031	2.087	2.151	2.224	2.307	2.404
130	1.880	1.924	1.971	2.020	2.074	2.134	2.203	2.280	2.370
140	1.874	1.918	1.963	2.018	2.062	2.119	2.183	2.256	2.339
150	1.868	1.911	1.956	2.001	2.050	2.106	2.166	2.235	2.313
160	1.863	1.905	1.948	1.992	2.040	2.093	2.151	2.216	2.290
170	1.858	1.898	1.941	1.983	2.030	2.081	2.136	2.199	2.269
180	1.853	1.892	1.934	1.975	2.020	2.069	2.123	2.183	2.250
190	1.848	1.887	1.928	1.968	2.011	2.059	2.111	2.168	2.233
200	1.843	1.882	1.921	1.960	2.003	2.049	2.100	2.155	2.218

Coefficient of thermal expansion $\alpha \cdot 10^5$ (deg^{-1}) of liquid propane [66]

p, atm \ t, °C →	20	40	60	80	100
20	313	384			
40	293	345	480	805	
60	277	312	406	603	929
80	261	287	353	480	656
100	248	265	313	400	510
150	223	227	251	297	354
200	205	204	218	251	294

Isothermal coefficient of compressibility $\beta \cdot 10^6$ (atm^{-1}) of liquid propane [66]

p, atm \ t, °C →	20	40	60	80	100
20	451	755			
40	420	674	1250	2810	
60	393	602	1040	2050	4600
80	364	544	884	1560	2980
100	343	492	758	1330	2090
150	295	394	542	640	1070
200	256	320	404	506	640

Viscosity of propane gas at a pressure of 1 bar [52]

t, °C	0	25	50	75	100	150	200	250	300	400	500	600
$\eta \cdot 10^7$, N · s/m²	75.0	81.1	87.8	94.2	100.6	113.0	124.8	136.2	147.5	171.5	194.0	218.0

Viscosity $\eta \cdot 10^7$ (N · s/m²) of propane gas and liquid at different temperatures and pressures [52]

p, atm \ t, °C →	24.5	52.5	92.7	100.8	125	151	201	250
1		88 5	98.7	100.8	106.7	113.1	125.2	136.2
20	967.0			107.0	112.0	117.5	128.5	139.0
35	995.0	748.0		127.0	124.0	126.0	134.0	142.5
40	1005.0	758.0		151.0	130.5	131.0	137.5	144.0
45	1015.0	768.0		240.0	141.5	136.5	141.0	146.0
50	1024.0	778.0	444.0	325.0	160.0	143.5	145.0	148.5
60	1042.0	796.0	477.0	416.0	230.0	166.0	153.5	154.0
75	1070.0	823.0	520.0	475.0	316.0	212.5	173.5	165.0
100	1112.0	870.0	585.0	545.0	414.0	296.5	217.0	190.0
150	1192.0	950.0	684.0	644.0	532.0	437.0	313.0	250.0
200	1264.0	1020.0	758.0	717.0	616.0	525.0	396.0	304.0
300	1398.0	1152.0	887.0	845.0	744.0	654.0	516.0	406.0
400	1526.0	1276.0	1005.0	963.0	860.0	766.0	620.0	504.0
500	1653.0	1398.0	1120.0	1078.0	967.0	870.0	712.0	588.0
600	1777.0	1517.0	1228.0	1185.0	1069.0	964.0	794.0	660.0
700	1904.0	1634.0	1328.0	1284.0	1160.0	1051.0	872.0	726.0
800	2030.0	1743.0	1427.0	1380.0	1250.0	1136.0	950.0	793.0

Viscosity η of liquid propane at low temperatures [63]

T, °K	81.5	88.1	93.1	96.8	101.6	106.7	111.6
$\eta \cdot 10^7$, N · s/m²	115 400	86 600	60 900	45 900	35 800	25 700	21 000
T, °K	119.4	141.8	144.4	149.8	160.0	169.6	175.8
$\eta \cdot 10^7$ N · s/m²	14 900	9 700	7 400	7 200	5 600	4 100	3 800

Heat capacity c_p (kJ/kg · deg) of propane at different temperatures [51]

T, °K \ p, bar →	0.1	0.5	1	2	3	4	5	6
230	1.35	1.36	2.25	2.25	2.25	2.25	2.25	2.25
240	1.39	1.40	1.42	2.26	2.26	2.26	2.26	2.26
250	1.43	1.44	1.46	1.53	2.27	2.27	2.27	2.27
260	1.48	1.49	1.51	1.55	1.66	1.29	2.29	2.29
270	1.53	1.54	1.56	1.59	1.67	1.81	2.34	2.34
280	1.57	1.57	1.60	1.62	1.67	1.76	1.87	2.42
290	1.61	1.62	1.63	1.66	1.70	1.74	1.81	1.93
300	1.66	1.67	1.68	1.71	1.74	1.77	1.80	1.86
310	1.70	1.71	1.73	1.75	1.77	1.80	1.83	1.87
320	1.75	1.75	1.78	1.80	1.81	1.83	1.86	1.89
330	1.80	1.80	1.81	1.83	1.85	1.87	1.89	1.91
340	1.84	1.85	1.86	1.88	1.89	1.91	1.93	1.94
350	1.89	1.90	1.91	1.92	1.93	1.95	1.95	1.98
360	1.94	1.95	1.95	1.95	1.96	1.98	1.99	2.01
370	1.98	1.99	1.99	2.00	2.01	2.02	2.04	2.05
380	2.03	2.04	2.04	2.05	2.06	2.07	2.08	2.09
390	2.08	2.09	2.09	2.10	2.11	2.12	2.12	2.13
400	2.13	2.13	2.13	2.14	2.15	2.16	2.16	2.17
420	2.22	2.22	2.23	2.24	2.25	2.26	2.26	2.27
440	2.31	2.31	2.32	2.32	2.33	2.33	2.34	2.35
460	2.41	2.41	2.42	2.42	2.43	2.43	2.44	2.44
480	2.50	2.50	2.51	2.51	2.52	2.52	2.53	2.53
500	2.58	2.58	2.58	2.59	2.59	2.60	2.60	2.60
520	2.67	2.67	2.67	2.68	2.68	2.69	2.69	2.69

continued

p, bar → / T, °K	0.1	0.5	1	2	3	4	5	6
540	2,73	2,73	2,73	2,74	2,74	2,74	2,74	2,75
560	2,80	2,80	2,80	2,81	2,81	2,81	2.81	2,82
580	2,85	2.85	2,86	2,86	2,87	2,87	2.87	2,87
600	2,91	2.91	2,91	2.91	2,92	2.92	2.92	2.92

p, bar → / T, °K	7	8	9	10	15	20	25	30
230	2.25	2,25	2.25	2,25	2.25	2,25	2.24	2.23
240	2,26	2.26	2.26	2,26	2.26	2.26	2.25	2,24
250	2,27	2,27	2.27	2.27	2.27	2,27	2.26	2.25
260	2.29	2,29	2.29	2,29	2.29	2.29	2,28	2,27
270	2.32	2.32	2,32	2.32	2,32	2.31	2,31	2,30
280	2.41	2.40	2,40	2,40	2.39	2.38	2.37	2,35
290	2.07	2.53	2,52	2.52	2.51	2,49	2.47	2.44
300	1.95	2.17	2,55	2.67	2,64	2,62	2.59	2,59
310	1.91	1,98	2.05	2,15	2,81	2,78	2,75	2,73
320	1.92	1,97	2.01	2.08	3,18	2,99	2.95	2.92
330	1,93	1.96	1,99	2.03	2,47	3,27	3,20	3.16
340	1,95	1,98	1.99	2,02	2.24	3,05	3.68	3.58
350	1,98	2,00	2,01	2.03	2,16	2.43	3,06	4,27
360	2,02	2.03	2,04	2,06	2,14	2.26	2,58	3.54
370	2.06	2,07	2,07	2,09	2,15	2.26	2.44	2.84
380	2.10	2,11	2,12	2.13	2,18	2,26	2,38	2,55
390	2,13	2,14	2,15	2,16	2,21	2,27	2,37	2,50
400	2,19	2,19	2,20	2,20	2,25	2,29	2.36	2,45
420	2,27	2,28	2,28	2,29	2,33	2,37	2,41	2,47
440	2,35	2.36	2,37	2,37	2,40	2,43	2,47	2,52
460	2,45	2,45	2,46	2.46	2,48	2.51	2,55	2,58
480	2,53	2,53	2,54	2.55	2,56	2.58	2,61	2,64
500	2,61	2.61	2,62	2.62	2,64	2,66	2,68	2,70
520	2.70	2.70	2,71	2.71	2.72	2,73	2.74	2,76
540	2,75	2,75	2,76	2,76	2,78	2,79	2,80	2,82
560	2,82	2,82	2,83	2.83	2,84	2,85	2,87	2,88
580	2,87	2 88	2,88	2,88	2,89	2,90	2,91	2,92
600	2,92	2.93	2,93	2,93	2,94	2,95	2.96	2,97

p, bar → / T, °K	35	40	50	60	70	80	90	100
230	2.23	2.22	2,21	2,21				
240	2,23	2.22	2,21	2.21				
250	2,24	2.23	2,22	2.22				
260	2,26	2.25	2,24	2.24				
270	2.29	2,28	2,27	2,27				
280	2,34	2,33	2,32	2,32	2,31	2,31	2,30	2,30
290	2.42	2,41	2,40	2,39	2,38	2,38	2,37	2,37
300	2.55	2,52	2,51	2,49	2,48	2,48	2,47	2,47
310	2,70	2,67	2,64	2,59	2,59	2,58	2,57	2,57
320	2,88	2,86	2,80	2,77	2,73	2,72	2,70	2,69
330	3,11	3,07	3,00	2,96	2,91	2,87	2,83	2,80
340	3,49	3,42	3,29	3.19	3,11	3,03	2,97	2.92
350	4,06	3.94	3,70	3,50	3.35	3,22	3,11	3,05
360	6,62				3,66	3.43	3,28	3,19
370	3,47	6.41			4,05	3,65	3,43	3,32
380	2,80	3,71			5,53	4,02	3,10	3.46
390	2,66	2,98			5.00	4.56	3,81	3,61
400	2,58	2,79						3,80
420	2,55	2,67	3,06	3.50				3,94
440	2,58	2,66	2,83	3.03	3,28			3,87

continued

T, °K \ p, bar →	35	40	50	60	70	80	90	100
460	2,62	2,67	2,78	2,91	3,06	3,24	3,45	3,64
480	2,67	2,70	2,77	2,88	3,00	3,16	3,34	3,47
500	2,72	2,75	2,80	2,88	2,98	3,10	3,24	3,35
520	2,78	2,80	2,84	2,90	2,98	3,08	3,17	3,25
540	2,84	2,86	2,89	2,93	2,98	3,07	3,14	3,19
560	2,88	2,91	2,93	2,96	3,01	3,06	3,11	3,16
580	2,92	2,94	2,97	2,99	3,02	3,06	3,10	3,14
600	2,98	2,99	3,01	3,03	3,04	3,07	3,10	3,14
T, °K \ p, bar →	**150**	**200**	**250**	**300**	**350**	**400**	**500**	**600**
280	2,30							
290	2,37							
300	2,45							
310	2,53	2,49	2,45	2,42	2,38	2,35	2,31	2,29
320	2,61	2,55	2,50	2,44	2,43	2,40	2,37	2,34
330	2,69	2,60	2,55	2,51	2,48	2,45	2,41	2,38
340	2,77	2,67	2,60	2,56	2,52	2,49	2,46	2,43
350	2,84	2,73	2,66	2,60	2,56	2,53	2,49	2,47
360	2,92	2,80	2,72	2,66	2,61	2,58	2,55	2,52
370	2,99	2,87	2,78	2,71	2,66	2,63	2,59	2,56
380	3,07	2,92	2,82	2,75	2,70	2,67	2,63	2,60
390	3,15	2,98	2,87	2,80	2,74	2,72	2,67	2,65
400	3,23	3,03	2,92	2,84	2,79	2,76	2,73	2,67
420	3,37	3,14	3,01	2,93	2,88	2,85	2,81	2,78
440	3,47	3,25	3,10	3,10	2,96	2,93	2,90	2,87
460	3,54	3,34	3,19	3,10	3,05	3,02	2,98	2,95
480	3,56	3,40	3,26	3,19	3,12	3,09	3,06	3,03
500	3,52	3,42	3,32	3,25	3,20	3,16	3,12	3,09
520	3,44	3,42	3,34					
540	3,38	3,41	3,34					
560	3,33	3,38	3,31					
580	3,31	3,36	3,29					
600	3,30	3,34	3,28					

Heat capacity c_p of liquid propane [153]

T, °K	90	100	110	120	130	140	150	160
c_p, kJ/kg · deg	1.918	1,929	1,939	1,951	1.967	1,982	1,999	2,018
T, °K	**170**	**180**	**190**	**200**	**210**	**220**	**230**	
c_p, kJ/kg · deg	2,039	2,063	2,092	2,122	2,156	2,191	2,231	

Thermal conductivity λ (W/m · deg) of propane gas at a pressure of 1 bar [15]

t, °C	λ · 10³	t, °C	λ · 10³	t, °C	λ · 10³	t, °C	λ · 10³
−20	12,8	100	27.4	220	44.8	350	66,8
0	15,0	120	30,1	240	48,0	400	76.0
20	17,3	140	32,9	260	51,2	450	85.7
40	19,7	160	35,7	280	54.5	500	95.8
60	22,2	180	38,7	300	57,9	550	106.4
80	24.7	200	41,7	320	61,3	—	—

Thermal conductivity $\lambda \cdot 10^3$ (W/m · deg) of propane liquid and gas [15]

p, bar \ t, °C →	50	60	80	100	120	140
1	21.0	22.2	24.7	27.4	30.1	32.9
10	22.2	23.3	25.7	28.3	31.0	33.7
20	80	25.4	27.5	29.9	32.2	34.9
30	82	77	30.5	31.7	33.8	36.3
40	84	79	68	37.2	36.4	38.0
50	86	80	71		40.5	41.3
60	88	82	73	63		45.3
70	89	83	75	66		
80	90	85	76	69	61	
100	92	88	79	73	67	
150	97	93	86	80	75	71
200	102	98	92	86	82	78
250	106	102	96	92	87	83
300	109	106	100	96	91	87

Surface tension of propane [42]

t, °C	−130	−120	−110	−100	−90	−80	−70	−60	−50	−40
$\sigma \cdot 10^3$, N/m	27.8	26.3	24.9	23.4	22.0	20.6	19.2	17.85	16.49	15.15

n – BUTANE (C_4H_{10})

$CH_3-CH_2-CH_2-CH_3$

Molecular weight 58.120

$t_{boil} = -0.50$ °C at 760 mm Hg; $t_{melt} = -138.33$ °C; $t_{cr} = 152.01$ °C;
$p_{cr} = 37.96$ bar; $\rho_{cr} = 228$ kg/m³

Thermodynamic properties of *n*-butane at different temperatures [62]:
c_p^0 (kJ/kg · deg), i^0 (kJ/kg) and s^0 (kJ/kg · deg)

T, °K	c_p^0	i_p^0	s^0	T, °K	c_p^0	i^0	s^0
0	0	0	0	800	3.474	1675.9	7.8430
200		189.6	4.754	900	3.706	2035.2	8.2659
250	1.478	258.8	5.064	1000	3.906	2416.2	8.6671
298.16	1.678	334.6	5.340	1100	4.080	2815.5	9.0475
300	1.686	337.8	5.349	1200	4.232	3231.9	9.4084
400	2.132	528.8	5.901	1300	4.364	3662.7	9.7521
500	2.546	763.3	6.426	1400	4.479	4105.8	10.08
600	2.903	1035.6	6.924	1500	4.580	4558.0	10.39
700	3.209	1341.4	7.396				

Saturated vapor pressure of *n*-butane [62]

t, °C	−130	−120	−110	−100	−90	−80	−70	−60	−50	−40	−30	−20	−10
p, mm Hg	0.019	0.096	0.38	1.23	3.42	8.41	16.62	37.8	71.2	126.1	211.7	339.1	521.7

t, °C	0	10	20	25	30	40	50	60	70	80
p, bar	1.032	1.483	2.074	2.43	2.83	3.78	4.96	6.39	8.10	10.13

t, °C	90	100	110	120	130	140	150	152.01
p, bar	12.50	15.29	18.52	22.23	26.48	31.29	36.73	37.96

Specific volume $v \cdot 10^{-3}$ (m^2/kg) of liquid n-butane at different temperatures and pressures [66]

p, bar \ t, °C →	20	40	60	80	90	100	110	120
20	1,700	1.778	1.862	1,969	2.039	2,126	2,229	2.345
30	1,695	1,771	1,852	1,953	2.019	2.099	2.194	2.302
40	1,691	1.765	1.843	1,940	2,000	2,075	2,163	2.264
50	1,687	1,760	1.834	1,926	1.983	2,053	2.137	2.231
60	1,683	1,754	1,827	1,913	1.967	2,034	2,113	2.202
70	1,680	1,748	1,819	1,901	1.953	2,016	2,091	2,176
80	1,676	1.743	1.811	1,890	1.939	2,000	2,071	2,153
90	1,672	1,739	1.804	1.880	1.927	1.985	2,054	2,132
100	1.668	1,734	1.797	1.870	1,916	1.971	2.038	2,113
120	1,662	1,725	1.784	1,852	1.895	1.947	2.008	2,081
140	1.656	1,716	1,771	1,836	1.877	1.926	1,984	2.052
160	1,649	1,707	1,760	1.822	1.860	1,907	1.963	2,029
180	1,643	1.699	1.745	1.809	1.846	1,891	1,945	2.008
200	1.637	1.691	1,739	1.797	1.833	1,877	1.929	1.991

Coefficient of compressibility z of n-butane [67]

p, bar \ t, °C →	37,78	71.11	104.44	137,78	171,11	204,44	237.78
0	1.000	1,000	1,000	1.000	1,000	1,000	1,000
10	0.040	0,041	0.846	0,887	0.916	0.936	0,951
20	0,081	0,069		0.749	0.823	0.869	0.898
30	0,120	0,116	0,119		0,712	0,795	0,846
40	0.159	0,155	0.155	0.170	0.566	0,713	0.790
50	0.197	0.193	0.193	0.206		0.625	0.732
60	0.237	0,229	0,229	0,240	0.301	0,535	0,679
70	0.276	0.266	0,265	0,275	0,318	0,470	0,629
80	0,314	0.303	0,300	0,310	0,342	0.443	0,592
90	0.352	0,340	0,336	0,344	0,371	0.444	0,568
100	0.390	0,375	0.370	0,377	0.400	0.457	0.557
110	0,428	0,412	0,404	0,409	0,431	0,476	0.558
120	0.466	0.448	0,439	0,441	0.460	0.500	0.568
130	0,504	0.484	0,473	0.473	0,490	0,525	0,583
140	0.542	0,521	0,508	0,508	0,520	0.549	0.599
160	0,615	0,589	0.571	0.571	0.572	0,606	0.643
180	0,688	0,657	0.637	0,632	0,637	0,654	0,689
200	0,760	0,725	0.702	0.692	0,695	0.707	0,734
220	0.833	0.792	0,767	0.754	0,750	0,760	0.781
240	0.907	0,861	0,831	0,814	0,805	0,814	0,829
260	0.980	0,930	0.894	0.874	0,861	0,867	0.877
280	1,053	0.996	0.959	0.932	0.916	0.920	0.925
300	1,126	1.064	1,023	0,990	0,971	0.970	0.972
320	1,195	1,130	1.085	1,048	1,027	1.020	1.017
340	1.265	1,197	1.146	1,107	1,080	1,069	1,065
360	1.334	1,264	1,204	1,164	1.133	1,120	1.113
380	1,401	1,327	1.263	1,221	1.187	1.170	1,160
400	1,470	1,390	1.324	1.280	1.240	1,219	1,205
420	1.542	1,454	1.384	1,335	1.293	1 270	1.255
440	1,612	1,518	1,441	1,390	1.345	1,318	1,301
460	1,682	1.581	1,500	1,445	1.396	1.366	1.347
480	1,752	1,644	1.559	1,500	1.448	1,415	1,393
500	1,819	1.707	1,618	1,554	1,499	1,464	1.438
520	1,886	1,770	1.676	1,609	1,550	1,512	1.482
540	1.959	1,831	1.735	1,663	1,602	1.559	1.528
560	2,019	1.894	1.793	1,716	1.654	1,607	1,572
580	2,085	1,955	1,851	1.770	1,706	1,654	1,615
600	2.151	2,016	1 911	1.824	1.757	1,702	1,660
620	2.220	2,082	1,969	1.878	1,806	1,750	1,705

continued

p, bar / t, °C →	37.78	71.11	104.44	137.78	171.11	204.44	237.78
640	2,288	2,143	2,015	1.930	1.858	1.797	1.750
660	2,353	2,201	2,075	1.983	1.905	1.844	1.795
680	2,408	2,263	2,138	2,036	1.953	1.890	1.839

Density ρ of liquid *n*-butane [65]

t, °C	−60	−50	−40	−30	−20	−10	0
$\varrho \cdot 10^{-3}$, kg/m³	0.6605	0,6511	0,6415	0,6317	0,6218	0,6115	0,6010
t, °C	10	20	25	30	40	50	
$\varrho \cdot 10^{-3}$, kg/m³	0,5902	0,5789	0,5732	0.5673	0,5552	0,5426	

Coefficient of thermal expansion $\alpha \cdot 10^5$ (deg⁻¹) of *n*-butane [66]

p, atm / t, °C →	20	40	60	80	100	120
20	226	225	247	321	446	504
40	217	212	227	287	393	457
60	209	201	210	259	355	424
80	202	191	195	239	327	399
100	195	182	184	223	306	379
150	182	164	162	197	273	348
200	169	151	148	183	255	328

Isothermal coefficient of compressibility $\beta \cdot 10^6$ (atm⁻¹) of liquid *n*-butane [66]

p, atm / t, °C →	20	40	60	80	100	120
20	247	355	532	833	1350	2000
40	238	335	488	730	1100	1560
60	230	319	450	641	918	1250
80	223	303	415	569	781	1030
100	215	289	386	510	669	854
150	200	256	323	395	479	580
200	185	229	273	316	358	417

Viscosity η of *n*-butane at a pressure of 1 bar [52]

t, °C	0	25	50	75	100	150	200	250	300	400	500	600
$\eta \cdot 10^7$, N · s/m²	68.2	74.9	81.4	88.1	94.7	107.0	118.5	130.0	142.0	165.0	188.0	210.0

Viscosity η of liquid *n*-butane [52]

t, °C	−70	−60	−50	−40	−30	−20	−10	0
$\eta \cdot 10^3$, N · s/m²	0.460	0.401	0,355	0.314	0.280	0.252	0.227	0.207

Viscosity $\eta \cdot 10^7$ (N · s/m²) of n-butane at different temperatures and pressures [68]

p, atm \ t, °C →	37.78	54,44	71.11	87.78	104.44	121.11	137.78	171,11	204,44	237.78
1.0	80.0	84,0	88,0	92.0	96,0	101	105	112	120	127
6.8	1415	1205	90,0	94,0	97,0	102	106	113	121	128
13.6	1430	1220	1050	885	101	103	107	114	122	129
20,4	1445	1235	1065	900	760	110	112	118	124	130
27,2	1460	1250	1078	915	775	615	122	124	128	132
34.0	1472	1265	1092	930	790	640	510	134	133	136
40.8	1485	1278	1105	945	805	665	535	152	142	142
47,6	1500	1293	1120	960	825	685	565	200	154	150
54,4	1512	1305	1135	975	840	705	590	294	166	158
68,0	1540	1335	1160	1005	868	740	630	405	205	178
102,1	1610	1400	1225	1075	940	820	715	530	360	255
136,1	1675	1465	1290	1140	1005	887	785	610	462	350
204.1	1795	1590	1412	1260	1125	1010	905	740	600	492
272,2	1920	1705	1522	1375	1233	1120	1015	842	703	595
340,2	2035	1820	1632	1480	1337	1222	1115	938	795	680
408.3	2150	1930	1735	1580	1432	1315	1208	1025	875	760
476.3	2270	2040	1838	1676	1528	1405	1293	1105	952	832
544,4	2375	2150	1940	1772	1618	1495	1375	1180	1022	896
612.4	2480	2260	2040	1865	1705	1580	1455	1253	1090	960
680.5	2585	2370	2140	1960	1795	1665	1535	1325	1155	1020

Thermal conductivity $\lambda \cdot 10^3$ (W/m · deg) of butane liquid and gas [15]

p, atm \ t, °C →	60	80	100	120	140	160	180
1	19,9	22,4	24,9	27,4	30,1	32,8	35,6
10	94	24,0	26,4	28,7	31,3	34,0	36,7
20	94	89	84	31,7	33,5	35.8	38.3
40	95	90	85	79	68		44,6
60	96	92	87	82	77	71	
80	98	94	89	85	81	76	73
100	99	95	91	87	84	80	77
150	102	98	94	90	88	86	84
200	105	101	98	94	92	89	88
250	108	104	101	97	95	93	92
300	111	107	103	100	98	96	95
400	115	112	108	105	103	101	100
500	118	115	112	110	108	106	105
600	122	119	116	114	112	110	109

Thermal conductivity λ of n-butane gas at a pressure of 1 bar [15]

t, °C	0	20	40	60	80	100	120	140	160	180	200
$\lambda \cdot 10^3$, W/m · deg	13.1	15.3	17.6	19.9	22,4	24.9	27.4	30.1	32.8	35,6	38.4

Surface tension σ of n-butane [62]

t, °C	−100	−90	−80	−70	−60	−50	−40	−30
$\sigma \cdot 10^3$, N/m	27.2	25.9	24.6	23.4	22.1	20.88	19,65	18.43

2-METHYLPROPANE (ISOBUTANE) (C_6H_{10})

$$CH_3-CH(CH_3)-CH_3$$

Molecular weight 58.120

$t_{boil} = -11.73$ °C at 760 mm Hg; $t_{melt} = -159.60$ °C; $t_{cr} = 134.98$ °C;
$p_{cr} = 36.47$ bar; $\rho_{cr} = 221$ kg/m³

Thermodynamic properties of isobutane at different temperatures [62]:
c^0_p (kJ/kg · deg), i^0 (kJ/kg) and s^0 (kJ/kg · deg)

T, °K	c^0_p	i^0	s^0	T, °K	c^0_p	i^0	s^0
0	0	0	0	800	3,493	1657,5	7,5793
200	1,235	166,0	4,502	900	3,721	2018,6	8,0044
250	1,448	233,0	4,800	1000	3,919	2399,7	8,4063
298.16	1,667	308,0	5,073	1100	4,093	2800,2	8,7882
300	1,675	311,0	5,082	1200	4,242	3218,7	9,1512
400	2,145	501,7	5,628	1300	4,374	3648,8	9,4963
500	2,566	738,4	6,156	1400	4,487	4090,4	9,8241
600	2,926	1013,6	6,656	1500	4,587	4542,1	10.134
700	3,231	1321,2	7.131				

Saturation vapor pressure of isobutane [65]

t, °C	−150	−140	−130	−120	−110	−100	−90
p, mm Hg	0.00115	0,0100	0,060	0,268	0.96	2.87	7.44
t, °C	−80	−70	−60	−50	−40	−30	−20
p, mm Hg	17,19	36,06	69,79	126,2	215,3	349,4	543,0

t, °C	−10	0	10	20	25	30	40	50	60
p, bar	1,081	1,553	2,18	2,98	3,45	3,99	5,25	6,79	8,63
t, °C	70	80	90	100	110	120	130	134,98	
p, bar	10,84	13,43	16,45	19,93	23,89	28,38	33,44	36,47	

Latent heat of vaporization r (kJ/kg) of isobutane [65]

t, °C	r	t, °C	r	t, °C	r	t, °C	r	t, °C	r
−150	458,2	−90	422,9	−30	381,1	30	324,9	90	231,2
−140	452,4	−80	417,1	−20	372,4	40	313,4	100	206,8
−130	446,6	−70	410,6	−10	363,8	50	300,4	110	177,9
−120	440,9	−60	403,4	0	355,2	60	286,0	120	141,9
−110	435,1	−50	396,2	10	345,8	70	270,2	130	86,45
−100	429,4	−40	389,0	20	335,7	80	252,1		

Specific volume v (dm^3/kg) of isobutane at different temperatures and pressures [69]

p, atm \ t, °C →	100	125	150	175	200	225	250	275
1	537.1	574,1	611,2	648,2	685.2	722,2	759.2	796,2
2	265.1	283,9	302.8	321,6	340.4	359.1	377,9	396,7
3	174.3	187,6	200,6	213.5	226.2	239,0	251,4	263,6
4	128.9	139,1	149,1	158.9	168,6	178.3	187,8	197,0
5	101.6	110,0	118,2	126.2	134,1	141.9	149,6	157,1
10	46,74	51,68	56,30	60.71	64.97	69,11	73,21	77,23
15	28.03	32.01	35,55	38.81	41.90	44.87	47,76	50,58
20		21,88	25,05	27.79	30,31	32,72	35,02	37,24
25		15,48	18.61	21.12	23,36	25,43	27,38	29,24
30			14,17	16,62	18,70	20.55	22.29	23,92
35			10,81	13.36	15.35	17,09	18.66	20,13
40			7,994	10,88	12,83	14.48	15.94	17,29
45			5,293	8.879	10.86	12.45	13.83	15,10
50			3.766	7.243	9.289	10,82	12,15	13,34
55				5.928	8,006	9.509	10,79	11,92
60				4,918	6,942	8,431	9,657	10,74
65				4,234	6,083	7.537	8.717	9,755
70				3,818	5.389	6,782	7,924	8,915
75					4,839	6.153	7,253	8,202
80					4,415	5.620	6,680	7,592
85					4.088	5.174	6,186	7,068
90					3.843	4.809	5,753	6,608
95					3,656	4.498	5,386	6,200
100						4,243	5.068	5.840
110						3.860	4.549	5.241
120						3.595	4.163	4,779
130							3,874	4,411
140							3,653	4,118
150								3,886
160								3.701

Specific volume $v \cdot 10^3$ (m^3/kg) of liquid isobutane at different temperatures and pressures [66]

p, bar \ t, °C →	20	40	60	80	90	100	110	120
20	1,771	1,861	1,967	2,106	2,199	2,320		
30	1,765	1,852	1,953	2,083	2,166	2,273	2,414	
40	1.759	1,844	1,941	2.061	2,137	2,232	2,352	2,517
50	1,753	1,835	1,929	2,042	2,112	2,197	2,302	2,440
60	1,747	1,829	1,918	2,024	2,089	2.166	2,259	2,378
70	1,742	1,821	1,907	2,009	2,069	2,139	2,223	2,327
80	1,737	1,814	1,897	1,994	2,050	2,115	2,192	2,284
90	1,732	1,807	1,887	1,980	2,033	2,094	2,165	2,248
100	1,727	1,800	1,878	1,967	2,018	2,075	2,141	2,218
110	1,722	1,794	1,869	1,956	2,004	2,058	2,120	2,191
120	1,717	1,787	1,861	1,945	1,991	2,043	2,101	2,168
130	1,712	1,781	1,853	1,934	1,979	2,029	2,084	2,147
140	1,708	1,776	1,846	1,925	1,968	2,016	2,069	2,128
150	1,704	1,770	1,839	1,916	1,957	2,004	2,055	2,112
160	1,699	1,765	1,832	1,907	1,948	1,993	2,042	2,097
170	1,695	1,760	1,826	1,900	1,939	1,983	2,030	2,084
180	1,691	1,755	1,820	1,892	1,932	1,974	2,019	2,071
190	1,687	1,750	1,814	1,885	1,923	1,965	2,010	2,060
200	1,683	1,745	1,809	1,878	1,916	1,957	2,000	2,050

Enthalpy difference i—i^0 (kJ/kg) of isobutane [69]

p, bar \ t, °C →	100	125	150	175	200	225	250	275
1	2.27	1.88	1.58	1.48	1.28	1.19	0.99	0.95
2	4.54	3.75	3.25	2.96	2.56	2.27	2.07	1.98
3	6.86	5.78	5.04	4.37	3.95	3.55	3.16	2.96
4	9.26	7.80	6.78	7.27	5.29	4.75	4.25	3.95
5	11.64	9.83	8.52	7.56	6.65	5.99	5.33	4.88
10	24.9	20.8	17.8	15.4	13.6	12.13	10.85	9.9
15	41.05	32.9	27.7	23.8	20.7	18.4	16.5	15.0
20		47.20	38.8	32.8	28.5	25.1	22.3	20.0
25		64.62	50.96	42.55	36.4	31.7	28.4	25.3
30			65.31	53.08	44.71	38.8	34.5	31.0
35			82.87	64.72	53.75	46.35	40.8	36.3
40			105.9	77.76	63.31	54.01	47.26	41.85
45			145.7	92.48	73.51	61.99	53.71	47.49
50			184.6	109.3	84.53	70.25	60.43	53.07
55				128.4	95.95	78.81	67.33	58.96
60				148.2	107.6	87.38	74.26	64.70
65				165.4	119.7	96.12	81.20	70.47
70				177.5	132.2	105.0	88.13	76.26
75					143.5	113.7	95.00	81.88
80					153.5	121.8	101.4	87.40
85					161.9	130.0	108.1	92.71
90					169.3	138.0	114.5	97.89
95					174.9	144.9	120.8	103.2
100						151.3	126.8	108.5
110						161.9	137.8	118.4
120						169.3	147.2	127.4
130							155.2	135.3
140							161.0	142.6
150								148.5
160								152.9

Heat capacity difference c_p—$c_p{}^0$ (kJ/kg · deg) of isobutane [69]

p, bar \ t, °C →	100	125	150	175	200	225	250	275
1	0.015	0.012	0.0087	0.0074	0.0059	0.0046	0.0042	0.0033
2	0.0295	0.0266	0.0178	0.0144	0.0119	0.0100	0.0083	0.0066
3	0.0470	0.0397	0.0276	0.0223	0.0177	0.0150	0.0118	0.0104
4	0.0643	0.0478	0.0374	0.0297	0.0246	0.0200	0.0167	0.0138
5	0.0841	0.0635	0.0487	0.0380	0.0316	0.0260	0.0217	0.0177
10	0.198	0.143	0.1061	0.1031	0.0671	0.0557	0.0403	0.0384
15	0.385	0.250	0.1779	0.1355	0.1072	0.0848	0.0714	0.0603
20		0.424	0.2800	0.1986	0.1521	0.1200	0.0990	0.0822
25		0.681	0.4155	0.2810	0.2067	0.1610	0.1280	0.1053
30			0.6164	0.3876	0.2718	0.2050	0.1620	0.1318
35			0.989	0.5427	0.3487	0.2560	0.1990	0.1604
40			2.140	0.7319	0.4473	0.3190	0.2390	0.1885
45				1.023	0.5705	0.3820	0.2830	0.2208
50				1.390	0.7136	0.4588	0.3340	0.2559
55				2.450	0.8816	0.5483	0.3880	0.2930
60				2.418	1.068	0.6385	0.4447	0.3349
65				2.402	1.258	0.7310	0.5029	0.3731
70				2.230	1.416	0.8268	0.5591	0.4136
75					1.509	0.9179	0.6155	0.4532
80					1.517	0.9980	0.6683	0.4908
85					1.469	1.079	0.7199	0.5264
90					1.359	1.141	0.7726	0.5600
95					1.243	1.162	0.8142	0.5910

continued

p, bar \ t, °C →	100	125	150	175	200	225	250	275
100						1.147	0.8429	0.6243
110						1.057	0.8730	0.6743
120						0.9208	0.8651	0.7074
130							0.8226	0.7219
140							0.7640	0.7154
150								0.6912
160								0.6562

Heat capacity c_p (kJ/kg · deg) of liquid isobutane [70]

T, °K	c_p	T, °K	c_p	T, °K	c_p	T, °K	c_p
120	1.727	160	1.838	200	1.969	240	2.140
130	1.749	170	1.875	210	2.003	250	2.189
140	1.774	180	1.909	220	2.044	260	2.233
150	1.805	190	1.941	230	2.088		

Density ρ (kg/m³) of saturated liquid isobutane [65]

t, °C	$\varrho \cdot 10^3$	t, °C	$\varrho \cdot 10^3$	t, °C	$\varrho \cdot 10^3$	t, °C	$\varrho \cdot 10^3$
−60	0.6457	−20	0.6033	20	0.5573	50	0.5182
−50	0.6352	−10	0.5923	25	0.5511	75	0.480
−40	0.6247	0	0.5810	30	0.5448	100	0.428
−30	0.6141	10	0.5694	40	0.5318	125	0.353

Coefficient of thermal expansion $\alpha \cdot 10^5$ (deg⁻¹) of liquid isobutane [66]

p, atm \ t, °C →	20	40	60	80	100
20	240	257	300	391	605
40	250	242	272	336	471
60	221	229	251	296	386
80	213	218	233	267	330
100	206	208	219	245	293
150	192	191	195	212	241
200	182	179	182	194	218

Isothermal coefficient of compressibility $\beta \cdot 10^6$ (atm⁻¹) of liquid isobutane [66]

p, atm \ t, °C →	20	40	60	80	100
20	362	496	733	1180	2260
40	342	459	650	989	1700
60	323	425	582	837	1320
80	306	394	522	718	1060
100	291	366	471	621	866
150	256	309	373	454	570
200	228	263	301	344	407

Viscosity η of isobutane gas at a pressure of 1 bar [52]

t, °C	0	25	50	75	100	150	200	250	300
$\eta \cdot 10^7$, N · s/m²	68.9	75.8	82.1	88.6	94.7	107.4	120.2	132.6	145.0

Viscosity $\eta \cdot 10^8$ (N · s/m³) of isobutane at different temperatures and pressures [52]

p, atm \ t, °C →	37.78	54.14	71 .11	87.78	104.44
1.0	765	795	825	857	887
1.36	775	802	831	866	898
2.72	792	812	852	887	921
4.08	821	842	873	911	942
6.80		898	925	957	994
10.21			1 010	1030	1060
13.61	13 440	10 710	8 960	1170	1140
17.01	13 760				1310
27.22	14 040	11 020	9 280	7800	
40.83	14 560	11 320	9 560	8110	
68.05	15 060	11 860	10 110	8620	
102.10	15 540	12 520	10 650	9130	
136.10	–	12 970	11 060	9540	
Saturated vapor	841	913	1 038	1344	
Saturated liquid	13 200	10 580	8 900	7530	

Viscosity η of liquid isobutane [52]

t, °C	–70	–60	–50	–40	–30	–20	–10	0
$\eta \cdot 10^3$, N · s/m²	0.530	0.454	0.392	0.343	0.301	0.267	0.238	0.214

Surface tension σ of isobutane [62]

t, °C	–100	–90	–80	–70	–60	–50	–40	–30
$\sigma \cdot 10^3$, N/m	25.2	23.9	22.6	21.4	20.14	18.90	17.68	16.48

n-PENTANE (C_5H_{12})

CH_3—$(CH_2)_3$—CH_3

Molecular weight 72.146

t_{boil} = 36.07 °CC at 760 mm Hg; t_{melt} = – 129.67 °C; t_{cr} = 196.62 °C;
p_{cr} = 33.74 bar; ρ_{cr} = 232 kg/m³

Thermodynamic properties of *n*-pentane [62] : $c_p{}^0$ (kJ/kg · deg), i^0 (kJ/kg) and s^0 (kJ/kg · deg)

T, °K	$c_p{}^0$	i^0	s^0	T, °K	$c_p{}^0$	i^0	s^0
0	0	0	0	800	3.441	1657.8	7.3129
200		182.6	4.259	900	3.666	2013.4	7.7308
250	1.468	251.3	4.565	1000	3.862	2390.3	8.1277
298.16	1.667	326.7	4.840	1100	4.032	2785.0	8.5043
300	1.675	329.7	4.851	1200	4.179	3197.0	8.8635
400	2.120	519.5	5.394	1300	4.308	3621.8	9.2030
500	2.529	752.6	5.9121	1400	4.420	4058.9	9.5268
600	2.881	1023.0	6.4030	1500	4.516	4504.6	9.8343
700	3.182	1325.9	6.8696				

Saturated vapor pressure of *n*-pentane [62, 65]

t, °C	−100	−90	−80	−70	−60	−50	−40	−30
p, mm Hg	0.064	0.234	0.722	1.94	4.66	10.15	20.41	38.33
t, °C	−20	−10	0	10	20	25	30	
p, mm Hg	67.83	114.07	183.48	283.81	424.14	512.49	614.81	

t, °C	40	50	60	70	80	90	100	110	120
p, bar	1.156	1.591	2.145	2.832	3.676	4.693	5.906	7.333	8.985
t, °C	130	140	150	160	170	180	190	196.62	
p, bar	10.94	13.20	15.79	18.74	22.08	25.84	30.04	33.74	

Heat capacity c_p of liquid *n*-pentane [71]

t, °C	—121.84	—116.19	—110.34	—104.78	—98.96	—93.09	—87.45	—82.63	—76.49	—66.11
c_p, kJ/kg · deg	1.952	1.955	1.964	1.964	1.968	1.972	1.981	1.988	1.992	2.016

t, °C	—57.32	—47.00	—38.35	—28.60	—18.94	—10.60	—3.15	5.92	13.25
c , kJ/kg · deg	2.030	2.051	2.085	2.122	2.149	2.187	2.208	2.280	2.314

Latent heat of vaporization r (kJ/kg) of *n*-pentane [65]

t, °C	r	t, °C	r	t, °C	r	t, °C	r
−120	448.6	−70	425.4	−30	403.9	10	377.8
−110	444.5	−60	420.1	−20	397.5	20	370.2
−100	439.9	−50	414.9	−10	391.1	30	362.7
− 90	435.2	−40	409.7	0	384.7	40	355.1
− 80	430.0						

Density ρ (kg/m^3) of saturated *n*-pentane vapor [65, 71]

t, °C	$\varrho \cdot 10^{-3}$	t, °C	$\varrho \cdot 10^{-3}$	t, °C	$\varrho \cdot 10^{-3}$	t, °C	$\varrho \cdot 10^{-3}$
30	0.002451	100	0.01626	170	0.0735	196.5	0.1841
40	0.003361	110	0.02024	180	0.0935	196.8	0.1925
50	0.004545	120	0.0250	186	0.1109	196.9	0.1960
60	0.006020	130	0.0310	190	0.1269	197.0	0.2005
70	0.007862	140	0.0386	193	0.1440	197.1	0.2090
80	0.01012	150	0.0476	195	0.1609	197.15	0.2168
90	0.01289	160	0.0591	196	0.1746	197.2	0.2323

Density ρ (kg/m^3) of liquid n-pentane [71]

t, °C	$\varrho \cdot 10^{-3}$	t, °C	$\varrho \cdot 10^{-3}$	t, °C	$\varrho \cdot 10^{-3}$	t, °C	$\varrho \cdot 10^{-3}$	t, °C	$\varrho \cdot 10^{-3}$
−130	0.7614	−40	0.6825	40	0.6062	130	0.4957	195	0.3065
−120	0.7528	−30	0.6734	50	0.5957	140	0.4787	196	0.2915
−110	0.7441	−20	0.6643	60	0.5850	150	0.4604	196.5	0.2809
−100	0.7354	−10	0.6550	70	0.5739	160	0.4394	196.8	0.2730
−90	0.7267	0	0.6455	80	0.5624	170	0.4162	196.9	0.2691
−80	0.7180	10	0.6360	90	0.5503	180	0.3867	197.0	0.2640
−70	0.7092	20	0.6262	100	0.5377	186	0.3643	197.1	0.2560
−60	0.7004	25	0.6213	110	0.5248	190	0.3445	197.15	0.2472
−50	0.6915	30	0.6163	120	0.5107	193	0.3253	197.2	0.2323

Specific volume $v \cdot 10^3$ (m^{3}kg) of liquid n-pentane at different temperatures and pressures [66]

p, bar \ t, °C →	20	40	60	80	90	100	110	120
10	1.591	1.644	1.703	1.774	1.813	1.859	1.908	1.965
20	1.588	1.640	1.698	1.766	1.805	1.848	1.896	1.950
30	1.584	1.636	1.693	1.759	1.797	1.839	1.884	1.936
40	1.581	1.632	1.688	1.753	1.789	1.830	1.874	1.924
50	1.578	1.628	1.683	1.746	1.781	1.823	1.864	1.911
60	1.575	1.625	1.678	1.740	1.774	1.814	1.855	1.900
70	1.572	1.621	1.673	1.735	1.768	1.806	1.845	1.889
80	1.569	1.617	1.669	1.729	1.762	1.798	1.836	1.878
90	1.567	1.614	1.665	1.724	1.756	1.791	1.828	1.869
100	1.566	1.610	1.660	1.718	1.749	1.784	1.820	1.860
110	1.562	1.607	1.656	1.713	1.744	1.777	1.813	1.851
120	1.558	1.604	1.653	1.708	1.738	1.771	1.805	1.843
130	1.556	1.601	1.649	1.703	1.733	1.765	1.798	1.835
140	1.553	1.597	1.645	1.699	1.727	1.759	1.792	1.827
150	1.551	1.595	1.641	1.694	1.722	1.753	1.785	1.820
160	1.548	1.592	1.638	1.690	1.717	1.748	1.779	1.813
170	1.546	1.589	1.634	1.685	1.713	1.743	1.774	1.807
180	1.543	1.586	1.631	1.681	1.708	1.738	1.768	1.801
190	1.541	1.583	1.628	1.677	1.704	1.733	1.763	1.795
200	1.539	1.581	1.624	1.673	1.699	1.728	1.758	1.783

Viscosity $\eta \cdot 10^7$ (N · s/m^2) of n-pentane at different temperatures and pressures [68]

p, atm \ t, °C →	25	50	75	100	125	150	175	185
1	2162	73.0	79.0	84.9	90.9	96.7	102.5	104.6
5	2172	1772	1429	87.2	92.5	97.8	103.6	105.8
10	2185	1782	1440	1154	984.6	100.7	105.3	107.5
15	2195	1796	1451	1167	947.1	108.6	111.1	112.6
20	2209	1807	1461	1179	960.6	743.0	120.1	120.3
25	2225	1817	1472	1192	972.4	763.0	551.0	136.4
30	2232	1826	1482	1203	985.5	778.0	580.0	482.5
33.12	2240	1832	1489	1211	993.4	787.0	594.0	508.0
35	2245	1836	1494	1216	998.5	798.0	601.0	520.0
40	2259	1848	1503	1227	1010	807.0	623.0	551.0
50	2282	1870	1523	1252	1033	834.0	660.0	595.0
60	2309	1892	1544	1273	1054	858.0	694.0	633.0
70	2333	1913	1567	1295	1078	883.0	722.0	662.0
80	2359	1935	1586	1316	1100	906.0	747.0	692.0
100	2408	1977	1629	1355	1139	950.0	799.0	742.0
150	2532	2083	1732	1450	1239	1046	900.0	848.0

continued

p, atm \ t, °C →	25	50	75	100	125	150	175	185
200	2656	2191	1832	1547	1333	1133	994.0	942.0
250	2786	2296	1925	1640	1420	1218	1076	1027
300	2915	2400	2020	1723	1505	1301	1153	1101
400	3168	2612	2213	1898	1665	1461	1299	1245
500	3431	2825	2393	2052	1818	1608	1444	1386

p, atm \ t, °C →	192	197,2	205	210	225	250	275
1	106.2	107.3	109.1	110.2	113.6	118.9	124.2
5	107.1	108.1	110.0	110.9	114.4	119.9	124.9
10	108.4	109.1	111.2	112.2	115.6	120.4	125.7
15	113.2	114.3	115.2	116.0	118.6	123.0	127.5
20	120.4	120.6	120.8	121.2	122.6	127.0	131.0
25	134.0	132.9	131.7	130.2	131.0	133.5	136.4
30	164.0	150.6	145.8	144.0	141.8	141.8	144.5
33.12	480.0	265.0	164.8	157.5	151.8	148.4	150.0
35	485.0	378.0	202.0	173.2	160.0	153.5	154.0
40	495.0	441.0	354.0	298.0	196.5	169.0	164.5
50	548.0	511.0	452.0	429.0	291.2	216.3	190.8
60	591.0	559.0	513.0	486.0	380.0	268.0	222.0
70	626.0	595.0	552.0	525.0	435.0	322.0	267.0
80	657.0	624.0	587.0	557.0	482.0	375.0	297.0
100	712.0	680.0	644.0	614.0	546.0	452.0	371.2
150	812.0	790.0	756.0	734.0	670.0	581.0	499.0
200	912.0	885.0	853.0	829.0	784.0	667.0	598.0
250	995.0	968.0	935.0	912.0	846.0	749.0	675.0
300	1170	1043	1010	987.0	925.0	825.0	747.0
400	1211	1189	1150	1129	1069	961.0	875.0
500	1353	1328	1285	1264	1201	1095	1008

Viscosity η ($N \cdot s/m^2$) of *n*-pentane gas at a pressure of 1 bar [52]

t, °C	$\eta \cdot 10^7$	t, °C	$\eta \cdot 10^7$	t, °C	$\eta \cdot 10^7$	t, °C	$\eta \cdot 10^7$	t, °C	$\eta \cdot 10^7$	t, °C	$\eta \cdot 10^7$
0	62.3	50	73.0	100	85.0	200	107.9	300	129.5	500	172.5
25	68.0	75	79.0	150	96.7	250	119.1	400	151.0	600	193.0

Viscosity η ($N \cdot s/m^2$) of saturated *n*-pentane [68]

t, °C	$\eta' \cdot 10^7$	$\eta'' \cdot 10^7$	t, °C	$\eta' \cdot 10^7$	$\eta'' \cdot 10^7$	t, °C	$\eta' \cdot 10^7$	$\eta'' \cdot 10^7$
40	1906	70.5	110	1048	90.7	180	502.2	142.1
50	1760	73.2	120	962.4	94.4	186	457.0	156.0
60	1618	75.8	130	884.7	98.7	190	421.0	167.7
70	1484	78.6	140	806.6	103.6	193	394.0	185.4
80	1355	81.8	150	733.2	109.2	195	366.0	200.3
90	1245	84.8	160	655.1	116.3	197.2	265.3	265.3
100	1142	88.0	170	579.5	127.1			

Viscosity η ($N \cdot s/m^2$) of liquid *n*-pentane [52]

t, °C	$\eta \cdot 10^3$	t, °C	$\eta \cdot 10^3$	t, °C	$\eta \cdot 10^3$
−120	2.31	−50	0.474	0	0.283
−100	1.25	−40	0.419	10	0.259
− 80	0.768	−30	0.375	20	0.240
− 70	0.640	−20	0.341	30	0.220
− 60	0.546	−10	0.311		

Coefficient of thermal expansion $\alpha \cdot 10^5$ (deg^{-1}) of liquid *n*-pentane [66]

p, atm \ t, °C →	20	40	60	80	100	120
20	157	167	185	209	244	295
40	152	162	178	199	230	272
60	148	158	171	190	217	252
80	145	153	166	183	206	236
100	143	149	160	176	197	223
150	135	141	150	163	179	194
200	129	135	142	153	167	183

Isothermal coefficient of compressibility $\beta \cdot 10^6$ (atm^{-1}) of liquid *n*-pentane [66]

p, atm \ t, °C →	20	40	60	80	100	120
20	202	248	313	401	534	742
40	195	238	296	375	489	661
60	188	229	280	350	449	592
80	182	218	266	327	412	531
100	176	210	253	307	381	484
150	164	190	224	265	317	385
200	152	174	199	229	267	314

Thermal coefficient of pressure $\gamma \cdot 10^5$ (deg^{-1}) of *n*-pentane [66]

p, atm \ t, °C →	20	40	60	80	100	120
20	38 739	33 774	29 510	26 028	22 879	18 981
40	19 527	17 084	14 991	13 286	11 749	10 281
60	13 122	11 521	10 174	9 071	8 064	7 108
80	9 931	8 770	7 774	6 980	6 250	5 552
100	7 984	7 119	6 350	5 735	5 159	4 619
120	6750	6015	5403	4913	4462	4018
140	5845	5248	4739	4328	3968	3608
160	5172	4669	4240	3904	3606	3304
180	4653	4227	3861	3589	3329	3087
200	4243	3867	3567	3337	3124	2904

Thermal conductivity λ of *n*-pentane gas at $p = 1$ bar [15]

t, °C	40	60	80	100	120	140	160	180	200
$\lambda \cdot 10^3$, W/m · deg	15.8	18.0	20.3	22.7	25.1	27.6	30.2	33.8	35.5

Thermal conductivity λ of liquid *n*-pentane [72]*

t, °C	0	10	20	30	40	50
λ, W/m · deg	0.1205	0.1182	0.1158	0.1134	0.1110	0.1085

*Values of λ have been calculated from the equation $\lambda = B\rho^{4/3}$, where $B = 0.216$, and the density ρ is given in gm/cm³.

Surface tension σ of n-pentane [62]

t, °C	−20	−10	0	10	20	25	30	40
$\sigma \cdot 10^3$, N/m	20.5	19.3	18.2	17.1	16.00	15.48	14.95	13.8

2-METHYLBUTANE (ISOPENTANE) (C_5H_{12})

$$CH_3-CH(CH_3)-CH_2-CH_3$$

Molecular weight 72.146

$t_{boil} = 27.85$ °C at 760 mm Hg; $t_{melt} = -159.9$ °C;
$t_{cr} = 187.8$ °C, $p_{cr} = 33.33$ bar; $\rho_{cr} = 234$ kg/m³

Thermodynamic properties of isopentane [62]: $c_p{}^0$ (kJ/kg · deg), i^0 (kJ/kg) and s^0 (kJ/kg · deg)

T, °K	$c_p{}^0$	i^0	s^0	T, °K	$c_p{}^0$	i^0	s^0
0	0	0	0	800	3.465	1642.2	7.2433
200		167.6	4.207	900	3.694	2001.5	7.6652
250	1.423	232.6	4.497	1000	3.895	2379.8	8.0644
298.16	1.647	307.3	4.765	1100	4.068	2772.7	8.4439
300	1.656	310.2	4.775	1200	4.218	3193.4	8.8049
400	2.118	498.8	5.313	1300	4.349	3620.5	9.1478
500	2.536	732.3	5.8332	1400	4.461	4061.5	9.4746
600	2.895	1003.9	6.3276	1500	4.558	4511.3	9.7844
700	3.203	1309.7	6.7988				

Saturated vapor pressure of isopentane [65]

t, °C	p, mm Hg	t, °C	p, mm Hg	t, °C	p, bar	t, °C	p, bar
−100	0.134	−30	58.33	30	1.090	120	10.69
−90	0.459	−20	100.71	40	1.511	130	12.93
−80	1.34	−10	165.05	50	2.048	140	15.49
−70	3.43	0	259.27	60	2.719	150	18.43
−60	7.89	10	392.43	70	3.541	160	21.75
−50	16.55	20	574.84	80	4.536	170	25.51
−40	32.16			90	5.721	180	29.71
				100	7.11	187.8	33. 3
				110	8.77		

Heat capacity c_p (kJ/kg · deg) of liquid isopentane [73]

T, °K	c_p	T, °K	c_p	T, °K	c_p	T, °K	c_p
115	1.710	160	1.811	210	1.942	260	2.119
120	1.721	170	1.834	220	1.973	270	2.161
130	1.743	180	1.859	230	2.007	280	2.204
140	1.765	190	1.885	240	2.041	290	2.249
150	1.787	200	1.913	250	2.079	300	2.295

Latent heat of vaporization r (kJ/kg) of isopentane [65]

t, °C	r	t, °C	r	t, °C	r	t, °C	r
−150	438.7	−100	418.4	−50	394.0	0	362.7
−140	435.8	−90	415.5	−40	388.2	10	355.7
−130	432.3	−80	410.3	−30	381.8	20	348.2
−120	428.3	−70	405.0	−20	376.0	30	340.6
−110	424.2	−60	399.8	−10	369.7	40	331.9

Density ρ (kg/m³) of saturated isopentane vapor [71]

t, °C	$\varrho \cdot 10^{-3}$	t, °C	$\varrho \cdot 10^{-3}$	t, °C	$\varrho \cdot 10^{-3}$	t, °C	$\varrho \cdot 10^{-3}$
0	0.0011	70	0.01013	140	0 04728	185	0 1574
10	0.001650	80	0.01287	150	0.05834	186	0.1676
20	0.002344	90	0.01621	160	0.07289	187	0.1833
30	0.003266	100	0.02020	170	0.09337	187.4	0.1951
40	0.004456	110	0.02513	176	0.1101	187.8	0.2343
50	0.005956	120	0.03106	180	0.1258		
60	0.007836	130	0.03831	183	0.1418		

Density ρ (kg/m³) of liquid isopentane [71, 65]

t, °C	$\varrho \cdot 10^{-3}$	t, °C	$\varrho \cdot 10^{-3}$	t, °C	$\varrho \cdot 10^{-3}$	t, °C	$\varrho \cdot 10^{-3}$
−120	0.7510	−20	0.6585	70	0.5656	170	0.3914
−110	0.7412	−10	0.6489	80	0.5540	176	0.3694
−100	0.7323	0	0.6392	90	0.5413	180	0.3498
− 90	0.7234	10	0.6294	100	0.5278	183	0.3311
− 80	0.7143	20	0.6196	110	0.5140	185	0.3142
− 70	0.7052	25	0.6146	120	0.4991	186	0.3028
− 60	0.6960	30	0.6092	130	0.4826	187	0.2857
− 50	0.6868	40	0.5988	140	0.4642	187.4	0.2761
− 40	0.6774	50	0.5881	150	0.4445	187.8	0.2343
− 30	0.6680	60	0.5769	160	0.4206		

Viscosity η of isopentane gas [52]

t, °C	0	25	50	75	100	150	200	250	300
$\eta \cdot 10^7$, N · s/m²	63.8	69.6	75.2	80.5	86.0	96.9	107.9	118.5	129.1

Thermal conductivity λ of liquid isopentane [72]*

t, °C	0	10	20	30	40	50
λ, W/m · deg	0.1190	0.1166	0.1142	0.1116	0.1091	0.1045

*Calculated from $\lambda = B\rho^{4/3}$, with $B = 0.216$, and ρ in gm/cm³.

Surface tension of isopentane [62]

t, °C	−20	−10	0	10	20	25	30
$\sigma \cdot 10^3$, N/m	19.4	18.27	17.17	16.08	15.00	14.46	13.93

n-HEXANE (C_6H_{14})

$CH_3(CH_2)_4CH_3$

Molecular weight 86.172
$t_{boil} = 68.74$ °C at 760 mm Hg; $t_{melt} = -95.32$ °C; $t_{cr} = 234.7$ ° C;
$p_{cr} = 30.31$ bar; $\sigma_{cr} = 234$ kg/m³
Thermodynamic properties of n-hexane [62]: c_p (kJ/kg · deg), i^0 (kJ/kg) and s^0 (kJ/kg · deg)

T, °K	$c_p{}^0$	i^0	s^0	T, °K	$c_p{}^0$	i^0	s^0
0	0	0	0	900	3.641	1999.8	7.3881
298.16	1.662	321.8	4.511	1000	3.833	2373.6	7.7822
300	1.670	324.9	4.522	1100	4.000	2766.0	8.1558
400	2.112	514.1	5.0631	1200	4.145	3174.3	8.5120
500	2.518	746.3	5.5796	1300	4.271	3595.5	8.8487
600	2.866	1015.1	6.0679	1400	4.380	4028.5	9.1694
700	3.163	1316.6	6.5324	1500	4.475	4470.8	9.4741
800	3.419	1646.2	6.9722	—	—	—	—

Saturated vapor pressure of n-hexane [65]

t, °C	p, mm Hg	t, °C	p, mm Hg	t, °C	p, bar	t, °C	p, bar
−90	0.0144	0	45.32	70	1.0537	160	9.036
−80	0.0579	10	75.69	80	1.4239	170	10.85
−70	0.194	20	121.23	90	1.8876	180	12.94
−60	0.563	25	151.26	100	2.460	190	15.32
−50	1.44	30	187.10	110	3.153	200	18.02
−40	3.34	40	279.44	120	3.986	210	21.08
−30	7.08	50	405.33	130	4.973	220	24.52
−20	13.97	60	572.75	140	6.128	230	28.37
−10	25.86			150	7.468	234.7	30.31

Specific volume $v \cdot 10^3$ (m³/kg) of liquid n-hexane at different temperatures and pressures [66]

p, bar \ t, °C →	70	80	100	120	140	160	180	200	210
10	1.627	1.656	1.717	1.788	1.870	1.973			
20	1.623	1.651	1.711	1.779	1.858	1.955	2.084	2.274	
30	1.619	1.647	1.705	1.771	1.847	1.940	2.059	2.230	2.350
40	1.615	1.642	1.699	1.763	1.836	1.925	2.036	2.190	2.296
50	1.611	1.638	1.693	1.756	1.827	1.910	2.014	2.155	2.249
60	1.607	1.633	1.688	1.749	1.817	1.897	1.995	2.124	2.207
70	1.603	1.629	1.683	1.742	1.808	1.884	1.977	2.096	2.171
80	1.599	1.625	1.678	1.736	1.800	1.872	1.960	2.071	2.138
90	1.596	1.621	1.673	1.729	1.791	1.861	1.944	2.047	2.109
100	1.592	1.617	1.668	1.723	1.783	1.851	1.930	2.026	2.082
120	1.585	1.610	1.659	1.711	1.768	1.832	1.903	1.988	2.038
140	1.579	1.603	1.650	1.701	1.754	1.814	1.880	1.956	1.999
160	1.574	1.596	1.642	1.690	1.742	1.798	1.859	1.928	1.966
180	1.568	1.590	1.634	1.680	1.730	1.784	1.841	1.904	1.938
200	1.562	1.584	1.627	1.672	1.719	1.770	1.824	1.883	1.914
220	1.556	1.578	1.619	1.663	1.709	1.758	1.809	1.864	1.893
240	1.551	1.572	1.613	1.655	1.700	1.747	1.795	1.847	1.874
260	1.546	1.566	1.606	1.648	1.692	1.736	1.783	1.831	1.858
280	1.541	1.561	1.600	1.642	1.683	1.726	1.771	1.818	1.843
300	1.536	1.556	1.594	1.635	1.675	1.717	1.761	1.806	1.829

Density ρ (kg/m^3) of saturated vapor of n-hexane [71]

t, °C	$\varrho \cdot 10^{-3}$	t, °C	$\varrho \cdot 10^{-3}$	t, °C	$\varrho \cdot 10^{-3}$	t, °C	$\varrho \cdot 10^{-3}$
0	0.0002	70	0.003367	140	0.01866	210	0.07899
10	0.0004	80	0.00446	150	0.02299	220	0.1011
20	0.0006	90	0.00585	160	0.02833	226	0.1203
30	0.0009	100	0.00754	170	0.03472	230	0.1405
40	0.0013	110	0.00956	180	0.04228	233	0.1658
50	0.0018	120	0.01202	190	0.05155	234	0.1807
60	0.002488	130	0.01504	200	0.06329	234.7	0.2344

Density ρ (kg/m^3) of liquid n-hexane [62]

t, °C	$\varrho \cdot 10^{-3}$	t, C	$\varrho \cdot 10^{-3}$	t, °C	$\varrho \cdot 10^{-3}$	t, °C	$\varrho \cdot 10^{-3}$
−100	0.7603	0	0.6772	90	0.5918	190	0.4570
−90	0.7526	10	0.6684	100	0.5814	200	0.4365
−80	0.7445	20	0.6594	110	0.5703	210	0.4124
−70	0.7364	25	0.6548	120	0.5588	220	0.3810
−60	0.7282	30	0.6502	130	0.5467	226	0.3557
−50	0.7199	40	0.6409	140	0.5343	230	0.3329
−40	0.7115	50	0.6315	150	0.5207	233	0.3040
−30	0.7031	60	0.6218	160	0.5063	234	0.2883
−20	0.6946	70	0.6122	170	0.4913	234.7	0.2344
−10	0.6860	80	0.6022	180	0.4751		

Latent heat of vaporization r (kJ/kg) of n-hexane [65]

t, °C	r	t, °C	r	t, °C	r	t, °C	r
−90	459.7	0	379.0	80	329.0	160	243.0
−80	416.4	10	373.7	90	320.7	170	229.3
−70	412.0	20	368.3	100	311.5	180	214.3
−60	407.7	30	362.5	110	301.3	190	197.3
−50	403.3	40	356.2	120	290.6	200	177.8
−40	398.9	50	349.4	130	279.4	210	155.5
−30	394.1	60	343.0	140	267.7	220	126.3
−20	389.2	70	336.2	150	255.6	230	82.60
−10	384.3						

Heat capacity c_p (kJ/kg · deg) of liquid n-hexane [74]

T, °K	c_p	T, °K	c_p	T, °K	c_p	T, °K	c_p
180	1.975	220	2.023	250	2.102	280	2.202
190	1.981	230	2.046	260	2.134	290	2.239
200	1.991	240	2.073	270	2.167	300	2.270
210	2.005						

Viscosity η (N · s/m^3) of saturated n-hexane [68]

t, °C	$\eta' \cdot 10^7$	$\eta'' \cdot 10^7$	t, °C	$\eta' \cdot 10^7$	$\eta'' \cdot 10^7$	t, °C	$\eta' \cdot 10^7$	$\eta'' \cdot 10^7$
−90	18200		30	2780		150	1059	97.4
−80	13800		40	2530		160	972	102.2
−70	11000		50	2330		170	888	107.7
−60	8920		60	2160		180	811	113.8
−50	7420		70	2001	73.0	190	731	121.3

continued

t, °C	$\eta' \cdot 10^7$	$\eta'' \cdot 10^7$	t, °C	$\eta' \cdot 10^7$	$\eta'' \cdot 10^7$	t, °C	$\eta' \cdot 10^7$	$\eta'' \cdot 10^7$
—40	6330		80	1835	75.4	200	655	130.6
—30	5470		90	1703	77.8	210	589	142.3
—20	4790		100	1537	80.2	220	512	158.6
—10	4260		110	1479	83.0	226	486	172.8
0	3810		120	1358	86.1	230	423	188.5
10	3430		130	1251	89.5	233	377	210
20	3070		140	1153	93.2	234.8	272	272

Viscosity η (N · s/m³) of n-hexane gas at a pressure of 1 bar

t, °C	$\eta \cdot 10^7$	t, °C	$\eta \cdot 10^7$	t, °C	$\eta \cdot 10^7$	t, °C	$\eta \cdot 10^7$
0	60.0	75	74.0	200	104.0	400	147.5
25	65.4	100	80.0	250	115.0	500	168.5
50	71.0	150	91.0	300	126.0	600	190.0

Viscosity $\eta \cdot 10^7$ (N · s/m³) of n-hexane at different temperatures and pressures [68]

p, atm \ t, °C →	25	50	75	100	125	150
1	2930	2330	73.5	79.5	85.0	90.7
5	2941	2344	1940	1598	1310	93.1
10	2960	2360	1952	1605	1323	1084
15	2976	2373	1967	1619	1336	1094
20	2992	2388	1982	1630	1348	1111
25	3010	2404	1996	1643	1360	1124
28	3020	2413	2000	1650	1370	1128
29.62	3025	2419	2007	1656	1375	1133
35	3043	2433	2020	1668	1383	1146
40	3060	2450	2030	1680	1395	1160
50	3091	2477	2058	1704	1420	1183
60	3125	2507	2084	1730	1442	1204
80	3196	2570	2134	1784	1491	1258
100	3264	2631	2185	1832	1533	1292
150	3432	2775	2308	1947	1647	1403
200	3596	2918	2435	2061	1760	1510
250	3761	3065	2556	2173	1868	1617
300	3935	3210	2680	2289	1978	1724
400	4270	3508	2986	2514	2190	1925
500	4613	3814	3199	2744	2400	2120

p, atm \ t, °C →	175	200	225	234,8	250	275
1	96.5	101.4	107.2	109.0	112.4	117.7
5	98.3	103.8	110.5	111.1	114.4	119.8
10	106.5	109.6	115.0	115.7	118.6	123.5
15	861.0	121.1	123.0	124.0	125.3	128.5
20	877.0	665.0	128.1	136.0	135.4	136.5
25	892.0	687.0	164.7	155.0	147.0	145.2
28	901.0	700.0	480.0	175.0	161.0	157.0
29.62	905.0	711.0	507.0	272.0	173.0	160.0
35	922.0	729.0	548.0	460.0	259.0	190.0
40	936.0	748.0	578.0	505.0	348.0	239.0
50	960.0	775.0	622.0	563.0	448.0	320.0
60	988.0	809.0	658.0	604.0	507.0	384.0

continued

p, atm \ t, °C →	175	200	225	234.8	250	275
80	1038	865.0	717.0	668.0	583.0	466.0
100	1084	918.0	768.0	721.0	643.0	525.0
150	1198	1026	881.0	834.0	758.0	650.6
200	1296	1124	975.0	924.0	853.0	745.0
250	1395	1295	1067	1020	947.0	835.0
300	1495	1307	1150	1105	1029	923.0
400	1684	1478	1313	1259	1181	1068
500	1864	1640	1463	1404	1319	1195

Thermal conductivity $\lambda \cdot 10^3$ (W/m · deg) of liquid and gaseous n-hexane [15]

t, °C \ p, bar →	1	20	50	100	150	200	300	400	500
0	132	133	135	137	139	141	145	150	154
20	126	127	129	132	134	136	140	144	149
40	120	121	124	126	128	130	135	139	143
60	114	116	118	121	123	125	130	134	138
80	18.3	110	113	115	118	120	125	130	134
100	20.5	106	109	111	114	116	121	126	130
120	22.8	101	103	106	109	111	117	122	126
140	25.1	97	99	102	105	108	114	119	124
160	27.5	92	95	98	101	105	112	117	122
180	30.0	87	92	95	99	103	109	115	120
200	32.5	81	87	92	96	99	106	112	117
220	35.1	39.3	83	89	93	97	104	110	115
240	37.8	41.0	77	86	91	95	102	108	113
260	40.5	43.4	69	83	89	94	101	107	112
280	43.2	45.5	62.0	80	87	92	99	105	111
300	46.1	48.3	58.8	78	86	91	98	104	110
320	49.0	51.2	59.3	77	85	90			
340	51.9	54.0	60.6	76	84	89			
360	54.9	56.9	62.6	76	83	88			

Surface tension σ (N/m) of n-hexane [64]

t, °C	$\sigma \cdot 10^3$	t, °C	$\sigma \cdot 10^3$	t, °C	$\sigma \cdot 10^3$	t, °C	$\sigma \cdot 10^3$
0	20.56	60	14.23	120	8.34	180	3.16
10	19.51	70	13.20	130	7.42	190	2.43
20	18.46	80	12.24	140	6.51	200	1.74
30	17.40	90	11.22	150	5.62	210	1.12
40	16.31	100	10.27	160	4.74	220	0.58
50	15.26	110	9.31	170	3.92		

n-HEPTANE (C_7H_{16})

$CH_3(CH_2)_5CH_3$

Molecular weight 100.198

t_{boil} = 98.43 °C at 760 mm Hg; t_{melt} = −90.59 °C; t_{cr} = 267.01 °C;
p_{cr} = 27.36 bar; ρ_{cr} = 235 kg/m³

Thermodynamic properties of *n*-heptane [62] : $c_p{}^0$ (kJ/kg · deg), i^0 (kJ/kg) and s^0 (kJ/kg · deg)

T, °K	$c_p{}^0$	i^0	s^0	T, °K	$c_p{}^0$	i^0	s^0
0	0	0	0	900	3.621	1989.5	7.1377
298.16	1.657	318.2	4.2716	1000	3.811	2361.4	7.5296
300	1.665	321.2	4.2825	1100	3.977	2751.2	7.9010
400	2.107	509.9	4.8222	1200	4.120	3156.9	8.9553
500	2.510	741.4	5.3370	1300	4.245	3575.5	8.5896
600	2.855	1009.2	5.8237	1400	4.349	4005.4	8.9075
700	3.149	1309.3	6.2858	1500	4.445	4444.6	9.2108
800	3.402	1637.8	6.7245				

Saturated vapor pressure of *n*-heptane [65]

t, °C	p, mm Hg	t, °C	p, mm Hg	t, °C	p, bar	t, °C	p, bar
−70	0.0186	20	35.43	100	1.0606	190	8.14
−60	0.0661	25	45.71	110	1.4061	200	9.71
−50	0.202	30	58.37	120	1.8330	210	11.51
−40	0.542	40	92.50	130	2.353	220	13.54
−30	1.31	50	141.62	140	2.979	230	15.86
−20	2.90	60	210.24	150	3.724	240	18.47
−10	5.93	70	303.63	160	4.599	250	21.38
0	11.37	80	427.78	170	5.60	260	24.65
10	20.58	90	589.37	180	6.78	267.01	27.36

Specific volume $v \cdot 10^3$ (m³ kg) of liquid *n*-heptane at high pressures [355]

p, bar \ t, °C →	30	50	100	150	200	250	300
0	1.4808	1.5191	1.6325	1.7897	2.0753	3.3368	
50	1.4699	1.5055	1.6091	1.7427	1.9361	2.2226	2.5866
100	1.4600	1.4937	1.5881	1.7072	1.8618	2.0654	2.3166
200	1.4423	1.4728	1.5561	1.6511	1.7707	1.9110	2.0788
300	1.4266	1.4548	1.5300	1.6134	1.7110	1.8215	1.9339
500	1.4001	1.4246	1.4887	1.5574	1.6302	1.7109	1.7930
1000	1.3502	1.3695	1.4184	1.4687	1.5182	1.5713	1.6257
1500	1.3137	1.3299	1.3707	1.4111	1.4499	1.4903	1.5333
2000	1.2848	1.2988	1.3345	1.3682	1.4011	1.4332	1.4713
3000	1.2403	1.2525	1.2809	1.3084	1.3329	1.3569	1.3854
5000	1.1793	1.1887	1.2110	1.2305	1.2472	1.2641	1.2794

Density of liquid ρ' and of saturated vapor ρ''(kg/m³) of *n*-heptane [65, 71]

t, °C	$\varrho' \cdot 10^{-3}$	$\varrho'' \cdot 10^{-3}$	t, °C	$\varrho' \cdot 10^{-3}$	$\varrho'' \cdot 10^{3}$	t, °C	$\varrho' \cdot 10^{-3}$	$\varrho'' \cdot 10^{-3}$
−90	0.7731		−40	0.7335		10	0.6920	0.00010
−80	0.7653		−30	0.7254		20	0.6836	0.00020
−70	0.7574		−20	0.7172		30	0.6751	0.0003
−60	0.7495		−10	0.7090		40	0.6665	0.0005
−50	0.7415		0	0.7005	0.00007	50	0.6579	0.0007

continued

t, °C	$\varrho' \cdot 10^{-3}$	$\varrho'' \cdot 10^{-3}$	t, °C	$\varrho' \cdot 10^{-3}$	$\varrho'' \cdot 10^{-3}$	t, °C	$\varrho' \cdot 10^{-3}$	$\varrho'' \cdot 10^{-3}$
60	0.6491	0.0011	160	0.5481	0.01511	250	0.3877	0.09461
70	0.6402	0.001460	170	0.5359	0.01848	256	0.3664	0.1117
80	0.6311	0.002000	180	0.5232	0.02242	260	0.3457	0.1287
90	0.6218	0.002703	190	0.5066	0.02711	262	0.3332	0.1397
100	0.6124	0.003597	200	0.4952	0.03304	264	0.3166	0.1538
110	0.6027	0.004706	210	0.4793	0.04005	265	0.3059	0.1631
120	0.5926	0.006075	220	0.4616	0.04892	266	0.2907	0.1778
130	0.5821	0.007764	230	0.4414	0.06002	266.5	0.2819	0.1895
140	0.5711	0.009785	240	0.4177	0.07446	266.56	0.2341	0.2341
150	0.5598	0.01222						

Heat capacity c_p (kJ/kg · deg) of *n*-heptane [75, 76]

t, °C	c_p	t, °C	c_p	t, °C	c_p	t, °C	c_p	t, °C	c_p
−85	2.02	−10	2.13	35	2.282	100	2.57	180	3.01
−80	2.02	0	2.16	40	2.301	110	2.62	190	3.07
−70	2.02	5	2.172	45	2.322	120	2.67	200	3.14
−60	2.02	10	2.190	50	2.34	130	2.72	210	3.21
−50	2.03	15	2.207	60	2.39	140	2.78	220	3.30
−40	2.05	20	2.226	70	2.43	150	2.83	230	3.41
−30	2.07	25	2.244	80	2.47	160	2.89	240	3.56
−20	2.10	30	2.263	90	2.52	170	2.95		

Latent heat of vaporization r (kJ/kg) of *n*-heptane [65]

t, °C	r	t, °C	r	t, °C	r	t, °C	r	t, °C	r
−90	407.8	−10	379.4	60	342.6	130	295.4	200	224.4
−80	405.3	0	375.6	70	336.3	140	287.4	210	210.6
−70	402.3	10	371.0	80	330.1	150	278.7	220	194.3
−60	399.4	20	366.0	90	323.4	160	269.5	230	176.3
−50	396.5	30	360.6	100	316.7	170	259.5	240	159.2
−40	393.6	40	354.7	110	310.0	180	248.6	250	128.7
−30	391.1	50	348.4	120	302.9	190	236.9	260	90.24
−20	383.1								

Viscosity η (N · s/m²) of saturated *n*-heptane [68]

t, °C	$\eta' \cdot 10^7$	$\eta'' \cdot 10^7$	t, °C	$\eta' \cdot 10^7$	$\eta'' \cdot 10^7$	t, °C	$\eta' \cdot 10^7$	$\eta'' \cdot 10^7$
20	4140		110	1809	75.9	200	867	106
30	3730		120	1672	78.2	210	795	112
40	3380		130	1546	80.7	220	722	119
50	3080		140	1427	83.4	230	652	127
60	2810		150	1318	86.3	240	581	138
70	2600		160	1217	89.7	250	517	152
80	2390		170	1121	93.2	260	447	179
90	2170		180	1028	97.0	265	378	213
100	1980	73.6	190	945	101	266.88	271	271

Viscosity $\eta \cdot 10^7$ ($N \cdot s/m^2$) of *n*-heptane at different temperatures and pressures [68]

p, atm \ t, °C →	25	50	75	100	125	150
1	3883	3039	2417	73.3	78.4	83.3
5	3905	3055	2431	1964	1611	1320
10	3931	3073	2446	1978	1623	1332
15	3950	3089	2461	1994	1637	1344
20	3969	3111	2477	2008	1648	1355
23	3982	3123	2489	2013	1655	1363
25	3991	3127	2492	2020	1660	1368
27.15	3999	3134	2498	2025	1666	1372
30	4016	3151	2510	2034	1674	1380
35	4028	3174	2523	2048	1687	1393
40	4051	3185	2540	2064	1700	1406
50	4094	3220	2570	2091	1727	1434
60	4136	3255	2607	2121	1755	1458
80	4218	3327	2673	2174	1805	1508
100	4308	3406	2727	2245	1861	1559
150	4529	3586	2884	2377	1996	1683
200	4763	3778	3044	2520	2123	1803
250	5015	3974	3208	2651	2239	1924
300	5279	4170	3362	2787	2358	2032
400	5761	4555	3689	3065	2593	2244
500	6295	4952	4020	3345	2829	2446

p, atm \ t, °C →	175	200	225	250	260	266.96	275
1	88.5	93.4	98.6	103.7	104.9	107.1	108.8
5	92.5	96.5	101.1	106.0	106.0	109.4	111.0
10	1081	867	109.1	111.7	113.0	114.3	115.6
15	1097	887	692.0	123.8	123.4	123.5	123.5
20	1111	905	717.0	144.0	140.0	138.0	136.2
23	1117	911	732.0	531.0	159.5	152.4	146.5
25	1122	923	742.0	544.0	450.0	168.0	155.9
27.15	1128	929	749.0	558.0	472.0	271.1	173.0
30	1135	938	764.0	581.0	500.0	430.0	300.0
35	1148	949	781.0	608.0	536.0	480.0	413.0
40	1161	967	800.0	632.0	565.0	522.0	468.0
50	1186	997	830.0	676.0	616.0	578.0	531.0
60	1211	1025	862.0	712.0	655.0	619.0	576.0
80	1264	1075	914.0	770.0	717.0	682.5	648.0
100	1313	1124	962.0	823.5	772.0	740.0	702.0
150	1431	1245	1080	939.0	888.0	856.0	820.0
200	1542	1350	1181	1038	988.0	956.0	919.0
250	1649	1452	1277	1131	1080	1049	1011
300	1753	1553	1374	1223	1170	1135	1095
400	1953	1738	1549	1390	1333	1293	1255
500	2146	1915	1716	1550	1500	1453	1410

Viscosity η ($N \cdot s/m^2$) of liquid *n*-heptane at low temperatures [52]

t, °C	$\eta \cdot 10^3$	t, °C	$\eta \cdot 10^3$	t, °C	$\eta \cdot 10^3$	t, °C	$\eta \cdot 10^3$
−90	3.85	−60	1.46	−30	0.807	0	0.526
−80	2.57	−50	1.18	−20	0.689	10	0.466
−70	1.92	−40	0.965	−10	0.599	20	0.414

Thermal conductivity $\lambda \cdot 10^3$ (W/m · deg) of liquid and gaseous n-heptane [15]

t, °C \ p, bar →	1	20	50	100	150	200	300	400	500
0	134	135	136	139	141	142	146	150	154
20	129	131	132	134	136	138	142	146	150
40	123	125	127	129	131	134	138	142	146
60	118	120	122	124	126	129	134	138	142
80	113	115	117	119	122	124	129	133	138
100	18.8	110	112	115	117	120	125	129	134
120	20.9	106	108	111	114	117	122	127	131
140	23.2	101	104	107	110	113	119	124	128
160	25.5	97	100	104	107	110	116	121	126
180	27.8	94	97	101	105	108	114	119	124
200	30.2	90	94	98	102	106	112	117	123
220	32.6	85	91	96	100	104	110	116	121
240	35.1	79	87	93	98	102	109	115	120
260	37.7	42.4	83	90	96	100	107	113	119
280	40.3	43.9	77	87	94	98	106	112	117
300	43.0	46.1	71	85	92	97	104	110	116
320	45.7	48.5	65.6	83	91	96			
340	48.5	50.9	63.2	82	90	95			
360	51.4	53.3	63.2	81	89	94			

Thermal conductivity λ of liquid n-heptane at a pressure of 1 bar [15]

t, °C	−80	−60	−40	−20	0	20	40	60	80
$\lambda \cdot 10^3$, W/m · deg	156	151	145	140	134	129	123	118	113

Surface tension σ (N/m) of n-heptane [64]

t, °C	$\sigma \cdot 10^3$	t, °C	$\sigma \cdot 10^3$	t, °C	$\sigma \cdot 10^3$	t, °C	$\sigma \cdot 10^3$
20	20.86	80	14.35	140	8.87	200	4.07
30	19.54	90	13.42	150	8.02	210	3.34
40	18.47	100	12.47	160	7.19	220	2.63
50	17.42	110	11.54	170	6.38	230	1.94
60	16.39	120	10.63	180	5.59	240	1.29
70	15.38	130	9.74	190	4.82		

n-OCTANE (C_8H_{18})

$CH_3(CH_2)_6CH_3$

Molecular weight 114.224

$t_{boil} = 125.66$ °C at 760 mm Hg; $t_{melt} = -56.78$ °C; $t_{cr} = 296.2$ °C;
$p_{cr} = 24.96$ bar; $\rho_{cr} = 235$ kg/m³

Thermodynamic properties of n-octane [62] : $c_p{}^0$ (kJ/kg · deg), i^0 (kJ/kg) and s^0 (kJ/kg · deg)

T, °K	$c_p{}^0$	i^0	s^0	T, °K	$c_p{}^0$	i^0	s^0
0	0	0	0	900	3.608	1982.6	6.9478
298.16	1.655	315.6	4.0894	1000	3.798	2352.8	7.3386
300	1.663	318.6	4.1001	1100	3.959	2741.1	7.7089
400	2.103	506.9	4.6390	1200	4.099	3145.4	8.0615
500	2.505	738.0	5.1529	1300	4.223	3561.9	8.3944
600	2.847	1005.2	5.6383	1400	4.330	3990.1	8.7108
700	3.140	1304.4	6.0991	1500	4.421	4426.7	9.0125
800	3.391	1631.8	6.5365				

Saturated vapor pressure of n-octane [65]

t, °C	p, mm Hg	t, °C	p, mm Hg	t, °C	p, bar	t, °C	p, bar
−30	0.237	50	50.36	130	1.1408	220	7.826
−20	0.593	60	78.67	140	1.4839	230	9.270
−10	1.35	70	119.03	150	1.9022	240	10.92
0	2.86	80	175.04	160	2.406	250	12.79
10	5.63	90	250.84	170	3.006	260	14.91
20	10.46	100	351.22	180	3.712	270	17.29
25	13.98	110	481.50	190	4.536	280	19.97
30	18.45	120	647.60	200	5.488	290	22.94
40	31.10			210	6.582	296.2	24.96

Density of liquid ρ' and of saturated vapor ρ'' (kg/m³) of n-octane [65, 71]

t, °C	$\varrho' \cdot 10^{-3}$	$\varrho'' \cdot 10^{-3}$	t, °C	$\varrho' \cdot 10^{-3}$	$\varrho'' \cdot 10^{-3}$	t, °C	$\varrho' \cdot 10^{-3}$	$\varrho'' \cdot 10^{-3}$
0	0.7185		100	0.6351	0.0017	200	0.5317	0.01965
10	0.7102		110	0.6260	0.0023	210	0.5189	0.02364
20	0.7022		120	0.6168	0.003247	220	0.5053	0.02874
30	0.6942	0.0001	130	0.6071	0.004219	230	0.4901	0.03484
40	0.6860	0.0002	140	0.5973	0.005405	240	0.4732	0.04237
50	0.6778	0.0003	150	0.5875	0.006863	250	0.4554	0.05118
60	0.6694	0.0004	160	0.5772	0.008591	260	0.4364	0.06223
70	0.6611	0.0006	170	0.5667	0.01071	270	0.4123	0.07716
80	0.6525	0.0009	180	0.5556	0.01316	280	0.3818	0.09833
90	0.6438	0.0013	190	0.5441	0.01613	290	0.3365	0.1346
						296.2	0.2327	0.2327

Specific volume $v \cdot 10^3$ (m³/kg) of liquid n-octane at different temperatures and pressures [66]

p, bar \ t, °C →	100	140	180	200	220	240	260	280
20	1.561	1.657	1.777	1.852	1.947	2.067	2.235	2.505
30	1.556	1.650	1.765	1.837	1.924	2.033	2.180	2.402
40	1.552	1.643	1.754	1.822	1.904	2.003	2.133	2.319
50	1.548	1.637	1.745	1.809	1.886	1.977	2.093	2.253
60	1.544	1.631	1.736	1.797	1.869	1.954	2.059	2.198
70	1.540	1.626	1.727	1 785	1.854	1.933	2.029	2.152
80	1.537	1.620	1.719	1.775	1.840	1.914	2.003	2.113
90	1.533	1.616	1.711	1.765	1.827	1.897	1.979	2.079
100	1.529	1.611	1.703	1.755	1.815	1.882	1.958	2.049
110	1.526	1.606	1.696	1.747	1.804	1.867	1.939	2.024
120	1.523	1.602	1.690	1.739	1.794	1.853	1.922	2.000
130	1.520	1.597	1.683	1.731	1.784	1.842	1.907	1.979
140	1.516	1.593	1.677	1.724	1.776	1.831	1.893	1.961
150	1.513	1.589	1.672	1.717	1.768	1.821	1.879	1.944
160	1.511	1.585	1.666	1.710	1.760	1.811	1.867	1.929
170	1.508	1.581	1.661	1.704	1.753	1.802	1.856	1.916
180	1.505	1.578	1.656	1.699	1.746	1.794	1.846	1.903
190	1.502	1.574	1.652	1.693	1.739	1.786	1.836	1.892
200	1.500	1.572	1.647	1.688	1.733	1.779	1.828	1.881

Heat capacity c_p of liquid n-octane [76, 77]

t, °C	−50	−40	−30	−20	−10	0	10	15	20	25	30	35
c_p, kJ/kg	2.02	2.03	2.06	2.08	2.11	2.14	2.173	2.189	2.205	2.223	2.241	2.260

Latent heat of vaporization r (kJ/kg) of n-octane [65]

t, °C	r	t, °C	r	t, °C	r	t, °C	r	t, °C	r
−50	388.9	20	365.5	90	327.0	160	277.1	230	209.3
−40	387.5	30	361.1	100	320.4	170	268.7	240	196.1
−30	384.2	40	356.3	110	313.8	180	261.0	250	181.5
−20	380.9	50	351.2	120	306.8	190	252.2	260	164.6
−10	377.2	60	345.7	130	299.5	200	242.7	270	145.2
0	373.6	70	339.8	140	292.2	210	232.4	280	121.0
10	369.5	80	333.6	150	284.8	220	221.4	290	80.65

Coefficient of thermal expansion $\alpha \cdot 10^5$ (deg^{-1}) of liquid n-octane [66]

p, atm \ t, °C →	100	160	200	240	280
20	138	174	225	339	700
40	133	163	201	280	485
60	129	154	183	239	365
80	126	146	169	209	291
100	122	139	157	188	242
150	116	127	138	153	176
200	111	119	128	133	144

Isothermal coefficient of compressibility $\beta \cdot 10^6$ (atm^{-1}) of liquid n-octane [66]

p, atm \ t, °C →	100	160	200	240	280
20	288	527	892	1770	4730
40	269	473	762	1400	3170
60	253	428	663	1130	2280
80	240	388	581	939	1720
100	224	355	510	793	1340
150	196	286	386	544	814
200	173	237	317	396	539

Temperature coefficient of pressure $\gamma \cdot 10^5$ (deg^{-1}) of liquid n-octane [66]

p, atm \ t, °C →	100	160	200	240	280
20	24 031	16 463	12 595	9576	7401
40	12 388	8 597	6 594	5001	3821
60	8 509	5 978	4 610	3508	2662
80	6 568	4 694	3 642	2786	2109
100	5 448	3 929	3 086	2368	1800
120	4 676	3 431	2 716	2117	1608
140	4 161	3 099	2 471	1938	1488
160	3 746	2 845	2 304	1822	1413
180	3 455	2 649	2 167	1740	1365
200	3 213	2 509	2 017	1685	1337

Viscosity η (N · s/m²) of saturated n-octane [68]

t, °C	$\eta' \cdot 10^7$	$\eta'' \cdot 10^7$	t, °C	$\eta' \cdot 10^7$	$\eta'' \cdot 10^7$	t, °C	$\eta' \cdot 10^7$	$\eta'' \cdot 10^7$
−60	24 700		70	3250		200	1090	92.6
−50	18 300		80	2980		210	1000	96.3
−40	14 300		90	2750		220	920	101
−30	11 600		100	2560		230	840	106
−20	9 670		110	2340		240	767	112
−10	8 290		120	2140		250	696	119
0	7 140		130	1940	74.5	260	627	127
10	6 220		140	1768	76.6	270	561	138
20	5 460		150	1633	78.7	280	492	152
30	4 860		160	1507	80.9	290	411	180
40	4 350		170	1391	83.3	296.2	264	264
50	3 920		180	1283	86.0			
60	3 560		190	1184	89.1			

Viscosity $\eta \cdot 10^7$ (N · s/m²) of n-octane at different temperatures and pressures [68]

p, atm \ t, °C →	50	75	100	125	150	175
1	3830	3043	2440	1982	77.7	82.1
5	3850	3062	2453	1998	1647	1348
10	3873	3079	2470	2014	1661	1364
15	3895	3100	2490	2033	1680	1375
20	3917	3117	2506	2048	1695	1395
22	3930	3128	2512	2055	1704	1405
24.97	3940	3138	2524	2066	1720	1415
30	3964	3156	2540	2084	1733	1429
35	3986	3174	2557	2100	1750	1446
40	4006	3193	2574	2118	1766	1461
50	4052	3233	2610	2150	1800	1496
60	4097	3271	2645	2186	1833	1528
80	4180	3350	2716	2254	1898	1583
100	4267	3429	2786	2313	1960	1648
150	4487	3624	2967	2494	2114	1790
200	4718	3826	3152	2661	2265	1938
250	4958	4025	3338	2838	2413	2080
300		4231	3523	2990	2562	2186
400		4658	3886	3321	2856	2375
500		5071	4265	3650	3150	2700

p, atm \ t, °C →	200	225	250	275	285	296.2
1	86.7	91.5	96.1	100.7	102.5	104.5
5	91.5	95.1	99.3	102.3	105.2	107.0
10	1119	886	109.3	111.2	112.3	113.2
15	1136	905	128.0	126.3	125.2	124.0
20	1152	926	729	127.5	150.0	142.3
22	1155	936	738	554	461	155.2
24.97	1158	945	751	584	480	264.5
30	1185	966	771	602	520	422
35	1203	985	790	629	552	469
40	1217	1004	810	653	582	504
50	1247	1037	841	694	627	558
60	1279	1068	881	732	670	605
80	1339	1136	945	795	734	670
100	1397	1192	1066	857	794	735
150	1525	1321	1139	976	917	857

continued

p, bar ↓ / t, °C →	200	225	250	275	285	296.2
200	1645	1436	1259	1088	1029	869
250	1762	1546	1353	1187	1124	1065
300	1873	1649	1451	1282	1221	1159
400	2095	1847	1645	1465	1402	1335
500	2308	2050	1822	1643	1569	1501

Thermal conductivity $\lambda \cdot 10^3$ (W/m · deg) of liquid and gaseous *n*-octane [15]

t, °C ↓ / p, bar →	1	20	50	100	150	200	300	400	500
0	137	138	139	141	143	145	148	151	155
20	132	133	134	136	138	140	144	147	150
40	126	128	129	131	133	135	139	142	146
60	121	123	124	126	128	130	134	138	142
80	116	118	119	121	124	126	130	134	138
100	111	112	114	116	119	121	126	130	134
120	106	107	110	112	115	118	123	127	131
140	21.4	104	107	109	113	116	121	125	129
160	23.6	101	104	107	111	114	119	124	129
180	25.8	98	101	105	109	112	118	123	127
200	28.0	95	98	103	106	110	116	121	126
220	30.4	91	95	100	105	109	115	120	125
240	32.8	87	92	98	103	107	113	119	124
260	35.2	82	89	96	101	105	112	117	123
280	37.7	73	84	93	98	103	109	115	121
300	40.2	44.7	79	90	96	101	107	113	119
320	42.8	45.9	73	88	95	100			
340	45.4	48.2	68	85	93	98			
360	48.0	50.4	65	83	91	96			

Thermal conductivity λ of liquid *n*-octane at a pressure of 1 bar [15]

t, °C	−40	−20	0	20	40	60	80	100	120
$\lambda \cdot 10^3$, W/m · deg	148	142	137	132	126	121	116	111	106

Surface tension σ (N/m) of *n*-octane [64]

t, °C	$\sigma \cdot 10^3$	t, °C	$\sigma \cdot 10^3$	t, °C	$\sigma \cdot 10^3$	t, °C	$\sigma \cdot 10^3$
−40	27.5	40	19.78	110	13.25	180	7.50
−30	26.52	50	18.79	120	12.39	190	6.74
−20	25.55	60	17.82	130	11.54	200	5.99
−10	24.59	70	16.87	140	10.70	210	5.25
0	23.70	80	15.94	150	9.88	220	4.52
10	22.73	90	15.03	160	9.07	230	3.80
20	21.76	100	14.13	170	8.28	240	3.10
30	20.79						

2, 2, 4-TRIMETHYLPENTANE (ISOOCTANE) (C_8H_{18})

$$CH_3-\overset{\overset{CH_3}{|}}{\underset{\underset{CH_3}{|}}{C}}-CH_2-\overset{\overset{CH_3}{|}}{CH}-CH_3$$

Molecular weight 114.224

$t_{boil} = 99.24$ °C at 760 mm Hg; $t_{melt} = -107.38$°C; $t_{cr} = 271.1$ °C;
$p_{cr} = 25.83$ bar; $\rho_{cr} = 237$ kg/m³

Thermodynamic properties of isooctane [62]: i^0 (kJ/kg) and s^0 (kJ/kg · deg)

T, °K	i^0	s^0	T, °K	i^0	s^0
0	0	0	600	985.4	5.312
298.16	270.7	3.7082	700	1295.6	5.785
300	273.6	3.7177	800	1627.7	6.229
400	467.4	4.282	900	1983.7	6.650
500	707.2	4.813	1000	2360.9	7.050

Saturated vapor pressure p of isooctane [65]

t, °C	p, mm Hg	t, °C	p, mm Hg	t, °C	p, bar	t, °C	p, bar	t, °C	p, bar
−30	1.65	30	62.41	100	1.0350	170	5.219	240	16.77
−20	3.51	40	97.20	110	1.3600	180	6.321	250	19.36
−10	6.97	50	146.51	120	1.7585	190	7.518	260	22.25
0	12.99	60	241.47	130	2.241	200	8.935	270	25.45
10	22.93	70	305.83	140	2.817	210	10.55	271.1	25.83
20	38.63	80	425.93	150	3.498	220	12.38		
25	49.34	90	580.68	160	4.295	230	14.45		

Heat capacity c_p (kJ/kg · deg) of liquid isooctane [76, 77]

t, °C	c_p	t, °C	c_p	t, °C	c_p	t, °C	c_p
−100	1.63	−50	1.78	−10	1.94	20	2.067
−90	1.66	−40	1.82	0	1.98	25	2.088
−80	1.68	−30	1.86	10	2.024	30	2.111
−70	1.71	−20	1.90	15	2.043	35	2.134
−60	1.75						

Latent heat of vaporization r (kJ/kg) of isooctane [65]

t, °C	r	t, °C	r	t, °C	r	t, °C	r	t, °C	r
−100	349.4	−20	324.1	60	292.2	140	246.4	210	182.9
−90	346.4	−10	320.4	70	287.4	150	239.0	220	170.1
−80	343.1	0	317.1	80	282.6	160	231.3	230	155.8
−70	340.2	10	313.4	90	277.5	170	222.9	240	139.3
−60	336.9	20	309.4	100	272.0	180	214.1	250	119.1
−50	334.0	30	305.4	110	266.2	190	204.6	260	92.02
−40	330.7	40	301.3	120	259.9	200	194.3	270	36.66
−30	327.4	50	296.9	130	253.3				

Density ρ (kg/m³) of saturated isooctane [45]

t, °C	ϱ′	ϱ″	t, °C	ϱ′	ϱ″	t, °C	ϱ′	ϱ″
−90	781.5		40	675.9	0.538	170	545.4	18.08
−80	773.3		50	667.4	0.795	180	532.7	22.00
−70	765.1		60	658.4	1.124	190	519.4	26.50
−60	757.0		70	649.5	1.548	200	504.3	32.21
−50	748.9		80	640.0	2.086	210	487.8	39.27
−40	740.7		90	630.8	2.815	220	470.6	47.62
−30	732.6		100	621.2	3.703	230	451.7	57.58
−20	724.3		110	611.2	4.833	240	430.0	70.63
−10	716.2		120	600.9	6.160	250	403.1	88.29
0	708.1	0.0823	130	590.7	7.799	260	366.7	113.20
10	700.0	0.139	140	580.1	9.747	270	290.5	186.00
20	692.4	0.225	150	569.2	12.06	271.1	236.0	236.0
30	684.1	0.350	160	557.9	14.84			

Density ρ (kg/m³) of isooctane at different temperatures and pressures [45]

p, bar \ T, °K →	290	300	320	340	360	380	400	420	440
1	695.1	687.0	670.0	652.4	634.0				
2	695.2	687.2	670.1	652.5	634.2	614.5			
5	695.5	687.4	670.5	653.0	634.9	615.5	595.3	574.0	549.6
10	696.0	687.8	671.0	653.6	635.8	616.8	597.3	576.7	553.2
20	696.9	688.7	672.0	655.0	637.9	619.5	600.7	580.7	558.7
30	697.7	689.5	673.0	656.4	639.7	621.9	603.4	583.7	562.7
40	698.5	690.5	674.0	657.6	641.4	624.0	605.9	586.7	566.3
60	700.4	692.3	676.2	660.2	644.4	627.7	610.5	592.0	572.8
80	702.1	694.0	678.2	662.6	647.2	631.3	614.5	596.8	578.5
100	703.7	695.8	680.4	665.0	649.9	634.5	618.0	601.1	583.7
120	705.3	697.5	682.5	667.3	652.5	637.5	621.5	605.0	588.4
140	706.9	699.4	684.5	669.6	655.2	640.3	624.5	608.8	592.6
160	708.5	701.1	686.5	672.0	657.6	643.0	627.9	612.6	596.9
180	710.0	702.9	688.6	674.2	660.0	645.6	631.0	616.0	600.8
200	711.6	704.5	690.6	676.5	662.5	648.3	634.0	619.1	604.6
250	715.7	709.0	695.9	682.0	668.5	654.4	640.9	626.7	613.0
300	719.3	712.9	700.0	687.0	674.0	660.2	647.0	633.5	620.3
350	722.5	716.2	703.9	691.4	678.7	665.7	652.5	639.5	626.7
400	725.6	719.5	707.5	695.4	683.2	670.7	657.7	644.9	632.8
450	728.5	722.5	711.0	699.1	687.4	675.0	662.5	650.1	638.5
500	731.0	725.5	714.2	702.9	691.2	679.3	667.0	655.3	643.9

p, bar \ T, °C →	460	480	500	520	540	545	550	560	570
10	527.0								
20	534.5	506.7	472.3	420.9					
30	539.7	514.3	483.6	445.3	387.0	366.9	336.3	247.5	172.5
40	544.2	520.1	492.4	460.0	418.2	405.5	388.7	352.5	318.0
50	548.3	525.4	499.7	470.7	435.7	425.7	414.3	391.1	364.3
60	552.0	530.3	506.2	479.4	449.0	440.3	431.5	413.1	390.7
80	559.3	538.9	517.0	493.6	468.1	461.4	454.7	440.3	424.7
100	565.5	546.4	526.3	505.2	482.4	476.6	470.6	458.4	445.5
120	571.1	553.0	534.3	514.9	494.0	488.7	483.3	472.3	461.3
140	576.3	559.0	541.3	523.3	504.0	498.8	493.8	483.8	473.2
160	580.9	564.4	547.5	530.6	512.7	507.7	503.2	493.9	484.0
180	585.4	569.5	553.5	537.3	520.3	515.8	511.4	502.5	493.4
200	589.5	574.2	558.9	543.4	527.2	522.9	518.7	510.6	501.7
250	598.8	584.6	570.6	556.5	542.2	538.5	534.9	527.4	519.6

continued

T, °K \ p, bar →	460	480	500	520	540	545	550	560	570
300	607.1	593.7	580.7	567.7	554.7	551.2	548.1	541.1	534.3
350	614.5	602.1	589.8	577.4	565.3	562.0	559.0	552.8	546.5
400	621.2	609.5	598.0	586.0	574.2	571.4	568.3	562.7	556.8
450	627.2	616.0	605.1	593.6	582.5	579.8	576.7	571.4	565.7
500	632.6	621.6	611.5	600.5	590.4	587.5	585.0	579.6	574.0

Viscosity η (N · s/m³) of saturated liquid isooctane [68]

t, °C	$\eta \cdot 10^7$	t, °C	$\eta \cdot 10^7$	t, °C	$\eta \cdot 10^7$	t, °C	$\eta \cdot 10^7$
100	2317	160	1455	210	972	260	536
110	2144	170	1349	220	886	265	472
120	1981	180	1249	230	805	268	420
130	1827	190	1153	240	723	270	370
140	1691	200	1060	250	635	271	287
150	1565						

Viscosity $\eta \cdot 10^7$ (N · s/m²) of liquid isooctane at different temperatures and pressures [68, 290]

t, °C \ p, kg/cm³ →	1	20	40	60	80	100	150	200	250	300	400	500
20	5080	5205	5332	5457	5592	5722	6068	6410	6760	7122	7858	8640
50	3588	3682	3785	3887	3985	4100	4357	4610	4875	5125	5650	6180
75	8243	2935	3025	3112	3200	3290	3505	3717	3927	4160	4550	4975
100		2395	2467	2542	2620	2695	2887	3075	3270	3445	3825	4200
125		1965	2040	2112	2182	2255	2435	2605	2760	2927	3255	3580
150		1625	1695	1765	1832	1902	2067	2212	2360	2510	2802	3095
175		1352	1427	1492	1560	1620	1775	1922	2067	2207	2470	2737
200		1115	1195	1268	1335	1402	1545	1682	1820	1950	2190	2430
225		882	985	1058	1125	1190	1340	1472	1600	1720	1952	2182
250		648	788	880	950	1020	1162	1292	1410	1525	1738	1950
260			700	805	882	952	1098	1227	1348	1455	1660	1863
265			662	770	850	920	1070	1195	1315	1425	1627	1825
268			638	753	830	905	1052	1178	1295	1405	1608	1805
271.1			617	735	812	885	1035	1160	1280	1390	1590	1775
275			580	710	792	865	1015	1138	1258	1367	1567	1763

Thermal conductivity $\lambda \cdot 10^4$ (W/m · deg) of isooctane [45]

T, °K \ p, bar →	1	5	10	15	20	25	30	35	40
290	983	984	986	987	989	990	992	993	995
300	961	962	964	966	967	969	971	972	974
310	937	939	941	943	945	947	949	951	953
320	914	916	918	920	922	925	927	929	931
330	889	892	894	896	899	901	904	907	909
340	865	867	870	873	876	878	881	884	887
350	841	843	846	849	852	855	858	861	864
360	818	820	823	826	829	832	835	838	842
370	793	796	799	802	805	809	812	816	819

continued

T, °K \ p, bar →	1	5	10	15	20	25	30	35	40
380	210	775	778	781	785	789	792	796	799
390	220	756	760	763	766	770	773	777	780
400	230	740	743	746	749	753	757	760	763
410	241	725	729	732	735	737	741	745	748
420	252	711	714	717	720	723	727	731	734
430	263	696	700	703	707	710	714	717	720
440	274	683	687	691	694	698	702	705	709
450	284		675	679	683	686	690	694	697
460	295		663	667	671	675	679	683	686
470	306		652	656	660	664	668	672	676
480	317			647	651	655	659	663	667
490	329			638	642	646	651	655	659
500	340	345		631	636	640	645	649	653
520	363	368			623	628	632	637	642
540	387	392	400	412	438		622	626	630
560	414	418	422	430	441	470	575	606	611
580	444	447	451	456	466	480			

T, °K \ p, bar →	45	50	75	100	150	200	300	400	500
290	996	998	1006	1014	1030	1047	1079	1110	1140
300	976	978	987	996	1013	1030	1064	1096	1126
310	955	957	967	977	995	1013	1048	1082	1112
320	934	936	946	957	976	996	1032	1067	1099
330	912	914	926	937	958	978	1017	1053	1085
340	890	892	905	917	939	961	1000	1038	1071
350	867	869	884	897	921	943	985	1023	1058
360	845	847	862	877	902	926	969	1008	1044
370	822	825	842	857	883	908	953	994	1030
380	802	805	821	837	865	891	938	979	1016
390	783	786	803	819	847	875	923	964	1002
400	766	769	785	801	831	859	909	950	989
410	751	754	770	786	815	844	895	937	976
420	737	740	755	771	801	830	882	924	963
430	724	727	742	759	789	817	870	912	951
440	712	715	731	747	777	806	858	900	940
450	700	704	720	736	767	795	846	889	930
460	690	693	710	726	757	785	836	879	920
470	680	683	701	717	748	776	827	870	912
480	671	674	693	710	740	768	819	863	904
490	663	667	686	703	734	762	812	857	898
500	657	661	680	697	728	756	806	851	892
520	646	650	669	687	719	748	798	843	883
540	635	639	659	678	711	741	792	837	878
560	616	621	644	663	699	729	781	826	868
580		590	615	639	675	706	760		

Surface tension σ of isooctane [62]

t, °C	0	10	20	25	30	40	50	60	70	80	90
$\sigma \cdot 10^3$, N/m	20.58	19.67	18.77	18.32	17.88	16.99	16.11	15.24	14.4	13.5	12.7

n-NONANE (C_9H_{20})

$CH_3(CH_2)_7CH_3$

Molecular weight 128.250

t_{boil} = 150.79 °C at 760 mm Hg; t_{melt} = – 53.50 °C; t_{cr} =322 °C;
p_{cr} = 22.88 bar; ρ_{cr} = 236 kg/m³

Thermodynamic properties of n-nonane [62] : $c_p{}^0$ (kJ/kg · deg), i^0 (kJ/kg) and s^0 (kJ/kg · deg)

T, °K	$c_p{}^0$	i^0	s^0	T, °K	$c_p{}^0$	i^0	s^0
0	0	0	0	900	3.597	1976.4	6.7984
298.16	1.652	313.5	3.9461	1000	3.784	2345.9	7.1876
300	1.660	316.6	3.9569	1100	3.944	2732.5	7.5565
400	2.099	504.6	4.4949	1200	4.085	3135.7	7.9082
500	2.500	735.3	5.0075	1300	4.209	3550.4	8.2396
600	2.841	1001.8	5.4921	1400	4.313	3976.8	8.5550
700	3.132	1300.2	5.9518	1500	4.404	4411.7	8.8553
800	3.381	1627.0	6.3880				

Saturated vapor pressure of n-nonane [65]

t, °C	p, mm Hg	t, °C	p, mm Hg	t, °C	p, bar
−20	0.117	70	47.29	160	1.2846
−10	0.301	80	72.71	170	1.6410
0	0.705	90	108.53	180	2.070
10	1.53	100	157.76	190	2.579
20	3.08	110	223.88	200	3.179
30	5.84	120	310.87	210	3.879
40	10.51	130	423.19	220	4.689
50	18.06	140	565.80	230	5.618
60	29.77	150	744.06	322	22.8

Heat capacity c_p (kJ/kg · deg) of liquid n-nonane [76, 77]

t, °C	c_p	t, °C	c_p	t, °C	c_p	t, °C	c_p
−45	2.05	−10	2.10	15	2.181	35	2.250
−40	2.05	0	2.13	20	2.197	40	2.270
−30	2.06	5	2.151	25	2.214	45	2.290
−20	2.08	10	2.166	30	2.232		

Latent heat of vaporization r (kJ/kg) of n-nonane [65]

t, °C	r	t, °C	r	t, °C	r	t, °C	r
−50	386.6	50	349.7	150	296.1	240	225.3
−40	383.6	60	345.1	160	290.3	250	213.8
−30	380.4	70	340.5	170	282.7	260	201.4
−20	377.1	80	335.6	180	276.9	270	187.7
−10	373.5	90	330.7	190	269.7	280	172.4
0	369.9	100	325.5	200	262.2	290	154.4
10	366.0	110	320.3	210	254.0	300	133.2
20	362.1	120	314.7	220	245.2	310	104.8
30	357.8	130	309.2	230	236.7	320	43.75
40	353.6	140	301.7				

Specific volume $v \cdot 10^3$ (m^3/kg) of liquid *n*-nonane at high pressures [355]

p, bar \ t, °C →	30	50	100	150	200	250	300
0	1.4086	1.4401	1.5300	1.6411	1.7989	2.1166	3.9977
50	1.4002	1.4304	1.5137	1.6124	1.7425	1.9259	2.1931
100	1.3921	1.4210	1.5003	1.5889	1.6945	1.8434	2.0321
200	1.3776	1.4041	1.4752	1.5545	1.6418	1.7464	1.8778
300	1.3646	1.3892	1.4542	1.5246	1.5998	1.6844	1.7871
500	1.3423	1.3641	1.4203	1.4790	1.5415	1.6085	1.6785
1000	1.2995	1.3171	1.3609	1.4044	1.4485	1.4928	1.5405
1500	1.2677	1.2828	1.3195		1.3896	1.4235	1.4616
2000	1.2422	1.2556	1.2877		1.3474	1.3753	1.4098
3000	1.2025	1.2141	1.2399		1.2860	1.3077	1.3341
5000	1.1475	1.1558	1.1759		1.2087	1.2238	1.2393

Density ρ (kg/m^3) of liquid *n*-nonane [65]

t, °C	$\varrho \cdot 10^{-3}$	t, °C	$\varrho \cdot 10^{-3}$	t, °C	$\varrho \cdot 10^{-3}$	t, °C	$\varrho \cdot 10^{-3}$
−50	0.7716	10	0.7254	60	0.6855	120	0.6350
−40	0.7640	20	0.7176	70	0.6773	130	0.6263
−30	0.7563	25	0.7137	80	0.6690	140	0.6174
−20	0.7487	30	0.7098	90	0.6606	150	0.6084
−10	0.7410	40	0.7018	100	0.6522		
0	0.7332	50	0.6936	110	0.6436		

Viscosity η of *n*-nonane gas [52]

t, °C	0	50	75	100	150	200	250	300
$\eta \cdot 10^7$, $N \cdot s/m^2$	47.5	55.4	59.2	63.0	70.2	77.8	85.0	92.0

Viscosity η ($N \cdot s/m^2$) of liquid *n*-nonane [52]

t, °C	$\eta \cdot 10^3$	t, °C	$\eta \cdot 10^3$	t, °C	$\eta \cdot 10^3$
−10	1.146	50	0.495	110	0.284
0	0.968	60	0.445	120	0.264
10	0.827	70	0.403	130	0.244
20	0.714	80	0.366	140	0.228
30	0.628	90	0.335	150	0.213
40	0.555	100	0.308		

Thermal conductivity λ (W/m · deg) of liquid *n*-nonane [78, 79]

t, °C	λ	t, °C	λ	t, °C	λ	t, °C	λ	t, °C	λ
−40	0.1465	0	0.1364	40	0.1264	80	0.1162	120	0.1061
−20	0.1414	20	0.1315	60	0.1213	100	0.1111	140	0.1010

Surface tension σ of *n*-nonane [65]

t, °C	0	10	20	25	30	40	50	75	100
$\sigma \cdot 10^3$, N/m	24.84	23.90	22.96	22.49	22.01	21.07	20.13	17.78	15.42

n-DECANE ($C_{10}H_{22}$)

$CH_3(CH_2)_8CH_3$

Molecular weight 142.276

t_{boil} = 174.12 °C at 760 mm Hg; t_{melt} = − 29.65 °C; t_{cr} = 346 °C;
p_{cr} = 21.17 bar; ρ_{cr} = 236 kg/m³ [52]

Thermodynamic properties of n-decane [62] : $c_p{}^0$ (kJ/kg · deg), i^0 (kJ/kg) and s^0 (kJ/kg · deg)

T, °K	$c_p{}^0$	i^0	s^0	T, °K	$c_p{}^0$	i^0	s^0
0	0	0	0	900	3.5881	1971.7	6.6783
298.16	1.650	311.78	3.8309	1000	3.7729	2240.0	7.0664
300	1.658	314.78	3.8415	1100	3.935	2725.8	7.4340
400	2.096	501.19	4.3789	1200	4.073	3127.2	7.7848
500	2.496	732.95	4.8910	1300	4.194	3541.0	8.1150
600	2.659	999.09	5.3745	1400	4.300	3965.7	8.4296
700	3.1258	1297.0	5.8330	1500	4.391	4399.8	8.7289
800	3.3736	1622.9	6.2683				

Saturated vapor pressure of n-decane [65]

t, °C	p, mm Hg	t, °C	p, mm Hg	t, °C	p, bar
−10	0.065	90	47.47	180	1.1737
0	0.172	100	71.72	190	1.4921
10	0.409	110	105.46	200	1.8740
20	0.900	120	151.31	210	2.3274
30	1.84	130	212.32	220	2.8603
40	3.56	140	291.95	230	3.482
50	6.50	150	394.09	240	4.199
60	11.33	160	523.05	250	5.022
70	18.94	170	683.50	346	21.07
80	30.49				

Latent heat of vaporization r (kJ/kg) of n-decane [65]

t, °C	r	t, °C	r	t, °C	r	t, °C	r	t, °C	r
−20	375.8	60	339.9	140	298.7	210	257.5	280	195.4
−10	371.7	70	334.9	150	293.1	220	250.4	290	183.3
0	367.6	80	329.9	160	287.5	230	242.8	300	169.8
10	363.2	90	324.9	170	281.9	240	234.6	310	154.2
20	358.7	100	319.9	180	276.0	250	225.7	320	134.8
30	354.0	110	314.6	190	270.2	260	216.3	330	110.4
40	349.3	120	309.3	200	264.0	270	206.3	340	72.69
50	344.6	130	304.0						

Specific volume $v \cdot 10^3$ (m³/kg) of liquid n-decane [66]

p, atm \ t, °C →	40	60	70	80	90	100	110	120
20	1.389	1.419	1.435	1.452	1.469	1.488	1.507	1.528
30	1.386	1.416	1.432	1.449	1.465	1.484	1.502	1.522
40	1.384	1.414	1.429	1.445	1.462	1.480	1.497	1.517
50	1.382	1.411	1.426	1.442	1.458	1.476	1.493	1.512
60	1.380	1.409	1.423	1.440	1.455	1.472	1.489	1.508
70	1.378	1.407	1.421	1.437	1.452	1.469	1.486	1.504
80	1.377	1.405	1.419	1.434	1.450	1.466	1.482	1.500
90	1.375	1.403	1.417	1.432	1.447	1.463	1.479	1.497

continued

p, atm \ t, °C →	40	60	70	80	90	100	110	120
100	1.373	1.401	1.415	1.430	1.445	1.461	1.476	1.494
110	1.372	1.399	1.413	1.428	1.442	1.458	1.474	1.491
120	1.370	1.397	1.411	1.426	1.440	1.456	1.471	1.488
130	1.369	1.395	1.409	1.424	1.438	1.454	1.469	1.486
140	1.367	1.394	1.407	1.422	1.436	1.452	1.467	1.483
150	1.366	1.392	1.406	1.420	1.434	1.450	1.465	1.481
160	1.365	1.391	1.404	1.419	1.432	1.448	1.463	1.479
170	1.363	1.389	1.403	1.417	1.431	1.446	1.461	1.477
180	1.362	1.388	1.401	1.415	1.429	1.444	1.459	1.475
190	1.361	1.387	1.400	1.414	1.428	1.443	1.457	1.473
200	1.360	1.386	1.399	1.413	1.426	1.441	1.456	1.471

Density ρ (kg/m³) of liquid n-decane [65]

t, °C	$\varrho \cdot 10^{-3}$	t, °C	$\varrho \cdot 10^{-3}$	t, °C	$\varrho \cdot 10^{-3}$	t, °C	$\varrho \cdot 10^{-3}$
−20	0.7601	25	0.7261	80	0.6830	130	0.6419
−10	0.7526	30	0.7222	90	0.6749	140	0.6334
0	0.7451	40	0.7145	100	0.6668	150	0.6250
10	0.7375	50	0.7067	110	0.6586	160	0.6165
20	0.7299	60	0.6989	120	0.6503	170	0.6080
		70	0.6910				

Coefficient of thermal expansion $\alpha \cdot 10^6$ (deg⁻¹) of liquid n-decane [66]

p, atm \ t, °C →	40	60	80	100	120	p, atm \ t, °C →	40	60	80	100	120
20	1061	1116	1187	1268	1361	120	958	993	1033	1072	1109
40	1029	1082	1137	1209	1279	140	946	981	1017	1055	1087
60	1006	1052	1106	1157	1218	160	939	970	1006	1039	1071
80	939	1030	1074	1122	1171	180	930	961	995	1026	1057
100	970	1010	1051	1096	1138	200	925	956	987	1016	1043

Heat capacity c_p (kJ/kg · deg) of liquid n-decane [76, 77]

t, °C	c_p	t, °C	c_p	t, °C	c_p	t, °C	c_p
−20	2.08	5	2.147	20	2.190	35	2.242
−10	2.10	10	2.161	25	2.206	40	2.261
0	2.14	15	2.175	30	2.224	45	2.280

Isothermal coefficient of compressibility $\beta \cdot 10^7$ (cm²/kg) of liquid n-decane [66]

p, atm \ t, °C →	40	60	80	100	120	p, atm \ t, °C →	40	60	80	100	120
20	1652	1994	2454	3066	3909	120	1077	1211	1378	1551	1769
40	1490	1800	2136	2642	3243	140	997	1118	1238	1396	1557
60	1365	1615	1921	2249	2741	160	945	1029	1138	1249	1397
80	1264	1474	1694	1973	2328	180	870	944	1029	1109	1246
100	1160	1339	1524	1756	2040	200	822	889	950	1010	1102

Temperature coefficient of pressure $\gamma \cdot 10^5$ (deg^{-1}) of liquid *n*-decane [66]

p, atm \ t, °C →	40	60	80	100	120
20	32 129	27 988	24 178	20 682	17 409
40	17 270	15 033	13 313	11 441	9 857
60	12 276	10 853	9 592	8 575	7 408
80	9 780	8 732	7 926	7 108	6 285
100	8 365	7 542	6 898	6 238	5 581
120	7409	6832	6249	5757	5225
140	6779	6266	5866	5396	4986
160	6211	5894	5524	5201	4791
180	5940	5660	5371	5136	4712
200	5629	5379	5196	5032	4733

Viscosity η of liquid *n*-decane [52]

t, °C	−30	−20	−10	0	10	20
$\eta \cdot 10^3$, N·s/m²	2.51	1.93	1.55	1.27	1.07	0.907

Thermal conductivity λ of liquid *n*-decane [78, 79]

t, °C	−20	0	20	40	60	80	100	120	140	160
λ, W/m · deg	0.1446	0.1399	0.1351	0.1305	0.1257	0.1209	0.1162	0.1114	0.1066	0.1020

Surface tension σ of *n*-decane [65]

t, °C	0	10	20	25	30	40	50	75	100
$\sigma \cdot 10^3$, N/m	25.73	24.81	23.89	23.43	22.98	22.06	21.14	18.84	16.54

n-UNDECANE ($C_{11}H_{24}$)

$CH_3(CH_2)_9CH_3$

Molecular weight 156.302

t_{boil} = 195.98 °C at 760 mm Hg; t_{melt} = − 25.57 °C; t_{cr} = 367 °C;
p_{cr} = 19.45 bar; ρ_{cr} = 237 kg/m³

Thermodynamic properties of *n*-undecane [62] : c_p^0 (kJ/kg · deg), i^0 (kJ/kg) and s^0 (kJ/kg · deg)

T, °K	c_p°	i°	s°
0	0	0	0
298.16	1.648	310.42	3.7367
300	1.657	313.52	3.7471
400	2.094	501.08	4.2842
500	2.493	731.23	4.7957
600	2.8317	996.91	5.2784
700	3.1205	1294.3	5.7363
800	3.3672	1619.6	6.1708
900	3.5808	1967.7	6.5799
1000	3.767	2335.3	6.9673
1100	3.925	2720.3	7.3343
1200	4.064	3121.0	7.6842
1300	4.184	3533.6	8.0137
1400	4.286	3957.1	8.3274
1500	4.377	4390.3	8.6258

Saturated vapor pressure of *n*-undecane [65]

t, °C	p, mm Hg	t, °C	p, mm Hg	t, °C	p, mm Hg	t, °C	p, mm Hg	t, °C	p, bar
0	0.040	50	2.33	100	32.86	150	211.23	200	1.1193
10	0.107	60	4.31	110	50.12	160	287.37	210	1.4148
20	0.259	70	7.60	120	74.38	170	384.28	220	1.7681
30	0.576	80	12.85	130	107.67	180	505.80	230	2.186
40	1.20	90	20.90	140	152.37	190	656.13	367	19.4

Latent heat of vaporization r of liquid *n*-undecane [62]

t, °C	25	195.9
r, kJ/kg	360.70	265.76

Heat capacity c_p of liquid *n*-undecane [71]

t, °C	−15	0	10	20	25
c_p, kJ/kg · deg *ad*	2.11	2.14	2.16	2.18	2.19

Specific volume $v \cdot 10^3$ (m³/kg) of liquid *n*-undecane at high pressures [355]

p, bar \ t, °C →	30	50	100	150	200	250	300
0	1.3646	1.3928	1.4706	1.5634	1.6762	1.8565	2.4796
50	1.3572	1.3843	1.4576	1.5418	1.6455	1.7844	1.9837
100	1.3503	1.3762	1.4467	1.5236	1.6131	1.7308	1.8790
200	1.3376	1.3617	1.4255	1.4955	1.5708	1.6600	1.7680
300	1.3263	1.3488	1.4076	1.4702	1.5372	1.6116	1.6982
500	1.3065	1.3267	1.3782	1.4308	1.4873	1.5461	1.6090
1000	1.2681	1.2847	1.3252	1.3647	1.4055	1.4445	1.4883
1500	1.2390	1.2535	1.2877	1.3197	1.3523	1.3823	1.4174
2000	1.2156	1.2286	1.2586	1.2869	1.3140	1.3394	1.3716
3000	1.1789	1.1901	1.2144	1.2348	1.2568	1.2771	1.3022
5000	1.1276	1.1351	1.1540	1.1689	1.1847	1.1986	1.2143

Viscosity η (N · s/m²) of liquid *n*-undecane [52]

t, °C	$\eta \cdot 10^3$	t, °C	$\eta \cdot 10^3$	t, °C	$\eta \cdot 10^3$	t, °C	$\eta \cdot 10^3$
−10	2.163	40	0.871	90	0.482	180	0.233
0	1.742	50	0.759	100	0.437	200	0.204
10	1.425	60	0.671	120	0.365		
20	1.182	70	0.597	140	0.311		
30	1.010	80	0.535	160	0.268		

Thermal conductivity λ of liquid *n*-undecane [78, 79]

t, °C	−20	0	20	40	60	80	100	120	140	160	180
λ, W/m · deg	0.1475	0.1430	0.1384	0.1338	0.1293	0.1247	0.1200	0.1154	0.1107	0.1061	0.1014

Surface tension σ of n-undecane [65]

t, °C	0	10	20	25	30	40	50	75	100
$\sigma \cdot 10^3$, N/m	26.57	25.68	24.78	24.34	23.89	23.00	22.10	19.87	17.63

n-DODECANE ($C_{12}H_{26}$)

$CH_3(CH_2)_{10}CH_3$

Molecular weight 170.328

$t_{boil} = 216.28$ °C at 760 mm Hg; $t_{melt} = -9.55$ °C; $t_{cr} = 386$ °C;
$p_{cr} = 18.13$ bar; $\rho_{cr} = 237$ kg/m³

Thermodynamic properties of n-dodecane [62]: c_p° (kJ/kg·deg), i° (kJ/kg) and s° (kJ/kg·deg)

T, °K	c_p°	i°	s°	T, °K	c_p°	i°	s°
0	0	0	0	900	3.5742	1964.2	6.4965
288.16	1.647	309.19	3.6570	1000	3.758	2331.2	6.8831
300	1.655	312.29	3.6678	1100	3.918	2715.1	7.2496
400	2.092	499.76	4.2042	1200	4.056	3115.0	7.5987
500	2.4900	729.53	4.7149	1300	4.174	3526.7	7.9275
600	2.8277	994.90	5.1972	1400	4.277	3949.5	8.2402
700	3.1158	1291.8	5.6544	1500	4.368	4381.1	8.5381
800	3.3616	1616.8	6.0882				

Saturated vapor pressure of n-dodecane [65]

t, °C	p, mm Hg	t, °C	p, mm Hg	t, °C	p, mm Hg	t, °C	p, bar
0	0.0092	80	5.43	150	114.33	220	1.1059
10	0.028	90	9.24	160	159.52	230	1.3890
20	0.073	100	15.14	170	218.38	240	1.7258
30	0.178	110	23.99	180	293.78	250	2.1227
40	0.399	120	36.85	190	388.94	386	18.1
50	0.833	130	55.07	200	507.38		
60	1.64	140	80.26	210	652.93		
70	3.05						

Latent heat of vaporization r of liquid n-dodecane [62]

t, °C	25	216,3
r, kJ/kg	360.02	256.63

Density ρ (kg/m³) of liquid n-dodecane [65]

t, °C	$\varrho \cdot 10^{-3}$	t, °C	$\varrho \cdot 10^{-3}$	t, °C	$\varrho \cdot 10^{-3}$	t, °C	$\varrho \cdot 10^{-3}$	t, °C	$\varrho \cdot 10^{-3}$
0	0.7633	40	0.7342	90	0.6968	140	0.6582	190	0.6172
10	0.7561	50	0.7268	100	0.6892	150	0.6502	200	0.6085
20	0.7488	60	0.7194	110	0.6815	160	0.6421	210	0.599
25	0.7452	70	0.7119	120	0.6738	170	0.6339		
30	0.7415	80	0.7044	130	0.6660	180	0.6256		

Viscosity η of liquid *n*-dodecane [52]

t, °C	−10	0	10	20	30	40	50	60	70	80	90	100
$\eta \cdot 10^3$, N · s/m²	2.90	2.264	1.827	1.492	1.253	1.064	0.919	0.803	0.709	0.632	0.566	0.510

Thermal conductivity λ of liquid *n*-dodecane [78, 79]

t, °C	0	20	40	60	80	100	120	140	160	180	200
λ, W/m ·deg	0.1463	0.1420	0.1377	0.1333	0.1288	0.1243	0.1199	0.1154	0.1109	0.1064	0.1019

Surface tension σ of *n*-dodecane [65]

t, °C	0	10	20	25	30	40	50	75	100
$\sigma \cdot 10^3$, N/m	27.24	26.34	25.48	25.04	24.60	23.72	22.85	20.65	18.45

n-TRIDECANE ($C_{13}H_{28}$)

$CH_3(CH_2)_{11}CH_3$

Molecular weight 184.354

t_{boil} = 235.47 °C at 760 mm Hg; t_{melt} = − 5.37 °C; t_{cr} = 404 °C;
p_{cr} = 17.2 bar; ρ_{cr} = 240 kg/m³

Thermodynamic properties of *n*-tridecane [62]: $c_p{}^0$ (kJ/kg · deg), i^0 (kJ/kg) and s^0 (kJ/kg · deg)

T, °K	$c_p{}^\circ$	i°	s°	T, °K	$c_p{}^\circ$	i°	s°
0	0	0	0	900	3.5691	1960.5	6.4267
298.16	1.646	308.22	3.5902	1000	3.752	2327.8	6.8128
300	1.654	311.28	3.6009	1100	3.911	2711.1	7.1786
400	2.091	498.62	4.1368	1200	4.047	3110.6	7.5270
500	2.4879	728.20	4.6474	1300	4.167	3521.4	7.8554
600	2.8247	993.20	5.1288	1400	4.269	3944.5	8.1676
700	3.1120	1289.9	5.5858	1500	4.360	4374.4	8.4649
800	3.3570	1614.4	6.0190				

Saturated vapor pressure of *n*-tridecane [65]

t, °C	p, mm Hg	t, °C	p, mm Hg	t, °C	p, mm Hg	t, °C	p, mm Hg	t, °C	p, bar
70	1.25	110	11.67	150	62.77	190	233.27	240	1.1230
80	2.33	120	18.55	160	89.76	200	309.99	404	17.2
90	4.16	130	28.60	170	125.71	210	405.87		
100	7.10	140	42.91	180	172.65	220	524.20		
						230	668.50		

Latent heat of vaporization r of *n*-tridecane [62]

t, °C	25.0	235.4
r, kJ/kg	359.50	247.54

Density ρ (kg/m³) of liquid *n*-tridecane [65]

t, °C	$\varrho \cdot 10^{-3}$	t, °C	$\varrho \cdot 10^{-3}$	t, °C	$\varrho \cdot 10^{-3}$	t, °C	$\varrho \cdot 10^{-3}$	t, °C	$\varrho \cdot 10^{-3}$	t, °C	$\varrho \cdot 10^{-3}$
0	0.7704	40	0.7418	90	0.7053	130	0.6752	170	0.6441	210	0.611
10	0.7633	50	0.7346	100	0.6978	140	0.6676	180	0.6362	220	0.601
20	0.7562	60	0.7273	110	0.6903	150	0.6599	190	0.6281	230	0.592
25	0,7527	70	0.7200	120	0.6828	160	0.6521	200	0.6198		
30	0.7491	80	0.7127								

Specific volume $v \cdot 10^3$ (m³/kg) of liquid *n*-tridecane at high pressures [355]

p, bar \ t, °C →	30	50	100	150	220	250	300
0	1.3348	1.3607	1.4316	1.5142	1.6161	1.7569	1.9907
50	1.3281	1.3530	1.4204	1.4966	1.5862	1.7011	1.8576
100	1.3219	1.3459	1.4105	1.4812	1.5615	1.6615	1.7840
200	1.3105	1.3330	1.3920	1.4558	1.5249	1.6050	1.6979
300	1.3002	1.3214	1.3761	1.4335	1.4959	1.5644	1.6406
500	1.2821	1.3013	1.3496	1.3982	1.4507	1.5041	1.5624
1000	1.2466	1.2625	1.3010	1.3377	1.3763	1.4119	1.4529
1500	1.2195	1.2335	1.2661	1.2959	1.3270	1.3543	1.3873
2000	1.1975	1.2101	1.2387	1.2657	1.2913	1.3149	1.3457
3000	1.1628	1.1737	1.1969	1.2213	1.2369	1.2562	1.2805
5000	1.1139	1.1210	1.1389	1.1527	1.1682	1.1814	1.1972

Viscosity η (N · s/m²) of liquid *n*-tridecane [52]

t, °C	$\eta \cdot 10^3$	t, °C	$\eta \cdot 10^3$	t, °C	$\eta \cdot 10^3$	t, °C	$\eta \cdot 10^3$	t, °C	$\eta \cdot 10^3$	t, °C	$\eta \cdot 10^3$
0	2.962	30	1.561	60	0.969	90	0.668	140	0.408	200	0.260
10	2.339	40	1.312	70	0.849	100	0.598	160	0.347		
20	1.878	50	1.114	80	0.751	120	0.489	180	0.299		

Thermal conductivity λ of liquid *n*-tridecane [78, 79]

t, °C	0	20	40	60	80	100	120	140	160	180	200	220
λ, W/m · deg	0.1483	0.1442	0.1401	0.1359	0.1317	0.1275	0.1232	0.1189	0.1146	0.1104	0.1061	0.1018

Surface tension σ of *n*-tridecane [65]

t, °C	0	10	20	25	30	40	50	75	100
$\sigma \cdot 10^3$, N/m	27.87	27.00	26.13	25.69	25.26	24.39	23.52	21.34	19.16

n-TETRADECANE ($C_{14}H_{30}$)

$CH_3(CH_2)_{12}CH_3$

Molecular weight 198.380

t_{boil} = 253.59 °C at 760 mm Hg; t_{melt} = 5.85 °C; t_{cr} = 422 °C;
p_{cr} = 16.2 bar; ρ_{cr} = 240 kg/m³

Thermodynamic properties of n-tetradecane [62] : c_p^0 (kJ/kg · deg), i^0 (kJ/kg) and s^0 (kJ/kg · deg)

T, °K	c_p^0	i^0	s^0	T, °K	c_p^0	i^0	s^0
0	0	0	0	900	3.5638	1958.6	6.3654
298.16	1.644	307.32	3.5321	1000	3.747	2324.4	6.7509
300	1.652	310.42	3.5427	1100	3.904	2707.1	7.1162
400	2.089	497.54	4.0784	1200	4.041	3105.9	7.4641
500	2.4854	727.00	4.5884	1300	4.161	3516.3	7.7918
600	2.8215	991.66	5.0693	1400	4.262	3937.5	8.1037
700	3.1082	1287.9	5.5257	1500	4.351	4367.3	8.4003
800	3.3526	1612.0	5.9584				

Saturated vapor pressure of n-tetradecane [65]

t, °C	p, mm Hg	t, °C	p, mm Hg	t, °C	p, mm Hg	t, °C	p, bar
120	9.31	170	72.79	220	334.34	260	1.167
130	14.85	180	102.28	230	433.10	422	16.2
140	22.97	190	140.99	240	553.9		
150	34.57	200	190.99	250	700.2		
160	50.73	210	254.58				

Latent heat of vaporization r of n-tetradecane [62]

t, °C	25.0	253.6
r, kJ/kg	359.1	240.6

Heat capacity c_p of liquid n-tetradecane [71]

t, °C	7.44	11.24	13.4	17.44
c_p, kJ/kg · deg	2.16	2.17	2.18	2.19

Density ρ (kg/m³) of liquid n-tetradecane [65]

t, °C	$\varrho \cdot 10^{-3}$	t, °C	$\varrho \cdot 10^{-3}$	t, °C	$\varrho \cdot 10^{-3}$	t, °C	$\varrho \cdot 10^{-3}$	t, °C	$\varrho \cdot 10^{-3}$
10	0.7697	50	0.7415	100	0.7055	150	0.6684	200	0.6293
20	0.7727	60	0.7343	110	0.6981	160	0.6607	210	0.621
25	0.7592	70	0.7272	120	0.6908	170	0.6530	220	0.613
30	0.7557	80	0.7200	130	0.6834	180	0.6452	230	0.605
40	0.7486	90	0.7127	140	0.6759	190	0.6373	240	0.595
								250	0.585

Viscosity η of liquid n-tetradecane [52]

t, °C	10	20	30	40	50	60	70	80	90	100
$\eta \cdot 10^3$, N · s/m²	2.96	2.322	1.889	1.560	1.323	1.135	0.988	0.868	0.769	0.685

Thermal conductivity λ of liquid *n*-tetradecane [78, 79]

t, °C	20	40	60	80	100	120	140	160	180	200	220	240
λ, W/m · deg	0.1455	0.1420	0.1384	0.1342	0.1300	0.1258	0.1216	0.1175	0.1134	0.1093	0.1051	0.1009

Surface tension σ of *n*-tetradecane [65]

t, °C	10	20	25	30	40	50	75	100
$\sigma \cdot 10^3$, N/m	27.56	26.69	26.26	25.83	24.97	24.11	21.94	19.79

n-PENTADECANE ($C_{15}H_{32}$)

$CH_3(CH_2)_{13}CH_3$

Molecular weight 212.406

$t_{boil} = 270.74$ °C at 760 mm Hg; $t_{melt} = 9.95$ °C; $t_{cr} = 437$ °C;
$p_{cr} = 15.2$ bar; $\rho_{cr} = 240$ kg/m³

Thermodynamic properties of *n*-pentadecane [62] : $c_p{}^0$ (kJ/kg · deg), i^0 (kJ/kg) and s^0 (kJ/kg · deg)

T, °K	$c_p{}^0$	i^0	s^0	T, °K	$c_p{}^0$	i^0	s^0
0	0	0	0	900	3.5605	1959.0	6.3147
298.16	1.644	306.65	3.4830	1000	3.743	2322.2	6.6998
300	1.652	309.72	3.4934	1100	3.901	2705.0	7.0646
400	2.0883	496.77	4.0289	1200	4.037	3102.9	7.4121
500	2.4842	726.12	4.5388	1300	4.155	3512.7	7.7395
600	2.8199	990.66	5.0193	1400	4.257	3933.3	8.0509
700	3.1061	1286.8	5.4752	1500	4.346	4362.2	8.3472
800	3.3497	1610.5	5.9077				

Saturated vapor pressure p of n-pentadecane [65]

t, °C	p, mm Hg	t, °C	p, mm Hg	t, °C	p, mm Hg	t, °C	p, bar
140	12.33	190	85.66	240	366.86	280	1.2346
150	19.10	200	118.33	250	470.33	437	15.2
160	28.79	210	160.65	260	595.9		
170	42.33	220	214.64	270	746.8		
180	60.84	230	282.54				

Latent heat of vaporization r of *n*-pentadecane [65]

t, °C	25.0	270.6
r, kJ/kg	358.72	232.58

Density ρ (kg/m³) of liquid n-pentadecane [65]

t, °C	$\varrho \cdot 10^{-3}$	t, °C	$\varrho \cdot 10^{-3}$	t, °C	$\varrho \cdot 10^{-3}$	t, °C	$\varrho \cdot 10^{-3}$	t, °C	$\varrho \cdot 10^{-3}$
10	0.7752	60	0.7404	120	0.6977	180	0.6532	240	0.605
20	0.7683	70	0.7333	130	0.6904	190	0.6455	250	0.596
25	0.7649	80	0.7262	140	0.6831	200	0.6377	260	0.587
30	0.7614	90	0.7191	150	0.6757	210	0.630	270	0.577
40	0.7544	100	0.7120	160	0.6683	220	0.622		
50	0.7474	110	0.7049	170	0.6608	230	0.614		

Viscosity η of liquid n-pentadecane [65]

t, °C	20	30	40	50	60	70	80	90	100
$\eta \cdot 10^3$, N · s/m²	2.841	2.291	1.873	1.570	1.335	1.155	1.010	0.888	0.786

Thermal conductivity λ of liquid n-pentadecane [78, 79]

t, °C	20	40	60	80	100	120	140	160	180	200	220	240	260
λ, W/m · deg	0.1775	0.1435	0.1395	0.1356	0.1317	0.1270	0.1240	0.1200	0.1161	0.1122	0.1083	0.1043	0.1004

Surface tension σ of n-pentadecane [65]

t, °C	10	20	25	30	40	50	75	100
$\sigma \cdot 10^3$, N/m	28.02	27.17	26.74	26.32	25.46	24.61	22.48	20.35

n-HEXADECANE ($C_{16}H_{34}$)

$CH_3(CH_2)_{14}CH_3$

Molecular weight 226.432

$t_{boil} = 287.05$ °C at 760 mm Hg; $t_{melt} = 18.8$ °C; $t_{cr} = 452$ °C;
$p_{cr} = 14.2$ bar; $\rho_{cr} =$ kg/m³

Thermodynamic properties of n-hexadecane [62] : $c_p{}^0$ (kJ/kg · deg), i^0 (kJ/kg) and s^0 (kJ/kg)

T, °K	$c_p{}^0$	i^0	s^0	T, °K	$c_p{}^0$	i^0	s^0
0	0	0	0	900	3.5573	1955.1	6.2694
298.16	1.643	306.03	3.4395	1000	3.739	2320.3	6.6542
300	1.651	309.13	3.4500	1100	3.896	2702.5	7.0188
400	2.0873	496.12	3.9853	1200	4.031	3100.0	7.3659
500	2.4828	725.36	4.4947	1300	4.151	3509.4	7.6929
600	2.8181	989.70	4.9751	1400	4.253	3929.5	8.0040
700	3.1037	1285.6	5.4307	1500	4.341	4358.8	8.2998
800	3.3470	1609.2	5.8628				

Saturated vapor pressure of n-hexadecane [65]

t, °C	p, mm Hg	t, °C	p, mm Hg	t, °C	p, mm Hg
190	51.88	230	185.32	260	409.83
200	73.27	240	244.76	270	522.00
210	101.64	250	318.71	280	654.67
220	139.24				

Latent heat of vaporization r of hexadecane [62]

t, °C	25.0	286.8
r, kJ/kg	358.34	227.43

Density ρ (kg/m^3) of liquid n-hexadecane [65]

t, °C	$\varrho \cdot 10^{-3}$	t, °C	$\varrho \cdot 10^{-3}$	t, °C	$\varrho \cdot 10^{-3}$	t, °C	$\varrho \cdot 10^{-3}$	t, °C	$\varrho \cdot 10^{-3}$	t, °C	$\varrho \cdot 10^{-3}$
20	0.7734	60	0.7459	110	0.7108	160	0.6747	210	0.637	250	0.604
25	0.7700	70	0.7389	120	0.7037	170	0.6674	220	0.629	260	0.596
30	0.7665	80	0.7319	130	0.6965	180	0.6599	230	0.621	270	0.587
40	0.7597	90	0.7249	140	0.6892	190	0.6522	240	0.612	280	0.578
50	0.7528	100	0.7179	150	0.6820	200	0.6447				

Viscosity η of liquid n-hexadecane [52]

t, °C	20	30	40	50	60	70	80	90	100	120	140	160	180	200	220	240
$\eta \cdot 10^3$, N · s/m^2	3.451	2.754	2.232	1.852	1.560	1.338	1.161	1.014	0.892	0.716	0.584	0.486	0.409	0.349	0.299	0.259

Thermal conductivity λ of liquid n-hexadecane [78, 79]

t, °C	40	60	80	100	120	140	160	180	200	220	240	260	280
λ, W/m · · deg	0.1454	0.1419	0.1380	0.1341	0.1302	0.1264	0.1225	0.1187	0.1148	0.1110	0.1072	0.1034	0.0996

Surface tension σ of liquid n-hexadecane [65]

t, °C	20	25	30	40	50	75	100
$\sigma \cdot 10^3$, N/m	27.64	27.22	26.79	25.95	25.11	23.00	20.90

n-HEPTADECANE ($C_{17}H_{36}$)

$CH_3(CH_2)_{15}CH_3$

Molecular weight 240.458

t_{boil} = 302.56 °C at 760 mm Hg; t_{melt} = 22.00 °C;
t_{cr} = 462 °C; p_{cr} = 13.2 bar; ρ_{cr} = 240 kg/m³

Thermodynamic properties of *n*-heptadecane [62]: c_p^0 (kJ/kg · deg), i^0 (kJ/kg) and s^0 (kJ/kg · deg)

T, °K	c_p^0	i^0	s^0	T, °K	c_p^0	i^0	s^0
0	0	0	0	900	3.5541	1953.4	6.2286
298.16	1.642	305.42	3.4007	1000	3.736	2318.1	6.6230
300	1.650	308.52	3.4111	1100	3.891	2699.9	6.9772
400	2.0862	495.42	3.9462	1200	4.027	3097.2	7.3240
500	2.4814	724.52	4.4554	1300	4.145	3506.0	7.6506
600	2.8161	988.71	4.9345	1400	4.248	3931.2	7.9614
700	3.1014	1284.4	5.3908	1500	4.337	4354.4	8.2569
800	3.3441	1607.7	5.8224				

Saturated vapor pressure *p* of *n*-heptadecane [65]

t, °C	p, mm Hg	t, °C	p, mm Hg	t, °C	p, mm Hg	t, °C	p, mm Hg	t, °C	p, bar
160	9.37	200	46.21	240	164.08	280	459.8	310	1.1794
170	14.50	210	65.14	250	216.44	290	557.6	462	13.169
180	21.84	220	90.13	260	281.68	300	718.3		
190	32.13	230	122.57	270	361.98				

Specific volume $v \cdot 10^3$ (m³/kg) of liquid *n*-heptadecane at high pressures [355]

p, bar \ t, °C →	50	100	150	200	250	300
0	1.3201	1.3831	1.4548	1.5361	1.6439	1.7726
50	1.3135	1.3737	1.4407	1.5158	1.6062	1.7169
100	1.3075	1.3648	1.4283	1.4980	1.5790	1.6732
200	1.2965	1.3496	1.4058	1.4677	1.5367	1.6126
300	1.2865	1.3362	1.3871	1.4437	1.5044	1.5689
500	1.2689	1.3133	1.3569	1.4044	1.4512	1.5038
1000	1.2343	1.2701	1.3035	1.3393	1.3706	1.4083
1500	1.2080	1.2385	1.2656	1.2947	1.3188	1.3494
2000	1.1866	1.2133	1.2386	1.2623	1.2839	1.3128
3000	1.1527	1.1746	1.1909	1.2114	1.2295	1.2528
5000	1.1029	1.1197	1.1319	1.1472	1.1593	1.1753

Density ρ (kg/m³) of liquid *n*-heptadecane [65]

t, °C	$\varrho \cdot 10^{-3}$	t, °C	$\varrho \cdot 10^{-3}$	t, °C	$\varrho \cdot 10^{-3}$	t, °C	$\varrho \cdot 10^{-3}$
30	0.7711	100	0.7231	170	0.6735	240	0.6204
40	0.7643	110	0.7162	180	0.6662	250	0.6123
50	0.7575	120	0.7092	190	0.6588	260	0.6041
60	0.7507	130	0.7022	200	0.6514	270	0.5957
70	0.7439	140	0.6951	210	0.6438	280	0.5871
80	0.7370	150	0.6879	220	0.6361	290	0.5782
90	0.7301	160	0.6807	230	0.6283	300	0.5689

Latent heat of vaporization r of n-heptadecane [62]

t, °C	25.0	301.8
r, kJ/kg	358.65	221.11

Viscosity η (N · s/m²) of liquid n-heptadecane [52]

t, °C	$\eta \cdot 10^3$	t, °C	$\eta \cdot 10^3$	t, °C	$\eta \cdot 10^3$	t, °C	$\eta \cdot 10^3$
30	3.291	80	1.340	160	0.546	240	0.296
40	2.652	90	1.161	180	0.460	260	0.260
50	2.169	100	1.014	200	0.392	280	0.229
60	1.829	120	0.794	220	0.339	300	0.203
70	1.557	140	0.655				

Thermal conductivity λ of liquid n-heptadecane [78, 79]

t, °C	40	60	80	100	120	140	160
λ, W/m · deg	0.1478	0.1437	0.1398	0.1360	0.1323	0.1286	0.1249
t, °C	180	200	220	240	260	280	300
λ, W/m · deg	0.1212	0.1175	0.1138	0.1101	0.1064	0.1026	0.0989

Surface tension σ of n-heptadecane [65]

t, °C	25	30	40	50	75	100
$\sigma \cdot 10^3$, N/m	27.64	27.22	26.38	25.54	23.45	21.35

n-OCTADECANE ($C_{18}H_{38}$)

$CH_3(CH_2)_{16}CH_3$

Molecular weight 254.484

t_{boil} = 317.38 °C at 760 mm Hg; t_{melt} = 28.20 °C;
t_{cr} = 477 °C; p_{cr} = 13.2 bar; ρ_{cr} = 240 kg/m³

Thermodynamic properties of n-octadecane [62]: $c_p{}^0$ (kJ/kg · deg), i^0 (kJ/kg) and s^0 (kJ/kg · deg)

T, °K	$c_p{}^\circ$	i°	s°	T, °K	$c_p{}^\circ$	i°	s°
0	0	0	0	900	3.5514	1952.0	6.1926
298.16	1.642	304.93	3.3663	1000	3.732	2316.3	6.5767
300	1.6498	307.99	3.3767	1100	3.889	2697.8	6.9406
400	2.0854	494.82	3.9115	1200	4.024	3094.9	7.2872
500	2.4803	723.80	4.4206	1300	4.142	3503.4	7.6134
600	2.8144	987.89	4.9003	1400	4.242	3922.5	7.9240
700	3.0995	1283.3	5.3551	1500	4.331	4350.7	8.2191
800	3.3418	1606.4	5.7868				

Saturated vapor pressure p of n-octadecane [65]

t, °C	p, mm Hg	t, °C	p, mm Hg	t, °C	p, mm Hg	t, °C	p, bar
180	13.15	230	81.40	280	326.9	320	1.0665
190	19.79	240	110.67	290	415.3	477	13.169
200	29.07	250	148.13	300	521.9		
210	41.78	260	195.40	310	649.3		
220	58.86	270	254.31				

Latent heat of vaporization r of n-octadecane [62]

t, °C	28.2	316.1
r, kJ/kg	355.32	215.49

Density ρ (kg/m³) of liquid n-octadecane [65]

t, °C	$\varrho \cdot 10^{-3}$	t, °C	$\varrho \cdot 10^{-3}$	t, °C	$\varrho \cdot 10^{-3}$	t, °C	$\varrho \cdot 10^{-3}$
30	0.7753	100	0.7279	170	0.6790	240	0.6270
40	0.7686	110	0.7210	180	0.6718	250	0.6192
50	0.7618	120	0.7140	190	0.6645	260	0.6113
60	0.7551	130	0.7071	200	0.6572	270	0.6032
70	0.7483	140	0.7001	210	0.6498	280	0.5948
80	0.7415	150	0.6931	220	0.6423	290	0.5861
90	0.7347	160	0.6861	230	0.6347	300	0.5770

Viscosity η of liquid n-octadecane [52]

t, °C	30	40	50	60	70	80	90	100
$\eta \cdot 10^3$, N · s/m²	3.813	3.060	2.491	2.060	1.748	1.484	1.297	1.131

Thermal conductivity λ of liquid n-octadecane [78, 79]

t, °C	40	60	80	100	120	140	160
λ, W/m · deg	0.1493	0.1456	0.1419	0.1382	0.1346	0.1309	0.1273
t, °C	180	200	220	240	260	280	300
λ, W/m · deg	0.1237	0.1200	0.1164	0.1137	0.1101	0.1064	0.1028

Surface tension σ of n-octadecane [65]

t, °C	30	40	50	75	100
$\sigma \cdot 10^3$, N/m	27.59	26.75	25.92	23.84	21.75

n-NONADECANE ($C_{19}H_{40}$)

$CH_3(CH_2)_{17}CH_3$

Molecular weight 268.510
$t_{boil} = 331.55$ °C at 760 mm Hg; $t_{melt} = 32.2$ °C; $t_{cr} = 487$ °C;
$p_{cr} = 12.2$ bar; $\rho_{cr} = 240$ kg/m³

Thermodynamic properties of *n*-nonadecane [62]: c_p^0 (kJ/kg · deg), i^0 (kJ/kg) and s^0 (kJ/kg · deg)

T, °K	c_p^0	i^0	s^0	T, °K	c_p^0	i^0	s^0
0	0	0	0	900	3.5488	1950.6	6.1602
298.16	1.6410	304.46	3.3355	1000	3.729	2314.8	6.5440
300	1.6493	307.56	3.3459	1100	3.885	2695.8	6.9078
400	2.0845	494.33	3.8805	1200	4.021	3092.6	7.2540
500	2.4791	723.22	4.3892	1300	4.138	3500.7	7.5800
600	2.8129	987.13	4.8688	1400	4.239	3919.5	7.8902
700	3.0976	1282.4	5.3235	1500	4.328	4347.3	8.1851
800	3.3395	1605.4	5.7547				

Saturated vapor pressure p of *n*-nonadecane [65]

t, °C	p, mm Hg	t, °C	p, mm Hg	t, °C	p, mm Hg	t, °C	p, bar
190	12.19	240	74.87	290	299.9	340	1.195
200	18.31	250	101.71	300	381.0	487	12.156
210	26.84	260	136.06	310	478.9		
220	38.52	270	179.4	320	595.8		
230	54.19	280	233.4	330	734.3		

Latent heat of vaporization r of *n*-nonadecane [62]

t, °C	32.1	329.7
r, kJ/kg	353.9	210.5

Density ρ (kg/m³) of liquid *n*-nonadecane [65]

t, °C	$\varrho \cdot 10^{-3}$	t, °C	$\varrho \cdot 10^{-3}$	t, °C	$\varrho \cdot 10^{-3}$	t, °C	$\varrho \cdot 10^{-3}$
40	0.7723	110	0.7254	180	0.6766	250	0.6250
50	0.7657	120	0.7186	190	0.6695	260	0.6170
60	0.7590	130	0.7116	200	0.6624	270	0.6089
70	0.7523	140	0.7046	210	0.6551	280	0.6007
80	0.7456	150	0.6976	220	0.6478	290	0.5924
90	0.7388	160	0.6906	230	0.6404	300	0.5840
100	0.7321	170	0.6836	240	0.6328		

Thermal conductivity λ of liquid *n*-nonadecane [78, 79]

t, °C	40	60	80	100	120	140	160	180
λ, W/m · deg	0.1507	0.1470	0.1433	0.1396	0.1359	0.1322	0.1286	0.1250
t, °C	200	220	240	260	280	300	320	
λ, W/m · deg	0.1214	0.1174	0.1142	0.1106	0.1070	0.1034	0.0998	

Surface tension σ of *n*-nonadecane [65]

t, °C	20	25	30	40	50	60	70	80	90	100
$\sigma \cdot 10^3$, N/M	28.7	28.2	27.8	26.9	26.0	25.3	24.6	23.9	23.2	22.5

n-EICHOSANE ($C_{20}H_{42}$)

$CH_3(CH_2)_{18}CH_3$

Molecular weight 282.536

$t_{boil} = 345.12$ °C at 760 mm Hg; $t_{melt} = 36.9$ °C; $t_{cr} = 502$ °C;
$p_{cr} = 11.1$ bar; $\rho_{cr} = 240$ kg/m³

Thermodynamic properties of *n*-eichosane [62]: $c_p{}^0$ (kJ/kg · deg), i^0 (kJ/kg) and s^0 (kJ/kg · deg)

T, °K	$c_p{}^0$	i^0	s^0	T, °K	$c_p{}^0$	i^0	s^0
0	0	0	0	900	3.5476	1950.0	6.1331
298.16	1.6410	304.14	3.3087	1000	3.729	2314.0	6.5168
300	1.6492	307.22	3.3191	1100	3.883	2695.0	6.8803
400	2.0844	493.98	3.8536	1200	4.019	3091.4	7.2264
500	2.4789	722.80	4.3624	1300	4.136	3500.8	7.5523
600	2.8125	986.74	4.8418	1400	4.237	3917.9	7.8623
700	3.0969	1282.0	5.2964	1500	4.326	4345.8	8.1569
800	3.3386	1604.8	5.7275				

Saturated vapor pressure p of *n*-eichosane [65]

t, °C	p, mm Hg	t, °C	p, mm Hg	t, °C	p, mm Hg	t, °C	p, bar
200	11.5	250	70.0	300	279.2	350	1.11
210	17.3	260	95.0	310	345.6	502	11.14
220	25.2	270	126.9	320	445.5		
230	36.1	280	167	330	554.2		
240	50.8	290	217	340	683.0		

Latent heat of vaporization r of *n*-eichosane [62]

t, °C	36.8	342.7
r, kJ/kg	352.7	204.5

Specific volume $v \cdot 10^3$ (m³/kg) of liquid *n*-eichosane at high pressures [355]

p, bar \ t, °C →	100	150	200	250	300
0	1.3598	1.4267	1.5013	1.5942	1.7135
50	1.3514	1.4141	1.4831	1.5637	1.6575
100	1.3429	1.4029	1.4676	1.5408	1.6238
200	1.3293	1.3819	1.4403	1.5038	1.5727
300	1.3171	1.3650	1.4184	1.4748	1.5345
500	1.2959	1.3372	1.3823	1.4260	1.4759
1000	1.2553	1.2870	1.3216	1.3508	1.3869
1500	1.2252	1.2510	1.2792	1.3017	1.3312
2000	1.2011	1.2255	1.2484	1.2689	1.2970
3000	1.1638	1.1790	1.1992	1.2167	1.2394
5000	1.1104	1.1219	1.1370	1.1487	1.1647

Density ρ (kg/m³) of liquid *n*-eichosane [65]

t, °C	$\varrho \cdot 10^{-3}$	t, °C	$\varrho \cdot 10^{-3}$	t, °C	$\varrho \cdot 10^{-3}$	t, °C	$\varrho \cdot 10^{-3}$
40	0.7756	110	0.7290	180	0.6808	250	0.6302
50	0.7690	120	0.7222	190	0.6738	260	0.6225
60	0.7624	130	0.7154	200	0.6668	270	0.6147
70	0.7558	140	0.7087	210	0.6597	280	0.6068
80	0.7491	150	0.7018	220	0.6525	290	0.5987
90	0.7424	160	0.6943	230	0.6452	300	0.5903
100	0.7357	170	0.6878	240	0.6378		

Viscosity η of liquid *n*-eichosane [52]

t, °C	40	50	60	70	80	90	100	120	140	160	180	200	220
$\eta \cdot 10^3$, N · s/m²	4.072	3.259	2.665	2.220	1.188	1.614	1.403	1.094	0.876	0.717	0.598	0.505	0.432

Thermal conductivity λ of liquid *n*-eichosane [78, 79]

t, °C	40	60	80	100	120	140	160	180
λ, W/m · deg	0.1522	0.1486	0.1450	0.1414	0.1378	0.1342	0.1306	0.1270
t, °C	200	220	240	260	280	300	320	340
λ, W/m · deg	0.1234	0.1198	0.1162	0.1126	0.1090	0.1054	0.1028	0.0992

Surface tension σ of *n*-eichosane [65]

t, °C	20	25	30	40	50	60	70	80	90	100
$\sigma \cdot 10^3$, N/m	29.0	28.6	28.1	27.2	26.4	25.7	25.0	24.3	23.7	23.0

NAPUTHENES

Cyclopentane (C_5H_{10})

$$\begin{array}{ccc} & CH_2 & \\ H_2C & & CH_2 \\ | & & | \\ H_2C & \text{———} & CH_2 \end{array}$$

Molecular weight 70.130

$t_{boil} = 49.262$ °C at 760 mmHg; $t_{melt} = -93.879$ ° C;
$t_{cr} = 238.60$ °C; $p_{cr} = 45.13$ bar; $\rho_{cr} = 270$ kg/m³

Thermodynamic properties of cyclopentane [62]: c^0_p (kJ/kg · deg), i^0 (kJ/kg) and s^0 (kJ/kg · deg)

T, °K	c_p^0	i^0	s^0	T, °K	c_p^0	i^0	s^0
0	0	0	0	900	3.365	1681.2	6.6464
298.16	1.183	214.9	4.179	1000	3.567	2028.0	7.0118
300	1.193	217.1	4.186	1100	3.742	2394.6	7.3610
400	1.686	361.1	4.597	1200	3.891	2776.0	7.6941
500	2.141	522.8	5.023	1300	4.021	3171.9	8.0105
600	2.529	787.3	5.449	1400	4.134	3579.6	8.3120
700	2.854	1056.9	5.865	1500	4.232	3998.7	8.6010
800	3.131	1356.4	6.2637				

Saturated vapor pressure of cyclopentane [65]

t, °C	p, mm Hg	t, °C	p, mm Hg	t, °C	p, bar	t, °C	p, bar	t, °C	p, bar
−80	0.32	−10	64.2	50	1.038	120	6.465	180	19.54
−70	0.82	0	106.5	60	1.419	130	7.950	190	22.87
−60	2.10	10	169.4	70	1.905	140	9.670	200	26.59
−50	4.85	20	259.6	80	2.516	150	11.67	210	30.74
−40	10.24	25	317.4	90	3.252	160	13.93	220	35.33
−30	20.07	30	385.0	100	4.146	170	16.58	230	40.39
−20	36.90	40	554.7	110	5.211				

Latent heat of vaporization r (kJ/kg) of cyclopentane [65]

t, °C	r	t, °C	r	t, °C	r	t, °C	r	t, °C	r
−90	469.8	−20	435.2	50	391.0	120	330.7	190	232.8
−80	465.7	−10	429.8	60	383.9	130	320.0	200	211.9
−70	460.9	0	423.9	70	376.1	140	308.6	210	187.4
−60	456.1	10	417.9	80	367.8	150	296.1	220	157.6
−50	450.7	20	411.9	90	359.4	160	282.4	230	115.2
−40	446.0	30	405.4	100	350.4	170	267.4		
−30	440.6	40	397.6	110	340.9	180	250.7		

Heat capacity c_p of liquid cyclopentane [80]

T, °K	180	190	200	210	220	230	240	250	260	270	280	290	300
c_p, kJ/kg · deg	1.426	1.441	1.460	1.483	1.509	1.538	1.569	1.604	1.643	1.685	1.727	1.772	1.817

Density ρ of liquid cyclopentane [65]

t, °C	−10	0	10	20	25	30	40
$\rho \cdot 10^{-3}$, kg/m³	0.7745	0.7648	0.7551	0.7454	0.7404	0.7356	0.7258

Viscosity η of liquid cyclopentane [52]

t, °C	0	10	20	30	40
$\eta \cdot 10^3$, N · s/m²	0.555	0.491	0.439	0.393	0.354

Surface tension σ of cyclopentane [65]

t, °C	13.5
$\sigma \cdot 10^3$, N/m	23.3

METHYLCYCLOPENTANE (C_6H_{12})

```
       CH2
      /   \
  H2C       CH - CH3
   |        |
  H2C ----- CH2
```

Molecular weight 84.156

$t_{boil} = 71.812$ °C at 760 mm Hg; $t_{melt} = -142.455$ °C;
$t_{cr} = 259.61$ °C; $p_{cr} = 37.84$ bar; $\rho_{cr} = 264$ kg/m³

Thermodynamic properties of methylcyclopentane [62]:
c_p^0 (kJ/kg · deg), i^0 (kJ/kg) and s^0 (kJ/kg · deg)

T, °K	c_p^0	i^0	s^0	T, °K	c_p^0	i^0	s^0
0	0	0	0	900	3.409	1752.9	6.6083
298.16	1.305	237.5	4,042	1000	3.604	2103.4	6.9774
300	1.316	240.1	4,051	1100	3.772	2472.6	7.3287
400	1.796	395.6	4,494	1200	3.916	2857.6	7.6640
500	2.236	597.7	4,943	1300	4.042	3255.6	7.9809
600	2.608	840.9	5,3849	1400	4.151	3665.1	8.2839
700	2.919	1117.5	5,8113	1500	4.246	4085.0	8.5754
800	3.184	1422.8	6,2192				

Saturated vapor pressure of methylcyclopentane [65]

t, °C	p, mm Hg	t, °C	p, mm Hg	t, °C	p, bar	t, °C	p, bar
−90	0.0139			80	1.2946	170	9.86
−80	0.0551	10	68.87	90	1.7170	180	11.73
−70	0.183	20	110.22	100	2.238	190	13.87
−60	0.524	30	170.04	110	2.872	200	16.28
−50	1.33	40	253.90	120	3.632	210	19.00
−40	3.07	50	368.27	130	4.533	220	22.05
−30	6.50	60	520.45	140	5.59	230	25.47
−20	12.78	70	718.53	150	6.82	240	29.24
−10	23.60			160	8.22		

Latent heat of vaporization r (kJ/kg) of methylcyclopentane [65]

t, °C	r	t, °C	r	t, °C	r	t, °C	r
−140	442.8	−40	407.0	60	356.2	160	276.1
−130	440.3	−30	402.5	70	350.2	170	265.2
−120	437.8	−20	398.0	80	343.8	180	253.2
−110	434.8	−10	393.0	90	336.8	190	240.3
−100	431.8	0	388.5	100	329.3	200	225.9
−90	427.4	10	383.6	110	321.9	210	209.4
−80	423.4	20	378.6	120	313.9	220	190.5
−70	419.4	30	373.6	130	305.0	230	169.2
−60	415.4	40	368.2	140	296.0	240	143.8
−50	410.9	50	362.2	150	286.1	250	108.0

Heat capacity c_p (kJ/kg · deg) of liquid methylcyclopentane [80]

T, °K	c_p	T, °K	c_p	T, °K	c_p	T, °K	c_p	T, °K	c_p
140	1.487	180	1.523	220	1.606	250	1.698	280	1.811
150	1.492	190	1.538	230	1.634	260	1.736	290	1.852
160	1.499	200	1.558	240	1.665	270	1.771	300	1.895
170	1.510	210	1.581						

Viscosity η ($N \cdot s/m^2$) of liquid methylcyclopentane [62]

t, °C	$\eta \cdot 10^3$	t, °C	$\eta \cdot 10^3$	t, °C	$\eta \cdot 10^3$	t, °C	$\eta \cdot 10^3$
−25	0.93	−5	0.695	15	0.538	35	0.427
−20	0.86	0	0.650	20	0.507	40	0.405
−15	0.80	5	0.609	25	0.478	45	0.384
−10	0.745	10	0.572	30	0.452	50	0.365

Surface tension σ of methylcyclopentane [65]

t, °C	13.5
$\sigma \cdot 10^3$, N/m	24.1

Density of liquid methylcyclopentane [65]

t, °C	−10	0	10	20	25	30	40
$\varrho \cdot 10^{-3}$, kg/m²	0.7765	0.7672	0.7579	0.7486	0.7439	0.7393	0.7300

ETHYLCYCLOPENTANE (C_7H_{14})

```
        CH2
      /     \
  H2C         CH — CH2 — CH3
   |          |
  H2C ———————— CH2
```

Molecular weight 98.182

$t_{boil} = 103.466$ °C at 760 mm Hg; $t_{melt} = -138.466$ °C;
$t_{cr} = 296.30$ °C; $p_{cr} = 33.96$ bar; $\rho_{cr} = 262$ kg/m³

Thermodynamic properties of ethylcyclopentane [62]:
c_p^0 (kJ/kg · deg) i^0 (kJ/kg) and s^0 (kJ/kg · deg)

T, °K	c_p^0	i^0	s^0	T, °K	c_p^0	i^0	s^0
0	0	0	0	900	3.434	1778.3	6.4689
298.16	1.343	247.0	3.856	1000	3.631	2131.1	6.8403
300	1.354	249.7	3.865	1100	3.800	2503.4	7.1934
400	1.871	408.7	4.3237	1200	3.945	2891.0	7.5298
500	2.261	613.38	4.7838	1300	4.071	3291.0	7.8496
600	2.631	858.34	5.2315	1400	4.180	3704.1	8.1515
700	2.943	1138.1	5.6647	1500	4.274	4128.0	8.4423
800	3.207	1445.3	6.0775				

Saturated vapor pressure of ethylcyclopentane [65]

t, °C	p, mm Hg	t, °C	p, mm Hg	t, °C	p, bar	t, °C	p, bar	t, °C	p, bar
0	10.06	70	262.8	110	1.216	170	4.874	230	13.75
10	18.09	80	370.0	120	1.585	180	5.93	240	15.98
20	31.01	90	509.5	130	2.036	190	7.10	250	18.47
30	50.9	100	687.9	140	2.579	200	8.46	260	21.24
40	80.4			150	3.236	210	10.01	270	24.31
50	122.9			160	3.986	220	11.76	280	27.70
60	182.1							290	31.43

Latent heat of vaporization s (kJ/kg) of ethylcyclopentane [65]

t, °C	r	t, °C	r	t, °C	r	t, °C	r	t, °C	r
−130	426.4	−40	396.1	50	357.7	140	306.2		
−120	423.4	−30	392.3	60	353.0	150	298.9	230	220.4
−110	420.4	−20	388.9	70	347.9	160	291.2	240	206.4
−100	417.0	−10	385.0	80	342.8	170	283.1	250	190.6
−90	413.6	0	380.8	90	337.3	180	274.2	260	172.7
−80	410.2	10	376.5	100	331.7	190	265.2	270	151.4
−70	406.8	20	372.2	110	325.8	200	255.4	280	124.5
−60	402.9	30	367.6	120	319.4	210	244.3	290	62.68
−50	399.5	40	362.9	130	313.0	220	232.8		

Density ρ of liquid ethylcyclopentane [65]

t, °C	10	20	25	30	40
$\rho \cdot 10^{-3}$, kg/m³	0.7750	0.7665	0.7622	0.7578	0.7491

Viscosity η (N · s/m²) of liquid ethylcyclopentane [62]

t, °C	$\eta \cdot 10^3$	t, °C	$\eta \cdot 10^3$	t, °C	$\eta \cdot 10^3$	t, °C	$\eta \cdot 10^3$
−20	0.96	0	0.724	25	0.536	40	0.456
−15	0.89	5	0.679	30	0.507	45	0.433
−10	0.829	10	0.639	35	0.480	50	0.412
−5	0.774	15	0.601				
		20	0.567				

1,1-DIMETHYLCYCLOPENTANE (C_7H_{14})

```
        CH2       CH3
       /    \    /
   H2C        C
    |         | \
   H2C ------CH2  CH3
```

Molecular weight 98.182

$t_{boil} = 87.846$ °C at 760 mm Hg; $t_{melt} = -69.795$ °C;
$t_{cr} = 277$ °C; $p_{cr} = 35.46$ bar; $\rho_{cr} = 280$ kg/m³

Thermodynamic properties of 1,1-dimethylcyclopentane [62]:
$c_p{}^0$ (kJ/kg · deg), i^0 (kJ/kg) and s^0 (kJ/kg · deg)

T, °K	$c_p{}^0$	i^0	s^0	T, °K	$c_p{}^0$	i^0	s^0
0	0	0	0	900	3.470	1791.7	6.2984
298.16	1.358	237.2	3.661	1000	3.660	2148.2	6.6736
300	1.371	240.1	3.672	1100	3.821	2522.2	7.0279
400	1.857	401.0	4.130	1200	3.961	2912.3	7.3678
500	2.303	609.75	4.594	1300	4.083	3313.6	7.6876
600	2.677	860.48	5.0464	1400	4.187	3726.3	7.9933
700	2.988	1143.6	5.4835	1500	4.277	4148.9	8.2884
800	3.248	1454.4	5.9009				

Saturated vapor pressure p of 1,1-dimethylcyclopentane [65]

t, °C	p, mm Hg	t, °C	p, mm Hg	t, °C	p, bar
−60	0.19370	20	59.84	90	1.0784
−50	0.5310	25	75.69	100	1.4263
−40	1.46	30	94.85	110	1.8550
−30	2.91	40	145.15	120	2.3756
−20	6.01	50	215.30	130	2.9998
−10	11.58	60	310.49	140	3.7397
0	21.03	70	436.72	150	4.6070
10	36.28	80	600.52	160	5.6137

Latent heat of vaporization r (kJ/kg) of 1,1-dimethylcyclopentane [65]

t, °C	r	t, °C	r	t, °C	r	t, °C	r	t, °C	r
−60	379.1	10	352.2	80	316.8	150	268.2	220	189.7
−50	375.6	20	347.5	90	311.3	160	259.7	230	173.5
−40	372.7	30	342.4	100	304.4	170	250.3	240	154.4
−30	369.3	40	337.7	110	298.0	180	240.5	250	130.9
−20	364.1	50	332.6	120	291.2	190	229.4	260	98.92
−10	360.3	60	327.5	130	284.0	200	217.5		
0	356.5	70	322.4	140	276.3	210	204.2		

Density ρ of liquid 1,1-dimethylcyclopentane [65]

t, °C	10	20	25	30	40
$\rho \cdot 10^{-3}$, kg/m^2	0.7636	0.7545	0.7499	0.7453	0.7360

CYCLOHEXANE (C_6H_{12})

CH$_2$

H$_2$C CH$_2$

H$_2$C CH$_2$

CH$_2$

Molecular weight 84.156

t_{boil} = 80.738 °C at 760 mm Hg; t_{melt} = 6.554 °C;
t_{cr} = 279.9 °C; p_{cr} = 40.3 bar; ρ_{cr} = 270 kg/m^3

Thermodynamic properties of cyclohexane [62]:
$c_p{}^0$ (kJ/kg · deg), i^0 (kJ/kg) and s^0 (kJ/kg · deg)

T, °K	$c_p{}^0$	i^0	s^0	T, °K	$c_p{}^0$	i^0	s^0
0	0	0	0	900	3.566	1764.1	6.1590
298.16	1.264	210.8	3.546	1000	3.771	2131.8	6.5466
300	1.273	213.1	3.554	1100	3.94	2517.4	6.915
400	1.782	365.8	3.989	1200	4.09	2919.3	7.264
500	2.262	568.39	4.440	1300	4.21	3337.2	7.597
600	2.678	816.10	4.890	1400	4.32	3761.1	7.910
700	3.028	1101.9	5.3302	1500	4.41	4201.4	8.214
800	3.321	1419.7	5.7536				

Saturated vapor pressure of cyclohexane [65]

t, °C	p, mm Hg	t, °C	p, mm Hg	t, °C	p, bar	t, °C	p, bar	t, °C	p, bar
10	47.49	50	271.80	90	1.3272	160	6.703	220	18.01
20	77.52	60	389.20	100	1.7462	170	8.059	230	20.82
25	97.58	70	543.83	110	2.260	180	9.601	240	23.96
30	121.73	80	743.28	120	2.881	190	11.34	250	27.45
40	184.69			130	3.622	200	13.30	260	31.32
				140	4.498	210	15.52	270	35.61
				150	5.52				

Latent heat of vaporization (kJ/kg) of cyclohexane [65]

t, °C	r	t, °C	r	t, °C	r	t, °C	r	t, °C	r
10	399.0	70	366.2	130	322.9	190	259.2	240	189.0
20	394.0	80	360.2	140	313.9	200	246.8	250	171.1
30	388.5	90	353.7	150	304.0	210	233.8	260	149.2
40	383.1	100	346.8	160	293.5	220	220.4	270	114.4
50	377.6	110	339.3	170	282.6	230	206.5	280	42.3
60	372.1	120	331.3	180	271.1				

Heat capacity c_p of liquid cyclohexane [81]

T, °K	280	290	295
c_p, kJ/kg · deg	1.786	1.839	1.853

Density ρ of liquid cyclohexane [65]

t, °C	10	20	25	30	40	50	60	70	80
$\varrho \cdot 10^{-3}$, kg/m³	0.78795	0.77857	0.77387	0.76915	0.75960	0.74993	0.7401	0.7301	0.7199

Viscosity η of cyclohexane gas at $p \leqslant 1$ bar [52]

t, °C	0	25	50	75	100	150	200	250	300	400	500	600
$\eta \cdot 10^7$, N · s/m²	65.3	71.2	77.0	81.7	87.8	98.6	109.0	119.1	129.1	148.2	167.0	186.0

Viscosity η of liquid cyclohexane [52]

t, °C	20	30	40	50	60	70	80
$\eta \cdot 10^3$, N · s/m²	0.970	0.822	0.706	0.610	0.538	0.474	0.426

Thermal conductivity λ of liquid cyclohexane [72]

t, °C	10	20	30	40	60	80
λ, W/m · deg	0.127	0.124	0.122	0.120	0.116	0.112

Surface tension σ of cyclohexane [65]

t, °C	10	20	25	30	40	50	75
$\sigma \cdot 10^3$, N/m	26.15	24.95	24.35	23.75	22.45	21.35	18.35

METHYLCYCLOHEXANE (C_7H_{14})

```
        CH2
      /     \
   H2C       CH—CH3
    |         |
   H2C       CH2
      \     /
        CH2
```

Molecular weight 98.182

$t_{boil} = 100.934$ °C at 760 mm Hg; $t_{melt} = -126.593$ °C;
$t_{cr} = 299.1$ °C; $P_{cr} = 34.7$ bar

Thermodynamic properties of methylcyclohexane [62]:
$c_p{}^0$ (kJ/kg · deg), i^0 (kJ/kg) and s^0 (kJ/kg · deg)

T, °K	$c_p{}^0$	i^0	s^0	T, °K	$c_p{}^0$	i^0	s^0
0	0	0	0	900	3.590	1819.8	6.2024
298.16	1.376	223.1	3.499	1000	3.786	2188.7	6.5909
300	1.386	225.9	3.508	1100	3.953	2575.0	6.959
400	1.891	389.6	3.975	1200	4.093	2978.0	7.308
500	2.354	602.50	4.4482	1300	4.213	3392.4	7.641
600	2.748	857.83	4.9126	1400	4.315	3820.5	7.957
700	3.080	1150.0	5.3628	1500	4.400	4253.5	8.259
800	3.357	1472.3	5.7931				

Saturated vapor pressure of methylcyclohexane [65]

t, °C	p, mm Hg	t, °C	p, mm Hg	t, °C	p, bar	t, °C	p, bar
−70	0.027	25	46.33	110	1.2986	210	10.10
−60	0.089	30	58.67	120	1.6820	220	11.86
−50	0.26	40	91.57	130	2.146	230	13.83
−40	0.66	50	138.31	140	2.704	240	16.02
−30	1.33	60	202.89	150	3.362	250	18.48
−20	3.27	70	289.89	160	4.134	260	21.20
−10	6.49	80	404.52	170	5.01	270	24.21
0	12.13	90	552.53	180	6.05	280	27.52
10	21.46	100	740.20	190	7.23	290	31.16
20	36.23			200	8.58		

Latent heat of vaporization r (kJ/kg) of methylcyclohexane [65]

t, °C	r	t, °C	r	t, °C	r	t, °C	r	t, °C	r
−120	412.3	−30	381.2	60	344.5	140	299.3	220	229.8
−110	409.3	−20	377.4	70	338.6	150	292.5	230	217.9
−100	406.4	−10	373.5	80	333.9	160	285.3	240	204.7
−90	402.5	0	369.3	90	328.8	170	277.6	250	189.7
−80	399.1	10	365.4	100	323.2	180	269.0	260	173.1
−70	395.7	20	361.2	110	317.7	190	260.5	270	153.5
−60	392.3	30	357.3	120	311.7	200	251.1	280	129.6
−50	388.9	40	353.0	130	305.7	210	240.9	290	96.37
−40	385.0	50	348.8						

Heat capacity of liquid methylcyclohexane [80]

T, °K	150	160	170	180	190	200	210	220
c_p, kJ/kg · deg	1.426	1.447	1.469	1.492	1.516	1.541	1.567	1.596
T, °K	230	240	250	260	270	280	290	300
c_p, kJ/kg · deg	1.627	1.661	1.696	1.732	1.770	1.808	1.848	1.888

Density ρ (kg/m³) of saturated liquid methylcyclohexane [65, 403]*

t, °C	ρ	t, °C	ρ	t, °C	ρ	t, °C	ρ	t, °C	ρ
0	786.8	60	734.5	120	678.9	180	614.1	240	530.0
10	778.1	70	725.6	130	668.9	190	601.7	250	512.8
20	769.4	80	716.6	140	658.6	200	589.1	260	494.3
30	760.6	90	707.4	150	648.1	210	575.9	270	473.9
40	751.9	100	698.1	160	637.3	220	561.6	280	440.0
50	743.2	110	688.6	170	626.0	230	546.4	290	402.0

*Reference [403] gives experimental data up to 700 bar.

Viscosity η of liquid methylcyclohexane [52]

t, °C	0	10	20	30	40
$\eta \cdot 10^3$, N · s/m²	0.991	0.847	0.731	0.639	0.562

Surface tension of methylcyclohexane [65]

t, °C	0	10	20	25	30	40	50	75	100
$\sigma \cdot 10^3$, N/m	25.80	24.74	23.68	23.15	22.62	21.56	20.50	17.85	15.20

ETHYLCYCLOHEXANE (C_8H_{16})

```
         CH2
        /   \
     H2C     CH—CH2—CH3
      |       |
     H2C     CH2
        \   /
         CH2
```

Molecular weight 112.208

t_{boil} = 131.783 °C at 760 mm Hg; t_{melt} = – 111.323 °C

Thermodynamic properties of ethylcyclohexane [62]:
$c_p{}^0$ (kJ/kg · deg), i^0 (kJ/kg) and s^0 (kJ/kg · deg)

T, °K	c_p	$i°$	$s°$	T, °K	c_p	$i°$	$s°$
0	0	0	0	900	3.59	1836.8	6.137
298.16	1.416	227.5	3.412	1000	3.780	2205.0	6.526
300	1.426	230.4	3.421	1100	3.944	2589.3	6.895
400	1.92	398.47	3.899	1200	4.082	2992.3	7.246
500	2.38	613.75	4.376	1300	4.197	3406.4	7.574
600	2.76	870.82	4.846	1400	4.302	3828.0	7.887
700	3.09	1164.8	5.298	1500	4.388	4264.5	8.190
800	3.36	1489.4	5.731				

Saturated vapor pressure of ethylcyclohexane [65]

t, °C	p, mm Hg	t, °C	p, mm Hg	t, °C	p, mm Hg	t, °C	p, bar
−30	0.25	30	16.76	90	216.02	140	1.253
−20	0.60	40	27.29	100	300.19	150	1.6020
−10	1.33	50	44.68	110	410.69	160	2.0216
0	2.73	60	69.17	120	550.22	170	2.520
10	5.28	70	103.83	130	724.77	180	3.108
20	9.64	80	151.63				

Latent heat of vaporization r (kJ/kg) of ethylcyclohexane [65]

t, °C	r	t, °C	r	t, °C	r	t, °C	r	t, °C	r
−110	402.6	−20	377.6	70	341.4	160	292.9	250	217.9
−100	400.3	−10	374.2	80	336.5	170	286.5	260	205.6
−90	397.7	0	370.5	90	332.0	180	279.8	270	192.1
−80	395.1	10	366.8	100	326.8	190	272.7	280	177.2
−70	392.5	20	363.0	110	321.6	200	265.3	290	160.4
−60	389.9	30	358.9	120	316.4	210	257.1	300	139.9
−50	386.9	40	354.4	130	310.8	220	248.5	310	113.8
−40	383.9	50	350.3	140	304.8	230	239.2	320	72.75
−30	380.9	60	345.9	150	298.8	240	228.7		

Heat capacity c_p (kJ/kg · deg) of liquid ethylcyclohexane [82]

T, °K	c_p	T, °K	c_p	T, °K	c_p	T, °K	c_p
170	1.466	210	1.566	250	1.697	290	1.854
180	1.489	220	1.596	260	1.733	298.16	1.889
190	1.512	230	1.627	270	1.772	300	1.897
200	1.538	240	1.661	280	1.812	310	1.941

Viscosity η of liquid ethylcyclohexane [52]

t, °C	0	10	20	30	40
$\eta \cdot 10^3$, N · s/m²	1.139	0.972	0.839	0.735	0.649

Surface tension σ of ethylcyclohexane [65]

t, °C	0	10	20	25	30	40	50	75	100
$\sigma \cdot 10^3$, N/m	27.87	26.77	25.67	25.12	24.57	23.47	22.37	19.62	16.87

OLEFINS

ETHYLENE (C_2H_4)

$CH_2{=}CH_2$

Molecular weight 28.052

$t_{boil} = -103.71$ °C at 760 mm Hg; $t_{melt} = -169.15$ °C;
$t_{cr} = 9.5$ ° C; $p_{cr} = 50.6$ bar; $\rho_{cr} = 220$ kg/m³

Thermodynamic properties of saturated ethylene [51]: v (dm³/kg), i (kJ/kg)and s (kJ/kg · deg)

t, °C	p, bar	v'	v''	i'	i''	s'	s''
0	40.94	2.914	9.728	−307.6	−134.4	−2.127	−1.493
1	41.88	2.959	9.342	−303.7	−137.9	−2.113	−1.509
2	42.84	3.007	8.965	−299.5	−141.7	−2.099	−1.525
3	43.81	3.059	8.591	−295.2	−145.6	−2.084	−1.542
4	44.79	3.117	8.220	−290.6	−149.8	−2.068	−1.560
5	45.80	3.182	7.851	−285.8	−154.2	−2.052	−1.579
6	46.82	3.255	7.482	−280.5	−159.1	−2.034	−1.598
7	47.86	3.336	7.111	−275.2	−164.0	−2.015	−1.618
8	48.92	3.487	6.532	−265.2	−173.6	−1.981	−1.655
9	50.00	3.975	5.317	−239.8	−198.6	−1.892	−1.746
9.5	50.6	4.550		−219.1		−1.820	

Thermodynamic properties of ethylene at different temperatures and pressures [51]:
v (dm³/kg), i (kJ/kg) and s (kJ/kg · deg)

p, bar	v	i	s	v	i	s
		t=0 °C			t=25 °C	
1.0	803.61	−1.89	−0.00465	878.71	35.88	0.12760
1.2	668.67	−2.25	−0.05957	731.41	35.57	0.07284
1.4	572.28	−2.61	−0.10615	626.21	33.26	0.02644
1.6	499.98	−2.98	−0.14662	547.30	34.94	−0.01385
1.8	443.75	−3.34	−0.18243	485.92	34.63	−0.04949
2.0	398.77	−3.71	−0.21455	436.83	34.31	−0.08144
2.5	317.79	−4.63	−0.28295	348.44	33.52	−0.14938
3.0	263.79	−5.56	−0.33928	289.52	32.72	−0.20525
3.5	225.22	−6.49	−0.38727	247.43	31.92	−0.25277
4.0	196.29	−7.43	−0.42918	215.86	31.12	−0.29419
4.5	173.78	−8.39	−0.46644	191.30	30.31	−0.33096
5.0	155.77	−9.34	−0.50004	171.65	29.50	−0.36406
6	128.75	−11.27	−0.55890	142.18	27.86	−0.42188
7	109.44	−13.23	−0.60950	121.11	26.21	−0.47139
8	94.94	−15.22	−0.65409	105.31	24.54	−0.51484
9	83.66	−17.24	−0.69409	93.02	22.85	−0.55368
10	74.62	−19.30	−0.73052	83.18	21.14	−0.58889
12	61.04	−23.51	−0.79531	68.41	17.68	−0.65106
14	51.31	−27.88	−0.85227	57.84	14.13	−0.70512
16	43.99	−32.42	−0.90367	49.91	10.50	−0.75335
18	38.26	−37.16	−0.95103	43.72	6.78	−0.79713
20	33.65	−42.12	−0.99546	38.76	2.96	−0.83755
25	25.23	−55.69	−1.0985	29.79	−7.05	−0.92806
30	19.42	−71.63	−1.1975	23.75	−17.87	−1.0090
35	14.97	−91.64	−1.3020	19.37	−29.70	−1.0846
40	11.27	−118.76	−1.4253	16.02	−42.82	−1.1581
45	2.842	−312.67	−2.1458	13.33	−57.70	−1.2326
50	2.777	−317.21	−2.1676	11.08	−74.92	−1.3107
60	2.670	−323.17	−2.1993	7.323	−122.66	−1.5016
70	2.601	−327.28	−2.2240	4.401	−195.64	−1.7657
80	2.547	−330.25	−2.2443	3.500	−233.10	−1.9042
90	2.504	−332.50	−2.2618	3.195	−248.51	−1.9671
100	2.467	−334.25	−2.2773	3.026	−257.77	−2.0079

continued

p, bar	*v*	*i*	*s*	*v*	*i*	*s*
120	2.407	−336.73	−2.3042	2.826	−268.57	−2.0637
140	2.358	−338.29	−2.3274	2.702	−274.95	−2.1036
160	2.318	−339.20	−2.3478	2.613	−279.09	−2.1353
180	2.283	−339.63	−2.3662	2.544	−281.87	−2.1619
200	2.253	−339.68	−2.3830	2.488	−283.75	−2.1851
250	2.190	−338.68	−2.4200	2.381	−285.91	−2.2331
300	2.140	−336.53	−2.4517	2.303	−285.85	−2.2721
350	2.098	−333.62	−2.4798	2.242	−284.41	−2.3054
400	2.063	−330.16	−2.5051	2.192	−282.08	−2.3347
450	2.032	−326.26	−2.5283	2.150	−279.07	−2.3609
500	2.004	−322.01	−2.5495	2.113	−275.54	−2.3847
600	1.957	−312.72	−2.5882	2.052	−267.58	−2.4280
700	1.917	−302.73	−2.6226	2.002	−258.58	−2.4658
800	1.884	−292.19	−2.6537	1.961	−248.82	−2.4996
900	1.854	−281.25	−2.6823	1.925	−238.50	−2.5302
1000	1.828	−270.07	−2.7088	1.893	−227.75	−2.5584
1200	1.783	−247.06	−2.7569	1.840	−205.39	−2.6088
1400	1.745	−223.63	−2.8000	1.797	−182.36	−2.6532
1600	1.712	−199.83	−2.8390	1.760	−158.83	−2.6932
1800	1.684	−175.70	−2.8747	1.727	−134.90	−2.7297
2000	1.659	−151.29	−2.9078	1.699	−110.62	−2.7632
2500	1.605	− 89.92	−2.9820	1.640	− 49.42	−2.8378
		$t=50$ °C			$t=75$ °C	
1.0	953.61	75.60	0.25546	1028.4	117.36	0.37991
1.2	793.97	75.33	0.20083	856.38	117.13	0.32540
1.4	679.94	75.06	0.15457	733.53	116.89	0.27924
1.6	594.42	74.78	0.11441	641.39	116.66	0.23918
1.8	527.90	74.51	0.07891	569.73	116.42	0.20380
2.0	474.69	74.24	0.04710	512.40	116.18	0.17209
2.5	378.90	73.55	−0.02050	409.20	115.59	0.10476
3.0	315.04	72.86	−0.07601	340.41	114.99	0.04953
3.5	269.43	72.17	−0.12318	291.26	114.40	0.00264
4.0	235.21	71.48	−0.16424	254.41	113.80	−0.03814
4.5	208.60	70.79	−0.20064	225.74	113.20	−0.07425
5.0	187.31	70.09	−0.23336	202.81	112.60	−0.10669
6	155.37	68.69	−0.29041	168.40	111.40	−0.16315
7	132.56	67.29	−0.33914	143.83	110.19	−0.21128
8	115.44	65.87	−0.38178	125.39	108.98	−0.25331
9	102.13	64.44	−0.41979	111.06	107.76	−0.29069
10	91.48	63.00	−0.45417	99.59	106.53	−0.32440
12	75.49	60.09	−0.51450	82.38	104.03	−0.38346
14	64.07	57.14	−0.56665	70.08	101.57	−0.43422
16	55.49	54.14	−0.61281	60.86	99.05	−0.47895
18	48.82	51.09	−0.65442	53.68	96.51	−0.51907
20	43.47	48.00	−0.69250	47.94	93.94	−0.55559
25	33.84	40.03	−0.77641	37.59	87.39	−0.63528
30	27.39	31.70	−0.84924	30.68	80.65	−0.70335
35	22.76	22.98	−0.91485	25.74	73.72	−0.76359
40	19.27	13.81	−0.97565	22.03	66.59	−0.81825
45	16.53	4.13	−1.0332	19.14	59.24	−0.86883
50	14.33	− 6.12	−1.0887	16.82	51.68	−0.91634
60	10.97	− 28.76	−1.1976	13.34	35.86	−1.0048
70	8.535	− 54.12	−1.3061	10.85	19.09	−1.0875
80	6.717	− 82.65	−1.4180	9.000	1.48	−1.1665
90	5.402	−111.86	−1.5269	7.586	− 16.61	−1.2423
100	4.541	−137.16	−1.6204	6.501	− 34.70	−1.3144
120	3.682	−169.56	−1.7457	5.048	− 67.70	−1.4420
140	3.293	−187.19	−1.8218	4.229	− 92.91	−1.5408
160	3.069	−197.92	−1.8746	3.754	−110.48	−1.6141
180	2.919	−204.92	−1.9147	3.453	−122.64	−1.6697
200	2.810	−209.80	−1.9476	3.246	−131.30	−1.7138
250	2.623	−216.83	−2.0112	2.927	−144.21	−1.7949

continued

p, bar	v	i	s	v	i	s
300	2.500	−219.62	−2.0594	2.736	−150.46	−1.8534
350	2.410	−220.12	−2.0989	2.606	−153.19	−1.8996
400	2.340	−219.20	−2.1327	2.507	−153.85	−1.9381
450	2.282	−217.31	−2.1625	2.430	−153.15	−1.9713
500	2.234	−214.59	−2.1891	2.366	−151.30	−2.0006
600	2.155	−207.71	−2.2358	2.266	−145.70	−2.0511
700	2.093	−199.45	−2.2759	2.190	−138.29	−2.0938
800	2.042	−190.27	−2.3115	2.128	−129.71	−2.1312
900	1.999	−180.40	−2.3436	2.077	−120.31	−2.1644
1000	1.962	−170.01	−2.3728	2.033	−110.27	−2.1946
1200	1.900	−148.18	−2.4249	1.962	−88.95	−2.2481
1400	1.850	−125.50	−2.4706	1.905	−66.49	−2.2947
1600	1.808	−102.23	−2.5114	1.857	−43.43	−2.3363
1800	1.772	−78.50	−2.5486	1.817	−19.90	−2.3740
2000	1.740	−54.38	−2.5826	1.782	4.05	−2.4086
2500	1.675	6.60	−2.6579	1.711	64.79	−2.4845
		t=100 °C			t=125 °C	
1.0	1103.0	161.25	0.50161	1177 6	207.30	0.62104
1.2	918.66	161.04	0.44719	980.86	207.12	0.56668
1.4	786.99	160.84	0.40111	840.37	206.94	0.52067
1.6	688.24	160.63	0.36114	735.00	206.76	0.48077
1.8	611.43	160.42	0.32483	653.05	206.58	0.44553
2.0	549.98	160.22	0.29421	587.48	206.40	0.41398
2.5	439.38	159.70	0.22709	469.47	205.95	0.34703
3.0	365.64	159.18	0.17207	390.80	205.50	0.29218
3.5	312.97	158.66	0.12540	334.60	205.04	0.24568
4.0	273.47	158.14	0.08483	292.45	204.59	0.20528
4.5	242.75	157.62	0.04893	259.67	204.14	0.16956
5.0	218.17	157.10	0.01671	233.44	203.68	0.13752
6	181.30	156.05	−0.03931	194.11	202.77	0.08184
7	154.96	155.00	−0.08700	166.01	201.86	0.03451
8	135.21	153.95	−0.12858	144.93	200.95	−0.00671
9	119.85	152.90	−0.16551	128.54	200.03	−0.04327
10	107.55	151.84	−0.19875	115.42	199.11	−0.07616
12	89.12	149.71	−0.25686	95.76	197.26	−0.13354
14	75.95	147.57	−0.30666	81.71	195.40	−0.18261
16	66.07	145.41	−0.35038	71.17	193.53	−0.22559
18	58.38	143.23	−0.38948	62.98	191.65	−0.26393
20	52.23	141.04	−0.42494	56.42	189.77	−0.29862
25	41.16	135.49	−0.50183	44.62	184.98	−0.37353
30	33.78	129.84	−0.56688	36.75	180.12	−0.43648
35	28.51	124.09	−0.62385	31.13	175.19	−0.49130
40	24.55	118.23	−0.67498	26.92	170.20	−0.54016
45	21.47	112.27	−0.72170	23.63	165.16	−0.58448
50	19.01	106.22	−0.76498	21.04	160.07	−0.62527
60	15.33	93.82	−0.84391	17.12	149.76	−0.69880
70	12.71	81.07	−0.91555	14.34	139.31	−0.76438
80	10.75	68.03	−0.98192	12.26	128.78	−0.82413
90	9.248	54.74	−1.0442	10.66	118.23	−0.87938
100	8.071	41.24	−1.1024	9.398	107.72	−0.93086
120	6.389	15.73	−1.2099	7.558	87.25	−1.0245
140	5.304	− 7.12	−1.3022	6.317	68.23	−1.1069
160	4.598	−25.89	−1.3790	5.455	51.26	−1.1790
180	4.123	−40.70	−1.4419	4.834	36.66	−1.2415
200	3.793	−52.08	−1.4936	4.400	24.66	−1.2947
250	3.294	−70.32	−1.5896	3.711	3.41	−1.3986
300	3.013	−80.04	−1.6577	3.324	− 9.02	−1.4738
350	2.828	−85.12	−1.7104	3.076	−16.25	−1.5320
400	2.695	−87.41	−1.7535	2.902	−20.05	−1.5790
450	2.593	−87.98	−1.7901	2.770	−21.86	−1.6188
500	2.511	−87.05	−1.8221	2.667	−21.86	−1.6533
600	2.385	−82.83	−1.8764	2.512	−19.07	−1.7112
700	2.292	−76.36	−1.9216	2.399	−13.61	−1.7591

continued

p, bar	v	i	s	v	i	s
800	2.218	−68.45	−1.9608	2.312	−6.43	−1.8002
900	2.158	−59.55	1.9955	2.241	1.91	−1.8363
1000	2.107	−49.93	−2.0269	2.182	11.07	−1.8688
1200	2.024	−29.14	−2.0815	2.089	31.27	−1.9250
1400	1.959	−6.94	−1.1290	2.016	53.15	−1.9734
1600	1.906	15.95	−2.1711	1.957	75.89	−2.0160
1800	1.862	39.36	−2.2093	1.907	99.19	−2.0545
2000	1.823	63.17	−2.2442	1.865	122.88	−2.0897
2500	1.745	123.68	−2.3208	1.780	183.17	−2.1669

p, bar	v	i	s	p, bar	v	i	s
			t=150 °C				
1.0	1252.0	255.58	0.73850	60	18.79	206.72	−0.56015
1.2	1043.0	255.38	0.68420	70	15.84	197.97	−0.62156
1.4	893.66	255.23	0.63826	80	13.64	189.17	−0.67707
1.6	781.68	255.07	0.59842	90	11.94	180.37	−0.72800
1.8	694.58	254.92	0.56325	100	10.59	171.62	−0.77520
2.0	624.90	254.76	0.53176	120	8.604	154.46	−0.86081
2.5	499.48	254.38	0.46497	140	7.241	138.27	−0.93632
3.0	415.86	254.00	0.41028	160	6.266	123.42	−1.0032
3.5	356.14	253.61	0.36394	180	5.552	110.20	−1.0622
4.0	311.34	253.22	0.32370	200	5.018	98.71	−1.1143
4.5	276.50	252.83	0.28814	250	4.157	76.84	−1.2196
5.0	248.63	252.44	0.25625	300	3.662	62.74	−1.2989
6	206.82	251.66	0.20090	350	3.345	53.92	−1.3608
7	176.96	250.88	0.15389	400	3.125	48.80	−1.4111
8	154.57	250.10	0.11298	450	2.961	45.91	−1.4537
9	137.15	249.31	0.07674	500	2.833	45.11	−1.4903
10	123.21	248.53	0.04418	600	2.646	46.51	−1.5514
12	102.31	246.95	−0.01255	700	2.512	50.92	−1.6015
14	87.38	245.36	−0.06096	800	2.410	57.26	−1.6442
16	76.19	243.76	−0.10325	900	2.328	64.97	−1.6815
18	67.48	242.15	−0.14091	1000	2.261	73.60	−1.7150
20	60.51	240.53	−0.17491	1200	2.155	93.07	−1.7731
25	47.98	236.44	−0.24809	1400	2.073	114.47	−1.8225
30	39.63	232.31	−0.30933	1600	2.008	136.87	−1.8655
35	36.66	228.13	−0.36236	1800	1.954	159.94	−1.9043
40	29.20	223.91	−0.40937	2000	1.907	183.47	−1.9397
45	25.72	219.66	−0.45181	2500	1.816	243.57	−2.0173
50	22.95	215.38	−0.49065				

Heat capacity c_p and c_v (kJ/kg · deg) of ethylene at different temperatures and pressures [51]

p, bar	c_p	c_v	c_p	c_v	c_p	c_v	c_p	c_v
	t=0 °C		t=25 °C		t=50 °C		t=75 °C	
1	1.472	1.168	1.549	1.245	1.629	1.328	1.713	1.413
2	1.483	1.169	1.558	1.246	1.637	1.329	1.720	1.414
3	1.495	1.171	1.568	1.248	1.645	1.331	1.727	1.416
5	1.521	1.174	1.588	1.251	1.662	1.334	1.740	1.419
7	1.550	1.178	1.609	1.255	1.679	1.338	1.754	1.422
10	1.594	1.185	1.644	1.261	1.707	1.344	1.776	1.427
15	1.69	1.199	1.714	1.273	1.759	1.355	1.816	1.436
20	1.82	1.216	1.800	1.286	1.819	1.367	1.859	1.446
25	2.00	1.238	1.905	1.302	1.887	1.380	1.907	1.457
30		1.266	2.034	1.320	1.964	1.394	1.960	1.468
35		1.303	2.21	1.341	2.055	1.408	2.017	1.478
40		1.354	2.48	1.367	2.169	1.423	2.079	1.489
45				1.398	2.300	1.440	2.149	1.500

continued

p, bar	c_p	c_v	c_p	c_v	c_p	c_v	c_p	c_v
50				1.438	2.461	1.458	2.228	1.511
60				1.530	2.95	1.500	2.417	1.534
70				1.559	3.8	1.543	2.640	1.557
80			5.4		4.3	1.582	2.921	1.579
90			4.7		4.6	1.601	3.23	1.621
100			4.1	1.39	4.6	1.603	3.52	1.615
120			3.43	1.36	4.1	1.582	3.704	1.630
140			3.13	1.35	3.71	1.565	3.630	1.628
160			2.92	1.344	3.43	1.554	3.469	1.622
180			2.78	1.342	3.23	1.548	3.308	1.617
200			2.70	1.341	3.071	1.545	3.172	1.615
250			2.54	1.339	2.853	1.543	2.937	1.614
300			2.45	1.339	2.726	1.544	2.796	1.615
350			2.39	1.340	2.644	1.548	2.703	1.619
400			2.34	1.344	2.585	1.553	2.639	1.624
450			2.30	1.352	2.538	1.559	2.589	1.630
500			2.26	1.362	2.505	1.566	2.553	1.636
600			2.22	1.378	2.456	1.580	2.499	1.649
700			2.18	1.389	2.424	1.593	2.463	1.662
800			2.16	1.397	2.401	1.605	2.437	1.674
900			2.14	1.404	2.383	1.615	2.418	1.686
1000			2.12	1.411	2.369	1.624	2.403	1.697
1200			2.10	1.424	2.348	1.641	2.383	1.716
1400			2.09	1.436	2.336	1.657	2.372	1.733
1600			2.08	1.447	2.328	1.673	2.365	1.749
1800			2.07	1.46	2.321	1.688	2.359	1.765
2000			2.06	1.47	2.315	1.703	2.353	1.780
2500			2.05		2.306	1.733	2.344	1.811

p, bar	c_p	c_v	c_p	c_v	c_p	c_v
	t=100 °C		t=125 °C		t=150 °C	
1	1.798	1.500	1.886	1.588	1.974	1.676
2	1.804	1.501	1.891	1.589	1.980	1.678
3	1.810	1.502	1.896	1.591	1.985	1.680
5	1.821	1.505	1.906	1.594	1.995	1.684
7	1.833	1.508	1.917	1.598	2.005	1.688
10	1.851	1.512	1.933	1.603	2.021	1.695
15	1.882	1.519	1.960	1.610	2.047	1.705
20	1.914	1.527	1.988	1.618	2.074	1.716
25	1.948	1.534	2.016	1.626	2.102	1.727
30	1.985	1.542	2.045	1.634	2.130	1.739
35	2.024	1.549	2.075	1.641	2.159	1.750
40	2.066	1.557	2.106	1.648	2.190	1.761
45	2.110	1.564	2.140	1.655	2.21	1.771
50	2.156	1.571	2.175	1.661	2.24	1.779
60	2.260	1.585	2.247	1.672	2.29	1.792
70	2.378	1.598	2.324	1.681	2.35	1.803
80	2.508	1.610	2.406	1.689	2.41	1.812
90	2.648	1.621	2.494	1.696	2.46	1.818
100	2.798	1.632	2.590	1.702	2.52	1.822
120	3.047	1.650	2.760	1.713	2.63	1.827
140	3.212	1.660	2.889	1.721	2.73	1.828
160	3.240	1.662	2.976	1.726	2.82	1.829
180	3.196	1.663	3.010	1.729	2.88	1.829
200	3.129	1.663	3.010	1.731	2.92	1.830
250	2.956	1.662	2.942	1.732	2.94	1.830
300	2.829	1.663	2.854	1.733	2.89	1.83
350	2.738	1.666	2.775	1.735	2.83	1.83
400	2.674	1.670	2.718	1.738	2.79	1.84
450	2.624	1.674	2.671	1.741	2.74	1.84
500	2.587	1.679	2.636	1.745	2.71	1.85
600	2.530	1.688	2.579	1.752	2.66	1.86

continued

p, bar	c_p	c_v	c_p	c_v	c_p	c_v
700	2.491	1.698	2.538	1.761	2.62	1.87
800	2.463	1.707	2.507	1.769	2.59	1.88
900	2.442	1.716	2.483	1.777	2.56	1.89
1000	2.425	1.724	2.464	1.783	2.54	1.89
1200	2.402	1.740	2.438	1.796	2.50	1.90
1400	2.391	1.754	2.425	1.807	2.48	1.91
1600	2.385	1.767	2.416	1.817	2.46	1.91
1800	2.380	1.779	2.409	1.827	2.45	1.92
2000	2.375	1.791	2.404	1.836	2.44	1.92
2500	2.368	1.819	2.396	1.858	2.43	1.93

Heat capacity c_p (kJ/kg · deg) of liquid ethylene [71]

t, °C	c_p	t, °C	c_p	t, °C	c_p	t, °C	c_p
−166.47	2.466	−154.13	2.439	−133.08	2.406	−114.61	2.394
−164.58	2.463	−147.26	2.432	−127.78	2.403	−108.93	2.396
−160.88	2.454	−140.56	2.421	−121.28	2.402	−104.45	2.403

Viscosity η (N · s/m²) of ethylene gas at a pressure of 1 bar [52]

t, °C	$\eta \cdot 10^7$	t, °C	$\eta \cdot 10^7$	t, °C	$\eta \cdot 10^7$	t, °C	$\eta \cdot 10^7$	t, °C	$\eta \cdot 10^7$
−50	79.2	25	102.7	100	126.0	250	167.0	500	226.0
−25	86.4	50	110.8	150	140.5	300	181.0		
0	94.1	75	118.0	200	154.5	400	204.9		

Viscosity $\eta \cdot 10^7$ (N · s/m²) of ethylene gas at different temperatures and pressures [83]

p, atm \ t, °C →	24	50	100	150	p, atm \ t, °C →	24	50	100	150
1	102.3	110.8	126.0	140.5	150	488.5	364.0	238.0	215.0
25	109.6	117.5	129.0	147.0	200	552.4	438.0	302.7	260.0
50	141.0	131.0	139.5	156.0	300	652.0	538.0	409.5	341.5
60	181.3	140.0	—	160.0	400	732.3	618.0	486.3	415.0
70	282.0	156.0	150.0	164.0	500	809.0	689.0	554.0	477.0
80	335.7	176.0	157.5	168.5	600	882.0	756.0	614.7	533.0
90	366.7	200.4	—	173.0	700	944.0	814.0	671.3	586.0
100	390.6	242.0	173.4	178.0	800	995.6	867.0	725.5	636.0
125	442.0	301.0	204.0	195.0					

Viscosity η (N · s/m²) of liquid ethylene [62, 65]

t, °C	$\eta \cdot 10^6$	t, °C	$\eta \cdot 10^6$	t, °C	$\eta \cdot 10^6$	t, °C	$\eta \cdot 10^6$	t, °C	$\eta \cdot 10$
−165	600	−150	387	−135	276	−120	211	−105	170
−160	508	−145	345	−130	251	−115	196	−100	160
−155	443	−140	307	−125	229	−110	182		

Thermal conductivity $\lambda \cdot 10^3$ (W/m · deg) of ethylene gas [36, 38]

T, °K \ p, bar →	1	50	60	70	80	90	100	120	140	160	180
300	20.5	31.4	40.4	58.9	64.5	68.7	72.0	77.5	82.5	86.6	90.0
310	21.7	30.8	35.9	41.7	54.5	60.2	65.0	71.7	76.8	81.1	85.2
320	22.9	30.3	33.3	39.8	46.3	53.0	57.5	65.5	71.5	76.2	80.5
330	24.2	30.4	33.0	37.3	41.9	47.7	51.8	59.7	66.0	71.0	75.7
340	25.6	30.9	33.5	36.5	40.0	44.0	47.5	55.3	61.7	66.9	71.3
350	26.9	31.9	34.0	36.5	39.3	42.1	45.3	52.5	58.7	63.4	68.7
360	28.3	33.2	35.2	37.2	39.8	41.5	44.5	50.7	56.4	61.1	65.6
370	29.7	34.5	36.1	38.0	39.7	41.4	43.9	49.5	54.4	58.9	63.2
380	31.2	35.8	34.7	39.0	40.4	42.1	44.1	48.3	52.8	57.2	61.2
390	32.9	37.1	38.8	40.3	41.7	42.9	44.4	48.3	52.5	56.2	60.2
400	34.4	38.4	40.2	41.6	43.0	44.0	45.3	48.6	52.4	56.0	59.8
410	39.5	39.7	41.4	42.9	44.2	45.2	46.3	49.4	52.7	55.8	59.4
420	37.5	41.0	42.7	44.2	45.5	46.4	47.5	50.2	53.2	56.1	59.3
430	39.2	42.3	44.1	45.5	46.8	47.7	48.8	51.2	53.8	56.5	59.5
440	40.8	43.8	45.6	46.9	48.1	49.1	50.2	52.4	54.6	57.0	59.8
450	42.4	45.2	47.0	48.3	49.4	50.6	51.6	53.6	55.6	57.8	60.4
460	44.0	46.5	48.4	49.7	50.9	52.0	53.0	54.8	56.6	58.7	61.2
470	45.7	47.9	49.8	51.1	52.4	53.4	54.4	56.1	57.8	59.7	62.0
480	47.3	49.4	51.2	52.6	53.9	54.8	55.8	57.5	59.2	60.9	62.8
490	48.9	50.9	52.7	54.1	55.4	56.2	57.2	59.0	60.6	62.2	63.9
500	50.5	52.4	54.2	55.5	56.9	57.6	58.7	60.4	61.8	63.6	64.5

T, °K \ p, bar →	200	300	400	500	600	700	800	1000	1200	1500
300	93.2	107	117	127	135	143	151	167	180	199
310	88.7	103	113	123	131	139	146	162	175	194
320	84.0	99.0	109	119	127	134	142	157	170	189
330	79.5	94.8	106	115	123	131	138	152	165	185
340	75.2	90.8	102	112	120	128	135	148	160	180
350	71.8	87.2	98.5	109	117	125	132	145	156	176
360	69.0	84.4	95.8	106	114	122	129	142	152	172
370	66.7	81.9	93.3	103	112	119	126	139	149	168
380	64.8	79.8	91.2	101	109	117	124	137	146	165
390	63.6	78.0	89.4	96.8	107	115	122	135	144	162
400	62.8	76.6	87.8	97.2	105	113	120	133	142	159
410	62.4	75.7	86.4	95.8	104	112	118	131	140	157
420	62.2	75.1	85.3	94.8	103	110	117	127	139	156
430	62.4	74.8	84.5	94.0	102	109	116	128	138	154
440	62.6	74.6	83.9	93.2	101	108	115	127	137	153
450	63.0	74.8	83.6	92.7	100	107	114	126	136	152
460	63.3	75.0	83.6	92.4	99.8	106	113	125	136	151
470	63.9	75.3	83.8	92.2	99.5	106	112	124	135	150
480	64.7	75.7	84.1	92.0	99.2	106	112	124	134	149
490	65.6	76.2	84.5	92.0	99.2	105	111	123	133	148
500	66.6	76.7	85.0	92.2	99.2	105	111	123	133	147

Thermal conductivity λ of liquid ethylene [85]

T, °K	110	125	150	175	200	225	250	275
λ, W/m · deg	0.250	0.235	0.212	0.189	0.164	0.138	0.111	0.077

Surface tension of ethylene [65]

t, °C	−120	−110	−100
$\sigma \cdot 10^3$, N/m	19.50	17.65	15.71

PROPYLENE (C_3H_6)

CH_3—CH=CH_2

Molecular weight 42.078

$t_{boil} = -47.70$ °C at 760 mm Hg; $t_{melt} = -185.25$ °C;
$t_{cr} = 91.9$ °C; $p_{cr} = 46.0$ bar; $\rho_{cr} = 233$ kg/m³

Saturated vapor pressure of propylene [65]

t, °C	p, mm Hg	t, °C	p, mm Hg	t, °C	p, bar	t, °C	p, bar
−180	$1.64 \cdot 10^{-5}$	−110	12.44	−40	1.425	30	12.98
−170	$4.96 \cdot 10^{-4}$	−100	30.4	−30	2.132	40	16.45
−160	$6.94 \cdot 10^{-3}$	−90	36.3	−20	3.08	50	20.54
−150	0.0572	−80	131.9	−10	4.30	60	25.38
−140	0.318	−70	242.9	0	5.82	70	31.00
−130	1.33	−60	419.3	10	7.74	80	37.47
−120	4.43	−50	685.1	20	10.10	90	44.88
				25	11.47	91.9	46.0

Density ρ (kg/m³) at different temperatures and pressures [86]

p, bar \ t, °C →	25	50	75	100	125	150
1	1.7229	1.592	1.453	1.366	1.279	1.202
10	20.325	17.825	16.031	14.63	13.48	12.56
30			67.796	54.30	47.05	42.14
50				174.62	98.10	80.96
100				413.56	316.8	238.0
200				453.41	418.8	378.1
300				482.62	455.4	427.0
400				507.79	483.7	456.8
600				535.56	521.6	501.7
800				558.35	544.9	527.6
1000				576.44	566.9	551.1
1200				592.73	583.8	569.1
1500				613.62	598.0	584.9
2000				767.19	625.7	614.1
2500					672.0	635.5

Density ρ (kg/m³) of saturated liquid propylene [62, 65]

t, °C	ϱ′	t, °C	ϱ′	t, °C	ϱ′	t, °C	ϱ′	t, °C	ϱ′
−160	741	−120	694	−80	647	−40	599	0	5455
−150	729	−110	682	−70	636	−30	5865	10	5305
−140	718	−100	671	−60	624	−20	5735	20	514
−130	706	−90	659	−50	6115	−10	560	25	505

Heat capacity c_p (kJ/kg · deg) of liquid propylene [86]

p, bar \ t, °C →	25	50	75	100	125	150
0	1.529	1.620	1.709	1.799	1.890	1.980
1	1.547	1.634	1.720	1.807	1.895	1.984
10	1.832	1.822	1.855	1.907	1.970	2.040
30				2.40	2.25	2.21
50				2.93	3.04	2.57
100				3.25	3.82	3.91
200				2.74	2.78	2.90

continued

p, bar \ t, °C →	25	50	75	100	125	150
300				2.60	2.64	2.68
400				2.53	2.55	2.58
600				2.46	2.47	2.49
800				2.42	2.43	2.45
1000				2.40	2.41	2.42
1200				2.39	2.39	2.40
2000				2.39	2.37	2.38
2500					2.37	2.37

Heat capacity c_p (kJ/kg · deg) of liquid propylene [71]

t, °C	c_p	t, °C	c_p	t, °C	c_p	t, °C	c_p	t, °C	c_p
−179.25	2.194	−157.52	2.106	−118.19	2.077	−85.39	2.098	−63.98	2.148
−174.50	2.169	−145.07	2.089	−111.28	2.077	−78.50	2.110	−56.75	2.152
−168.98	2.139	−138.60	2.085	−104.15	2.081	−71.39	2.135	−49.76	2.177
−163.28	2.127	−131.95	2.072	−96.45	2.089				

Enthalpy i (kJ/kg) of propylene gas [86]

p, bar \ t, °C →	25	50	75	100	125	150
0	40.37	79.71	121.32	165.18	211.28	259.66
1	37.72	77.48	119.42	163.55	209.84	258.38
10	9.28	54.87	100.81	147.85	196.34	246.43
30				103.26	160.82	216.60
50				3.10	112.05	180.55
100				−118.91	−29.78	69.04
200				−134.69	−64.70	7.62
300				−134.57	−69.08	−2.45
400				−130.05	−66.64	−2.40
600				−115.66	−54.17	7.91
800				−97.82	−37.27	23.74
1000				−78.20	−18.15	42.26
1200				−57.58	2.23	62.16
1500				−25.43	34.21	93.75
2000				−32.15	89.47	148.68
2500					145.90	205.08

Latent heat of vaporization r (kJ/kg) of propylene [65]

t, °C	r	t, °C	r	t, °C	r	t, °C	r	t, °C	r
−180	557.2	−120	509.4	−60	452.7	0	378.1	60	246.8
−170	549.2	−110	500.5	−50	442.8	10	362.2	70	210.9
−160	542.3	−100	491.5	−40	431.8	20	345.3	80	165.2
−150	534.3	−90	482.6	−30	419.9	30	326.4	90	69.6
−140	526.3	−80	472.6	−20	407.0	40	301.5		
−130	518.4	−70	462.7	−10	393.0	50	276.6		

Entropy s (kJ/kg · deg) of propylene gas [86]

p, bar \ t, °C →	25	50	75	100	125	150
1	0.1327	0.2607	0.3857	0.5080	0.6280	0.7462
10	−0.3864	−0.2394	−0.1024	0.0281	0.1536	0.2757
30				−0.2794	−0.1302	0.0060
50				−0.6099	−0.3285	−0.1614
100				−0.9804	−0.7498	−0.5090
200				−1.0854	−0.9042	−0.7278
300				−1.1421	−0.9727	−0.8102
400				−1.1843	−1.0203	−0.8634
600				−1.2486	−1.0895	−0.9380
800				−1.2988	−1.1422	−0.9932
1000				−1.3407	−1.1854	−1.0380
1200				−1.3771	−1.2225	−1.0761
1500				−1.4247	−1.2705	−1.1250
2000				−1.4913	−1.3369	−1.1921
2500					−1.3924	−1.2479

Compressibility factor z of propylene gas [87]

p, bar \ t, °C →	30	50	75	100	125	150	175	200	225	250
5	0.9257	0.9407	0.9532	0.9646	0.9708	0.9763	0.9809	0.9842	0.9868	0.9890
10	0.8447	0.8777	0.9038	0.9265	0.9407	0.9522	0.9613	0.9684	0.9735	0.9778
15		0.8064	0.8540	0.8867	0.9101	0.9277	0.9418	0.9525	0.9604	0.9666
20		0.7147	0.7973	0.8427	0.8779	0.9027	0.9218	0.9375	0.9470	0.9553
25			0.7291	0.7975	0.8452	0.8770	0.9016	0.9211	0.9341	0.9455
30			0.6429	0.7502	0.8100	0.8508	0.8810	0.9044	0.9211	0.9339
35				0.6947	0.7728	0.8240	0.8601	0.8874	0.9082	0.9233
40				0.6299	0.7345	0.7963	0.8394	0.8707	0.8952	0.9137
45				0.5515	0.6942	0.7683	0.8185	0.8545	0.8824	0.9037
50				0.4298	0.6496	0.7393	0.7977	0.8386	0.8699	0.8936
52				0.3614						
54				0.2989						
55				0.2763	0.6019	0.7099	0.7769	0.8227	0.8576	0.8835
56				0.2668						
58				0.2593						
60				0.2578	0.5510	0.6799	0.7558	0.8071	0.8453	0.8743
65				0.2618	0.4990	0.6495	0.7348	0.7917	0.8335	0.8650
70				0.2698	0.4503	0.6198	0.7141	0.7769	0.8218	0.8558
75				0.2797	0.4157	0.5915	0.6942	0.7620	0.8103	0.8470
80				0.2918	0.3948	0.5651	0.6751	0.7473	0.7994	0.8383
85				0.3045	0.3863	0.5420	0.6572	0.7277	0.7890	0.8301
90				0.3173	0.3855	0.5228	0.6408	0.7209	0.7792	0.8223
95				0.3299	0.3882	0.5086	0.6262	0.7092	0.7701	0.8149
100				0.3427	0.3927	0.4992	0.6133	0.6983	0.7617	0.8079
105				0.3554	0.4000	0.4940	0.6026	0.6889	0.7538	0.8020
110				0.3679	0.4091	0.4916	0.5940	0.6804	0.7466	0.7964
115				0.3802	0.4186	0.4916	0.5878	0.6729	0.7400	0.7914
120				0.3929	0.4284	0.4939	0.5835	0.6664	0.7345	0.7869
125				0.4057	0.4383	0.4984	0.5810	0.6614	0.7297	0.7829
130				0.4185	0.4487	0.5042	0.5807	0.6579	0.7259	0.7792
135				0.4313	0.4594	0.5106	0.5815	0.6559	0.7229	0.7760
140				0.4445	0.4703	0.5178	0.5840	0.6551	0.7205	0.7735
145				0.4576	0.4816	0.5255	0.5875	0.6553	0.7192	0.7717
150				0.4703	0.4931	0.5402	0.5915	0.6563	0.7184	0.7706
155				0.4830	0.5045	0.5423	0.5963	0.6580	0.7186	0.7701
160				0.4959	0.5160	0.5514	0.6018	0.6602	0.7193	0.7701
165				0.5084	0.5275	0.5605	0.6080	0.6634	0.7206	0.7705
170				0.5213	0.5389	0.5698	0.6147	0.6671	0.7225	0.7714

continued

p, bar \ t, °C →	30	50	75	100	125	150	175	200	225	250
175				0.5335	0.5504	0.5795	0.6216	0,6717	0.7247	0.7726
180				0,5462	0.5617	0 5890	0.6290	0.6767	0.7272	0.7744
185				0.5590	0.5734	0.5989	0.6368	0.6821	0.7306	0.7767
190				0.5719	0.5846	0,6091	0.6445	0.6879	0.7345	0.7793
195				0.5847	0.5963	0,6191	0.6526	0.6940	0.7388	0.7822
200				0.5977	0.6079	0,6292	0.6609	0.7002	0.7436	0.7858
205				0,6105	0.6197	0.6395	0.6694	0.7080	0.7488	0.7897
210				0.6229	0.6312	0.6500	0.6782	0.7129	0.7540	0.7939
215				0.6356	0.6426	0.6604	0.6875	0.7195	0.7595	0.7982

Viscosity η of propylene gas at a pressure of 1 bar [52]

t, °C	0	25	50	75	100	150	200	250	300
$\eta \cdot 10^7$, N · s/m²	78.4	85.5	93.0	100.2	107.3	121.1	134.0	147.0	159.2

Viscosity $\eta \cdot 10^7$ (N · s/m²) of propylene liquid and gas at different temperatures and pressures [52]

p, atm \ t, °C →	18	53	85	100	150	200	250
1	83.9	94.2	103.2	107.5	121.2	134	146.8
25	1068			119	131.2	142.3	153
50	1116	778	514	280.5	155	154.7	166
75	1162	828	588	497	240	185.3	182
100	1205	870	640	550	340	229.4	206
125	1248	908	687	603	410	278.2	235
150	1288	944	728	647	460	326	269.5
200	1366	1013	803	724	544	408.5	338
300	1510	1146	935	852	674	533	446.5
400	1640	1270	1046	965	785	635	542
500	1770	1390	1150	1068	877	727	630
600	1894	1500	1250	1162	967	805.5	705
700	2010	1610	1346	1250	1048	880.5	774
800	2130	1710	1440	1337	1125	950	845

Viscosity η (N · s/m²) of liquid propylene at low temperatures [63]

T, °K	$\eta \cdot 10^7$	T, °K	$\eta \cdot 10^7$	T, °K	$\eta \cdot 10^7$	T, °K	$\eta \cdot 10^7$
88.7	14 460	98.0	5370	123.0	1310	159.8	450
89.8	12 730	102.6	3580	134.2	900	174.8	370
90.1	12 400	111.1	2150	141.9	670		
94.3	7 840	119.0	1550	150.0	550		

Thermal conductivity $\lambda \cdot 10^3$ (W/m · deg) of propylene at different temperatures and pressures [84]

t, °C \ p, bar →	1	10	20	46	100	150	200	300	400	500
0	14.0	117.9	119.0	121.2	125.4	129.4	133.1	139.8	145.7	151.4
25	16.6	17.9	112.0	114.2	118.5	122.7	126.4	133.4	139.6	145.5
50	19.4	20.3	22.8	105.5	111.5	116.1	120.0	127.1	133.4	139.4

continued

t, °C \ p, bar →	1	10	20	46	100	150	200	300	400	500
75	22.4	23.2	25.0	89.6	102.0	107.8	112.7	120.4	126.8	133.1
100	25.6	26.3	27.7	39.8	85.3	97.0	103.3	112.9	119.7	126.2
125	28.8	29.5	30.7	37.2	70.6	86.3	93.5	105.8	113.8	120.5
150	32.0	32.7	33.8	38.5	61.9	77.2	85.8	99.6	108.9	115.8
175	35.4	36.0	37.0	41.0	56.4	70.6	80.5	94.2	104.6	111.8
200	38.9	39.4	40.4	43.7	54.2	66.4	76.7	89.9	100.9	108.7
225	42.5	43.0	43.9	46.8	54.3	64.3	73.9	86.7	97.6	105.9
250	46.2	46.7	47.5	50.0	56.0	63.8	72.4	84.4	94.9	103.6
275	49.9	50.4	51.1	53.5	58.7	64.9	72.2	82.8	93.0	102.0
300	53.7	54.2	54.8	57.1	61.8	66.9	72.8	82.5	91.9	100.9
325	57.4	57.9	58.5	60.7	65.0	69.4	74.3	83.2	91.9	100.5
350	61.2	61.7	62.3	64.4	68.6	72.9	77.0	85.2	93.2	101.0

1-BUTENE (C_4H_8)

$CH_2{=}CH-CH_2-CH_3$

Molecular weight 56.104

$t_{boil} = -6.26$ °C at 730 mm Hg; $t_{melt} = -185.35$ °C;
$t_{cr} = 146.4$ °C; $p_{cr} = 40.2$ bar; $\rho_{cr} = 233$ kg/m^3

Thermodynamic properties of 1-butene [62]:
$c_p{}^0$ (kJ/kg · deg), i^0 (kJ/kg) and s (kJ/kg · deg)

T, °K	$c_p{}^0$	i^0	s^0	T, °K	$c_p{}^0$	i^0	s^0
0	0	0	0	900	3.320	1842.6	8.0876
298.16	1.528	307.2	5.451	1000	3.494	2182.9	8.4466
300	1.535	309.6	5.461	1100	3.646	2540.4	8.7969
400	1.943	483.8	5.944	1200	3.778	2911.3	9.1093
500	2.308	697.8	6.433	1300	3.893	3294.9	9.4168
600	2.622	944.1	6.882	1400	3.993	3689.0	9.7094
700	2.889	1219.4	7.307	1500	4.080	4092.7	9.9877
800	3.120	1520.2	7.7078				

Saturated vapor pressure of 1-butene [65]

t, °C	p, mm Hg	t, °C	p, mm Hg	t, °C	p, bar	t, °C	p, bar
−130	0.0309	−60	50.05	0	1.285	80	11.93
−120	0.148	−50	93.04	10	1.838	90	14.68
−110	0.561	−40	162.80	20	2.557	100	17.89
−100	1.77	−30	270.35	25	2.991	110	21.59
−90	4.80	−20	429.07	30	3.472	120	25.84
−80	11.53	−10	654.6	40	4.62	130	30.68
−70	25.05			50	6.02	140	36.15
				60	7.63	146.4	4.02
				70	9.59		

Density of liquid 1-butene [65]

t, °C	−80	−70	−60	−50	−40	−30	−20	−10	0	10	20
$\varrho \cdot 10^{-3}$, kg/m^3	0.703	0.694	0.6835	0.6732	0.6627	0.6519	0.6409	0.6297	0.6182	0.6065	0.5945

Heat capacity (kJ/kg · deg) of liquid 1-butene [89]

T, °K	c_p	T, °K	c_p	T, °K	c_p	T, °K	c_p	T, °K	c_p
85	1.968	120	1.892	160	1.897	200	1.963	240	2.075
90	1.944	130	1.886	170	1.907	210	1.987	250	2.112
100	1.921	140	1.886	180	1.920	220	2.012	255	2.131
110	1.904	150	1.890	190	1.939	230	2.041		

Latent heat of vaporization r (kJ/kg) of 1-butene [65]

t, °C	r	t, °C	r	t, °C	r	t, °C	r	t, °C	r
−180	508.2	−110	473.2	−40	423.9	30	356.0	90	265.7
−170	504.5	−100	467.2	−30	415.7	40	344.0	100	245.5
−160	500.0	−90	461.2	−20	406.7	50	331.4	110	223.1
−150	494.8	−80	454.5	−10	397.0	60	317.2	120	196.3
−140	489.6	−70	447.0	0	387.3	70	301.5	130	161.2
−130	484.3	−60	439.6	10	377.6	80	284.3	140	111.9
−120	479.1	−50	431.4	20	367.2				

Compressibility factor z of 1-butene [88]

p, atm \ t, °C →	37.78	71.12	104.45	137.78	171.12	p, atm \ t, °C →	37.78	71.12	104.45	137.78	171.12
0	1.000	1.000	1.000	1.000	1.000	360	1.275	1.213	1.166	1.134	1.112
20	0.077	0.075	—	0.783	0.846	380	1.340	1.274	1.224	1.188	1.163
40	0.150	0.148	0.156	0.178	0.632	400	1.404	1.335	1.282	1.242	1.214
60	0.225	0.222	0.228	0.239	—	420	1.469	1.396	1.341	1.297	1.265
80	0.300	0.295	0.298	0.307	0.354	440	1.534	1.458	1.400	1.352	1.316
100	0.375	0.365	0.364	0.373	0.410	460	1.600	1.520	1.458	1.406	1.367
120	0.447	0.434	0.430	0.438	0.465	480	1.666	1.580	1.514	1.460	1.418
140	0.519	0.502	0.495	0.500	0.522	500	1.732	1.640	1.570	1.513	1.469
160	0.589	0.570	0.560	0.562	0.578	520	1.798	1.700	1.626	1.566	1.519
180	0.659	0.635	0.622	0.621	0.633	540	1.863	1.759	1.681	1.618	1.568
200	0.729	0.700	0.684	0.680	0.689	560	1.927	1.818	1.736	1.671	1.616
220	0.799	0.766	0.746	0.738	0.744	580	1.991	1.878	1.791	1.722	1.664
240	0.869	0.831	0.807	0.796	0.799	600	2.055	1.938	1.846	1.773	1.712
260	0.939	0.895	0.869	0.853	0.852	620	2.118	1.998	1.900	1.825	1.760
280	1.008	0.959	0.930	0.910	0.905	640	2.180	2.056	1.954	1.876	1.808
300	1.076	1.023	0.990	0.967	0.957	660	2.240	2.114	2.008	1.926	1.856
320	1.143	1.087	1.049	1.024	1.009	680	2.300	2.170	2.062	1.974	1.902
340	1.210	1.150	1.108	1.079	1.061						

Viscosity η of 1-butene gas at a pressure of 1 bar [52]

t, °C	0	25	50	75	100	150	200	250	300
$\eta \cdot 10^7$, N · s/m²	70.8	77.5	84.1	90.6	97.1	109.8	122.8	135.5	148.3

cis-2-BUTENE (C_4H_8)

$$CH_3\diagdown CH{=}CH \diagup CH_3$$

Molecular weight 56.104

$t_{boil} = 3.720$ °C at 760 mmHg; $t_{melt} = -138.910$ °C; $t_{cr} = 155$ °C;
$p_{cr} = 41.5$ bar; $\rho_{cr} = 238$ kg/m³

Thermodynamic properties of *cis*-2-butene [62]:
c_p^0 (kJ/kg · deg), i^0 (kJ/kg) and s^0 (kJ/kg · deg)

T, °K	c_p^0	i^0	s^0	T, °K	c_p^0	i^0	s^0
0	0	0	0	900	3.261	1771.7	7.8862
298.16	1.408	294.4	5.366	1000	3.444	2106.8	8.2392
300	1.415	297.1	5.375	1100	3.603	2459.8	8.5757
400	1.816	458.5	5.840	1200	3.741	2827.0	8.8951
500	2.193	659.6	6.283	1300	3.861	3207.6	9.1989
600	2.522	896.3	6.713	1400	3.965	3599.4	9.4892
700	2.806	1162.7	7.124	1500	4.056	4001.7	9.7661
800	3.050	1456.0	7.5145				

Saturated vapor pressure of *cis*-2-butene [65]

t, °C	p, mm Hg	t, °C	p, mm Hg	t, °C	p, mm Hg	t, °C	p, bar	t, °C	p, bar
−130	0.0078	−80	5.67	−30	170.3	10	1.279	40	3.370
−120	0.0457	−70	13.18	−20	278.6	20	1.812	50	4.45
−110	0.203	−60	27.86	−10	436.4	25	2.135	60	5.76
−100	0.724	−50	54.35	0	658.0	30	2.500	155	41.5
−90	2.17	−40	98.05						

Density of liquid *cis*-2-butene [65]

t, °C	−50	−40	−30	−20	−10	0	10
$\rho \cdot 10^{-3}$, kg/m³	0.6994	0.6885	0.6776	0.6667	0.6558	0.6449	0.6340

Heat capacity c_p (kJ/kg · deg) of liquid *cis*-2-butene [89]

T, °K	c_p	T, °K	c_p	T, °K	c_p	T, °K	c_p	T, °K	c_p
140	2.007	170	1.972	200	1.980	230	2.020	260	2.095
150	1.988	180	1.971	210	1.989	240	2.041	270	2.135
160	1.976	190	1.974	220	2.002	250	2.066		

Latent heat of vaporization *r* (kJ/kg) of *cis*-2-butene [65]

t, °C	r	t, °C	r	t, °C	r	t, °C	r	t, °C	r
−130	514.2	−70	476.1	−10	429.1	50	364.9	110	266.4
−120	508.2	−60	469.4	0	419.4	60	351.5	120	244.0
−110	502.2	−50	462.0	10	409.7	70	337.3	130	217.2
−100	496.3	−40	453.8	20	399.3	80	322.4	140	184.3
−90	489.6	−30	446.3	30	388.8	90	306.0	150	138.8
−80	482.8	−20	437.3	40	376.9	100	287.3		

Viscosity of *cis*-2-butene gas at a pressure of 1 bar [52]

t, °C	0	25	50	75	100	150	200	250	300
$\eta \cdot 10^7$, N · s/m²	69.4	75.9	82.5	88.9	95.2	107.6	119.2	130.1	141.0

trans-2-BUTENE (C_4H_8)

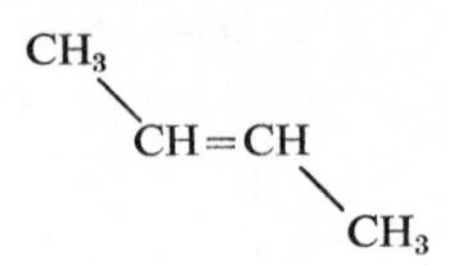

Molecular weight 56.104
t_{boil} = 0.88 °C at 760 mm Hg; t_{melt} = − 105.550 °C;
t_{cr} = 155 °C; p_{cr} = 41.5 bar; ρ_{cr} = 238 kg/m³

Thermodynamic properties of *trans*-2-butene [62]:
c_p^0 (kJ/kg · deg), i^0 (kJ/kg) and s^0 (kJ/kg · deg)

T, °K	c_p^0	i^0	s^0	T, °K	c_p^0	i^0	s^0
0	0	0	0	900	3.314	1838.9	7.9123
298.16	1.566	312.7	5.288	1000	3.476	2178.4	8.2698
300	1.573	315.5	5.297	1100	3.631	2534.4	8.6078
400	1.942	491.2	5.803	1200	3.764	2904.6	8.9295
500	2.290	703.2	6.272	1300	3.881	3286.7	9.2355
600	2.597	947.0	6.717	1400	3.982	3680.0	9.5273
700	2.864	1220.9	7.138	1500	4.071	4083.0	9.8049
800	3.097	1521.0	7.5354				

Saturated vapor pressure of *trans*-2-butene [65]

t, °C	−100	−90	−80	−70	−60	−50	−40	−30	−20	−10	0
p, mm Hg	1.05	2.98	7.44	16.68	34.24	65.2	116.5	197.0	317.9	492.1	734.8
t, °C	10	20	30	40	50	60	155				
p, bar	1.416	1.992	2.732	3.67	4.81	6.22	41.5				

Density of liquid *trans*-2-butene [65]

t, °C	−50	−40	−30	−20	−10	0	10
$\varrho \cdot 10^{-3}$, kg/m³	0.6814	0.6705	0.6596	0.6487	0.6378	0.6269	0.6160

Heat capacity c_p of liquid *trans*-2-butene [89]

T, °K	175	180	190	200	210	220	230	240	250	260
c_p, kJ/kg · deg	1.968	1.974	1.989	2.008	2.028	2.054	2.082	2.110	2.141	2.177

Latent heat of vaporization r (kJ/kg) of *trans*-2-butene [65]

t, °C	r	t, °C	r	t, °C	r	t, °C	r	t, °C	r
−100	480.6	−40	439.6	10	397.0	60	338.1	110	250.8
− 90	473.9	−30	432.1	20	386.6	70	323.1	120	226.1
− 80	467.9	−20	423.9	30	375.4	80	307.5	130	197.8
− 70	461.2	−10	415.7	40	363.4	90	290.3	140	160.4
− 60	454.5	0	406.7	50	351.5	100	271.6	150	102.2
− 50	447.0								

Viscosity of *trans*-2-butene gas at a pressure of 1 bar [52]

t, °C	0	25	50	75	100	150	200	250	300
$\eta \cdot 10^7$, $N \cdot s/m^2$	69.4	75.9	82.5	88.9	95.2	107.6	119.2	130.1	141.0

ISOBUTYLENE (C_4H_8)

$$CH_3-\underset{\displaystyle CH_3}{\underset{|}{C}}=CH_2$$

Molecular weight 56.104

$t_{boil} = -6.900$ °C at 760 mm Hg; $t_{melt} = -140.350$ °C;
$t_{cr} = 144.73$ °C; $p_{cr} = 39.69$ bar; $\rho_{cr} = 234$ kg/m³

Thermodynamic properties of isobutylene [62]:
c_p^0 (kJ/kg · deg), i^0 (kJ/kg) and s^0 (kJ/kg · deg)

T, °K	c_p^0	i^0	s^0	T, °K	c_p^0	i^0	s^0
0	0	0	0	900	3.323	1850.8	7.900
298.16	1.590	304.6	5.237	1000	3.496	2191.9	8.258
300	1.596	307.6	5.246	1100	3.648	2550.1	8.600
400	1.983	486.6	5.762	1200	3.778	2921.8	8.923
500	2.406	702.6	6.239	1300	3.893	3306.1	9.230
600	2.634	951.53	6.692	1400	3.993	3700.9	9.522
700	2.896	1227.7	7.118	1500	4.081	4179.3	9.801
800	3.124	1529.2	7.520				

Saturated vapor pressure of isobutylene [65]

t, °C	p, mm Hg	t, °C	p, mm Hg	t, °C	p, bar	t, °C	p, bar
−140	0.0062	−70	26.9	0	1.315	70	9.82
−130	0.038	−60	53.3	10	1.87	80	12.26
−120	0.175	−50	98.2	20	2.58	90	15.09
−110	0.646	−40	171	25	3.01	100	18.37
−100	1.99	−30	282	30	3.50	110	22.16
− 90	5.30	−20	445	40	4.64	120	26.34
− 80	12.5	−10	675	50	6.06	130	31.28
				60	7.77	140	36.70

Density of liquid isobutylene [65]

t, °C	−70	−60	−50	−40	−30	−20	−10	0	10
$\varrho \cdot 10^{-3}$, kg/m³	0.6948	0.6841	0.6733	0.6624	0.6515	0.6405	0.6294	0.6180	0.6065

Heat capacity c_p (kJ/kg · deg) of liquid isobutylene [89]

T, °K	c_p	T, °K	c_p	T, °K	c_p	T, °K	c_p	T, °K	c_p
140	1.904	170	1.941	200	2.005	230	2.086	250	2.150
150	1.915	180	1.960	210	2.034	240	2.116	255	2.173
160	1.926	190	1.981	220	2.059				

Latent heat of vaporization r (kJ/kg) of isobutylene [65]

t, °C	r	t, °C	r	t, °C	r	t, °C	r	t, °C	r
−140	485.8	−80	452.2	−20	408.2	40	346.3	100	247.0
−130	480.6	−70	445.5	−10	400.0	50	333.6	110	223.1
−120	474.6	−60	438.8	0	391.1	60	319.4	120	194.0
−110	469.4	−50	432.1	10	381.4	70	303.7	130	156.7
−100	463.4	−40	424.6	20	370.9	80	286.6	140	100.8
−90	458.2	−30	416.4	30	359.7	90	267.9		

Viscosity of isobutylene gas at a pressure of 1 bar [52]

t, °C	0	25	50	75	100	150	200	250	300
$\eta \cdot 10^7$, N · s/m²	73.2	80.1	87.0	93.8	100.6	114.1	127.3	140.8	154.2

1-PENTENE (C_5H_{10})

$CH_2{=}CH-CH_2-CH_2-CH_3$

Molecular weight 70.130

$t_{boil} = 29.968$ °C at 760 mm Hg; $t_{melt} = -165.220$ °C;

$t_{cr} = 201$ °C; $p_{cr} = 40.4$ bar

Thermodynamic properties of 1-pentene [62] c_p^0 (kJ/kg · deg), i^0 (kJ/kg) and s^0 (kJ/kg · deg)

T, °K	c_p^0	i^0	s^0	T, °K	c_p^0	i^0	s^0
0	0	0	0	900	3.362	1871.0	7.6100
298.16	1.564	313.2	4.934	1000	3.535	2216.1	7.9729
300	1.571	315.9	4.945	1100	3.686	2577.2	8.3168
400	1.976	493.6	5.453	1200	3.817	2952.8	8.6434
500	2.342	710.79	5.935	1300	3.931	3340.8	8.9538
600	2.660	961.17	6.3903	1400	4.030	3739.6	9.2493
700	2.929	1240.00	6.8207	1500	4.118	4147.4	9.5323
800	3.161	1544.4	7.2267				

Saturated vapor pressure p of 1-pentene [65]

t, °C	p, mm Hg	t, °C	p, mm Hg	t, °C	p, bar	t, °C	p, bar	t, °C	p, bar
−60	6.70	0	235.42	40	1.4162	100	6.900	160	21.56
−50	14.24	10	359.40	50	1.9318	110	8.515	170	25.40
−40	28.02	20	530.70	60	2.5797	120	10.54	180	29.76
−30	51.59	25	637.65	70	3.380	130	12.73	190	34.70
−20	89.71	30	760.83	80	4.354	140	15.26	200	40.26
−10	148.49			90	5.520	150	18.19	201	40.4

Density ρ of liquid 1-pentene [65]

t, °C	10	20	26	30
$\varrho \cdot 10^{-3}$, kg/m³	0.6508	0.6405	0.6353	0,6300

Heat capacity c_p (kJ/kg · deg) of liquid 1-pentene [91]

T, °K	c_p	T, °K	c_p	T, °K	c_p	T, °K	c_p	T, °K	c_p
110	1,844	160	1,849	200	1,904	240	2,004	280	2,141
120	1,837	170	1,858	210	1,925	250	2,034	290	2,182
130	1,835	180	1,871	220	1,949	260	2,068	298,16	2,216
140	1,838	190	1.886	230	1.975	270	2,103	300	2.224
150	1,843								

Latent heat of vaporization r (kJ/kg) of 1-pentene [65]

t, °C	r	t, °C	r	t, °C	r	t, °C	r	t, °C	r
−160	460,3	−80	428,0	0	381.5	70	327,8	140	243.0
−150	456.7	−70	423,3	10	374.3	80	318,2	150	232,2
−140	453,1	−60	417,9	20	367,2	90	308,6	160	207,8
−130	448,9	−50	412,5	30	359,4	100	297.9	170	185,1
−120	445,4	−40	407.2	40	352,2	110	286,0	180	157,6
−110	441.2	−30	401.2	50	344,5	120	272,8	190	119,4
−100	437,0	−20	394,6	60	336.1	130	258.5	200	47,8
− 90	432.2	−10	388,0						

Compressibility factor z of 1-pentene [90]

p, bar \ t, °C →	80	100	125	150	175	200	225
10	0,040	0,046					
20	0,084	0,085	0,081	0.085			
30	0,124	0,124	0,123		0,140		
40	0,164	0,164	0,160	0.164	0,176	0.290	
50	0.203	0.202	0,197		0,214	0,248	0,426
60	0,242	0,240	0,235	0,240	0.251	0,269	0,345
70	0.280	0.278	0,274	0,278	0.288	0,300	0,343
80	0,320	0.315	0.313	0.315	0.323	0,333	0.366
90	0,359	0,353	0,352	0,353	0,359	0,367	0,393
100	0,400	0.390	0.391	0,391	0.393	0,401	0,421
110	0,440	0,428	0,429	0,427	0.427	0,435	0,450
120	0,481	0,465	0,464	0,462	0,461	0,468	0.478
130	0,519	0,503	0,500	0,496	0,494	0,500	0,506
140	0,557	0,541	0,535	0,531	0.528	0,532	0,536
150	0,595	0.579	0,571	0,564	0,561	0,565	0,565
160	0,632	0,618	0,607	0,598	0,595	0,596	0,594
170	0,670	0,654	0,643	0.631	0,628	0.631	0.623
180	0,707	0,691	0,679	0,666	0,661	0,659	0,651
190	0.745	0,729	0,714	0,700	0,694	0,688	0,680
200	0,784	0,766	0.749	0,733	0,726	0,719	0,708
210	0,822	0,802	0,783	0,767	0.758	0,750	0,738
220	0,862	0,838	0,818	0,800	0,791	0,780	0,767
230	0,901	0,873	0,852	0,832	0,822	0,811	0,795
240	0,940	0,908	0,886	0,865	0,854	0,841	0,823
250	0,979	0,943	0,920	0,897	0,885	0,872	0.850

continued

p, bar \ t, °C →	80	100	125	150	175	200	225
260	1.017	0.978	0.954	0.930	0.916	0.902	0.877
270	1.053	1.013	0.987	0.962	0.946	0.931	0.904
280	1.089	1.047	1.020	0.995	0.977	0.959	0.930
290	1.123	1.082	1.053	1.028	1.007	0.986	0.958
300	1.157	1.118	1.087	1.060	1.038	1.012	0.985
310	1.190	1.153	1.121	1.091	1.069	1.039	1.014

Viscosity η of liquid 1-pentene [62]

t, °C	−90	−85	−80	−75	−70	−65	−60	−55	−50	−45
$\eta \cdot 10^3$, N · s/m²	0.85	0.77	0.70	0.64	0.59	0.54	0.50	0.46	0.43	0.40
t, °C	−40	−35	−30	−25	−20	−15	−10	−5	0	
$\eta \cdot 10^3$, N · s/m²	0.38	0.35	0.33	0.31	0.30	0.28	0.27	0.25	0.24	

cis-2-PENTENE (C_5H_{10})

```
CH3          CH2—CH3
   \        /
    C  =  C
   /        \
  H          H
```

Molecular weight 70.130

t_{boil} = 36.942 °C at 760 mm Hg; t_{melt} = − 151.390 °C

Thermodynamic properties of *cis*-2-pentene [62]:
c_p^0 (kJ/kg · deg), i^0 (kJ/kg) and s^0 (kJ/kg · deg)

T, °K	c_p^0	i^0	s^0	T, °K	c_p^0	i^0	s^0
0	0	0	0	900	3.329	1809.5	7.5383
298.16	1.452	289.2	4.941	1000	3.509	2152.2	7.8995
300	1.460	291.8	4.948	1100	3.664	2509.8	8.2410
400	1.885	459.4	5.431	1200	3.800	2882.9	8.5646
500	2.272	668.0	5.891	1300	3.917	3265.6	8.8738
600	2.604	912.2	6.3348	1400	4.019	3665.6	9.1675
700	2.880	1183.2	6.7586	1500	4.108	4072.7	9.4499
800	3.122	1487.1	7.1580				

Saturated vapor pressure of *cis*-2-pentene [65]

t, °C	p, mm Hg	t, °C	p, mm Hg	t, °C	p, mm Hg	t, °C	p, bar	t, °C	p, bar
−60	4.11	−20	63.34	20	408.27	40	1.1238	80	3.622
−50	9.11	−10	107.52	25	494.66	50	1.5537	90	4.638
−40	18.61	0	174.34	30	594.93	60	2.1006	100	5.849
−30	35.40	10	271.54			70	2.7837	110	7.277

Density ρ (kg/m³) of liquid *cis*-2-pentene [65]

t, °C	$\varrho \cdot 10^{-3}$	t, °C	$\varrho \cdot 10^{-3}$	t, °C	$\varrho \cdot 10^{-3}$	t, °C	$\varrho \cdot 10^{-3}$	t, C°	$\varrho \cdot 10^{-3}$
−70	0.7405	−40	0.7138	−10	0,6862	20	0,6555	40	0.6341
−60	0.7316	−30	0,7048	0	0,6763	25	0.6502	50	0.6234
−50	0.7227	−20	0,6956	10	0.6660	30	0,6468		

Heat capacity c_p (kJ/kg · deg) of liquid *cis*-2-pentene [91]

T, °K	c_p	T, °K	c_p	T, °K	c_p	T, °K	c_p	T, °K	c_p
125	1,910	160	1.849	200	1.894	240	1.969	280	2,096
130	1,901	170	1,858	210	1,907	250	1,998	290	2,133
140	1,888	180	1.871	220	1,924	260	2,029	298.16	2,165
150	1,879	190	1.884	230	1,944	270	2,061	300	2,172

Latent heat of vaporization r (kJ/kg) of *cis*-2-pentene [65]

t °C	r	t, °C	r	t, °C	r	t, °C	r	t, °C	r
−150	491.9	−80	458,5	−10	417.3	60	361,2	130	275,2
−140	487,7	−70	453,1	0	410.7	70	351,6	140	259.1
−130	483,6	−60	447.2	10	403,6	80	340.9	150	240,6
−120	478.8	−50	441.8	20	395,8	90	329.5	160	218.5
−110	474,0	−40	435.8	30	387.4	100	317,6	170	194,0
−100	469,2	−30	429.8	40	379.1	110	304.5	180	163.6
− 90	463.9	−20	423,9	50	370,1	120	290.1	190	119,4

trans-2-PENTENE (C_5H_{10})

```
CH3        H
   \      /
    C = C
   /      \
  H        CH2 - CH3
```

Molecular weight 70.130

t_{boil} = 36.353 °C at 760 mm Hg; t_{melt} = − 140.244 °C

Thermodynamic properties of *trans*-2-pentene [62]:
$c_p{}^0$ (kJ/kg · deg), i^0 (kJ/kg) and s^0 (kJ/kg · deg)

T, °K	$c_p{}^0$	i^0	s^0	T, °K	$c_p{}^0$	i^0	s^0
0	0	0	0	900	3.334	1841,1	7,5025
298.16	1.547	300,7	4.857	1000	3,511	2183,8	7,8637
300	1,554	303,4	4.867	1100	3.664	2542,6	8,2052
400	1.950	478,4	5,369	1200	3.798	2915.2	8,5293
500	2.313	692,5	5,843	1300	3,914	3300,8	8,8386
600	2.508	940.3	6,2936	1400	4,015	3697,2	9.1323
700	2,898	1216,1	6,7192	1500	4.102	4104,4	9,4129
800	3.131	1517,6	7,1222				

Saturated vapor pressure p of *trans*-2-pentene [65]

t, °C	p, mm Hg	t, °C	p, mm Hg	t, °C	p, mm Hg	t, °C	p, bar	t, °C	p, bar
−60	4,35	−20	65,43	20	417.47	40	1.1465	80	3.689
−50	9,58	−10	110,68	25	505,45	50	1,5839	90	4.723
−40	19,42	0	178,96	30	607,54	60	2,1404	100	5.956
−30	36,73	10	278,14			70	2,8355	110	7,412

Density ρ (kg/m^3) of liquid *trans*-2-pentene [65]

t, °C	ϱ · 10⁻³	t, °C	ϱ · 10⁻³	t, °C	ϱ · 10⁻³	t, °C	ϱ · 10⁻³	t, °C	ϱ · 10⁻³
−70	0,7314	−40	0,7052	−10	0,6770	20	0,6482	40	0,6275
−60	0,7227	−30	0,6960	0	0.6675	25	0.6431	50	0.6163
−50	0,7140	−20	0,6866	10	0,6580	30	0,6381		

Heat capacity c_p (kJ/kg · deg) of liquid *trans*-2-pentene [91]

T, °K	c_p	T, °K	c_p	T, °K	c_p	T, °K	c_p	T, °K	c_p
135	1.821	170	1,866	210	1,946	250	2.059	290	2.207
140	1,827	180	1,882	220	1,971	260	2.093	298.16	2,240
150	1,838	190	1,901	230	1,998	270	2,130	300	2,247
160	1,851	200	1,922	240	2.027	280	2.168		

Latent heat of vaporization r (kJ/kg) of *trans*-2-pentene [65]

t, °C	r	t, °C	r	t, °C	r	t, °C	r	t, °C	r
−140	474.6	−70	440.6	0	399.4	70	342.1	140	251.9
−130	469.8	−60	435.2	10	392.2	80	331.9	150	233.4
−120	465.7	−50	429.8	20	385.1	90	320.6	160	213,1
−110	460.9	−40	423.9	30	377.3	100	309.2	170	188.6
−100	456.1	−30	418.5	40	368.9	110	296.7	180	158.8
−90	451,3	−20	412.5	50	360.6	120	283.0	190	118.8
−80	446.0	−10	406.0	60	351.6	130	268.0		

1-HEXENE (C_6H_{12})

$CH_2{=}CH-CH_2-CH_2-CH_2-CH_3$

Molecular weight 84.156

t_{boil} = 63.485 °C at 760 mm Hg; t_{melt} = − 139.819 °C

Thermodynamic properties of 1-hexene [62]:
c_p^0 (kJ/kg · deg), i^0 (kJ/kg) and s^0 (kJ/kg · deg)

T, °K	c_p^0	i^0	s^0	T, °K	c_p^0	i^0	s^0
0	0	0	0				
298.16	1.574	309.8	4.574	900	3.386	1879.6	7.2695
300	1,581	312.7	4.584	1000	3,559	2227.3	7.8341
400	1,991	491.6	5.0959	1100	3,710	2591.0	7,9814
500	2,362	708.0	5,5814	1200	3,842	2969.6	8,3107
600	2,682	962.66	6,0401	1300	3,956	3359.6	8.6227
700	2,952	1423.8	6.4735	1400	4,055	3760.6	8,9202
800	3,185	1550.7	6.8834	1500	4,141	4170.0	9.2042

Saturated vapor pressure of 1-hexene [65]

t, °C	p, mm Hg	t, °C	p, mm Hg	t, °C	p, mm Hg	t, °C	p, bar	t, °C	p, bar
−60	0,82	−10	33,43	30	228.71	70	1.2398	110	3.610
−50	2,04	0	57.63	40	337.90	80	1.6626	120	4.537
−40	4.59	10	94,87	50	485.30	90	2.1885	130	5.629
−30	9.52	20	150.31	60	679.57	100	2.8326		
−20	18,39								

Density of saturated liquid 1-hexene [65, 403]*

t, °C	0	10	20	30	40	50	75	100	125	150	175	200
ϱ kg/m³	691.7	682.5	673.2	663.7	654.1	644.7	619	592	562	528	490	438

*Reference [403] gives experimental data up to 700 bar.

Latent heat of vaporization r (kJ/kg) of 1-hexene [65]

t, °C	r	t, °C	r	t, °C	r	t, °C	r	t, °C	r
−130	438.3	−50	403.0	20	366.2	90	316.4	160	241.8
−120	433.8	−40	398.5	30	359.7	100	308.0	170	226,9
−110	429.8	−30	393.5	40	353,2	110	298.5	180	210,4
−100	425.4	−20	388,5	50	346,8	120	289.0	190	192.0
− 90	421.4	−10	383,1	60	339.8	130	278.6	200	170.1
− 80	416.9	0	377,6	70	332,3	140	267.2	210	148.8
− 70	412,4	10	372.1	80	324.9	150	255.2	220	106,0
− 60	408,0								

Viscosity η (N · s/m²) of liquid 1-hexene [62]

t, °C	$\eta \cdot 10^3$	t, °C	$\eta \cdot 10^3$	t, C	$\eta \cdot 10^3$	t, °C	$\eta \cdot 10^3$	t, °C	$\eta \cdot 10^3$
−55	0.69	−35	0.51	−15	0.39	5	0,31	25	0.25
−50	0.63	−30	0,47	−10	0.37	10	0,29	30	0.24
−45	0.58	−25	0,44	− 5	0.35	15	0.27	35	0.23
−40	0.54	−20	0.42	0	0,33	20	0.26	40	0,22

Thermal conductivity $\lambda \cdot 10^3$ (W/m · deg) of 1-hexene at different temperatures and pressures [84]

t, °C \ p, bar →	1	10	20	50	100	150	200	300	400	500
0	127,4	127.8	128.2	129.1	130,7	132.3	133,8	136.8	139,7	142.5
25	120.8	121.3	121.8	122,8	124.6	126,4	128.1	131,3	134.4	137,4
50	114,4	114,9	115,4	116.4	118,4	120.4	122.4	126.0	129,5	132.9
75	17,4	108,6	109.2	110.4	112.7	115,0	117,2	121.1	124.8	128.3
100	20.1	102,6	103.2	104.8	107,4	109.8	112,1	116.2	120.1	123.9
125	22.8	96.6	97,3	99,2	102.2	104.9	107,4	111.9	116,1	120.1
150	25.6	90,6	91,2	93,8	97,3	100,5	103,3	108,2	112.7	116,8
175	28,4	29,6	85.0	88.2	92.6	96,5	99.7	104.7	109,3	113,5
200	31,4	32,4	77,4	82,6	88,0	93.0	96.4	101.6	106,3	110.4
225	34,5	35,4	37,8	75,6	83.9	89,7	93.3	98.5	103,3	107,6
250	37,6	38,5	40,0	66,1	78,8	86,1	90,3	95,6	100,5	105,0
275	40.8	41,7	42,8	57,4	74,1	82,7	87,3	92,8	98.1	102.7
300	44,1	44,9	45,8	54,9	70,5	79,4	84,2	90,1	95.5	100,5
325	47,5	48,2	49.1	55.5	67,5	76.4	81,1	87,4	93,2	98,4
350	50,9	51,6	52.5	57.4	65,2	73.4	78.2	84.9	91.0	96.5

Surface tension of 1-hexene [65]

t, °C	0	10	20	25	30	40	50
$\sigma \cdot 10^3$, N/m	20,58	19,55	18.52	18.00	17,49	16.46	15.43

1-HEPTENE (C_7H_{14})

$CH_2{=}CH{-}(CH_2)_4{-}CH_3$

Molecular weight 98.182

t_{boil} = 93.643 °C at 760 mm Hg; t_{melt} = − 119.029 °C

Thermodynamic properties of 1-heptene [62]: $c_p{}^0$ (kJ/kg · deg), i^0 (kJ/kg) and s^0 (kJ/kg · deg)

T, °K	$c_p{}^0$	i^0	s^0	T, °K	$c_p{}^0$	i^0	s^0
0	0	0	0				
298.16	1.582	307.9	4.3169	900	3,403	1886,4	7,0275
300	1.589	309.9	4.3271	1000	3,577	2235,6	7,3950
400	2,003	490.62	4.8418	1100	3,73	2601,0	7,7434
500	2,376	710.72	5.3304	1200	3.86	2981.4	8,0743
600	2.696	1219.9	5.7914	1300	3.97	3373.2	8,3873
700	2,968	1246.8	6,2271	1400	4.07	3775,8	8,6862
800	3,201	1555.5	6.6395	1500	4,16	4186.8	8.9710

Saturated vapor pressure of 1-heptene [65]

t, °C	p, mm Hg	t, °C	p, mm Hg	t, °C	p, mm Hg	t, °C	p, bar	t, °C	p, bar
−60	0.100	0	14.57	50	169,46	100	1.2180	140	3.345
−50	0.294	10	25 92	60	249.11	110	1,6046	150	4.161
−40	0.763	20	43.96	70	356.58	120	2,0797	160	5.118
−30	1,79	30	71,47	80	498.32	130	2.6556		
−20	3,87	40	111,90	90	681,48				
−10	7.75								

Density of liquid 1-heptene [65]

t, °C	10	20	25	30	40
$\varrho \cdot 10^{-3}$, kg/m³	0.7057	0.6970	0.6927	0.6882	0.6793

Heat capacity c_p (kJ/kg · deg) of liquid 1-heptene [55]

T, °K	c_p	T, °K	c_p	T, °K	c_p	T, °K	c_p	T, °K	c_p
155	1.827	190	1,867	220	1.920	250	1,997	280	2.103
160	1.831	200	1,882	230	1,941	260	2.028	290	2,142
170	1.842	210	1,901	240	1,967	270	2,065	300	2.194
180	1.855								

Latent heat of vaporization r (kJ/kg) of 1-heptene [65]

t, °C	r	t, °C	r	t, °C	r	t, °C	r	t, °C	r
−80	404.2	−10	375.6	60	339.8	130	293.4	200	220.9
−70	400.4	0	371,4	70	333.9	140	285.3	210	206.8
−60	396.6	10	366.7	80	327.9	150	276.3	220	189.3
−50	392.3	20	361.6	90	321,5	160	266.9	230	171.8
−40	388.4	30	356.5	100	315.1	170	257.1	240	150.1
−30	384.2	40	351.4	110	308.3	180	246.0	250	122.0
−20	379.9	50	345.8	120	301,0	190	234.1	260	78.0

Viscosity η ($N \cdot s/m^2$) of liquid 1-heptene [62]

t, °C	$\eta \cdot 10^3$	t, °C	$\eta \cdot 10^3$	t, °C	$\eta \cdot 10^3$	t, °C	$\eta \cdot 10^3$	t, °C	$\eta \cdot 10^3$
0	0,44	20	0.35	40	0.29	60	0,25	80	0,22
5	0,41	25	0.34	45	0,28	65	0,24	85	0,21
10	0,39	30	0,32	50	0,27	70	0,23	90	0,20
15	0,37	35	0,31	55	0.26	75	0.22	95	0.20

Thermal conductivity $\lambda \cdot 10^3$ (W/m · deg) of 1-heptene at different temperatures and pressures [84]

t, °C \ p, bar →	1	10	20	50	100	150	200	300	400	500
0	131.2	131,6	132,0	132.8	134,4	135,8	137,4	140,6	143,7	146.6
25	124,9	125,4	125,8	126.8	128.5	130,2	131.9	135.2	138,5	141.6
50	118,7	119.2	119,7	120,8	122.8	124,7	126.5	130.0	133.4	136,7
75	112,9	113.3	113.8	115,0	117.1	119,2	121.3	125,4	129.3	132.9
100	18.8	107.4	108.0	109,4	111.9	114,3	116,6	120,9	125.1	129,0
125	21,4	101.7	102,3	103,9	106,8	109,7	112.3	116,8	121.0	125,1
150	24,0	96,3	97,0	98,8	102,0	105,1	108,1	112.9	117.3	121,4
175	26,7	91,0	91,9	94,0	97,8	101,3	104,5	109,3	113,8	118.0
200	29,5	31,4	86,6	89,9	94,2	98,0	101,2	106.1	110.6	114.9
225	32.3	33,8	80,9	85,3	90,4	94,7	97,9	102,9	107,5	112,0
250	35,3	36,4	40,0	79,6	86,5	91,5	94,8	100,0	104.8	109,5
275	38,3	39,3	41,4	71,0	82.2	88,5	91,9	97,3	102.3	107,1
300	41,3	42,3	43,8	61,0	77,8	85,1	89,0	94,6	99,9	104,9
325	44,4	45,4	46,4	56.8	73,6	81,9	86,2	92.0	97,5	102.8
350	47,6	48.5	49,7	56,6	70,3	78,7	83,4	89.5	95.4	101,0

Surface tension of 1-heptene [65]

t, °C	0	10	20	25	30	40	50	75
$\sigma \cdot 10^3$ N/m	22,40	21.41	20,42	19,93	19,43	18.44	17,45	14,98

1-OCTENE (C_8H_{16})

$$CH_2=CH-(CH_2)_5-CH_3$$

Molecular weight 112.208

t_{boil}= 121.280 °C at 760 mm Hg; t_{melt} = − 101.736 °C

Thermodynamic properties of 1-octene [62]: c_p^0 (kJ/kg · deg), i^0 (kJ/kg) and s^0 (kJ/kg · deg)

T, °K	c_p^0	i^0	s^0	T, °K	c_p^0	i^0	s^0
0	0	0	0				
298.16	1,588	306.5	4,1246	900	3,416	1891,6	6,8464
300	1,596	309,3	4,1351	1000	3,589	2242,3	7.2154
400	2,011	489,92	4,6518	1100	3.742	2609,1	7,5650
500	2,386	710,94	5,1421	1200	3,873	2990.8	7,8974
600	2,708	965,58	5,6051	1300	3,985	3383.6	8.2116
700	2,981	1249.5	6,0427	1400	4,085	3787,34	8,5130
800	3,214	1559.6	6,4569	1500	4,171	4199,99	8,7966

Saturated vapor pressure of 1-octene [65]

t, °C	p, mm Hg	t, °C	p, mm Hg	t, °C	p, mm Hg	t, °C	p, bar
−30	0.336	20	13.20	70	139.96	130	1,2843
−20	0.815	30	22.77	80	203.93	140	1,6619
−10	1.81	40	37.83	90	289,86	150	2.1202
0	3.73	50	60.49	100	402,83	160	2.6698
10	7.19	60	93.43	110	548.53	170	3,322
				120	733,19	180	4.086

Density of liquid 1-octene [65]

t, °C	−10	0	10	20	25	30	40	50	60
$\varrho \cdot 10^{-3}$, kg/m³	0,7398	0,7316	0,7232	0,7149	0,7108	0.7064	0.6979	0.6892	0,6805

Latent heat of vaporization r (kJ/kg) of 1-octene [65]

t, °C	r	t, °C	r	t, °C	r	t, °C	r	t, °C	r
−100	399.9	−20	372,4	60	338,0	140	294,0	220	223 5
− 90	397,0	−10	368,2	70	333,2	150	287.3	230	209,7
− 80	393.6	0	364.5	80	328,3	160	279.8	240	196,6
− 70	390,3	10	360,4	90	323,1	170	271.6	250	182,1
− 60	386,9	20	356.3	100	317,5	180	262.7	260	164.9
− 50	383.2	30	351.8	110	311,9	190	253.0	270	144,9
− 40	379,8	40	347.4	120	306.3	200	244.8	280	118.6
− 30	376,1	50	342,9	130	300,3	210	233.6	290	79,8

Viscosity η (N · s/m²) of liquid 1-octene [62]

t, °C	$\eta \cdot 10^3$	t, °C	$\eta \cdot 10^3$	t, °C	$\eta \cdot 10^3$	t, °C	$\eta \cdot 10^3$	t, °C	$\eta \cdot 10^3$	t, °C	$\eta \cdot 10^3$
0	0,613	20	0.470	40	0.383	60	0.317	80	0.271	100	0.235
5	0.571	25	0.447	45	0,364	65	0.304	85	0.261	105	0.23
10	0,533	30	0,425	50	0,347	70	0,292	90	0,251	110	0.22
15	0.498	35	0,403	55	0.331	75	0.281	95	0.243	115	0.21

Thermal conductivity λ of 1-octene gas at a pressure of 1 bar [84]

t, °C	20	40	60	80	100	120	140	160	180	200	220
$\lambda \cdot 10^3$, W/m · deg	10.2	12.0	13.8	15,7	17.6	19,6	21.7	23.7	25,8	27.9	30.0

Surface tension of 1-octene [65]

t, °C	0	10	20	25	30	40	50	75	100
$\sigma \cdot 10^3$, N/m	23.83	22,87	21.97	21.44	20.95	19.99	19.03	16.64	14.24

CYCLIC ALIPHATIC COMPOUNDS

CYCLOPENTENE (C_5H_8)

```
       CH2
      /   \
    HC     CH2
    ||      |
    HC-----CH2
```

Molecular weight 68.114

$t_{boil} = 44.242$ °C at 760 mm Hg; $t_{melt} = -135.076$ °C

Thermodynamic properties of cyclopentene [62]: $c_p{}^0$ (kJ/kg · deg), i^0 (kJ/kg) and s^0 (kJ/kg · deg)

T, °K	$c_p{}^0$	i^0	s^0	T, °K	$c_p{}^0$	i^0	s^0
0	0	0	0				
298.16	1,103	212,8	4,256	900	3.019	1539.1	6,4925
300	1.111	214,6	4.262	1000	3.193	1849,6	6,8195
400	1.542	347.2	4,640	1100	3.342	2176.6	7.1305
500	1,944	521.9	5,028	1200	3.470	2517.6	7,4274
600	2.286	733,95	5.414	1300	3,580	2870.4	7.7096
700	2,573	977.17	5.789	1400	3,675	3233.1	7.9788
800	2,814	1247,1	6,1488	1500	3.758	3605.2	8.2351

Saturated vapor pressure of cyclopentene [65]

t, °C	p, mm Hg	t, °C	p, mm Hg	t, °C	p, bar	t, °C	p, bar
−50	6,39	0	130,37	50	1,2237	90	3,776
−40	13,23	10	205,39	60	1,6693	100	4,798
−30	25.50	20	312,18	70	2,2342	110	6.013
−20	46,23	30	459,64	80	2,9274	120	7,438
−10	79,46	40	657,87				

Density of liquid cyclopentene [65]

t, °C	10	20	25	30	40
$\varrho \cdot 10^{-3}$, kg/m³	0,7827	0.7720	0,7665	0,7612	0,7500

Latent heat of vaporization r (kJ/kg) of cyclopentene [65]

t, °C	r	t, °C	r	t, °C	r	t, °C	r
−130	501,6	−40	454,9	50	397,7	140	306.1
−120	496,7	−30	449.3	60	389,7	150	292,0
−110	491,8	−20	443,2	70	381.7	160	276.6
−100	486.8	−10	437.7	80	372.5	170	259,4
− 90	481,3	0	431.5	90	363,3	180	241,0
− 80	476,4	10	425.4	100	352.8	190	219.0
− 70	470.9	20	418,6	110	342,4	200	194,9
− 60	465.9	30	411.8	120	330.7	210	164,1
− 50	460.4	40	405.1	130	319.0	220	121,1

Surface tension of cyclopentene [65]

t, °C	0	10	20	25	30	40
$\sigma \cdot 10^3$, N/m	25,25	23,94	22.65	21.99	21,32	20,03

CYCLOHEXENE (C_6H_{10})

```
       CH2
      /   \
    HC     CH2
    ||     |
    HC     CH2
      \   /
       CH2
```

Molecular weight 82.140

t_{boil} = 82.979 °C at 760 mm Hg; t_{melt} = − 103.512 °C

Thermodynamic properties of cyclohexene [62]: $c_p{}^0$ (kJ/kg · deg), i^0 (kJ/kg) and s^0 (kJ/kg · deg)

T, °K	$c_p{}^0$	i^0	s^0	T, °K	$c_p{}^0$	i^0	s^0
0	0	0	0				
298.16	1,279	212,4	3,786	900	3,228	1672,8	6,2673
300	1,288	214.8	3,794	1000	3,396	2004,6	6,6164
400	1,766	367,8	4,230	1100	3,539	2351,2	6,9472
500	2,180	565.77	4.670	1200	3,662	2712,1	7.2612
600	2,520	801,25	5,0990	1300	3,768	3083,2	7,5578
700	2,799	1067,8	5,5093	1400	3,859	3464,4	7,8402
800	3,032	1359,9	5,8988	1500	3,938	3854.9	8,1093

Saturated vapor pressure of cyclohexene [65]

t, °C	p, mm Hg	t, °C	p, mm Hg	t, °C	p, mm Hg	t, °C	p, bar	t, °C	p, bar
−60	0,246	−10	13,85	40	169,44	90	1.2450	130	3,447
−50	0,663	0	24,99	50	250,57	100	1,6443	140	4,294
−40	1,60	10	42,88	60	360,47	110	2,1358	150	5,287
−30	3.54	20	70,38	70	505,90	120	2,7324		
−20	7,24	30	111,11	80	694,37				

Density ρ of liquid cyclohexene [65]

t, °C	10	20	25	30	40
$\varrho \cdot 10^{-3}$, kg/m³	0,8205	0.8110	0,8060	0,8014	0,7916

Latent heat of vaporization r (kJ/kg) of cyclohexene [65]

t, °C	r	t, °C	r	t, °C	r	t, °C	r	t, °C	r
−100	464,8	−20	429,7	60	387,9	140	330.8	220	235,5
− 90	460.8	−10	424,6	70	381,8	150	321,6	230	218,2
− 80	456.2	0	420,0	80	375,6	160	311,9	240	198,3
− 70	452,1	10	414,9	90	369,0	170	301,2	250	175,3
− 60	447,5	20	409,8	100	362,4	180	290,0	260	146,8
− 50	443,4	30	404,2	110	355,3	190	278,3	270	105,5
− 40	438,8	40	399,1	120	347,6	200	265,6		
− 30	434,3	50	393,5	130	339,5	210	251,3		

Viscosity of liquid cyclohexene [52]

t, °C	0	10	20	30	40
$\eta \cdot 10^3$, N · s/m²	0,883	0,759	0,660	0,581	0,515

Surface tension of cyclohexene [65]

t, °C	0	10	20	25	30	40	50	75
$\sigma \cdot 10^3$, N/m	29.00	27.80	26.61	26.01	25.41	24.22	23.02	20.03

DIENES

PROPADIENE (ALLENE) (C_3H_4)

$CH_2{=}C{=}CH_2$

Molecular weight 40.062

$t_{boil} = -34.32$ °C at 760 mm Hg; $t_{melt} = -135.25$ °C;

$t_{cr} = 120.7$ °C; $p_{cr} = 52.5$ bar

Thermodynamic properties of propadiene [62]: $c_p{}^0$ (kJ/kg · deg), i^0 (kJ/kg) and s^0 (kJ/kg · deg)

T, °K	$c_p{}^0$	i^0	s^0	T, °K	$c_p{}^0$	i^0	s^0
0	0	0	0				
100	0,8997	84,4	4.638	800	2.656	1392.8	8,114
200	1,158	186,8	5,337	900	2.801	1665.6	8,436
298,16	1,473	315,3	6,092	1000	2.926	1952.1	8.737
300	1,480	318,2	6.102	1100	3,035	2249.6	9,021
400	1,798	482,4	6,572	1200	3.131	2558.2	9.290
500	2,071	676,1	7.004	1300	3.213	2875,9	9,544
600	2,299	895.4	7,402	1400	3.286	3201.0	9.785
700	2,491	1134.6	7.771	1500	3.350	3533.1	10.01

Saturated vapor pressure of propadiene [65]

t, °C	−130	−120	−110	−100	−90	−80	−70	−60	−50	−40
p, mm Hg	0.359	1.314	4,04	10.76	25,5	54.9	108,9	201,5	351,4	582,5

t, °C	−30	−20	−10	0	10	20	25	30	40	50	60	70
p, bar	1.22	1.84	2.68	3.81	5.28	7.14	8.24	9.47	12.4	15.8	20.0	24.8

Density of liquid propadiene [65]

t, °C	−70	−60	−50	−40	−30
$\varrho \cdot 10^{-3}$, kg/m³	0.7064	0.6944	0.6822	0.6699	0,6575

Latent heat of vaporization r (kJ/kg) of propadiene [65]

t, °C	r	t, °C	r	t, °C	r	t, °C	r	t, °C	r
−130	586.2	−70	548.6	−20	494.3	30	415.9	80	303.0
−120	581.0	−60	538,2	−10	480,7	40	397.1	90	270,6
−110	574.8	−50	528.8	0	466,1	50	376.2	100	229.9
−100	568.5	−40	518.3	10	450.4	60	353.2	110	172.4
−90	562,2	−30	506,8	20	433.7	70	329.2	120	47.0
−80	555,9								

Surface tension of propadiene [65]

t, °C	−50	−40	−30	−20
$\sigma \cdot 10^3$, N/m	21.99	20.44	18.90	17.35

1,3-BUTADIENE (C_4H_6)

$CH_2{=}CH{-}CH{=}CH_2$

Molecular weight 54.088

t_{boil} = —4.47 °C at 760 mm Hg; t_{melt} = — 108.915 °C;

t_{cr} = 152 °C; p_{cr} = 43.3 bar; ρ_{cr} = 0.245 g/cm³

Thermodynamic properties of 1,3-butadiene [62] : c_p^0 (kJ/kg · deg), i^0 (kJ/kg) and s^0 (kJ/kg · deg)

T, °K	c_p^0	i^0	s^0	T, °K	c_p^0	i^0	s^0
0	0	0	0				
298.16	1.471	280.6	5.156	900	3,004	1717.8	7.640
300	1.479	283.3	5.166	1000	3,136	2024.8	7,9629
400	1.880	451.7	5.648	1100	3.252	2344.8	8.2679
500	2,207	656.7	6.104	1200	3.353	2674.9	8,5550
600	2.464	890.72	6.529	1300	3.442	3014.6	8.8275
700	2.674	1148.1	6.926	1400	3.519	3362,4	9.0852
800	2.851	1424.8	7.295	1500	3.587	3717.5	9.3298

Thermodynamic properties of saturated 1,3-butadiene [92] :
v (dm³/kg), i and r (kJ/kg), s (kJ/kg · deg)

t, °C	p	v′	v″	i′	i″	r	s′	s″
	mm Hg							
−100	1.5	1.3253	$1.40 \cdot 10^5$	301.9	803.5	501.6	2.569	5,4768
− 70	21,8	1.3836	$1.07 \cdot 10^4$	360,0	834.5	473,9	2.883	5.2159
− 50	83.8	1,4257	3050	399.3	855.7	456,4	3.068	5,1129
− 40	148	1,4483	1795	419,35	866,9	447.6	3,156	5.0756
− 30	248	1.4718	1112	439,70	878,5	438.8	3,241	5,0459
− 20	396	1.4965	719.8	460.42	890,0	429.6	3,325	5,0225
− 15	493	1.5092	587.6	470.89	895,9	425.0	3,365	5,0128
− 10	608	1.5224	483.9	481,48	902,3	420.8	3,406	5.0045
− 5	742	1.5360	401.7	492,16	908.06	415.9	3,446	4.9974
	bar							
0	1.20	1.5499	335.9	502.96	914,16	411.2	3,486	4.9911
5	1.44	1,5642	282,9	513,84	920,24	406,4	3.525	4.9861
10	1,72	1.5790	239.7	524,90	926,10	401.2	3,565	4,9819
15	2,04	1,5943	204.4	536,04	932,24	396,2	3,604	4.9785
20	2.40	1,6102	175.3	547,34	938,34	391,0	3,642	4,9756
25	2.81	1,6266	151,0	558,77	944.17	385,4	3,681	4,9735
30	3.26	1.6436	130,8	570,32	950,22	379.9	3,719	4.9718
35	3,78	1.6613	113.7	582,05	956.25	374.2	3,757	4,9710
40	4,34	1,6798	99.3	594,06	962,26	368.2	3,794	4,9706
45	4.98	1,6990	87,09	605,91	968.11	362.2	3.832	4,9706
50	5.68	1,7191	76,60	618,01	973,91	355.9	3,870	4.9710
55	6,45	1,7403	67.55	630,57	979.67	349,1	3,908	4.9718
60	7.30	1,7625	59,78	642,7	985,10	342.4	3,945	4.9727
65	8.22	1,7858	53,04	655.6	990,80	335.2	3,982	4,9735
70	9.24	1.8105	47,16	668,6	996,60	328.0	4,019	4.9752
75	10.33	1,8366	42,02	681,6	1001.9	320.3	4,056	4.9764
80	11,53	1.8644	37,51	695,0	1007.1	312,1	4,094	4.9777
85	12,81	1,8941	33,53	708.4	1012,2	303.8	4.131	4,9789
90	14.20	1,9259	30,00	721,8	1017.0	295,2	4,168	4.9802
95	15,71	1.9603	26,87	736,9	1021.6	284.7	4.204	4,982
100	17.33	1.9976	24.07	749.4	1026,1	276.7	4.241	4,982
105	19,06	2.0384	21.55	764.1	1030.0	265.9	4,279	4,982
110	20.93	2,083	19.30	778.7	1034,1	255,4	4,316	4,982
115	22.93	2,133	17,24	795.5	1038.3	242,8	4,354	4,982
120	25.08	2,190	15.37	808.0	1038.3	230,3	4.392	4.978
125	27.39	2.257	13.63	826.9	1042.5	215,6	4.430	4,974
130	29.84	2,33	12.02	841,5	1042.5	201,0	4.472	4.970
131.12	30.40	2,35	11.67	845,7	1042.5	196.8	4.480	4,966

continued

t, °C	p	v′	v″	i′	i″	r	s′	s″
132.23	31.02	2.38	11.33	849.9	1042.5	192,6	4,492	4,966
133,34	31.64	2,40	10,99	854.1	1042.5	188,4	4.501	4.961
134.45	32,19	2,42	10.66	858,3	1042,5	184.2	4.509	4.961
135.57	32.81	2.45	10.32	862.5	1042.5	180.0	4,518	4.957
136,68	33.43	2.47	9.982	866.7	1042,5	175.8	4,530	4,953
137.79	34,05	2.50	9,676	870.8	1038.3	167.5	4,538	4.949
138.90	34.74	2,53	9.302	875.0	1038,3	163.3	4.551	4.945
140,01	35.36	2.56	8.990	879.2	1034.1	154.9	4.564	4.940
141,12	36.05	2.60	8.615	883.4	1034.1	150.7	4.572	4.936
142.23	36.74	2.65	8,240	887.6	1034.1	146.5	4.584	4.932

Heat capacity c_p (kJ/kg · deg) of 1,3-butadiene gas at different temperatures and pressures [92]

p, bar \ t, °C →	0	20	40	60	80	100	120	140
0	1.36	1,45	1,54	1,62	1,71	1.80	1,88	1.96
1	1.39	1,47	1,56	1.64	1,72	1.81	1.89	1.98
2		1.50	1,58	1.66	1,74	1,82	1,90	1,99
3			1.60	1.68	1,76	1.84	1,92	2,00
4			1.63	1.71	1.78	1,86	1,93	2.01
5				1.74	1,80	1.88	1.95	2,02
6				1.77	1.82	1,89	1.96	2,03
7				1.81	1,85	1,90	1,98	2,05
8					1.87	1.93	2,00	2,06
9					1,90	1.96	2,02	2,08
10					1,93	1.98	2.04	2,09
11					1.97	2.01	2,06	2,11
12						2.04	2,09	2,13
13						2.07	2,12	2.15
14						2,11	2.15	2,17

Heat capacity (kJ/kg · deg) of liquid 1,3-butadiene [92]

T, °K	c_p	T, °K	c_p	T, °K	c_p	T, °K	c_p	T, °K	c_p
165	1,91	190	1.93	220	1,98	250	2,08	280	2,19
170	1,91	200	1,94	230	2,01	260	2,11	290	2.24
180	1,92	210	1,96	240	2.04	270	2,15	300	2,30

Compressibility factor z of 1,3-butadiene gas [92]

Saturated vapor			Superheated vapor								
p, bar	t, °C	z	p, bar \ t, °C →	0	20	40	60	80	100	120	140
1	−4.7	0.963	1	0,964	0,970	0.975	0.980	0,985	0,988	0.989	0.991
2	14.6	0,940	2		0,943	0.953	0,961	0,969	0.975	0.980	0.982
3	27,4	0.920	3			0.929	0,943	0.954	0,963	0,968	0,972
4	36,3	0.903	4			0,907	0,925	0,938	0,949	0.957	0,963
5	45.0	0,885	5				0,904	0,922	0.934	0.945	0.955
6	52,2	0,871	6				0,883	0.904	0,920	0.934	0,944
7	58,5	0,856	7				0.859	0,887	0,905	0.921	0.934
8	64.6	0.842	8					0.868	0.891	0.910	0.925

Viscosity η of liquid 1,3-butadiene [52]

t, °C	−20	−10	0	10	20	30	40	50	60
$\eta \cdot 10^3$, N · s/m	0.244	0,214	0,188	0,167	0.149	0.133	0,119	0.106	0,095

2-METHYL-1,3-BUTADIENE (ISOPRENE) (C_5H_8)

$$CH_2{=}C(CH_3){-}CH{=}CH_2$$

Molecular weight 68.114

t_{boil} = 34.067 °C at 760 mm Hg; t_{melt} = − 145.950 °C

Thermodynamic properties of 2-methyl-1,3-butadiene [62]: c_p^0 (kJ/kg · deg), i^0 (kJ/kg) and s^0 (kJ/kg · deg)

T, °K	c_p^0	i^0	s^0	T, °K	c_p^0	i^0	s^0
0	0	0	0				
298.16	1.54	274.9	4.637	900	3.11	1764.8	7.210
300	1.55	278.4	4.646	1000	3.25	2077.7	7,542
400	1.95	452.4	5.14	1100	3,37	2413.9	7.862
500	2.28	666.95	5,62	1200	3.48	2758.8	8.157
600	2.54	907.30	6.06	1300	3.58	3108,5	8.440
700	2.77	1174.7	6.473	1400	3,66	3468.1	8.710
800	2,95	1460.5	6.854	1500	3.72	3835.7	8.962

Saturated vapor pressure of 2-methyl-1,3-butadiene [65]

t, °C	−50	−40	−30	−20	−10	0	10	20	30
p, mm Hg	11.21	22.40	41.85	73.74	123.54	198.09	305.59	455.64	659.18
t, °C	40	50	60	70	80	90	100		
p, bar	1.2374	1.7012	2.2889	3.0202	3.915	4.996	6.282		

Density of liquid 2-methyl-1,3-butadiene [65]

t, °C	10	20	25	30	40
$\varrho \cdot 10^{-3}$, kg/m³	0.6910	0.6810	0.6759	0.6708	0.6602

Latent heat of vaporization r (kJ/kg) of 2-methyl-1,3-butadiene [65]

t, °C	r	t, °C	r	t, °C	r	t, °C	r
−140	480.7	−50	438.3	40	371.9	120	285.2
−130	476,4	−40	432.1	50	363,3	130	269.8
−120	472,7	−30	426.0	60	355.3	140	253.2
−110	469.0	−20	419.2	70	345,4	150	234.2
−100	464.7	−10	411.8	80	335.0	160	213.3
− 90	459.8	0	404.5	90	323.9	170	188.7
− 80	454.8	10	397.1	100	311.6	180	157.3
− 70	449.9	20	389.1	110	298.7	190	113.1
− 60	444.4	30	380.5				

Thermal conductivity λ (W/m · deg) of liquid 2-methyl-1,3-butadiene [79]

t, °C	λ	t, °C	λ	t, °C	λ	t, °C	λ	t, °C	λ
−140	0.1758	−100	0.1689	−60	0.1536	−20	0.1376	10	0.1256
−130	0.1750	−90	0.1656	−50	0.1496	−10	0.1336	20	0.1216
−120	0.1738	−80	0.1616	−40	0.1456	0	0.1296	30	0.1176
−110	0.1717	−70	0.1576	−30	0.1416				

ALKYNES

ACETYLENE (C_2H_2)

Molecular weight 26.036

$t_{boil} = -84.0$ °C at 760 mm Hg, (temperature of sublimation); $t_{melt} = -81.0$ °C;
$t_{cr} = 35.5$ °C; $p_{cr} = 62.4$ bar; $\rho_{cr} = 230$ kg/m³

Thermodynamic properties of acetylene [62]: c_p^0 (kJ/kg · deg), i^0 (kJ/kg) and s^0 (kJ/kg · deg)

T, °K	c_p^0	i^0	s^0	T, °K	c_p^0	i^0	s^0
0	0	0	0				
298.16	1.690	385.0	7.728	900	2.487	1693.7	10.053
300	1.696	388.1	7.738	1000	2.563	1946.5	10.319
400	1.928	570.1	8.260	1100	2.633	2206.7	10.567
500	2.088	771.4	8.708	1200	2.696	2473.3	10.799
600	2.210	986.4	9.100	1300	2.753	2745.9	11.018
700	2.313	1212.8	9.449	1400	2.804	3023.9	11.224
800	2.404	1448.8	9.764	1500	2.850	3307.1	11.419

Thermodynamic properties of saturated acetylene [51]: ρ (kg/m³), i (kJ/kg) and s (kJ/kg · deg)

T, °K	p, bar	ϱ′	ϱ″	i′	i″	s′	s″
192.4	1.283	609	2.16	377.94	1019.1	4.128	7.461
200.9	2.026	605	3.32	411.60	1027.9	4.300	7.369
209.4	3.039	593	4.82	445.48	1036.2	4.463	7.285
221.5	5.065	573	7.91	493.20	1047.1	4.689	7.184
230.4	7.091	557	11.0	528.79	1053.0	4.840	7.122
240.7	10.13	538	15.7	565.64	1058.8	4.995	7.042
253.2	15.20	511	23.8	602.48	1062.2	5.137	6.954
263.0	20.26	489	32.4	628.44	1062.2	5.234	6.883
271.6	25.33	469	41.6	653.98	1060.9	5.330	6.829
278.9	30.39	449	51.7	680.36	1057.6	5.418	6.774
284.9	35.45	432	62.9	704.22	1052.6	5.497	6.720
290.4	40.52	414	75.4	727.67	1042.1	5.581	6.665
300.0	50.65	371	107	778.33	1017.8	5.740	6.540
307.8	60.78	298	164	850.34	969.2	5.970	6.356
308.7	62.45	230	230	908.95	909.0	6.163	6.163

Thermodynamic properties of acetylene at different temperatures and pressures [51]: ρ (kg/m³) c_p (kJ/kg · deg), i (kJ/kg) and s (kJ/kg · deg)

T, °K	ϱ	c_p	i	s	ϱ	c_p	i	s
	p=0.1 bar				p=0.5 bar			
170	0.18483	1.3126	995.33	8.1341				
180	0.17553	1.3486	1008.73	8.2103	0.88339	1.3775	1006.30	7.6874
190	0.16522	1.3825	1022.37	8.2840	0.83604	1.4063	1020.24	7.7623
200	0.15694	1.4147	1036.40	8.3556	0.79270	1.4356	1034.43	7.8352

continued

T, °K	ϱ	c_p	i	s	ϱ	c_p	i	s
210	0,14937	1,4457	1050,68	8,4255	0,75342	1,4633	1048,92	7,9059
220	0,14257	1,4746	1065,25	8,4933	0,71755	1,4905	1063,66	7,9746
230	0,13636	1,5035	1080.15	8,5599	0,68620	1,5177	1078,73	8,0416
240	0,13041	1,5307	1095.35	8,6244	0,65690	1,5437	1094,01	8,1065
250	0.12539	1.5583	1110.80	8,6876	0,63015	1,5692	1109.59	8,1701
260	0,12056	1.5855	1126.54	8,7492	0.60551	1,5968	1125.41	8,2325
270	0,11609	1,6128	1142.49	8.8094	0,58271	1,6224	1141,49	8,2928
280	0,11195	1,6387	1158.78	8,8685	0.56156	1.6467	1157,78	8,3522
290	0,10809	1,6642	1175,28	8,9263	0.54201	1,6722	1174.36	8.4100
300	0,10448	1,6885	1192,02	8,9832	0.52378	1,6965	1191.19	8.4674
310	0.10111	1.7124	1209,02	9.0389	0.50674	1,7208	1208,27	8.5231
320	0.097947	1,7367	1226,31	9.0937	0.49077	1,7446	1225,56	8,5779
			p=1 bar				p=2 bar	
190	1.6980	1,4394	1017.35	7,5312				
200	1.6057	1,4637	1031.88	7,6053				
210	1,5237	1,4867	1046,66	7,6773	3.120	1.5353	1042,09	7,4408
220	1,4498	1.5114	1061.65	7,7468	2.958	1,5516	1057.50	7,5124
230	1.3835	1,5357	1076,89	7,8147	2,815	1,5692	1073,12	7.5819
240	1,3236	1,5596	1092.34	7,8804	2,686	1,5889	1088,90	7,6493
250	1.2680	1,5822	1108,04	7.9444	2.569	1,6081	1104.90	7,7146
260	1.2176	1,6065	1123,99	8.0068	2.4632	1.6291	1121,06	7.7778
270	1,1710	1,6303	1140.15	8.0680	2,3656	1,6496	1137,47	7,8398
280	1,1278	1,6546	1156,56	8,1278	2,2776	1,6722	1154,09	7,9001
290	1.0877	1.6793	1173.22	8.1860	2,1939	1,6952	1170.92	7,9591
300	1.0508	1.7032	1190,14	8.2434	2,1180	1.7178	1188,00	8,0169
310	1,0162	1,7275	1207,26	8,2995	2.0455	1.7404	1205.25	8,0738
320	0,98435	1,7518	1224.64	8,3548	1,9792	1.7626	1222.80	8,1295
			p=3 bar				p=5 bar	
210	4,793	1.5914	1037.28	7,2955				
220	4,529	1.5985	1053.23	7,3696				
230	4,297	1,6081	1069.22	7,4408	7,442	1.6982	1061.14	7.2532
240	4,091	1,6207	1085,39	7,5094	7,044	1.6948	1078,10	7.3252
250	3.906	1.6387	1101.67	7.5760	6.695	1.6998	1095.06	7,3947
260	3,738	1,6546	1118.17	7,6405	6,384	1.7078	1112,10	7,4617
270	3,585	1,6722	1134.79	7,7033	6,107	1.7191	1129.22	7,5262
280	3.446	1.6915	1151.62	7,7644	5,853	1,7317	1146,47	7,5886
290	3.317	1,7111	1168,62	7,8239	5.623	1.7480	1163,89	7,6497
300	3,199	1.7224	1185,83	7.8825	5.412	1.7639	1181,47	7,7092
310	3,089	1.7530	1203.24	7.9398	5.218	1.7823	1199.18	7,7674
320	2,987	1.7756	1220,91	7.9960	5.039	1.7799	1217.10	7,8243
			p=7 bar				p=10 bar	
240	20.21	1,7832	1070,31	7.1950				
250	9.662	1.7735	1088.11	7.2674	14,51	1.9054	1076.89	7.1217
260	9,172	1,7689	1105,78	7,3369	13,67	1.8765	1095,77	7.1958
270	8,741	1.7718	1123,49	7,4039	12,94	1.8606	1114.48	7.2666
280	8,357	1.7786	1141,24	7.4680	12,31	1.8539	1133,03	7.3340
290	8,011	1.7882	1159,03	7.5304	11.76	1.8510	1151.54	7.3985
300	7.694	1.7995	1176.99	7.5915	11.25	1.8539	1170,08	7,4613
310	7,406	1.8125	1195,04	7.6505	10.81	1.8627	1188.67	7.5224
320	7.140	1.8271	1213.25	7.7087	10.39	1.8673	1207.35	7.5819
			p=15 bar				p=20 bar	
260	22.26	2.1269	1077.18	7.0146				
270	20.78	2.0561	1098.07	7.0933	30.00	2.3492	1079.32	6.9501
280	19.56	2.0084	1118.38	7.1670	27.87	2.2236	1102.13	7.0326
290	18.54	1.9795	1138.31	7.2365	26.09	2.1453	1123.95	7.1092
300	17.63	1.9649	1158.03	7.3034	24.63	2.0967	1145.13	7.1808
310	16.83	1.9569	1177.58	7.3679	23.37	2.0662	1165.90	7.2490
320	16.11	1.9523	1197.13	7.4299	22.28	2.0423	1186.46	7.3143

continued

T, °K	ϱ	c_p	i	s	ϱ	c_p	i	s
	$p=25$ bar				$p=30$ bar			
280	37.80	2.5502	1083.42	6.9112			1060.98	6.7893
290	34.82	2.3764	1107.95	6.9970	45.08	2.7160	1089.95	6.8910
300	32.46	2.2705	1131.15	7.0757	41.38	2.5054	1115.78	6.9790
310	30.55	2.2014	1153.46	7.1485	38.50	2.3752	1140.11	7.0585
320	28.90	2.1709	1175.23	7.2176	36.16	2.2835	1163.34	7.1322
	$p=35$ bar				$p=40$ bar			
290	57.86		1068.35	6.7826				
300	51.76		1098.57	6.8852	64.39		1078.64	6.7902
310	47.45	2.6017	1125.58	6.9740	57.72	2.8864	1109.50	6.8910
315		2.5117	1138.31	7.0146	55.18	2.7549	1123.61	6.9363
320	44.10	2.4522	1150.70	7.0539	52.94	2.6791	1137.18	6.9790
	$p=50$ bar				$p=60$ bar			
300	107.1		1017.89	6.5456				
310	84.87		1070.15	6.7177	138.2		1003.87	6.4728
315	78.97		1089.07	6.7784	116.1		1041.38	6.5934
320	74.38		1106.19	6.8324	104.2		1067.17	6.6746
	$p=70$ bar				$p=80$ bar			
310	353.4		831.04	5.9017	411.6		800.52	5.7958
315	217.5		929.14	6.2471	340.5		852.93	5.9633
320	155.6		1009.44	6.4690	256.6		921.64	6.1797
	$p=90$ bar				$p=100$ bar			
310	453.0		782.22	5.7292	485.6		766.77	5.6731
315	393.8		824.72	5.8649	432.3		806.88	5.8012
320	333.6		875.08	6.0135	381.0		846.61	5.9264

Viscosity η of acetylene gas at 1 atmosphere [52]

t, °C	0	25	50	75	100	150
$\eta \cdot 10^7$, N · s/m²	95.5	103.3	111.0	118.8	126.5	141.7

Surface tension of acetylene [65]

t, °C	−80	−70	−60	−50
$\sigma \cdot 10^3$, N/m	18.92	16.99	15.06	13.13

METHYLACETYLENE (C_3H_4)

$$CH_3{-}C \equiv CH$$

Molecular weight 40.062

$t_{boil} = -23.22$ °C at 760 mm Hg; $t_{melt} = -102.7$ °C;
$t_{cr} = 127.6$ °C; $p_{cr} = 53.5$ bar

Thermodynamic properties of methylacetylene [62]: $c_p{}^0$ (kJ/kg · deg), i^0 (kJ/kg) and s^0 (kJ/kg · deg)

T, °K	$c_p{}^0$	i^0	s^0	T, °K	$c_p{}^0$	i^0	s^0
0	0	0	0	900	2.770	1667.4	8.534
298.16	1.515	324.4	6.197	1000	2.896	1951.0	8.833
300	1.520	327.2	6.206	1100	3.006	2245.7	9.114
400	1.811	494.1	6.684	1200	3.103	2551.9	9.381
500	2.063	688.0	7.115	1300	3.187	2866.4	9.632
600	2.278	905.3	7.511	1400	3.261	3189.3	9.871
700	2.464	1142.7	7.877	1500	3.327	3518.5	10.10
800	2.627	1397.4	8.217				

Saturated vapor pressure of methylacetylene [65]

t, °C	p, mm Hg	t, °C	p, mm Hg	t, °C	p, bar	t, °C	p, bar	t, °C	p, bar
−100	4.1	−60	107.2	−20	1.17	20	5.77	50	10.84
−90	10.9	−50	196	−10	1.84	30	6.79	60	14.38
−80	25.7	−40	338	0	2.79	40	8.00	70	18.64
−70	54.7	−30	553	10	4.05				

Density of liquid methylacetylene [65]

t, °C	−60	−50	−40	−30	−20
$\varrho \cdot 10^{-3}$, kg/m³	0.716	0.703	0.690	0.678	0.666

Latent heat of vaporization (kJ/kg) of methylacetylene [65]

t, °C	r	t, °C	r	t, °C	r	t, °C	r	t, °C	r
−100	636.4	−50	584.2	0	518.3	50	429.5	90	321.9
−90	627.0	−40	571.6	10	502.6	60	406.5	100	283.2
−80	616.6	−30	559.1	20	487.0	70	380.4	110	235.1
−70	606.1	−20	546.5	30	469.2	80	353.2	120	170.3
−60	595.6	−10	533.0	40	450.4				

1-BUTYNE (ETHYLACETYLENE) (C_4H_6)

$CH_3—CH_2—C\equiv CH$

Molecular weight 54.088

t_{boil} = 8.07 °C at 760 mm Hg; t_{melt} = − 125.720 °C; t_{cr} = 190.5 °C

Thermodynamic properties of 1-Butyne [62]: $c_p{}^0$ (kJ/kg · deg), i^0 (kJ/kg) and s^0 (kJ/kg · deg)

T, °K	$c_p{}^0$	i^0	s^0	T, °K	$c_p{}^0$	i^0	s^0
0	0	0	0				
298.16	1.506	295.7	5.380	900	2.943	1698.2	7.8098
300	1.512	298.0	5.388	1000	3.084	1999.2	8.1262
400	1.848	466.8	5.872	1100	3.206	2313.5	8.4265
500	2.139	666.4	6.316	1200	3.313	2640.1	8.7089
600	2.386	893.20	6.728	1300	3.406	2976.0	8.9792
700	2.598	1142.4	7.113	1400	3.488	3321.2	9.2346
800	2.782	1411.8	7.472	1500	3.559	3673.4	9.4776

Saturated vapor pressure of 1-butyne [65]

t, °C	−50	−40	−30	−20	−10	0	t, °C	10	20	30	40
p, mm Hg	26.5	62.1	125	223	365	556	p, bar	1.06	1.47	1.70	1.96

Latent heat of vaporization r (kJ/kg) of 1-butyne [65]

t, °C	r	t, °C	r	t, °C	r	t, °C	r
−120	549.5	−40	493.0	40	423.4	120	316.6
−110	544.1	−30	485.3	50	413.3	130	298.0
−100	537.9	−20	476.8	60	401.7	140	277.1
− 90	531.7	−10	469.0	70	390.1	150	253.1
− 80	524.8	0	460.5	80	375.4	160	225.2
− 70	517.8	10	452.0	90	363.8	170	193.5
− 60	509.3	20	442.7	100	349.1	180	146.3
− 50	501.6	30	433.4	110	333.6	190	36.4

2-BUTYNE (DIMETHYLACETYLENE) (C_4H_6)

$CH_3—C\equiv C—CH_3$

Molecular weight 54.088

$t_{boil} = 26.99$ °C at 760 mm Hg; $t_{melt} = -32.260$ °C; $t_{cr} = 215.0$ °C

Thermodynamic properties of 2-butyne [62]: $c_p{}^0$ (kJ/kg · deg), i^0 (kJ/kg) and s^0 (kJ/kg · deg)

T, °K	$c_p{}^0$	i^0	s^0	T, °K	$c_p{}^0$	i^0	s^0
0	0	0	0	900	2.892	1660.2	7.577
298.16	1.442	306.6	5.233	1000	3.041	1957.4	7.8902
300	1.447	309.2	5.250	1100	3.172	2267.8	8.1858
400	1.751	469.0	5.707	1200	3.285	2591.4	8.4676
500	2.040	658.9	6.131	1300	3.383	2924.2	8.7338
600	2.297	876.2	6.525	1400	3.469	3267.0	8.9877
700	2.522	1117.6	6.896	1500	3.543	3617.7	9.2300
800	2.720	1380.0	7.247				

Saturated vapor pressure of 2-butyne [65]

t, °C	−30	−20	−10	0	10	20	25	t, °C	30	40	50	60
p, mm Hg	52.4	93	156	252	389	581	702	p, bar	1.12	1.59	2.20	2.99

Latent heat of vaporization r (kJ/kg) of 2-butyne [65]

t, °C	r	t, °C	r	t, °C	r	t, °C	r	t, °C	r
−30	536.4	20	496.1	70	447.4	120	381.6	170	283.3
−20	528.6	30	487.6	80	435.8	130	365.3	180	256.2
−10	520.9	40	479.1	90	423.4	140	348.3	190	224.5
0	513.2	50	469.0	100	410.2	150	329.0	200	184.2
10	504.6	60	458.2	110	396.3	160	307.3	210	120.0

AROMATIC HYDROCARBONS

BENZENE (C_6H_6)

CH
HC CH
HC CH
CH

Molecular weight 78.108

t_{boil} = 80.100 °C at 760 mm Hg; t_{melt} = 5.533 °C;
t_{cr} = 289.45 °C; p_{cr} = 49.2 bar; ρ_{cr} = 304 kg/m³

Thermodynamic properties of saturated benzene [93]: v (m³/kg), i and r (kJ/kg) and s (kJ/kg · deg)

T, °K	p, bar	v'	v''	i'	i''	r	s'	s''
280	0.0530	1.110	5609	−273.0	163.5	436.5	2.1347	3.6936
290	0.0877	1.122	3505	−258.5	173.4	431.9	2.1858	3.6749
300	0.139	1.135	2272	−243.7	183.6	427.3	2.2369	3.6683
310	0.215	1.149	1521	−227.9	194.2	422.1	2.2880	3.6495
320	0.322	1.163	1048	−211.8	205.1	416.9	2.3392	3.6420
330	0.467	1.178	741.4	−195.1	216.3	411.4	2.3906	3.6379
340	0.662	1.194	536.9	−177.8	227.9	405.7	2.4420	3.6353
350	0.917	1.209	397.1	−160.0	239.7	399.7	2.4937	3.6357
360	1.243	1.227	299.3	−141.6	251.7	393.3	2.5454	3.6381
370	1.654	1.244	229.5	−122.7	264.0	386.7	2.5972	3.6424
380	2.164	1.263	178.7	−103.2	276.5	379.7	2.6491	3.6484
390	2.786	1.283	141.0	− 83.1	289.2	372.3	2.7010	3.6556
400	3.536	1.304	112.7	− 62.1	302.1	364.2	2.7528	3.6644
405	3.963	1.314	101.2	− 52.1	308.6	360.7	2.7787	3.6692
410	4.428	1.326	91.10	− 41.5	315.1	356.6	2.8045	3.6742
415	4.932	1.338	82.21	− 30.8	321.2	352.0	2.8303	3.6795
420	5.479	1.349	74.37	− 19.9	328.2	348.1	2.8561	3.6850
425	6.069	1.361	67.41	− 8.9	334.8	343.7	2.8818	3.6907
430	6.704	1.374	61.24	2.1	341.4	339.3	2.9074	3.6965
435	7.388	1.387	55.74	13.3	348.0	334.7	2.9330	3.7026
440	8.121	1.401	50.83	24.6	354.7	330.1	2.9586	3.7088
445	8.906	1.415	46.42	36.0	361.3	325.3	2.9841	3.7151
450	9.746	1.430	42.47	47.5	367.9	320.4	3.0095	3.7215
455	10.64	1.446	38.90	59.1	374.5	315.4	3.0349	3.7280
460	11.60	1.462	35.69	70.9	381.1	310.2	3.0603	3.7346
465	12.61	1.479	32.77	82.7	387.7	305.0	3.0856	3.7413
470	13.69	1.496	30.13	94.7	394.2	299.5	3.1108	3.7480
475	14.84	1.515	27.73	106.8	400.7	293.9	3.1361	3.7547
480	16.06	1.534	25.53	119.1	407.1	288.0	3.1613	3.7614
485	17.34	1.555	23.53	131.5	413.6	282.1	3.1865	3.7681
490	18.70	1.577	21.69	144.1	419.9	275.8	3.2119	3.7748
495	20.14	1.600	19.99	156.8	426.1	269.3	3.2372	3.7813
500	21.66	1.626	18.44	169.7	432.3	262.6	2.2627	3.7878
505	23.27	1.653	17.00	182.9	438.3	255.4	3.2883	3.7940
510	24.96	1.682	15.67	196.3	444.1	247.8	3.3142	3.8001
515	26.74	1.714	14.43	210.0	449.8	239.8	3.3404	3.8059
520	28.62	1.749	13.27	224.1	455.2	231.1	3.3669	3.8114
525	30.60	1.788	12.19	238.6	460.4	221.8	3.3940	3.8165
530	32.69	1.831	11.17	253.6	465.3	211.7	3.4217	3.8211
535	34.88	1.881	10.20	269.3	469.7	200.4	3.4503	3.8249
540	37.19	1.940	9.277	285.8	473.5	187.7	3.4802	3.8279
545	39.62	2.012	8.382	303.4	476.6	173.2	3.5119	3.8296
550	42.18	2.104	7.496	322.8	478.5	155.7	3.5462	3.8293
555	44.87	2.236	6.587	344.9	478.4	133.5	3.5853	3.8257
560	47.71	2.482	5.556	373.7	473.9	100.2	3.6357	3.8145
561	48.30	2.519	5.305	381.8	471.7	89.9	3.6498	3.8101
562	48.89	2.746	5.014	392.7	468.5	75.8	3.6691	3.8038
562.6	49.24	3.290	3.290	432.6	432.6	0	3.7380	3.7380

Thermodynamic properties of benzene at different temperatures and pressures [93]: v (m³/kg), i (kJ/kg) and s (kJ/kg · deg)

T, °K	v	i	s	v	i	s
		p=1 bar			p=2 bar	
280	0.001110	−272.0	2.1346	0.001110	−272.8	2.1345
300	0.001135	−243.4	2.2368	0.001135	−243.3	2.2366
325	0.001171	−203.5	2.3648	0.001171	−203.4	2.3647
350	0.001210	−160.0	2.4937	0.001210	−160.0	2.4935
375	0.3909	272.3	3.7169	0.001254	−113.0	2.6232
400	0.4184	307.6	3.8077	0.2054	305.5	3.7306
425	0.4458	345.0	3.8983	0.2195	343.1	3.8217
450	0.4731	384.6	3.9887	0.2335	382.9	3.9124
475	0.5002	426.2	4.0785	0.2474	424.6	4.0026
500	0.5274	469.8	4.1677	0.2612	468.3	4.0921
525	0.5544	515.2	4.2562	0.2749	513.8	4.1808
550	0.5814	562.3	4.3439	0.2886	561.1	4.2686
575	0.6084	611.1	4.4306	0.3083	609.9	4.3554
600	0.6353	661.4	4.5163	0.3159	660.4	4.4414
		p=4 bar			p=6 bar	
280	0.001110	−272.7	2.1342	0.001109	−272.5	2.1340
300	0.001135	−243.2	2.2364	0.001135	−243.0	2.2361
325	0.001170	−203.3	2.3644	0.001170	−203.1	2.3641
350	0.001209	−159.8	2.4932	0.001209	−159.7	2.4929
375	0.001253	−112.9	2.6228	0.001253	−112.8	2.6224
400	0.001303	− 62.5	2.7527	0.001303	− 62.5	2.7523
425	0.1062	339.2	3.7419	0.06828	335.0	3.6921
450	0.1136	379.3	3.8335	0.07350	375.6	3.7848
475	0.1208	421.4	3.9243	0.07859	418.0	3.8764
500	0.1280	465.4	4.0144	0.08359	462.3	3.9671
525	0.1352	511.1	4.1035	0.08852	508.3	4.0568
550	0.1422	558.6	4.1918	0.09338	556.0	4.1454
575	0.1492	607.6	4.2789	0.09820	605.2	4.2330
600	0.1562	658.2	4.3651	0.1030	656.0	4.3194
		p=8 bar			p=10 bar	
280	0.001109	−272.4	2.1337	0.001109	−272.2	2.1335
300	0.001135	−242.9	2.2358	0.001135	−242.7	2.2356
325	0.001170	−203.0	2.3638	00.01170	−202.8	2.3635
350	0.001209	−159.6	2.4925	0.001209	−159.5	2.4922
375	0.001253	−112.7	2.6220	0.001252	−112.6	2.6217
400	0.001302	− 62.4	2.7518	0.001302	− 62.3	2.7514
425	0.001361	− 8.9	2.8813	0.001360	− 8.8	2.8808
450	0.05336	371.6	3.7482	0.001430	− 47.5	3.0095
475	0.05740	414.5	3.8408	0.04462	410.8	3.8117
500	0.06133	459.1	3.9392	0.04792	455.8	3.9039
525	0.06517	505.4	4.0225	0.05112	502.4	3.9948
550	0.06894	553.3	4.1116	0.05425	550.6	4.0844
575	0.07265	602.8	4.1994	0.05731	600.3	4.1727
600	0.07633	653.7	4.2862	0.06033	651.4	4.2598
		p=20 bar			p=30 bar	
280	0.001108	−271.2	2.1322	0.001107	−270.6	2.1310
300	0.001134	−242.0	2.2342	0.001133	−241.2	2.2329
325	0.001169	−202.1	2.3620	0.001167	−201.5	2.3606
350	0.001207	−158.8	2.4906	0.001206	−158.2	2.4889
375	0.001250	−112.0	2.6198	0.001248	−111.4	2.6180
400	0.001299	− 61.8	2.7493	0.001297	− 61.4	2.7472
425	0.001356	− 8.6	2.8783	0.001353	− 8.2	2.8758
450	0.001424	47.6	3.0064	0.001419	47.6	3.0034
475	0.001510	106.7	3.1340	0.001502	106.3	3.1302
500	0.02064	436.2	3.8022	0.001612	168.8	3.2581
525	0.02272	485.5	3.8982	0.01263	462.2	3.8214

continued

T, °K	v	i	s	v	i	s
550	0.02465	535.6	3.9914	0.01443	516.9	3.9230
575	0.02648	586.8	4.0826	0.01597	570.9	4.0190
600	0.02822	639.2	4.1717	0.01737	625.3	4.1117
		p=40 bar			p=45 bar	
280	0.001107	−269.9	2.1298	0.001106	−269.6	2.1292
300	0.001132	−240.5	2.2316	0.001131	−240.1	2.2309
325	0.001166	−200.8	2.3591	0.001166	−200.4	2.3584
350	0.001204	−157.5	2.4873	0.001203	−157.2	2.4865
375	0.001246	−110.9	2.6162	0.001245	−110.6	2.6153
400	0.001294	−60.9	2.7451	0.001293	−60.6	2.7441
425	0.001349	−7.9	2.8734	0.001347	−7.7	2.8722
450	0.001414	47.8	3.0005	0.001411	47.8	2.9991
475	0.001493	106.1	3.1265	0.001489	106.0	3.1248
500	0.001597	167.8	3.2530	0.001590	167.4	3.2506
525	0.001752	235.8	3.3855	0.001736	234.6	3.3816
550	0.008649	488.6	3.8510	0.002047	318.9	3.5381
575	0.01042	550.5	3.9611	0.008376	537.0	3.9294
600	0.01178	608.7	4.0603	0.009833	599.0	4.0350
		p=50 bar			p=60 bar	
280	0.001106	−269.2	2.1286	0.001105	−268.4	2.1274
300	0.001131	−239.8	2.2303	0.001130	−239.0	2.2289
325	0.001165	−200.0	2.3577	0.001164	−199.4	2.3562
350	0.001203	−156.9	2.4858	0.001201	−156.2	2.4842
375	0.001244	−110.3	2.6144	0.001243	−109.7	2.6127
400	0.001292	−60.4	2.7431	0.001289	−59.9	2.7411
425	0.001346	−7,6	2.8711	0.001342	−7.2	2.8688
450	0.001409	47.9	2.9977	0.001404	48.1	2.9950
475	0.001486	105.9	3.1230	0.001478	105.8	3.1197
500	0.001583	167.1	3.2483	0.001571	166.5	3.2440
525	0.001722	233.6	3.3780	0.001696	231.9	3.3716
550	0.001980	314.4	3.5280	0.001897	308.9	3.5145
575	0.006478	517.9	3.8897	0.002595	425.0	3.7208
600	0.008206	587.6	4.0086	0.005488	556.4	3.9453
		p=80 bar			p=100 bar	
280	0.001104	−266.9	2.1250	0.001102	−265.3	2.1226
300	0.001128	−237.5	2.2264	0.001127	−236.0	2.2238
325	0.001162	−197.9	2.3534	0.001160	−196.5	2.3507
350	0.001198	−154.9	2.4811	0.001196	−153.6	2.4780
375	0.001239	−108.5	2.6092	0.001235	−107.3	2.6058
400	0.001284	−58.9	2.7372	0.001280	−57.8	2.7334
425	0.001336	−6.4	2.8643	0.001330	−5.6	2.8600
450	0.001395	48.5	2.9898	0.001386	49.1	2.9848
475	0.001464	105.8	3.1134	0.001452	105.9	3.1075
500	0.001548	165.6	3.2360	0.001529	165.2	3.2289
525	0.001655	229.6	3.3607	0.001622	228.2	3.3518
550	0.001801	302.9	3.4971	0.001740	299.8	3.4849
575	0.002042	395.3	3.6614	0.001902	387.2	3.6404
600	0.002646	481.5	3.8081	0.002179	458.7	3.7622
		p=200 bar			p=300 bar	
280	0.001095	−257.6	2.1110	0.001088	−249.8	2.1000
300	0.001116	−228.5	2.2116	0.001110	−220.7	2.1999
325	0.001149	−189.3	2.3373	0.001139	−181.9	2.3248
350	0.001183	−146.8	2.4635	0.001171	−139.7	2.4500
375	0.001219	−101.0	2.5899	0.001204	−94.3	2.5754
400	0.001259	−52.2	2.7158	0.001240	−45.9	2.7002
425	0.001302	−0.7	2.8405	0.001278	5.0	2.8237
450	0.001349	53.0	2.9630	0.001319	58.2	2.9450
475	0.001400	108.5	3.0831	0.001361	113.2	3.0638
500	0.001456	166.2	3.2012	0.001405	170.3	3.1809

continued

T, °K	v	i	s	v	i	s
525	0.001516	227.2	3.3202	0.001451	230.8	3.2989
550	0.001580	296.1	3.4482	0.001498	299.2	3.4259
575	0.001652	377.1	3.5925	0.001547	378.4	3.5670
600	0.001740	436.6	3.6938	0.001603	436.2	3.6637
		$p=400$ bar			$p=500$ bar	
280	0.001081	−241.6	2.0894	0.001075	−233.9	2.0794
300	0.001102	−213.1	2.1888	0.001095	−205.3	2.1784
325	0.001130	−174.4	2.3131	0.001121	−166.8	2.3020
350	0.001160	−132.5	2.4375	0.001149	−125.0	2.4258
375	0.001191	− 87.3	2.5621	0.001179	− 80.1	2.5498
400	0.001223	− 39.3	2.6862	0.001208	− 32.2	2.6733
425	0.001258	11.4	2.8089	0.001239	18.2	2.7956
450	0.001293	64.2	2.9295	0.001271	70.9	2.9159
475	0.001330	119.0	3.0478	0.001304	125.6	3.0340
500	0.001367	176.0	3.1646	0.001336	182.6	3.1508
525	0.001404	236.4	3.2824	0.001367	243.1	3.2687
550	0.001441	304.7	3.4092	0.001398	311.4	3.3956
575	0.001480	383.0	3.5486	0.001430	389.1	3.5340
600	0.001522	438.4	3.6430	0.001465	443.7	3.6269

Heat capacity c_p (kJ/kg · deg) of saturated liquid benzene [42, 93, 382]

T, °K	280	300	325	350	375	400	425	450	475	500
c_p	1.69	1.73	1.80	1.87	1.96	2.08	2.20	2.33	2.46	2.60

Heat capacity c_p (kJ/kg · deg) of liquid benzene at different pressures [93]

p, bar \ T, °K →	375	400	425	450	475	p, bar \ T, °K →	375	400	425	450	475
2	1.96					100	1.91	2.03		2.22	2.30
4		2.08	2.20			200	1.89	2.01		2.19	2.26
8						300	1.88	2.00		2.17	2.24
10				2.32		400	1.87	1.98		2.15	2.23
16					2.45	500	1.86	1.97		2.14	2.22
50	1.93	2.05		2.26	2.36						

Viscosity η ($N \cdot s/m^2$) of saturated benzene [52, 93]

T, °K	$\eta' \cdot 10^6$	$\eta'' \cdot 10^6$	T, °K	$\eta' \cdot 10^6$	$\eta'' \cdot 10^6$	T, °K	$\eta' \cdot 10^6$	$\eta'' \cdot 10^6$
285	735	7.39	375	258	9.89	465	124	13.1
290	675	7.54	380	246	10.0	470	120	13.4
295	628	7.68	385	235	10.2	475	116	13.6
300	580	7.83	390	224	10.3	480	112	13.8
305	544	7.96	395	214	10.5	485	108	14.1
310	510	8.10	400	205	10.7	490	105	14.4
315	481	8.23	405	196	10.8	495	101	14.7
320	452	8.36	410	188	11.0	500	97.9	15.0
325	426	8.49	415	180	11.2	505	94.5	15.3
330	405	8.63	420	173	11.3	510	91.0	15.6
335	385	8.76	425	166	11.5	515	87.7	16.0
340	355	8.90	430	160	11.7	520	84.2	16.4
345	348	9.03	435	154	11.9	525	80.7	16.8

continued

T, °K	$\eta' \cdot 10^6$	$\eta'' \cdot 10^6$	T, °K	$\eta' \cdot 10^6$	$\eta'' \cdot 10^6$	T, °K	$\eta' \cdot 10^6$	$\eta'' \cdot 10^6$
350	331	9.17	440	148	12.1	530	77.1	17.2
355	315	9.31	445	143	12.3	535	73.3	17.7
360	299	9.45	450	138	12.5	540	69.3	18.3
365	285	9.60	455	133	12.7	545	65.0	18.9
370	271	9.74	460	128	12.9	550	59.6	19.6

Viscosity $\eta \cdot 10^6$ (N · s/m²) of benzene at different temperatures and pressures [93]

T, °K → / p, bar	325	350	375	400	425	450	475	500	525	550	600	650	700
1	427	331	9.79	10.4	11.0	11.6	12.2	12.8	13.4	14.0	15.3	16.5	17.6
2	427	331	258	10.5	11.1	11.7	12.3	12.9	13.5	14.1	15.3	16.5	17.6
4	427	332	259	205	11.3	11.9	12.4	13.0	13.6	14.2	15.4	16.6	17.7
6	428	332	259	205	11.5	12.1	12.6	13.2	13.7	14.3	15.5	16.7	17.8
8	429	333	260	206	166	12.3	12.8	13.3	13.9	14.4	15.6	16.7	17.8
10	430	334	260	206	167	138	13.0	13.5	14.0	14.6	15.7	16.8	17.9
15	431	335	262	207	168	139	116	14.2	14.6	15.0	16.0	17.2	18.1
20	432	336	263	208	169	139	117	14.7	15.0	15.4	16.3	17.3	18.3
25	434	338	264	209	170	140	118	98.6	15.7	15.9	16.7	17.6	18.5
30	435	339	265	210	171	141	119	99.7	16.6	16.6	17.1	17.9	18.7
35	437	340	266	211	171	142	120	101	82.2	17.5	17.9	18.2	19.0
40	438	342	268	213	172	143	120	102	83.9	18.8	18.3	18.6	19.3
45	440	343	269	214	173	144	121	103	85.4	63.1	19.0	19.1	19.6
50	442	345	270	215	174	145	122	104	86.8	66.8	19.9	19.6	19.9
60	445	347	272	217	176	146	124	106	89.4	72.1	22.6	20.8	20.7
70	448	350	275	219	178	148	126	108	91.6	76.0	30.9	22.1	21.7
80	451	353	277	221	180	150	127	110	94.1	79.3	42.3	25.8	22.9
90	454	356	280	223	182	152	129	111	96.2	82.2	50.6	28.4	24.4
100	457	358	282	225	184	154	131	113	98.3	84.8	56.6	32.6	26.2
150	472	372	295	236	194	163	139	122	107	95.6	71.9	53.4	39.6
200	488	386	307	247	204	171	148	130	116	104	84.9	66.8	52.5
300	519	415	333	270	224	189	164	145	131	120	101	83.2	71.3
400	551	444	359	293	244	208	181	161	146	134	115	99.5	85.8
500	584	474	386	317	265	227	198	176	160	148	128	112	98.3

Thermal conductivity λ of benzene vapor at a pressure of 1 bar [15]

T, °K	325	350	375	400	425	450
$\lambda \cdot 10^4$, W/m · deg	125	150	176	202	228	254

Thermal conductivity λ (W/m · deg) of liquid benzene [15]

t, °C	λ	t, °C	λ	t, °C	λ	t, °C	λ
10	0.149	50	0.1375	90	0.125	130	0.113
20	0.1465	60	0.1345	100	0.122	140	0.110
30	0.1435	70	0.1315	110	0.119	150	0.1065
40	0.1405	80	0.1285	120	0.116	160	0.103

Surface tension of benzene [65]

t, °C	10	20	25	30	40	50	60	70	80
$\sigma \cdot 10^3$, N/m	30 24	28.88	28.18	27.49	26.14	24.88	23.66	22.4	21.2

TOLUENE (C_7H_8)

—CH_3

Molecular weight 92.134

$t_{boil} = 110.625$ °C at 760 mm Hg; $t_{melt} = -94.991$ °C;
$t_{cr} = 320.8$ °C; $p_{cr} = 40.5$ bar; $\rho_{cr} = 290$ kg/m³

Thermodynamic properties of toluene [62]: c_p^0 (kJ/kg · deg), i^0 (kJ/kg) and s^0 (kJ/kg · deg)

T, °K	c_p^0	i^0	s^0	T, °K	c_p^0	i^0	s^0
0	0	0	0	900	2.691	1425.6	5.5700
298.16	1.127	195.7	3.472	1000	2.826	1701.7	5.8608
300	1.134	197.8	3.479	1100	2.941	1990.3	6.1358
400	1.511	330.3	3.858	1200	3.040	2289.7	6.3961
500	1.842	498.43	4.141	1300	3.125	2598.2	6.6429
600	2.116	696.78	4.5931	1400	3.198	2914.1	6.8769
700	2.343	920.02	4.9366	1500	3.262	3237.6	7.1000
800	2.532	1164.2	5.2624				

Saturated vapor pressure of toluene [65]

t, °C	−70	−60	−50	−40	−30	−20	−10	0	10	20
p, mm Hg	0.009	0.033	0.104	0.289	0.720	1.63	3.43	6.72	12.43	21.84

t, °C	25	30	40	50	60	70	80	90	100	110
p, mm Hg	28.44	36.67	59.16	92.12	138.9	203.7	291.2	406.7	556.3	746.6

t, °C	120	130	140	150	160	170	180	190	200	210	220
p, bar	1.312	1.704	2.180	2.752	3.433	4.233	5.165	6.241	7.474	9.094	10.93

t, °C	230	240	250	260	270	280	290	300	310
p, bar	12.98	15.26	17.77	20.50	23.48	26.69	30.15	33.82	37.74

Latent heat of vaporization r (kJ/kg) of toluene [65]

t, °C	r	t, °C	r	t, °C	r	t, °C	r	t, °C	r
−90	452.1	0	423.0	90	376.7	170	324.0	250	242.2
−80	449.8	10	419.0	100	370.8	180	315.8	260	227.6
−70	447.1	20	414.4	110	364.4	190	307.2	270	211.8
−60	444.4	30	409.4	120	358.5	200	298.1	280	193.6
−50	441.7	40	404.0	130	352.2	210	288.5	290	172.7
−40	438.5	50	399.0	140	345.3	220	278.5	300	147.2
−30	434.9	60	393.5	150	338.5	230	267.2	310	112.2
−20	431.2	70	388.1	160	331.7	240	255.4	320	30.4
−10	427.1	80	382.2						

Density ρ (kg/m³) of liquid toluene [65]

t, °C	$\rho \cdot 10^{-3}$	t, °C	$\rho \cdot 10^{-3}$	t, °C	$\rho \cdot 10^{-3}$	t, °C	$\rho \cdot 10^{-3}$	t, °C	$\rho \cdot 10^{-3}$	t, °C	$\rho \cdot 10^{-3}$
−100	0.9799	−60	0.9413	−20	0.9039	20	0.8669	50	0.8388	90	0.8000
−90	0.9701	−50	0.9318	−10	0.8947	25	0.8623	60	0.8293	100	0.7900
−80	0.9604	−40	0.9225	0	0.8855	30	0.8576	70	0.8197	110	0.7798
−70	0.9508	−30	0.9132	10	0.8762	40	0.8483	80	0.8099		

Viscosity η (N · s/m²) of toluene vapor at $p \leqslant 1$ bar [52]

t, °C	$\eta \cdot 10^7$	t, °C	$\eta \cdot 10^7$	t, °C	$\eta \cdot 10^7$	t, °C	$\eta \cdot 10^7$	t, °C	$\eta \cdot 10^7$	t, °C	$\eta \cdot 10^7$
0	76.5	50	76.3	100	89.1	200	112.0	300	133.5	500	174.5
25	69.8	75	82.6	150	100.8	250	123.0	400	154.5	600	195.0

Viscosity η (N · s/m²) of liquid toluene [94]

t, °C	$\eta \cdot 10^3$	t, °C	$\eta \cdot 10^3$	t, °C	$\eta \cdot 10^3$	t, °C	$\eta \cdot 10^3$	t, °C	$\eta \cdot 10^3$
0	0.768	30	0.522	60	0.381	100	0.271	160	0.172
10	0.667	40	0.466	70	0.348	120	0.231	180	0.150
20	0.586	50	0.420	80	0.319	140	0.199		

Heat capacity of liquid toluene [42]

t, °C	−50	0	20	50	100
c_p, kJ/kg · deg	1.51	1.63	1.67	1.80	1.97

Thermal conductivity λ of liquid toluene [15]

t, °C	−80	−60	−40	−20	0	20	30	40	50	60
λ, W/m · deg	0.159	0.154	0.149	0.144	0.140	0.135	0.132	0.130	0.127	0.125
t, °C	70	80	100	120	140	160	180	200	220	240
λ, W/m · deg	0.123	0.120	0.116	0.111	0.106	0.102	0.097	0.092	0.087	0.083

Surface tension of toluene [62]

t, °C	0	10	20	25	30	40	50	60	70	80	90	100
$\sigma \cdot 10^3$, N/m	30.92	29.70	28.53	27.29	27.32	26.15	25.04	23.94	22.9	21.8	20.7	19.6

o-XYLENE (C_8H_{10})

$-CH_3$

$-CH_3$

Molecular weight 106.160

$t_{boil} = 144.411$ °C at 760 mm Hg; $t_{melt} = -25.182$ °C; $t_{cr} = 358.44$ °C;
$p_{cr} = 38.08$ bar; $\rho_{cr} = 287$ kg/m³

Thermodynamic properties of o-xylene [62]: $c_p°$ (kJ/kg · deg), $i°$ (kJ/kg) and s^0 (kJ/kg · deg)

T, °K	$c_p°$	$i°$	s^0	T, °K	$c_p°$	$i°$	s^0
0	0	0	0	900	2.792	1509.2	5.5350
298.16	1.256	219.9	3.325	1000	2.932	1795.7	5.8367
300	1.263	222.2	3.333	1100	3.053	2095.4	6.1219
400	1.618	366.4	3.745	1200	3.156	2405.8	6.3920
500	1.937	544.51	4.1416	1300	3.245	2726.1	6.6472
600	2.208	752.12	4.5198	1400	3.322	3054.6	6.8914
700	2.436	984.50	4.8775	1500	3.389	3390.3	7.1232
800	2.628	1237.9	5.2155				

Saturated vapor pressure of o-xylene [65, 402]

t, °C	p, mm Hg	t, °C	p, mm Hg	t, °C	p, bar	t, °C	p, bar	t, °C	p, bar
−20	0.243	60	40.80	150	1.172	240	7.500	330	26.87
−10	0.574	70	63.19	160	1.505	250	8.820	340	30.32
0	1.25	80	94.98	170	1.907	260	10.32	350	34.36
10	2.55	90	138.99	180	2.388	270	12.00	355	36.50
20	4.88	100	198.51	190	2.956	280	13.90	356	36.96
30	8.86	110	277.34	200	3.622	290	16.02	357	37.42
40	15.34	120	379.80	210	4.390	300	18.35	358	37.88
50	25.49	130	510.67	220	5.280	310	20.95	358.44	38.08
		140	675.23	230	6.305	320	23.79		

Density (kg/m³) of o-xylene at different temperatures and pressures [95]

p, bar \ t, °C →	25	50	100	150	200	250	275
1	876.0	855.5	811.0				
50	879.5	859.0	816.0	772.0	723.5	667.0	635.0
100	882.5	863.0	821.0	779.0	733.0	682.5	656.0
150	886.0	867.0	826.0	785.5	742.0	695.5	671.5
200	889.0	870.5	830.5	792.0	750.0	706.5	684.0
250	892.0	873.5	835.0	797.0	757.0	716.0	695.0
300	895.0	877.0	839.0	802.5	764.0	724.5	705.0
350	898.0	880.0	843.0	807.5	770.0	732.0	714.0
400	901.0	883.0	847.0	812.5	776.0	740.0	722.0

Density ρ (kg/m³) of liquid o-xylene at p = 1 bar and different temperatures [62]

t, °C	ρ	t, °C	ρ	t, °C	ρ	t, °C	ρ	t, °C	ρ	t, °C	ρ
−30	921.8*)	0	896.9	30	871.9	60	846.4	90	820.4	120	793.5
−20	913.5	10	888.6	40	863.4	70	837.8	100	811.6	130	784.4
−10	905.2	20	880.2	50	854.9	80	829.2	110	802.6	140	775.3

*Supercooled liquid.

Heat capacity c_p of liquid *o*-xylene [96]

T, °K	250	260	270	280	290	300
c_p, kJ/kg · deg	1.63	1.65	1.67	1.70	1.72	1.74

Latent heat of vaporization (kJ/kg) of *o*-xylene [65]

t, °C	r	t, °C	r	t, °C	r	t, °C	r	t, °C	r
−20	427.9	60	391.2	140	349.8	220	300.1	300	214.2
−10	423.6	70	386.5	150	343.9	230	292.2	310	198.4
0	419.2	80	381.4	160	338.4	240	283.6	320	180.6
10	414.9	90	376.2	170	332.5	250	274.1	330	159.7
20	410.6	100	371.1	180	326.6	260	263.8	340	133.7
30	405.8	110	366.0	190	320.2	270	252.8	350	97.4
40	401.1	120	360.9	200	313.9	280	241.0		
50	396.4	130	355.4	210	307.2	290	228.4		

Viscosity η (N · s/m²) of liquid *o*-xylene [62]

t, °C	$\eta \cdot 10^3$	t, °C	$\eta \cdot 10^3$	t, °C	$\eta \cdot 10^3$	t, °C	$\eta \cdot 10^3$	t, °C	$\eta \cdot 10^3$	t, °C	$\eta \cdot 10^3$
−5	1.215	25	0.756	50	0.557	75	0.432	100	0.345	125	0.283
0	1.108	30	0.708	55	0.528	80	0.412	105	0.331	130	0.272
5	1.017	35	0.664	60	0.501	85	0.393	110	0.318	135	0.263
10	0.939	40	0.625	65	0.476	90	0.376	115	0.305	140	0.254
15	0.870	45	0.589	70	0.453	95	0.360	120	0.294	145	0.245
20	0.809										

Surface tension of *o*-xylene [62]

t, °C	0	10	20	25	30	40	50	60	70	80	90	100
$\sigma \cdot 10^3$, N/m	32.28	31.16	30.03	29.48	28.93	27.84	26.76	25.70	24.7	23.6	22.6	21.5

m-XYLENE (C_8H_{10})

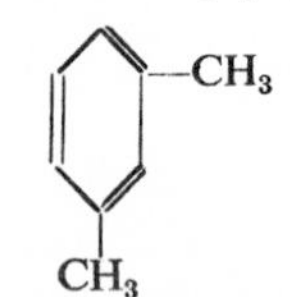

Molecular weight 106.160

$t_{boil} = 139.103$ °C at 760 mm Hg; $t_{melt} = -47.872$ °C; $t_{cr} = 346.0$ °C; $p_{cr} = 36.5$ bar; $\rho_{cr} = 270$ kg/m³

Thermodynamic properties of *m*-xylene [62]: c_p^0 (kJ/kg · deg), i^0 (kJ/kkg) and s^0 (kJ/kg · deg)

T, °K	c_p^0	i^0	s^0	T, °K	c_p^0	i^0	s^0
0	0	0	0	900	2.786	1486.0	5.5524
298.16	1.202	210.0	3.372	1000	2.928	1772.2	5.8533
300	1.209	212.3	3.379	1100	3.049	2071.4	6.1380
400	1.579	352.0	3.779	1200	3.153	2381.8	6.4078
500	1.910	526.88	4.1676	1300	3.243	2701.6	6.6638
600	2.189	732.12	4.5411	1400	3.316	3029.8	6.9067
700	2.423	962.93	4.8969	1500	3.384	3365.4	7.1386
800	2.619	1215.4	5.2337				

Saturated vapor pressure of *m*-xylene [62, 95]

t, °C	p, mm Hg	t, °C	p, mm Hg	t, °C	p, bar	t, °C	p, bar	t, °C	p, bar	t, °C	p, bar
−30	0.127	60	49.35	140	1.0376	210	4.96	275	14.41	340	33.83
−20	0.324	70	75.83	150	1.3454	220	5.94	280	15.47	342	34.70
−10	0.753	80	113.2	160	1.7203	225	6.51	290	17.78	343.6	35.41
0	1.62	90	164.5	170	2.1719	230	7.08	300	20.32	344	35.60
10	3.24	100	233.6	175	2.44	240	8.38	310	23.14	345	36.06
20	6.14	110	324.5	180	2.70	250	9.85	320	26.30	346	36.5
30	11.02	120	442.0	190	3.33	260	11.53	325	28.05		
40	18.89	130	591.5	200	4.09	270	13.40	330	29.85		
50	31.09										

Density ρ (kg/m³) of *m*-xylene at different temperatures and pressures [95]

p, bar \ t, °C →	20	50	100	150	200	250	275
1	864.9	840.6	796.7	747.4			
50	868.4	844.7	802.6	755.1	702.5	643.8	613.5
100	871.8	848.7	807.4	762.3	713.2	661.2	636.9
150	875.2	852.6	812.5	769.2	722.9	675.9	655.7
200	878.5	856.3	817.1	775.5	731.6	688.6	670.8
250	881.6	859.9	821.8	781.5	739.8	699.9	684.4
300	884.7	863.4	826.2	787.1	748.3	710.1	696.4
350	887.7	866.8	830.4	742.8	754.3	719.5	707.3
400	890.6	870.1	834.5	797.7	760.9	728.1	717.3

Density ρ of liquid *m*-xylene at low temperatures [62]

°C	−50	−40	−30	−20	−10	0	10	20
ρ, kg/m³	923.0 *)	914.7	906.3	897.9	889.5	881.1	872.6	864.2

*Supercooled liquid.

Heat capacity c_p of liquid *m*-xylene [96]

T, °K	220	230	240	250	260	270	280	290	300
c_p, kJ/kg · deg	1.51	1.54	1.56	1.59	1.61	1.64	1.67	1.69	1.72

Latent heat of vaporization r (kJ/kg) of *m*-xylene [62]

t, °C	r	t, °C	r	t, °C	r	t, °C	r	t, °C	r
−40	422.0	40	395.6	120	356.5	200	303.3	280	224.8
−30	419.6	50	391.2	130	350.6	210	295.8	290	209.8
−20	416.9	60	386.5	140	344.3	220	287.9	300	193.3
−10	413.7	70	382.2	150	338.0	230	279.6	310	175.5
0	410.6	80	377.4	160	331.3	240	270.6	320	153.4
10	407.4	90	372.3	170	324.6	250	260.7	330	125.4
20	403.9	100	367.2	180	321.8	260	249.7	340	82.8
30	399.9	110	362.1	190	310.8	270	237.8		

Viscosity η $(N \cdot s/m^2)$ of liquid *m*-xylene [94]

t, °C	$\eta \cdot 10^3$	t, °C	$\eta \cdot 10^3$	t, °C	$\eta \cdot 10^3$	t, °C	$\eta \cdot 10^3$	t, °C	$\eta \cdot 10^3$
0	0.80	30	0.55	60	0.403	90	0.313	120	0.250
10	0.70	40	0.490	70	0.369	100	0.285	130	0.233
20	0.61	50	0.433	80	0.339	110	0.269		

Thermal conductivity λ of liquid *m*-xylene [97]

t, °C	0	25	50	75	100	125
λ, W/m · deg	0.136	0.131	0.127	0.121	0.117	0.110

Surface tension of *m*-xylene [65]

t, °C	0	10	20	25	30	40	50	60	70	80	90	100
$\sigma \cdot 10^3$, N/m	30.92	29.78	28.63	28.08	27.54	26.44	25.36	24.26	23.2	22.2	21.1	20.1

n-XYLENE (C_8H_{10})

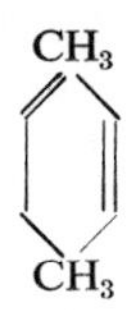

Molecular weight 106.160

$t_{boil} = 138.351$ °C at 760 mm Hg; $t_{melt} = 13.263$ °C; $t_{cr} = 345.0$ °C;
$p_{cr} = 36.17$ bar; $\rho_{cr} = 281$ kg/m³

Thermodynamic properties of *n*-xylene [62]: $c_p{}^0$ (kJ/kg · deg), i^0 (kJ/kg) and s^0 (kJ/kg · deg)

T, °K	$c_p{}^0$	i^0	s^0	T, °K	$c_p{}^0$	i^0	s^0
0	0	0	0	900	2.776	1480.0	5.4889
298.16	1.196	211.3	3.322	1000	2.919	1765.1	5.7890
300	1.202	213.5	3.329	1100	3.042	2063.5	6.0730
400	1.566	352.2	3.726	1200	3.147	2373.1	6.3423
500	1.895	525.74	4.1116	1300	3.238	2692.6	6.5979
600	2.176	729.60	4.4828	1400	3.316	3020.3	6.8405
700	2.411	959.14	4.8365	1500	3.384	3355.6	7.0720
800	2.608	1210.4	5.1718				

Saturated vapor pressure of *n*-xylene [65, 402]

t, °C	p, mm Hg	t, °C	p, mm Hg	t, °C	p, bar	t, °C	p, bar	t, °C	p, bar
20	6.50	80	117.15	140	1.059	220	5.988	300	20.37
30	11.62	90	169.81	150	1.370	230	7.125	310	23.25
40	19.83	100	240.42	160	1.749	240	8.417	320	26.44
50	32.51	110	333.19	170	2.203	250	9.900	330	30.03
60	51.41	120	452.83	180	2.745	260	11.55	340	33.96
70	78.74	130	604.60	190	3.382	270	13.42	342	34.80
				200	4.126	280	15.50	344	35.71
				210	4.989	290	17.82	345	36.17

Density ρ (Kg/m^3) of *n*-xylene at different temperatures and pressures [95]

p, bar \ t, °C →	10	20	30	40	50	100	150	200	250	275
1	869.7	861.0	852.5	843.7	835.0	789.5				
50					839.0	795.5	750.0	700.0	643.0	607.0
100					843.5	801.0	757.5	711.5	659.5	630.7
150					848.0	806.5	764.0	721.0	673.5	648.0
200					852.0	812.3	770.0	730.0	685.0	663.0
250					856.0	816.5	776.5	737.7	696.0	675.7
300					859.0	820.0	782.5	745.0	705.5	686.5
350					862.0	824.6	787.3	751.5	713.8	696.3
400					866.0	829.0	792.5	758.0	720.8	703.5

Heat capacity c_p of liquid *n*-xylene [98]

t, °C	20	40	60	80	100	120	140	160	180	200
c_p, kJ/kg · deg	1.698	1.758	1.821	1.890	1.962	2.036	2.111	2.187	2.263	2.343

Heat of vaporization (kJ/kg) of *n*-xylene [65]

t, °C	r	t, °C	r	t, °C	r	t, °C	r	t, °C	r
20	400.7	90	366.4	160	327.7	230	275.3	300	188.9
30	396.0	100	361.3	170	321.4	240	265.8	310	170.4
40	391.2	110	355.7	180	314.7	250	255.6	320	148.3
50	386.5	120	350.2	190	307.6	260	244.5	330	119.9
60	381.8	130	344.7	200	300.1	270	232.7	340	73.7
70	376.6	140	339.2	210	292.2	280	219.7		
80	371.5	150	333.7	220	284.0	290	205.1		

Viscosity of liquid *n*-xylene [94]

t, °C	10	20	30	40	50	60	70	80	90	100	110	120	130
$\eta \cdot 10^3$, $N \cdot s/m^2$	0.74	0.64	0.57	0.51	0.456	0.414	0.377	0.345	0.317	0.292	0.270	0.251	0.233

Surface tension of *n*-xylene [62]

t, °C	20	25	30	40	50	60	70	80	90	100
$\sigma \cdot 10^3$, N/m	28.31	27.76	27.22	26.13	25.06	24.02	23.0	22.0	21.0	20.1

ETHYLBENZENE (C_8H_{10})

$-CH_2-CH_3$

Molecular weight 106.160

$t_{boil} = 136.186$ °C at 760 mm Hg; $t_{melt} = -94.975$ °C; $t_{cr} = 346.4$ °C;
$p_{cr} = 37.5$ bar; $\rho_{cr} = 290$ kg/m³; $\lambda = 0.112$ kcal/m · hr · deg for liquid at 30 °C [75]

Thermodynamic properties of ethylbenzene [62]:
$c_p{}^0$ (kJ/kg · deg), i^0 (kJ/kg) and s^0 (kJ/kg · deg)

T, °K	$c_p{}^0$	i^0	s^0	T, °K	$c_p{}^0$	i^0	s^0
0	0	0	0				
298.16	1.210	210.4	3.398	900	2.811	1504.4	5.610
300	1.218	212.6	3.405	1000	2.949	1792.5	5.915
400	1.608	354.0	3.810	1100	3.067	2093.5	6.200
500	1.946	532.28	4.205	1200	3.169	2405.0	6.471
600	2.226	741.43	4.586	1300	3.256	2726.5	6.728
700	2.456	975.98	4.947	1400	3.332	3055.8	6.972
800	2.648	1231.4	5.288	1500	3.398	3392.6	7.204

Saturated vapor pressure of ethylbenzene [65]

t, °C	p, mm Hg	t, °C	p, mm Hg	t, °C	p, mm Hg	t, °C	p, bar	t, °C	p, bar
−30	0.153	30	12.63	90	181.92	140	1.1211	190	3.546
−20	0.386	40	21.50	100	256.95	150	1.4477	200	4.317
−10	0.889	50	35.17	110	355.26	160	1.8440	210	5.208
0	1.90	60	55.48	120	481.72	170	2.319	220	6.229
10	3.77	70	84.76	130	641.72	180	2.883		
20	7.08	80	125.80						

Density ρ (kg/m³) of liquid ethylbenzene [62]

t, °C	$\rho \cdot 10^{-3}$	t, °C	$\rho \cdot 10^{-3}$	t, °C	$\rho \cdot 10^{-3}$	t, °C	$\rho \cdot 10^{-3}$	t, °C	$\rho \cdot 10^{-3}$	t, °C	$\rho \cdot 10^{-3}$
−90	0.9637	−50	0.9283	−10	0.8932	30	0.8583	70	0.8224	110	0.7854
−80	0.9548	−40	0.9195	0	0.8845	40	0.8495	80	0.8133	120	0.7759
−70	0.9460	−30	0.9107	10	0.8758	50	0.8405	90	0.8041	130	0.7663
−60	0.9371	−20	0.9019	20	0.8670	60	0.8315	100	0.7948	140	0.7567

Heat capacity c_p of ethylbenzene [99]

T, °K	180	190	200	210	220	230	240	250	260	270	280	290	300
c_p, kJ/kg · deg	1.483	1.495	1.509	1.526	1.544	1.565	1.587	1.612	1.638	1.666	1.695	1.726	1.757

Latent heat of vaporization (kJ/kg) of ethylbenzene [65]

t, °C	r	t, °C	r	t, °C	r	t, °C	r	t, °C	r
−90	436.6	0	408.2	90	363.2	180	312.8	270	234.3
−80	434.6	10	404.3	100	358.1	190	306.0	280	221.2
−70	431.9	20	399.9	110	353.0	200	299.0	290	207.1
−60	429.1	30	391.6	120	347.5	210	291.5	300	191.7
−50	425.9	40	386.9	130	342.3	220	283.6	310	171.6
−40	422.8	50	382.6	140	336.8	230	275.3	320	150.3
−30	419.6	60	377.8	150	330.9	240	266.2	330	122.3
−20	416.1	70	373.1	160	325.0	250	256.4	340	80.1
−10	412.1	80	368.0	170	319.1	260	245.7		

Viscosity η of liquid ethylbenzene [52]

t, °C	−20	−10	0	10	20	30	40	50	60	70	80
$\eta \cdot 10^3$, N · s/m²	1.170	1.021	0.873	0.757	0.671	0.596	0.530	0.482	0.436	0.397	0.363

Surface tension of ethylbenzene [62]

t, °C	0	10	20	25	30	40	50	60	70	80	90	100
$\sigma \cdot 10^3$, N/m	31.38	30.18	29.04	28.48	27.93	26.79	25.74	24.74	23.7	22.7	21.7	20.7

ISOPROPYLBENZENE (CUMENE) (C_9H_{12})

C_6H_5—CH(CH_3)(CH_3)

Molecular weight 120.186

t_{boil} = 152.392 °C at 760 mm Hg; t_{melt} = − 96.035 °C; t_{cr} = 363 °C;
p_{cr} = 31.4 bar; ρ_{cr} = 280 kg/m³

Thermodynamic properties of isopropylbenzene [62]:
$c_p{}^0$ (kJ/kg · deg), i^0 (kJ/kg) and s^0 (KJ/kg · deg)

T, °K	$c_p{}^0$	i^0	s^0	T, °K	$c_p{}^0$	i^0	s^0
0	0	0	0				
298.16	1.263	212.14	3.235	900	2.90	1552.0	5.528
300	1.270	214.62	3.242	1000	3.04	1849.1	5.838
400	1.672	361.54	3.664	1100	3.16	2159.5	6.134
500	2.02	546.83	4.075	1200	3.27	2479.9	6.416
600	2.31	764.17	4.469	1300	3.36	2814.3	6.680
700	2.54	1006.6	4.841	1400	3.43	3152.1	6.931
800	2.74	1270.2	5.197	1500	3.504	3496.93	7.171

Saturated vapor pressure of cumene [65]

t, °C	p, mm Hg	t, °C	p, mm Hg	t, °C	p, mm Hg	t, °C	p, bar	t, °C	p, bar
−20	0.144	40	11.00	100	155.02	160	1.2290	200	3.0146
−10	0.356	50	18.62	110	218.65	170	1.5656	210	3.673
0	0.807	60	30.31	120	301.98	180	1.9698	220	4.434
10	1.70	70	47.63	130	404.19	190	2.4498	230	5.306
20	3.34	80	72.54	140	544.86				
30	6.22	90	107.40	150	714.00				

Density ρ (kg/m³) of liquid isopropylbenzene [62]

t, °C	$\varrho \cdot 10^{-3}$	t, °C	$\varrho \cdot 10^{-3}$	t, °C	$\varrho \cdot 10^{-3}$	t, °C	$\varrho \cdot 10^{-3}$	t, °C	$\varrho \cdot 10^{-3}$	t, °C	$\varrho \cdot 10^{-3}$
0	0.8786	20	0.8618	30	0.8534	50	0.8366	70	0.8199	90	0.8031
10	0.8702	25	0.8575	40	0.8450	60	0.8283	80	0.8115		

Heat capacity c_p of liquid isopropylbenzene [100]

t, °C	25	50	75	100
c_p, kJ/kg · deg	1.78	1.87	1.97	2.03

Latent heat of vaporization (kJ/kg) of isopropylbenzene [65]

t, °C	r	t, °C	r	t, °C	r	t, °C	r	t, °C	r
−90	407.8	10	377.9	110	336.1	210	282.8	310	178.7
−80	407.5	20	374.1	120	331.2	220	276.2	320	171.7
−70	404.4	30	370.2	130	326.4	230	268.9	330	154.3
−60	401.2	40	366.4	140	321.5	240	260.9	340	133.0
−50	398.1	50	362.2	150	316.6	250	252.9	350	105.2
−40	395.0	60	358.0	160	311.4	260	243.8	360	55.7
−30	391.8	70	353.9	170	306.2	270	234.4		
−20	388.3	80	349.7	180	300.6	280	224.3		
−10	384.9	90	345.2	190	295.0	290	212.8		
0	381.4	100	340.6	200	289.1	300	200.6		

Viscosity η of liquid isopropylbenzene [52]

t, °C	0	10	20	30	40
$\eta \cdot 10^3$, N · s/m²	1.075	0.915	0.788	0.691	0.611

Thermal conductivity λ of liquid isopropylbenzene [72]

t, °C	0	20	40	60	80	100
λ, W/m · deg	0.1285	0.1256	0.1221	0.1192	0.1157	0.1128

Surface tension of isopropylbenzene [62]

t, °C	20	25	30	40	50	60	70	80	90
$\sigma \cdot 10^3$, N/m	28.20	27.68	27.17	26.09	25.08	24.07	23.1	22.2	21.2

n-BUTYLBENZENE ($C_{10}H_{14}$)

C_6H_5—CH_2—CH_2—CH_2—CH_3

Molecular weight 134.212

t_{boil} = 183.270 °C at 760 mm Hg; t_{melt} = − 87.970 °C;
t_{cr} = 387.8 °C; ρ_{cr} = 269.7 kg/m³

Thermodynamic properties of *n*-butylbenzene [62]: $c_p{}^0$ (kJ/kg · deg), i^0 (kJ/kg) and s^0 (kJ/kg · deg)

T, °K	$c_p{}^0$	i^0	s^0	T, °K	$c_p{}^0$	i^0	s^0
0	0	0	0	900	2.959	1598.6	5.6151
298.16	1.306	232.5	3.2772	1000	3.104	1902.3	5.9346
300	1.313	234.8	3.2857	1100	3.2292	2218.9	6.2362
400	1.708	386.10	3.7178	1200	3.3368	2547.8	6.5227
500	2.056	574.86	4.1377	1300	3.4295	2886.6	6.7935
600	2.346	795.41	4.5384	1400	3.5097	3233.57	7.0506
700	2.587	1042.2	4.9184	1500	3.5796	3588.00	7.2961
800	2.788	1311.4	5.2778				

Saturated vapor pressure of n-butylbenzene [65]

t, °C	p, mm Hg	t, °C	p, mm Hg	t, °C	p, mm Hg	t, °C	p, bar
0	0.140	70	14.74	130	166.48	190	1.1917
10	0.330	80	23.72	140	229.53	200	1.5018
20	0.717	90	36.95	150	310.73	210	1.8714
30	1.46	100	55.89	160	413.67	220	2.3078
40	2.79	110	82.32	170	542.29	230	2.8185
50	5.08	120	118.35	180	700.88	240	3.411
60	8.83					250	4.094

Density ρ of liquid n-butylbenzene [65]

t, °C	10	20	25	30	40
$\rho \cdot 10^{-3}$, kg/m³	0.8065	0.7992	0.7955	0.7918	0.7844

Latent heat of vaporization (kJ/kg) of n-butylbenzene [65]

t, °C	r	t, °C	r	t, °C	r	t, °C	r	t, °C	r	t, °C	r
−80	408.7	0	383.4	80	351.3	160	312.6	240	266.4	320	197.8
−70	405.9	10	379.7	90	346.9	170	307.3	250	259.9	330	185.0
−60	403.1	20	375.9	100	342.2	180	301.1	260	253.0	340	170.4
−50	400.0	30	372.2	110	337.6	190	296.4	270	245.5	350	153.5
−40	396.8	40	368.1	120	332.9	200	290.8	280	237.4	360	133.8
−30	393.7	50	364.1	130	327.9	210	284.8	290	228.7	370	108.3
−20	390.3	60	360.0	140	322.9	220	278.9	300	219.3	380	67.1
−10	386.9	70	355.7	150	317.9	230	272.7	310	209.0		

Viscosity η of liquid n-butylbenzene [52]

t, °C	10	20	30	40	50	60	70	80
$\eta \cdot 10^3$, N · s/m²	1.204	1.020	0.880	0.767	0.681	0.608	0.544	0.492

VINYLBENZENE (C_8H_8)

C_6H_5—CH=CH₂

Molecular weight 104.144

t_{boil} = 145.2 °C at 760 mm Hg; t_{melt} = − 30.628 °C

Thermodynamic properties of vinylbenzene [62]: $c_p{}^0$ (kJ/kg · deg), i^0 (kJ/kg) and s^0 (kJ/kg · deg)

T, °K	$c_p{}^0$	i^0	s^0	T, °K	$c_p{}^0$	i^0	s^0
0	0	0	0	900	2.610	1419.0	5.406
298.16	1.173	200.4	3.316	1000	2.730	1686.4	5.688
300	1.180	202.5	3.322	1100	2.833	1965.0	5.954
400	1.540	338.8	3.712	1200	2.921	2252.8	6.203
500	1.847	508.93	4.091	1300	2.996	2548.7	6.440
600	2.096	706.23	4.450	1400	3.062	2851.8	6.665
700	2.300	926.37	4.789	1500	3.118	3160.9	6.878
800	2.468	1164.8	5.107				

Saturated vapor pressure of vinylbenzene [65]

t, °C	p, mm Hg	t, °C	p, mm Hg	t, °C	p, mm Hg	t, °C	p, mm Hg	t, °C	p, mm Hg
0	1.28	30	8.59	60	39.0	90	133.0	120	367.8
10	2.54	40	14.8	70	60.3	100	190.6	130	497.3
20	4.79	50	24.4	80	90.7	110	267.3	140	661.3

Latent heat of vaporization r (kJ/kg) of vinylbenzene [65]

t, °C	r	t, °C	r	t, °C	r	t, °C	r	t, °C	r
−30	434.9	50	405.2	130	366.6	210	314.8	290	233.2
−20	432.1	60	400.8	140	361.0	220	307.1	300	218.7
−10	429.3	70	396.4	150	355.0	230	299.1	310	202.6
0	425.7	80	391.5	160	348.9	240	290.2	320	184.5
10	422.1	90	387.1	170	342.9	250	280.6	330	163.2
20	417.7	100	382.3	180	336.5	260	269.7	340	136.3
30	413.6	110	377.1	190	329.6	270	258.5	350	98.1
40	409.2	120	371.8	200	322.4	280	246.4		

Viscosity η ($N \cdot s/m^2$) of liquid vinylbenzene [52]

t, °C	$\eta \cdot 10^3$	t, °C	$\eta \cdot 10^3$	t, °C	$\eta \cdot 10^3$	t, °C	$\eta \cdot 10^3$	t, °C	$\eta \cdot 10^3$
0	1.047	30	0.648	60	0.453	90	0.349	120	0.269
10	0.879	40	0.565	70	0.413	100	0.309	130	0.249
20	0.749	50	0.502	80	0.374	110	0.289	140	0.232

Surface tension σ of vinylbenzene at 20 °C is equal to $32 \cdot 10^{-3}$ N/m.

NAPHTHALENE ($C_{10}H_8$)

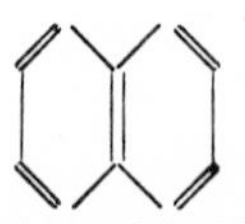

Molecular weight 128.164

$t_{boil} = 217.955$ °C at 760 mm Hg; $t_{melt} = 80.290$ °C; $t_{cr} = 478.2$ °C;
$p_{cr} = 39.7$ bar; $\rho_{cr} = 314$ kg/m^3; $\sigma = 32.0$ erg/cm^2 at 80.8 °C

Thermodynamic properties of naphthalene [62]: i^0 (kJ/kg) and s^0 (kJ/kg · deg)

T, °K	i^0	s^0	T, °K	i^0	s^0
0	0	0	900	1301.7	4.5682
298.16	166.3	2.628	1000	1553.1	4.8329
300	168.2	2.634	1100	1814.8	5.0821
400	291.9	2.987	1200	2085.3	5.3177
500	448.7	3.3359	1300	2363.1	5.5398
600	632.8	3.7035	1400	2647.8	5.7509
700	838.8	3.9880	1500	2937.4	5.9505
800	1062.9	4.2870			

Saturated vapor pressure of naphthalene [65]

t, °C	p, mm Hg	t, °C	p, mm Hg	t, °C	p, mm Hg	t, °C	p, bar	t, °C	p, bar
0	0.003	80	7.53	160	165.9	220	1.060	300	4.97
10	0.015	90	12.14	170	222.9	230	1.321	310	5.82
20	0.055	100	18.95	180	295.0	240	1.629	320	6.79
30	0.164	110	28.78	190	385.0	250	1.993	330	7.86
40	0.428	120	42.61	200	496.1	260	2.53	340	9.05
50	1.00	130	61.66	210	631.6	270	2.99	350	10.33
60	2.11	140	87.37			280	3.57	360	11.85
70	4.12	150	121.5			290	4.23	370	13.37

Density ρ' and ρ'' (kg/m³) of saturated naphthalene [42]

t, °C	$\rho' \cdot 10^{-3}$	$\rho'' \cdot 10^{-3}$	t, °C	$\rho' \cdot 10^{-3}$	$\rho'' \cdot 10^{-3}$	t, °C	$\rho' \cdot 10^{-3}$	$\rho'' \cdot 10^{-3}$
220	0.873	0.0033	270	0.835	0.0094	310	0.804	0.0150
230	0.865	0.0040	280	0.827	0.0118	320	0.794	0.0170
240	0.858	0.0047	290	0.820	0.0123	330		0.0194
250	0.850	0.0058	300	0.812	0.0129	340		0.0218
260	0.842	0.0070						

Latent heat of vaporization r (kJ/kg) of naphthalene [65]

t, °C	r	t, °C	r	t, °C	r	t, °C	r	t, °C	r
90	391.1	170	362.0	250	325.7	330	281.9	410	210.4
100	387.8	180	357.7	260	320.8	340	275.4	420	197.3
110	384.5	190	353.5	270	315.6	350	268.2	430	182.9
120	380.9	200	349.2	280	310.7	360	260.3	440	166.7
130	377.3	210	344.7	290	305.1	370	251.9	450	147.3
140	373.7	220	340.1	300	299.6	380	242.7	460	123.8
150	369.8	230	335.5	310	294.0	390	232.9	470	90.2
160	366.2	240	330.6	320	288.1	400	222.1		

Enthalpy i(kJ/kg) of saturated naphthalene [42]

t, °C	i′	i″	t, °C	i′	i″	t, °C	i′	i″
220	293	609.2	260	407	722.2	300	524.6	828.1
230	322	637.2	270	436.3	749.0	310	554.3	852.4
240	350	665.3	280	465.6	776.2	320	584.5	875.4
250	378	693.3	290	494.9	802.6			

BIPHENYL ($C_{12}H_{10}$)

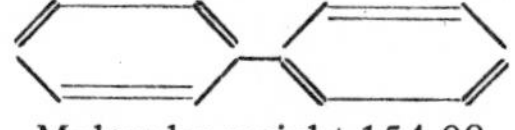

Molecular weight 154.08

$t_{boil} = 255.6$ °C at $p = 1$ atm; $t_{melt} = 69.1$ °C; $t_{cr} = 528$ °C;
$p_{cr} = 41.8$ bar; $\rho_{cr} = 323$ kg/m³

Thermodynamic properties of saturated biphenyl [101, 131]: ρ (kg/m³), c_p (kJ/kg · deg), i and r (kJ/kg), η (N · s/m²) λ (W/m · deg) and Pr

t, °C	p, mm Hg	ρ'	ρ''	c_p'	i′	i″	r	$\eta' \cdot 10^3$	λ′	Pr′
80		985		1.792				1.25	0.137	16.4
100	4.3	970	0.025	1.854	53	451	398	0.960	0.134	13.3
120		954		1.915			386	0.760	0.131	11.1

continued

t, °C	p, mm Hg	ϱ'	ϱ''	c'_p	i'	i''	r	$\eta' \cdot 10^3$	λ'	Pr'
140		937		1.977			374	0.618	0.128	9.5
160	54.4	922		2.040			362	0.516	0.125	8.4
180	105	905		2.100			350	0.438	0.122	7.5
200	190	889	0.868	2.163	258	596	338	0.376	0.119	6.8
220	327	872		2.225			327	0.325	0.116	6.2
240	534	855		2.287			316	0.284	0.113	5.7
	p, bar									
260	1.08	838		2.349			305	0.251	0.110	5.4
280	1.74	820		2.411			294	0.224	0.107	5.0
300	2.38	801	9.1	2.473	505	788	283	0.198	0.104	4.7
320	3.38	782		2.535			272	0.177	0.101	4.4
340	4.47	762		2.597			261	0.160	0.098	4.2
360	6.55	740		2.659			249	0.144	0.095	4.0
380	8.8	717		2.720			237	0.129	0.093	3.8
400		691	39	2.782	782	1008	226	0.116	0.090	3.6

Thermal conductivity λ of biphenyl vapor [376]

T, °K	450	475	500	525	550	575	600	625	650
$\lambda \cdot 10^3$, W/m · deg	18.4	19.8	21.4	23.2	25.2	27.2	29.4	31.8	34.6

Surface tension of biphenyl [101]

t, °C	100	125	150	175	200	225	250
σ, dyne/cm	32.3	29.7	27.2	24.7	22.3	20.1	17.8

HYDROCARBONS OF THE DIPHENYLMETHANE SERIES (HIGH-TEMPERATURE HEAT TRANSFER AGENTS/COOLANTS/) [102]

Compound	Symbol	Chemical formula	Mol. wt.	t_{melt} °C	t_{boil} at p = = 1 atm
Ditoluene-methane	DTM	$CH_3C_6H_4—CH_2—C_6H_4CH_3$	196	−32	292
Dixylene-methane	DXM	$(CH_3)_2C_6H_3—CH_2—C_6H_3(CH_3)_2$	224	−40	324
Dicumene-methane	DCM	$(CH_3)_2CHC_6H_4—CH_2—C_6H_4CH(CH_3)_2$	252	−22	335
Tetraiso-propyldiphenyl-methane	TDM	$[(CH_3)_2CH]_2C_6H_3—CH_2—C_6H_3[CH(CH_3)_2]_2$	336	−8	384

Boiling temperature (°C) of hydrocarbons of the diphenylmethane series

p, kg/cm²	DTM	DXM	DCM	TDM	p, kg/cm²	DTM	DXM	DCM	TDM
1.0	292	324	335	384	3.5	363	391	408	
1.5	314		360		4.0	372	400	418	420
2.0	332	364	374	395	4.5	380	407	426	
2.5	345	372	388		5.0	388	412	431	427
3.0	354	382	398	408					

Density ρ (gm/cm³) of liquid hydrocarbons of the diphenylmethane series

t, °C	DTM	DXM	DCM	TDM	t, °C	DTM	DXM	DCM	TDM
5.8		0.990			65	0.949		0.919	
7.0				0.941	75	0.942			
20	0.9825	0.9795	0.9475	0.928	75.7		0.935		
32.7				0.919	80	0.938			0.887
34		0.970			95	0.927		0.899	
35	0.971				120	0.910			
44.6	0.9635				135			0.8725	
46				0.910	150	0.888			
50	0.960		0.929		166	0.879			
60				0.900	170			0.8425	
63		0.9485			201	0.848			

Heat capacity c_p (kcal/kg · deg) of liquid hydrocarbons of the diphenylmethane series

DTM		DTM		DCM		DCM	
t, °C	c_p	t, °C	c_p	t, °C	c_p	t, °C	c_p
20	0.371	150	0.460	20	0.343	150	0.411
50	0.392	300	0.562	50	0.359	300	0.491
80	0.412			80	0.374		

Viscosity $\eta \cdot 10^2$ (g/cm · s) of liquid hydrocarbons of the diphenylmethane series

t, °C	DTM	DXM	DCM	TDM	t, °C	DTM	DXM	DCM	TDM
20	5.27	29.2	6.89	253	95	1.02	1.96	0.98	1.71
35	3.66	12.1	4.05	—	110	—	—	—	1.07
50	2.59	6.08	2.65	—	130	—	—	—	0.79
65	1.90	3.92	1.90	13.2	150	0.636	—	0.582	0.578
80	1.39	2.58	1.33	7.05					

Thermal conductivity λ (kcal/m · hr · deg) of liquid hydrocarbons of the diphenylmethane series

DTM		DTM		DCM [386]		DCM		TDM	
t, °C	λ	t, °C	λ	t, °C	λ	t, °C	λ	t, °C	λ
25.9	0.118	67.4	0.104	20	0.109	80	0.104	20	0.094
48.2	0.107	91.7	0.102	40	0.107	100	0.102	44	0.090
65.1	0.106	96.2	0.099	60	0.106	150	0.098	75.5	0.082

MONOISOPROPYLDIPHENYL ($C_{15}H_{16}$)

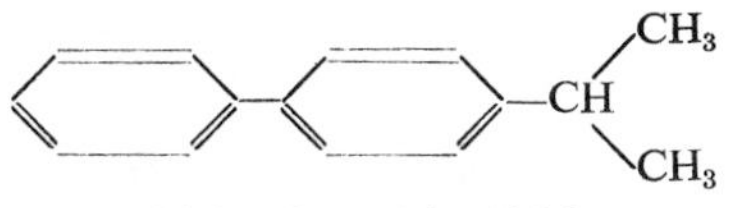

Molecular weight 196.3

Thermodynamic properties of liquid monoisopropyldiphenyl [103]:
ρ (kg/m³), c_p (kJ/kg · deg), r (kJ/kg), η (N · s/m²) and λ (kJ/kg · deg)

t, °C	p, mm Hg	ϱ	c_p	r	$\eta \cdot 10^3$	λ
20		969	1.72		14.1	0.127
40		962	1.81		6.29	0.124
60		953	1.87		3.47	0.121
80		943	1.93		2.22	0.119
100	1.5	932	2.00	322	1.57	0.116

continued

t, °C	p, mm Hg	ϱ	c_p	r	$\eta \cdot 10^3$	λ
120	3.5	920	2.07	317	1.17	0.114
140	8.5	907	2.14	314	0.890	0.112
160	19	893	2.20	311	0.690	0.109
180	39	879	2.27	307	0.555	0.107
200	77	861	2.34	304	0.456	0.104
220	142	845	2.42	300	0.384	0.102
240	249	827	2.50	295	0.330	0.100
260	418	809	2.58	290	0.289	0.098
280	671	791	2.67	283	0.254	0.094
300	1042	773	2.75	275	0.224	0.091
320	1570	753	2.85	266	0.198	0.087
340	2291	734	2.95	255	0.175	0.084
360	3266	714	3.06	242	0.155	0.081
380	4539	694	3.17	228	0.137	0.079
400	6194	674	3.30	213	0.124	0.077

Surface tension σ (dyne/cm) of monoisopropyldiphenyl [104]

t, °C	σ	t, °C	σ	t, °C	σ
20	35.0	120	26.8	220	18.6
40	33.4	140	25.2	240	17.0
60	31.8	160	23.6	260	15.5
80	30.1	180	21.9	280	14.0
100	28.5	200	20.3	300	12.6

HALOGEN-SUBSTITUTED HYDROCARBONS

METHYL CHLORIDE (CH_3Cl) [108]

Molecular weight 50.49
$t_{boil} = -23.74$ °C at $p = 1$ atm; $t_{melt} = -97.6$ °C; $t_{cr} = 143.1$ °C;
$p_{cr} = 66.72$ bar; $v_{cr} = 2.70$ dm³/kg

Thermodynamic properties of saturated methyl chloride [105]:
v' (dm³/kkg), v'' (m³/kg), i and r (kJ/kg) and s (kJ/kg · deg)

t, °C	p, bar	v'	v''	i'	i''	r	s'	s''
−60	0.156	0.936	2.235	409.82	870.36	460.54	0.6272	2.7882
−55	0.212	0.944	1.680	417.02	873.50	456.48	0.6612	2.7538
−50	0.280	0.953	1.295	424.42	876.60	452.18	0.6942	2.7212
−45	0.368	0.961	1.008	431.72	879.62	447.90	0.7272	2.6902
−40	0.474	0.970	0.794	439.12	882.72	443.60	0.7592	2.6617
−35	0.607	0.978	0.632	446.52	885.69	439.17	0.7902	2.6345
−30	0.767	0.986	0.508	454.12	888.66	434.54	0.8222	2.6090
−25	0.959	0.995	0.412	461.52	891.51	429.99	0.8522	2.5851
−20	1.188	1.003	0.338	469.22	894.44	425.22	0.8832	2.5625
−15	1.457	1.013	0.279	478.82	897.28	418.46	0.9132	2.5416
−10	1.772	1.022	0.233	484.42	900.01	415.59	0.9422	2.5209
− 5	2.136	1.032	0.195	492.22	902.56	410.34	0.9712	2.5014
0	2.557	1.042	0.1648	500.00	905.07	405.07	1.0000	2.4830
5	3.037	1.053	0.1402	507.87	907.46	399.59	1.0282	2.4650
10	3.582	1.064	0.1198	516.12	909.76	393.64	1.0562	2.4482
15	4.198	1.075	0.1031	523.57	911.94	388.37	1.0842	2.4319
20	4.893	1.086	0.0891	531.57	914.07	382.50	1.1122	2.4164
25	5.667	1.098	0.0774	539.61	916.08	376.47	1.1382	2.4013
30	6.525	1.110	0.0675	547.65	917.93	370.88	1.1652	2.3867
35	7.472	1.123	0.0591	555.77	919.64	363.87	1.1922	2.3724

continued

t, °C	p, bar	v′	v″	i′	i″	r	s′	s″
40	8.516	1.135	0.0520	563.93	921.32	357.39	1.2182	2.3594
45	9.664	1.149	0.0460	572.14	922.87	350.73	1.2442	2.3460
50	10.92	1.164	0.0408	580.39	924.29	343.90	1.2702	2.3343
55	12.28	1.180	0.0363	588.63	925.55	336.92	1.2952	2.3231
60	13.75	1.196	0.0324	597.01	926.76	329.75	1.3202	2.3105

Heat capacity of methyl chloride [105]

t, °C	25	100
c_p°, kJ/kg · deg	0.804	0.921

Viscosity of methyl chloride gas at a pressure of 1 bar [105]

t, °C	−20	−10	0	10	20	30	40	50
$\eta \cdot 10^7$, N · s/m²	94	98	101	105	108	112	115	119

Viscosity of liquid methyl chloride [105]

t, °C	−20	−10	0	10	20	30
$\eta \cdot 10^3$, N · s/m²	0.309	0.301	0.289	0.276	0.265	0.250

TRICHLOROMONOFLUOROMETHANE (FREON-11) ($CFCl_3$)

Molecular weight 137.39

$t_{boil} = 23.7$ °C at $p = 1$ atm; $t_{melt} = -111.0$ °C; $t_{cr} = 198.0$ °C;
$v_{cr} = 1.805$ dm³/kg

Thermodynamic properties of saturated trichloromonofluoromethane [106]:
v (m³/kg), i and r (kJ/kg) and s (kJ/kg · deg)

t, °C	p, bar	v′ · 10³	v″	i′	i″	r	s′	s″
−60	0.01279	0.6006	10.070	449.09	659.81	210.72	0.7899	1.7785
−50	0.02647	0.6084	5.094	457.32	664.72	207.40	0.8276	1.7570
−45	0.03702	0.6124	3.721	461.47	667.20	205.73	0.8460	1.7478
−40	0.05093	0.6164	2.763	465.65	669.71	204.06	0.8642	1.7394
−38	0.05760	0.6180	2.463	467.33	670.72	203.39	0.8714	1.7363
−36	0.06499	0.6197	2.200	469.02	671.74	202.72	0.8785	1.7333
−34	0.07316	0.6213	1.971	470.71	672.75	202.04	0.8856	1.7304
−32	0.08216	0.6230	1.769	472.40	673.77	201.37	0.8927	1.7277
−30	0.09206	0.6247	1.591	474.10	674.79	200.69	0.8997	1.7250
−28	0.1029	0.6264	1.434	475.80	675.81	200.01	0.9066	1.7225
−26	0.1149	0.6281	1.295	477.51	676.84	199.33	0.9136	1.7201
−24	0.1279	0.6298	1.172	479.21	677.87	198.65	0.9204	1.7178
−22	0.1421	0.6316	1.062	480.93	678.90	197.97	0.9273	1.7156
−20	0.1576	0.6333	0.9647	482.64	679.29	197.29	0.9341	1.7134
−18	0.1745	0.6351	0.8778	484.36	680.96	196.60	0.9409	1.7114
−16	0.1928	0.6369	0.8001	486.09	682.00	195.92	0.9476	1.7095
−14	0.2126	0.6387	0.7305	487.81	683.04	195.23	0.9543	1.7076
−12	0.2341	0.6405	0.6681	489.54	684.08	194.53	0.9609	1.7058
−10	0.2573	0.6423	0.6120	491.28	685.12	193.84	0.9675	1.7041
−8	0.2824	0.6441	0.5614	493.02	686.16	193.14	0.9741	1.7025
−6	0.3093	0.6460	0.5159	494.76	687.20	192.45	0.9806	1.7010
−4	0.3384	0.6480	0.4747	496.50	688.25	191.75	0.9871	1.6995
−2	0.3695	0.6498	0.4374	498.25	689.29	191.04	0.9936	1.6981

continued

t, °C	p, bar	$v' \cdot 10^3$	v''	i'	i''	r	s'	s''
0	0.4030	0.6517	0.4037	500.00	690.34	190.34	1.0000	1.6968
2	0.4388	0.6536	0.3730	501.75	691.38	189.63	1.0064	1.6956
4	0.4771	0.6556	0.4351	503.50	692.43	188.93	1.0127	1.6944
6	0.5181	0.6576	0.3197	505.26	693.47	188.22	1.0190	1.6932
8	0.5617	0.6596	0.2966	507.02	694.52	187.50	1.0253	1.6922
10	0.6083	0.6616	0.2755	508.77	695.56	186.79	1.0315	1.6912
12	0.6579	0.6637	0.2561	510.54	696.61	186.07	1.0377	1.6902
14	0.7106	0.6657	0.2384	512.30	697.65	185.35	1.0438	1.6893
16	0.7666	0.6678	0.2222	514.07	698.70	184.63	1.0499	1.6885
18	0.8261	0.6700	0.2073	515.84	699.74	183.90	1.0560	1.6877
20	0.8891	0.6721	0.1936	517.61	700.78	183.17	1.0621	1.6869
22	0.9558	0.6743	0.1810	519.39	701.82	182.43	1.0681	1.6862
24	1.026	0.6765	0.1694	521.17	702.86	181.69	1.0741	1.6855
26	1.101	0.6787	0.1587	522.95	703.90	180.95	1.0800	1.6849
28	1.180	0.6809	0.1488	524.73	704.93	180.20	1.0859	1.6843
30	1.263	0.6832	0.1397	526.52	705.97	179.45	1.0918	1.6838
32	1.350	0.6855	0.1312	528.31	707.00	178.69	1.0977	1.6833
34	1.442	0.6878	0.1233	530.10	708.03	177.93	1.1035	1.6828
36	1.539	0.6901	0.1161	531.90	709.05	177.16	1.1093	1.6824
38	1.641	0.6925	0.1093	533.70	710.08	176.38	1.1151	1.6820
40	1.748	0.6949	0.1030	535.50	711.10	175.60	1.1208	1.6816
42	1.860	0.6973	0.09719	537.31	712.12	174.81	1.1266	1.6812
44	1.978	0.6998	0.09174	539.12	713.13	174.01	1.1323	1.6809
46	2.102	0.7023	0.08667	540.93	714.14	173.21	1.1380	1.6806
48	2.231	0.7048	0.08194	542.75	715.15	172.40	1.1436	1.6804
50	2.366	0.7073	0.07752	544.57	716.15	171.58	1.1492	1.6802
52	2.508	0.7099	0.07338	546.40	717.15	170.75	1.1548	1.6799
54	2.655	0.7125	0.06952	548.23	718.15	169.91	1.1604	1.6797
56	2.810	0.7151	0.06590	550.07	719.14	169.07	1.1659	1.6796
58	2.971	0.7178	0.06251	551.91	720.12	168.21	1.1715	1.6794
60	3.138	0.7205	0.05932	553.76	721.11	167.35	1.1770	1.6793
70	4.088	0.7346	0.04608	563.06	725.93	162.87	1.2042	1.6788
80	5.240	0.7497	0.03626	572.52	730.61	158.09	1.2310	1.6787
90	6.619	0.7660	0.02884	582.13	735.10	152.97	1.2574	1.6787
100	8.253	0.7838	0.02315	591.93	739.39	147.46	1.2835	1.6786
110	10.168	0.8034	0.01872	601.93	743.43	141.50	1.3092	1.6785
120	12.393	0.8252	0.01523	612.16	747.19	135.03	1.3346	1.6780
130	14.959	0.8499	0.01242	622.63	750.60	127.97	1.3596	1.6771
140	17.896	0.8785	0.01014	633.38	753.60	120.22	1.3843	1.6753

Thermodynamic properties of trichloromonofluoromethane [106]: v (m^3/kg), i (kJ/kg) and s (kJ/kg · deg)

t, °C	v	i	s	v	i	s
		p=0.03 bar			p=0.05 bar	
−40	4.696	669.76	1.7716	2.814	669.72	1.7405
−30	4.898	674.91	1.7932	2.936	674.87	1.7622
−20	5.100	680.17	1.8144	3.057	680.14	1.7834
−10	5.302	685.53	1.8352	3.179	685.50	1.8042
− 0	5.504	690.99	1.8555	3.300	690.95	1.8245
10	5.707	696.54	1.8755	3.422	696.50	1.8445
20	5.909	702.17	1.8950	3.543	702.14	1.8640
30	6.111	707.89	1.9142	3.664	707.86	1.8832
40	6.313	713.69	1.9330	3.786	713.66	1.9021
50	6.515	719.57	1.9515	3.907	719.54	1.9205
60	6.717	725.52	1.9697	4.028	725.49	1.9387
70	6.919	731.54	1.9875	4.150	731.52	1.9565
80	7.121	737.64	2.0050	4.271	737.61	1.9740
90	7.323	743.79	2.0221	4.392	743.77	1.9912
100	7.525	750.01	2.0390	4.514	749.99	2.0081
110	7.727	756.29	2.0556	4.635	756.27	2.0247

continued

t, °C	v	i	s	v	i	s
120	7.929	762.62	2.0720	4.756	762.60	2.0410
130	8.131	769.01	2.0880	4.877	768.99	2.0571
140	8.333	775.46	2.1038	4.999	775.44	2.0729
150	8.535	781.95	2.1193	5.120	781.93	2.0884
160	8.737	788.49	2.1346	5.241	788.47	2.1037
170	8.939	795.07	2.1496	5.362	795.06	2.1187
180	9.140	801.70	2.1644	5.483	801.69	2.1335
190	9.342	808.38	2.1790	5.605	808.36	2.1480
200	9.544	815.09	2.1933	5.726	815.07	2.1624
210	9.746	821.84	2.2075	5.847	821.82	2.1785
220	9.948	828.63	2.2214	5.968	828.61	2.1904
230	10.15	835.46	2.2351	6.089	835.44	2.2041
240	10.35	842.32	2.2486	6.210	842.30	2.2176
250	10.55	849.21	2.2619	6.332	849.20	2.2309
		p=0.1 bar			p=0.2 bar	
−20	1.525	680.04	1.7412			
−10	1.586	685.41	1.7620	0.7894	685.22	1.7196
0	1.647	690.87	1.7824	0.8201	690.69	1.7400
10	1.708	696.42	1.8023	0.8507	696.25	1.7600
20	1.769	702.06	1.8219	0.8814	701.90	1.7796
30	1.829	707.78	1.8411	0.9119	707.63	1.7989
40	1.890	713.59	1.8600	0.9425	713.44	1.8177
50	1.951	719.47	1.8785	0.9731	719.33	1.8362
60	2.012	725.43	1.8966	1.004	725.29	1.8544
70	2.073	731.46	1.9144	1.034	731.33	1.8722
80	2.133	737.55	1.9319	1.065	737.43	1.8897
90	2.194	743.71	1.9491	1.095	743.59	1.9070
100	2.255	749.93	1.9660	1.126	749.82	1.9239
110	2.316	756.21	1.9826	1.156	756.10	1.9405
120	2.376	762.55	1.9990	1.187	762.44	1.9568
130	2.437	768.94	2.0150	1.217	768.84	1.9729
140	2.498	775.39	2.0303	1.247	775.29	1.9887
150	2.558	781.88	2.0463	1.278	781.78	2.0042
160	2.619	788.42	2.0616	1.308	788.33	2.0195
170	2.680	795.01	2.0767	1.339	794.92	2.0346
180	2.740	801.64	2.0915	1.370	801.55	2.0494
190	2.801	808.32	2.1060	1.400	808.23	2.0639
200	2.862	815.03	2.1204	1.430	814.95	2.0783
210	2.922	821.73	2.1345	1.460	821.70	2.0924
220	2.933	828.58	2.1484	1.491	828.50	2.1063
230	3.044	835.40	2.1621	1.521	835.33	2.1201
240	3.104	842.27	2.1756	1.552	842.19	2.1336
250	3.165	849.16	2.1889	1.582	849.09	2.1469
		p=0.4 bar			p=0.6 bar	
0	0.4067	690.34	1.6973			
10	0.4222	695.92	1.7173	0.2794	695.58	1.6920
20	0.4377	701.58	1.7370	0.2898	701.26	1.7117
30	0.4532	707.33	1.7563	0.3003	707.02	1.7311
40	0.4686	713.15	1.7752	0.3107	712.85	1.7500
50	0.4841	719.05	1.7937	0.3211	718.77	1.7686
60	0.4995	725.02	1.8119	0.3314	724.75	1.7868
70	0.5149	731.07	1.8298	0.3418	730.80	1.8047
80	0.5302	737.18	1.8473	0.3521	736.92	1.8223
90	0.5456	743.35	1.8646	0.3624	743.11	1.8396
100	0.5610	749.58	1.8815	0.3727	749.35	1.8565
110	0.5763	755.88	1.8981	0.3830	755.65	1.8732
120	0.5916	762.23	1.9145	0.3933	762.01	1.8896
130	0.6069	768.63	1.9306	0.4036	763.42	1.9057
140	0.6222	775.09	1.9464	0.4139	774.88	1.9215
150	0.6376	781.59	1.9620	0.4241	781.40	1.9371
160	0.6528	788.14	1.9773	0.4344	787.95	1.9524
170	0.6681	794.74	1.9923	0.4446	794.56	1.9675

continued

t, °C	v	i	s	v	i	s
180	0.6834	801.38	2.0071	0.4548	801.20	1.9823
190	0.6987	808.06	2.0217	0.4651	807.89	1.9969
200	0.7140	814.78	2.0361	0.4753	814.62	2.0113
210	0.7292	821.55	2.0502	0.4855	821.39	2.0254
220	0.7445	828.34	2.0641	0.4957	828.19	2.0394
230	0.7597	835.18	2.0779	0.5059	835.03	2.0531
240	0.7750	842.05	2.0914	0.5161	841.90	2.0666
250	0.7902	848.95	2.1047	0.5263	848,81	2.0800
		p=0.8 bar			p=1 bar	
20	0.2159	700.93	1.6936			
30	0.2238	706.70	1.7130	0.1779	706.39	1.6988
40	0.2317	712.55	1.7320	0.1842	712.25	1.7178
50	0.2395	718.48	1.7506	0.1906	718.19	1.7365
60	0.2474	724.48	1.7689	0.1969	724.20	1.7548
70	0.2552	730.54	1.7868	0.2033	730.28	1.7728
80	0.2630	736.67	1.8044	0.2196	736.42	1.7904
90	0.2708	742.86	1.8217	0.2159	742.62	1.8077
100	0.2786	749.12	1.8387	0.2221	748.88	1.8248
110	0.2864	755.43	1.8554	0.2284	755.20	1.8415
120	0.2942	761.79	1.8718	0.2347	761.58	1.8579
130	0.3019	768.21	1.8879	0.2409	768.00	1.8740
140	0.3097	774.68	1.9038	0.2471	774.48	1.8900
150	0.3174	781.20	1.9193	0.2533	781.01	1.9055
160	0.3251	787.77	1.9347	0.2596	787.58	1.9209
170	0.3328	794.38	1.9498	0.2658	794.19	1.9360
180	0.3406	801.03	1.9646	0.2720	800,85	1.9508
190	0.3483	807.72	1.9792	0.2782	807.55	1.9654
200	0.3560	814.46	1.9936	0.2844	814.29	1.9798
210	0.3637	821.23	2.0077	0.2905	821.07	1.9940
220	0.3713	828.04	2.0217	0.2967	827.88	2.0080
230	0.3790	834.88	2.0355	0.3029	834.73	2.0217
240	0.3867	841,76	2.0490	0.3091	841.61	2.0353
250	0.3944	848.67	2.0623	0.3152	848.53	2.0456
		p=1.5 bar			p=2 bar	
40	0.1210	711.49	1.6917			
50	0.1254	717.46	1.7105	0.09269	716.71	1.6915
60	0.1297	723.50	1.7289	0.09602	722.79	1.7100
70	0.1340	729.61	1.7469	0.09933	728.92	1.7282
80	0.1383	735.77	1.7646	0.1026	735.12	1.7460
90	0.1426	742.00	1.7820	0.1059	741.38	1.7634
100	0.1468	748.29	1.7991	0.1092	747.69	1.7806
110	0.1511	754.63	1.8159	0.1124	754.06	1.7974
120	0.1553	761.03	1.8324	0.1156	760.48	1.8140
130	0.1595	767.43	1.8486	0.1189	766.94	1.8302
140	0.1638	773.97	1.8645	0.1221	773.46	1.8462
150	0.1680	780.52	1.8801	0.1253	780.02	1.8619
160	0.1720	787.10	1.8955	0.1285	786.63	1.8773
170	0.1764	793.74	1.9107	0,1316	793.28	1.8925
180	0.1805	800.41	1.9256	0.1348	799.97	1.9074
190	0.1847	807.12	1.9402	0.1380	806.70	1.9221
200	0.1889	813.88	1.9546	0.1412	813.46	1.9366
210	0.1931	820.67	1.9688	0.1443	820.27	1.9508
220	0.1972	827.49	1.9828	0.1475	827.11	1.9648
230	0.2014	834.36	1.9966	0.1506	833.98	1.9786
240	0.2055	841.25	2.0102	0.1537	840.89	1.9922
250	0.2097	848.18	2.0235	0.1569	847.83	2.0056
		p=3 bar			p=4 bar	
60	0.06231	721.31	1.6325			
70	0.06462	727.52	1.7008	0.04721	726.06	1.6804
80	0.06692	733.79	1.7188	0.04902	732.40	1.6987
90	0.06920	740.10	1.7365	0.05081	738.79	1.7165
100	0.07146	746.47	1.7538	0.05257	745.21	1.7340

continued

t, °C	v	i	s	v	i	s
110	0.07370	752.89	1.7707	0.05432	751.69	1.7511
120	0.07593	759.35	1.7874	0.05605	758.21	1.7679
130	0.07815	765.86	1.8038	0.05774	764.77	1.7844
140	0.08035	772.42	1.8198	0.05948	771.37	1.8006
150	0.08255	779.02	1.8356	0.06118	778.01	1.8164
160	0.08474	785.67	1.8511	0.06286	784.69	1.8321
170	0.08692	792.35	1.8664	0.06454	791.41	1.8474
180	0.08909	799.07	1.8814	0.06621	798.17	1.8625
190	0.09125	805.83	1.8962	0.06787	804.96	1.8773
200	0.09340	812.63	1.9107	0.06952	811.79	1.8919
210	0.09555	819.46	1.9250	0.07117	818.65	1.9063
220	0.09770	826.35	1.9390	0.07281	825.55	1.9204
230	0.09984	833.23	1.9529	0.07445	832.47	1.9343
240	0.1020	840.16	1.9665	0.07608	839.43	1.9480
250	0.1041	847.12	1.9800	0.07770	846.41	1.9615
		p=6 bar			p=8 bar	
90	0.03232	736.01	1.6864			
100	0.03361	742.59	1.7043	0.02404	739.76	1.6813
110	0.03488	749.19	1.7218	0.02508	746.54	1.6992
120	0.03612	755.83	1.7389	0.02610	753.32	1.7168
130	0.03735	762.50	1.7557	0.02709	760.13	1.7339
140	0.03857	769.20	1.7721	0.02807	766.95	1.7506
150	0.03977	775.94	1.7883	0.02903	773.79	1.7670
160	0.04096	782.70	1.8041	0.02998	780.66	1.7831
170	0.04214	789.50	1.8196	0.03091	787.55	1.7988
180	0.04331	796.34	1.8349	0.03184	794.46	1.8143
190	0.04447	803.20	1.8499	0.03275	801.40	1.8294
200	0.04563	810.09	1.8646	0.03366	808.36	1.8443
210	0.04677	817.01	1.8791	0.03456	815.35	1.8589
220	0.04791	823.97	1.8933	0.03545	822.37	1.8733
230	0.04904	830.95	1.9073	0.03633	829.41	1.8875
240	0.05017	837.96	1.9211	0.03721	836.47	1.9014
250	0.05129	844.99	1.9347	0.03805	843.56	1.9151
		p=10 bar			p=12 bar	
110	0.01912	743.68	1.6800			
120	0.02001	750,66	1.6980	0.01589	747.78	1.6812
130	0.02088	757.63	1.7156	0.01669	754.96	1.6993
140	0.02173	764.60	1.7327	0.01745	762.10	1.7169
150	0.02255	771.56	1.7494	0.01819	769.23	1.7340
160	0.02336	778.54	1.7658	0.01881	776.34	1.7507
170	0.02415	785.53	1.7818	0.01962	783.45	1.7670
180	0.02493	792.54	1.7974	0.02031	790.56	1.7829
190	0.02570	799.56	1.8128	0.02098	797.68	1.7985
200	0.02646	806.60	1.8279	0.02165	804.81	1.8138
210	0.02721	813.67	1.8426	0.02230	811.95	1.8287
220	0.02795	820.75	1.8572	0.02295	819.11	1.8434
230	0.02869	827.85	1.8714	0.02359	826.27	1.8578
240	0.02942	834.97	1.8855	0.02422	833.46	1.8720
250	0.03014	842.12	1.8993	0,02484	840.66	1.8859
		p=14 bar			p=16 bar	
130	0.01363	752.08	1.6842			
140	0.01435	759.46	1.7024	0.01197	756.59	1.6885
150	0.01504	766.77	1.7200	0.01264	764.15	1.7068
160	0.01571	774.04	1.7371	0.01327	771.62	1.7244
170	0.01635	781.29	1.7537	0.01388	779.04	1.7414
180	0,01698	788.52	1.7700	0.01447	786.41	1.7550
190	0.01759	795.75	1.7858	0.01504	793.76	1.7742
200	0.01819	802.98	1.8013	0.01559	801.09	1.7899
210	0.01878	810.20	1.8164	0.01613	808.42	1.8053
220	0.01936	817.44	1.8313	0.01666	815.74	1.8203
230	0.01993	824.68	1.8459	0.01718	823.06	1.8351

continued

t, °C	v	i	s	v	i	s
240	0.02049	831.93	1.8602	0.01769	830.38	1.8496
250	0.02105	839.19	1.8742	0.01819	837.71	1.8637
		p=18 bar			p=20 bar	
150	0.01072	761.32	1.6939	0.009114	758.19	1.6808
160	0.01134	769.05	1.7122	0.009748	766.27	1.7001
170	0.01193	776.67	1.7298	0.01033	774.16	1.7184
180	0.01249	784.21	1.7468	0.01088	781.91	1.7360
190	0.01303	791.71	1.7633	0.01140	789.57	1.7529
200	0.01355	799.16	1.7793	0.01190	797.17	1.7693
210	0.01405	806.59	1.7950	0.01238	804.72	1.7852
220	0.01455	814.01	1.8102	0.01285	812.24	1.8008
230	0.01503	821.41	1.8252	0.01330	819.74	1.8159
240	0.01550	828.81	1.8398	0.01374	827.22	1.8307
250	0.01597	836.21	1.8542	0.01418	834.69	1.8452
		p=22 bar			p=25 bar	
170	0.008985	771.45	1.7071			
180	0.009534	779.47	1.7254			
190	0.01005	787.33	1.7429			
200	0.01053	795.10	1.7597	0.008854	791.81	1.7456
210	0.01100	802.79	1.7760	0.009306	799.76	1.7626
220	0.01144	810.43	1.7918	0.009736	807.61	1.7759
230	0.01188	818.03	1.8072	0.01015	815.39	1.7947
240	0.01230	825.60	1.8222	0.01055	823.11	1.8101
250	0.01271	833.16	1.8369	0.01093	830.80	1.8251

Viscosity of trichloromonofluoromethane gas at a pressure of 1 bar [105]

t, °C	−25	−20	0	20	40	60	80	100
$\eta \cdot 10^7$, N · s/m²	98.0	100.0	107	113	119	124	130	135

Viscosity of liquid trichloromonofluoromethane [105]

t, °C	−40	−30	−20	−10	0	10	20	30	40	50
$\eta \cdot 10^3$, N · s/m²	0.940	0.805	0.685	0.595	0.540	0.480	0.440	0.405	0.375	0.345

Thermal conductivity of trichloromonofluoromethane gas at a pressure of 1 bar [356]

t, °C	0	20	40	60	80	100	120	140
$\lambda \cdot 10^4$, W/m · deg	77	86	95	105	114	123	132	142

Thermal conductivity λ (W/m · deg) of liquid trichloromonofluoromethane [107]

t, °C	λ	t, °C	λ	t, °C	λ	t, °C	λ
−60	0.112	−10	0.098	30	0.087	70	0.075
−50	0.109	0	0.095	40	0.084	80	0.073
−40	0.107	10	0.093	50	0.081	90	0.070
−30	0.104	20	0.090	60	0.078	100	0.067
−20	0.101						

DICHLORODIFLUOROMETHANE (FREON-12) (CF_2Cl_2)

Molecular weight 120.92
$t_{boil} = -29.8$ °C at $p = 1$ atm; $t_{melt} = -155.0$ °C;
$t_{cr} = 111.8$ °C; $p_{cr} = 41.32$ bar; $v_{cr} = 1.780$ dm³/kg

Thermodynamic properties of dichlorodifluoromethane [46]:
v' (dm³/kg), v'' (m³/kg), i and r(kJ/kg) and s (kJ/kg · deg)

t, °C	p, bar	v'	v''	i'	i''	r	s'	s''
−70	0.1223	0.6258	1.1336	439.51	622.77	183.26	0.7433	1.6454
−68	0.1393	0.6280	1.0028	441.19	623.73	182.54	0.7516	1.6414
−66	0.1581	0.6302	0.8962	442.87	624.68	181.81	0.7598	1.6374
−64	0.1780	0.6323	0.7963	444.55	625.61	181.06	0.7679	1.6335
−62	0.2005	0.6345	0.7083	446.23	626.56	180.33	0.7760	1.6300
−60	0.2264	0.6368	0.6397	447.93	627.50	179.57	0.7839	1.6263
−58	0.2540	0.6390	0.5760	449.64	628.46	178.82	0.7918	1.6230
−56	0.2846	0.6412	0.5190	451.34	629.40	178.06	0.7996	1.6197
−54	0.3176	0.6435	0.4668	453.04	630.35	177.31	0.8075	1.6166
−52	0.3539	0.6458	0.4223	454.74	631.31	176.57	0.8152	1.6136
−50	0.3933	0.6482	0.3830	456.42	632.27	175.85	0.8227	1.6107
−48	0.4380	0.6505	0.3473	458.11	633.23	175.12	0.8302	1.6070
−46	0.4835	0.6528	0.3170	459.79	634.19	174.40	0.8376	1.6054
−44	0.5327	0.6551	0.2894	461.47	635.14	173.67	0.8450	1.6029
−40	0.6467	0.6600	0.2417	464.84	637.05	172.21	0.8597	1.5983
−38	0.7129	0.6625	0.2213	466.54	638.01	171.47	0.8669	1.5961
−36	0.7796	0.6650	0.2033	468.25	638.96	170.71	0.8742	1.5940
−34	0.8508	0.6676	0.1874	469.96	639.91	169.95	0.8814	1.5920
−32	0.9284	0.6702	0.1725	471.68	640.85	169.17	0.8885	1.5901
−30	1.0143	0.6728	0.1591	473.41	641.81	168.40	0.8956	1.5882
−28	1.108	0.6755	0.1468	475.13	642.75	167.62	0.9027	1.5865
−26	1.202	0.6782	0.1359	476.85	643.71	166.86	0.9097	1.5848
−24	1.302	0.6809	0.1260	478.58	644.65	166.07	0.9167	1.5832
−22	1.412	0.6836	0.1169	480.32	645.69	165.37	0.9237	1.5817
−20	1.527	0.6864	0.1086	482.08	646.53	164.45	0.9307	1.5803
−18	1.649	0.6892	0.1011	483.84	647.46	163.62	0.9376	1.5789
−16	1.779	0.6921	0.09417	485.60	648.38	162.78	0.9445	1.5775
−14	1.919	0.6950	0.08782	487.36	649.31	161.95	0.9515	1.5763
−12	2.067	0.6980	0.08190	489.14	650.29	161.09	0.9584	1.5751
−10	2.219	0.7010	0.07650	490.93	651.15	160.22	0.9653	1.5739
−8	2.377	0.7040	0.07192	492.73	652.09	159.36	0.9723	1.5728
−6	2.550	0.7071	0.06728	494.54	653.01	158.47	0.9792	1.5718
−4	2.734	0.7104	0.06289	496.36	653.93	157.57	0.9861	1.5707
−2	2.926	0.7137	0.05901	498.17	654.94	156.67	0.9931	1.5697
0	3.125	0.7171	0.05530	500.00	655.74	155.74	1.0000	1.5688
2	3.330	0.7203	0.05198	501.87	656.62	154.75	1.0069	1.5679
4	3.555	0.7237	0.04887	503.76	657.47	153.71	1.0136	1.5671
6	3.788	0.7271	0.04605	505.67	658.31	152.64	1.0202	1.5663
8	4.031	0.7306	0.04340	507.58	659.15	151.57	1.0269	1.5655
10	4.285	0.7342	0.04084	509.48	660.00	150.52	1.0335	1.5647
12	4.550	0.7379	0.03860	511.41	660.84	149.43	1.0401	1.5640
14	4.831	0.7416	0.03642	513.35	661.68	148.33	1.0468	1.5633
16	5.123	0.7454	0.03440	515.29	662.51	147.22	1.0535	1.5626
18	5.428	0.7492	0.03254	517.25	663.34	146.09	1.0602	1.5620
20	5.739	0.7532	0.03079	519.21	664.16	144.95	1.0669	1.5613
22	6.065	0.7572	0.02914	521.18	664.97	143.79	1.0735	1.5607
24	6.408	0.7613	0.02758	523.14	665.76	142.62	1.0802	1.5601
26	6.765	0.7654	0.02616	525.11	666.54	141.43	1.0868	1.5595
28	7.140	0.7696	0.02481	527.09	667.31	140.22	1.0934	1.5589
30	7.529	0.7740	0.02351	529.08	668.07	138.98	1.1000	1.5583
32	7.931	0.7786	0.02233	531.11	668.81	137.70	1.1066	1.5578
34	8.344	0.7832	0.02122	533.15	669.53	136.38	1.1132	1.5572
36	8.771	0.7879	0.02014	535.20	670.23	135.03	1.1198	1.5566
38	9.217	0.7926	0.01914	537.28	670.93	133.65	1.1264	1.5560
40	9.687	0.7975	0.01818	539.37	671.62	132.25	1.1331	1.5554
42	10.17	0.8026	0.01729	541.47	672.29	130.82	1.1397	1.5548
44	10.67	0.8078	0.01645	543.59	672.93	129.24	1.1464	1.5542

continued

t, °C	p, bar	v′	v″	i′	i″	r	s′	s″
46	11.18	0.8133	0.01566	545.72	673.56	127.84	1.1531	1.5536
48	11.72	0.8189	0.01490	547.89	674.17	126.28	1.1598	1.5530
50	12.28	0.8248	0.01418	550.09	674.67	124.67	1.1665	1.5523
52	12.85	0.8308	0.01349	552.33	675.33	123.00	1.1733	1.5517
54	13.44	0.8371	0.01286	554.59	675.88	121.29	1.1801	1.5510
56	14.05	0.8436	0.01226	556.86	676.40	119.54	1.1869	1.5502
58	14.68	0.8503	0.01169	559.13	676.89	117.76	1.1937	1.5490
60	15.34	0.8571	0.01111	561.43	677.36	115.93	1.2006	1.5486
62	16.02	0.8642	0.01057	563.75	677.80	114.05	1.2074	1.5477
64	16.72	0.8717	0.01008	566.10	678.21	112.11	1.2143	1.5468
66	17.44	0.8796	0.009608	568.47	678.59	110.12	1.2212	1.5459
68	18.18	0.8877	0.009150	570.88	678.94	108.06	1.2281	1.5448
70	18.94	0.8962	0.008705	573.35	679.24	105.89	1.2351	1.5436
75	20.96	0.9193	0.007693	579.72	679.84	100.12	1.2530	1.5406
80	23.13	0.9460	0.006780	586.30	680.10	93.80	1.2713	1.5369
85	25.47	0.9769	0.005960	593.22	680.08	86.86	1.2900	1.5325
90	27.99	1.0136	0.005205	600.30	679.47	79.17	1.3103	1.5291
95	30.70	1.0578	0.004498	607.47	678.20	70.73	1.3287	1.5200
100	33.60	1.1123	0.003843	614.79	676.11	61.32	1.3468	1.5111
105	36.72	1.2006	0.003198	623.84	672.45	48.61	1.3699	1.4985
110	40.05	1.3767	0.002505	635.55	665.44	29.89	1.3995	1.4775
111.8	41.32	1.7801	0.0017801	649.81	649.81	0	1.4363	1.4363

Thermodynamic properties of dichlorodifluoromethane [46] : v (m^3/kg), i (kJ/kg) and s (kJ/kg deg)

t, °C	v	i	s	v	i	s	v	i	s
	p=0.2 bar			p=0.5 bar			p=1 bar		
−60	0.725	627.6	1.634						
−50	0.760	632.7	1.658						
−40	0.795	637.9	1.681	0.314	637.3	1.618			
−30	0.830	643.3	1.704	0.329	642.7	1.640	0.161	641.8	1.589
−20	0.865	648.7	1.726	0.343	648.3	1.662	0.168	647.4	1.612
−10	0.900	654.3	1.748	0.357	653.9	1.684	0.176	653.1	1.634
0	0.935	660.0	1.769	0.371	659.6	1.705	0.183	658.9	1.655
10	0.970	665.8	1.790	0.385	665.4	1.726	0.190	664.7	1.676
20	1.005	671.7	1.810	0.399	671.4	1.746	0.197	670.7	1.697
30	1.040	677.7	1.830	0.413	677.4	1.766	0.205	676.7	1.718
40	1.075	683.8	1.850	0.427	683.5	1.786	0.212	682.9	1.738
50	1.110	690.0	1.870	0.441	689.7	1.806	0.219	689.2	1.757
60	1.145	696.3	1.889	0.455	696.0	1.825	0.226	695.5	1.776
70	1.180	702.6	1.908	0.469	702.4	1.844	0.233	701.9	1.795
80	1.215	709.1	1.926	0.483	708.8	1.862	0.240	708.4	1.814
90	1.250	715.6	1.944	0.497	715.3	1.880	0.247	715.0	1.832
100	1.285	722.1	1.962	0.511	721.9	1.898	0.254	721.6	1.850
120	1.354	735.6	1.997	0.538	735.4	1.933	0.268	735.1	1.886
140	1.423	749.3	2.031	0.566	749.1	1.967	0.282	748.8	1.920
160	1.492	763.2	2.064	0.594	763.1	2.000	0.296	762.9	1.953
180	1.561	777.4	2.096	0.622	777.2	2.032	0.310	777.0	1.985
200	1.629	791.8	2.127	0.650	791.6	2.064	0.324	791.4	2.016
220	1.697	806.4	2.157	0.678	806.2	2.095	0.338	806.0	2.046
240	1.765	821.2	2.186	0.706	821.0	2.124	0.352	820.8	2.076
260	1.834	836.1	2.215	0.734	836.0	2.152	0.366	835.8	2.105
280	1.903	821.5	2.243	0.762	851.1	2.180	0.380	850.9	2.133
300	1.972	866.5	2.271	0.790	866.3	2.208	0.394	866.2	2.161
	p=2 bar			p=3 bar			p=4 bar		
−10	0.0850	651.1	1.582						
0	0.0890	657.4	1.604	0.0579	656.0	1.572			
10	0.0930	663.4	1.626	0.0605	662.0	1.594	0.0441	660.5	1.570
20	0.0970	669.5	1.647	0.0631	668.2	1.616	0.0462	666.8	1.593

continued

t, °C	v	i	s	v	i	s	v	i	s
30	0.101	675.6	1.668	0.0657	674.4	1.637	0.0482	673.1	1.614
40	0.104	681.8	1.688	0.0683	680.7	1.657	0.0502	679.5	1.635
50	0.108	688.1	1.708	0.0708	687.1	1.687	0.0522	686.0	1.655
60	0.111	694.5	1.727	0.0733	693.6	1.697	0.0542	692.6	1.675
70	0.115	701.0	1.746	0.0758	700.1	1.716	0.0561	699.2	1.695
80	0.119	707.5	1.765	0.0783	706.7	1.735	0.0580	705.8	1.714
90	0.122	714.1	1.783	0.0808	713.3	1.754	0.0599	712.5	1.733
100	0.126	720.8	1.801	0.0832	720.1	1.772	0.0617	719.3	1.751
120	0.133	734.4	1.837	0.0880	733.7	1.808	0.0654	733.1	1.787
140	0.140	748.2	1.871	0.0928	747.5	1.844	0.0691	746.9	1.821
160	0.147	762.2	1.904	0.0975	761.7	1.877	0.0728	761.1	1.855
180	0.154	776.4	1.936	0.1022	775.9	1.908	0.0764	775.4	1.887
200	0.161	790.9	1.967	0.1070	790.5	1.939	0.0800	790.0	1.918
220	0.168	805.6	1.997	0.1118	805.2	1.969	0.0835	804.7	1.947
240	0.175	820.4	2.027	0.1167	820.0	1.999	0.0871	819.6	1.978
260	0.182	835.4	2.056	0.1212	835.0	2.028	0.0906	834.7	2.007
280	0.189	850.6	2.084	0.1258	850.2	2.056	0.0942	849.9	2.036
300	0.196	865.8	2.111	0.1304	865.5	2.083	0.0978	865.2	2.063
		$p=5$ bar			$p=6$ bar			$p=8$ bar	
20	0.0360	665.3	1.574						
30	0.0377	671.8	1.595	0.0308	670.4	1.579			
40	0.0394	678.4	1.616	0.0322	677.1	1.600	0.0230	674.3	1.575
50	0.0411	685.0	1.637	0.0336	683.8	1.621	0.0242	681.2	1.597
60	0.0427	691.6	1.657	0.0350	690.5	1.642	0.0253	688.1	1.618
70	0.0443	698.2	1.677	0.0364	697.2	1.662	0.0264	695.0	1.638
80	0.0460	704.7	1.697	0.0377	703.9	1.682	0.0275	702.0	1.658
90	0.0477	711.7	1.716	0.0391	710.8	1.701	0.0286	709.0	1.678
100	0.0494	718.5	1.734	0.0404	717.7	1.720	0.0296	716.0	1.697
120	0.0522	732.3	1.770	0.0429	731.6	1.757	0.0316	730.1	1.734
140	0.0550	746.3	1.805	0.0454	745.6	1.791	0.0336	744.3	1.769
160	0.0579	760.5	1.838	0.0479	759.9	1.825	0.0355	758.7	1.803
180	0.0608	774.8	1.871	0.0504	774.3	1.858	0.0374	773.3	1.836
200	0.0637	789.5	1.902	0.0528	789.0	1.889	0.0393	788.0	1.867
220	0.0666	804.2	1.932	0.0553	803.8	1.920	0.0412	802.9	1.898
240	0.0695	819.2	1.962	0.0578	818.8	1.950	0.0430	817.9	1.928
260	0.0723	834.3	1.992	0.0602	833.9	1.979	0.0449	833.1	1.957
280	0.0752	849.5	2.020	0.0625	849.1	2.007	0.0467	848.4	1.985
300	0.0781	864.9	2.047	0.0649	864.5	2.034	0.0485	863.8	2.013
		$p=10$ bar			$p=15$ bar			$p=20$ bar	
50	0.0185	678.5	1.575						
60	0.0195	685.7	1.597	0.0115	678.0	1.552			
70	0.0205	692.9	1.618	0.0123	686.2	1.575			
80	0.0214	700.0	1.639	0.0131	694.1	1.598	0.00874	686.6	1.562
90	0.0223	707.1	1.659	0.0138	701.8	1.620	0.00943	695.4	1.587
100	0.0232	714.3	1.678	0.0145	709.5	1.641	0.0101	703.9	1.610
120	0.0249	728.6	1.715	0.0158	724.5	1.680	0.0112	719.9	1.651
140	0.0265	743.0	1.751	0.0170	739.5	1.717	0.0122	735.6	1.691
160	0.0281	757.5	1.786	0.0181	754.5	1.753	0.0131	751.2	1.728
180	0.0296	772.2	1.819	0.0192	769.5	1.787	0.0140	766.6	1.762
200	0.0312	787.0	1.851	0.0203	784.5	1.819	0.0149	782.0	1.796
220	0.0327	802.0	1.882	0.0214	799.7	1.851	0.0157	797.4	1.827
240	0.0342	817.1	1.912	0.0225	815.0	1.882	0.0165	812.9	1.858
260	0.0357	832.4	1.941	0.0235	830.4	1.911	0.0173	828.5	1.888
280	0.0372	847.7	1.970	0.0245	845.9	1.940	0.0181	844.1	1.919
300	0.0386	863.2	1.998	0.0255	861 6	1.968	0.0189	859.9	1.945
		$p=30$ bar			$p=40$ bar			$p=50$ bar	
100	0.00523	687.2	1.546						
120	0.00643	709.1	1.602	0.00376	692.1	1.545	0.00141	645.6	1.421
140	0.00732	727.1	1.647	0.00478	716.5	1.607	0.00314	702.1	1.559
160	0.00807	744.1	1.687	0.00551	736.1	1.653	0.00393	726.7	1.621
180	0.00876	760.5	1.724	0.00612	753.9	1.694	0.00451	746.7	1.666

continued

t, °C	v	i	s	v	i	s	v	i	s
200	0.00941	776.7	1.759	0.00666	771.1	1.730	0.00500	765.1	1.706
220	0.01001	792.6	1.792	0.00718	787.8	1.766	0.00545	782.8	1.743
240	0.01061	808.6	1.824	0.00765	804.3	1.798	0.00586	799.9	1.777
260	0.01120	824.6	1.855	0.00811	820.7	1.830	0.00625	816.7	1.809
280	0.01176	840.6	1.885	0.00855	836.9	1.860	0.00662	833.3	1.840
300	0.01231	856.5	1.913	0.00899	853.3	1.889	0.00698	850.0	1.869
		p=60 bar			p=80 bar			p=100 bar	
140	0.00195	680.6	1.505	0.00129	658.5	1.444			
160	0.00286	715.7	1.588	0.00170	692.2	1.523	0.00136	679.2	1.482
180	0.00344	739.0	1.640	0.00220	722.5	1.592	0.00166	708.4	1.554
200	0.00391	759.1	1.683	0.00261	746.6	1.642	0.00197	735.4	1.611
220	0.00431	777.6	1.723	0.00295	767.6	1.688	0.00225	758.2	1.659
240	0.00468	795.4	1.758	0.00325	787.0	1.728	0.00249	779.4	1.701
260	0.00502	812.8	1.791	0.00352	805.4	1.762	0.00272	799.0	1.739
280	0.00534	829.9	1.823	0.00378	823.6	1.795	0.00292	817.7	1.773
300	0.00565	846.8	1.853	0.00402	840.8	1.826	0.00311	835.4	1.805

Viscosity of dichlorodifluoromethane gas at a pressure of 1 bar [105]

t, °C	−20	0	20	40	60	80	100
$\eta \cdot 10^7$, $N \cdot s/m^2$	111	117	122	128	133	139	145

Viscosity η ($N \cdot s/m^2$) of liquid dichlorodifluoromethane [109]

T, °K	$\eta \cdot 10^3$	T, °K	$\eta \cdot 10^3$	T, °K	$\eta \cdot 10^3$	T, °K	$\eta \cdot 10^3$	T, °K	$\eta \cdot 10^3$
213	0.498	237	0.394	261	0.325	285	0.277	309	0.243
217	0.477	241	0.380	265	0.316	289	0.271	313	0.238
221	0.458	245	0.368	269	0.307	293	0.265	317	0.233
225	0.440	249	0.356	273	0.299	297	0.259	321	0.229
229	0.423	253	0.345	277	0.292	301	0.253	325	0.224
233	0.408	257	0.335	281	0.284	305	0.248	329	0.220

Thermal conductivity of dichlorodifluoromethane gas at a pressure of 1 bar [383]

T, °K	250	273,15	300	350	400	450	500
$\lambda \cdot 10^4$, W/m · deg	72	84	97	123	151	179	209

Thermal conductivity λ (W/m · deg) of liquid dichlorodifluoromethane [107]

t, °C	λ	t, °C	λ	t, °C	λ	t, °C	λ
−80	0.112	−30	0.092	20	0.073	60	0.058
−70	0.108	−20	0.088	30	0.069	70	0.053
−60	0.104	−10	0.085	40	0.065	80	0.047
−50	0.100	0	0.081	50	0.061	90	0.042
−40	0.096	10	0.077				

Surface tension of dichlorodifluoromethane [105]

t, °C	0	10	20	30
$\sigma \cdot 10^3$, N/m	12.0	11.0	9.0	7.5

MONOCHLOROTRIFLUOROMETHANE (FREON-13) (CF_3Cl)

Molecular weight 104.47
$t_{boil} = -81.5$ °C at $p = 1$ atm; $t_{melt} = -180.0$ °C;
$t_{cr} = 29.13$ °C; $p_{cr} = 39.0$ bar; $v_{cr} = 1.75$ dm³/kg

Thermodynamic properties of saturated monochlorotrifluoromethane [46]:
v' (dm³/kg), v'' (m³/kg), i and r (kJ/kg) and s (kJ/kg · deg)

t, °C	p, bar	v'	v''	i'	i''	r	s'	s''
−110	0.1614	0.6151	0.7925	393.01	554.42	161.41	0.5108	1.5034
−108	0.1889	0.6178	0.6845	394.51	555.25	160.74	0.5205	1.4965
−106	0.2187	0.6206	0.6004	396.23	556.10	159.87	0.5302	1.4899
−104	0.2520	0.6234	0.5272	397.85	556.94	159.09	0.5400	1.4834
−102	0.2892	0.6262	0.4628	399.47	557.78	158.31	0.5498	1.4775
−100	0.3310	0.6291	0.4034	401.10	558.63	157.53	0.5597	1.4717
−98	0.3774	0.6320	0.3576	402.77	559.47	156.70	0.5695	1.4662
−96	0.4299	0.6350	0.3182	404.46	560.31	155.85	0.5794	1.4609
−94	0.4876	0.6380	0.2835	406.17	561.15	154.98	0.5892	1.4557
−92	0.5535	0.6411	0.2539	407.86	561.99	154.13	0.5990	1.4508
−90	0.6263	0.6442	0.2262	409.52	562.84	153.32	0.6089	1.4461
−88	0.7041	0.6473	0.2033	411.29	563.68	152.39	0.6185	1.4416
−86	0.7875	0.6504	0.1829	413.06	564.51	151.45	0.6279	1.4373
−84	0.8800	0.6536	0.1647	414.83	565.33	150.50	0.6373	1.4332
−82	0.9830	0.6568	0.1487	416.60	566.16	149.56	0.6467	1.4292
−80	1.094	0.6601	0.1346	418.40	566.99	148.59	0.6560	1.4253
−78	1.218	0.6633	0.1222	420.20	567.82	147.62	0.6654	1.4216
−76	1.346	0.6666	0.1112	422.00	568.63	146.63	0.6744	1.4181
−74	1.482	0.6700	0.1012	423.81	569.43	145.62	0.6834	1.4147
−72	1.631	0.6735	0.09247	425.65	570.24	144.59	0.6925	1.4114
−70	1.797	0.6770	0.08467	427.51	571.04	143.53	0.7016	1.4082
−68	1.974	0.6806	0.07767	429.37	571.83	142.46	0.7109	1.4052
−66	2.162	0.6843	0.07116	431.23	572.61	141.38	0.7200	1.4022
−64	2.363	0.6881	0.06545	433.10	573.39	140.29	0.7289	1.3994
−62	2.574	0.6921	0.06035	434.97	574.16	139.19	0.7379	1.3966
−60	2.803	0.6960	0.05565	436.88	574.93	138.05	0.7465	1.3940
−58	3.046	0.7002	0.05144	438.70	575.68	136.98	0.7552	1.3914
−56	3.302	0.7044	0.04654	440.62	576.43	135.81	0.7640	1.3890
−54	3.583	0.7086	0.04404	442.51	577.18	134.67	0.7726	1.3866
−52	3.879	0.7130	0.04083	444.40	577.91	133.51	0.7813	1.3842
−50	4.183	0.7177	0.03797	446.30	578.63	132.33	0.7899	1.3819
−48	4.511	0.7223	0.03532	448.23	579.35	131.12	0.7985	1.3797
−46	4.868	0.7271	0.03291	450.21	580.04	129.83	0.8070	1.3776
−44	5.231	0.7319	0.03067	452.21	580.72	128.51	0.8154	1.3755
−42	5.616	0.7370	0.02856	454.21	581.39	127.18	0.8236	1.3735
−40	6.017	0.7421	0.02664	456.22	582.05	125.83	0.8318	1.3715
−38	6.439	0.7474	0.02491	458.24	582.69	124.45	0.8398	1.3696
−36	6.896	0.7527	0.02330	460.26	583.32	123.06	0.8477	1.3676
−34	7.371	0.7582	0.02179	462.28	583.94	121.66	0.8554	1.3657
−32	7.870	0.7640	0.02040	464.31	584.56	120.25	0.8638	1.3638
−30	8.393	0.7699	0.01911	466.34	585.12	118.78	0.8726	1.3619
−28	8.940	0.7761	0.01794	468.38	585.69	117.31	0.8812	1.3600
−26	9.520	0.7825	0.01682	470.46	586.24	115.78	0.8898	1.3582
−24	10.13	0.7891	0.01578	472.56	586.74	114.18	0.8983	1.3563
−22	10.65	0.7959	0.01481	474.68	587.23	112.55	0.9066	1.3545
−20	11.40	0.8029	0.01390	476.82	587.68	110.86	0.9146	1.3526
−18	12.08	0.8101	0.01305	478.95	588.11	109.16	0.9226	1.3507
−16	12.80	0.8174	0.01226	481.09	588.51	107.42	0.9307	1.3488
−14	13.55	0.8252	0.01154	483.23	588.89	105.66	0.9387	1.3468
−12	14.32	0.8326	0.01095	485.39	589.24	103.85	0.9470	1.3448
−10	15.13	0.8427	0.01024	487.63	589.55	101.92	0.9554	1.3427
− 8	15.97	0.8520	0.00964	489.95	589.82	99.87	0.9640	1.3406
− 6	16.85	0.8609	0.00907	492.35	590.05	97.70	0.9729	1.3383
− 4	17.75	0.8721	0.00853	494.83	590.23	95.40	0.9818	1.3360
− 2	18.70	0.8824	0.00800	497.40	590.36	92.96	0.9909	1.3336
− 0	19.70	0.8934	0.00750	500.00	590.44	90.44	1.0000	1.3310
2	20.74	0.9049	0.00703	502.60	590.46	87.86	1.0089	1.3284

continued

t, °C	p, bar	v'	v''	i'	i''	r	s'	s''
4	21.80	0.9179	0.00659	505.20	590.43	82.23	1.0178	1.3256
6	22.91	0.9316	0.00618	507.89	590.34	82.45	1.0270	1.3226
8	24.02	0.9468	0.00580	510.66	590.17	79.51	1.0362	1.3193
10	25.23	0.9652	0.00544	513.44	589.94	76.50	1.0455	1.3157
12	26.47	0.9827	0.00510	516.25	589.52	73.27	1.0552	1.3110
14	27.75	1.0038	0.00477	519.10	588.95	69.85	1.0654	1.3079
16	29.03	1.0262	0.00443	522.26	588.15	65.89	1.0756	1.3035
18	30.41	1.0538	0.00411	525.35	587.07	61.72	1.0866	1.2981
20	31.84	1.0859	0.00377	529.15	585.69	56.54	1.0985	1.2913
22	33.31	1.1230	0.00342	533.12	583.75	50.63	1.1117	1.2825
24	34.72	1.1714	0.00305	537.92	581.90	43.98	1.1270	1.2719
26	36.42	1.2968	0.00239	544.16	576.40	32.24	1.1472	1.2544
29.13	39.00	1.7517	0.00175	562.02	562.02	0	1.2078	1.2078

Thermodynamic properties of monochlorotrifluoromethane [46] : v (m³/kg), i (kJ/kg) and s (kJ/kg · deg)

t, °C	v	i	s	v	i	s	v	i	s
	p=0.2 bar			p=0.5 bar			p=1 bar		
−90	0.722	563.7	1.540	0.284	563.1	1.462			
−80	0.762	568.7	1.556	0.302	568.1	1.491	0.142	567.1	1.429
−70	0.802	573.8	1.592	0.318	573.3	1.518	0.155	572.4	1.447
−60	0.843	579.0	1.617	0.334	578.6	1.544	0.165	577.8	1.484
−50	0.883	584.4	1.642	0.351	584.0	1.569	0.173	583.3	1.510
−40	0.924	589.9	1.666	0.367	589.6	1.593	0.182	588.9	1.530
−30	0.964	595.5	1.689	0.384	595.2	1.617	0.190	594.6	1.559
−20	1.004	601.3	1.713	0.400	601.0	1.640	0.198	600.5	1.583
−10	1.044	607.3	1.736	0.416	607.0	1.663	0.206	606.5	1.606
0	1.084	613.3	1.759	0.432	613.0	1.685	0.215	612.6	1.629
10	1.124	619.5	1.781	0.448	619.2	1.707	0.223	618.9	1.651
20	1.164	625.8	1.802	0.464	625.5	1.729	0.231	625.2	1.673
30	1.204	632.2	1.824	0.480	631.9	1.751	0.239	631.6	1.695
40	1.244	638.7	1.846	0.496	638.4	1.772	0.247	638.2	1.716
50	1.284	645.4	1.866	0.512	645.1	1.792	0.255	644.9	1.737
60	1.324	652.1	1.887	0.528	651.9	1.814	0.263	651.6	1.757
70	1.364	658.9	1.907	0.545	658.8	1.834	0.271	658.5	1.778
80	1.404	665.9	1.927	0.561	665.7	1.854	0.280	665.5	1.798
90	1.444	672.9	1.947	0.577	672.8	1.874	0.288	672.5	1.818
100	1.484	680.0	1.966	0.593	679.9	1.894	0.296	679.7	1.837
120	1.563	694.6	2.004	0.624	694.5	1.931	0.312	694.3	1.875
140	1.643	709.5	2.041	0.656	709.4	1.968	0.328	709.2	1.913
160	1.723	724.7	2.077	0.688	724.6	2.004	0.344	724.5	1.949
180	1.803	740.3	2.112	0.720	740.2	2.039	0.360	740.0	1.984
200	1.882	756.1	2.146	0.752	756.0	2.073	0.376	755.9	2.018
220	1.961	772.2	2.180	0.784	772.1	2.106	0.392	772.0	2.051
240	2.040	788.5	2.212	0.816	788.4	2.138	0.408	788.3	2.084
260	2.120	805.0	2.243	0.848	805.0	2.170	0.424	804.9	2.115
280	2.200	821.8	2.274	0.880	821.8	2.201	0.440	821.7	2.146
300	2.280	838.8	2.304	0.912	838.7	2.211	0.456	838.6	2.176
	p=2 bar			p=3 bar			p=4 bar		
−60	0.0801	576.2	1.425						
−50	0.0845	518.9	1.451	0.0548	580.5	1.414	0.0399	578.9	1.386
−40	0.0889	587.7	1.476	0.0579	586.3	1.440	0.0423	585.0	1.413
−30	0.0932	593.5	1.501	0.0609	592.3	1.465	0.0447	591.2	1.439
−20	0.0975	599.5	1.525	0.0639	598.4	1.490	0.0471	597.4	1.464
−10	0.1018	605.6	1.548	0.0669	604.6	1.514	0.0494	603.6	1.489
0	0.1060	611.7	1.571	0.0697	610.9	1.537	0.0516	610.0	1.512
10	0.1102	618.0	1.594	0.0726	617.2	1.560	0.0538	616.4	1.535
20	0.1143	624.4	1.616	0.0755	623.7	1.582	0.0560	622.9	1.557
30	0.1185	630.9	1.639	0.0783	630.2	1.604	0.0581	629.5	1.579

continued

t, °C	v	i	s	v	i	s	v	i	s
40	0.1226	637.5	1.660	0.0810	636.9	1.626	0.0603	636.2	1.601
50	0.1268	644.2	1.681	0.0838	643.6	1.647	0.0625	643.0	1.623
60	0.1308	651.0	1.702	0.0866	650.5	1.668	0.0646	649.9	1.644
70	0.1350	658.0	1.722	0.0893	657.4	1.688	0.0666	656.8	1.664
80	0.1390	665.0	1.742	0.0921	664.5	1.709	0.0687	663.9	1.685
90	0.143	672.1	1.762	0.0950	671.6	1.729	0.0709	671.1	1.705
100	0.147	679.2	1.781	0.0977	678.8	1.748	0.0730	678.3	1.724
120	0.155	693.9	1.819	0.1031	693.5	1.787	0.0771	693.0	1.763
140	0.163	708.8	1.857	0.1086	708.5	1.824	0.0812	708.1	1.800
160	0.171	724.1	1.893	0.1140	723.8	1.860	0.0853	723.4	1.836
180	0.179	739.7	1.928	0.1195	739.4	1.895	0.0894	739.1	1.872
200	0.187	755.6	1.962	0.1249	755.3	1.930	0.0935	755.1	1.906
220	0.195	771.7	1.995	0.1303	771.4	1.963	0.0975	771.2	1.939
240	0.204	788.1	2.028	0.1356	787.8	1.996	0.1016	787.6	1.972
260	0.212	804.6	2.060	0.1410	804.4	2.027	0.1056	804.2	2.004
280	0.220	821.4	2.091	0.1464	821.2	2.058	0.1097	821.0	2.035
300	0.228	838.4	2.121	0.1518	838.2	2.088	0.1138	838.1	2.065
		p=5 bar			p=6 bar			p=8 bar	
−40	0.0330	583.6	1.391	0.0267	582.0	1.371			
−30	0.0350	589.9	1.417	0.0285	588.6	1.399	0.0203	585.7	1.368
−20	0.0370	596.2	1.443	0.0302	595.0	1.425	0.0217	592.5	1.395
−10	0.0388	602.6	1.468	0.0318	601.5	1.450	0.0230	599.3	1.421
0	0.0407	609.1	1.492	0.0334	608.1	1.475	0.0243	606.1	1.447
10	0.0425	615.5	1.515	0.0350	614.7	1.498	0.0256	612.9	1.471
20	0.0443	622.1	1.537	0.0365	621.4	1.521	0.0268	619.7	1.495
30	0.0461	628.8	1.560	0.0381	628.1	1.544	0.0280	626.6	1.518
40	0.0478	635.5	1.582	0.0396	634.9	1.566	0.0291	633.5	1.540
50	0.0496	642.3	1.603	0.0410	641.8	1.588	0.0303	640.4	1.562
60	0.0513	649.2	1.625	0.0425	648.7	1.609	0.0314	647.5	1.584
70	0.0530	656.3	1.645	0.0439	655.8	1.630	0.0325	654.6	1.605
80	0.0547	663.4	1.666	0.0453	662.9	1.650	0.0336	661.8	1.625
90	0.0564	670.6	1.686	0.0458	670.1	1.669	0.0347	669.1	1.646
100	0.0581	677.9	1.706	0.0482	677.4	1.690	0.0358	676.5	1.666
120	0.0615	692.6	1.744	0.0510	692.2	1.729	0.0380	691.4	1.705
140	0.0648	707.7	1.782	0.0538	707.4	1.767	0.0401	706.6	1.742
160	0.0681	723.1	1.818	0.0566	722.8	1.802	0.0422	722.1	1.779
180	0.0714	738.8	1.854	0.0594	738.5	1.839	0.0443	737.8	1.815
200	0.0747	754.7	1.888	0.0621	754.5	1.873	0.0464	753.8	1.849
220	0.0780	770.9	1.921	0.0648	770.7	1.906	0.0485	770.1	1.883
240	0.0812	787.3	1.954	0.0676	787.1	1.939	0.0506	786.6	1.916
260	0.0844	804.0	1.986	0.0703	803.8	1.971	0.0526	803.3	1.948
280	0.0876	820.8	2.017	0.0730	820.6	2.002	0.0547	820.2	1.979
300	0.0908	837.9	2.047	0.0757	837.7	2.032	0.0568	837.3	2.009
		p=10 bar			p=15 bar			p=20 bar	
−20	0.0165	589.7	1.369						
−10	0.0177	596.9	1.397	0.0104	589.7	1.344			
0	0.0188	604.0	1.423	0.0113	598.2	1.374			
10	0.0199	611.0	1.449	0.0122	605.7	1.402	0.00821	599.2	1.362
20	0.0209	618.0	1.473	0.0130	613.3	1.428	0.00896	607.9	1.392
30	0.0219	625.0	1.496	0.0138	620.8	1.454	0.00964	616.0	1.419
40	0.0229	632.1	1.519	0.0145	628.3	1.478	0.01026	624.0	1.445
50	0.0238	639.1	1.541	0.0152	635.6	1.501	0.01087	631.9	1.470
60	0.0248	646.3	1.563	0.0159	643.1	1.524	0.01143	639.6	1.493
70	0.0257	653.5	1.584	0.0166	650.5	1.545	0.01198	647.4	1.516
80	0.0266	660.8	1.605	0.0172	658.0	1.567	0.01250	655.1	1.538
90	0.0275	668.1	1.626	0.0178	665.6	1.588	0.01303	662.9	1.560
100	0.0284	675.5	1.645	0.0185	673.1	1.609	0.01353	670.6	1.581
120	0.0302	690.5	1.685	0.0197	688.4	1.649	0.01451	686.2	1.622
140	0.0319	705.9	1.723	0.0209	704.0	1.688	0.01546	702.0	1.661
160	0.0336	721.5	1.759	0.0221	719.7	1.724	0.01638	717.9	1.699
180	0.0353	737.2	1.796	0.0233	735.6	1.761	0.01730	734.1	1.735
200	0.0370	753.3	1.830	0.0245	751.9	1.796	0.01820	750.5	1.770

continued

t, °C	v	i	s	v	i	s	v	i	s
220	0.0387	769.6	1.864	0.0256	768.3	1.830	0.01908	767.0	1.805
240	0.0404	786.1	1.897	0.0267	784.9	1.863	0.01996	783.7	1.838
260	0.0420	802.9	1.929	0.0279	801.8	1.895	0.02082	800.6	1.870
280	0.0437	819.8	1.960	0.0290	818.8	1.926	0.02168	817.8	1.902
300	0.0454	836.9	1.991	0.0301	836.0	1.957	0.02254	835.0	1.933
	$p=30$ bar			$p=40$ bar			$p=50$ bar		
20	0.00448	591.2	1.314						
30	0.00530	603.8	1.355	0.00148	553.8	1.182			
40	0.00591	613.8	1.387	0.00348	598.6	1.324	0.00158	565.5	1.210
50	0.00645	623.2	1.416	0.00411	611.7	1.366	0.00252	594.7	1.302
60	0.00693	632.2	1.445	0.00460	622.7	1.399	0.00314	611.0	1.352
70	0.00736	640.7	1.469	0.00502	632.6	1.428	0.00358	623.5	1.389
80	0.00775	648.8	1.493	0.00540	642.0	1.455	0.00395	634.1	1.420
90	0.00817	657.2	1.516	0.00575	650.9	1.480	0.00428	644.2	1.448
100	0.00856	665.3	1.540	0.00607	659.5	1.503	0.00458	653.7	1.474
120	0.00926	681.6	1.581	0.00668	677.0	1.549	0.00512	672.0	1.521
140	0.00998	698.0	1.621	0.00725	693.9	1.591	0.00562	689.5	1.565
160	0.01065	714.4	1.660	0.00779	710.9	1.631	0.00608	707.2	1.607
180	0.01129	730.9	1.697	0.00831	727.7	1.669	0.00652	724.5	1.646
200	0.01193	747.6	1.734	0.00882	744.7	1.706	0.00694	741.9	1.684
220	0.01255	764.5	1.768	0.00930	761.8	1.740	0.00735	759.2	1.719
240	0.01315	781.4	1.802	0.00977	779.0	1.775	0.00775	776.6	1.754
260	0.01376	798.5	1.835	0.01024	796.3	1.808	0.00814	794.2	1.788
280	0.01436	815.8	1.867	0.01071	813.7	1.840	0.00852	811.8	1.820
300	0.01495	833.2	1.898	0.01127	831.4	1.871	0.00889	829.5	1.852
	$p=60$ bar			$p=80$ bar			$p=100$ bar		
40	0.00120	551.5	1.161						
50	0.00159	574.3	1.231						
60	0.00215	596.4	1.301	0.00136	575.1	1.226			
70	0.00261	612.5	1.348	0.00161	592.0	1.277	0.00129	581.3	1.237
80	0.00299	625.4	1.385	0.00188	607.4	1.322	0.00144	595.5	1.278
90	0.00331	636.8	1.417	0.00215	621.6	1.361	0.00162	609.3	1.317
100	0.00359	647.4	1.446	0.00240	634.2	1.395	0.00180	622.6	1.353
120	0.00409	667.0	1.497	0.00284	656.6	1.453	0.00215	647.0	1.417
140	0.00454	685.5	1.543	0.00322	677.2	1.504	0.00245	669.2	1.471
160	0.00495	703.5	1.586	0.00356	696.3	1.550	0.00276	689.4	1.519
180	0.00533	721.3	1.626	0.00388	715.0	1.592	0.00303	709.0	1.563
200	0.00570	739.0	1.664	0.00419	733.5	1.632	0.00328	728.1	1.605
220	0.00606	756.6	1.700	0.00446	751.6	1.669	0.00352	746.9	1.643
240	0.00640	774.3	1.736	0.00474	769.8	1.705	0.00376	765.6	1.681
260	0.00674	792.1	1.770	0.00501	788.0	1.740	0.00398	784.2	1.717
280	0.00705	809.9	1.802	0.00526	806.1	1.773	0.00419	802.7	1.750
300	0.00739	827.8	1.834	0.0551	824.3	1.806	0.00440	821.2	1.783

Thermal conductivity of monochlorotrifluoromethane at $p = 1$ bar [383]

T, °K	250	273.15	300	350	400	450	500
$\lambda \cdot 10^4$, W/m · deg	91	105	122	153	184	216	249

Thermal conductivity of liquid monochlorotrifluoromethane [107]

t, °C	−80	−70	−60	−50	−40	−30	−20	−10	0
λ, W/m · deg	0.0984	0.0933	0.0882	0.0831	0.0780	0.0729	0.0678	0.0618	0.0545

Surface tension of monochlorotrifluoromethane [105]

t, °C	−30	−20	−10	0	10	20	30
$\sigma \cdot 10^3$, N/m	23.5	22.0	20.5	18.5	17.3	16.0	14.0

DICHLOROMONOFLUOROMETHANE (FREON-21) ($CHFCl_2$)

Molecular weight 102.92
$t_{boil} = 8.90$ °C at $p = 1$ atm; $t_{melt} = -135.0$ °C;
$t_{cr} = 178.2$ °C; $p_{cr} = 51.81$ bar; $v_{cr} = 1.905$ dm³/kg

Thermodynamic properties of saturated dichloromonofluoromethane [358]:
v' (dm³/kg), v'' (m³/kg), i and r (kJ/kg) and s (kJ/kg · deg)

t, °C	p, bar	v'	v''	i'	i''	r	s'	s''
−60	0.0253	0.6435	6.7994	444.55	713.63	269.08	0.7718	2.0342
−58	0.0292	0.6452	5.9323	446.25	714.62	268.37	0.7797	2.0271
−56	0.0337	0.6469	5.1909	447.95	715.61	267.66	0.7876	2.0202
−54	0.0387	0.6486	4.5548	449.67	716.61	266.94	0.7955	2.0136
−52	0.0444	0.6503	4.0077	451.40	717.61	266.21	0.8033	2.0051
−50	0.0508	0.6520	3.5356	453.14	718.42	265.28	0.8111	2.0008
−48	0.0579	0.6538	3.1271	454.88	719.62	264.74	0.8189	1.9948
−46	0.0658	0.6555	2.7728	456.64	720.63	263.99	0.8267	1.9889
−44	0.0747	0.6573	2.4646	458.40	721.63	263.23	0.8344	1.9831
−42	0.0845	0.6591	2.1957	460.18	722.64	262.46	0.8421	1.9776
−40	0.0954	0.6609	1.9607	461.96	723.65	261.69	0.8498	1.9722
−38	0.1074	0.6627	1.7548	463.76	724.66	260.90	0.8575	1.9670
−36	0.1207	0.6646	1.5738	465.57	725.67	260.10	0.8652	1.9619
−34	0.1354	0.6664	1.4145	467.39	726.68	259.29	0.8728	1.9570
−32	0.1514	0.6683	1.2739	469.21	727.69	258.48	0.8804	1.9522
−30	0.1691	0.6702	1.1496	471.06	728.71	257.65	0.8880	1.9476
−28	0.1884	0.6721	1.0394	472.91	729.72	256.81	0.8950	1.9431
−26	0.2095	0.6741	0.9415	474.77	730.73	255.96	0.9031	1.9388
−24	0.2324	0.6760	0.8544	476.63	731.73	255.10	0.9107	1.9345
−22	0.2575	0.6780	0.7768	478.53	732.75	254.22	0.9182	1.9304
−20	0.2847	0.6800	0.7074	480.42	733.76	253.34	0.9257	1.9264
−18	0.3142	0.6820	0.6453	482.33	734.76	252.43	0.9332	1.9226
−16	0.3461	0.6841	0.5896	484.25	735.77	251.52	0.9407	1.9188
−14	0.3806	0.6861	0.5396	486.18	736.78	250.60	0.9481	1.9151
−12	0.4179	0.6882	0.4945	488.12	737.78	249.66	0.9556	1.9116
−10	0.4581	0.6903	0.4540	490.06	738.77	248.71	0.9630	1.9081
−8	0.5014	0.6924	0.4173	492.03	739.77	247.74	0.9705	1.9048
−6	0.5479	0.6946	0.3842	494.01	740.77	246.76	0.9779	1.9015
−4	0.5978	0.6967	0.3542	495.99	741.76	245.77	0.9853	1.8984
−2	0.6513	0.6989	0.3269	497.99	742.75	244.76	0.9926	1.8953
0	0.7085	0.7012	0.3022	500.00	743.74	243.74	1.0000	1.8923
2	0.7697	0.7034	0.2797	502.02	744.72	242.70	1.0073	1.8894
4	0.8351	0.7057	0.2592	504.05	745.70	241.65	1.0147	1.8866
6	0.9047	0.7080	0.2405	506.09	746.67	240.58	1.0220	1.8839
8	0.9789	0.7103	0.2234	508.14	747.65	239.51	1.0293	1.8812
10	1.0578	0.7127	0.2077	510.20	748.61	238.41	1.0366	1.8786
12	1.1417	0.7151	0.1934	512.27	749.57	237.30	1.0439	1.8761
14	1.2306	0.7175	0.1803	514.35	750.53	236.18	1.0511	1.8736
16	1.3250	0.7199	0.1682	516.45	751.49	235.04	1.0583	1.8712
18	1.4248	0.7224	0.1571	518.54	752.43	233.89	1.0655	1.8689
20	1.5305	0.7249	0.1469	520.65	753.37	232.72	1.0727	1.8666
22	1.6422	0.7274	0.1375	522.77	754.31	231.54	1.0799	1.8644
24	1.7601	0.7300	0.1288	524.90	755.25	230.35	1.0871	1.8623
26	1.8844	0.7326	0.1207	527.04	756.17	229.13	1.0942	1.8602
28	2.0154	0.7352	0.1133	529.18	757.09	227.91	1.1013	1.8581
30	2.1534	0.7379	0.1066	531.33	758.00	226.67	1.1084	1.8561
32	2.2985	0.7406	0.1001	533.50	758.91	225.41	1.1155	1.8542
34	2.4509	0.7433	0.0942	535.66	759.81	224.15	1.1225	1.8523
36	2.6110	0.7461	0.0887	537.84	760.71	222.87	1.1296	1.8505

continued

t, °C	p, bar	v'	v''	i'	i''	r	s'	s''
38	2.7790	0.7489	0.0836	540.02	761.59	221.57	1.1360	1.8487
40	2.9550	0.7518	0.0788	542.21	762.47	220.26	1.1445	1.8469
42	3.1394	0.7567	0.0744	544.41	763.35	218.94	1.1505	1.8452
44	3.3326	0.7576	0.0703	546.61	764.21	217.60	1.1574	1.8435
46	3.5343	0.7606	0.0664	548.82	765.07	216.25	1.1643	1.8419
48	3.7452	0.7637	0.0628	551.04	765.92	214.88	1.1712	1.8403
50	3.9655	0.7667	0.0595	553.26	766.76	213.50	1.1780	1.8387
52	4.1954	0.7699	0.0563	555.48	767.59	212.11	1.1848	1.8372
54	4.4351	0.7730	0.0534	557.71	768.42	210.71	1.1916	1.8357
56	4.6850	0.7763	0.0506	559.95	769.24	209.29	1.1984	1.8342
58	4.9452	0.7795	0.0481	562.19	770.05	207.86	1.2051	1.8328
60	5.2160	0.7829	0.0456	564.44	770.85	206.41	1.2118	1.8314
62	5.4978	0.7863	0.0434	566.69	771.64	204.95	1.2184	1.8300
64	5.7907	0.7897	0.0412	568.94	772.42	203.48	1.2251	1.8286
66	6.0950	0.7932	0.0392	571.20	773.19	201.99	1.2317	1.8273
68	6.4110	0.7968	0.0373	573.46	773.95	200.49	1.2383	1.8260
70	6.7389	0.8004	0.0355	575.73	774.71	198.98	1.2448	1.8247
72	7.0791	0.8041	0.0338	578.00	775.45	197.45	1.2513	1.8234
74	7.4318	0.8079	0.0322	580.27	776.18	195.91	1.2578	1.8222
76	7.7972	0.8117	0.0307	582.55	776.90	194.35	1.2643	1.8209
78	8.1757	0.8154	0.0293	584.83	777.61	192.78	1.2707	1.8197
80	8.5676	0.8196	0.0280	587.12	778.31	191.19	1.2771	1.8185
82	8.9730	0.8236	0.0267	589.40	779.00	189.60	1.2835	1.8173
84	9.3924	0.8278	0.0255	591.70	779.68	187.98	1.2898	1.8161
86	9.8259	0.8320	0.0244	593.99	780.34	196.35	1.2961	1.8150
88	10.274	0.8363	0.0233	596.29	780.99	184.70	1.3024	1.8138
90	10.737	0.8407	0.0223	598.59	781.63	183.04	1.3086	1.8127
92	11.214	0.8453	0.0213	600.90	782.26	181.36	1.3149	1.8115
94	11.708	0.8499	0.0204	603.21	782.87	179.66	1.3211	1.8104
96	12.217	0.8546	0.0195	604.53	783.47	177.94	1.3272	1.8093
98	12.741	0.8594	0.0187	607.85	784.05	176.20	1.3334	1.8081
100	13.283	0.8643	0.0179	610.18	784.62	174.44	1.3395	1.8070
102	13.840	0.8694	0.0171	612.51	785.18	172.67	1.3456	1.8059
104	14.415	0.8746	0.0164	614.85	785.72	170.87	1.3517	1.8048
106	15.007	0.8799	0.0157	617.20	786.24	169.04	1.3578	1.8036
108	15.617	0.8854	0.0151	619.55	786.75	167.20	1.3638	1.8025
110	16.245	0.8910	0.0144	621.91	787.23	165.32	1.3699	1.8013
112	16.891	0.8968	0.0138	624.28	787.70	163.42	1.3759	1.8002
114	17.555	0.9027	0.0133	626.66	788.15	161.49	1.3819	1.7990
116	18.239	0.9088	0.0127	629.05	788.58	159.53	1.3879	1.7978
118	18.942	0.9151	0.0122	631.45	788.99	157.54	1.3939	1.7966
120	19.666	0.9216	0.0117	633.86	789.37	155.51	1.3998	1.7954
122	20.409	0.9284	0.0112	636.29	789.73	153.44	1.4058	1.7942
124	21.173	0.9353	0.0108	638.73	790.07	151.34	1.4118	1.7929
126	21.958	0.9425	0.0103	641.19	790.38	149.19	1.4178	1.7916
128	22.764	0.9499	0.00992	643.67	790.66	146.99	1.4238	1.7902
130	23.593	0.9576	0.00951	646.16	790.91	144.75	1.4298	1.7889
132	24.444	0.9657	0.00912	648.69	791.14	142.45	1.4359	1.7875
134	25.318	0.9740	0.00875	651.23	791.32	140.09	1.4419	1.7860
136	26.215	0.9827	0.00839	653.80	791.47	137.67	1.4480	1.7845
138	27.136	0.9918	0.00804	656.41	791.59	135.18	1.4518	1.7829
140	28.081	1.0013	0.00770	659.05	791.66	132.61	1.4603	1.7813
142	29.052	1.0113	0.00738	661.72	791.69	129.97	1.4665	1.7796
144	30.048	1.0218	0.00707	664.44	791.66	127.22	1.4728	1.7778
146	31.070	1.0328	0.00677	667.20	791.59	124.39	1.4792	1.7759
148	32.118	1.0445	0.00647	670.02	791.46	121.44	1.4856	1.7740
150	33.195	1.0569	0.00619	672.89	791.25	118.36	1.4922	1.7719
152	34.299	1.0701	0.00591	675.83	790.98	115.15	1.4988	1.7697
154	35.431	1.0843	0.00565	678.85	790.63	111.78	1.5056	1.7673
156	36.593	1.0995	0.00539	681.95	790.19	108.24	1.5126	1.7648
158	37.785	1.1160	0.00513	685.15	789.65	104.50	1.5197	1.7621
160	39.008	1.1340	0.00488	688.47	788.99	100.52	1.5270	1.7591
162	40.262	1.1538	0.00464	691.92	788.18	96.26	1.5347	1.7559
164	41.549	1.1758	0.00439	695.54	787.21	91.67	1.5426	1.7523

continued

t, °C	p, bar	v′	v″	i′	i″	r	s′	s″
166	42.869	1.2007	0.00415	699.35	786.04	86.69	1.5510	1.7484
168	44.223	1.2293	0.00391	703.42	784.61	81.19	1.5598	1.7439
170	45.612	1.2631	0.00367	707.82	782.83	75.01	1.5694	1.7387
172	47.037	1.3047	0.00342	712.68	780.57	67.89	1.5799	1.7324
174	48.499	1.3590	0.00315	718.28	777.55	59.27	1.5920	1.7246
176	49.999	1.4398	0.00284	725.26	773.04	47.78	1.6072	1.7135
178	51.539	1.6320	0.00236	737.40	762.88	25.48	1.6336	1.6901
178.25	51.812	1.9048	0.00190	748.74	748.74	0	1.6586	1.6586

Thermodynamic properties of dichloromonofluoromethane at different temperatures and pressures [342]: ρ (kg/m^3), i (kJ/kg) and s (kJ/kg · deg)

t, °C	ϱ	i	s	ϱ	i	s	υ	i	s
	p=1 bar			p=5 bar			p=10 bar		
0	1415.9	500.01	1.0000	1416.8	500.18	0.99953	1418.0	500.40	0.99914
5	1405.7	505.50	1.0196	1406.7	505.67	1.0192	1407.8	505.88	1.0186
10	4.5206	735.81	1.8472	1396.2	510.98	1.0379	1397.4	511.19	1.0373
15	4.4333	738.86	1.8582	1395.4	516.17	1.0558	1386.7	516.36	1.0553
20	4.3496	741.92	1.8686	1374.3	521.24	1.0732	1375.6	521.43	1.0726
25	4.2691	744.99	1.8790	1362.9	526.24	1.0900	1364.3	526.42	1.0894
30	4.1924	748.08	1.8892	1351.2	531.18	1.1035	1352.6	531.35	1.1058
35	4.1184	751.18	1.8994	1339.2	536.08	1.1225	1340.7	536.24	1.1218
40	4.0472	754.30	1.9095	1326.9	540.95	1.1382	1328.5	541.10	1.1375
50	3.9125	760.58	1.9294	1301.4	550.67	1.1690	1303.2	550.81	1.1682
60	3.7871	766.93	1.9490	20.670	759.51	1.8030	1276.6	560.56	1.1981
70	3.6700	773.35	1.9682	19.838	766.50	1.8239	1248.6	570.42	1.2276
80	3.5604	779.84	1.9871	19.087	773.48	1.8442	1218.9	580.48	1.2567
90	3.4574	786.40	2.0056	18.404	780.47	1.8640	40.561	771.94	1.7907
100	3.3605	793.03	2.0239	17.778	787.48	1.8832	38.722	779.64	1.8118
110	3.2691	799.74	2.0418	17.202	794.53	1.9020	37.102	787.27	1.8322
120	3.1827	806.51	2.0594	16.668	801.61	1.9204	35.656	794.86	1.8518
130	3.1010	813.36	2.0767	16.172	808.73	1.9384	34.352	802.43	1.8709
140	3.0234	820.28	2.0937	15.709	815.90	1.9560	33.167	809.99	1.8895
150	2.9498	827.27	2.1104	15.275	823.11	1.9733	32.082	817.55	1.9076
160	2.8797	834.33	2.1269	14.868	830.38	1.9903	31.083	825.13	1.9253
170	2.8130	841.45	2.1432	14.485	837.69	2.0069	30.158	832.72	1.9427
180	2.7494	848.65	2.1592	14.122	845.06	2.0233	29.298	840.35	1.9596
190	2.6887	855.91	2.1750	13.780	852.48	2.0395	28.495	848.00	1.9763
200	2.6306	863.23	2.1905	13.455	859.95	2.0554	27.743	855.69	1.9926
	p=20 bar			p=30 bar			p=40 bar		
0	1420.2	500.84	0.99816	1422.4	501.27	0.99718	1424.6	501.71	0.99622
5	1410.2	506.30	1.0176	1412.5	506.72	1.0166	1414.7	507.15	1.0156
10	1399.8	511.60	1.0362	1402.2	512.01	1.0352	1404.5	512.42	1.0341
15	1389.2	516.76	1.0541	1391.6	517.16	1.0530	1394.0	517.56	1.0519
20	1378.2	521.81	1.0714	1380.7	522.20	1.0703	1383.2	522.58	1.0691
25	1367.0	526.79	1.0882	1369.6	527.16	1.0870	1372.2	527.53	1.0858
30	1355.5	531.70	1.1045	1358.2	532.06	1.1033	1360.9	532.42	1.1020
35	1343.7	536.58	1.1205	1346.5	536.92	1.1192	1349.4	536.26	1.1179
40	1331.6	541.42	1.1362	1334.6	541.75	1.1348	1337.6	542.07	1.1334
50	1306.6	551.09	1.1667	1310.0	551.37	1.1652	1313.2	551.66	1.1638
60	1280.4	560.79	1.1965	1284.2	561.03	1.1949	1287.8	561.28	1.1933
70	1252.9	570.59	1.2257	1257.2	570.78	1.2240	1261.2	570.98	1.2222
80	1223.9	580.58	1.2547	1228.7	580.70	1.2527	1233.4	580.84	1.2508
90	1193.0	590.80	1.2834	1198.7	590.81	1.2812	1204.0	590.90	1.2791
100	1159.9	601.33	1.3122	1165.6	601.25	1.3097	1172.9	601.22	1.3073
110	1123.8	612.25	1.3413	1131.9	612.03	1.3384	1139.5	611.85	1.3357
120	1083.6	623.72	1.3710	1093.8	623.26	1.3675	1103.2	622.90	1.3642
130	80.802	787.10	1.7860	1050.9	635.12	1.3974	1062.9	634.47	1.3934

continued

t, °C	ϱ	i	s	ϱ	i	s	ϱ	i	s
140	76.302	796.02	1.8079	1000.0	647.95	1.4289	1016.8	646.78	1.4236
150	72.511	804.71	1.8287	131.33	787.41	1.7634	960.87	660.29	1.4560
160	69.243	813.23	1.8487	121.11	798.12	1.7884	883.36	676.30	1.4933
170	66.376	821.64	1.8678	113.26	808.13	1.8113	185.68	789.16	1.7527
180	63.827	829.97	1.8864	106.90	817.71	1.8326	166.96	801.92	1.7811
190	61.535	838.24	1.9044	101.57	826.99	1.8528	153.89	813.27	1.8059
200	59.457	846.48	1.9219	96.991	836.08	1.8722	143.87	823.84	1.8284
		p=50 bar			p=60 bar			p=80 bar	
0	1426.7	502.15	0.99526	1428.8	502.59	0.99432	1432.9	503.48	0.99245
5	1416.9	507.58	1.0146	1419.1	508.01	1.0136	1423.3	508.87	1.0116
10	1406.8	512.84	1.0331	1409.0	513.26	1.0320	1413.4	514.10	1.0300
15	1396.4	517.96	1.0506	1398.7	518.37	1.0498	1403.2	519.18	1.0476
20	1385.7	522.98	1.0680	1388.1	523.37	1.0669	1392.7	524.16	1.0647
25	1374.7	527.91	1.0846	1377.2	528.29	1.0835	1382.1	529.06	1.0812
30	1363.6	532.78	1.1008	1366.1	533.15	1.0998	1371.2	533.89	1.0972
35	1352.1	537.61	1.1166	1354.8	537.96	1.1154	1360.0	538.68	1.1129
40	1340.5	542.41	1.1321	1343.3	542.74	1.1308	1348.7	543.43	1.1283
50	1316.4	551.96	1.1623	1319.5	552.27	1.1609	1325.4	552.80	1.1582
60	1291.3	561.54	1.1917	1294.7	561.80	1.1902	1301.3	562.36	1.1873
70	1265.2	571.19	1.2206	1269.0	571.42	1.2189	1276.3	571.89	1.2157
80	1237.8	580.99	1.2489	1242.1	581.16	1.2471	1250.3	581.54	1.2437
90	1209.1	590.98	1.2771	1214.0	591.09	1.2751	1223.2	591.35	1.2713
100	1178.8	601.21	1.3051	1184.4	601.23	1.3029	1195.0	601.35	1.2987
110	1146.5	611.73	1.3330	1153.1	611.65	1.3306	1165.3	611.59	1.3259
120	1111.7	622.61	1.3612	1119.7	622.39	1.3584	1134.0	622.09	1.3531
130	1073.7	633.94	1.3898	1083.5	633.52	1.3864	1100.7	632.91	1.3804
140	1031.1	645.88	1.4191	1043.6	645.16	1.4150	1064.9	644.12	1.4079
150	981.54	658.69	1.4498	998.50	657.49	1.4445	1025.7	655.79	1.4358
160	919.68	672.98	1.4831	945.22	670.83	1.4757	982.11	668.06	1.4645
170	828.16	690.74	1.5236	877.12	685.96	1.5102	932.06	681.18	1.4944
180	285.48	775.13	1.7116	771.64	705.56	1.5538	872.06	695.55	1.5264
190	234.20	794.36	1.7535	454.78	754.11	1.6595	795.12	712.05	1.5624
200	208.20	808.46	1.7836	315.13	786.30	1.7284	687.96	732.54	1.6061
		p=100 bar			p=150 bar			p=200 bar	
0	1436.9	504.38	0.99062	1446.4	506.62	0.98612	1455.2	508.90	0.98186
5	1427.4	509.74	1.0097	1437.1	511.94	1.0051	1446.1	514.16	1.0006
10	1417.6	514.94	1.0280	1427.6	517.09	1.0232	1436.8	519.26	1.0185
15	1407.5	520.00	1.0456	1417.8	522.10	1.0406	1427.3	524.23	1.0358
20	1397.2	524.96	1.0625	1407.8	527.00	1.0573	1417.7	529.09	1.0524
25	1386.7	529.84	1.0769	1397.7	531.82	1.0736	1407.8	533.86	1.0684
30	1376.0	534.64	1.0949	1387.3	536.58	1.0894	1397.8	538.56	1.0841
35	1365.1	539.41	1.1105	1376.8	541.28	1.1048	1387.6	543.22	1.0993
40	1353.9	544.14	1.1258	1366.2	545.95	1.1199	1377.3	547.84	1.1142
50	1331.1	553.54	1.1555	1344.3	555.23	1.1492	1356.3	557.01	1.1433
60	1307.5	562.94	1.1844	1321.9	564.50	1.1777	1334.8	566.16	1.1714
70	1283.1	572.40	1.2126	1298.9	573.80	1.2054	1312.9	575.34	1.1988
80	1257.9	581.97	1.2404	1275.2	583.19	1.2326	1290.4	584.59	1.2256
90	1231.8	591.67	1.2677	1250.9	592.69	1.2594	1267.6	593.93	1.2519
100	1204.7	601.55	1.2947	1226.0	602.33	1.2258	1244.2	603.39	1.2778
110	1176.4	611.64	1.3216	1200.3	612.13	1.3119	1220.4	612.99	1.3033
120	1146.8	621.96	1.3483	1173.8	622.11	1.3377	1196.0	622.73	1.3286
130	1115.7	632.54	1.3750	1146.4	632.27	1.3634	1171.1	632.62	1.3535
140	1082.7	643.43	1.4017	1118.1	642.65	1.3888	1145.7	642.68	1.3782
150	1047.4	654.67	1.4286	1088.7	653.24	1.4142	1119.6	652.90	1.4027
160	1009.3	666.33	1.4559	1058.0	664.08	1.4395	1092.9	663.30	1.4270
170	967.59	678.52	1.4837	1025.9	675.17	1.4648	1065.5	673.86	1.4511
180	920.97	691.36	1.5123	992.33	686.54	1.4902	1037.3	684.61	1.4750
190	867.78	705.09	1.5422	956.88	698.22	1.5156	1008.4	695.54	1.4988
200	805.67	720.03	1.5740	919.43	710.24	1.5412	978.79	706.65	1.5225

Viscosity of dichloromonofluoromethane gas at $p \leqslant 1$ bar [105]

t, °C	−20	0	20	40	60	80	100
$\eta \cdot 10^7$, N · s/m²	100	106	112	118	124	130	136

Viscosity η (N · s/m²) of liquid dichloromonofluoromethane [109]

T, °K	$\eta \cdot 10^3$	T, °K	$\eta \cdot 10^3$	T, °K	$\eta \cdot 10^3$	T, °K	$\eta \cdot 10^3$	T, °K	$\eta \cdot 10^3$
209	0.918	237	0.560	261	0.400	285	0.302	309	0.238
213	0.849	241	0.527	265	0.380	289	0.289	313	0.229
217	0.787	245	0.497	269	0.362	293	0.277	317	0.221
221	0.732	249	0.469	273	0.345	297	0.266	321	0.214
225	0.682	253	0.444	277	0.329	301	0.256	325	0.207
229	0.638	257	0.421	281	0.315	305	0.247	329	0.200
233	0.597								

Thermal conductivity λ (W/m · deg) of dichloromonofluoromethane gas at a pressure of $p \leqslant 1$ bar [383]

T, °K	250	273.15	300	350	400	450
$\lambda \cdot 10^4$	66	75	86	109	138	172

Thermal conductivity λ (W/m · deg) of liquid dichloromonofluoromethane [107]

t, °C	λ	t, °C	λ	t, °C	λ	t, °C	λ	t, °C	λ
−40	0.123	−10	0.113	20	0.102	50	0.091	80	0.080
−30	0.120	0	0.109	30	0.098	60	0.087	90	0.076
−20	0.116	10	0.106	40	0.095	70	0.083	100	0.072

MONOCHLORODIFLUOROMETHANE (FREON-22) (CHF_2Cl)

Molecular weight 86.48

$t_{boil} = -40.8$ °C at $p = 1$ atm; $t_{melt} = -160.0$ °C;
$t_{cr} = 96$ °C; $p_{cr} = 49.86$ bar; $v_{cr} = 1.95$ dm³/kg;
$\sigma = 8.5$ erg/cm² at $t = 26$°C

Thermodynamic properties of saturated monochlorodifluoromethane [110]: v (dm³/kg), i and r (kJ/kg) and s (kJ/kg · deg)

t, °C	p, bar	v'	v''	i'	i''	r	s'	s''
−100	0.0199	0.6421	8359	389.11	658.41	269.29	0.4979	2.0532
− 95	0.0313	0.6465	5457	394.50	660.83	266.32	0.5285	2.0235
− 90	0.0478	0.6511	3665	399.90	663.26	263.36	0.5583	1.9963
− 85	0.0712	0.6558	2526	405.30	665.70	260.40	0.5873	1.9714
− 80	0.1034	0.6608	1782	410.72	668.15	257.43	0.6157	1.9485
− 75	0.1469	0.6659	1284	416.14	670.60	254.46	0.6434	1.9276
− 70	0.2045	0.6713	943.5	421.58	673.04	251.46	0.6705	1.9083
− 65	0.2794	0.6769	705.5	427.02	675.48	248.46	0.6969	1.8906
− 60	0.3752	0.6827	536.1	432.48	677.90	245.42	0.7228	1.8742
− 55	0.4958	0.6888	413.4	437.95	680.31	242.36	0.7481	1.8591
− 50	0.6459	0.6952	323.2	443.43	682.69	239.26	0.7729	1.8451
− 45	0.8302	0.7019	255.7	448.93	685.06	236.13	0.7972	1.8321
− 40	1.054	0.7089	204.7	454.46	687.38	232.92	0.8211	1.8220
− 35	1.322	0.7162	165.5	460.02	689.67	229.65	0.8446	1.8089
− 30	1.641	0.7239	135.1	465.60	691.92	226.32	0.8677	1.7985
− 25	2.017	0.7319	111.3	471.22	694.13	222.91	0.8904	1.7887

continued

t, °C	p, bar	v′	v″	i′	i″	r	s′	s″
−20	2.456	0.7404	92.41	476.88	696.28	219.40	0.9129	1.7796
−15	2.966	0.7493	77.29	482.59	698.38	215.79	0.9350	1.7710
−10	3.552	0.7586	65.08	488.34	700.42	212.08	0.9569	1.7629
− 5	4.222	0.7684	55.14	494.15	702.39	208.24	0.9786	1.7552
0	4.983	0.7786	46.98	500.00	704.28	204.28	1.0000	1.7479
2	5.315	0.7828	44.13	502.36	705.01	202.65	1.0085	1.7450
4	5.663	0.7871	41.49	504.73	705.73	201.00	1.0170	1.7422
6	6.028	0.7915	39.03	507.11	706.44	199.33	1.0254	1.7395
8	6.411	0.7960	36.75	509.49	707.13	197.64	1.0338	1.7368
10	6.811	0.8005	34.62	511.89	707.81	195.92	1.0422	1.7341
12	7.229	0.8052	32.64	514.30	708.47	194.17	1.0506	1.7315
14	7.667	0.8099	30.79	516.72	709.11	192.39	1.0589	1.7289
16	8.123	0.8147	29.07	519.16	709.74	190.58	1.0673	1.7264
18	8.600	0.8196	27.45	521.60	710.35	188.75	1.0755	1.7238
20	9.097	0.8246	25.94	524.05	710.94	186.89	1.0838	1.7213
22	9.615	0.8297	24.53	526.51	711.51	185.00	1.0920	1.7188
24	10.154	0.8350	23.21	528.99	712.06	183.07	1.1002	1.7163
26	10.716	0.8403	21.96	531.48	712.58	181.10	1.1084	1.7138
28	11.300	0.8458	20.80	533.99	713.09	179.10	1.1166	1.7113
30	11.908	0.8515	19.70	536.51	713.57	177.06	1.1248	1.7089
32	12.539	0.8573	18.67	539.05	714.03	174.98	1.1330	1.7064
34	13.196	0.8634	17.69	541.60	714.46	172.86	1.1411	1.7039
36	13.876	0.8696	16.78	544.17	714.86	170.69	1.1493	1.7015
38	14.582	0.8761	15.91	546.76	715.24	168.48	1.1574	1.6989
40	15.315	0.8829	15.10	549.36	715.58	166.22	1.1656	1.6964
42	16.074	0.8900	14.32	551.98	715.89	163.91	1.1737	1.6938
44	16.862	0.8974	13.59	554.63	716.17	161.54	1.1819	1.6912
46	17.677	0.9050	12.90	557.31	716.42	159.11	1.1901	1.6886
48	18.521	0.9130	12.25	560.01	716.62	156.61	1.1982	1.6859
50	19.395	0.9213	11.63	562.75	716.78	154.03	1.2065	1.6832
52	20.299	0.9300	11.04	565.52	716.90	151.38	1.2148	1.6804
54	21.235	0.9392	10.48	568.33	716.98	148.65	1.2231	1.6775
56	22.202	0.9488	9.946	571.17	717.01	146.84	1.2315	1.6746
58	23.202	0.9588	9.439	574.03	716.97	142.94	1.2999	1.6715
60	24.236	0.9693	8.956	576.94	716.88	139.94	1.2483	1.6684
62	25.30	0.9804	8.495	579.90	716.73	136.83	1.2569	1.6652
64	26.41	0.9921	8.054	582.91	716.50	133.59	1.2656	1.6618
66	27.55	1.004	7.633	585.99	716.20	130.21	1.2743	1.6583
68	28.72	1.017	7.229	589.14	715.82	126.68	1.2833	1.6546
70	29.94	1.031	6.842	592.34	715.34	123.00	1.2922	1.6506
72	31.19	1.046	6.469	595.61	714.76	119.15	1.3014	1.6466
74	32.48	1.062	6.111	598.96	714.05	115.09	1.3107	1.6422
76	33.82	1.079	5.764	602.42	713.22	110.80	1.3201	1.6375
78	35.20	1.097	5.429	605.94	712.22	106.28	1.3298	1.6325
80	36.62	1.118	5.104	609.57	711.05	101.48	1.3396	1.6270
81	37.35	1.130	4.944	611.44	710.38	98.94	1.3447	1.6241
82	38.08	1.141	4.785	613.35	709.65	96.30	1.3499	1.6210
83	38.84	1.153	4.629	615.31	708.85	93.54	1.3552	1.6178
84	39.60	1.167	4.474	617.34	707.98	90.64	1.3606	1.6144
85	40.37	1.182	4.319	619.45	707.04	87.59	1.3661	1.6107
86	41.16	1.205	4.166	621.61	705.98	84.37	1.3720	1.6069
87	41.96	1.222	4.01	623.8	704.8	81.0	1.378	1.603
88	42.77	1.240	3.86	626.2	703.5	77.3	1.384	1.598
89	43.59	1.259	3.70	628.7	702.1	73.4	1.390	1.593
90	44.43	1.278	3.54	631.1	700.4	69.3	1.397	1.588
92	46.14	1.341	3.21	637.0	696.4	59.4	1.413	1.575
94	47.91	1.448	2.83	644.6	690.3	45.7	1.433	1.557
96.13	49.86	1.95	1.95	667.3	667.3	0	1.493	1.493

Thermodynamic properties of superheated vapor of Freon-22 (monochlorodifluoromethane) [110]: v (dm^3/kg), i (kJ/kg) and s (kJ/kg · deg)

t, °C	v	i	s	v	i	s
	p=0,05 bar, t_s=−89.46 °C			p=0.1 bar, t_s=−80.47 °C		
t_s	3517	663.53	1.9935	1839	667.92	1.9506
−80	3701	668.43	2.0195	1844	668.17	1.9518
−70	3895	673.74	2.0463	1942	673.51	1.9788
−60	4089	679.16	2.0724	2039	678.97	2.0050
−50	4282	684.70	2.0978	2137	684.54	2.0306
−40	4475	690.37	2.1226	2234	690.23	2.0555
−30	4668	696.16	2.1469	2331	696.03	2.0799
−20	4861	702.07	2.1707	2428	701.95	2.1037
−10	5054	708.10	2.1941	2524	707.99	2.1271
0	5247	714.24	2.2170	2621	714.15	2.1501
10	5440	720.51	2.2395	2718	720.43	2.1727
20	5633	726.90	2.2617	2814	726.82	2.1949
30	5825	733.40	2.2835	2911	733.33	2.2167
40	6018	740.02	2.3050	3007	739.95	2.2382
50	6210	746.75	2.3261	3103	746.69	2.2594
60	6403	753.60	2.3470	3200	753.54	2.2802
70	6595	760.55	2.3676	3296	760.50	2.3008
80	6788	767.62	2.3879	3393	767.57	2.3211
90	6980	774.79	2.4079	3489	774.75	2.3412
100	7173	782.07	2.4277	3585	782.03	2.3610
110	7365	789.46	2.4472	3681	789.42	2.3805
120	7558	796.95	2.4665	3778	796.92	2.3998
130	7750	804.55	2.4856	3874	804.52	2.4189
140	7942	812.24	2.5044	3970	812.21	2.4377
150	8135	820.03	2.5231	4067	820.00	2.4564
160	8327	827.92	2.5415	4163	827.89	2.4748
170	8520	835.90	2.5597	4259	835.87	2.4930
180	8712	843.97	2.5777	4355	843.94	2.5110
190	8904	852.13	2.5955	4452	852.10	2.5288
200	9097	860.38	2.6132	4548	860.36	2.5465
210	9289	868.72	2.6303	4644	868.70	2.5640
220	9482	877.14	2.6478	4740	877.12	2.5812
230	9674	885.64	2.6649	4836	885.62	2.5982
240	9866	894.22	2.6818	4933	894.20	2.6151
250	10 060	902.88	2.6985	5029	902.86	2.6318
	p=0.5 bar, t_s=−54.85 °C			p=1.0 bar, t_s=−41.12 °C		
t_s	410.3	680.38	1.8568	214.9	686.86	1.8227
−50	420.2	683.19	1.8714			
−40	440.4	689.06	1.8971	216.1	687.54	1.8257
−30	460.5	695.00	1.9221	226.6	693.68	1.8514
−20	480.5	701.04	1.9464	237.0	699.88	1.8764
−10	500.3	707.18	1.9702	247.2	706.14	1.9007
0	520.0	713.42	1.9935	257.4	712.49	1.9243
10	539.7	719.77	2.0163	267.4	718.93	1.9475
20	559.3	726.22	2.0387	277.5	725.46	1.9702
30	578.9	732.78	2.0607	287.4	732.08	1.9924
40	598.4	739.45	2.0823	297.3	731.81	2.0142
50	617.9	746.23	2.1036	307.2	745.63	2.0356
60	637.4	753.11	2.1246	317.1	752.55	2.0568
70	656.9	760.10	2.1453	326.9	759.69	2.0776
80	676.3	767.19	2.1657	336.7	766.72	2.0980
90	695.7	774.39	2.1858	346.5	773.95	2.1182
100	715.1	781.70	2.2056	356.3	781.28	2.1382
110	734.5	789.11	2.2251	366.1	788.72	2.1578
120	753.8	796.62	2.2445	375.8	796.25	2.1772
130	773.2	804.23	2.2636	385.6	803.88	2.1964
140	792.6	811.94	2.2825	395.3	811.61	2.2153
150	811.9	819.74	2.3012	405.1	819.43	2.2340
160	831.2	827.64	2.3197	414.8	827.34	2.2525
170	850.5	835.64	2.3379	424.5	835.35	2.2708
180	869.9	843.72	2.3559	434.2	843.45	2.2889

continued

t, °C	v	i	s	v	i	s
190	889.2	851.90	2.3737	443.9	851.63	2.3067
200	908.5	860.16	2.3914	453.6	859.90	2.3243
210	927.8	868.50	2.4089	463.3	868.26	2.3418
220	947.1	876.93	2.4261	473.0	876.70	2.3592
230	966.4	885.44	2.4432	482.6	885.22	2.3763
240	985.7	894.03	2.4601	492.3	893.82	2.3932
250	1005	902.70	2.4769	502.0	902.49	2.4099
	$p=2.0$ bar, $t_s=-24.00$ °C			$p=3.0$ bar, $t_s=-14.69$ °C		
t_s	112.9	694.83	1.7923	76.44	698.51	1.7705
−20	115.1	697.44	1.8028			
−10	120.6	703.99	1.8281	78.27	701.72	1.7828
0	125.9	710.57	1.8526	82.07	708.57	1.8083
10	131.2	717.20	1.8765	85.79	715.41	1.8329
20	136.4	723.89	1.8997	89.43	722.28	1.8567
30	141.6	730.65	1.9224	93.01	729.20	1.8799
40	146.8	737.50	1.9446	96.55	736.17	1.9026
50	151.9	744.43	1.9664	100.0	743.21	1.9247
60	156.9	751.45	1.9878	103.5	750.32	1.9464
70	162.0	758.56	2.0088	106.9	757.51	1.9676
80	167.0	765.76	2.0295	110.4	764.78	1.9885
90	172.0	773.05	2.0498	113.8	772.14	2.0091
100	176.9	780.44	2.0699	117.1	779.59	2.0293
110	181.9	787.92	2.0897	120.5	787.12	2.0492
120	186.8	795.50	2.1092	123.8	794.75	2.0689
130	191.8	803.17	2.1285	127.2	802.46	2.0883
140	196.7	810.94	2.1475	130.5	810.26	2.1074
150	201.6	818.79	2.1663	133.8	818.15	2.1262
160	206.5	826.73	2.1849	137.1	826.13	2.1449
170	211.4	834.77	2.2032	140.4	834.19	2.1633
180	216.3	842.90	2.2213	143.7	842.34	2.1814
190	221.2	851.11	2.2392	147.0	850.58	2.1994
200	226.1	859.40	2.2570	150.3	858.89	2.2172
210	231.0	867.78	2.2745	153.6	867.29	2.2348
220	235.9	876.24	2.2918	156.9	875.77	2.2521
230	240.8	884.78	2.3089	160.1	884.33	2.2693
240	245.6	893.39	2.3259	163.4	892.96	2.2863
250	250.5	902.08	2.3427	166.7	901.66	2.3031
	$p=4.0$ bar, $t_s=-6.58$ °C			$p=5$ bar, $t_s=0.10$ °C		
t_s	58.08	701.77	1.7576	46.83	704.32	1.7477
0	60.07	706.46	1.7749			
10	63.01	713.54	1.8004	49.29	711.59	1.7739
20	65.87	720.61	1.8250	51.70	718.87	1.7992
30	68.67	727.69	1.8487	54.04	726.13	1.8235
40	71.42	734.80	1.8717	56.32	733.39	1.8470
50	74.12	741.95	1.8942	58.56	740.67	1.8699
60	76.78	749.17	1.9162	60.75	747.99	1.8922
70	79.43	756.44	1.9378	62.91	755.36	1.9140
80	82.05	763.79	1.9589	65.05	762.79	1.9354
90	84.64	771.22	1.9796	67.17	770.29	1.9563
100	87.22	778.73	2.0000	69.27	777.86	1.9769
110	89.78	786.31	2.0201	71.35	785.51	1.9971
120	92.33	793.98	2.0398	73.42	793.23	2.0170
130	94.87	801.74	2.0593	75.48	801.02	2.0366
140	97.40	809.58	2.0785	77.53	808.90	2.0559
150	99.91	817.51	2.0975	79.57	816.86	2.0749
160	102.4	825.52	2.1162	81.60	824.90	2.0937
170	104.9	833.61	2.1346	83.62	833.02	2.1122
180	107.4	841.79	2.1529	85.64	841.22	2.1305
190	109.9	850.05	2.1709	87.65	849.51	2.1486
200	112.4	858.39	2.1887	89.65	857.88	2.1665
210	114.9	866.81	2.2063	91.65	866.32	2.1842
220	117.4	875.31	2.2238	93.65	874.84	2.2016

continued

t, °C	v	i	s	v	i	s
230	119.8	883.88	2.2410	95.64	883.43	2.2188
240	122.3	892.53	2.2580	97.63	892.10	2.2359
250	124.8	901.25	2.2748	99.61	900.84	2.2528
	p=6 bar, t_s=5.85 °C			p=8 bar, t_s=15.47 °C		
t_s	39.21	706.39	1.7397	29.51	709.58	1.7270
10	40.12	709.55	1.7510			
20	42.23	717.08	1.7771	30.31	713.22	1.7396
30	44.26	724.53	1.8021	31.98	721.13	1.7661
40	46.23	731.94	1.8262	33.59	728.90	1.7914
50	48.16	739.36	1.8495	35.13	736.63	1.8156
60	50.04	746.79	1.8721	36.63	744.32	1.8390
70	51.89	754.26	1.8942	38.10	751.99	1.8617
80	53.72	761.77	1.9158	39.53	759.68	1.8838
90	55.52	769.34	1.9369	40.94	767.40	1.9054
100	57.30	776.97	1.9576	42.33	775.17	1.9265
110	59.07	784.67	1.9780	43.70	782.99	1.9472
120	60.82	792.44	1.9980	45.05	790.87	1.9675
130	62.56	800.29	2.0177	46.39	798.81	1.9874
140	64.28	808.21	2.0371	47.72	806.81	2.0070
150	66.00	816.20	2.0563	49.04	814.88	2.0263
160	67.71	824.28	2.0751	50.36	823.03	2.0453
170	69.42	832.44	2.0937	51.66	831.25	2.0641
180	71.11	840.67	2.1121	52.96	839.54	2.0826
190	72.80	848.98	2.1303	54.25	847.90	2.1009
200	74.49	857.37	2.1482	55.53	856.34	2.1189
210	76.17	865.83	2.1659	56.81	864.85	2.1367
220	77.84	874.37	2.1834	58.09	873.43	2.1543
230	79.51	882.98	2.2006	59.36	882.08	2.1716
240	81.18	891.67	2.2177	60.63	890.80	2.1888
250	82.85	900.42	2.2346	61.89	899.59	2.2058
	p=10 bar, t_s=23.44 °C			p=12 bar, t_s=30.30 °C		
t_s	23.57	711.90	1.7170	19.54	713.64	1.7085
30	24.55	717.44	1.7355			
40	25.95	725.67	1.7622	20.80	722.17	1.7362
50	27.28	733.74	1.7875	22.01	730.66	1.7629
60	28.56	741.71	1.8118	23.15	738.97	1.7882
70	29.80	749.62	1.8352	24.24	747.15	1.8124
80	31.00	757.52	1.8579	25.30	755.27	1.8357
90	32.18	765.41	1.8800	26.33	763.36	1.8583
100	33.33	773.33	1.9015	27.33	771.43	1.8802
110	34.47	781.27	1.9225	28.31	779.52	1.9016
120	35.59	789.26	1.9431	29.27	787.63	1.9225
130	36.69	797.30	1.9633	30.22	793.77	1.9430
140	37.78	805.40	1.9831	31.15	803.96	1.9630
150	38.87	813.55	2.0026	32.07	812.20	1.9827
160	39.94	821.77	2.0218	32.98	820.50	2.0021
170	41.00	830.05	2.0407	33.89	828.55	2.0211
180	42.06	838.40	2.0593	34.79	837.26	2.0399
190	43.11	846.82	2.0777	35.68	848.73	2.0584
200	44.16	855.31	2.0958	36.57	854.27	2.0767
210	45.20	863.87	2.1137	37.45	862.87	2.0947
220	46.23	872.49	2.1314	38.33	871.54	2.1124
230	47.26	881.18	2.1489	39.20	880.27	2.1299
240	48.29	889.94	2.1661	40.07	889.07	2.1473
250	49.31	898.76	2.1831	40.93	897.93	2.1645
	p=14 bar, t_s=36.37 °C			p=16 bar, t_s=41.81 °C		
t_s	16.62	714.94	1.7010	14.40	715.87	1.6940
40	17.06	718.34	1.7119			
50	18.20	727.36	1.7404	15.30	723.78	1.7189
60	19.26	736.07	1.7668	16.31	732.97	1.7469
70	20.26	744.57	1.7919	17.25	741.84	1.7731

continued

t, °C	v	i	s	v	i	s
80	21.21	752.94	1.8159	18.13	750.50	1.7980
90	22.13	761.23	1.8391	18.98	759.03	1.8218
100	23.03	769.48	1.8615	19.80	767.47	1.8447
110	23.90	777.72	1.8833	20.59	775.87	1.8669
120	24.75	785.96	1.9046	21.36	784.25	1.8885
130	25.59	794.22	1.9253	22.12	792.63	1.9096
140	26.42	802.51	1.9456	22.86	801.02	1.9301
150	27.23	810.83	1.9655	23.58	809.44	1.9503
160	28.03	819.20	1.9851	24.30	817.90	1.9700
170	28.82	827.62	2.0043	25.01	826.40	1.9894
180	29.60	836.10	2.0232	25.71	834.94	2.0085
190	30.38	844.64	2.0418	26.40	843.53	2.0272
200	31.15	853.23	2.0602	27.09	852.18	2.0457
210	31.92	861.88	2.0783	27.77	860.88	2.0639
220	32.68	870.59	2.0961	28.45	869.64	2.0818
230	33.44	879.36	2.1137	29.12	878.45	2.0995
240	34.19	888.20	2.1311	29.79	887.32	2.1170
250	34.94	897.09	2.1483	30.45	896.25	2.1342
	p=18 bar, t_s=46.77 °C			p=20 bar, t_s=51.35 °C		
t_s	12.65	716.50	1.6875	11.23	716.87	1.6813
60	13.98	729.65	1.7278	12.08	726.03	1.7091
70	14.88	738.96	1.7553	12.97	735.89	1.7383
80	15.72	747.95	1.7812	13.78	745.28	1.7653
90	16.52	756.75	1.8058	14.54	754.37	1.7907
100	17.28	765.41	1.8293	15.26	763.26	1.8148
110	18.01	773.98	1.8520	15.94	772.03	1.8380
120	18.72	782.50	1.8739	16.60	780.72	1.8602
130	19.41	791.01	1.8952	17.24	789.37	1.8821
140	20.09	799.52	1.9161	17.87	797.99	1.9033
150	20.75	808.04	1.9365	18.48	806.61	1.9239
160	21.40	816.58	1.9565	19.08	815.24	1.9440
170	22.04	825.15	1.9760	19.67	823.89	1.9638
180	22.68	833.76	1.9952	20.25	832.57	1.9832
190	23.31	842.41	2.0141	20.83	841.29	2.0022
200	23.93	851.11	2.0327	21.40	850.05	2.0209
210	24.54	859.87	2.0510	21.96	858.86	2.0393
220	25.15	868.67	2.0691	22.52	867.71	2.0574
230	25.76	877.53	2.0869	23.07	876.61	2.0753
240	26.36	886.44	2.1044	23.62	885.57	2.0929
250	26.96	895.41	2.1217	24.16	894.57	2.1103
	p=30 bar, t_s=70.10 °C			p=40 bar, t_s=84.52 °C		
t_s	6.822	715.31	1.6505	4.394	707.50	1.6112
80	7.715	728.84	1.6893			
90	8.443	740.51	1.7219	5.024	719.70	1.6464
100	9.080	751.21	1.7510	5.800	735.41	1.6891
110	9.659	761.33	1.7778	6.403	748.28	1.7231
120	10.20	771.08	1.8029	6.921	759.84	1.7529
130	10.71	780.58	1.8268	7.387	770.67	1.7801
140	11.19	789.92	1.8497	7.818	781.02	1.8055
150	11.66	799.15	1.8717	8.223	791.06	1.8295
160	12.11	808.30	1.8931	8.607	800.88	1.8524
170	12.55	817.40	1.9139	8.975	810.55	1.8745
180	12.98	826.48	1.9341	9.331	820.11	1.8958
190	13.40	835.55	1.9539	9.676	829.60	1.9165
200	13.81	844.63	1.9733	10.01	839.04	1.9367
210	14.21	853.72	1.9923	10.34	848.45	1.9564
220	14.61	862.83	2.0110	10.66	857.85	1.9756
230	15.01	871.96	2.0294	10.98	867.24	1.9945
240	15.40	881.13	2.0474	11.29	876.64	2.0130
250	15.78	890.33	2.0651	11.59	886.05	2.0312

continued

t, °C	v	i	s	v	i	s
	p=50 bar			p=60 bar		
100	3.365	707.51	1.6020			
110	4.275	730.58	1.6631	2.461	698.18	1.5698
120	4.864	746.06	1.7030	3.364	727.52	1.6455
130	5.342	759.16	1.7360	3.918	745.26	1.6901
140	5.760	771.05	1.7651	4.355	759.66	1.7254
150	6.139	782.22	1.7918	4.731	772.47	1.7560
160	6.491	792.92	1.8168	5.069	784.33	1.7837
170	6.823	803.29	1.8405	5.380	795.60	1.8094
180	7.138	813.43	1.8631	5.672	806.44	1.8336
190	7.440	823.41	1.8849	5.948	817.00	1.8567
200	7.731	833.27	1.9060	6.211	827.34	1.8788
210	8.014	843.05	1.9264	6.465	837.53	1.9001
220	8.290	852.77	1.9463	6.711	847.60	1.9207
230	8.559	862.45	1.9657	6.949	857.59	1.9407
240	8.822	872.10	1.9847	7.181	867.52	1.9603
250	9.080	881.74	2.0034	7.408	877.41	1.9794

Thermodynamic properties of saturated Freon-22 gas (monochlorodifluoromethane) [110]: c_p (kJ/kg · deg), η (N · s/m²), ν (m²/kg) λ (W/m · deg), α (m²/kg), σ (N/m), β (deg⁻¹) and Pr

t, °C	$\eta \cdot 10^7$	$\nu \cdot 10^8$	$\lambda \cdot 10^2$	$a \cdot 10^3$	Pr	t, °C	$\eta \cdot 10^7$	$\nu \cdot 10^8$	$\lambda \cdot 10^2$	$a \cdot 10^3$	Pr
−40	101.7	218	0.831	2.91	0.749	90	153.0	525	1.464	6.90	0.761
−30	106.1	238	0.880	3.20	0.744	100	156.5	553	1.513	7.23	0.764
−20	110.4	259	0.929	3.49	0.741	110	160.0	580	1.561	7.57	0.766
−10	114.6	281	0.977	3.79	0.740	120	163.4	609	1.610	7.91	0.769
0	118.7	303	1.026	4.09	0.740	130	166.8	638	1.659	8.26	0.772
10	122.8	325	1.075	4.39	0.741	140	170.1	667	1.708	8.61	0.775
20	126.8	348	1.123	4.69	0.742	150	173.4	696	1.756	8.96	0.778
30	130.7	372	1.172	5.00	0.744	160	176.7	726			
40	134.5	396	1.221	5.31	0.746	170	179.9	757			
50	138.3	421	1.269	5.62	0.749	180	183.1	788			
60	142.1	446	1.318	5.93	0.752	190	186.3	819			
70	145.8	472	1.367	6.25	0.755	200	189.4	851			
80	149.4	498	1.416	6.57	0.758						

Physical properties of saturated Freon-22 (monochlorodifluoromethane) [110]

t, °C	c_p	$\eta \cdot 10^4$	$\nu \cdot 10^7$	λ	$a \cdot 10^2$	$\sigma \cdot 10^3$	$\beta \cdot 10^4$	Pr
−100	1.075			0.1487	8.46	28.1	11.2	
−95	1.077			0.1462	8.55	27.3	11.5	
−90	1.079			0.1436	8.65	26.5	11.9	
−85	1.081			0.1411	8.55	25.7	12.4	
−80	1.083			0.1385	8.45	24.8	12.9	
−75	1.085			0.1360	8.35	24.0	13.5	
−70	1.087			0.1334	8.25	23.2	14.1	
−65	1.089	4.35	2.94	0.1309	8.14	22.4	14.7	3.61
−60	1.091	4.14	2.83	0.1283	8.03	21.5	15.3	3.52
−55	1.094	3.95	2.72	0.1258	7.92	20.7	16.0	3.44
−50	1.097	3.78	2.63	0.1232	7.81	19.9	16.8	3.37
−45	1.101	3.63	2.55	0.1207	7.69	19.0	17.6	3.31
−40	1.105	3.49	2.47	0.1181	7.57	18.2	18.4	3.26
−35	1.110	3.36	2.41	0 1156	7.45	17.4	19.2	3.22
−30	1.116	3.24	2.34	0.1130	7.33	16.6	20.1	3.20
−25	1.123	3.13	2.29	0.1105	7.20	15.8	21.1	3.18
−20	1.130	3.02	2.24	0.1079	7.07	15.0	22.1	3.16
−15	1.138	2.92	2.19	0.1054	6.93	14.1	23.1	3.15

continued

t, °C	c_p	$\eta \cdot 10^4$	$\nu \cdot 10^7$	λ	$a \cdot 10^2$	$\sigma \cdot 10^3$	$\beta \cdot 10^4$	Pr
−10	1.148	2.83	2.15	0.1028	6.79	13.3	24.1	3.16
− 5	1.159	2.75	2.11	0.1003	6.65	12.5	25.2	3.18
0	1.171	2.67	2.08	0.0977	6.50	11.7	26.3	3.20
5	1.185	2.60	2.05	0.0952	6.35	10.9	27.6	3.23
10	1.199	2.53	2.02	0.0926	6.19	10.2	29.1	3.27
15	1.215	2.46	2.00	0.0901	6.03	9.4	30.8	3.32
20	1.232	2.40	1.98	0.0875	5.86	8.7	32.7	3.38
25	1.250	2.34	1.96	0.0850	5.69	7.9	35.0	3.44
30	1.270	2.29	1.95	0.0824	5.52	7.2	37.7	3.53
35	1.292	2.24	1.94	0.0798	5.34	6.5	41.0	3.62
40	1.319	2.19	1.94	0.0772	5.15	5.8	44.9	3.74
45	1.353	2.15	1.94	0.0744	4.94	5.2	49.4	3.90
50	1.395	2.10	1.94	0.0714	4.72	4.5	55.0	4.10
55	1.446	2.06	1.94	0.0681	4.47	3.9	61.7	4.37
60	1.526			0.0646	4.12	3.3	69.6	
65	1.607			0.0608	3.68	2.7		
70	1.720			0.0565	3.20	2.1		
75						1.6		
80						1.1		
85						0.7		

Heat capacity c_p (kJ/kg · deg) and ratio of heat capacities c_p/c_v for Freon-22 (monochlorodifluoromethane)[110]

t, °C	c_p	c_p/c_v	c_p	c_p/c_v	c_p	c_p/c_v
	Ideal gas ($p=0$)		$p=1$ bar, $t_s=-41.12$ °C		$p=2$ bar, $t_s=-24.00$ °C	
t_s			0.611	1.237	0.654	1.247
−80	0.520	1.227				
−60	0.545	1.214				
−40	0.571	1.203	0.611	1.235		
−20	0.596	1.193	0.623	1.215	0.654	1.241
0	0.620	1.183	0.639	1.200	0.660	1.217
20	0.644	1.175	0.658	1.187	0.673	1.200
40	0.667	1.169	0.678	1.177	0.689	1.187
60	0.690	1.162	0.698	1.169	0.706	1.176
80	0.712	1.156	0.718	1.162	0.725	1.168
100	0.733	1.151	0.738	1.155	0.744	1.160
120	0.754	1.146	0.758	1.150	0.762	1.154
140	0.774	1.142	0.777	1.145	0.781	1.148
160	0.793	1.138	0.796	1.141	0.799	1.143
180	0.812	1.134	0.814	1.137	0.817	1.139
200	0.829	1.131	0.832	1.133	0.834	1.135
220	0.846	1.128	0.848	1.130	0.850	1.132
240	0.862	1.125	0.864	1.127	0.865	1.129
	$p=3$ bar, $t_s=-14.69$ °C		$p=4$ bar, $t_s=-6.58$ °C		$p=5$ bar, $t_s=0{,}10$ °C	
t_s	0.687	1.262	0.715	1.276	0.741	1.290
0	0.684	1.238	0.710	1.262		
20	0.689	1.215	0.707	1.231	0.726	1.249
40	0.700	1.197	1.713	1.209	0.727	1.221
60	0.715	1.184	0.724	1.193	0.734	1.202
80	0.732	1.174	0.739	1.180	0.764	1.187
100	0.749	1.165	0.755	1.170	0.760	1.176
120	0.767	1.158	0.771	1.162	0.776	1.166
140	0.785	1.152	0.788	1.155	0.792	1.159
160	0.802	1.146	0.805	1.149	0.808	1.152
180	0.819	1.142	0.822	1.144	0.825	1.147
200	0.836	1.137	0.838	1.139	0.840	1.142
220	0.852	1.134	0.854	1.136	0.856	1.137
240	0.867	1.130	0.869	1.132	0.870	1.134

continued

t, °C	c_p	c_p/c_v	c_p	c_p/c_v	c_p	c_pc_v
	$p=6$ bar, $t_s=5.85$ °C		$p=8$ bar, $t_s=15.47$ °C		$p=10$ bar, $t_s=23.44$ °C	
t_s	0.764	1.305	0.810	1.336	0.854	1.369
40	0.741	1.235	0.774	1.266	0.814	1.305
60	0.745	1.211	0.768	1.233	0.794	1.258
80	0.754	1.194	0.771	1.210	0.789	1.228
100	0.767	1.181	0.779	1.193	0.793	1.206
120	0.781	1.171	0.791	1.180	0.801	1.190
140	0.796	1.162	0.804	1.170	0.812	1.178
160	0.812	1.155	0.818	1.162	0.825	1.168
180	0.827	1.149	0.833	1.154	0.838	1.160
200	0.843	1.144	0.847	1.148	0.852	1.153
220	0.858	1.139	0.862	1.143	0.866	1.147
240	0.872	1.135	0.876	1.139	0.879	1.142
	$p=12$ bar, $t_s=30.30$ °C		$p=14$ bar, $t_s=36.49$ °C		$p=16$ bar, $t_s=41.81$ °C	
t_s	0.899	1.406	0.944	1.445	0.994	1.492
40	0.862	1.354	0.925	1.419		
60	0.824	1.287	0.859	1.323	0.901	1.366
80	0.810	1.247	0.833	1.270	0.858	1.296
100	0.808	1.221	0.824	1.236	0.842	1.254
120	0.813	1.201	0.825	1.213	0.838	1.225
140	0.821	1.186	0.831	1.195	0.841	1.205
160	0.832	1.175	0.840	1.182	0.847	1.190
180	0.844	1.165	0.850	1.171	0.857	1.177
200	0.857	1.158	0.862	1.163	0.867	1.168
220	0.870	1.151	0.874	1.155	0.879	1.160
240	0.883	1.146	0.886	1.149	0.890	1.153
	$p=18$ bar, $t_s=46.77$ °C		$p=20$ bar, $t_s=53.51$ °C		$p=24$ bar, $t_s=59.55$ °C	
t_s	1.047	1.543	1.079	1.567	1.243	1.743
60	0.952	1.420	1.018	1.491	1.234	1.731
80	0.888	1.326	0.922	1.361	1.010	1.453
100	0.861	1.273	0.882	1.294	0.933	1.346
120	0.851	1.239	0.866	1.253	0.900	1.286
140	0.851	1.215	0.862	1.226	0.886	1.249
160	0.856	1.197	0.864	1.206	0.882	1.223
180	0.863	1.184	0.870	1.190	0.884	1.204
200	0.872	1.173	0.878	1.178	0.890	1.189
220	0.883	1.164	0.888	1.168	0.897	1.178
240	0.894	1.157	0.898	1.160	0.906	1.168
	$p=30$ bar, $t_s=70.10$ °C		$p=35$ bar, $t_s=77.72$ °C		$p=40$ bar, $t_s=84.52$ °C	
t_s	1.544	2.063	1.975	2.546	2.846	3.520
80	1.241	1.706	1.751	2.283		
100	1.036	1.453	1.168	1.594	1.386	1.830
120	0.961	1.349	1.027	1.417	1.114	1.507
140	0.927	1.290	0.969	1.332	1.018	1.381
160	0.912	1.253	0.941	1.282	0.973	1.313
180	0.907	1.227	0.929	1.247	0.952	1.270
200	0.908	1.207	0.925	1.223	0.942	1.240
220	0.912	1.192	0.926	1.205	0.940	1.219
240	0.918	1.180	0.929	1.191	0.941	1.202

Viscosity $\eta \cdot 10^7$ ($N \cdot s/m^2$) of Freon-22 (monochlorodifluoromethane) at different temperatures and pressures [110]

p, bar \ t, °C →	0	20	40	60	80	100	120	140	160	180	200
2	122	129	136	143	150	156	163	170	177	183	190
4	134	137	140	145	151	157	164	170	177	183	189
6		145	146	148	153	159	165	171	178	184	189
8		154	151	151	154	160	166	172	178	184	190

continued

p, bar \ t, °C →	0	20	40	60	80	100	120	140	160	180	200
10			158	157	159	163	168	174	179	185	191
12			164	163	164	167	171	176	181	187	193
14			169	168	169	171	175	178	183	188	195
16				174	174	176	179	181	185	191	197
18				181	181	181	183	185	189	195	200
20				187	186	187	188	190	193	198	203

TRICHLOROTRIFLUOROETHANE (FREON-113) ($C_2F_3Cl_3$)

Molecular weight 187.39

$t_{boil} = 47.68\ °C$ at $p = 1$ atm; $t_{melt} = -36.6\ °C$;

$t_{cr} = 214.1\ °C$; $p_{cr} = 34.12$ bar; $v_{cr} = 1.735\ dm^3/kg$

Thermodynamic properties of saturated trichlorotrifluoroethane [105]:
v' (dm^3/kg), v'' (m^3/kg), i and r (kJ/kg) and s (kJ/kg · deg)

t, °C	p, bar	v'	v''	i'	i''	r	s'	s''
−30	0.0283	0.5925	3.798	473.25	640.13	166.88	0.8966	1.5828
−25	0.0386	0.5964	2.838	477.64	643.19	165.55	0.9142	1.5811
−20	0.0520	0.6004	2.149	482.04	646.24	164.20	0.9318	1.5803
−15	0.0690	0.6044	1.649	486.48	649.34	162.86	0.9493	1.5803
−10	0.0905	0.6085	1.281	490.96	652.44	161.48	0.9765	1.5803
−5	0.1172	0.6127	1.006	495.48	655.58	160.10	0.9832	1.5803
0	0.1500	0.6169	0.7993	500.00	658.68	158.68	1.0000	1.5807
5	0.1902	0.6212	0.6409	504.56	661.82	157.26	1.0163	1.5815
10	0.2387	0.6257	0.5186	509.17	665.00	155.83	1.0327	1.5828
15	0.2968	0.6302	0.4234	513.82	668.18	154.36	1.0490	1.5845
20	0.3657	0.6348	0.3485	518.46	671.36	152.90	1.0649	1.5866
25	0.4469	0.6395	0.2892	523.19	674.63	151.44	1.0808	1.5887
30	0.5420	0.6443	0.2416	527.93	677.86	149.93	1.0967	1.5912
35	0.6526	0.6493	0.2032	532.74	681.16	148.42	1.1126	1.5941
40	0.7802	0.6543	0.1720	537.56	684.47	146.91	1.1281	1.5974
45	0.9269	0.6596	0.1465	542.41	687.78	145.37	1.1436	1.6004
50	1.0943	0.6649	0.1255	547.35	691.17	143.82	1.1581	1.6037
55	1.285	0.6704	0.1080	552.34	694.60	142.26	1.1742	1.6075
60	1.499	0.6761	0.0934	557.32	697.99	140.67	1.1892	1.6117
65	1.741	0.6819	0.0812	562.38	701.47	139.09	1.2043	1.6155
70	2.012	0.6878	0.0708	567.53	704.99	137.46	1.2190	1.6196
75	2.314	0.6939	0.0621	572.68	708.50	135.82	1.2378	1.6238
80	2.651	0.7002	0.0546	577.92	712.10	134.18	1.2483	1.6284

Density $\rho \cdot 10^{-3}$ (kg/m^3) of liquid trichlorotrifluoroethane [111]

t, °C \ p, bar →	5	10	15	20	25	30	35
20	1.586	1.586	1.587	1.588	1.589	1.590	1.591
30	1.561	1.561	1.562	1.563	1.564	1.565	1.566
40	1.535	1.536	1.537	1.538	1.539	1.541	1.542
50	1.510	1.512	1.513	1.514	1.515	1.517	1.518
60	1.485	1.486	1.487	1.489	1.490	1.492	1.494
70	1.459	1.460	1.462	1.464	1.465	1.468	1.469
80	1.432	1.434	1.436	1.437	1.439	1.441	1.444
90	1.403	1.405	1.408	1.410	1.412	1.415	1.417
100	1.372	1.375	1.378	1.381	1.384	1.387	1.390
110		1.347	1.350	1.353	1.355	1.359	1.362
120		1.314	1.318	1.321	1.325	1.328	1.333
130			1.284	1.287	1.292	1.296	1.300

continued

t, °C \ p, bar →	5	10	15	20	25	30	35
140			1.246	1.252	1.257	1.263	1.268
150			1.207	1.213	1.219	1.225	1.232
160				1.171	1.181	1.189	1.195
170				1.120	1.134	1.144	1.153
180					1.081	1.093	1.103
185					1.051	1.063	1.073
190						1.030	1.041
195						0.995	1.009
200							0.975
205							0.934

Heat capacity $c_p{}^0$ of trichlorotrifluoroethane gas [105]

t, °C	0	25	50	75	100
$c_p{}^0$, kcal/kg · deg	0.149	0.155	0.160	0.166	0.172

Heat capacity c_p (kJ/kg · deg) of liquid trichlorotrifluoroethane [111]

t, °C \ p, bar →	5	10	15	20	25	30	35
−20	0.904	0.904	0.900	0.900	0.896	0.896	0.892
−10	0.913	0.913	0.908	0.904	0.904	0.900	0.900
0	0.925	0.921	0.917	0.913	0.913	0.908	0.908
10	0.934	0.929	0.925	0.921	0.917	0.913	0.913
20	0.946	0.942	0.938	0.929	0.925	0.921	0.921
30	0.955	0.950	0.946	0.938	0.934	0.929	0.925
40	0.963	0.959	0.955	0.946	0.942	0.938	0.934
50	0.976	0.971	0.963	0.958	0.949	0.946	0.942
60	0.988	0.980	0.971	0.966	0.958	0.954	0.945
70	1.00	0.992	0.984	0.975	0.966	0.962	0.954
80	1.01	1.00	0.996	0.987	0.975	0.970	0.962
90	1.03	1.01	1.01	0.999	0.987	0.979	0.970
100	1.05	1.03	1.02	1.01	1.00	0.991	0.983
110		1.05	1.04	1.03	1.02	1.00	0.996
120		1.08	1.06	1.05	1.03	1.02	1.01
130			1.08	1.07	1.06	1.04	1.03
140			1.12	1.10	1.08	1.07	1.05
150			1.16	1.13	1.11	1.09	1.07
160				1.17	1.15	1.12	1.10
170				1.22	1.19	1.16	1.13
180					1.26	1.21	1.18
185					1.34	1.24	1.19
190						1.30	1.22
195						1.40	1.26
200							1.33
205							1.52

Enthalpy i (kJ/kg) of liquid trichlorotrifluoroethane [111]

t, °C \ p, bar →	5	10	15	20	25	30	35
−20	481.82	482.02	482.32	482.72	483.02	483.32	486.09
−10	490.92	491.12	491.42	491.72	492.02	492.33	492.53
0	500.38	500.44	500.73	500.90	501.15	501.37	501.58
10	509,59	509.69	509.89	510.07	510.32	510.49	510.65

continued

t, °C \ p, bar →	5	10	15	20	25	30	35
20	519.01	519.10	519.27	519.36	519.57	519.70	519.82
30	528.43	528.47	528.55	528.81	528.90	528.98	529.07
40	538.10	538.14	538.18	538.22	538.27	538.31	538.35
50	547.77	547.73	547.74	547.77	547.77	547.73	547.73
60	557.78	557.73	557.56	557.43	557.35	557.23	557.19
70	567.49	567.36	567.19	567.06	566.98	566.80	566.68
80	577.66	577.44	577.10	576.89	576.72	576.46	576.25
90	587.83	587.45	587.12	586.89	586.55	586.24	585.91
100	598.17	597.70	597.32	596.85	596.52	596.11	595.65
10		608.94	607.74	607.13	606.63	606.10	605.51
20		618.58	618.04	617.50	616.92	616.34	615.67
130			628.94	628.01	627.39	626.58	625.75
140			640.01	638.92	638.08	637.10	636.10
150			651.31	650.11	649.02	647.87	646.66
160				661.56	660.27	658.91	657.57
170				673.35	671.89	670.29	668.57
180					684.10	682.09	680.03
185					690.04	688.07	685.91
190						694.72	691.96
195						701.43	698.16
200							704.66
205							711.80

Entropy s (kJ/kg · deg) of liquid trichlorotrifluoroethane [111]

t, °C \ p, bar →	5	10	15	20	25	30	35
−20	0.9302	0.9302	0.9302	0.9302	0.9292	0.9292	0.0929
−10	0.9652	0.9652	0.9652	0.9652	0.9652	0.9642	0.9642
0	0.9992	0.9992	0.9992	0.9992	0.9992	0.9982	0.9982
10	1.0331	1.0327	1.0322	1.0318	1.0314	1.0314	1.0310
20	1.0657	1.0649	1.0645	1.0641	1.0636	1.0632	1.0628
30	1.0976	1.0967	1.0963	1.0955	1.0950	1.0945	1.0937
40	1.1281	1.1273	1.1269	1.1260	1.1256	1.1247	1.1238
50	1.1595	1.1574	1.1570	1.1561	1.1552	1.1544	1.1536
60	1.1892	1.1876	1.1867	1.1853	1.1845	1.1833	1.1824
70	1.2181	1.2165	1.2152	1.2138	1.2130	1.2116	1.2104
80	1.2470	1.2453	1.2437	1.2422	1.2405	1.2393	1.2380
90	1.2755	1.2730	1.2717	1.2698	1.2686	1.2665	1.2652
100	1.3039	1.3009	1.2985	1.2971	1.2954	1.2933	1.2916
110		1.3286	1.3235	1.3243	1.3218	1.3197	1.3180
120		1.3558	1.3528	1.3506	1.3480	1.3459	1.3439
130			1.3801	1.3773	1.3744	1.3719	1.3694
140			1.4073	1.4041	1.4008	1.3974	1.3949
150			1.4341	1.4304	1.4267	1.4232	1.4199
160				1.4572	1.4530	1.4487	1.4454
170				1.4843	1.4797	1.4747	1.4713
180					1.5067	1.5014	1.4968
185					1.5207	1.5147	1.5097
190						1.5285	1.5231
195						1.5426	1.5364
200							1.5501
205							1.5651

Viscosity of trichlorotrifluoroethane at $p = 1$ bar [105]

t, °C	−30	−20	−10	0	25	50
$\eta \cdot 10^7$, N · s/m²	89.4	91.8	94.2	96.7	102.6	108.5

Viscosity η (N · s/m²) of liquid trichlorotrifluoroethane [109]

T, °K	$\eta \cdot 10^3$	T, °K	$\eta \cdot 10^3$	T, °K	$\eta \cdot 10^3$	T, °K	$\eta \cdot 10^3$
241	1.69	265	1.08	289	0.744	313	0.542
245	1.56	269	1.01	293	0.704	317	0.517
249	1.44	273	0.948	297	0.666	321	0.493
253	1.34	277	0.890	301	0.631	325	0.471
257	1.24	281	0.837	305	0.599	329	0.451
261	1.16	285	0.789	309	0.570	333	0.431

Thermal conductivity of trichlorotrifluoroethane gas at a pressure $p \approx 1$ bar [356]

t, °C	0	10	20	30	40	50	60	70	80	90	100	110
$\lambda \cdot 10^4$, W/m · deg	74	79	84	90	93	98	102	108	112	117	122	126

Thermal conductivity λ of liquid trichlorotrifluoroethane [107]

t, °C	−20	−10	0	10	20	30	40	50	60	70	80	90
λ, W/m deg	0.0867	0.0844	0.0822	0.0799	0.0777	0.0754	0.0732	0.0709	0.0687	0.0664	0.0642	0.0619

DICHLOROTETRAFLUOROETHANE (FREON-114) ($C_2F_4Cl_2$) [108]

Molecular weight 170.91

$t_{boil} = 3.50$ °C at $Op = 1$ atm; $t_{melt} = -94.0$ °C; $t_{cr} = 145.8$ °C;
$p_{cr} = 32.7$ bar; $v_{cr} = 1.715$ dm³/kg; $\sigma = 13.0$ erg/cm² at 26°C

Thermodynamic properties of saturated dichlorotetrafluoroethane (freon-114) [105]:
v (dm³/kg), v'' (m³/kg), i and r (kJ/kg) and s (kJ/kg · deg)

t, °C	p, bar	v'	v''	i'	i''	r	s'	s''
−40	0.131	0.6060	0.8468	466.92	613.63	146.71	0.8742	1.5037
−35	0.175	0.6111	0.6554	470.72	616.60	145.88	0.8902	1.5028
−30	0.226	0.6162	0.5142	474.52	619.58	145.06	0.9062	1.5024
−25	0.291	0.6213	0.4069	478.52	622.59	144.07	0.9212	1.5020
−20	0.371	0.6266	0.3250	482.62	625.60	142.98	0.9372	1.5016
−15	0.466	0.6321	0.2627	486.82	628.70	141.88	0.9532	1.5024
−10	0.581	0.6376	0.2139	491.12	631.72	140.60	0.9682	1.5028
− 5	0.718	0.6434	0.1754	495.52	634.81	139.29	0.9842	1.5041
0	0.880	0.6494	1.1450	500.00	637.96	137.96	1.0000	1.5049
5	1.069	0.6554	0.1207	504.52	641.89	137.37	1.0152	1.5062
10	1.289	0.6617	0.1013	509.32	644.24	134.92	1.0314	1.5079
15	1.544	0.6681	0.0854	514.12	647.42	133.30	1.0469	1.5095
20	1.836	0.6749	0.0725	519.12	650.60	131.48	1.0628	1.5112
25	2.169	0.6818	0.0619	524.12	653.78	129.66	1.0787	1.5133
30	2.548	0.6888	0.0531	529.32	657.05	127.73	1.0942	1.5152
35	2.974	0.6961	0.0458	534.72	660.31	125.59	1.1101	1.5179
40	3.453	0.7040	0.0397	540.02	663.58	123.56	1.1260	1.5204
45	3.988	0.7119	0.0345	545.52	666.84	121.32	1.1415	1.5229
50	4.583	0.7203	0.0302	551.22	670.19	118.97	1.1570	1.5254
55	5.239	0.7288	0.0265	556.82	673.50	116.68	1.1725	1.5280
60	5.963	0.7381	0.0233	562.62	676.89	114.27	1.1842	1.5309

Heat capacity $c_p{}^0$ of dichlorotetrafluoroethane [105]

t, °C	−20	−10	0	25	50	75	100
bar $c_p{}^0$, kJ/kg · deg	0.6117	0.6209	0.6301	0.6536	0.6770	0.7004	0.7243

Viscosity η ($N \cdot s/m^2$) of liquid dichlorotetrafluoroethane [109]

T, °K	$\eta \cdot 10^3$	T, °K	$\eta \cdot 10^3$	T, °K	$\eta \cdot 10^3$	T, °K	$\eta \cdot 10^3$
209	1.36	241	0.759	273	0.484	305	0.339
213	1.26	245	0.712	277	0.461	309	0.326
217	1.16	249	0.671	281	0.439	313	0.314
221	1.07	253	0.632	285	0.420	317	0.302
225	0.996	257	0.597	289	0.401	321	0.292
229	0.927	261	0.565	293	0.384	325	0.281
233	0.865	265	0.536	297	0.368	329	0.272
237	0.809	269	0.509	301	0.353	333	0.263

Heat capacity λ (W/m · deg) of liquid dichlorotetrafluoroethane [107]

t, °C	λ	t, °C	λ	t, °C	λ	t, °C	λ
−40	0.0870	0	0.0760	40	0.0644	80	0.0523
−30	0.0842	10	0.0729	50	0.0616	90	0.0487
−20	0.0814	20	0.0702	60	0.0587	100	0.0450
−10	0.0786	30	0.0673	70	0.0556		

MONOCHLORODIFLUOROETHANE (FREON-142) ($C_2H_3F_2Cl$)

Molecular weight 100.48

$t_{boil} = -9.25$ °C at $p = 1$ atm; $t_{melt} = -130.8$ °C;

$t_{cr} = 136.8$ °C; $p_{cr} = 41.5$ bar; $v_{cr} = 2.32$ dm^3/kg

Thermodynamic properties of monochlorodifluoroethane (freon-142) in ideal state [108]: c_p^0 (kJ/kg · deg), i^0 (kJ/kg) and s^0 (kJ/kg · deg)

T, °K	c_p^0	i^0	s^0	T, °K	c_p^0	i^0	s^0
250	0.7382	121.2	2.918	400	0.9882	251.8	3.319
298	0.8228	159.0	3.054	500	1.118	356.2	3.555
300	0.8261	160.6	3.060	600	1.215	473.9	3.767

Thermodynamic properties of saturated monochlorodifluoroethane (freon-142) [105]: v' (dm^3/kg), v'' (m^3/kg), i (kJ/kg) and s (kJ/kg · deg)

t, °C	p, bar	v'	v''	i'	i''	r	s'	s''
−30	0.4026	0.8013	0.4851	464.38	696.65	232.27	0.8622	1.8173
−25	0.5118	0.8085	0.3879	470.15	699.92	229.77	0.8852	1.8114
−20	0.6425	0.8159	0.3138	475.98	703.50	227.52	0.9092	1.8064
−15	0.7993	0.8238	0.2559	481.89	706.28	224.39	0.9322	1.8014
−10	0.9836	0.8322	0.2107	487.85	709.42	221.57	0.9552	1.7967
−5	1.200	0.8414	0.1747	493.90	712.48	218.58	0.9772	1.7926
0	1.452	0.8511	0.1460	500.00	715.41	215.41	1.0000	1.7884
5	1.745	0.8615	0.1228	506.15	718.26	212.11	1.0222	1.7846
10	2.079	0.8724	0.1039	512.39	721.06	208.67	1.0444	1.7813
15	2.463	0.8841	0.0884	518.71	723.74	205.03	1.0662	1.7779
20	2.896	0.8962	0.07659	525.12	726.34	201.22	1.0879	1.7746
25	3.387	0.9089	0.06509	531.53	728.85	197.32	1.1097	1.7712
30	3.938	0.9222	0.05627	538.06	731.32	193.26	1.1310	1.7683
35	4.557	0.9363	0.04883	544.63	733.67	189.04	1.1524	1.7658
40	5.245	0.9508	0.04257	551.29	736.01	184.72	1.1733	1.7633
45	6.012	0.9654	0.03722	557.99	738.23	180.24	1.1938	1.7603
50	6.857	0.9817	0.03267	564.77	740.36	175.59	1.2148	1.7582
55	7.794	0.9984	0.02877	571.64	742.42	170.78	1.2357	1.7561
60	3.819	1.015	0.02535	578.54	744.72	166.18	1.2554	1.7540

continued

t, °C	p, bar	v'	v''	i'	i''	r	s'	s''
65	9.954	1.032	0.02239	585.54	746.64	161.10	1.2755	1.7515
70	11.18	1.051	0.01984	592.61	748.53	155.92	1.2952	1.7499
75	12.53	1.070	0.01760	599.73	750.29	150.56	1.3148	1.7473
80	14.00	1.090	0.01566	606.92	751.96	145.04	1.3349	1.7457

Viscosity η ($N \cdot s/m^2$) of liquid monochlorodifluoroethane [109]

T, °K	$\eta \cdot 10^3$	T, °K	$\eta \cdot 10^3$	T, °K	$\eta \cdot 10^3$	T, °K	$\eta \cdot 10^3$
241	0.515	265	0.405	289	0.331	313	0.278
245	0.494	269	0.390	293	0.321	317	0.271
249	0.473	273	0.377	297	0.311	321	0.265
253	0.454	277	0.364	301	0.303	325	0.258
257	0.436	281	0.352	305	0.294	329	0.253
261	0.420	285	0.341	309	0.286	333	0.246

Thermal conductivity of liquid monochlorodifluoroethane [107]

t, °C	−80	−70	−60	−50	−40	−30	−20	−10	0
λ, W/m · deg	0.126	0.122	0.118	0.115	0.111	0.107	0.103	0.0988	0.0948
t, °C	10	20	30	40	50	60	70	80	90
λ, W/m · deg	0.0909	0.0869	0.0830	0.0790	0.0751	0.0711	0.0688	0.0618	0.0561

OCTAFLUORO-CYCLOBUTANE (C_4F_8)

Molecular weight 200.04

$t_{boil} = -6.42$ °C at $p = 1$ atm; $t_{melt} = -40.2$ °C;
$t_{cr} = 115$ °C; $p_{cr} = 27.83$ bar; $v_{cr} = 1.613$ dm^3/kg

Thermodynamic properties of saturated octafluoro-cyclobutane [113]:
v (m^3/kg), i and r (kJ/kg) and s (kJ/kg · deg)

t, °C	p, bar	$v' \cdot 10^3$	v''	i'	i''	r	s'	s''
−40	0.1926	0.5776	0.4954	459.57	587.35	127.77	0.8405	1.3885
−38	0.2158	0.5799	0.4453	461.52	588.64	127.12	0.8488	1.3894
−36	0.2412	0.5822	0.4011	463.47	589.93	126.46	0.8570	1.3903
−34	0.2691	0.5845	0.3621	465.43	591.23	125.80	0.8653	1.3913
−32	0.2995	0.5869	0.3275	467.39	592.53	125.13	0.8734	1.3923
−30	0.3326	0.5893	0.2968	469.37	593.83	124.46	0.8816	1.3935
−28	0.3687	0.5917	0.2695	471.35	595.13	123.78	0.8897	1.3946
−26	0.4078	0.5941	0.2452	473.34	596.44	123.10	0.8978	1.3959
−24	0.4502	0.5966	0.2235	475.35	597.75	122.41	0.9058	1.3971
−22	0.4960	0.5991	0.2040	477.35	599.07	121.71	0.9139	1.3985
−20	0.5455	0.6016	0.1866	479.37	600.38	121.01	0.9219	1.3999
−18	0.5989	0.6041	0.1709	481.40	601.70	120.30	0.9298	1.4013
−16	0.6564	0.6067	0.1568	483.43	603.02	119.59	0.9377	1.4028
−14	0.7181	0.6093	0.1440	485.47	604.34	118.87	0.9456	1.4043
−12	0.7844	0.6119	0.1325	487.52	605.66	118.14	0.9535	1.4059
−10	0.8554	0.6145	0.1221	489.58	606.98	117.40	0.9613	1.4075
−8	0.9313	0.6172	0.1127	491.65	608.31	116.66	0.9691	1.4091
−6	1.012	0.6199	0.1041	493.72	609.63	115.91	0.9769	1.4108
−4	1.099	0.6227	0.09635	495.81	610.96	115.15	0.9847	1.4125

continued

t, °C	p, bar	$v' \cdot 10^3$	v''	i'	i''	r	s'	s''
−2	1.191	0.6255	0.08926	497.90	612.28	114.38	0.9924	1.4142
0	1.290	0.6283	0.08279	500.00	613.61	113.61	1.0000	1.4160
2	1.394	0.6312	0.07687	502.10	614.94	112.84	1.0077	1.4178
4	1.505	0.6341	0.07147	504.21	616.26	112.05	1.0153	1.4196
6	1.622	0.6370	0.06652	506.34	617.59	111.25	1.0230	1.4215
8	1.747	0.6400	0.06198	508.48	618.92	110.44	1.0306	1.4234
10	1.878	0.6430	0.05781	510.63	620.25	109.62	1.0382	1.4253
12	2.018	0.6461	0.05397	512.78	621.57	108.79	1.0457	1.4272
14	2.165	0.6492	0.05044	514.94	622.89	107.95	1.0532	1.4292
16	2.320	0.6524	0.04718	517.11	624.21	107.10	1.0607	1.4311
18	2.483	0.6557	0.04417	519.29	625.53	106.53	1.0682	1.4331
20	2.655	0.6590	0.04139	521.47	626.85	105.39	1.0756	1.4351
22	2.836	0.6624	0.03882	523.66	628.17	104.51	1.0830	1.4371
24	3.046	0.6659	0.03644	525.86	629.49	103.62	1.0904	1.4391
26	3.226	0.6694	0.03423	528.07	630.80	102.72	1.0978	1.4412
28	3.436	0.6730	0.03217	530.29	632.11	101.81	1.1051	1.4432
30	3.656	0.6766	0.03027	532.52	633.41	100.89	1.1125	1.4453
32	3.886	0.6803	0.02849	534.76	634.72	99.96	1.1198	1.4474
34	4.127	0.6842	0.02684	537.01	636.02	99.01	1.1271	1.4494
36	4.379	0.6882	0.02530	539.26	637.31	98.05	1.1343	1.4515
38	4.643	0.6922	0.02386	541.53	638.61	97.08	1.1416	1.4536
40	4.918	0.6963	0.02252	543.80	639.89	96.09	1.1488	1.4556
50	6.482	0.7187	0.01698	555.33	646.25	90.91	1.1847	1.4660
60	8.393	0.7447	0.01293	567.15	652.41	85.25	1.2203	1.4762
70	10.698	0.7759	0.009902	579.35	658.28	78.93	1.2558	1.4859
80	13.453	0.8155	0.007579	592.07	663.71	71.64	1.2917	1.4946
90	16.720	0.8693	0.005748	605.58	668.42	62.84	1.3287	1.5017
100	20.574	0.9507	0.004244	620.47	671.78	51.31	1.3682	1.5057
102	21.423	0.9722	0.003967	623.70	672.16	48.46	1.3767	1.5058
104	22.299	0.9965	0.003695	627.06	672.40	45.34	1.3853	1.5055
106	23.204	1.024	0.003425	630.56	672.43	41.87	1.3943	1.5047
108	24.139	1.057	0.003152	634.28	672.19	37.91	1.4038	1.5033
110	25.105	1.098	0.002869	638.27	671.55	33.27	1.4140	1.5009
112	26.101	1.157	0.002561	642.79	670.18	27.39	1.4255	1.4966
115	27.828	1.613	0.001613	658.1	658.1	0.00	1.467	1.467

Thermodynamic properties of octafluoro-cyclobutane at different temperatures and pressures [113] v (m^3/kg), i (kJ/kg) and s (kJ/kg · deg)

t, °C	v	i	s	v	i	s
		p=0.5 bar			p=1 bar	
−20	0.2041	600.48	1.4038			
−10	0.2131	607.76	1.4320			
0	0.2220	615.18	1.4597	0.1083	614.20	1.4282
10	0.2308	622.77	1.4870	0.1130	621.88	1.4558
20	0.2395	630.51	1.5138	0.1176	629.71	1.4830
30	0.2482	638.40	1.5403	0.1221	637.68	1.5097
40	0.2568	646.43	1.5664	0.1266	645.78	1.5360
50	0.2654	654.62	1.5921	0.1311	654.02	1.5619
60	0.2740	662.95	1.6175	0.1355	662.40	1.5875
70	0.2825	671.42	1.6424	0.1399	670.92	1.6127
80	0.2910	680.03	1.6673	0.1442	679.57	1.6375
90	0.2995	688.78	1.6917	0.1486	688.35	1.6620
100	0.3080	697.66	1.7158	0.1529	697.26	1.6862
110	0.3165	706.67	1.7396	0.1572	706.30	1.7101
120	0.3249	715.80	1.7632	0.1615	715.46	1.7337
130	0.3333	725.07	1.7864	0.1658	724.74	1.7571
140	0.3418	734.45	1.8094	0.1700	734.15	1.7801
150	0.3502	743.95	1.8322	0.1743	743.66	1.8029
160	0.3586	753.57	1.8546	0.1786	753.30	1.8254
170	0.3670	763.30	1.8768	0.1828	763.04	1.8476

continued

t, °C	v	i	s	v	i	s
180	0.3754	773.14	1.8988	0.1870	772.90	1.8696
190	0.3838	783.09	1.9205	0.1913	782.86	1.8913
200	0.3922	793.14	1.9420	0.1955	792.92	1.9128
210	0.4005	803.29	1.9632	0.1997	803.09	1.9341
220	0.4089	813.55	1.9842	0.2039	813.35	1.9551
230	0.4173	823.90	2.0050	0.2082	823.70	1.9759
240	0.4257	834.34	2.0255	0.2124	834.15	1.9965
250	0.4340	844.87	2.0459	0.2166	844.69	2.0168
260	0.4424	855.49	2.0660	0.2208	855.32	2.0369
270	0.4507	866.20	2.0859	0.2250	866.04	2.0568
280	0.4591	876.99	2.1056	0.2292	876.83	2.0765
290	0.4675	887.86	2.1250	0.2334	887.71	2.0960
300	0.4758	898.81	2.1443	0.2376	898.66	2.1153
310	0.4842	909.83	2.1634	0.2418	909.69	2.1344
320	0.4925	920.93	2.1822	0.2460	920.79	2.1533
330	0.5009	932.10	2.2009	0.2502	931.97	2.1719
340	0.5092	943.34	2.2194	0.2544	943.21	2.1904
350	0.5176	954.64	2.2377	0.2586	954.52	2.2087
360	0.5259	966.01	2.2558	0.2627	965.89	2.2268
370	0.5342	977.44	2.2737	0.2669	977.32	2.2447
380	0.5426	988.93	2.2914	0.2711	988.82	2.2625
390	0.5509	1000.48	2.3090	0.2753	1000.37	2.2800
		$p=2$ bar			$p=4$ bar	
20	0.05653	628.03	1.4499			
30	0.05904	636.16	1.4772			
40	0.06147	644.42	1.5040	0.02871	641.42	1.4680
50	0.06386	652.79	1.5303	0.03011	650.10	1.4953
60	0.06621	661.28	1.5562	0.03146	658.86	1.5220
70	0.06853	669.89	1.5817	0.03277	667.69	1.5481
80	0.07082	678.62	1.6067	0.03404	676.62	1.5727
90	0.07308	687.47	1.6315	0.03529	685.64	1.5989
100	0.07533	696.45	1.6558	0.03651	694.76	1.6237
110	0.07756	705.54	1.6799	0.03771	707.99	1.6481
120	0.07978	714.76	1.7036	0.03889	713.31	1.6721
130	0.08198	724.09	1.7271	0.04007	722.73	1.6958
140	0.08418	733.53	1.7502	0.04122	732.26	1.7191
150	0.08636	743.09	1.7731	0.04237	741.90	1.7422
160	0.08853	752.75	1.7956	0.04351	751.64	1.7649
170	0.09070	762.53	1.8179	0.04464	761.47	1.7874
180	0.09286	772.41	1.8400	0.04577	771.41	1.8096
190	0.09502	782.39	1.8618	0.04689	781.45	1.8315
200	0.09717	792.48	1.8833	0.04800	791.58	1.8531
210	0.09931	802.66	1.9046	0.04911	801.81	1.8745
220	0.1015	812.94	1.9257	0.05021	812.13	1.8956
230	0.1036	823.32	1.9465	0.05131	822.54	1.9165
240	0.1057	833.78	1.9671	0.05241	833.04	1.9372
250	0.1079	844.34	1.9875	0.05350	843.62	1.9576
260	0.1100	854.98	2.0076	0.05459	854.29	1.9778
270	0.1121	865.71	2.0275	0.05568	865.05	1.9978
280	0.1142	876.51	2.0473	0.05676	875.88	2.0176
290	0.1164	887.4	2.0668	0.05785	886.79	2.0371
300	0.1185	898.37	2.0861	0.05893	897.77	2.0565
310	0.1206	909.41	2.1052	0.06000	908.83	2.0756
320	0.1227	920.52	2.1241	0.06108	919.96	2.0945
330	0.1248	931.70	2.1428	0.06216	931.16	2.1132
340	0.1269	942.95	2.1613	0.06323	942.43	2.1318
350	0.1291	954.27	2.1796	0.06431	953.76	2.1501
360	0.1312	965.65	2.1977	0.06538	965.16	2.1682
370	0.1333	977.09	2.2156	0.06645	976.62	2.1862
380	0.1354	988.59	2.2334	0.06752	988.13	2.2040
390	0.1375	1000.15	2.2509	0.06859	999.70	2.2215

continued

t, °C	v	i	s	v	i	s
		$p=6$ bar			$p=8$ bar	
50	0.01871	647.05	1.4712			
60	0.01976	656.16	1.4990	0.01379	653.07	1.4798
70	0.02076	665.29	1.5260	0.01467	662.60	1.5080
80	0.02172	674.46	1.5523	0.01549	672.08	1.5352
90	0.02263	683.68	1.5780	0.01627	681.55	1.5617
100	0.02352	692.97	1.6033	0.01700	691.05	1.5875
110	0.02439	702.34	1.6281	0.01771	700.59	1.6127
120	0.02524	711.79	1.6524	0.01839	710.19	1.6374
130	0.02607	721.32	1.6764	0.01906	719.85	1.6617
140	0.02689	730.95	1.6999	0.01971	729.59	1.6855
150	0.02770	740.67	1.7232	0.02035	739.41	1.7090
160	0.02850	750.49	1.7461	0.02098	749.30	1.7321
170	0.02928	760.39	1.7687	0.02160	759.28	1.7549
180	0.03006	770.39	1.7910	0.02221	769.35	1.7774
190	0.03084	780.48	1.8130	0.02281	779.50	1.7995
200	0.03161	790.67	1.8348	0.02341	789.73	1.8214
210	0.03237	800.94	1.8563	0.02400	800.05	1.8430
220	0.03313	811.29	1.8775	0.02459	810.46	1.8643
230	0.03388	821.74	1.8985	0.02517	820.95	1.8853
240	0.03463	832.28	1.9192	0.02575	831.52	1.9061
250	0.03538	842.90	1.9397	0.02632	842.17	1.9267
260	0.03613	853.60	1.9600	0.02689	852.90	1.9470
270	0.03687	864.38	1.9800	0.02746	863.71	1.9671
280	0.03761	875.24	1.9998	0.02803	874.59	1.9870
290	0.03834	886.17	2.0194	0.02860	885.55	2.0066
300	0.03908	897.18	2.0388	0.02916	896.58	2.0260
310	0.03981	908.26	2.0580	0.02972	907.68	2.0452
320	0.04054	919.41	2.0770	0.03027	918.85	2.0642
330	0.04127	930.63	2.0957	0.03083	930.09	2.0830
340	0.04200	941.91	2.1142	0.03139	941.39	2.1016
350	0.04273	953.25	2.1326	0.03194	952.76	2.1200
360	0.04346	964.67	2.1508	0.03249	964.18	2.1382
370	0.04418	976.14	2.1688	0.03304	975.67	2.1562
380	0.04490	987.67	2.1865	0.03359	987.21	2.1740
390	0.04562	999.26	2.2041	0.03414	998.81	2.1916
		$p=10$ bar			$p=15$ bar	
70	0.01091	659.50	1.4915			
80	0.01168	669.42	1.5201			
90	0.01239	679.23	1.5474	0.006993	671.91	1.5144
100	0.01305	688.98	1.5739	0.007627	682.83	1.5440
110	0.01367	698.73	1.5997	0.008182	693.39	1.5720
120	0.01426	708.50	1.6249	0.008686	703.78	1.5987
130	0.01484	718.31	1.6495	0.009155	714.07	1.6246
140	0.01539	728.17	1.6737	0.009590	724.31	1.6497
150	0.01593	738.09	1.6974	0.01001	734.56	1.6742
160	0.01646	748.08	1.7207	0.01042	744.84	1.6982
170	0.01698	758.14	1.7437	0.01081	755.14	1.7217
180	0.01749	768.28	1.7663	0.01119	765.49	1.7448
190	0.01799	778.49	1.7886	0.01156	775.89	1.7675
200	0.01849	788.78	1.8106	0.01192	786.34	1.7898
210	0.01898	799.16	1.8323	0.01228	796.85	1.8118
220	0.01946	809.60	1.8537	0.01263	807.42	1.8335
230	0.01994	820.14	1.8748	0.01297	818.06	1.8548
240	0.02042	830.74	1.8957	0.01331	828.77	1.8759
250	0.02089	841.43	1.9163	0.01364	839.55	1.8967
260	0.02135	852.19	1.9367	0.01398	850.40	1.9173
270	0.02182	863.03	1.9569	0.01430	861.32	1.9375
280	0.02228	873.94	1.9768	0.01463	872.30	1.9576
290	0.02274	884.92	1.9965	0.01495	883.35	1.9774
300	0.02320	895.98	2.0159	0.01527	894.47	1.9969
310	0.02366	907.10	2.0351	0.01559	905.65	2.0163
320	0.02411	918.29	2.0542	0.01591	916.89	2.0354

continued

t, °C	v	i	s	v	i	s
330	0.02457	929.55	2.0730	0.01622	928.20	2.0545
340	0.02502	940.87	2.0916	0.01654	939.57	2.0730
350	0.02547	952.25	2.1100	0.01685	951.00	2.0915
360	0.02592	963.70	2.1282	0.01716	962.48	2.1098
370	0.02636	975.20	2.1463	0.01747	974.02	2.1279
380	0.02681	986.76	2.1641	0.01778	985.62	2.1458
390	0.02726	998.37	2.1817	0.01809	997.28	2.1635
		$p=20$ bar			$p=25$ bar	
100	0.004561	673.43	1.5108			
110	0.005252	686.30	1.5449	0.002939	672.25	1.5028
120	0.005783	697.94	1.5749	0.003860	689.76	1.5480
130	0.006238	709.07	1.6028	0.004395	702.79	1.5807
140	0.006647	719.93	1.6294	0.004822	714.74	1.6100
150	0.007023	730.65	1.6551	0.005192	726.18	1.6373
160	0.007375	741.29	1.6799	0.005526	737.35	1.6634
170	0.007709	751.90	1.7041	0.005835	748.37	1.6886
180	0.008029	762.50	1.7278	0.006124	759.30	1.7130
190	0.008337	773.11	1.7509	0.006399	770.18	1.7367
200	0.008636	783.75	1.7737	0.006662	781.05	1.7599
210	0.008926	794.43	1.7960	0.006916	791.92	1.7827
220	0.009209	805.15	1.8180	0.007161	802.81	1.8050
230	0.009485	815.92	1.8396	0.007400	813.73	1.8269
240	0.009759	826.75	1.8609	0.007633	824.68	1.8485
250	0.01003	837.64	1.8819	0.007861	835.68	1.8697
260	0.01029	848.58	1.9026	0.008085	846.72	1.8906
270	0.01055	859.58	1.9231	0.008304	857.82	1.9112
280	0.01081	870.64	1.9432	0.008521	868.96	1.9316
290	0.01106	881.76	1.9632	0.008734	880.16	1.9516
300	0.01131	892.95	1.9829	0.008945	891.42	1.9714
310	0.01156	904.19	2.0023	0.009153	902.72	1.9910
320	0.01181	915.49	2.0215	0.009360	914.08	2.0103
330	0.01206	926.85	2.0405	0.009564	925.50	2.0294
340	0.01230	938.27	2.0593	0.009766	936.97	2.0468
350	0.01254	949.74	2.0778	0.009967	948.49	2.0669
360	0.01278	961.27	2.0962	0.01017	960.06	2.0853
370	0.01302	972.85	2.1143	0.01036	971.69	2.1035
380	0.01326	984.48	2.1321	0.01056	983.36	2.1215
390	0.01350	996.16	2.1496	0.01076	995.09	2.1394
400	0.01373	1007.91	2.1676	0.01095	1006.86	2.1570
		$p=30$ bar			$p=40$ bar	
120	0.001898	668.82	1.4909	0.001065	646.73	1.4317
130	0.003022	693.88	1.5540	0.001267	665.05	1.4777
140	0.003541	708.27	1.5893	0.001812	688.85	1.5360
150	0.003938	720.96	1.6197	0.002309	707.37	1.5803
160	0.004275	732.93	1.6476	0.002684	722.29	1.6152
170	0.004575	744.50	1.6740	0.002991	735.66	1.6457
180	0.004849	755.85	1.6994	0.003256	748.23	1.6738
190	0.005105	767.07	1.7238	0.003494	760.34	1.7002
200	0.005347	778.21	1.7476	0.003713	772.17	1.7255
210	0.005578	789.30	1.7709	0.003917	783.82	1.7498
220	0.005799	800.39	1.7936	0.004109	795.35	1.7735
230	0.006013	811.47	1.8158	0.004292	806.82	1.7965
240	0.006220	822.57	1.8376	0.004468	818.24	1.8190
250	0.006422	833.69	1.8591	0.004637	829.64	1.8410
260	0.006619	844.85	1.8802	0.004801	841.05	1.8626
270	0.006812	856.04	1.9010	0.004960	852.46	1.8838
280	0.007001	867.28	1.9216	0.005116	863.89	1.9046
290	0.007187	878.56	1.9417	0.005268	875.34	1.9251
300	0.007371	889.88	1.9617	0.005417	886.83	1.9454
310	0.007552	901.26	1.9814	0.005563	898.35	1.9653
320	0.007730	912.68	2.0008	0.005707	909.90	1.9849
330	0.007907	924.15	2.0200	0.005848	921.49	2.0043

continued

t, °C	v	i	s	v	i	s
340	0.008081	935.68	2.0389	0.005988	933.13	2.0234
350	0.008254	947.25	2.0576	0.006126	944.80	2.0423
360	0.008426	958.87	2.0761	0.006262	956.52	2.0610
370	0.008596	970.54	2.0944	0.006397	968.27	2.0794
380	0.008764	982.26	2.1125	0.006531	980.07	2.0976
390	0.008932	994.01	2.1304	0.006663	991.91	2.1156
400	0.009098	1005.82	2.1480	0.006794	1003.79	2.1334
		$p=60$ bar			$p=80$ bar	
150	0.001217	685.44	1.5211			
160	0.001375	700.98	1.5573			
170	0.001577	716.84	1.5935			
180	0.001786	731.92	1.6272	0.001301	721.11	1.5968
190	0.001981	746.09	1.6581	0.001410	735.07	1.6272
200	0.002163	759.54	1.6869	0.001530	748.98	1.6569
210	0.002330	772.49	1.7139	0.001653	762.61	1.6854
220	0.002487	785.07	1.7397	0.001774	775.91	1.7127
230	0.002634	797.41	1.7645	0.001890	788.91	1.7388
240	0.002774	809.57	1.7884	0.002002	801.67	1.7639
250	0.002907	821.59	1.8116	0.002109	814.24	1.7882
260	0.003035	833.54	1.8343	0.002213	826.66	1.8117
270	0.003158	845.42	1.8563	0.002313	838.97	1.8346
280	0.003277	857.26	1.8779	0.002409	851.19	1.8569
290	0.003392	869.09	1.8991	0.002503	863.35	1.8786
300	0.003505	880.90	1.9199	0.002594	875.47	1.9000
310	0.003614	892.72	1.9404	0.002683	887.57	1.9209
320	0.003722	904.54	1.9605	0.002769	899.64	1.9414
330	0.003827	916.38	1.9803	0.002854	911.71	1.9616
340	0.003930	928.24	1.9998	0.002937	923.79	1.9815
350	0.004032	940.13	2.0190	0.003019	935.86	2.0010
360	0.004132	952.03	2.0379	0.003099	947.95	2.0202
370	0.004230	963.97	2.0567	0.003178	960.05	2.0392
380	0.004327	975.94	2.0751	0.003255	972.18	2.0579
390	0.004423	987.93	2.0933	0.003332	984.32	2.0764
400	0.004518	999.96	2.1113	0.003407	996.48	2.0946

t, °C	v	i	s	t, °C	v	i	s
			$p=100$ bar				
200	0.001274	742.80	1.6380	310	0.002154	883.03	1.9049
210	0.001348	755.94	1.6655	320	0.002226	895.32	1.9258
220	0.001429	769.12	1.6925	330	0.002297	907.58	1.9463
230	0.001513	782.24	1.7189	340	0.002366	919.83	1.9664
240	0.001598	795.24	1.7444	350	0.002435	932.08	1.9862
250	0.001683	808.09	1.7692	360	0.002502	944.32	2.0057
260	0.001766	820.81	1.7933	370	0.002567	956.57	2.0249
270	0.001848	833.41	1.8167	380	0.002632	968.83	2.0438
280	0.001927	845.92	1.8396	390	0.002696	981.10	2.0625
290	0.002005	858.34	1.8618	400	0.002759	993.38	2.0809
300	0.002089	870.71	1.8836				

Viscosity η ($N \cdot s/m^2$) of liquid octafluoro-cyclobutane [109]

T, °K	$\eta \cdot 10^3$	T, °K	$\eta \cdot 10^3$	T, °K	$\eta \cdot 10^3$	T, °K	$\eta \cdot 10^3$
245	0.907	269	0.601	293	0.426	317	0.318
249	0.843	273	0.565	297	0.404	321	0.304
253	0.784	277	0.532	301	0.384	325	0.291
257	0.731	281	0.502	305	0.366	329	0.279
261	0.684	285	0.475	309	0.349	333	0.268
265	0.640	289	0.449	313	0.333		

CARBON TETRACHLORIDE (CCl_4)

Molecular weight 153.8

$t_{boil} = -22.8$ °C; $t_{melt} = 76.7$ °C; $r = 46$ cal/g; $q = 3.75$ cal/g;
$t_{cr} = 283.2$ °C; $p_{cr} = 45.6$ bar; $\rho_{cr} = 588$ kg/m³

Thermodynamic properties of carbon tetrachloride [108]:
$c_p{}^0$ (kJ/kg · deg), i^0 (kJ/kg) and s^0 (kJ/kg · deg)

T, °K	$c_p{}^0$	i^0	s^0	T, °K	$c_p{}^0$	i^0	s^0
273	0.5254	99.03		500	0.6286	231.8	85.21
283	0.5327			600	0.6484	295.63	89.48
293	0.5401			700	0.6615	361.29	93.20
298.1	0.5428	112.3	74.03	800	0.6705	427.93	96.47
300	0.5439	113.2	74.15	900	0.6770	495.39	99.43
400	0.5967	170.4	80.18	1000	0.6816	563.22	102.00

Saturated vapor pressure of carbon tetrachloride [71]

t, °C	mm Hg	t, °C	mm Hg	t, °C	p, bar	t, °C	p, bar	t, °C	p, bar
−20	9.92	30	139.6	90	1.482	160	7.383	230	22.73
−10	18.81	40	210.9	100	1.942	170	8.852	240	26.17
0	33.08	50	309.0	110	2.506	180	10.53	250	29.57
10	55.65	60	439.0	120	3.187	190	12.41	260	34.03
20	89.55	70	613.8	130	4.001	200	14.58	270	38.65
				140	4.965	210	17.01	280	43.75
				150	6.071	220	19.72	283.05	46.49

Density ρ (kg/m³) of saturated carbon tetrachloride [71]

t, °C	$\varrho' \cdot 10^{-3}$	$\varrho'' \cdot 10^{-3}$	t, °C	$\varrho' \cdot 10^{-3}$	$\varrho'' \cdot 10^{-3}$	t, °C	$\varrho' \cdot 10^{-3}$	$\varrho'' \cdot 10^{-3}$
0	1.6325		100	1.4343	0.01027	210	1.1566	0.08787
10	1.6132		110	1.4124	0.01307	220	1.1227	0.1040
20	1.5940		120	1.3902	0.01639	230	1.0857	0.1232
30	1.5748		130	1.3680	0.02037	240	1.0444	0.1464
40	1.5552		140	1.3450	0.03040	250	0.9980	0.1754
50	1.5361		160	1.2982	0.03650	260	0.9409	0.2146
60	1.5163		170	1.2734	0.04367	270	0.8666	0.2710
70	1.4963	0.004570	180	1.2470	0.05249	280	0.7634	0.3597
80	1.4765	0.006083	190	1.2192	0.06250	283.2	0.558	0.558
90	1.4554	0.007955	200	1.1888	0.07418			

Heat capacity of liquid carbon tetrachloride [114]

T, °K	260	270	280	290	300	310	320
c_p, kJ/kg · deg	0.8386	0.8482	0.8545	0.8600	0.8637	0.8654	0.8667

Viscosity of carbon tetrachloride gas at $p = 1$ bar [42]

t, °C	0	100	200	300	400	500	600
$\eta \cdot 10^7$, N · s/m²	93.3	124	153	182	212	240	269

Viscosity η ($N \cdot s/m^2$) of liquid carbon tetrachloride [94]

t, °C	$\eta \cdot 10^3$	t, °C	$\eta \cdot 10^3$	t, °C	$\eta \cdot 10^3$	t, °C	$\eta \cdot 10^3$	t, °C	$\eta \cdot 10^3$
−10	1.68	30	0.84	70	0.52	100	0.387	140	0.276
0	1.35	40	0.74	80	0.472	110	0.352	160	0.234
10	1.13	50	0.65	90	0.426	120	0.323	180	0.201
20	0.97	60	0.59						

Thermal conductivity λ ($W/m \cdot deg$) of carbon tetrachloride vapor [15]

T, °K	$\lambda \cdot 10^4$	t, °C	$\lambda \cdot 10^4$	t, °C	$\lambda \cdot 10^4$	t, °C	$\lambda \cdot 10^4$
300	69	400	101	475	123	550	144
325	77	425	109	500	130	575	151
350	85	450	116	525	137	600	158
375	93						

Thermal conductivity λ ($W/m \cdot deg$) of liquid carbon tetrachloride [15]

t, °C	λ	T, °K	λ	T, °K	λ	T, °K	λ
−20	0.113	40	0.0997	100	0.0864	160	0.0731
−10	0.1108	50	0.0975	110	0.0840	170	0.0710
0	0.1087	60	0.0953	120	0.0820	180	0.0688
10	0.1065	70	0.0930	130	0.0797	190	0.0666
20	0.1042	80	0.0908	140	0.0775	200	0.0645
30	0.1019	90	0.0886	150	0.0753		

Surface tension σ (N/m) of carbon tetrachloride [64]

t, °C	$\sigma \cdot 10^3$	t, °C	$\sigma \cdot 10^3$	t, °C	$\sigma \cdot 10^3$	t, °C	$\sigma \cdot 10^3$	t, °C	$\sigma \cdot 10^3$	t, °C	$\sigma \cdot 10^3$
0	29.5	50	23.3	100	17.3	150	11.7	200	6.5	250	2.1
10	28.2	60	22.1	110	16.1	160	10.6	210	5.5	260	1.4
20	26.9	70	20.9	120	15.0	170	9.5	220	4.6	270	0.7
30	25.7	80	19.7	130	13.9	180	8.5	230	3.7	283.2	0.0
40	24.5	90	18.5	140	12.8	190	7.5	240	2.9		

CHLOROBENZENE (C_6H_5Cl)

Molecular weight 112.6

$t_{melt} = -45.2$ °C; $q = 15.9$ cal/g; $t_{boil} = 132$ °C; $r = 77.6$ cal/g;
$t_{cr} = 359.2$ °C; $p_{cr} = 45.2$ bar; $\rho_{cr} = 365$ kg/m³

Saturated vapor pressure of chlorobenzene [115]

t, °C	mm Hg	t, °C	mm Hg	t, °C	p, bar	t, °C	p, bar
0	2.52	70	97.90	140	1.252	230	7.982
10	4.86	80	144.75	150	1.608	240	9.434
20	8.76	90	208.35	160	2.044	250	11.02
30	15.45	100	292.75	170	2.559	260	12.85
40	26.00	110	402.55	180	3.158	270	14.91
50	41.98	120	542.80	190	3.868	329.2	31.90
60	65.54	130	718.95	200	4.693	358.8	45.08
				210	5.636	359.2	45.22
				220	6.739		

Density ρ (kg/m^3) of liquid chlorobenzene [71]

t, °C	$\varrho \cdot 10^{-3}$	t, °C	$\varrho \cdot 10^{-3}$	t, °C	$\varrho \cdot 10^{-3}$	t, °C	$\varrho \cdot 10^{-3}$	t, °C	$\varrho \cdot 10^{-3}$	t, °C	$\varrho \cdot 10^{-3}$
0	1.128	60	1.064	120	1.000	180	0.922	240	0.836	290	0.745
10	1.117	70	1.053	130	0.984	190	0.909	250	0.820	300	0.723
20	1.106	80	1.042	140	0.972	200	0.896	260	0.802	310	0.702
30	1.096	90	1.031	150	0.960	210	0.882	270	0.783	320	0.675
40	1.085	100	1.019	160	0.948	220	0.867	280	0.765	330	0.640
50	1.074	110	1.008	170	0.935	230	0.852				

Viscosity η (N · s/m^2) of liquid chlorobenzene [94]

t, °C	$\eta \cdot 10^3$	t, °C	$\eta \cdot 10^3$	t, °C	$\eta \cdot 10^3$	t, °C	$\eta \cdot 10^3$	t, °C	$\eta \cdot 10^3$
0	1.06	40	0.64	80	0.435	120	0.320	160	0.240
10	0.91	50	0.57	90	0.400	130	0.295	170	0.225
20	0.80	60	0.52	100	0.370	140	0.275	180	0.210
30	0.71	70	0.475	110	0.345	150	0.255	190	0.195

Thermal conductivity of liquid chlorobenzene [72]

t, °C	0	30	60	90	120
λ, W/m · deg	0.133	0.127	0.122	0.117	0.112

Surface tension σ (N/m) of chlorobenzene [64]

t, °C	$\sigma \cdot 10^3$	t, °C	$\sigma \cdot 10^3$	t, °C	$\sigma \cdot 10^3$	t, °C	$\sigma \cdot 10^3$	t, °C	$\sigma \cdot 10^3$	t, °C	$\sigma \cdot 10^3$
0	36.0	60	28.7	120	21.8	180	15.2	240	9.2	290	4.7
10	34.8	70	27.5	130	20.7	190	14.2	250	8.3	300	3.9
20	33.5	80	26.4	140	19.6	200	13.2	260	7.4	310	3.1
30	32.3	90	25.2	150	18.5	210	12.2	270	6.5	320	2.4
40	31.1	100	24.0	160	17.4	220	11.2	280	5.6	330	1.7
50	29.9	110	22.9	170	16.3	230	10.2				

TETRACHLORODIPHENYL ($C_{12}H_6Cl_4$)

Molecular weight 292.0

$t_{melt} = -7$ °C; $t_{boil} = 340$ °C at $p = 1$ atm

Thermodynamic properties of tetrachlorodiphenyl [116, 117]:
ρ (kg/m^3), c_p (kJ/kg · deg), η (N · s/m^2) and λ (W/m · deg)

t, °C	p, bar	ϱ	$\eta \cdot 10^3$	λ	c_p	t, °C	p, bar	ϱ	$\eta \cdot 10^3$	λ	c_p
30	–	1440	112	1.05	1.21	200	0.024	1270	0.98		1.84
60	–	1410	17.6	1.16	1.40	300	0.48	1170	0.49		
100	0.0002	1370	3.92	1.40	1.70	340	0.98				

ALCOHOLS

METHANOL (METHYL ALCOHOL) (CH_4O)

Molecular weight 32.0

$t_{melt} = -98$ °C; $q = 100.4$ kJ/kg; $t_{boil} = 64.71$ °C;
$t_{cr} = 240$ °C; $p_{cr} = 79.5$ bar; $\rho_{cr} = 275$ kg/m³

Saturated vapor pressure of methanol [115]

t, °C	p, mm Hg	t, °C	p, mm Hg	t, °C	p, bar	t, °C	p, bar
−44.0	1	12.1	60	84.0	2.03	203.5	40.52
−25.3	5	21.2	80	112.5	5.06	214.0	50.65
−16.2	10	34.8	200	138.0	10.13	224.0	60.78
− 6.0	20	49.9	400	167.8	20.26	240.0	79.72
5.0	40	64.7	760	186.5	30.39		

Latent heat of vaporization r (kJ/kg) of methanol [64]

t, °C	r	t, °C	r	t, °C	r	t, °C	r	t, °C	r
0	1210.0	50	1147.2	100	1030.0	150	866.7	200	636.4
10	1201.6	60	1130.4	110	1000.6	160	829.0	210	565.2
20	1191.1	70	1109.5	120	971.3	170	787.1	220	473.1
30	1178.6	80	1084.4	130	939.9	180	741.1	230	351.7
40	1163.9	90	1059.3	140	904.3	190	690.8	240	0

Density ρ (kg/m³) of saturated liquid methanol [71]

t, °C	$\varrho' \cdot 10^{-3}$	$\varrho'' \cdot 10^{-3}$	t, °C	$\varrho' \cdot 10^{-3}$	$\varrho'' \cdot 10^{-3}$	t, °C	$\varrho' \cdot 10^{-3}$	$\varrho'' \cdot 10^{-3}$
0	0.8100		100	0.7140	0.003984	200	0.5530	0.05075
10	0.8008		110	0.7020	0.005376	210	0.5255	0.06521
20	0.7915		120	0.6900	0.007142	220	0.4900	0.08635
30	0.7825		130	0.6770	0.009379	225	0.4675	0.1003
40	0.7740		140	0.6640	0.01216	230	0.4410	0.1187
50	0.7650		150	0.6495	0.01562	232	0.4295	0.1277
60	0.7555	0.001006	160	0.6340	0.01994	234	0.4145	0.1381
70	0.7460	0.001465	170	0.6160	0.02526	236	0.3955	0.1505
80	0.7355	0.002084	180	0.5980	0.03186	238	0.3705	0.1681
90	0.7250	0.002907	190	0.5770	0.04010	240	0.275	0.275

Heat capacity of methanol gas at $p = 1$ bar [42]

t, °C	0	100	200	300	400	500	600
c_p, kJ/kg · deg	1.43	1.72	1.99	2.24	2.47	2.69	2.90

Heat capacity of liquid methanol [42]

t, °C	−50	0	20	30	40	50
c_p, kJ/kg · deg	2.30	2.42	2.46	2.49	2.52	2.55

Viscosity of methanol gas at $p \leqslant 1$ bar [42]

t, °C	0	100	200	300	400	500	600
$\eta \cdot 10^7$, $N \cdot s/m^2$	88	123	157	191	226	261	296

Viscosity $\eta \cdot 10^7$ ($N \cdot s/m^2$) of methanol at different temperatures and pressures [52, 118]

p, atm \ t, °C →	150	200	231	250	270	p, atm \ t, °C →	150	200	231	250	270
1	139	156	166	172	179	200	1700	1108	842	710	580
25				176	182	300	1820	1228	967	843	723
50	1483	876		179	185	400	1931	1333	1072	943	827
75	1524	917	580	197	191	500	2033	1428	1163	1037	917
100	1562	958	645	368	220	600	2136	1515	1245	1113	996
125	1594	999	710	520	340	700	2236	1600	1324	1186	1066
150	1632	1037	762	610	465	800	2329	1685	1398	1260	1134

Viscosity η ($N \cdot s/m^2$) of liquid methanol [42]

t, °C	$\eta \cdot 10^3$	t, °C	$\eta \cdot 10^3$	t, °C	$\eta \cdot 10^3$	t, °C	$\eta \cdot 10^3$	t, °C	$\eta \cdot 10^3$	t, °C	$\eta \cdot 10^3$
−100	16	−40	1.75	30	0.509	90	0.240	150	0.121	210	0.0646
− 90	8.8	−30	1.39	40	0.446	100	0.214	160	0.109	220	0.0583
− 80	5.7	−20	1.16	50	0.393	110	0.190	170	0.098	230	0.0528
− 70	4.02	−10	0.970	60	0.347	120	0.170	180	0.0883	240	0.0460
− 60	2.98	0	0.817	70	0.306	130	0.152	190	0.0794		
− 50	2.26	20	0.578	80	0.271	140	0.136	200	0.0716		

Thermal conductivity $\lambda \cdot 10^4$ (W/m · deg) of methanol [119]

T, °K \ p, bar →	1	5	10	15	20	25	30	35
290	2038	2039	2042	2044	2047	2050	2053	2055
300	2000	2002	2005	2008	2012	2015	2018	2021
310	1964	1967	1970	1973	1976	1980	1983	1986
320	1932	1935	1938	1941	1945	1948	1951	1955
330	1902	1905	1908	1911	1915	1918	1921	1925
340		1878	1882	1885	1888	1892	1895	1898
350		1854	1857	1860	1864	1867	1870	1873
360		1831	1834	1837	1841	1844	1847	1851
370		1810	1813	1816	1820	1823	1826	1829
380	238	1792	1795	1798	1801	1804	1807	1810
390	249		1776	1780	1782	1785	1788	1792
400	261		1758	1762	1764	1767	1770	1773
410	272		1740	1743	1746	1749	1753	1756
420	282	318		1725	1728	1731	1735	1740
430	293	325				1714	1718	1721
440	304	331				1696	1700	1704
450	316	340				1677	1682	1686
460	327	348						
470	338	356	379	403	429	455		
480	351	366	387	409	432	456		
490	363	376	394	414	435	457		
500	375	387	403	421	440	460		
510	388	398	412	427	445	463	484	508
520	401	410	422	436	451	469	487	508
530	414	421	432	445	459	474	490	508

continued

T, °K \ p, bar →	1	5	10	15	20	25	30	35
540	427	434	443	454	467	480	494	509
550	441	447	455	465	475	487	500	512
560	454	460	468	476	485	495	505	516
570	468	473	479	486	493	502	512	522

T, °K \ p, bar →	40	45	50	75	100	150	200	300	400
290	2058	2061	2064	2080	2095	2123	2150	2200	2247
300	2024	2027	2029	2045	2059	2088	2116	2166	2215
310	1989	1992	1996	2012	2026	2055	2082	2133	2182
320	1958	1961	1964	1980	1995	2025	2051	2103	2151
330	1928	1931	1935	1950	1967	1995	2022	2074	2123
340	1902	1905	1908	1924	1940	1968	1995	2047	2096
350	1876	1880	1883	1898	1914	1943	1970	2021	2072
360	1854	1857	1860	1876	1891	1920	1948	1999	2050
370	1833	1836	1839	1855	1870	1899	1927	1979	2030
380	1813	1816	1819	1835	1850	1879	1907	1960	2011
390	1795	1798	1801	1817	1832	1862	1889	1943	1993
400	1776	1780	1783	1799	1815	1845	1872	1926	1977
410	1760	1763	1766	1782	1798	1829	1856	1911	1963
420	1743	1747	1750	1766	1782	1813	1840	1896	1949
430	1725	1729	1733	1750	1766	1797	1826	1881	1936
440	1707	1711	1715	1734	1750	1782	1811	1868	1923
450	1690	1694	1698	1717	1734	1766	1797	1855	1910
460			1678	1698	1716	1750	1782	1842	1898
470			1658	1678	1698	1733	1767	1827	1885
480			1626	1655			1750	1814	1872
490							1734	1799	1859
500							1713	1785	1846
510	537	571	610				1692	1770	1834
520	531	556	584				1664	1754	1820
530	527	547	570				1632	1738	1807
540	525	542	559				1592	1719	1794
550	525	538	553				1543	1698	1780
560	527	539	553	642			1480	1674	1766
570	532	543	555	633					

Surface tension σ (N/m) of methanol [64]

t, °C	$\sigma \cdot 10^3$	t, °C	$\sigma \cdot 10^3$	t, °C	$\sigma \cdot 10^3$	t, °C	$\sigma \cdot 10^3$	t, °C	$\sigma \cdot 10^3$
0	24.5	50	20.1	100	15.7	150	10.4	200	4.5
10	23.5	60	19.3	110	14.7	160	9.3	210	3.3
20	22.6	70	18.4	120	13.6	170	8.1	220	2.1
30	21.8	80	17.5	130	12.6	180	6.9	230	0.9
40	20.9	90	16.6	140	11.5	190	5.7	235	0.34

ETHANOL (ETHYL ALCOHOL) (C_2H_6O)

C_2H_5OH

Molecular weight 46.1

$t_{melt} = -114.5$ °C; $q = 104.7$ kJ/kg; $t_{boil} = 78.3$ °C;
$t_{cr} = 243.1$ °C; $p_{cr} = 63.9$ bar; $\rho_{cr} = 280$ kg/m³

Saturated vapor pressure of ethanol [115]

t, °C	p, mm Hg	t, °C	p, mm Hg	t, °C	p, bar	t, °C	p, bar
−31.3	1	26.0	60	97.5	2.03	218.0	40.52
−12.0	5	34.9	100	126.0	5.06	230.0	50.65
− 2.3	10	48.4	200	151.8	10.13	242.0	60.78
8.0	20	63.5	400	183.0	20.26	243.1	63.92
19.0	40	78.4	760	203.0	30.39		

Thermal properties of 96% (Volume) saturated aqueous solution of ethanol [120]: p (bar), t (°C) and v (m³kg)

p	t	$v' \cdot 10^3$	v''	p	t	$v' \cdot 10^3$	v''
0.02	2.8	1.216	27.81	16.68	172.5	1.598	0.0432
0.05	17.0	1.234	11.69	17.66	175.1	1.611	0.0405
0.10	28.9	1.249	6.07	18.64	177.7	1.625	0.03820
0.20	41.7	1.266	3.164	19.62	180.1	1.638	0.03617
0.29	49.9	1.278	2.161	20.60	182.4	1.652	0.03420
0.39	56.0	1.287	1.649	21.58	184.6	1.665	0.03243
0.49	60.9	1.295	1.337	22.56	186.8	1.679	0.03080
0.98	78.0	1.321	0.697	23.54	188.9	1.692	0.02930
1.47	88.0	1.339	0.475	24.52	190.9	1.707	0.02797
1.96	95.6	1.354	0.3618	25.51	192.8	1.720	0.02673
2.45	102.4	1.368	0.2926	26.49	194.7	1.733	0.02557
2.94	107.8	1.381	0.2456	27.47	196.5	1.746	0.02453
3.43	112.6	1.392	0.2117	28.45	198.3	1.760	0.02350
3.92	117.0	1.403	0.1862	29.43	200.0	1.773	0.02248
4.41	121.0	1.413	0.1663	30.41	201.7	1.787	0.02158
4.90	124.5	1.422	0.1502	31.39	203.3	1.800	0.02080
5.89	130.9	1.441	0.1243	32.37	204.9	1.814	0.01995
6.87	136.5	1.458	0.1066	33.35	206.5	1.829	0.01919
7.85	141.5	1.475	0.0937	34.34	208.1	1.843	0.01843
8.83	146.0	1.490	0.0837	35.32	209.6	1.856	0.01777
9.81	150.2	1.504	0.0750	36.30	211.1	1.871	0.01710
10.79	153.9	1.518	0.0680	37.28	212.5	1.885	0.01651
11.77	157.4	1.532	0.0622	38.26	213.9	1.899	0.01593
12.75	160.7	1.545	0.0573	39.24	215.3	1.913	0.01536
13.73	163.8	1.558	0.0532	40.22	216.6	1.927	0.01487
14.72	166.8	1.572	0.0494	41.20	217.9	1.942	0.01439
15.70	169.7	1.585	0.0462	42.18	219.2	1.957	0.01392
43.16	220.5	1.972	0.01345	56.90	236.5	2.259	0.00854
44.14	221.7	1.981	0.01305	57.88	237.5	2.288	0.00824
45.13	223.0	2.003	0.01261	58.86	238.6	2.322	0.00794
46.11	224.2	2.019	0.01222	59.84	239.6	2.361	0.00766
47.09	225.4	2.035	0.01185	60.82	240.6	2.407	0.00738
48.07	226.5	2.053	0.01150	61.80	241.5	2.452	0.00709
49.05	227.7	2.073	0.01112	62.78	242.5	2.506	0.00679
50.03	228.9	2.093	0.01076	63.76	243.5	2.583	0.00650
51.01	230.0	2.112	0.01043	64.75	244.5	2.650	0.00618
51.99	231.1	2.132	0.01011	65.73	245.5	2.717	0.00587
52.97	232.2	2.154	0.00977	66.71	246.4	2.814	0.00549
53.96	233.3	2.177	0.00950	67.69	247.3	2.945	0.00503
54.94	234.4	2.202	0.00916	68.57	248.2	3.742	0.00374
55.92	235.5	2.230	0.00884				

Enthalpy and latent heat of vaporization of 96% (volume) saturated aqueous solution of ethanol [120] : i and r (kJ/kg)

t, °C	p, bar	i'	i''	r	t, °C	p, bar	i'	i''	r
0	0.012	−5.44	1042.9	1048.4	130	5.75	376.0	1236.4	860.4
10	0.031	18.8	1058.0	1039.2	140	7.53	413.2	1247.2	834.0
20	0.058	43.5	1073.5	1030.0	150	9.78	451.8	1256.0	804.3
30	0.104	68.7	1089.8	1021.2	160	12.56	491.5	1264.4	772.9
40	0.180	94.6	1106.6	1011.9	170	15.8	533.0	1271.1	738.1
50	0.296	121.4	1122.1	1000.6	180	19.6	576.5	1275.3	698.8
60	0.472	149.5	1138.4	988.9	190	24.0	622.6	1273.2	650.6
70	0.729	178.4	1153.5	975.1	200	29.4	670.7	1269.0	598.3
80	1.086	208.5	1168.5	960.0	210	35.6	722.2	1259.0	536.7
90	1.588	239.5	1184.0	944.5	220	42.8	777.5	1246.0	468.5
100	2.26	271.7	1198.7	927.0	230	51.0	837.4	1224.6	387.3
110	3.15	305.2	1212.1	906.9	240	60.2	909.8	1190.3	280.5
120	4.29	340.0	1225.5	885.5	248.2	68.6	1067.6	1067.6	0

Specific volume $v \cdot 10^3$ (m³/kg) of 96% (volume) aqueous solution of ethanol [120]

t, °C \ p, bar →	1	5	10	15	20	25	30	35
0	1.213	1.212	1.212	1.212	1.211	1.211	1.210	1.210
10	1.225	1.224	1.224	1.224	1.223	1.223	1.222	1.222
20	1.238	1.237	1.236	1.236	1.235	1.235	1.234	1.234
30	1.251	1.250	1.249	1.249	1.248	1.248	1.247	1.247
40	1.266	1.265	1.264	1.263	1.262	1.262	1.262	1.261
50	1.280	1.279	1.278	1.277	1.276	1.276	1.276	1.275
60	1.295	1.294	1.293	1.292	1.291	1.290	1.290	1.289
70	1.310	1.309	1.308	1.307	1.306	1.305	1.304	1.304
80	687	1.325	1.324	1.323	1.322	1.321	1.320	1.319
90	707	1.343	1.342	1.341	1.340	1.339	1.338	1.337
100	726	1.363	1.362	1.361	1.360	1.359	1.358	1.357
110	747	1.386	1.385	1.384	1.383	1.381	1.380	1.379
120	766	1.411	1.410	1.408	1.407	1.405	1.404	1.403
130	787	149.6	1.438	1.436	1.435	1.433	1.431	1.430
140	807	154.3	1.469	1.467	1.465	1.463	1.461	1.459
150	827	158.8	1.504	1.502	1.499	1.496	1.494	1.492
160	848	163.3	76.6	1.542	1.539	1.536	1.533	1.530
170	862	167.6	79.4	49.2	1.584	1.580	1.577	1.573
180	888	171.9	81.8	51.4	1.638	1.634	1.629	1.624
190	909	176.2	84.2	53.2	37.38	1.699	1.692	1.685
200	928	180.5	86.6	55.1	39.13	29.09	1.771	1.761
210	949	184.8	89.1	57.8	40.7	30.67	23.75	18.44
220	968	189.0	91.4	58.7	42.2	32.13	25.16	20.04
230	989	193.3	93.7	60.4	43.6	33.44	26.50	21.35
240	1009	197.5	95.9	62.0	45.0	34.69	27.75	22.65
250	1029	201.7	98.2	63.7	46.4	35.89	28.85	23.75
260	1059	205.9	100.6	65.4	47.7	37.02	29.90	24.73
270	1069	210.1	102.8	66.9	49.0	38.10	30.88	25.67
280	1090	214.3	105.0	68.4	50.2	39.15	31.80	26.55
290	1110	218.5	107.1	70.0	51.4	40.2	32.68	27.34
300	1129	222.6	109.3	71.3	52.5	41.1	33.50	28.07
310	1150	236.7	111.2	72.8	53.6	42.1	34.31	28.79
320	1169	230.8	113.4	74.2	54.7	43.0	35.12	29.52
330	1189	234.8	115.4	75.6	55.9	43.9	35.93	30.24
340	1209	238.8	117.6	77.1	56.9	44.8	36.72	30.94
350	1229	242.8	119.7	78.6	58.0	45.7	37.52	31.64

continued

t, °C \ p, bar →	40	45	50	60	70	80	90	100
0	1.209	1.208	1.208	1.207	1.206	1.204	1.204	1.202
10	1.221	1.220	1.220	1.219	1.218	1.216	1.216	1.214
20	1.233	1.232	1.232	1.231	1.230	1.228	1.228	1.226
30	1.246	1.245	1.245	1.243	1.242	1.241	1.241	1.239
40	1.260	1.259	1.259	1.257	1.256	1.255	1.254	1.252
50	1.274	1.273	1.273	1.271	1.270	1.269	1.268	1.266
60	1.288	1.287	1.287	1.285	1.284	1.283	1.282	1.280
70	1.303	1.302	1.302	1.300	1.299	1.297	1.296	1.294
80	1.319	1.318	1.318	1.316	1.315	1.313	1.312	1.310
90	1.337	1.336	1.335	1.333	1.332	1.330	1.329	1.327
100	1.357	1.356	1.355	1.353	1.351	1.349	1.347	1.345
110	1.378	1.377	1.376	1.374	1.371	1.369	1.367	1.365
120	1.401	1.400	1.399	1.396	1.394	1.391	1.388	1.386
130	1.428	1.426	1.425	1.422	1.419	1.416	1.413	1.410
140	1.457	1.455	1.454	1.450	1.446	1.443	1.439	1.436
150	1.489	1.487	1.485	1.480	1.476	1.473	1.468	1.464
160	1.527	1.524	1.521	1.515	1.510	1.505	1.500	1.496
170	1.569	1.566	1.563	1.555	1.549	1.543	1.537	1.531
180	1.620	1.614	1.610	1.602	1.594	1.586	1.578	1.571
190	1.679	1.673	1.667	1.661	1.650	1.634	1.624	1.615
200	1.752	1.743	1.734	1.727	1.710	1.690	1.677	1.665
210	1.848	1.836	1.824	1.800	1.779	1.759	1.740	1.724
220	15.86	1.958	1.936	1.898	1.867	1.839	1.815	1.794
230	17.33	14.25	11.19	2.047	1.993	1.949	1.912	1.881
240	18.66	15.44	12.83	8.16	2.204	2.105	2.039	1.988
250	19.84	16.66	14.08	10.00	5.81	2.438	2.255	2.155
260	20.82	17.72	15.19	11.21	8.15	4.80	2.84	2.462
270	21.71	18.60	16.09	12.20	9.36	6.98	4.72	3.256
280	22.55	19.44	16.93	13.06	10.22	8.04	6.08	4.45
290	23.31	20.17	17.61	13.78	10.98	8.79	7.03	5.53
300	23.98	20.80	18.22	14.38	11.59	9.45	7.75	6.35
310	24.64	21.41	18.81	14.93	12.12	10.02	8.35	7.00
320	25.30	22.03	19.39	15.47	12.63	10.53	8.86	7.55
330	25.96	22.64	19.98	16.00	13.15	11.03	9.37	8.04
340	26.61	23.23	20.56	16.43	13.65	11.50	9.82	8.48
350	27.25	23.83	21.11	17.02	14.11	11.93	10.25	8.90

t, °C \ p, bar →	120	140	160	180	200	250	300	350
0	1.200	1.198	1.196	1.194	1.192	1.188	1.183	1.180
10	1.212	1.210	1.208	1.206	1.204	1.199	1.193	1.190
20	1.224	1.222	1.220	1.218	1.216	1.210	1.204	1.199
30	1.237	1.234	1.232	1.230	1.228	1.222	1.215	1.210
40	1.250	1.247	1.244	1.242	1.240	1.234	1.226	1.221
50	1.264	1.260	1.257	1.255	1.252	1.246	1.238	1.233
60	1.277	1.274	1.270	1.268	1.265	1.259	1.251	1.245
70	1.291	1.288	1.284	1.282	1.279	1.272	1.264	1.258
80	1.307	1.303	1.299	1.296	1.293	1.286	1.278	1.271
90	1.324	1.320	1.316	1.312	1.309	1.301	1.293	1.286
100	1.342	1.337	1.333	1.329	1.326	1.317	1.309	1.301
110	1.360	1.355	1.351	1.347	1.344	1.335	1.326	1.317
120	1.381	1.376	1.371	1.367	1.364	1.354	1.344	1.334
130	1.405	1.399	1.394	1.390	1.385	1.374	1.363	1.353
140	1.430	1.423	1.418	1.413	1.407	1.395	1.384	1.373
150	1.457	1.450	1.444	1.438	1.432	1.418	1.405	1.394
160	1.487	1.479	1.472	1.465	1.458	1.443	1.427	1.415
170	1.521	1.511	1.502	1.495	1.486	1.469	1.452	1.437
180	1.558	1.546	1.534	1.525	1.516	1.496	1.478	1.461
190	1.599	1.584	1.571	1.560	1.549	1.525	1.505	1.485
200	1.645	1.627	1.613	1.599	1.587	1.559	1.534	1.512
210	1.697	1.674	1.655	1.638	1.625	1.593	1.564	1.541

continued

t, °C \ p, bar →	120	140	160	180	200	250	300	350
220	1.759	1.730	1.705	1.685	1.667	1.628	1.597	1.569
230	1.831	1.794	1.763	1.736	1.714	1.667	1.632	1.600
240	1.916	1.868	1.828	1.795	1.766	1.710	1.668	1.631
250	2.025	1.954	1.902	1.860	1.826	1.757	1.708	1.666
260	2.160	2.069	1.988	1.934	1.874	1.811	1.752	1.703
270	2.447	2.241	2.120	2.035	1.950	1.870	1.800	1.742
280	2.942	2.488	2.291	2.160	2.033	1.940	1.854	1.787
290	3.552	2.819	2.502	2.321	2.157	2.022	1.917	1.835
300	4.32	3.260	2.773	2.520	2.296	2.120	1.984	1.890
310	5.02	3.761	3.087	2.739	2.447	2.224	2.061	1.957
320	5.59	4.28	3.449	2.977	2.614	2.342	2.146	2.027
330	6.06	4.70	3.821	3.269	2.803	2.474	2.235	2.105
340	6.50	5.15	4.21	3.572	3.008	2.605	2.330	2.187
350	6.90	5.54	4.58	3.933	3.219	2.736	2.425	2.270

Heat capacity of ethanol gas at $p = 1$ bar [42]

t, °C	0	100	200	300	400	500	600
c_p, kJ/kg · deg	1.34	1.69	2.01	2.32	2.61	2.89	3.16

Heat capacity c_p (kcal/kg · deg) of 96% (volume) aqueous solution of ethanol at different temperatures and pressures [122, 123]

t, °C \ p, kg/cm² →	75	100	125	150	175	200	225	250
190	1.054	1.036	1.018	1.005	0.994	0.983	0.974	0.963
200	1.089	1.065	1.043	1.025	1.010	0.997	0.987	0.976
210	1.137	1.099	1.071	1.045	1.028	1.012	1.000	0.988
220	1.213	1.143	1.104	1.070	1.047	1.029	1.014	1.001
230	1.344	1.211	1.148	1.102	1.070	1.047	1.029	1.014
240	1.677	1.320	1.206	1.139	1.096	1.067	1.044	1.027
250	14.02	1.520	1.285	1.186	1.127	1.089	1.060	1.039
260	2.006	2.100	1.415	1.248	1.168	1.115	1.078	1.052
270	1.324	3.148	1.644	1.342	1.214	1.145	1.098	1.065
280	1.083	2.096	1.940	1.453	1.268	1.177	1.119	1.078
290	0.951	1.488	1.969	1.570	1.325	1.212	1.140	1.093
300	0.870	1.200	1.657	1.609	1.377	1.244	1.160	1.106
310	0.817	1.044	1.370	1.522	1.396	1.268	1.175	1.119
320	0.780	0.946	1.182	1.367	1.356	1.269	1.181	1.124
330	0.754	0.880	1.053	1.219	1.278	1.240	1.175	1.123
340	0.734	0.834	0.968	1.106	1.187	1.193	1.156	1.114
350	0.721	0.800	0.908	1.018	1.102	1.131	1.122	1.094
360	0.709	0.776	0.861	0.955	1.029	1.072	1.078	1.064
370	0.700	0.755	0.824	0.905	0.972	1.014	1.034	1.033

Heat capacity c_p (kcal/kg · deg) of saturated liquid ethanol [124]

t, °C	c_p'	t, °C	c_p'	t, °C	c_p'	t, °C	c_p'	t, °C	c_p'
0	0.541	30	0.593	60	0.665	90	0.755	120	0.863
10	0.557	40	0.615	70	0.693	100	0.789	130	0.903
20	0.574	50	0.639	80	0.723	110	0.825	140	0.945

Enthalpy i (kJ/kg) of ethanol [120]

t, °C \ p, bar →	0	1	5	10	20	30
0	1042.9	−5.44	−5.2	−4.60	−3.77	−2.93
10	1058.8	18.8	19.3	19.7	20.5	21.4
20	1074.8	43.5	44.0	44.4	45.2	46.0
30	1091.1	68.7	69.1	69.5	70.3	71.2
40	1107.8	94.6	95.0	95.5	96.3	97.1
50	1125.0	121.4	121.8	122.2	123.1	123.9
60	1141.7	149.5	149.9	150.3	151.1	151.6
70	1158.9	178.4	178.8	179.2	180.0	180.4
80	1176.1	1170.2	208.5	208.9	209.8	210.2
90	1193.7	1189.0	239.5	239.9	240.7	241.2
100	1211.7	1207.9	271.7	272.1	272.6	273.4
110	1229.7	1225.9	305.2	305.6	306.1	306.5
120	1248.1	1244.7	340.0	340.0	340.4	340.8
130	1266.9	1263.6	1241.8	376.0	376.0	376.4
140	1286.2	1283.2	1264.8	413.2	412.8	413.2
150	1305.9	1302.9	1287.0	1253.9	450.9	451.3
160	1325.5	1323.0	1308.8	1283.2	490.7	490.7
170	1345.6	1343.5	1330.6	1310.0	532.1	531.7
180	1366.2	1364.1	1352.3	1334.8	576.5	575.3
190	1387.1	1385.0	1374.1	1358.6	1308.4	621.3
200	1408.4	1406.3	1395.9	1382.1	1341.0	670.7
210	1429.8	1427.7	1417.6	1405.1	1369.9	1307.5
220	1451.1	1449.0	1439.8	1428.5	1398.8	1348.1
230	1472.5	1470.8	1462.9	1451.6	1426.0	1385.8
240	1494.3	1492.6	1485.0	1475.0	1452.8	1419.7
250	1516.5	1514.8	1508.5	1498.5	1479.2	1451.6
260	1539.1	1537.4	1531.1	1521.9	1505.2	1481.7
270	1561.7	1560.4	1554.6	1545.3	1531.1	1510.6
280	1584.7	1583.9	1578.0	1569.6	1556.6	1539.1
290	1607.7	1607.3	1602.3	1593.9	1582.2	1566.3
300	1630.8	1630.3	1625.3	1618.6	1607.3	1592.7
310	1653.8	1653.4	1648.3	1642.9	1632.4	1618.6
320	1677.2	1676.8	1671.8	1667.2	1657.1	1644.2
330	1701.1	1700.7	1695.6	1691.5	1681.8	1669.7
340	1725.4	1725.0	1719.9	1716.2	1706.5	1694.8
350	1749.7	1749.2	1744.2	1740.9	1731.7	1720.4

t, °C \ p, bar →	40	50	60	70	80	90
0	−2.09	−1.26	−0.42	0.84	1.67	2.51
10	22.2	23.0	23.9	24.7	25.5	26.4
20	46.9	47.7	48.6	49.4	50.2	51.1
30	72.0	72.8	73.7	74.5	75.4	76.2
40	97.6	98.4	99.2	100.1	100.9	101.7
50	124.3	125.2	126.0	126.9	127.7	128.5
60	152.4	153.2	154.1	154.9	155.3	156.2
70	181.3	182.1	183.0	183.4	184.2	185.1
80	211.0	211.8	212.7	213.1	213.9	214.8
90	242.0	242.4	243.2	243.7	244.5	245.3
100	273.8	274.2	275.1	275.5	276.3	276.7
110	306.9	307.3	308.1	308.6	309.0	309.4
120	341.2	341.6	342.1	342.5	342.9	343.3
130	376.8	377.2	377.2	377.6	378.1	378.1
140	413.2	413.6	413.7	413.7	414.1	414.1
150	450.9	451.3	451.3	450.9	451.3	450.9
160	490.3	490.3	490.3	489.8	489.8	489.4
170	531.3	530.9	530.9	530.0	529.6	529.2
180	574.4	573.6	573.2	571.9	571.1	570.2
190	620.1	618.8	618.0	615.9	614.6	613.4
200	668.2	666.1	664.9	662.4	660.3	658.6

continued

t, °C \ p, bar →	40	50	60	70	80	90
210	720.5	717.2	715.1	711.3	708.8	706.7
220	1276.1	772.5	769.5	764.1	760.7	758.2
230	1331.0	1237.2	829.0	822.3	818.1	814.8
240	1377.9	1306.7	1184.4	896.4	888.0	880.5
250	1418.1	1366.6	1297.9	1143.8	1006.5	965.9
260	1454.5	1416.0	1370.8	1301.7	1215.8	1101.5
270	1487.6	1458.3	1424.3	1379.1	1319.7	1243.9
280	1519.0	1495.5	1470.0	1435.6	1392.9	1339.4
290	1548.3	1528.6	1507.2	1480.0	1448.2	1408.9
300	1576.7	1559.2	1539.9	1517.3	1493.0	1462.9
310	1603.5	1587.2	1569.6	1550.0	1530.7	1506.0
320	1629.9	1614.4	1598.9	1580.5	1563.8	1543.7
330	1656.3	1642.1	1627.4	1609.8	1594.8	1576.7
340	1683.1	1669.3	1655.9	1639.1	1624.9	1608.6
350	1709.5	1696.5	1684.3	1668.8	1655.0	1639.1

t, °C \ p, bar →	100	150	200	250	300	350
0	3.35	7.95	12.56	16.7	21.4	26.0
10	27.2	31.8	36.4	40.6	45.2	49.4
20	51.9	56.5	60.7	64.9	69.1	73.7
30	77.0	81.2	85.4	90.0	94.2	98.4
40	102.6	107.2	111.4	115.6	119.7	123.9
50	129.4	133.6	137.7	141.9	146.1	149.9
60	157.0	161.2	165.4	169.1	173.3	177.1
70	185.5	189.2	193.4	197.6	201.4	205.2
80	215.2	219.0	223.2	226.9	230.3	234.0
90	245.8	249.1	253.3	256.6	260.0	263.8
100	277.2	280.5	284.3	287.6	290.6	294.3
110	309.8	312.8	316.5	319.4	322.4	325.7
120	343.7	345.8	349.6	352.5	355.0	358.4
130	378.5	380.2	383.5	386.4	389.0	391.9
140	413.7	415.3	418.7	421.6	424.1	426.6
150	450.5	451.8	455.1	457.2	459.7	461.8
160	489.0	489.8	492.8	494.0	496.1	497.8
170	528.8	529.2	531.7	532.1	533.4	535.1
180	569.8	569.8	571.1	571.1	572.3	573.6
190	612.5	612.1	612.5	612.5	612.9	613.4
200	657.3	656.5	656.1	655.6	655.2	654.4
210	705.1	703.4	702.1	699.2	699.2	697.1
220	756.1	751.5	749.9	746.9	744.0	741.1
230	811.8	803.9	800.9	796.3	791.3	787.1
240	875.5	860.0	854.1	846.6	840.3	834.8
250	949.1	919.4	907.7	898.9	890.5	883.0
260	1044.2	982.2	964.2	952.1	942.4	933.6
270	1173.6	1048.8	1022.0	1006.5	994.8	984.7
280	1283.2	1122.9	1081.4	1061.8	1048.8	1037.1
290	1361.5	1197.0	1142.2	1118.7	1102.8	1089.8
300	1426.0	1271.1	1202.4	1175.6	1157.6	1143.4
310	1476.7	1337.7	1261.9	1232.2	1212.5	1197.0
320	1519.0	1395.5	1320.1	1287.8	1266.5	1249.8
330	1555.4	1447.4	1375.8	1341.9	1320.1	1302.1
340	1588.5	1495.1	1429.0	1394.2	1372.0	1353.2
350	1620.7	1541.2	1479.2	1444.4	1422.2	1403.4

Viscosity of ethanol at $p \leqslant 1$ bar [42]

t, °C	0	100	200	300	400	500	600
$\eta \cdot 10^7$, N · s/m²	78.5	108	137	167	197	227	257

Viscosity ($N \cdot s/m^2$) of 96% (volume) saturated aqueous solution of ethanol [121]

t, °C	0	10	20	30	40	50	60	70	80	90	100	110	120
$\eta'' \cdot 10^5$	0.774	0.809	0.835	0.869	0.900	0.930	0.959	0.990	1.030	1.059	1.092	1.125	1.157
$\eta' \cdot 10^3$	1.799	1.464	1.198	0.985	0.819	0.690	0.588	0.500	0.432	0.369	0.318	0.278	0.243
t, °C	130	140	150	160	170	180	190	200	210	220	230	240	
$\eta'' \cdot 10^5$	1.189	1.219	1.254	1.293	1.329	1.369	1.411	1.464	1.529	1.618	1.728	1.948	
$\eta' \cdot 10^3$	0.215	0.190	0.168	0.150	0.134	0.120	0.107	0.0950	0.0836	0.0725	0.0614	0.0488	

Viscosity $\eta \cdot 10^5$ ($N \cdot s/m^2$) of 96% (volume) aqueous solution of ethanol at different temperatures and pressures [121]

t, °C \ p, kg/cm² →	1	20	50	70	80	90	100	120	150	200	300	400	500	600
0	179.9	181.6	184.3	185.9	186.8	187.8	188.6	190.3	193.0	197.4	206.1	214.9	224.4	234.3
10	146.4	148.0	150.2	151.2	151.9	152.7	154.0	155.2	157.1	160.2	168.1	175.8	183.3	191.4
20	119.8	120.9	122.5	123.7	124.0	124.6	125.4	126.5	128.2	130.8	137.2	143.7	149.7	155.9
30	98.5	99.3	100.6	101.5	102.0	102.5	103.0	104.0	105.2	107.6	112.3	117.6	123.0	128.9
40	81.9	82.5	84.0	84.5	84.9	85.2	85 6	86.4	87.6	89.7	93.9	98.2	103.1	108.0
50	69.0	69.5	70.4	71.0	71.2	71.6	71.9	72.7	73.6	75.3	79.0	83.0	87.1	91.1
60	58.8	59.2	60.0	60.6	60.8	61.2	61.4	61.9	62.7	65.2	67.3	70.6	74.1	77.6
70	50.0	50.5	51.4	51.7	52.0	52.3	52.7	53.3	54.1	55.3	58.0	60.7	63.7	66.7
80	1.03	43.5	44.4	44.8	45.0	45.3	45.6	46.1	46.7	48.0	50.0	52.5	55.4	58.2
90	1.06	37.4	38.6	39.0	39.2	39.5	39.8	40.2	40.9	41.9	44.0	46.0	48.6	51.2
100	1.083	32.3	33.6	34.2	34.4	34.7	35.0	35.4	36.0	36.9	38.8	40.6	43.0	45.5
110	1.117	28.3	29.5	30.0	30.2	30.4	30.7	31.1	31.8	33.0	34.6	36.2	38.5	40.8
120	1.146	24.8	26.0	26.4	26.6	26.8	27.0	27.4	28.2	29.4	31.0	32.5	34.7	36.8
130	1.174	22.0	23.0	23.4	23.6	23.8	24.1	24.5	25.2	26.2	27.8	29.6	31.3	33.5
140	1.202	19.4	20.5	20.9	21.1	21.3	21.5	21.8	22.5	23.7	25.3	27.0	28.8	30.7
150	1.232	17.2	18.14	18.64	18.9	19.14	19.36	19.89	20.5	21.6	23.3	25.0	26.6	28.2
160	1.259	15.3	16.04	16.54	16.8	17.04	17.25	17.82	18.42	19.58	21.4	22.95	24.57	26.09
170	1.289	13.5	14.30	14.78	15.0	15.25	15.49	15.95	16.65	17.69	19.4	20.95	22.51	24.09
180	1.317	12.0	12.74	13.19	13.44	13.69	13.90	14.30	15.01	16.01	17.8	19.16	20.62	22.08
190	1.346	1.379	11.25	11.65	11.95	12.14	12.34	12.81	13.49	14.42	16.10	17.56	18.94	20.25
200	1.376	1.408	9.87	10.34	10.6	10.82	11.03	11.50	12.12	13.02	14.71	16.11	17.40	18.62
210	1.403	1.434	8.65	9.18	9.37	9.59	9.80	10.30	10.90	11.78	13.40	14.82	16.01	17.21
220	1.433	1.471	7.44	8.04	8.25	8.50	8.71	9.62	9.80	10.65	12.22	13.60	14.83	15.98
230	1.459	1.490	1.68	6.83	7.14	7.40	7.65	8.09	8.76	9.68	11.21	12.57	13.78	14.95
240	1.488	1.508	1.64	5.43	6.00	6.35	6.64	7.19	7.90	8.84	10.36	11.69	12.91	14.05
250	1.511	1.54	1.63	2.21	4.19	5.21	5.68	6.33	7.10	8.08	9.62	10.93	12.14	13.25
260	1.540	1.57	1.63	1.90	2.42	4.02	4.72	5.54	6.37	7.38	8.96	10.23	11.40	12.46
270	1.569	1.60	1.66	1.84	2.05	2.50	3.60	4.71	5.64	6.72	8.33	9.61	10.70	11.76
280	1.594	1.63	1.68	1.83	1.94	2.14	2.56	3.74	4.88	6.10	7.76	9.04	10.08	11.11
290	1.625	1.65	1.70	1.83	1.93	2.04	2.22	2.96	4.20	5.52	7.23	8.53	9.54	10.54
300	1.649	1.68	1.73	1.84	1.92	2.01	2.15	2.63	3.66	4.98	6.74	8.03	9.04	10.00
310	1.680	1.70	1.76	1.85	1.92	2.00	2.11	2.44	3.27	4.54	6.29	7.54	8.56	9.52
320	1.704	1.72	1.78	1.87	1.93	2.00	2.09	2.34	2.96	4.16	5.88	7.08	8.10	9.06
330	1.730	1.76	1.82	1.89	1.94	2.00	2.08	2.29	2.78	3.84	5.52	6.66	7.67	8.61
340	1.759	1.78	1.85	1.91	1.96	2.01	2.08	2.25	2.65	3.57	5.19	6.27	7.25	8.17

Thermal conductivity $\lambda \cdot 10^4$ (W/m · deg) of 100% and 96% (volume) ethanol at low temperatures [15]

t, °C	−60	−50	−40	−30	−20	−10	0	10	20	30	40	50	60
100%-	1865	1840	1820	1795	1770	1750	1725	1700	1680	1655	1635	1610	1585
96%-	1950	1930	1910	1890	1870	1850	1830	1810	1790	1770	1750	1730	1710

Thermal conductivity $\lambda \cdot 10^4$ (W/m · deg) of 100% ethanol [119]

T, °K \ p, bar →	1	5	10	15	20	25	30	35
290	1705	1707	1709	1711	1713	1715	1717	1719
300	1675	1677	1679	1681	1683	1685	1687	1689
320	1619	1621	1623	1626	1628	1631	1633	1635
340	1571	1573	1575	1578	1580	1583	1585	1588
350	1548	1550	1553	1556	1559	1561	1565	1568
360		1528	1531	1534	1537	1540	1543	1546
370		1507	1510	1513	1516	1520	1523	1526
380		1487	1491	1494	1497	1500	1504	1507
390	246	1468	1472	1475	1479	1482	1486	1489
400	258		1454	1457	1460	1464	1468	1471
410	270		1436	1440	1443	1447	1450	1454
420	282	302	1419	1422	1426	1430	1433	1437
430	293	313		1405	1409	1414	1416	1420
440	304	322		1389	1392			
450	316	331	346		1375			
460	328	341	356					
470	340	351	367	385	406	429		
480	352	363	377	394	414	437		
490	365	375	389	405	424	446		
500	378	387	400	416	435	457		
510	391	400	413	428	446	466	489	515
520	404	413	425	439	454	472	491	512
530	417	425	437	449	463	478	494	512
540	430	438	449	460	473	486	500	515
550	444	451	461	471	482	494	507	520
560	458	465	473	482	492	503	514	527
570	472	478	485	494	503	513	524	535

T, °K \ p, bar →	40	45	50	75	100	150	200	300	400
290	1721	1723	1525	1735	1746	1767	1790	1835	1870
300	1692	1694	1696	1708	1718	1739	1762	1805	1843
320	1638	1640	1643	1655	1668	1690	1713	1755	1794
340	1591	1593	1596	1610	1623	1649	1672	1715	1752
350	1571	1574	1575	1589	1603	1630	1653	1697	1734
360	1549	1552	1555	1569	1584	1610	1635	1679	1718
370	1529	1532	1535	1550	1565	1593	1619	1663	1703
380	1510	1513	1517	1532	1548	1576	1602	1647	1689
390	1493	1496	1499	1515	1530	1560	1586	1632	1676
400	1474	1477	1481	1498	1514	1544	1571	1618	1664
410	1457	1460	1464	1480	1497	1529	1555	1604	1652
420	1440	1443	1447	1464	1481	1513	1540	1590	1641
430	1423	1427	1430	1447	1465	1497	1525	1577	1631
440					1448	1482	1510	1563	1621
450					1432	1466	1496	1552	1610
460					1416	1450	1482	1540	1601
470					1400	1435	1467	1528	1592
480					1384	1420	1453	1517	1583
490					1368	1405	1439	1505	1573
500					1351	1389	1424	1494	1564
510	545	580	620		1332	1373	1410	1482	1553
520	537	566	599			1355	1396	1469	1542
530	533	555	583			1334	1382	1455	1531
540	532	550	571			1308	1365	1442	1520
550	535	550	567			1278	1345	1426	1507
560	540	553	568			1244	1320	1410	1494
570	547	560	573			1207	1291	1391	1481

Surface tension σ (N/m) of ethanol [64]

t, °C	$\sigma \cdot 10^3$	t, °C	$\sigma \cdot 10^3$	t, °C	$\sigma \cdot 10^3$	t, °C	$\sigma \cdot 10^3$	t, °C	$\sigma \cdot 10^3$
0	24.4	50	20.1	100	15.5	150	10.1	200	4.3
10	23.6	60	19.2	110	14.5	160	9.0	210	3.3
20	22.8	70	18.3	120	13.4	170	7.8	220	2.2
30	21.9	80	17.3	130	12.3	180	6.7	230	1.1
40	21.0	90	16.4	140	11.2	190	5.5	240	0 1

1-PROPANOL (n-PROPYL ALCOHOL) (C_3H_8O)

$CH_3CH_2CH_2OH$

Molecular weight 60.1

$t_{melt} = -126$ °C; $q = 86.6$ kJ/kg; $t_{boil} = 97.8$ °C; $t_{cr} = 263.7$ °C;
$p_{cr} = 50.5$ bar; $\rho_{cr} = 273$ kg/m³; $\sigma = 23.7$ erg/cm² at 20°C

Saturated vapor pressure of propanol [115]

t, °C	p, mm Hg	t, °C	p, mm Hg	t, °C	p, bar	t, °C	p, bar
−15.0	1	43.5	60	117.0	2.03	232.3	30.39
− 5.0	5	52.8	100	149.0	5.06	250.0	40.52
14.7	10	66.8	200	177.0	10.13	263.7	50.55
25.3	20	82.0	400	210.8	20.26		
36.4	40	97.8	760				

Density ρ (kg/m³) of saturated 1-propanol [71]

t, °C	$\varrho' \cdot 10^{-3}$	$\varrho'' \cdot 10^{-3}$	t, °C	$\varrho' \cdot 10^{-3}$	$\varrho'' \cdot 10^{-3}$	t, °C	$\varrho' \cdot 10^{-3}$	$\varrho'' \cdot 10^{-3}$
0	0.8193		130	0.6995	0.00605	220	0.5485	0.0556
20	0.8035	(0.0001)	140	0.6875	0.00805	230	0.5230	0.0704
40	0.7875	(0.0002)	150	0.6740	0.01050	240	0.4920	0.0904
60	0.7700	(0.0004)	160	0.6600	0.01380	250	0.4525	0.1180
80	0.7520	0.00104	170	0.6450	0.01770	260	0.3905	0.1610
90	0.7425	0.00156	180	0.6285	0.0225	263.15	0.3450	
100	0.7325	0.00226	190	0.6110	0.02820	263.50	0.3380	
110	0.7220	0.00320	200	0.5920	0.0353	263.70	0.2734	0.2734
120	0.7110	0.00443	210	0.5715	0.0442			

Heat capacity of 1-propanol gas at $p = 1$ bar [42]

t, °C	0	100	200	300	400	500	600
c_p, kJ/kg · deg	1.28	1.65	2.00	2.34	2.67	2.98	3.30

Latent heat of vaporization r (kJ/kg) of 1-propanol [64, 126, 127]

t, °C	r	t, °C	r	t, °C	r	t, °C	r
0	833	70	741	140	594	210	393
10	823	80	724	150	569	220	356
20	810	90	703	160	544	230	314
30	798	100	687	170	515	240	264
40	784	110	666	180	486	250	209
50	770	120	645	190	456	260	138
60	756	130	620	200	427	263.7	0

Viscosity η ($N \cdot s/m^2$) of saturated liquid 1-propanol [45, 52]

t, °C	$\eta \cdot 10^3$	t, °C	$\eta \cdot 10^3$	t, °C	$\eta \cdot 10^3$	t, °C	$\eta \cdot 10^3$	t, °C	$\eta \cdot 10^3$
−70	54.6	−20	6.90	30	1.72	100	0.447	150	0.216
−60	31.6	−10	5.10	40	1.38	110	0.387	160	0.188
−50	20.2	0	3.85	60	0.920	120	0.337	170	0.165
−40	13.5	10	2.89	80	0.630	130	0.291	180	0.148
−30	9.50	20	2.20	90	0.530	140	0.250	200	0.119

Viscosity of 1-propanol gas at $p \leqslant 1$ bar [52]

t, °C	0	50	100	150	200	250	300	400	500
$\eta \cdot 10^7$, $N \cdot s/m^2$	71.5	85.5	97.0	111	125	138	150	175	201

Viscosity η ($N \cdot s/m^2$) of 1-propanol at different temperatures and pressures [45]

p, bar	$\eta \cdot 10^5$
323.15 °K	
1.0	112.0
10.8	112.7
50.0	117.1
122.6	123.3
198.1	131.6
275.6	139.6
345.7	145.7
415.3	152.6
494.1	161.1
373.15 °K	
1.1	44.70
10.8	45.17
50.0	46.59
98.1	48.73
147.6	50.85
196.2	52.10
295.2	56.88
395.2	61.02
494.1	65.22
423.15 °K	
5.8	21.60
10.8	21.85
50.0	23.07
98.1	24.64
196.2	27.22
295.2	30.10
395.2	32.54
494.1	34.84
473.15 °K	
17.7	11.88
50.0	12.75
98.1	13.97
196.2	16.13
295.2	18.08
395.2	19.88
494.1	21.53
523.15 °K	
1.0	1.374
9.8	1.366
21.5	1.363
30.4	1.408
35.3	1.452
40.2	1.512
43.2	5.674
45.1	5.809
50.0	6.133
98.1	8.116
196.2	10.29
245.7	11.17
295.2	12.00
395.2	13.54
494.1	14.85
538.150 °K	
1.0	1.412
10.8	1.430
20.6	1.429
30.4	1.472
45.1	1.628
50.0	1.762
52.0	2.078
53.0	3.343
53.6	3.918
54.9	4.172
55.9	4.559
59.5	5.137
65.1	5.550
69.8	5.736
74.4	6.054
98.1	7.028
117.7	7.657
147.1	8.444
196.2	9.239
295.2	10.92
395	12.30
494.1	13.64
553.15 °K	
1.0	1.450
10.8	1.460
20.6	1.456
40.2	1.553
50.0	1.699
54.7	1.824
64.5	2.449
64.7	2.485
68.7	3.138
69.2	3.388
79.1	4.909
98.1	5.672
147.1	7.118
196.2	8.113
295.2	9.908
395.2	11.26
494.1	12.43

Thermal conductivity $\lambda \cdot 10^4$ (W/m · deg) of 1-propanol at different temperatures and pressures [119]

T, °K \ p, bar →	1	5	10	15	20	25	30	35
300	1560	1561	1563	1565	1567	1569	1571	1573
320	1519	1520	1523	1525	1527	1529	1531	1533
340	1479	1481	1483	1485	1487	1490	1492	1494
350	1460	1461	1464	1466	1468	1471	1473	1475
360	1440	1443	1445	1448	1450	1452	1455	1458
370	1421	1424	1427	1429	1432	1434	1437	1439
380		1407	1409	1412	1414	1416	1419	1422

continued

T, °K \ p, bar →	1	5	10	15	20	25	30	35
390		1389	1391	1394	1396	1399	1401	1404
400		1371	1374	1376	1379	1381	1384	1387
410	251	1362	1355	1359	1362	1364	1368	1371
420	262	1335	1338	1341	1344	1346	1350	1354
430	273		1321	1324	1328	1330	1333	1337
440	284		1303	1307	1310	1314	1317	1321
450	296			1291	1294	1298	1302	1306
460	309			1275	1279	1282	1286	1290
470	322	335	352		1263	1266	1271	1275
480	335	346	362		1245	1249	1254	1258
490	349	358	372			1230	1235	1239
500	361	370	383					
510	375	382	394					
520	388	394	405	418	433	453	478	
530	401	407	416	427	441	459	481	512
540	414	420	429	439	452	467	486	510
550	428	433	441	451	463	477	493	514
560	441	446	454	463	474	486	501	519
570	458	461	469	478	487	498	511	525

T, °K \ p, bar →	40	45	50	75	100	150	200	300	400
300	1575	1576	1578	1588	1597	1615	1634	1669	1704
310	1556	1557	1558	1569	1578	1597	1617	1653	1687
320	1535	1538	1539	1550	1560	1580	1600	1637	1672
330	1515	1517	1520	1531	1542	1562	1583	1622	1657
340	1496	1498	1501	1513	1524	1545	1567	1607	1642
350	1478	1480	1483	1495	1507	1529	1551	1593	1629
360	1460	1463	1465	1478	1490	1512	1535	1578	1615
370	1442	1445	1447	1460	1473	1496	1520	1564	1601
380	1425	1427	1430	1444	1456	1480	1506	1549	1588
390	1406	1409	1413	1427	1440	1465	1491	1535	1575
400	1390	1393	1396	1411	1425	1450	1476	1522	1563
410	1374	1377	1380	1395	1409	1435	1463	1508	1550
420	1357	1360	1364	1380	1394	1421	1449	1495	1538
430	1340	1343	1348	1365	1380	1408	1435	1482	1526
440	1325	1328	1332	1350	1366	1394	1421	1469	1514
450	1310	1313	1318	1335	1351	1380	1408	1456	1502
460	1294	1298	1302	1320	1337	1366	1395	1444	1490
470	1279	1283	1287	1305	1322	1353	1382	1431	1478
480	1263	1267	1270	1289	1308	1339	1369	1419	1466
490	1243	1248	1251	1272	1292	1326	1356	1407	1454
500			1230	1252	1275	1311	1343	1395	1443
510			1204	1229	1255	1296	1331	1383	1432
520			1173	1203	1235	1280	1317	1371	1420
530			1130	1175	1212	1263	1303	1358	1408
540	545				1186	1244	1288	1346	1396
550	540	576			1156	1222	1271	1334	1383
560	540	566	599		1120	1197	1253	1320	1370
570	542	562	586		1077	1170	1233	1306	1356

2-PROPANOL (ISOPROPYL ALCOHOL) (C_3H_8O)

$$CH_3—\underset{\displaystyle OH}{\underset{|}{CH}}—CH_3$$

Molecular weight 60.1

$t_{melt} = -89$ °C; $q = 89.2$ kJ/kg; $t_{boil} = 82.5$ °C; $r = 699.9$ kJ/kg at t_{boil};
$t_{cr} = 235.6$ °C; $p_{cr} = 53.7$ bar; $\rho_{cr} = 274$ kg/m³

Saturated vapor pressure of 2-propanol [115]

t, °C	−26.1	−7.0	2.4	12.7	23.8	30.5	39.5	53.0	67.8	82.5
p, mm Hg	1	5	10	20	40	60	100	200	400	760
t, °C	101.3	130.2	155.7	186.0	205.0	220.2	232.0	235.0		
p, bar	2.03	5.06	10.13	20.26	30.39	40.52	50.65	53.69		

Density of liquid 2-propanol [71]

t, °C	0	10	15	20	25	30
$\rho \cdot 10^{-3}$, kg/m³	0.8012	0.7932	0.7892	0.7851	0.7809	0.7769

Heat capacity of 2-propanol gas [130]

t, °C	100	120	140	160	180
c_p^0, kJ/kg · deg	1.775	1.846	1.918	1.989	2.059
c_p at p = 1 bar kJ/kg · deg	2.016	1.946	1.976	2.026	2.084

Latent heat of vaporization of 2-propanol [128–130]

t, °C	40	50	60	70	80	90	100
r, kJ/kg	737	723	705	687	670	648	628

Thermal conductivity $\lambda \cdot 10^4$ (W/m · deg) of 2-propanol [119]

T, °K \ p, bar →	1	5	10	15	20	25	30	35
300	1400	1401	1403	1405	1407	1409	1411	1413
320	1364	1366	1368	1370	1372	1374	1377	1379
340	1329	1332	1334	1336	1338	1339	1342	1344
350	1311	1313	1315	1317	1319	1322	1324	1326
360		1294	1297	1299	1301	1304	1306	1309
370		1275	1277	1280	1283	1286	1288	1291
380		1258	1261	1263	1266	1270	1272	1274
390	242	1243	1245	1248	1251	1254	1257	1259
400	254	1228	1231	1233	1236	1239	1241	1244
410	265		1216	1219	1222	1222	1228	1230
420	277	289	1201	1204	1207	1210	1213	1216
430	288	300		1189	1192	1195	1198	1201

continued

T, °K \ p, bar →	1	5	10	15	20	25	30	35
440	299	311		1173	1176	1179	1184	1187
450	310	322			1158	1162	1166	1170
460	323	334				1144	1147	1152
470	335	346	364	386	418	463	1132	1136
480	347	357	373	394	421	458		
490	360	370	384	400	423	454		
500	373	382	394	408	427	452		
510	386	394	405	417	433	452	477	509
520	400	406	415	426	438	454	473	498
530	412	418	426	436	446	458	475	496
540	426	431	438	446	455	464	477	496
550	440	444	450	456	464	473	483	497
560	454	457	462	468	474	482	490	499

T, °K \ p, bar →	40	45	50	75	100	150	200	300	400
300	1415	1417	1419	1429	1439	1460	1480	1522	1562
320	1381	1383	1385	1394	1404	1424	1446	1490	1531
340	1346	1348	1350	1360	1371	1392	1415	1460	1502
350	1328	1330	1333	1344	1355	1377	1400	1445	1487
360	1311	1313	1316	1328	1339	1362	1385	1431	1473
370	1293	1296	1299	1312	1323	1347	1371	1417	1460
380	1277	1280	1283	1296	1309	1333	1358	1403	1446
390	1262	1264	1267	1281	1295	1320	1345	1390	1434
400	1247	1249	1252	1266	1280	1306	1332	1378	1422
410	1233	1236	1238	1252	1267	1294	1320	1366	1410
420	1219	1222	1225	1239	1254	1282	1308	1354	1399
430	1204	1207	1210	1226	1242	1270	1296	1343	1389
440	1191	1194	1196	1213	1230	1258	1285	1332	1379
450	1174	1178	1182	1199	1216	1246	1274	1322	1370
460	1156	1161	1165	1184	1203	1235	1264	1312	1361
470	1141	1145	1148	1168	1188	1222	1252	1302	1353
480			1128	1151	1172	1209	1241	1294	1345
490			1104	1132	1155	1195	1230	1285	1338
500			1077	1110	1137	1181	1219	1276	1330
510	552	612			1118	1166	1207	1266	1321
520	532	578	648		1095	1151	1194	1256	1313
530	523	556	606		1072	1135	1180	1246	1304
540	517	543	578		1047	1117	1164	1235	1295
550	513	532	556		1017	1097	1148	1224	1286
560	510	524	540		974	1072	1130	1213	1277

Viscosity of 2-propanol gas at $p \leqslant 1$ bar [52]

t, °C	0	50	100	150	200	250	300	400	500
$\eta \cdot 10^7$, $N \cdot s/m^2$	72.0	85.5	98.5	111	124	137	150	176	202

Viscosity η ($N \cdot s/m^2$) of saturated 2-propanol [52]

t, °C	$\eta' \cdot 10^7$	$\eta'' \cdot 10^7$	t, °C	$\eta' \cdot 10^7$	$\eta'' \cdot 10^7$	t, °C	$\eta' \cdot 10^7$	$\eta'' \cdot 10^7$
−60	661 000		40	13 300		170	1470	119
−50	376 000	65.0	60	8 000		180	1300	122
−40	230 000		80	5 200		190	1160	127
−30	149 000		100	3 760	98.0	200	1010	133

continued

t, °C	$\eta' \cdot 10^7$	$\eta'' \cdot 10^7$	t, °C	$\eta' \cdot 10^7$	$\eta'' \cdot 10^7$	t, °C	$\eta' \cdot 10^7$	$\eta'' \cdot 10^7$
−20	101 000		110	3 250	101	210	865	141
−10	68 000		120	2 820	104	220	725	152
0	46 000	72.0	130	2 460	107	230	580	185
10	32 600		140	2 140	110	233	477	222
20	23 900		150	1 885	113	235	282	282
30	17 600		160	1 665	116			

Viscosity $\eta \cdot 10^7$ ($N \cdot s/m^2$) of 2-propanol at different temperatures and pressures [52]

p, atm \ t, °C →	155	200	230	240	260	p, atm \ t, °C →	155	200	230	240	260
1	113	124	132	135	140	200	2397	1487	1128	1030	858
25	1820			143	144	300	2678	1690	1313	1209	1040
50	1919	1079	626	180	166	400	2951	1888	1485	1375	1206
75	2002	1157	782	627	405	500	3216	2070	1646	1537	1357
100	2088	1232	873	759	569	600	3458	2244	1800	1685	1500
125	2168	1300	951	842	663	700	3692	2418	1945	1830	1633
150	2246	1368	1017	915	741	800	3926	2587	2090	1971	1763

Surface tension of 2-propanol [64]

t, °C	−10	0	10	20	30	40	50	60	70	80	90	100
$\sigma \cdot 10^3$, N/m	26.3	25.5	24.6	23.8	23.0	22.1	21.2	20.4	19.6	18.8	18.0	17.2

n-BUTANOL (BUTYL ALCOHOL) ($C_4H_{10}O$)

$CH_3CH_2CH_2CH_2OH$

Molecular weight 74.1

$t_{melt} = -90$ °C; $q = 125.2$ kJ/kg; $t_{boil} = 117.5$ °C;
$r = 590.4$ kJ/kg; $t_{cr} = 288$ °C; $p_{cr} = 49.6$ bar

Saturated vapor pressure of *n*-butanol [115]

t, °C	−1.2	20.0	30.2	41.5	53.4	60.3	70.1	84.3	100.8	117.5
p, mm Hg	1	5	10	20	40	60	100	200	400	760
t, °C	139.8	172.5	203.0	237.0	259.0	277.0	288.0			
p, bar	2.03	5.06	10.13	20.26	30.39	40.52	49.03			

Density of liquid *n*-butanol [71]

t, °C	0	10	20	25	30	35
$\varrho \cdot 10^{-3}$, kg/m³	0.8246	0.8171	0.8096	0.8057	0.8020	0.7984

Heat capacity of *n*-butanol at $p = 1$ bar [42]

t, °C	0	100	200	300	400	500	600
c_p, kJ/kg · deg	1.24	1.64	2.03	2.41	2.78	3.14	3.50

Viscosity of n-butanol gas at $p \leqslant 1$ bar [42]

t, °C	0	100	200	300	400	500	600
$\eta \cdot 10^7$, $N \cdot s/m^2$	66	90	113	136	161	182	206

Viscosity η ($N \cdot s/m^2$) of liquid n-butanol [94]

t, °C	$\eta \cdot 10^3$	t, °C	$\eta \cdot 10^3$	t, °C	$\eta \cdot 10^3$	t, °C	$\eta \cdot 10^3$	t, °C	$\eta \cdot 10^3$	t, °C	$\eta \cdot 10^3$
−50	34.7	−20	10.3	10	3.87	40	1.78	70	0.93	100	0.54
−40	22.4	−10	7.4	20	2.95	50	1.41	80	0.76	110	0.46
−30	14.6	0	5.19	30	2.28	60	1.14	90	0.63		

Thermal conductivity of n-butanol at low temperatures [72, 79]

t, °C	−80	−60	−40	−20	0	20	40	60
λ, W/m · deg	0.169	0.166	0.163	0.160	0.157	0.154	0.151	0.148

Thermal conductivity $\lambda \cdot 10^4$ (W/m · deg) of n-butanol [45]

T, °K \ p, bar →	1	5	10	15	20	25	30	35
290	1558	1559	1561	1562	1564	1565	1567	1569
300	1540	1541	1544	1544	1546	1548	1549	1551
320	1502	1504	1506	1508	1510	1512	1514	1516
340	1465	1469	1471	1473	1475	1477	1479	1481
360	1429	1430	1433	1435	1438	1441	1442	1445
380	1392	1394	1397	1400	1402	1405	1408	1411
390	1375	1377	1380	1382	1384	1388	1390	1392
400		1360	1362	1365	1367	1370	1373	1375
410		1342	1345	1348	1350	1353	1355	1358
420		1325	1327	1330	1333	1335	1338	1341
430		1306	1309	1311	1314	1317	1320	1323
440	273	1288	1291	1294	1297	1300	1303	1306
450	285		1274	1277	1280	1282	1286	1289
460	298		1256	1259	1262	1263	1268	1271
470	311	324	1235	1238	1242	1244	1249	1252
480	324	336		1216	1220	1224	1228	1232
490	336	348		1192	1196	1200	1205	1209
500	349	359			1171	1174	1181	1186
510	362	371				1144	1150	1157
520	374	383	399	418		1106	1116	1125
530	387	395	408	424	443			
540	399	406	417	431	446			
550	412	418	427	438	450			
560	425	429	436	444	456	472	494	
570	437	440	444	451	459	469	482	500
580	450	451	454	457	462	468	476	486

T, °K \ p, bar →	40	45	50	75	100	150	200	300	400
290	1570	1571	1573	1580	1588	1602	1618	1652	1687
300	1553	1554	1555	1563	1571	1586	1603	1638	1674
320	1518	1519	1521	1530	1539	1555	1574	1611	1647
340	1483	1485	1487	1496	1506	1525	1545	1584	1621
360	1447	1449	1452	1463	1474	1494	1515	1557	1594

continued

T, °K \ p, bar →	40	45	50	75	100	150	200	300	400
380	1413	1415	1418	1430	1442	1463	1485	1530	1568
390	1395	1398	1400	1414	1426	1448	1471	1517	1555
400	1378	1381	1383	1397	1410	1432	1456	1503	1542
410	1361	1363	1366	1380	1394	1416	1441	1490	1529
420	1343	1346	1349	1363	1377	1401	1427	1476	1517
430	1326	1329	1332	1346	1360	1387	1412	1462	1504
440	1309	1311	1314	1329	1345	1372	1397	1448	1491
450	1292	1295	1298	1313	1328	1357	1383	1435	1479
460	1274	1277	1280	1296	1311	1342	1369	1422	1466
470	1256	1259	1262	1280	1295	1327	1355	1409	1454
480	1235	1239	1243	1262	1279	1312	1341	1396	1442
490	1213	1218	1223	1244	1263	1298	1326	1382	1430
500	1191	1196	1201	1226	1247	1281	1312	1369	1418
510	1163	1170	1177	1205	1230	1266	1297	1355	1406
520	1133	1142	1150	1184	1212	1250	1282	1342	1393
530					1194	1234	1267	1328	1381
540					1175	1218	1252	1314	1368
550					1155	1200	1236	1300	1355
560					1134	1182	1220	1285	1341
570	522	556	613		1108	1162	1201	1269	1328
580	500	517	546		1077	1140	1182	1252	1314

Surface tension σ (N/m) of n-butanol [64]

t, °C	$\sigma \cdot 10^3$	t, °C	$\sigma \cdot 10^3$	t, °C	$\sigma \cdot 10^3$	t, °C	$\sigma \cdot 10^3$	t, °C	$\sigma \cdot 10^3$
0	26.2	30	23.8	60	21.4	90	18.8	120	16.1
10	25.4	40	23.0	70	20.5	100	17.8	130	15.1
20	24.6	50	22.1	80	19.6	110	17.0	140	14.2

GLYCEROL ($C_3H_8O_3$)

CH_2—OH
|
CH—OH
|
CH_2—OH

Molecular weight 92.1

$t_{melt} = 18.0$ °C; $t_{boil} = 290$ °C at $p = 1$ atm

Saturated vapor pressure of glycerol [131]

t, °C	125.5	153.8	167.2	182.2	189.0	208.0	220.1	240.0	263.0	290.0
p, mm Hg	1	5	10	20	40	60	100	200	400	760

Density of liquid glycerol [343]

t, °C	20	40	60	80	100	120	140	160	180	200	220	240
ϱ, kg/m³	1260	1250	1238	1224	1208	1188	1167	1143	1117	1090	1059	1025

Heat capacity of liquid glycerol [343]

t, °C	20	40	60	80	100	120	140	160	180	200	220	240
c_p, kJ/kg · deg	2.35	2.45	2.56	2.67	2.79	2.90	3.01	3.12	3.23	3.34	3.46	3.60

Viscosity η ($N \cdot s/m^2$) of liquid glycerol [131]

t,°C	η.10³	t,°C	η.10³	t,°C	η.10³	t,°C	η.10³
0	12 100	40	330	80	35	140	1.8
5	7 050	50	180	90	21	160	1.0
10	3 950	60	102	100	13	180	0.45
20	1 480	70	59	120	5.2	200	0.22
30	600						

Thermal conductivity of liquid glycerol [97]

t, °C	25	50	75	100	125	150
λ, W/m · deg	0.279	0.283	0.286	0.289	0.292	0.296

Surface tension σ (N/m) of glycerol [131]

t,°C	σ.10³	t,°C	σ.10³	t,°C	σ.10³	t,°C	σ.10³
20	59.4	60	57.4	100	54.2	130	51.1
30	59.0	70	56.7	110	53.2	140	50.0
40	58.5	80	55.9	120	52.2	150	48.8
50	58.0	90	55.0				

ETHERS

ETHYL ETHER ($C_4H_{10}O$)

$C_2H_5OC_2H_5$

Molecular weight 74.1

$t_{melt} = -116.3$ °C; $q = 100.5$ kJ/kg; $t_{boil} = 34.6$ °C;
$t_{cr} = 193.8$ °C; $p_{cr} = 36.1$ bar, $\rho_{cr} = 265$ kg/m³

Saturated vapor pressure of ethyl ether [115]

t,°C	p, mm Hg	t,°C	p, bar	t,°C	p, bar	t °C	p, bar	t,°C	p, bar
−10	112.3	40	1.228	90	5.106	140	14.73	185	31.48
0	184.9	50	1.701	100	6.471	150	17.68	190	34.01
10	290.8	60	2.311	110	8.107	160	21.03	192	35.10
20	439.8	70	3.070	120	10.01	170	24.89	193	35.72
34.6	760	80	3.964	130	12.21	180	29.02	193.8	36.06

Density ρ (kg/m³) of saturated ethyl ether [71]

t,°C	ρ'.10⁻³	ρ''.10⁻³	t,°C	ρ'.10⁻³	ρ''.10⁻³	t,°C	ρ'.10⁻³	ρ''.10⁻³
0	0.7362	0.000827	80	0.6402	0.01155	160	0.4947	0.06911
10	0.7248	0.001264	90	0.6250	0.01477	170	0.4658	0.08731
20	0.7135	0.001870	100	0.6105	0.01867	180	0.4268	0.1135
30	0.7019	0.002677	110	0.5942	0.02349	185	0.4018	0.1320
40	0.6894	0.003731	120	0.5764	0.02934	190	0.3663	0.1620
50	0.6764	0.005079	130	0.5580	0.03638	192	0.3468	0.1826
60	0.6658	0.006771	140	0.5385	0.04488	193	0.3300	0.2012
70	0.6532	0.00892	150	0.5179	0.05551	193.8	0.265	0.265

Heat capacity of ethyl ether gast at $p = 1$ bar [42]

t, °C	0	100	200	300	400	500	600
c_p, kJ/kg · deg	1.44	1.84	2.22	2.59	2.94	3.27	3.61

Latent heat of vaporization r (kJ/kg) of ethyl ether [64]

t, °C	r	t, °C	r	t, °C	r	t, °C	r
30	353.8	80	307.7	130	249.1	170	165.4
40	345.4	90	297.3	140	234.5	180	134.0
50	337.0	100	286.8	150	215.6	190	81.6
60	328.7	110	274.2	160	192.6	193.8	0
70	318.2	120	261.7				

Viscosity of ethyl ether gas at $p \leqslant 1$ bar [42]

t, °C	0	100	200	300	400	500	600
$\eta \cdot 10^7$, N · s/m²	68.5	93.0	117	139	165	188	212

Viscosity $\eta \cdot 10^7$ (N · s/m²) of ethyl ether at different temperatures and pressures [52]

p, atm \ t, °C →	135.5	185	203	225	249	p, atm \ t, °C →	135.5	185	203	225	249
1	101	113	118	123	129	125	1020	716	632	539	446
20			124	125	130	150	1060	762	682	592	502
30	840		139	132	133	200	1138	840	764	676	592
40	860	443	199	153	145	300	1277	973	897	814	728
50	880	507	372	198	167	400	1414	1100	1020	937	849
60	902	546	438	279	199	500	1550	1215	1132	1051	955
70	921	580	483	363	243	600	1658	1321	1237	1150	1051
80	940	611	519	411	294	800	1894	1522	1437	1336	1224
100	975	660	577	477	376						

Viscosity η (N · s/m²) of liquid ethyl ether [94]

t, °C	$\eta \cdot 10^3$	t, °C	$\eta \cdot 10^3$	t, °C	$\eta \cdot 10^3$	t, °C	$\eta \cdot 10^3$
−120	4.25	−70	0.79	−20	0.364	30	0.220
−110	2.54	−60	0.65	−10	0.328	40	0.199
−100	1.71	−50	0.55	0	0.296	60	0.166
−90	1.24	−40	0.470	10	0.268	80	0.140
−80	0.97	−30	0.410	20	0.243	100	0.118

Thermal conductivity of ethyl ether gas at $p = 1$ bar [42]

t, °C	0	100	200	300	400	500	600
$\lambda \cdot 10^4$, W/m · deg	130	228	352	500	673	864	1082

Thermal conductivity of liquid ethyl ether [79]

t, °C	−80	−60	−40	−20	0	20
λ, W/m · deg	0.170	0.163	0.156	0.149	0.143	0.136

Surface tension σ (N/m) of ethyl ether [64]

t, °C	$\sigma \cdot 10^3$	t, °C	$\sigma \cdot 10^3$	t, °C	$\sigma \cdot 10^3$	t, °C	$\sigma \cdot 10^3$
0	19.4	50	13.5	100	8.0	150	3.1
10	18.2	60	12.4	110	7.0	160	2.3
20	17.0	70	11.3	120	5.9	170	1.5
30	15.8	80	10.2	130	4.9	180	0.8
40	14.6	90	9.1	140	4.0	190	0.2

PHENYL ETHER ($C_{12}H_{10}O$)

Molecular weight 170.08

$t_{melt} = 27$ °C; $t_{boil} = 259$ °C at $p = 1$ atm;

$t_{cr} = 532$ °C; $p_{cr} = 34.5$ bar

Thermodynamic properties of saturated phenyl ether [131]:
ρ (kg/m³), c_p (kJ/kg · deg), i and r (kJ/kg)

t, °C	p, bar	ϱ'	ϱ''	c_p'	i'	i''	r
220		905					
230		899					
240		893					
250	0.832	884					
260	1.056	875	4.5	2.6	487.8	762.8	275.1
270	1.28	864	5.7	2.7	514.6	784.6	270.0
280	1.57	853	6.8	2.7	541.4	806.4	265.0
290	1.90	842	8.3	2.7	568.6	828.6	260.0
300	2.28	831	9.9	2.7	595.8	851.2	255.4
310	2.73	820	12.7	2.8	623.4	874.2	250.8
320	3.21	810	15.5	2.8	651.0	897.2	246.2
330	3.79	800	18.8	2.8	679.1	920.8	241.6
340	4.41	789	20.2	2.8	707.2	944.1	237.0
350	5.14	779	22.1	2.8	735.6	968.0	232.4
360	5.94	768	24.0	2.8	764.1	991.8	227.8
370	6.84			2.9	793.0	1016.1	223.2

ETHYL ACETATE ($C_4H_8O_2$)

$CH_3COOC_2H_5$

Molecular weight 88.1

$t_{melt} = -82.6$ °C; $q = 118.9$ kJ/kg; $t_{boil} = 77.1$ °C;
$t_{cr} = 250.1$ °C; $p_{cr} = 38.5$ bar; $\rho_{cr} =$ kg/m³; $\lambda = 0.123$ kcal/m · hr · deg at 30 °C

Saturated vapor pressure of ethyl acetate [115]

t, °C	p, mm Hg	t, °C	p, mm Hg	t, °C	p, bar	t, °C	p, bar	t, °C	p, bar
−20	6,55	30	118,7	80	1,110	160	8,489	230	28,35
−10	12,95	40	186,2	90	1,506	170	10,32	240	33,06
0	24,30	50	282,2	100	2,022	180	12,42	245	35,64
10	42,7	60	415.4	110	2.667	190	14.83	247	36,70
20	72,8	70	596,3	120	3,447	200	17,60	249	37,82
				130	4,395	210	20,75	250	38,38
				140	5,552	220	24,33	250,1	38,49
				150	6,888				

Latent heat of vaporization r (kJ/kg) of ethyl acetate [64]

t, °C	r	t, °C	r	t, °C	r	t, °C	r	t, °C	r
80	360.1	120	324.5	160	278,4	200	217,7	230	150.7
90	351.7	130	314,0	170	265,9	210	198,9	240	113,0
100	343.3	140	303.5	180	251.2	220	177,9	250.1	0
110	334.9	150	291.0	190	234.5				

Density ρ (kg/m³) of saturated ethyl acetate [71]

t, °C	$\varrho' \cdot 10^{-3}$	$\varrho'' \cdot 10^{-3}$	t, °C	$\varrho' \cdot 10^{-3}$	$\varrho'' \cdot 10^{-3}$	t, °C	$\varrho' \cdot 10^{-3}$	$\varrho'' \cdot 10^{-3}$
0	0,92436	0,0001	100	0.7972	0.006158	200	0.6210	0.05797
10	0,9127	0,0002	110	0.7831	0.008006	210	0.5944	0.07128
20	0,9005	0,0003	120	0.7683	0.01030	220	0.5648	0.08905
30	0,8885	0,0005	130	0.7533	0.01314	230	0.5281	0,1131
40	0,8762	0.0008	140	0.7378	0.01650	240	0.4778	0,1499
50	0,8686	0,0012	150	0.7210	0,02070	245	0.4401	0,1802
60	0,8508	0.0018	160	0.7033	0.02577	247	0.4195	0,1996
70	0,8376	0,002561	170	0.6848	0.03165	249	0.3839	0,2288
80	0,8245	0,003495	180	0,6653	0.03883	250.1	0.3077	0,3077
90	0,8192	0,004677	190	0.6441	0.04751			

Heat capacity of ethyl acetate gas at $p = 1$ bar [42]

t, °C	0	100	200	300	400	500	600
c_p, kJ/kg · deg	1.17	1.46	1.74	2.00	2.26	2,50	2,73

Viscosity of ethyl acetate gas at $p \leqslant 1$ bar [42]

t, °C	0	100	200	300	400	500	600
$\eta \cdot 10^7$ N · s/m²	69	95	121	146	170	197	224

Viscosity η ($N \cdot s/m^2$) of liquid ethyl acetate [125]

t, °C	$\eta \cdot 10^3$	t, °C	$\eta \cdot 10^3$	t, °C	$\eta \cdot 10^3$	t, °C	$\eta \cdot 10^3$
20	0.477	100	0.212	180	0.104	230	0.059
40	0.380	120	0.177	200	0.086	240	0.048
60	0.308	140	0.149	220	0.068	247	0.036
80	0.250	160	0.125				

Thermal conductivity of ethyl acetate gas at $p \leqslant 1$ bar [42]

t, °C	0	100	200	300	400	500	600
$\lambda \cdot 10^4$, W/m · deg	92.0	166	263	384	523	683	870

Surface tension σ (N/m) of ethyl acetate [64]

t, °C	$\sigma \cdot 10^3$	t, °C	$\sigma \cdot 10^3$	t, °C	$\sigma \cdot 10^3$	t, °C	$\sigma \cdot 10^3$	t, °C	$\sigma \cdot 10^3$
0	27.0	50	20.5	100	14.4	150	8.7	200	3.7
10	25.6	60	19.3	110	13.3	160	7.6	210	2.8
20	24.3	70	18.1	120	12.1	170	6.6	220	2.0
30	23.0	80	16.8	130	10.9	180	5.7	230	1.2
40	21.7	90	15.6	140	9.8	190	4.7	240	0.5

ACETONE (METHYL KETONE) (C_3H_6O)

$$H_3C-\underset{\underset{O}{\|}}{C}-CH_3$$

Molecular weight 58.1

$t_{melt} = -93.2$ °C; $q =$ kJ/kg; $t_{boil} = 56.1$ °C;

$r = 524$ kJ/kg at t_{boil}; $t_{cr} = 235.0$ °C; $p_{cr} = 47.6$ bar; $\rho_{cr} = 273$ kg/m³

Saturated vapor pressure of acetone [115]

t, °C	−59.4	−40.5	−31.1	−20.8	−9.4	−2.0	7.7	22.7	39.5	56.5
p, mm Hg	1	5	10	20	40	60	100	200	400	760
t, °C	78.6	113.0	144.5	181.0	205.0	214.5	235.0			
p, bar	2.02	5.06	10.13	20.26	30.39	40.52	47.61			

Density of liquid acetone [71]

t, °C	0	10	20	30	40	50	60	70	80
$\varrho \cdot 10^3$, kg/m³	0.8130	0.8019	0.7905	0.7788	0.7674	0.7564	0.7446	0.7326	0.7205

Heat capacity of acetone gas [42]

t, °C	0	100	200	300	400	500	600
c_p, kJ/kg · deg	1.26	1.54	1.79	2.02	2.24	2.43	2.59

Heat capacity of liquid acetone [132, 133]

t, °C	−50	−25	0	10	20	30	40	50
c_p, kJ/kg · deg	2.03	2.06	2,11	2.14	2.16	2.19	2.22	2,25

Viscosity of acetone at $p = 1$ bar [42]

t, °C	0	100	200	300	400	500	600
$\eta \cdot 10^7$, N · s/m²	68,6	94,0	121	147	174	200	228

Viscosity $\eta \cdot 10^7$ (N · s/m²) of acetone at different temperatures and pressures [52]

p, atm \ t, °C →	203	231	240	263.4	p, атм \ t, °C →	203	231	240	263.5
1	122	129	131	137	150	1011	801	736	654
15	—	—	133	139	200	1090	885	834	746
30	—	—	140	143	300	1232	1024	970	885
45		—	177	161	400	1362	1138	1085	995
60		569	493	249	500	1482	1248	1194	1100
75		622	562	423	600	1586	1349	1292	1194
100	916	698	641	531	800	1785	1536	1460	

Thermal conductivity of acetone gas [42]

t, °C	0	100	200	300	400	500	600
$\lambda \cdot 10^4$, W/m · deg	97,2	173	269	386	521	674	847

Thermal conductivity of liquid acetone [97]

t, °C	0	25	50
λ, W/m · deg	0.174	0,169	0.163

Surface tension of acetone [64]

t, °C	0	10	20	30	40	50	60	70	80
$\sigma \cdot 10^3$, N/m	26,2	25,0	23.7	22.5	21.2	19.9	18.6	17.4	16 2

CARBOXYLIC ACIDS

ACETIC ACID ($C_2H_4O_2$)

CH_3—COOH

Molecular weight 60.05

t_{melt} = 16.7 °C; q = 194 kJ/kg; t_{boil} = 118 °C; t_{cr} = 321.6 °C;
p_{cr} = 57.9 bar; ρ_{cr} = 351 kg/m³; c_p at 20 °C = 2.03 kJ/kg · deg

Saturated vapor pressure of acetic acid [71]

t, °C	p, mm Hg	t, °C	p, mm Hg	t, °C	p, bar	t, °C	p, bar	t, °C	p, bar
20	11.80	70	137.10	130	1.386	200	7.775	270	27.52
30	19.90	80	202.1	140	1.841	210	9.497	280	32.15
40	34.00	90	292.8	150	2.499	220	11.52	300	42.72
50	56.20	100	416.5	160	3.211	230	13.87	310	49.24
60	88.30	110	582.6	170	4.076	240	16.66	320	56.72
				180	5.109	250	19.81	321.6	58.84
				190	6.309	260	23.43		

Density ρ (kg/m³) of saturated acetic acid [71]

t, °C	$\rho' \cdot 10^{-3}$	$\rho'' \cdot 10^{-3}$	t, °C	$\rho' \cdot 10^{-3}$	$\rho'' \cdot 10^{-3}$	t, °C	$\rho' \cdot 10^{-3}$	$\rho'' \cdot 10^{-3}$
20	1.0491	0.0000764	130	0.9265	0.004275	240	0.7571	0.04227
30	1.0392	0.0001264	140	0.9091	0.005515	250	0.7364	0.05163
40	1.0284	0.0002012	150	0.8963	0.00703	260	0.7136	0.06165
50	1.0175	0.0003100	160	0.8829	0.00887	270	0.6900	0.07365
60	1.0060	0.0004221	170	0.8694	0.01084	280	0.6629	0.0883
70	0.9948	0.000673	180	0.8555	0.01370	290	0.6334	0.1073
80	0.9835	0.000959	190	0.8413	0.01681	300	0.5950	0.1331
90	0.9718	0.001338	200	0.8265	0.02052	310	0.5423	0.1718
100	0.9599	0.001833	210	0.8109	0.02488	320	0.4615	
110	0.9483	0.002468	220	0.7941	0.03021	321.6	0.3506	0.3506
120	0.9362	0.003271	230	0.7764	0.03626			

Latent heat of vaporization r (kJ/kg) of acetic acid [64]

t, °C	r	t, °C	r	t, °C	r	t, °C	r	t, °C	r
20	352.1	80	383.5	140	384.3	200	356.7	250	316.9
30	358.8	90	386.9	150	380.6	210	350.4	260	303.5
40	365.1	100	389.8	160	376.4	220	343.7	270	288.0
50	370.1	110	391.0	170	371.8	230	336.2	280	265.9
60	375.1	120	390.2	180	367.2	240	327.4		
70	379.3	130	388.1	190	362.2				

Viscosity of acetic acid gas at $p \leqslant 1$ bar [52]

t, °C	50	75	100	150	200	250	300	400
$\eta \cdot 10^2$, N · s/m²	82.5	91.2	100	117	134	151	167	198

Viscosity of liquid acetic acid [94]

t, °C	30	40	50	60	80	100	120	130
$\eta \cdot 10^3$, N · s/m²	0.79	0.69	0.62	0.55	0.453	0.377	0.320	0.297

Thermal conductivity of liquid acetic acid [97]

t, °C	25	50	75
λ, W/m · deg	0.171	0.167	0.162

Surface tension σ (N/m) of acetic acid [64]

t, °C	$\sigma \cdot 10^3$	t, °C	$\sigma \cdot 10^3$	t, °C	$\sigma \cdot 10^3$	t, °C	$\sigma \cdot 10^3$
20	27.8	80	21.8	140	15.9	200	10.4
30	26.8	90	20.8	150	15.0	210	9.4
40	25.8	100	19.8	160	14.1	220	8.5
50	24.8	110	18.8	170	13.2	230	7.6
60	23.8	120	17.9	180	12.2	240	6.6
70	22.8	130	16.9	190	11.3	250	5.7

BENZOIC ACID ($C_7H_6O_2$)

C_6H_5—COOH

Molecular weight 122.12

$t_{melt} = 122.36$ °C; $q = 142$ kJ/kg; $t_{boil} = 250$ °C;

r at $t_{boil} = 704$ kJ/kg

Saturated vapor pressure of benzoic acid [115, 134]

t, °C	132.1	146.7	162.6	172.8	186.2	205.8	227.0	250.0
p, mm Hg	10	20	40	60	100	200	400	760

Density of liquid benzoic acid [134]

t, °C	130	140	150	160	170	180
$\varrho \cdot 10^{-3}$, kg/m³	1.0749	1.0658	1.0567	1.0476	1.0385	1.0294

Heat capacity of liquid benzoic acid [135]

T, °K	395.52	400	410
C_p, kJ/kg · deg	8.5906	8.6842	8.9080

ANILINE (C_6H_7N)

C_6H_5—NH_2

Molecular weight 93.1

$t_{melt} = -6.2$ °C; $q = 113$ kJ/kg; $t_{boil} = 184.4$ °C;

r at $t_{boil} = 448$ kJ/kg: $t_{cr} = 426{,}0$ °C; $p_{cr} = 53.1$ bar; $\rho_{cr} = 340$ kg/m³

Saturated vapor pressure of aniline [115]

t, °C	34.8	57.9	69.4	82.0	96.7	106.0	119.9	140.1	161.9	184.4
p, mm Hg	1	5	10	20	40	60	100	200	400	760
t, °C	212.8	254.8	292.7	342.0	375.5	400.0	422.4	426.0		
p, bar	2.02	5.06	10.13	20.26	30.39	40.52	50.65	53.08		

Density ρ (kg/m³) of liquid aniline [71]

t, °C	$\rho \cdot 10^{-3}$	t, °C	$\rho \cdot 10^{-3}$	t, °C	$\rho \cdot 10^{-3}$	t, °C	$\rho \cdot 10^{-3}$
0	1.0373	50	0.9990	100	0.9524	150	0.9050
10	1.0299	60	0.9901	110	0.9425	160	0.8960
20	1.0225	70	0.9813	120	0.9328	170	0.8873
30	1.0152	80	0.9718	130	0.9234	180	0.8780
40	1.0070	90	0.9625	140	0.9141		

Heat capacity of liquid aniline [136–138]

t, °C	0	20	40	60	80	100	120	140
c_p, kJ/kg · deg	2.03	2.07	2.12	2.17	2.23	2.32	2.51	2.78

Viscosity η of liquid aniline [94]

t, °C	0	10	20	30	40	50	60	70	80	90	100	110	120
$\eta \cdot 10^3$, N · s/m²	10.2	6.5	4.40	3.12	2.30	1.80	1.50	1.28	1.10	0.94	0.80	0.69	0.59

Thermal conductivity of liquid aniline [97]

t, °C	0	25	50	75	100	125	150
λ, W/m · deg	0.186	0.181	0.177	0.172	0.167	0.163	0.159

Surface tension σ (N/m) of aniline [64]

t, °C	$\sigma \cdot 10^3$	t, °C	$\sigma \cdot 10^3$	t, °C	$\sigma \cdot 10^3$	t, °C	$\sigma \cdot 10^3$
0	45	50	39.5	100	33.7	150	27.9
10	44	60	38.4	110	32.5	160	26.8
20	42.9	70	37.2	120	31.4	170	25.7
30	41.8	80	36.0	130	30.2	180	24.6
40	40.7	90	34.9	140	29.1		

NITROBENZENE ($C_6H_5NO_2$)

Molecular weight 123.1
$t_{melt} = 5.7$ °C; $q = 98.5$ kJ/kg; $t_{boil} = 210.6$ °C;
at t_{boil} $r = 410$ kJ/kg; at 20 °C $c_p = 1.51$ kJ/kg · deg

Saturated vapor pressure of nitrobenzene [115]

t, °C	44.4	71.6	84.9	99.3	115.4	125.8	139.9	161.2	185.8	210.6
p, mm Hg	1	5	10	20	40	60	100	200	400	760

Density of liquid nitrobenzene [71]

t, °C	0	5	10	15	20	25	30	35	40	45	50
$\rho \cdot 10^{-3}$, kg/m³	1.223	1.218	1.213	1.208	1.203	1.198	1.193	1.189	1.184	1.179	1.174

Heat capacity of liquid nitrobenzene [359]

t, °C	10	20	30	40	50	60	70
c_p, kJ/kg · deg	1.470	1.489	1.512	1.539	1.570	1.606	1.645

Viscosity of liquid nitrobenzene [94]

t, °C	0	10	20	30	40	50	60	80	100
$\eta \cdot 10^3$, N · s/m²	3.09	2.46	2.01	1.69	1.44	1.24	1.09	0.87	0.70

Thermal conductivity of liquid nitrobenzene [97]

t, °C	0	25	50	75	100	125
λ, W/m · deg	0.154	0.150	0.146	0.143	0.140	0.136

Surface tension σ (N/m) nitrobenzene [64]

t, °C	$\sigma \cdot 10^3$	t, °C	$\sigma \cdot 10^3$	t, °C	$\sigma \cdot 10^3$	t, °C	$\sigma \cdot 10^3$
0	46.4	60	39.0	110	33.3	160	27.9
10	45.2	70	37.9	120	32.2	170	26.8
20	43.9	80	36.7	130	31.1	180	25.8
30	42.7	90	35.5	140	30.1	190	24.7
40	41.5	100	34.4	150	29.0	200	23.6
50	40.2						

Chapter 5

NITROGEN AND AMMONIA

NITROGEN (N_2)

Molecular weight 28.016

$t_{boil} = 77.35$ °K at 760 mm Hg; $t_{melt} = 63.15$ °K; $t_{cr} = 126.25$ °K;
$p_{cr} = 33.96$ bar; $\rho_{cr} = 304$ kg/m³

Thermodynamic properties of saturated nitrogen [141, 142]:
v (dm³/kg), c_p (kJ/kg · deg), i and r (kJ/kg) and s (kJ/kg · deg)

T, °K	p, bar	v'	v''	c_p'	i'	i''	r	s'	s''
63.15	0.1253	1.155	1477	1.928	−148.5	64.1	212.6	2.459	5.826
64	0.1462	1.159	1282	1.929	−146.8	64.9	211.7	2.435	5.793
65	0.1743	1.165	1091	1.930	−144.9	65.8	210.7	2.516	5.757
66	0.2065	1.170	933.1	1.931	−142.9	66.8	209.7	2.545	5.722
67	0.2433	1.176	802.6	1.932	−141.0	67.7	208.7	2.753	5.688
68	0.2852	1.181	693.8	1.933	−139.1	68.7	207.8	2.600	5.656
69	0.3325	1.187	602.5	1.935	−137.1	69.6	206.7	2.629	5.625
70	0.3859	1.193	525.6	1.935	−135.2	70.5	205.7	2.657	5.595
71	0.4457	1.199	460.4	1.939	−133.3	71.4	204.7	2.683	5.566
72	0.5126	1.205	405.0	1.941	−131.4	72.3	203.7	2.709	5.538
73	0.5871	1.211	357.6	1.943	−129.4	73.2	202.6	2.736	5.511
74	0.6696	1.217	316.9	1.945	−127.4	74.1	201.4	2.763	5.485
75	0.7609	1.224	281.8	1.948	−125.4	74.9	200.3	2.789	5.460
76	0.8614	1.230	251.4	1.951	−123.4	75.7	199.1	2.816	5.436
77	0.9719	1.237	224.9	1.954	−121.4	76.5	197.9	2.842	5.412
77.35	1.013	1.239	216.9	1.955	−120.8	76.8	197.6	2.849	5.404
78	1.093	1.244	201.9	1.957	−119.5	77.3	196.8	2.866	5.389
79	1.225	1.251	181.7	1.960	−117.6	78.1	195.7	2.890	5.367
80	1.369	1.258	164.0	1.964	−115.6	78.9	194.5	2.913	5.345
81	1.525	1.265	148.3	1.968	−113.6	79.6	193.2	2.938	5.324
82	1.694	1.273	134.5	1.973	−111.6	80.3	191.9	2.963	5.303
83	1.877	1.281	122.3	1.978	−109.7	81.0	190.7	2.986	5.283
84	2.074	1.289	111.4	1.983	−107.7	81.7	189.3	3.009	5.263
85	2.287	1.297	101.7	1.989	−105.7	82.3	188.0	3.032	5.244
86	2.515	1.305	93.02	1.996	−103.7	82.9	186.6	3.055	5.225
87	2.760	1.314	85.24	2.003	−101.7	83.5	185.1	3.078	5.206
88	3.022	1.322	78.25	2.011	− 99.7	84.0	183.7	3.100	5.188
89	3.302	1.331	71.96	2.019	− 97.7	84.5	182.2	3.123	5.170
90	3.600	1.340	66.28	2.028	− 95.6	85.0	180.5	3.147	5.152
91	3.918	1.349	61.14	2.037	− 93.5	85.4	178.9	3.169	5.134
92	4.256	1.359	56.48	2.048	− 91.5	85.8	177.3	3.190	5.117
93	4.615	1.369	52.25	2.060	− 89.4	86.2	175.6	3.212	5.100
94	4.995	1.379	48.39	2.073	− 87.3	86.5	173.8	3.235	5.084
95	5.398	1.390	44.87	2.086	− 85.2	86.8	172.0	3.256	5.067
96	5.824	1.400	41.66	2.101	− 83.1	87.1	170.2	3.277	5.050
97	6.274	1.411	38.72	2.117	− 81.0	87.3	168.3	3.299	5.034
98	6.748	1.423	36.02	2.135	− 78.8	87.5	166.3	3.320	5.017
99	7.248	1.435	33.54	2.155	− 76.6	87.6	164.2	3.342	5.001
100	7.775	1.447	31.26	2.176	− 74.5	87.7	162.2	3.363	4.985
101	8.328	1.459	29.16	2.199	− 72.3	87.7	160.0	3.385	4.969
102	8.910	1.472	27.22	2.225	− 70.1	87.7	157.8	3.406	4.953

continued

T, °K	p, bar	v′	v″	c_p′	i′	i″	r	s′	s″
103	9.520	1.485	25.43	2.254	−67.8	87.7	155.5	3.426	4.936
104	10.16	1.499	23.77	2.285	−65.6	87.6	153.2	3.447	4.920
105	10.83	1.514	22.23	2.319	−63.8	87.4	150.7	3.469	4.904
106	11.53	1.529	20.79	2.356	−61.0	87.2	148.2	3.489	4.887
107	12.27	1.544	19.46	2.398	−58.6	86.9	145.5	3.501	4.871
108	13.03	1.560	18.22	2.445	−56.2	86.5	142.8	3.532	4.854
109	13.83	1.578	17.06	2.500	−53.8	86.1	139.9	3.554	4.837
110	14.67	1.597	15.98	2.566	−51.4	85.6	137.0	3.575	4.820
111	15.54	1.617	14.96	2.645	−48.9	85.1	134.0	3.596	4.803
112	16.45	1.639	14.00	2.736	−46.3	84.4	130.7	3.618	4.785
113	17.39	1.662	13.10	2.836	−43.7	83.6	127.3	3.640	4.767
114	18.36	1.687	12.26	2.945	−41.0	82.8	123.8	3.662	4.748
115	19.40	1.714	11.47	3.063	−38.1	81.8	119.9	3.687	4.729
116	20.47	1.744	10.71		−35.1	80.7	115.8	3.711	4.709
117	21.58	1.776	9.996		−31.9	79.4	111.3	3.737	4.688
118	22.72	1.811	9.314		−28.6	77.9	106.5	3.764	4.666
119	23.92	1.849	8.660		−25.1	76.2	101.3	3.792	4.643
120	25.15	1.892	8.031		−21.4	74.3	95.7	3.821	4.619
121	26.44	1.942	7.421		−17.3	72.1	89.4	3.853	4.592
122	27.77	2.000	6.821		−12.9	69.4	82.3	3.887	4.562
123	29.14	2.077	6.225		−8.0	66.4	74.4	3.924	4.529
124	30.57	2.177	5.636		−2.3	62.6	64.9	3.968	4.491
125	32.05	2.324	5.016		5.1	57.9	52.8	4.024	4.444
126	33.57	2.637	4.203		17.4	49.5	32.1	4.118	4.365
126.25	33.96	3.289	3.289		34.8	34.8	0	4.252	4.252

Thermodynamic properties of nitrogen and gas [141, 142]:
v (dm³/kg), c_p (kJ/kg · deg), i (kJ/kg) and s (kJ/kg · deg)

T, °K	v	c_p	i	s	v	c_p	i	s
	p=1 bar				p=2 bar			
65	1.1650	1.929	−144.8	2.515				
70	1.1927	1.936	−135.1	2.656				
75	1.2237	1.948	−125.4	2.789				
80	228.0	1.151	80.0	5.447				
85	244.0	1.107	85.6	5.516	117.6	1.186	83.0	5.290
90	259.7	1.086	91.1	5.578	126.0	1.140	88.8	5.356
95	275.3	1.075	96.5	5.636	134.2	1.117	94.4	5.417
100	290.8	1.070	101.9	5.691	142.3	1.104	100.0	5.474
105	306.2	1.066	107.2	5.743	150.3	1.095	105.5	5.527
110	321.5	1.063	112.5	5.793	158.2	1.089	111.0	5.578
115	336.8	1.061	117.8	5.841	166.1	1.084	116.4	5.626
120	352.0	1.059	123.1	5.886	173.9	1.079	121.8	5.672
125	367.2	1.057	128.4	5.929	181.7	1.075	127.2	5.716
130	382.3	1.055	133.7	5.970	189.4	1.072	132.6	5.758
135	397.4	1.053	138.9	6.010	197.1	1.069	137.9	5.799
140	412.5	1.052	144.2	6.048	204.8	1.066	143.2	5.838
150	442.6	1.050	154.7	6.120	220.0	1.061	153.9	5.911
160	472.6	1.048	165.2	6.188	235.2	1.057	164.5	5.979
170	502.6	1.046	175.7	6.252	250.3	1.054	175.0	6.043
180	532.5	1.045	186.1	6.312	265.4	1.052	185.5	6.103
190	562.4	1.044	196.6	6.368	280.5	1.050	196.0	6.160
200	592.3	1.043	207.0	6.421	295.5	1.048	206.5	6.214
210	622.1	1.043	217.4	6.472	310.5	1.047	217.0	6.265
220	652.0	1.042	227.9	6.521	325.5	1.046	227.5	6.314
230	681.8	1.042	238.3	6.567	340.5	1.045	238.0	6.360
240	711.6	1.042	248.7	6.611	355.5	1.044	248.4	6.404
250	741.4	1.042	259.1	6.654	370.4	1.044	258.8	6.447
260	771.1	1.041	269.5	6.695	385.3	1.044	269.2	6.488
270	800.9	1.041	280.0	6.734	400.2	1.043	279.7	6.528
280	830.7	1.041	290.4	6.772	415.2	1.043	290.1	6.566
290	860.4	1.041	300.8	6.809	430.1	1.043	300.5	6.603

continued

T, °K	v	c_p	i	s	v	c_p	i	s
300	890.2	1.041	311,2	6.844	445.0	1.043	311,0	6.638
310	919.9	1.041	321.6	6.878	459.9	1.043	321,4	6,672
320	949.6	1.041	332.0	6.911	474.8	1.043	331.8	6,705
330	979.4	1,042	342,4	6.943	489.7	1,043	342,3	6,737
340	1009	1.042	352,8	6.974	504.6	1.043	352.7	6.768
350	1039	1,042	363,3	7,005	519.5	1.043	363.1	6,798
375	1113	1.043	389.3	7.077	556.7	1,044	389.2	6,870
400	1187	1,045	415.4	7.144	593,9	1.046	415.3	6.938
425	1262	1,047	441.6	7.207	631.0	1.048	441.5	7.001
450	1336	1.050	467.8	7.267	668.2	1.050	467.7	7,061
475	1410	1.053	494.1	7.324	705,4	1.053	494.0	7,118
500	1484	1.056	520,4	7.378	742,5	1.057	520.4	7,172
550	1633	1.065	573.4	7.479	816.8	1.065	573.4	7,273
600	1781	1.075	626.9	7.572	891,0	1.075	626.9	7.366
650	1930	1.086	681.0	7.659	965.3	1.086	681.0	7.453
700	2078	1.098	735,6	7.740	1039	1.098	735.6	7.534
750	2227	1.110	790.8	7.816	1114	1.110	790.8	7,610
800	2375	1.122	846.6	7.888	1188	1.122	846.6	7.682
850	2523	1.134	903,0	7.956	1262	1.134	903.0	7.750
900	2672	1.146	960,0	8,021	1336	1.146	960.0	7.815
950	2820	1.157	1017.5	8,083	1411	1.157	1017.6	7.878
1000	2969	1.167	1075.6	8.143	1485	1.167	1075,7	7,938
1050	3117	1.177	1134,2	8.200	1559	1.177	1134.3	7.995
1100	3266	1.187	1193.3	8.255	1633	1.187	1193,4	8,050
1150	3414	1.196	1252,9	8.308	1707	1.196	1253.0	8,103
1200	3562	1.204	1312,9	8.359	1782	1.204	1313.0	8,154
1250	3711	1.212	1373.3	8.408	1856	1.212	1373.4	8,203
1300	3859	1.219	1434,0	8.456	1930	1.219	1434.1	8,251
		$p=3$ bar				$p=4$ bar		
90	81,25	1.203	86.4	5.218				
95	87.05	1.164	92.3	5.281	63,39	1.218	90.1	5.180
100	92.71	1.142	98.1	5.340	67.86	1,185	96.1	5.242
105	98.26	1.127	103,8	5.396	72.21	1,163	102.0	5.299
110	103.7	1.116	109.4	5.448	76.47	1.147	107.8	5.353
115	109.1	1,108	115.0	5.498	80.65	1,134	113,5	5,404
120	114.5	1.101	120,5	5.545	84.78	1,124	119,1	5,452
125	119.8	1.095	126.0	5,590	88.86	1.115	124.7	5.497
130	125.1	1,089	131.5	5.632	92.89	1.107	130,3	5.540
135	130.3	1,084	136.9	5.673	96.89	1.100	135,8	5.582
140	135,5	1.080	142,3	5.713	100.9	1.094	141.3	5.622
150	145.8	1.072	153.0	5.787	108.7	1.083	152.2	5.697
160	156.1	1.066	163.7	5.856	116.5	1.075	163.0	5.767
170	166.3	1.062	174.3	5.920	124.2	1.069	173.7	5.832
180	176.4	1,058	184.9	5.981	131.9	1,064	184.4	5,893
190	186.5	1.055	195.5	6.038	139.5	1.060	195.0	5,951
200	196.6	1,053	206.0	6.092	147.1	1.057	205.6	6.005
210	206.7	1.051	216.6	6,143	154.7	1.055	216.2	6.056
220	216.7	1,049	227.1	6,192	162.3	1.053	226.7	6,105
230	226.7	1,048	237,6	6,239	169.9	1,051	237.2	6,152
240	236.7	1,047	248.0	6,283	177.4	1,050	247.7	6.197
250	246.7	1.046	258,5	6.326	184.9	1.049	258.2	6,240
260	256.7	1,046	269.0	6.367	192,4	1,048	268.7	6.281
270	266.7	1.045	279.4	6.407	199.9	1.047	279.1	6,320
280	276.7	1,045	289.9	6.445	207,4	1.047	289.6	6,358
290	286.7	1,045	300.3	6.482	214.9	1,046	300.1	6.395
300	296.6	1.044	310.7	6,517	222.4	1.046	310,5	6.431
310	306.6	1.044	321.2	6,551	229.9	1.046	321,0	6.465
320	316.5	1.044	331.6	6,584	237.4	1.045	331.5	6,498
330	326.5	1.044	342,1	6.616	244.9	1.045	341,9	6,530
340	336.4	1.044	352,5	6.647	252.3	1.045	352.4	6.561
350	346.4	1.044	363,0	6,678	259.8	1.045	362.8	6.592
375	371.2	1.045	389,1	6.750	278.5	1.046	388,9	6.664
400	396.0	1.046	415.2	6.817	297.1	1.047	415.1	6.731

continued

T, °K	v	c_p	i	s	v	c_p	i	s
425	420.8	1.048	441.4	6,880	315.7	1.049	441.3	6,795
450	445.6	1.051	467.6	6.940	334.3	1.051	467,6	6.855
475	470.4	1,054	493.9	6.997	353,9	1.054	493.9	6,912
500	495.2	1.058	520,3	7,052	371.5	1.058	520.3	6.966
550	544.8	1,066	573,4	7.153	408.7	1.066	573.4	7.067
600	594,3	1.076	626.9	7.246	445.9	1.076	626.9	7,160
650	643,8	1,087	681.0	7.332	483.0	1.087	681,0	7.247
700	693.3	1,098	735.6	7,413	520,2	1.099	735,7	7.328
750	742.8	1.110	790.8	7,490	557.3	1.111	790.9	7.404
800	792,3	1.122	846.7	7,562	594,4	1.123	846.7	7.476
850	841,8	1.134	903.1	7.630	631,6	1.135	903,1	7.545
900	891,3	1.146	960.1	7,695	668.7	1.146	960.1	7,610
950	940.8	1.157	1017.7	7.757	705.8	1.157	1017.7	7,672
1000	990.2	1,167	1075.8	7,817	742.9	1.168	1075.8	7.732
1050	1040	1.177	1134,4	7,874	780.0	1.176	1134.5	7.789
1100	1089	1.187	1193.5	7.929	817.1	1.187	1193.6	7,844
1150	1139	1,196	1253.0	7,982	854,2	1.196	1253.1	7,897
1200	1188	1.204	1313,0	8,033	891.3	1,204	1313.1	7.948
1250	1238	1,212	1373.4	8,082	928.4	1.212	1373,5	7.997
1300	1287	1.219	1434,2	8.130	965.5	1.219	1434.3	8,045
		p=5 bar				p=6 bar		
65	1,1640	1,926	−144,5	2,513				
70	1,1916	1,933	−134,8	2,654				
75	1,2224	1,943	−125,1	2,786				
80	1.2568	1,959	−115,4	2,911				
85	1,2955	1,984	−105.5	3,030				
90	1.3394	2.024	− 95,5	3.145				
95	49,11	1,283	87,8	5.097				
100	52,89	1,234	94,1	5,162	42,85	1.292	91,9	5,092
105	56,53	1,203	100,2	5,221	46.05	1,248	98,2	5,154
110	60.08	1,181	106,1	5,276	49.13	1,218	104.4	5,211
115	63.54	1,163	112.0	5.328	52.11	1,195	110,4	5.265
120	66,94	1,149	117.8	5,377	55.02	1,176	116,3	5,315
125	70,28	1,137	123.5	5.424	57.88	1,160	122.2	5.363
130	73,58	1,126	129.1	5.469	60.70	1,146	128,0	5,408
135	76.84	1.117	134.7	5,511	63.47	1,134	133.7	5,451
140	80.07	1.109	140,3	5,551	66.21	1.124	139,3	5,492
150	86.45	1,095	151.3	5.627	71.61	1,108	150.5	5,569
160	92.75	1,085	162.2	5,697	76.92	1.095	161.5	5.640
170	98,99	1.077	173.0	5.763	82.17	1,085	172,4	5,706
180	105.2	1,071	183.8	5,825	87.38	1,077	183,2	5.768
190	111.3	1,066	194,5	5,883	92,55	1,071	193.9	5,826
200	117.5	1.062	205.1	5.937	97,69	1,067	204.6	5,881
210	123.6	1,059	215,7	5.989	102,8	1,063	215.3	5,933
220	129.7	1.056	226,3	6,038	107,9	1,060	225,9	5.982
230	135,7	1,054	236,8	6.085	113.0	1,058	236,5	6,029
240	141.8	1,053	247,3	6,129	118,0	1.056	247,1	6.074
250	147,8	1 051	257.9	6,172	123,1	1,054	257,6	6,117
260	153,9	1 050	268,4	6,213	128,1	1.052	268.1	6,158
270	159,9	1 049	278,9	6,253	133,2	1,051	278,6	6.198
280	165,9	1 049	289,4	6,291	138,2	1.050	289.1	6.236
290	171,9	1,048	299.8	6.328	143,2	1.050	299.6	6.273
300	177,9	1,047	310.3	6,364	148,2	1.049	310,1	6.309
310	183,9	1,047	320.8	6.398	153.2	1.049	320,6	6,343
320	189.9	1,047	331.3	6.431	158,2	1,048	331,1	6,376
330	195,9	1,046	341,7	6.463	163,2	1,048	341,6	6,409
340	201,9	1,046	352,2	6,495	168,2	1,048	352.0	6,440
350	207,9	1,046	362.7	6.525	173,2	1,048	362,5	6,470
375	222,8	1.047	388.8	6,597	185,7	1.048	388,7	6,542
400	237,7	1.048	415.0	6.665	198,2	1.049	414,9	6,610
425	252.7	1,050	441.2	6.728	210.6	1,051	441.1	6,674
450	267,6	1,052	467,5	6.788	223.0	1,053	467.4	6,734
475	282.5	1.055	493.9	6.845	235.5	1.056	493.8	6,791

continued

T, °K	v	c_p	i	s	v	c_p	i	s
500	297.4	1.058	520.3	6,900	247.9	1.059	520.2	6,845
550	327.1	1,066	573.4	7,001	272.7	1.067	573.3	6,947
600	356.9	1.076	626.9	7.094	297,5	1.077	626.9	7,040
650	386.6	1.087	681.0	7,181	322.3	1,088	681.0	7,126
700	416.3	1,099	735.7	7.262	347.1	1,099	735.7	7,207
750	446.0	1,111	791.0	7.338	371,9	1.111	791,0	7.284
800	475.7	1.123	846,8	7,410	396.7	1,123	846.9	7,356
850	505,4	1,135	903,2	7,478	421.4	1.135	903.3	7,424
900	535.1	1,146	960.2	7.543	446.1	1,146	960.3	7,489
950	564.8	1.157	1017,8	7.606	470,9	1.157	1017.9	7.551
1000	594.5	1,168	1075,9	7.666	495.6	1,168	1076.0	7,611
1050	624.2	1.178	1134,5	7,723	520.4	1,178	1134.6	7,668
1100	653.9	1,187	1193,6	7.778	545.1	1,187	1193.7	7.723
1150	683.6	1.196	1253.2	7.830	569.8	1.196	1253,3	7.776
1200	713.3	1,204	1313,2	7,881	594.6	1.204	1313.3	7.827
1250	743.0	1.212	1373.6	7,931	619.3	1,212	1373.7	7,876
1300	772.7	1.219	1434.4	7,979	644.1	1,219	1434.5	7.924
		p=8 bar				p=10 bar		
65					1.1629	1.922	−144.1	2.511
70					1,1902	1.928	−134.4	2,651
75					1.2208	1.938	−124.8	2,783
80					1.2548	1.953	−115,0	2.907
85					1.2930	1,976	−105,2	3.026
90					1.3362	2,012	− 95.3	3.141
95					1.3858	2,070	− 85.1	3.251
100					1.4440	2,164	− 74.5	3.360
105	32.83	1.360	94.1	5.040	24.75	1.516	89.5	4.942
110	35.36	1.305	100.8	5.102	27.01	1.417	96.8	5,010
115	37.74	1,265	107.2	5.160	29.11	1.350	103.7	5,072
120	40.10	1,234	113.4	5,213	31.10	1.304	110.4	5.129
125	42.36	1.210	119.5	5.263	33.02	1.264	116.8	5.181
130	44.57	1.189	125.5	5.310	34.88	1.237	123.0	5.230
135	46.74	1.172	131.4	5.354	36.69	1.213	129.1	5.276
140	48.87	1.157	137.3	5.397	38.46	1.192	135.2	5.320
150	53.04	1.133	148.7	5.476	41.90	1.160	146.9	5.401
160	57.13	1.115	159.9	5.548	45.25	1.136	158.4	5.475
170	61.15	1.101	171.0	5.615	48.54	1.118	169.7	5.543
180	65.12	1,091	182.0	5,678	51.77	1,104	180.8	5,607
190	69.05	1.082	192.8	5.737	54.96	1.094	191.8	5.666
200	72.95	1.076	203.6	5,792	58.12	1,086	202.7	5.722
210	76.83	1.071	214.4	5.844	61.26	1.079	213.5	5.775
220	80.69	1,067	225.1	5,894	64.38	1.074	224.2	5.825
230	84.54	1,064	235.7	5,942	67.48	1,070	235.0	5.873
240	88.37	1.061	246.3	5.987	70.56	1,067	245.7	5,919
250	92.18	1,059	256.9	6.030	73.64	1,064	256.3	5.962
260	95.99	1.057	267.5	6,071	76.71	1,061	266.9	6.003
270	99.79	1,055	278.1	6.111	79.76	1,059	277.5	6,043
280	103.6	1.054	288.6	6,150	82.81	1,058	288.1	6.082
290	107.4	1,053	299.1	6,187	85.85	1,056	298.7	6.119
300	111.2	1,052	309.7	6.222	88.89	1,055	309.2	6.155
310	114.9	1.051	320.2	6,257	91.92	1,054	319.8	6.190
320	118.7	1.051	330.7	6.290	94.95	1.053	330.3	6.223
330	122.4	1,050	341.2	6,322	97.97	1.053	340.9	6.255
340	126.2	1,050	351.7	6,354	101.0	1.052	351.4	6.285
350	130.0	1.050	362.2	6.384	104.0	1.052	361.9	6.317
375	139.4	1.050	388.5	6.456	111.5	1.052	388.2	6.389
400	148.7	1.051	414.7	6,524	119.0	1,052	414,5	6,457
425	158.1	1.052	441.1	6,588	126.5	1.053	440.8	6.521
450	167.4	1.054	467.3	6,648	134.0	1.055	467.2	6,582
475	176.7	1.057	493.7	6.705	141.5	1.058	493.6	6.639
500	186.1	1,060	520.1	6.760	149.0	1.061	520.1	6.693
550	204.7	1,068	573.3	6,861	163.9	1,069	573.3	6.794
600	223.3	1.077	626.9	6.954	178.8	1,078	626.9	6.888

continued

T, °K	v	c_p	i	s	v	c_p	i	s
650	241.9	1,088	681,1	7,041	193,7	1,089	681.1	6.975
700	260.5	1,100	735,8	7,122	208,6	1.100	735.8	7.056
750	279.1	1,111	791,0	7,198	223.5	1,112	791.1	7.132
800	297.7	1.123	846,9	7.270	238.3	1.124	847.0	7,204
850	316.3	1.135	903,4	7.339	253,2	1.136	903.5	7.273
900	334.8	1.146	960,4	7.404	268.0	1.147	960.5	7.338
950	353.4	1,157	1018,0	7.466	282.9	1.158	1018.1	7.400
1000	372,0	1.168	1076,1	7.526	297.8	1.168	1076.3	7.460
1050	390.5	1.178	1134.8	7.583	312.6	1.178	1134.9	7.517
1100	409,1	1.187	1193,9	7.638	327.5	1.187	1194.0	7.572
1150	427.6	1,196	1253,5	7,691	342.3	1,196	1253.6	7.625
1200	446.2	1.204	1313,5	7.742	357,2	1.204	1313,6	7,676
1250	464.7	1.212	1373,9	7.791	372.0	1,212	1374.0	7,725
1300	483.3	1.219	1434,7	7,839	386.8	1.219	1434,8	7.773
		$p=15$ bar				$p=20$ bar		
65	1.1618	1,918	−143,6	2,508	1.1607	1,914	−143,2	2,506
70	1,1889	1,924	−134,0	2.648	1,1876	1,919	−133.7	2,646
75	1.2192	1,932	−124,4	2,780	1,2176	1,927	−124.0	2,776
80	1,2529	1,946	−114,7	2.903	1,2510	1,940	−114.4	2,900
85	1,2906	1,968	−104,9	3,022	1.2883	1,960	−104,6	3,018
90	1,3331	2,001	− 95,0	3,136	1,3301	1,991	− 94.7	3,132
95	1.3817	2,055	− 84,9	3,246	1,3778	2.040	− 84,7	3,241
100	1,4384	2.140	− 74,4	3,354	1,4331	2,117	− 74.3	3,347
105	1,5071	2,283	− 63,4	3.462	1.4994	2,245	− 63.4	3.454
110	1.5959	2,555	− 51,4	3,575	1,5835	2.476	− 51,7	3,565
115	17,30	1.688	93.7	4,887	1,704	3.029	− 38,2	3,685
120	18,94	1.547	101,8	4.956	12.57	2,021	91.1	4.802
125	20.46	1,452	109,2	5.017	14.00	1.752	100,5	4.879
130	21,88	1.386	116,3	5,073	15.27	1,598	108.8	4.944
135	23,24	1.334	123,2	5,124	16,43	1,496	116,5	5.002
140	24,55	1.294	129,7	5.172	17.52	1.422	123.6	5,056
150	27,05	1.234	142,4	5,259	19,56	1.322	137,5	5.150
160	29.54	1.193	154,4	5,337	21,47	1,257	150,4	5,233
170	31,85	1.168	166,4	5,409	23.30	1.212	162.7	5,308
180	34,11	1,140	177,7	4.474	25.06	1.179	174,6	5,376
190	36.08	1,124	189,0	5,536	26.78	1,155	186.3	5,439
200	38,52	1.111	200.2	5.593	28,47	1.137	197.8	5.498
210	40.68	1.100	211,2	5.647	30,12	1,122	209.1	5,553
220	42,81	1,092	222,2	5,698	31,75	1.111	220.2	5,605
230	44.93	1.086	233.1	5.747	33.37	1.102	231.3	5,654
240	47.04	1,081	243,9	5.783	34,98	1,095	242.3	5.701
250	49.14	1,076	254,7	5,837	36,57	1.089	253.2	5.746
260	51.22	1.072	265,5	5.879	38,15	1.084	264,1	5,788
270	53.30	1.069	276,2	5.919	39,72	1.080	274.9	5,829
280	55.37	1.067	286,8	5,958	41.28	1.076	285.7	5.868
290	57,43	1.065	297,5	5.995	42,84	1,073	296.4	5.906
300	59,49	1,063	308,2	6.031	44,39	1,071	307.1	5.942
310	61.54	1,061	318.8	6,066	45,94	1,069	317,8	5.977
320	63,58	1,060	329,4	6,100	47.48	1.067	328.5	6,011
330	65.63	1.059	340,0	6,133	49,02	1.065	339,2	6,044
340	67,66	1,058	350,6	6,164	50,56	1,064	349.8	6.076
350	69.70	1,057	361,1	6,195	52,09	1.063	360,4	6.107
375	74.77	1,056	387.6	6.268	55,90	1.061	387.0	6,180
400	79.83	1.056	414.0	6,336	59,70	1,060	413.5	6.248
425	84.88	1,057	440.4	6.400	63.49	1.060	440.0	6,312
450	89.91	1,058	466.8	6,461	67.27	1.061	466.5	6,373
475	94.92	1.060	493.3	6.518	71.04	1.063	493.1	6.431
500	99.97	1.063	519.8	6.572	74.80	1.066	519.7	6.485
550	110.0	1.070	573.2	6.674	82.30	1.073	573.2	6.587
600	119.9	1,079	626,9	6.767	89.79	1.081	627,0	6,681
650	130.0	1,090	681.2	6.854	97.26	1.091	681.3	6.768
700	139.9	1.101	735,9	6,935	104.7	1,102	736.1	6.849
750	149,9	1,112	791,3	7,012	112,2	1.113	791.5	6,925

continued

T. °K	v	c_p	i	s	v	c_p	i	s
800	159.9	1.124	847.2	7.084	119.6	1.125	847.5	6.997
850	169.8	1.136	903.7	7.154	127.1	1.137	904.0	7.066
900	179.8	1.147	960.8	7.218	134.5	1.148	961.1	7.132
950	189.8	1.158	1018.4	7.280	142.0	1.159	1018.8	7.194
1000	199.7	1.168	1076.5	7.340	149.4	1.169	1077.0	7.254
1050	209.7	1.178	1135.2	7.397	156.8	1.179	1135.7	7.311
1100	219.6	1.187	1194.4	7.452	164.2	1.188	1194.8	7.366
1150	229.5	1.196	1254.0	7.505	171.7	1.197	1254.4	7.419
1200	239.5	1.204	1314.1	7.556	179.1	1.205	1314.5	7.470
1250	249.4	1.212	1374.5	7.615	186.5	1.213	1374.9	7.519
1300	259.4	1.219	1435.3	7.653	194.0	1.220	1435.7	7.567
		$p=25$ bar				$p=30$ bar		
65	1.1607	1.911	−142.8	2.503	1.1584	1.907	−142.4	2.501
70	1.1876	1.915	−133.3	2.643	1.1850	1.911	−132.9	2.640
75	1.2176	1.922	−123.7	2.773	1.2145	1.918	−123.3	2.770
80	1.2510	1.934	−114.0	2.896	1.2472	1.928	−113.7	2.893
85	1.2883	1.952	−104.3	3.014	1.2836	1.945	−104.0	3.010
90	1.3272	1.981	−94.5	3.127	1.3243	1.971	−94.2	3.123
95	1.3739	2.026	−84.5	3.236	1.3702	2.013	−84.3	3.231
100	1.4279	2.097	−74.2	3.341	1.4229	2.077	−74.0	3.336
105	1.4920	2.211	−63.4	3.447	1.4850	2.180	−63.4	3.440
110	1.5720	2.409	−51.9	3.555	1.5614	2.352	−52.1	3.546
115	1.6820	2.834	−39.0	3.671	1.6631	2.690	−39.6	3.658
120	8.163	3.765	75.0	4.626	1.8309	3.825	−24.1	3.791
125	9.892	2.360	89.4	4.743	6.644	4.733	72.3	4.573
130	11.18	1.941	100.0	4.826	8.270	2.616	89.0	4.705
135	12.28	1.726	109.1	4.895	9.419	2.082	100.6	4.792
140	13.27	1.591	117.4	4.955	10.39	1.824	110.3	4.862
150	15.07	1.426	132.4	5.059	12.05	1.553	127.0	4.978
160	16.71	1.329	146.2	5.148	13.52	1.412	141.8	5.073
170	18.25	1.265	159.1	5.226	14.88	1.324	155.4	5.156
180	19.72	1.221	171.5	5.297	16.17	1.265	168.3	5.230
190	21.15	1.188	183.6	5.362	17.40	1.223	180.7	5.297
200	22.54	1.164	195.3	5.422	18.59	1.192	192.8	5.359
210	23.90	1.145	206.8	5.479	19.75	1.168	204.6	5.416
220	25.24	1.130	218.2	5.532	20.89	1.150	216.2	5.470
230	26.56	1.119	229.5	5.582	22.02	1.136	227.6	5.521
240	27.86	1.110	240.6	5.629	23.13	1.124	238.9	5.569
250	29.15	1.102	251.6	5.674	24.22	1.115	250.1	5.615
260	30.44	1.096	262.6	5.717	25.31	1.107	261.2	5.659
270	31.72	1.090	273.6	6.758	26.39	1.101	272.3	5.700
280	32.99	1.086	284.5	5.798	27.46	1.095	283.3	5.740
290	34.25	1.082	295.3	5.836	28.52	1.090	294.2	5.778
300	35.50	1.079	306.1	5.873	29.58	1.086	305.1	5.815
310	36.75	1.076	316.9	5.908	30.63	1.083	315.9	5.851
320	38.00	1.074	327.6	5.942	31.68	1.080	326.7	5.886
330	39.24	1.072	338.3	5.975	32.72	1.078	337.5	5.919
340	40.48	1.070	349.0	6.007	33.76	1.075	348.3	5.951
350	41.71	1.068	359.7	6.038	34.79	1.073	359.0	5.982
375	44.78	1.066	386.4	6.112	37.37	1.070	385.8	6.056
400	47.84	1.064	413.0	6.181	39.93	1.068	412.5	6.125
425	50.88	1.064	439.6	6.245	42.48	1.067	439.2	6.189
450	53.91	1.064	466.2	6.306	45.02	1.067	465.9	6.250
475	56.94	1.066	492.8	6.363	47.55	1.069	492.6	6.308
500	59.96	1.068	519.5	6.418	50.07	1.071	519.3	6.363
550	65.98	1.074	573.1	6.520	55.10	1.076	573.0	6.465
600	71.98	1.083	627.0	6.614	60.12	1.084	627.0	6.559
650	77.97	1.092	681.4	6.701	65.12	1.093	681.5	6.646
700	83.95	1.103	736.3	6.782	70.11	1.104	736.4	6.727
750	89.92	1.114	791.7	6.858	75.09	1.116	791.9	6.804
800	95.89	1.126	847.7	6.931	80.06	1.127	848.0	6.877
850	101.9	1.137	904.3	7.000	85.03	1.138	904.6	6.946
900	107.8	1.148	961.4	7.065	90.00	1.149	961.8	7.011

continued

T, °K	v	c_p	i	s	v	c_p	i	s
950	113.8	1,159	1019.1	7.127	94.97	1.160	1019.5	7.073
1000	119.7	1.169	1077.3	7.187	99.93	1.170	1077.7	7.133
1050	125.7	1.179	1136.0	7,245	104.9	1.179	1136.4	7.190
1100	131.6	1,188	1195.2	7,300	109.8	1.188	1195.6	7.245
1150	137.6	1,197	1254.8	7.353	114.8	1.197	1255.2	7.298
1200	143.5	1,205	1314.9	7,404	119.8	1.205	1315,3	7.349
1250	149.4	1,213	1375.4	7.453	124,7	1.213	1375.8	7.399
1300	155.4	1,220	1436.2	7,501	129.7	1.220	1436.6	7.447
		p=35 bar				p=40 bar		
65	1.1574	1.903	−142.0	2.498	1.1563	1.900	−141.6	2.495
70	1.1837	1.907	−132.5	2.637	1.1824	1.903	−132.1	2.634
75	1.2130	1.913	−122.9	2,767	1.2115	1.908	−122.5	2.764
80	1.2454	1.922	−113.3	2.890	1.2436	1.917	−113.0	2.886
85	1.2814	1.938	−103.7	3.006	1.2791	1.931	−103.4	3.002
90	1.3214	1.962	−93.9	3,119	1.3187	1.958	−93.7	3.114
95	1.3666	2.000	−84.0	3.226	1.3630	1.989	−83.8	3.221
100	1.4181	2.060	−73.9	3.330	1.4135	2.043	−73.7	3.325
105	1.4784	2.152	−63.4	3.434	1.4720	2.127	−63.3	3.427
110	1.5516	2.302	−52.3	3.538	1.5423	2.261	−52.4	3.530
115	1.6465	2.579	−40.1	3.646	1.6315	2.491	−40.6	3.636
120	1.7898	2.977	−25.8	3.769	1.7585	2.929	−27.0	3.752
125	2.142	3.593	0.7	3.984	2.002	3.750	−5.2	3.932
130	5.867	4.687	71.1	4.527	3.282	15.03	35.4	4.265
135	7.262	2.721	90.2	4.676	5.488	4.090	76.0	4.544
140	8.271	2.162	102.2	4.768	6.623	2.690	91.8	4.667
150	9.884	1.710	121.2	4.903	8.241	1.906	115.0	4.832
160	11.25	1.506	137.2	5.006	9.534	1.615	132.4	4.944
170	12.48	1.389	151.6	5.094	10.68	1.460	147.7	5.037
180	13.63	1.312	165.1	5.171	11.73	1.363	161.8	5.117
190	14.72	1.260	177.9	5.240	12.72	1.298	175.1	5.189
200	15.78	1.221	190.3	5.304	13.67	1.251	187.8	5.255
210	16.80	1.192	202.4	5.363	14.59	1.217	200.2	5.315
220	17.80	1.170	214.2	5.418	15.48	1.191	212.2	5.371
230	18.78	1.153	225.8	5.469	16.36	1.170	224.0	5.423
240	19.75	1.139	237.3	5.518	17.22	1.154	235.6	5.473
250	20.70	1.128	248.6	5.564	18.07	1.141	247.1	5.520
260	21.64	1.119	259.8	5.608	18.91	1.130	258.4	5.564
270	22.58	1.111	271.0	5.650	19.74	1.121	269.7	5.606
280	23.51	1.104	282.1	5.690	20.56	1.114	280.9	5.647
290	24.43	1.099	293.1	5.729	21.37	1.108	292.0	5.686
300	25.35	1.094	304.0	5.766	22.18	1.102	303.0	5.724
310	26.26	1.090	315.0	5.802	22.98	1.097	314.0	5.760
320	27.16	1.087	325.8	5.837	23.78	1.093	325.0	5.794
330	28.06	1.084	336.7	5.871	24.58	1.090	335.9	5.827
340	28.96	1.081	347.5	5.903	25.37	1.087	346.8	5.860
350	29.85	1.079	358.3	5.934	26.15	1.084	357.6	5.892
375	32.07	1.075	385.2	6.008	28.11	1.079	384.7	5.967
400	34.28	1.072	412.1	6.077	30.05	1.076	411.6	6.036
425	36.48	1.071	438.8	6.142	31.98	1.074	438.5	6.101
450	38.67	1.070	465.6	6.204	33.90	1.073	465.3	6.163
475	40.84	1.071	492.4	6.262	35.81	1.074	492.2	6.221
500	43.01	1.073	519.2	6.316	37.72	1.075	519.0	6.276
550	44.33	1.078	573.0	6.419	41.51	1.080	572.9	6.379
600	51.64	1.086	627.1	6.513	45.29	1.087	627.1	6.473
650	55.93	1.095	681.6	6.600	49.05	1.096	681.7	6.560
700	60.21	1.105	736.6	6.681	52.80	1.107	736.7	6.641
750	64.49	1.116	792.1	6.758	56.55	1.117	792.3	6.718
800	68.76	1.128	848.2	6.831	60.29	1.128	848.4	6.791
850	73.03	1.139	904.9	6.900	64.02	1.139	905.1	6.860
900	77.29	1.150	962.1	6.965	67.75	1.150	962.4	6.925
950	81.55	1.160	1019.8	7.027	71.48	1.161	1020.1	6.987
1000	85.80	1.170	1078.1	7.087	75.21	1.171	1078.4	7.047
1050	90.05	1.180	1136.8	7.145	78.93	1.180	1137.2	7.105

continued

T, °K	v	c_p	i	s	v	c_p	i	s
1100	94.30	1.189	1196.2	7.200	82.65	1.189	1196.4	7.160
1150	98,55	1.198	1255.7	7.253	86.37	1.198	1256.1	7.213
1200	102,8	1,206	1315.8	7.304	90.08	1.206	1316.2	7.264
1250	107,0	1,213	1376.3	7.353	93.80	1.214	1376.7	7.313
1300	111,3	1.220	1437.1	7.401	97.52	1.221	1437.5	7.361
		p=45 bar				p=50 bar		
65	1.1552	1,896	−141.2	2,493	1.1541	1.893	−140.7	2.491
70	1,1812	1,899	−131.7	2.632	1.180	1.895	−131.3	2.629
75	1.2100	1,903	−122.2	2.761	1.2085	1.899	−121.8	2.758
80	1,2418	1.911	−112.6	2.883	1.2400	1.906	−112.3	2.879
85	1,2769	1.924	−103.0	2.999	1.2748	1.918	−102.7	2.995
90	1.3160	1.945	− 93.4	3.110	1.3133	1.937	− 93.1	3.106
95	1,3596	1,977	− 83.6	3.217	1.3562	1.967	− 83.3	3.212
100	1,4090	2.028	− 73.6	3.319	1.4046	2.013	− 73.4	3.314
105	1.4659	2,104	− 63.2	3.421	1.4601	2.083	− 63.1	3,415
110	1,5336	2,223	− 52.5	3.522	1.5254	2,190	− 52.5	3,515
115	1,6180	2.419	− 40.9	3.626	1,6055	2.358	− 41.2	3.616
120	1,7329	2,812	− 28.0	3.737	1.7111	2.682	− 28.7	3.723
125	1,929	3,498	− 8.8	3.892	1,876	3.311	− 11.4	3.862
130	2.403	7,062	17.0	4.104	2.181	4.753	9.7	4.046
135	3,966	6,710	54.7	4.376	2.999	6.878	38.4	4.260
140	5.284	3.528	79.0	4.554	4.204	4.574	65.8	4.447
150	6,951	2,152	108.3	4.762	5.915	2.450	101.1	4.692
160	8.201	1.740	127.5	4.885	7.136	1.880	122.4	4,829
170	9,276	1,538	143.8	4.984	8.159	1.622	139.7	4.935
180	10,25	1.417	158.5	5.068	9.076	1.475	155.2	5.023
190	11,17	1,338	172.2	5.143	9.926	1.380	169.4	5,100
200	12,04	1,283	185.3	5.210	10,73	1.315	182.9	5.169
210	12,87	1.242	198.0	5.272	11.50	1.268	195.8	5.232
220	13.68	1,212	210.2	5.329	12.25	1.233	208.2	5.290
230	14.48	1.188	222.2	5.382	12.98	1.206	220.4	5.344
240	15.26	1,169	234.0	5.432	13.69	1.184	232.4	5.395
250	16.02	1.154	245.6	5.480	14.39	1.167	244.1	5.443
260	16.77	1.142	257.1	5.525	15.07	1.153	255.7	5.489
270	17,52	1.132	268.5	5.567	15.75	1.142	267.2	5.532
280	18,26	1,123	279.7	5.608	16.42	1.132	278.6	5.573
290	18.99	1.116	290.9	5.648	17.09	1.124	289.9	5.613
300	19.72	1.110	302.0	5.686	17.75	1.117	301.1	5.651
310	20,44	1.104	313.1	5.722	18.40	1.111	312.2	5.688
320	21.15	1.100	324.1	5.757	19.05	1.106	323.9	5.723
330	21,86	1,096	335.1	5.791	19.70	1.102	334.3	5.757
340	22.57	1.092	346.1	5.823	20.34	1.098	345.3	5.790
350	23,28	1.089	357.0	5.855	20.98	1.094	356.3	5.821
375	25.03	1.084	384.1	5.930	22.56	1.088	383.6	5.897
400	26.76	1.080	411.1	6.000	24.13	1.083	410.7	5.967
425	28.48	1,077	438.1	6.065	25.69	1.080	437.8	6.032
450	30.19	1.076	465.0	6.127	27.23	1.079	464.8	6.094
475	31,90	1.076	491.9	6.185	28.77	1.079	491.7	6.152
500	33,60	1,078	518.9	6.240	30.31	1,080	518.7	6.208
550	36.98	1.082	572.8	6.343	33.36	1.084	572,8	6.311
600	40.34	1,089	627.1	6.437	36.39	1.090	627.2	6.405
650	43.69	1.098	681.8	6,524	39.41	1.099	681.9	6.493
700	47.04	1.108	736.9	6.606	42.42	1.109	737.0	6.575
750	50,37	1.118	792.5	6.683	45.42	1.119	792.7	6.652
800	53,69	1.129	848.7	6.756	48.42	1.130	849.0	6.724
850	57.02	1.140	905.4	6.825	51.41	1.141	905.7	6.793
900	60,34	1,151	962.7	6.890	54.40	1,151	963.0	6,859
950	63.65	1,161	1020.5	6,952	57.39	1.161	1020.8	6.921
1000	66.96	1.171	1078.8	7.012	60.37	1.171	1079.2	6.981
1050	70,27	1.181	1137.6	7.070	63.35	1.181	1138.0	7.038
1100	73.58	1.190	1196.8	7.125	66.33	1.190	1197.2	7.093
1150	76.89	1.198	1256.5	7.178	69.31	1.198	1256.9	7.146
1200	80.20	1.206	1316.6	7.229	72.28	1.206	1317.1	7.197

continued

T. °K	v	c_p	i	s	v	c_p	i	s
1250	83.50	1.214	1377.1	7.278	75.26	1.214	1377.6	7.247
1300	86.80	1.221	1438.0	7.326	78.23	1.221	1438.4	7.295
		p=60 bar				p=80 bar		
65	1.152	1.186	−139.9	2.486	1.148	1.873	−138.2	2.476
70	1.177	1.887	−130.5	2.624	1.173	1.873	−128.9	2.613
75	1.206	1.890	−121.0	2.752	1.200	1.874	−119.5	2.740
80	1.237	1.896	−111.5	2.873	1.230	1.877	−110.1	2.860
85	1.271	1.906	−102.1	2.988	1.262	1.883	−100.7	2.974
90	1.308	1.922	− 92.5	3.098	1.298	1.895	− 91.3	3.083
95	1.349	1.947	− 82.8	3.203	1.337	1.913	81.7	3.186
100	1.396	1.987	− 73.0	3.304	1.380	1.942	− 72.1	3.285
105	1.449	2.045	− 62.9	3.403	1.429	1.985	− 62.3	3.382
110	1.510	2.132	− 52.5	3.501	1.484	2.046	− 52.2	3.476
115	1.583	2.262	− 41.5	3.599	1.547	2.131	− 41.8	3.570
120	1.675	2.448	− 29.8	3.701	1.621	2.233	− 30.9	3.664
125	1.803	2.736	− 15.0	3.820	1.713	2.364	− 18.2	3.765
130	1.994	3.346	3.2	3.970	1.831	2.558	− 4.1	3.875
135	2.338	4.465	25.2	4.124	1.992	2.904	11.2	3.991
140	2.944	4.810	48.0	4.296	2.222	3.306	27.6	4.107
150	4.397	3.102	85.8	4.556	2.918	3.334	60.7	4.342
160	5.554	2.198	111.6	4.723	3.742	2.688	90.9	4.537
170	6.498	1.807	131.4	4.843	4.511	2.166	115.0	4.683
180	7.325	1.597	148.4	4.940	5.198	1.847	134.9	4.797
190	8.080	1.468	163.6	5.023	5.820	1.649	152.3	4.891
200	8.787	1.382	177.9	5.096	6.397	1.518	168.1	4.972
210	9.459	1.321	191.4	5.162	6.940	1.428	182.8	5.044
220	10.11	1.276	204.3	5.222	7.457	1.362	196.7	5.109
230	10.73	1.242	216.9	5.278	7.955	1.313	210.1	5.168
240	11.34	1.215	229.2	5.330	8.438	1.276	223.0	5.223
250	11.94	1.194	241.2	5.379	8.908	1.246	235.6	5.275
260	12.53	1.177	253.1	5.426	9.368	1.222	248.0	5.323
270	13.11	1.163	264.8	5.470	9.819	1.203	260.1	5.369
280	13.68	1.151	276.3	5.512	10.26	1.187	272.0	5.413
290	14.24	1.141	287.8	5.552	10.70	1.173	283.8	5.454
300	14.80	1.132	299.2	5.591	11.13	1.162	295.5	5.493
310	15.35	1.125	310.5	5.628	11.56	1.152	307.1	5.531
320	15.90	1.119	321.7	5.663	11.98	1.143	318.6	5.568
330	16.45	1.114	332.8	5.697	12.40	1.136	330.0	5.603
340	16.99	1.109	343.9	5.731	12.82	1.130	341.3	5.637
350	17.53	1.105	355.0	5.763	13.23	1.124	352.6	5.669
375	18.86	1.096	382.5	5.839	14.25	1.113	380.5	5.746
400	20.18	1.090	409.8	5.909	15.26	1.105	408.2	5.818
425	21.49	1.087	437.1	5.975	16.26	1.100	435.8	5.885
450	22.79	1.085	464.2	6.037	17.25	1.096	463.2	5.948
475	24.08	1.084	491.3	6.096	18.23	1.094	490.6	6.007
500	25.37	1.084	518.4	6.152	19.20	1.093	517.9	6.063
550	27.92	1.088	572.7	6.255	21.13	1.094	572.6	6.167
600	30.46	1.093	627.2	6.350	23.05	1.099	627.5	6.262
650	32.98	1.101	682.1	6.438	24.96	1.106	682.6	6.351
700	35.50	1.111	737.4	6.520	26.86	1.115	738.1	6.433
750	38.10	1.121	793.2	6.597	28.74	1.124	794.1	6.510
800	40.51	1.131	849.5	6.670	30.63	1.134	850.5	6.583
850	43.01	1.142	906.3	6.739	32.51	1.144	907.5	6.652
900	45.50	1.152	963.6	6.804	34.38	1.154	965.0	6.718
950	47.99	1.162	1021.5	6.866	36.25	1.164	1023.0	6.781
1000	50.48	1.172	1079.9	6.926	38.12	1.174	1081.4	6.841
1050	52.97	1.182	1138.8	6.984	39.99	1.183	1140.3	6.898
1100	55.45	1.191	1198.1	7.039	41.86	1.192	1199.7	6.953
1150	57.93	1.199	1257.8	7.092	43.72	1.200	1259.5	7.006
1200	60.41	1.207	1317.9	7.143	45.58	1.208	1319.7	7.057
1250	62.89	1.214	1378.5	7.194	47.45	1.215	1380.3	7.107
1300	65.37	1.221	1439.5	7.241	49.31	1.222	1441.2	7.155

continued

T, °K	v	c_p	i	s	v	c_p	i	s
	$p=100$ bar				$p=150$ bar			
70	1.1682	1.860	−127.2	2.603	1.157	1.830	−123.1	2.578
75	1.1946	1.859	−117.9	2.729	1.182	1.827	−114.0	2.702
80	1.2235	1.860	−108.6	2.848	1.209	1.824	−104.9	2.819
85	1.2549	1.864	− 99.3	2.960	1.238	1.823	−95.7	2.929
90	1.2891	1.871	− 90.0	3.068	1.268	1.825	− 86.6	3.035
95	1.3262	1.885	− 80.6	3.170	1.301	1.830	− 77.5	3.134
100	1.3668	1.906	− 71.1	3.267	1.337	1.841	− 68.3	3.228
105	1.4115	1.938	− 61.5	3.362	1.375	1.858	− 59.1	3.319
110	1.4612	1.984	− 51.7	3.454	1.416	1.883	− 49.7	3.407
115	1.5170	2.044	− 41.7	3.544	1.460	1.915	− 40.2	3.492
120	1.5807	2.106	− 31.3	3.634	1.509	1.948	− 30.6	3.575
125	1.6550	2.185	− 19.8	3.727	1.562	1.987	− 20.4	3.658
130	1.7436	2.286	− 7.8	3.823	1.620	2.032	− 10.0	3.743
135	1.8530	2.423	5.4	3.920	1.687	2.086	1.0	3.823
140	1.994	2.651	19.0	4.018	1.762	2.146	12.2	3.902
150	2.390	2.911	47.4	4.218	1.948	2.270	34.9	4.064
160	2.913	2.704	75.8	4.401	2.182	2.321	58.0	4.213
170	3.476	2.340	101.0	4.554	2.457	2.239	80.9	4.352
180	4.023	2.027	122.8	4.679	2.755	2.091	102.6	4.476
190	4.537	1.800	141.8	4.782	3.062	1.934	122.7	4.585
200	5.019	1.640	159.0	4.870	3.369	1.793	141.3	4.680
210	5.474	1.526	174.8	4.947	3.671	1.677	158.6	4.765
220	5.907	1.443	189.6	5.016	3.965	1.582	174.9	4.841
230	6.322	1.381	203.7	5.079	4.252	1.505	190.3	4.909
240	6.724	1.333	217.3	5.137	4.532	1.444	205.0	4.972
250	7.115	1.296	230.4	5.190	4.804	1.395	219.2	5.030
260	7.496	1.266	243.2	5.240	5.070	1.355	233.0	5.084
270	7.869	1.241	255.7	5.287	5.331	1.321	246.4	5.134
280	8.235	1.221	268.0	5.332	5.587	1.293	259.4	5.182
290	8.595	1.204	280.2	5.375	5.838	1.270	272.2	5.227
300	8.950	1.189	292.2	5.416	6.086	1.250	284.8	5.269
310	9.300	1.177	304.0	5.454	6.330	1.233	297.2	5.310
320	9.647	1.167	315.7	5.491	6.571	1.218	309.5	5.349
330	9.990	1.158	327.3	5.527	6.809	1.205	321.6	5.386
340	10.33	1.150	338.8	4.562	7.044	1.194	333.6	5.422
350	10.67	1.143	350.3	5.596	7.278	1.184	345.5	5.456
375	11.50	1.129	378.7	5.674	7.852	1.164	374.8	5.537
400	12.32	1.119	406.8	5.746	8.415	1.149	403.7	5.612
425	13.13	1.111	434.7	5.813	8.969	1.138	432.3	5.681
450	13.93	1.106	462.4	5.877	9.516	1.130	460.7	5.746
475	14.72	1.103	490.0	5.937	10.06	1.124	488.9	5.807
500	15.51	1.101	517.5	5.993	10.59	1.120	516.9	5.865
550	17.07	1.101	572.6	6.098	11.65	1.117	572.8	5.971
600	18.61	1.105	627.7	6.194	12.70	1.118	628.6	6.068
650	20.14	1.111	683.1	6.283	13.73	1.122	684.6	6.158
700	21.67	1.119	738.8	6.366	14.76	1.128	740.8	6.241
750	23.19	1.128	795.0	6.443	15.78	1.136	797.4	6.319
800	24.70	1.137	851.6	6.516	16.80	1.144	854.4	6.393
850	26.21	1.147	908.7	6.585	17.81	1.153	911.8	6.463
900	27.71	1.157	966.3	6.651	18.82	1.162	969.7	6.529
950	29.21	1.166	1024.4	6.714	19.83	1.172	1028.0	6.592
1000	30.71	1.176	1082.9	6.774	20.83	1.180	1086.0	6.652
1050	32.21	1.185	1141.9	6.832	21.83	1.188	1145.9	6.710
1100	33.71	1.193	1201.3	6.887	22.83	1.196	1205.6	6.766
1150	35.20	1.201	1261.2	6.940	23.83	1.204	1265.6	6.819
1200	36.69	1.209	1321.5	6.991	24.83	1.212	1326.0	6.870
1250	38.18	1.216	1382.1	7.040	25.83	1.219	1386.7	6.920
1300	39.67	1.223	1443.1	7.088	26.82	1.225	1447.8	6.968
	$p=200$ bar				$p=300$ bar			
70	1.1473	1.804	−119.0	2.555	1.1294	1.761	−110.6	2.513
75	1.1706	1.800	−110.0	2.677	1.1502	1.756	−101.8	2.632

continued

T. °K	v	c_p	i	s	v	c_p	i	s
80	1.1956	1.796	−101.0	2.792	1.1723	1.752	− 93.0	2.744
85	1.2221	1.792	− 92.0	2.901	1.1956	1.747	− 84.3	2.850
90	1.2504	1.791	− 83.1	3.004	1.2199	1.744	− 75.5	2.951
95	1.2802	1.792	− 74.1	3.101	1.2452	1.743	− 66.8	3.045
100	1.3118	1.797	− 65.1	3.194	1.2715	1.744	− 58.1	3.135
105	1.3452	1.807	− 56.1	3.282	1.2988	1.748	− 49.4	3.221
110	1.3805	1.823	− 47.0	3.368	1.3271	1.755	− 40.6	3.303
115	1.4181	1.843	− 37.9	3.450	1.3565	1.764	− 31.8	3.382
120	1.4581	1.863	− 28.6	3.530	1.3871	1.776	− 23.0	3.459
125	1.5008	1.891	− 19.1	3.609	1.4190	1.789	− 14.0	3.532
130	1.5466	1.919	− 9.3	3.687	1.4523	1.802	− 4.9	3.605
135	1.5959	1.955	1.0	3.763	1.4870	1.815	4.2	3.677
140	1.650	1.987	11.1	3.837	1.523	1.828	13.4	3.744
150	1.776	2.044	31.6	3.980	1.605	1.848	32.3	3.873
160	1.925	2.075	52.1	4.113	1.695	1.860	50.7	3.992
170	2.096	2.058	72.8	4.238	1.794	1.858	69.3	4.105
180	2.284	1.989	93.1	4.354	1.900	1.824	87.8	4.210
190	2.484	1.896	112.5	4.459	2.012	1.774	105.8	4.308
200	2.691	1.798	131.0	4.554	2.129	1.719	123.2	4.398
210	2.901	1.708	148.5	4.640	2.251	1.663	140.1	4.480
220	3.111	1.628	165.2	4.717	2.375	1.610	156.5	4.556
230	3.319	1.559	181.1	4.788	2.501	1.562	172.4	4.626
240	3.525	1.500	196.4	4.853	2.628	1.519	187.8	4.692
250	3.728	1.451	211.2	4.913	2.756	1.480	202.8	4.753
260	3.928	1.409	225.5	4.969	2.884	1.445	217.4	4.810
270	4.125	1.373	239.4	5.022	3.011	1.414	231.7	4.864
280	4.320	1.343	252.9	5.071	3.138	1.387	245.7	4.915
290	4.512	1.317	266.2	5.118	3.264	1.363	259.5	4.963
300	4.701	1.294	279.3	5.162	3.390	1.341	273.0	5.009
310	4.888	1.274	292.1	5.204	3.515	1.321	286.3	5.053
320	5.073	1.257	304.8	5.244	3.638	1.304	299.4	5.095
330	5.255	1.242	317.3	5.283	3.760	1.288	312.4	5.135
340	5.436	1.229	329.6	5.320	3.882	1.273	325.2	5.173
350	5.615	1.217	341.8	5.355	4.003	1.260	337.9	5.210
375	6.055	1.193	371.9	5.439	4.301	1.233	369.0	5.296
400	6.486	1.175	401.5	5.515	4.594	1.211	399.5	5.374
425	6.910	1.161	430.7	5.585	4.883	1.194	429.6	5.447
450	7.328	1.150	459.6	5.651	5.167	1.181	459.3	5.515
475	7.741	1.142	488.2	5.713	5.448	1.170	488.7	5.579
500	8.150	1.136	516.7	5.772	5.726	1.162	517.8	5.639
550	8.956	1.130	573.4	5.880	6.274	1.152	575.6	5.749
600	9.751	1.129	629.8	5.978	6.814	1.148	633.1	5.849
650	10.54	1.131	686.3	6.069	7.347	1.148	690.5	5.941
700	11.32	1.136	743.0	6.153	7.874	1.151	747.9	6.026
750	12.09	1.143	800.0	6.231	8.396	1.155	805.6	6.105
800	12.86	1.150	857.3	6.305	8.915	1.161	863.5	6.180
850	13.62	1.158	915.0	6.375	9.431	1.168	921.7	6.251
900	14.38	1.166	973.1	6.442	9.944	1.176	980.3	6.318
950	15.14	1.175	1031.7	6.505	10.45	1.183	1039.3	6.381
1000	15.90	1.184	1090.7	6.565	10.96	1.191	1098.6	6.442
1050	16.65	1.192	1150.0	6.623	11.47	1.198	1158.3	6.500
1100	17.40	1.200	1209.8	6.679	11.98	1.205	1218.4	6.556
1150	18.16	1.207	1270.0	6.732	12.48	1.212	1278.9	6.610
1200	18.91	1.214	1330.5	6.784	12.98	1.219	1339.7	6.662
1250	19.66	1.221	1391.4	6.834	13.49	1.225	1400.8	6.712
1300	20.40	1.227	1452.6	6.882	13.99	1.231	1462.2	6.760
	$p=400$ bar				$p=500$ bar			
75	1.1325	1.724	− 93.4	2.591	1.1169	1.699	− 85.0	2.554
80	1.1525	1.721	− 84.8	2.701	1.1351	1.697	− 76.5	2.662
85	1.1732	1.717	− 76.2	2.805	1.1539	1.696	− 68.0	2.765
90	1.1947	1.715	− 67.6	2.904	1.1733	1.695	− 59.5	2.863
95	1.2169	1.713	− 59.1	2.997	1.1931	1.695	− 51.1	2.955
100	1.2397	1.713	− 50.5	3.085	1.2134	1.695	− 42.6	3.042

continued

T. °K	v	c_p	i	s	v	c_p	i	s
105	1.2631	1.715	−41.9	3.170	1.2340	1.695	−34.1	3.125
110	1.2870	1.718	−33.4	3.251	1.2549	1.695	−25.6	3.205
115	1.3116	1.723	−24.8	3.327	1.2763	1.697	−17.2	3.281
120	1.3369	1.728	−16.1	3.402	1.2981	1.699	− 8.7	3.355
125	1.3629	1.735	− 7.5	3.473	1.3204	1.701	− 0.2	3.426
130	1.3898	1.741	1.4	3.544	1.3432	1.703	8.3	3.495
135	1.4175	1.747	10.2	3.609	1.3663	1.706	16.8	3.561
140	1.446	1.753	13.9	3.675	1.390	1.708	25.4	3.623
150	1.509	1.763	36.8	3.799	1.442	1.715	42.6	3.740
160	1.576	1.770	54.2	3.912	1.497	1.721	59.6	3.849
170	1.647	1.770	71.9	4.019	1.554	1.724	76.8	3.954
180	1.722	1.740	89.5	4.119	1.614	1.696	93.9	4.052
190	1.801	1.697	106.7	4.212	1.675	1.654	110.7	4.143
200	1.882	1.652	123.4	4.298	1.737	1.610	127.0	4.226
210	1.966	1.609	139.7	4.378	1.801	1.569	142.9	4.304
220	2.052	1.568	155.6	4.452	1.867	1.532	158.4	4.376
230	2.140	1.531	171.1	4.521	1.934	1.500	173.5	4.444
240	2.229	1.498	186.2	4.585	2.003	1.472	188.4	4.507
250	2.319	1.469	201.0	4.646	2.072	1.448	203.0	4.566
260	2.410	1.442	215.6	4.703	2.142	1.427	217.4	4.622
270	2.502	1.417	229.9	4.757	2.213	1.408	231.6	4.676
280	2.594	1.395	244.0	4.808	2.284	1.390	245.6	4.727
290	2.686	1.375	257.8	4.857	2.355	1.374	259.7	4.776
300	2.778	1.356	271.4	4.903	2.427	1.358	273.0	4.822
310	2.870	1.339	284.9	4.947	2.499	1.343	286.5	4.866
320	2.961	1.323	298.2	4.989	2.571	1.330	299.9	4.908
330	3.052	1.308	311.4	5.030	2.643	1.318	313.2	4.949
340	3.142	1.295	324.4	5.069	2.714	1.306	326.3	4.988
350	3.232	1.283	337.3	5.106	2.785	1.295	329.3	5.026
375	3.455	1.256	369.1	5.194	2.962	1.270	371.3	5.115
400	3.675	1.234	400.2	5.274	3.138	1.249	402.8	5.196
425	3.893	1.216	430.8	5.348	3.312	1.231	433.8	5.271
450	4.108	1.202	460.0	5.417	3.484	1.216	464.4	5.341
475	4.320	1.190	490.9	5.482	3.654	1.204	494.6	5.406
500	4.531	1.181	520.5	5.542	3.823	1.194	524.6	5.468
550	4.946	1.168	579.2	5.654	4.156	1.180	583.9	5.581
600	5.355	1.162	637.4	5.756	4.484	1.173	642.7	5.683
650	5.758	1.160	695.5	5.849	4.808	1.170	701.3	5.777
700	6.157	1.162	753.6	5.935	5.130	1.171	759.8	5.864
750	6.553	1.166	811.7	6.015	5.449	1.173	818.4	5.944
800	6.946	1.171	870.1	6.090	5.765	1.177	877.2	6.020
850	7.336	1.177	928.8	6.161	6.079	1.183	936.2	6.092
900	7.724	1.183	987.8	6.229	6.392	1.189	995.5	6.160
950	8.110	1.190	1047.1	6.293	6.703	1.195	1055.1	6.224
1000	8.495	1.197	1106.8	6.354	7.013	1.202	1115.0	6.285
1050	8.878	1.204	1166.8	6.413	7.321	1.209	1175.3	6.344
1100	9.260	1.211	1227.1	6.469	7.628	1.215	1235.9	6.401
1150	9.640	1.217	1287.8	6.523	7.934	1.221	1296.8	6.455
1200	10.02	1.223	1348.8	6.575	8.239	1.227	1358.0	6.507
1250	10.40	1.229	1410.2	6.625	8.544	1.233	1419.5	6.557
1300	10.78	1.235	1471.8	6.673	8.848	1.238	1481.3	6.606
		$p=600$ bar				$p=700$ bar		
130	1.304	1.434	18.7	3.473	1.274	1.413	26.6	3.433
135	1.325	1.451	26.1	3.528	1.293	1.425	33.8	3.487
140	1.347	1.509	33.6	3.582	1.312	1.482	41.1	3.541
150	1.392	1.629	49.3	3.691	1.352	1.604	56.6	3.648
160	1.439	1.692	66.0	3.798	1.393	1.671	73.0	3.753
170	1.487	1.698	83.0	3.901	1.435	1.681	89.8	3.855
180	1.536	1.671	99.8	3.998	1.478	1.656	106.5	3.951
190	1.587	1.629	116.3	4.087	1.522	1.615	122.9	4.040
200	1.639	1.585	132.4	4.169	1.566	1.570	138.8	4.121
210	1.692	1.543	148.1	4.245	1.611	1.528	154.3	4.196
220	1.746	1.507	163.3	4.316	1.656	1.491	169.4	4.266

continued

T, °K	v	c_p	i	s	v	c_p	i	s
230	1.800	1.476	178.2	4.382	1.702	1.460	184.1	4.332
240	1.855	1.450	192.8	4.445	1.749	1.435	198.6	4.394
250	1.911	1.429	207.2	4.504	1.796	1.414	212.8	4.452
260	1.968	1.411	221.4	4.559	1.844	1.397	226.9	4.507
270	2.025	1.395	235.5	4.612	1.892	1.382	240.8	4.559
280	2.083	1.380	249.4	4.663	1.941	1.369	254.6	4.609
290	2.141	1.367	263.1	4.711	1.990	1.358	268.2	4.657
300	2.200	1.364	276.7	4.757	2.039	1.348	281.7	4.703
310	2.259	1.342	290.2	4.801	2.089	1.338	295.1	4.747
320	2.318	1.331	303.5	4.843	2.139	1.329	308.5	4.789
330	2.376	1.320	316.7	4.884	2.189	1.320	321.7	4.830
340	2.435	1.310	329.9	4.924	2.239	1.311	334.8	4.869
350	2.494	1.301	343.0	4.962	2.289	1.303	347.9	4.907
375	2.641	1.278	375.2	5.051	2.413	1.283	380.2	4.997
400	2.786	1.258	406.9	5.133	2.537	1.265	412.1	5.079
425	2.930	1.241	438.1	5.208	2.660	1.248	443.5	5.155
450	3.073	1.226	469.0	5.278	2.782	1.234	474.5	5.226
475	3.215	1.214	499.5	5.344	2.903	1.222	505.2	5.292
500	3.355	1.204	529.7	5.406	3.024	1.212	535.6	5.354
550	3.633	1.190	589.5	5.520	3.262	1.197	595.8	5.469
600	3.907	1.181	648.7	5.623	3.497	1.188	655.4	5.573
650	4.178	1.178	707.7	5.718	3.729	1.184	714.7	5.668
700	4.447	1.177	766.6	5.805	3.960	1.183	773.8	5.756
750	4.713	1.180	825.5	5.886	4.189	1.185	833.0	5.838
800	4.978	1.184	884.5	5.963	4.416	1.188	892.3	5.914
850	5.241	1.188	943.8	6.035	4.642	1.193	951.8	5.986
900	5.503	1.194	1003.4	6.103	4.867	1.198	1011.6	6.054
950	5.763	1.200	1063.3	6.167	5.091	1.204	1071.7	6.119
1000	6.022	1.207	1123.4	6.229	5.314	1.210	1132.0	6.181
1050	6.281	1.213	1183.9	6.288	5.536	1.216	1192.6	6.240
1100	6.538	1.219	1244.7	6.345	5.757	1.222	1253.6	6.297
1150	6.794	1.225	1305.8	6.399	5.978	1.228	1314.9	6.352
1200	7.050	1.231	1367.2	6.451	6.198	1.234	1376.4	6.404
1250	7.305	1.237	1428.9	6.501	6.418	1.239	1438.2	6.454
1300	7.560	1.242	1490.8	6.550	6.637	1.244	1500.3	6.503
		$p=800$ bar				$p=900$ bar		
130	1.248	1.400	34.8	3.399				
135	1.265	1.406	41.8	3.452	1.242	1.394	49.8	3.419
140	1.283	1.462	48.9	3.504	1.258	1.446	56.9	3.470
150	1.318	1.585	64.2	3.609	1.290	1.570	72.0	3.575
160	1.355	1.656	80.4	3.714	1.323	1.644	88.2	3.678
170	1.393	1.670	97.1	3.815	1.357	1.661	104.7	3.779
180	1.431	1.646	113.7	3.910	1.392	1.640	121.2	3.873
190	1.470	1.606	130.0	3.998	1.427	1.600	137.4	3.961
200	1.509	1.560	145.8	4.079	1.462	1.555	153.2	4.042
210	1.548	1.518	161.2	4.154	1.497	1.511	168.6	4.117
220	1.588	1.480	176.2	4.224	1.532	1.473	183.5	4.186
230	1.628	1.448	190.8	4.289	1.568	1.441	198.0	4.251
240	1.669	1.423	205.2	4.350	1.604	1.415	212.3	4.312
250	1.710	1.403	219.3	4.408	1.641	1.394	226.3	4.369
260	1.751	1.386	233.2	4.462	1.677	1.377	240.2	4.423
270	1.793	1.372	247.0	4.514	1.714	1.364	253.9	4.475
280	1.835	1.360	260.7	4.564	1.751	1.353	267.5	4.524
290	1.877	1.350	274.2	4.612	1.788	1.344	281.0	4.571
300	1.920	1.341	287.7	4.657	1.826	1.336	294.4	4.617
310	1.963	1.333	301.1	4.701	1.864	1.329	307.7	4.661
320	2.006	1.325	314.4	4.743	1.902	1.322	320.9	4.703
330	2.049	1.318	327.6	4.784	1.940	1.315	334.1	4.743
340	2.092	1.310	340.7	4.823	1.978	1.309	347.2	4.782
350	2.135	1.303	353.8	4.861	2.016	1.302	360.3	4.820
375	2.244	1.286	386.1	4.951	2.112	1.287	392.6	4.909
400	2.352	1.269	418.0	5.033	2.207	1.272	424.6	4.992
425	2.459	1.254	449.6	5.109	2.302	1.258	456.3	5.069

continued

T, °K	v	c_p	i	s	v	c_p	i	s
450	2.565	1.240	480.8	5.180	2.397	1.245	487.6	5.141
475	2.671	1.228	511.6	5.247	2.491	1.234	518.5	5.208
500	2.776	1.218	542.2	5.310	2.584	1.224	549.2	5.270
550	2.984	1.203	602.6	5.425	2.768	1.208	610.0	5.386
600	3.190	1.193	662.5	5.529	2.951	1.198	670.1	5.491
650	3.393	1.188	722.1	5.625	3.132	1.193	729.8	5.587
700	3.595	1.187	781.4	5.713	3.311	1.191	789.4	5.675
750	3.795	1.189	840.8	5.795	3.489	1.192	849.0	5.757
800	3.994	1.192	900.3	5.872	3.665	1.195	908.7	5.834
850	4.192	1.196	960.0	5.944	3.842	1.199	968.5	5.907
900	4.389	1.201	1020.0	6.012	4.017	1.204	1028.5	5.975
950	4.585	1.207	1080.2	6.077	4.192	1.209	1088.8	6.040
1000	4.781	1.213	1140.7	6.139	4.366	1.215	1149.5	6.102
1050	4.976	1.219	1201.5	6.199	4.540	1.221	1210.4	6.162
1100	5.170	1.225	1262.6	6.256	4.713	1.227	1271.6	6.219
1150	5.364	1.231	1324.0	6.311	4.886	1.233	1333.1	6.274
1200	5.558	1.236	1385.6	6.363	5.058	1.238	1394.9	6.326
1250	5.751	1.242	1448.5	6.413	5.230	1.244	1456.9	6.377
1300	5.943	1.247	1509.8	6.462	5.401	1.249	1519.2	6.426

$p = 1000$ bar

T, °K	v	c_p	i	s	T, °K	v	c_p	i	s
135	1.221	1.385	58.1	3.389	375	2.006	1.288	399.7	4.873
140	1.236	1.435	65.1	3.440	400	2.092	1.274	431.7	4.956
150	1.266	1.558	80.1	3.543	425	2.177	1.261	463.4	5.033
160	1.296	1.634	96.1	3.645	450	2.262	1.249	494.7	5.105
170	1.327	1.653	112.6	3.746	475	2.346	1.238	525.8	5.172
180	1.358	1.634	129.1	3.840	500	2.430	1.228	556.7	5.235
190	1.390	1.596	145.2	3.928	550	2.596	1.212	617.6	5.351
200	1.422	1.551	160.9	4.009	600	2.760	1.202	678.0	5.456
210	1.454	1.507	176.2	4.083	650	2.922	1.196	738.0	5.552
220	1.487	1.468	191.1	4.152	700	3.083	1.194	797.7	5.641
230	1.519	1.436	205.6	4.217	750	3.243	1.195	857.3	5.723
240	1.551	1.409	219.8	4.277	800	3.402	1.197	917.1	5.800
250	1.584	1.388	233.8	4.334	850	3.561	1.201	977.1	5.873
260	1.617	1.371	247.6	4.388	900	3.719	1.206	1037.3	5.942
270	1.650	1.358	261.3	4.440	950	3.876	1.211	1097.7	6.008
280	1.683	1.347	274.8	4.489	1000	4.033	1.217	1158.4	6.070
290	1.717	1.338	288.2	4.536	1050	4.189	1.223	1219.4	6.129
300	1.751	1.331	301.5	4.581	1100	4.345	1.229	1280.7	6.186
310	1.785	1.324	314.8	4.625	1150	4.501	1.235	1342.4	6.241
320	1.819	1.318	328.0	4.667	1200	4.657	1.240	1404.2	6.293
330	1.853	1.312	341.2	4.707	1250	4.812	1.245	1466.3	6.344
340	1.887	1.307	354.3	4.746	1300	4.967	1.250	1528.7	6.399
350	1.921	1.301	367.3	4.784					

Specific volume v (m^3/kg) of dissociated nitrogen [143] (*cf* page 600)

p, bar \ T, °K →	1250	1500	1750	2000	2200	2400	2600	2800
0.1	37.10	44.52	51.92	59.36	65.29	71.23	77.17	83.10
0.2	18.55	22.26	25.97	29.68	32.65	35.62	38.58	41.55
0.4	9.276	11.13	12.99	14.84	16.32	17.81	19.29	20.77
0.6	6.184	7.421	8.662	9.894	10.88	11.87	12.86	13.85
1	3.711	4.453	5.200	5.937	6.530	7.124	7.718	8.313
2	1.856	2.227	2.600	2.969	3.266	3.563	3.859	4.156
4	0.9286	1.114	1.301	1.485	1.634	1.782	1.930	2.079
6	0.6194	0.7431	0.8677	0.9905	1.089	1.188	1.287	1.386
10	0.3721	0.4464	0.5210	0.5948	0.6541	0.7135	0.7728	0.8322

continued

T, °K \ p, bar →	1250	1500	1750	2000	2200	2400	2600	2800
20	0.1866	0.2238	0.2612	0.2980	0.3277	0.3573	0.3870	0.4167
40	0.09389	0.1125	0.1312	0.1496	0.1644	0.1793	0.1941	0.2089
60	0.06298	0.07538	0.08787	0.1001	0.1100	0.1199	0.1298	0.1397
100	0.03824	0.04570	0.05320	0.06055	0.06648	0.07241	0.07834	0.08427
200	0.01969	0.02344	0.02716	0.03087	0.03383	0.03680	0.03976	0.04272
300	0.01352	0.01601	0.01847	0.02097	0.02295	0.02492	0.02689	0.02887
500	0.008555	0.01007	0.01157	0.01305	0.01423	0.01542	0.01650	0.01778
1000	0.004817	0.005589	0.006335	0.007088	0.007681	0.008271	0.008861	0.009451

p, bar \ T, °K →	3000	3200	3400	3600	3800	4000	4200	4400
0.1	89.04	94.98	100.93	106.9	112.9	119.0	125.4	132.0
0.2	44.51	47.49	50.46	53.44	56.44	59.48	65.27	65.78
0.4	22.26	23.74	25.23	95.72	28.21	29.72	31.25	32.82
0.6	14.64	15.83	16.82	17.81	18.81	19.81	20.82	21.86
1	8.905	9.498	10.09	10.69	11.28	11.88	12.49	13.10
2	4.452	4.750	5.047	5.344	5.642	5.940	6.241	6.546
4	2.227	2.375	2.524	2.672	2.821	2.970	3.120	3.271
6	1.485	1.584	1.683	1.782	1.881	1.980	2.080	2.181
10	0.8915	0.9509	1.010	1.070	1.129	1.189	1.248	1.308
20	0.4463	0.4760	0.5057	0.5354	0.5651	0.5948	0.6246	0.6546
40	0.2238	0.2386	0.2534	0.2683	0.2831	0.2980	0.3129	0.3278
60	0.1496	0.1594	0.1693	0.1792	0.1891	0.1990	0.2089	0.2189
100	0.09020	0.09613	0.1021	0.1080	0.1139	0.1199	0.1258	0.1318
200	0.04568	0.04865	0.05161	0.05457	0.05754	0.06051	0.06348	0.06645
300	0.03084	0.03281	0.03479	0.03676	0.03874	0.04072	0.04269	0.04467
500	0.01896	0.02014	0.02133	0.02251	0.02370	0.02488	0.02607	0.02725
1000	0.01004	0.01063	0.01122	0.01181	0.01240	0.01299	0.01359	0.01418

p, bar \ T, °K →	4600	4800	5000	5200	5400	5600	5800	6000
0.1	139.1	147.0	156.1	167.0	180.2	196.5	216.5	240.6
0.2	69.17	72.84	76.94	81.65	87.20	93.89	102.0	111.9
0.4	34.45	36.19	38.07	40.17	42.57	45.39	48.32	52.72
0.6	22.93	24.05	25.26	26.59	28.08	29.79	31.79	34.17
1	13.73	14.39	15.09	15.84	16.66	17.59	18.66	19.91
2	6.856	7.175	7.508	7.859	8.239	8.655	9.120	9.649
4	3.424	3.581	3.742	3.910	4.087	4.278	4.486	4.717
6	2.282	2.385	2.491	2.601	2.715	2.837	2.969	3.112
10	1.369	1.430	1.493	1.557	1.624	1.884	1.768	1.849
20	0.6847	0.7150	0.7458	0.7773	0.8095	0.8430	0.8780	0.9151
40	0.3428	0.3579	0.3731	0.3885	0.4043	0.4205	0.4372	0.4547
60	0.2289	0.2389	0.2490	0.2592	0.2696	0.2802	0.2911	0.3025
100	0.1377	0.1437	0.1498	0.1559	0.1620	0.1683	0.1747	0.1813
200	0.06943	0.07242	0.07542	0.07844	0.08149	0.08458	0.08771	0.09091
300	0.04666	0.04865	0.05065	0.05265	0.05468	0.05672	0.05879	0.06089
500	0.02844	0.02963	0.03083	0.03203	0.03324	0.03445	0.03568	0.03936
1000	0.01477	0.01537	0.01596	0.01656	0.01716	0.01777	0.01837	0.01899

Enthalpy *i* (kJ/kg) of dissociated nitrogen at high temperatures and different pressures [143]

p, bar \ T, °K →	1250	1500	1750	2000	2200	2400	2600	2800	3000	3200	3400	3600
0.1	1373	1680	1995	2313	2572	2832	3093	3356	3620	3887	4157	4436
0.2	1373	1680	1995	2313	2572	2832	3093	3356	3620	3886	4155	4430
0.4	1373	1680	1995	2313	2572	2832	3093	3356	3620	3886	4154	4426

continued

p. bar → T. °K	1250	1500	1750	2000	2200	2400	2600	2800	3000	3200	3400	3600
0.6	1373	1680	1995	2314	2572	2832	3093	3356	3620	3885	4153	4424
1	1373	1680	1995	2314	2572	2832	3093	3356	3620	3885	4152	4423
2	1373	1680	1995	2314	2572	2832	3093	3356	3620	3885	4152	4421
4	1374	1681	1995	2314	2572	2832	3094	3356	3620	3885	4152	4420
6	1374	1681	1996	2314	2572	2832	3094	3357	3620	3885	4152	4420
10	1374	1681	1996	2315	2573	2833	3094	3357	3621	3886	4152	4420
20	1375	1682	1997	2316	2574	2834	3096	3358	3622	3887	4153	4420
40	1377	1684	1999	2318	2577	2837	3098	3361	3625	3889	4155	4422
60	1379	1686	2002	2321	2579	2839	3101	3363	3627	3892	4158	4425
100	1382	1691	2006	2326	2584	2844	3106	3368	3632	3898	4163	4429
200	1392	1701	2017	2338	2596	2857	3118	3381	3645	3909	4175	4441
300	1402	1712	2029	2350	2609	2869	3131	3393	3657	3922	4187	4453
500	1424	1733	2051	2374	2633	2894	3156	3418	3682	3946	4211	4477
1000	1480	1786	2114	2433	2693	2955	3216	3479	3742	4006	4271	4537
T. °K → p. bar	3800	4000	4200	4400	4600	4800	5000	5200	5400	5600	5800	6000
0.1	4729	5049	5415	5856	6415	7146	8123	9438	11 196	13 506	16 455	20 052
0.2	4715	5020	5358	5749	6223	6819	7590	8602	9 933	11 672	13 908	16 706
0.4	4706	5000	5318	5673	6087	6588	7213	8008	9 032	10 350	12 038	14 164
0.6	4702	4991	5300	5639	6027	6485	7045	7745	8 631	9 760	11 195	13 001
1	4698	4982	5282	5606	5967	6383	6877	7480	8 229	9 166	10 344	11 816
2	4694	4974	5264	5572	5906	6279	6708	7214	7 823	8 566	9 481	10 610
4	4691	4967	5251	5548	5863	6209	6589	7026	7 536	8 142	8 869	9 750
6	4690	4965	5246	5538	5844	6174	6536	6943	7 409	7 953	8 598	9 368
10	4689	4962	5241	5527	5826	6142	6484	6830	7 282	7 765	8 326	8 984
20	4689	4961	5236	5518	5808	6111	6431	6776	7 155	7 576	8 052	8 598
40	4691	4961	5235	5512	5797	6090	6396	6719	7 066	7 444	7 860	8 327
60	4693	4963	5235	5512	5793	6082	6381	6695	7 028	7 386	7 777	8 208
100	4697	4967	5238	5513	5792	6076	6369	6673	6 992	7 331	7 695	8 091
200	4709	4978	5248	5521	5797	6078	6364	6658	6 963	7 283	7 620	7 980
300	4721	4989	5260	5532	5806	6085	6368	6658	6 957	7 267	7 593	7 937
500	4745	5013	5282	5554	5827	6104	6384	6669	6 962	7 264	7 577	7 906
1000	4803	5071	5340	5610	5882	6156	6433	6714	7 001	7 293	7 595	7 908

Entropy *s* (kJ/kg · deg) of dissociated nitrogen at high temperatures and different pressures [143]

T. °K → p. bar	1250	1500	1750	2000	2200	2400	2600	2800
0.1	9.094	9.317	9.510	9.681	9.804	9.917	10.022	10.119
0.2	8.888	9.112	9.306	9.476	9.599	9.712	9.816	9.914
0.4	8.682	8.906	9.099	9.270	9.393	9.506	9.611	9.708
0.6	8.561	8.785	8.977	9.150	9.272	9.386	9.490	9.588
0.8	8.476	8.700	8.892	9.064	9.187	9.300	9.405	9.502
1	8.410	8.634	8.825	8.998	9.121	9.234	9.339	9.436
2	8.204	8.428	8.622	8.792	8.915	9.028	9.133	9.230
4	7.999	8.222	8.415	8.586	8.710	8.823	8.927	9.025
6	7.878	8.102	8.245	8.466	8.589	8.702	8.807	8.904
10	7.726	7.950	8.145	8.314	8.438	8.551	8.655	8.753
20	7.520	7.745	7.938	8.109	8.232	8.345	8.450	8.547
40	7.314	7.539	7.635	7.903	8.026	8.139	8.244	8.341
60	7.194	7.418	7.612	7.783	7.906	8.019	8.124	8.221
100	7.040	7.266	7.460	7.631	7.754	7.868	7.972	8.070
200	6.834	7.059	7.253	7.426	7.549	7.662	7.767	7.864
300	6.713	6.938	7.132	7.305	7.428	7.542	7.646	7.744
500	6.557	6.784	6.982	7.153	7.277	7.390	7.495	7.592
1000	6.343	6.572	6.772	6.946	7.070	7.184	7.289	7.387

continued

T. 10³ °K → / p. bar	3000	3200	3400	3600	3800	4000	4200	4400
0.1	10.211	10.296	10.379	10.458	10.537	10.619	10.709	10.811
0.2	10.005	10.091	10.172	10.251	10.328	10.406	10.488	10.579
0.4	9.799	9.885	9.966	10.044	10.120	10.195	10.272	10.355
0.6	9.679	9.764	9.846	9.923	9.998	10.072	10.148	10.226
0.8	9.593	9.679	9.760	9.837	9.912	9.985	10.059	10.136
1	9.527	9.613	9.694	9.771	9.845	9.918	9.991	10.067
2	9.321	9.407	9.488	9.565	9.638	9.710	9.781	9.853
4	9.116	9.201	9.282	9.359	9.432	9.503	9.572	9.641
6	8.995	9.081	9.162	9.238	9.311	9.382	9.450	9.518
10	8.844	8.929	9.010	9.086	9.159	9.229	9.297	9.364
20	8.638	8.723	8.804	8.880	8.953	9.023	9.090	9.156
40	8.432	8.518	8.598	8.675	8.747	8.817	8.883	8.948
60	8.312	8.398	8.478	8.554	8.627	8.696	8.763	8.827
100	8.160	8.246	8.326	8.403	8.475	8.544	8.610	8.674
200	7.955	8.040	8.121	8.197	8.269	8.338	8.404	8.468
300	7.835	7.920	8.000	8.077	8.149	8.218	8.284	8.347
500	7.684	7.769	7.849	7.925	7.998	8.066	8.132	8.195
1000	7.478	7.563	7.644	7.720	7.792	7.861	7.926	7.989

T. °K → / p. bar	4600	4800	5000	5200	5400	5600	5800	6000
0.1	10.935	11.091	11.290	11.548	11.879	12.299	12.816	13.425
0.2	10.685	10.811	10.968	11.167	11.418	11.734	12.126	12.600
0.4	10.447	10.554	10.681	10.837	11.029	11.269	11.565	11.925
0.6	10.312	10.410	10.524	10.661	10.828	11.034	11.285	11.591
0.8	10.219	10.311	10.417	10.543	10.695	10.879	11.104	11.377
1	10.147	10.235	10.336	10.454	10.595	10.766	10.972	11.222
2	9.927	10.006	10.094	10.193	10.308	10.443	10.603	10.794
4	9.711	9.784	9.862	9.948	10.044	10.154	10.282	10.431
6	9.586	9.656	9.730	9.810	9.898	9.997	10.110	10.240
10	9.430	9.498	9.567	9.641	9.720	9.808	9.907	10.018
20	9.220	9.284	9.350	9.418	9.489	9.565	9.649	9.742
40	9.011	9.074	9.136	9.199	9.265	9.333	9.406	9.486
60	8.889	8.951	9.012	9.074	9.136	9.201	9.270	9.343
100	8.736	8.797	8.857	8.916	8.976	9.038	9.102	9.169
200	8.529	8.589	8.647	8.705	8.763	8.821	8.880	8.941
300	8.408	8.468	8.525	8.582	8.639	8.695	8.752	8.811
500	8.256	8.315	8.372	8.428	8.483	8.538	8.593	8.649
1000	8.050	8.108	8.165	8.220	8.274	8.327	8.380	8.433

Ratio of molecular weight M of undissociated gas to the molecular weight of mixture M_m [144]

T. 10³ °K → / p. atm	5	6	7	8	9	10	12	14	16
0.2	1.015	1.251	1.737	1.955	1.990	2.117	2.530	3.318	3.92
0.4	1.010	1.179	1.610	1.915	1.981	2.075	2.375	3.050	3.65
0.6	1.008	1.148	1.532	1.883	1.971	1.999	2.313	2.900	3.56
0.8	1.007	1.128	1.478	1.850	1.966	1.997	2.272	2.802	3.46
1.0	1.007	1.116	1.441	1.822	1.960	1.996	2.244	2.728	3.38
2.0		1.082	1.326	1.715	1.924	1.987	2.173	2.536	3.12
4.0		1.058	1.236	1.585	1.861	1.965	2.123	2.380	2.86
6.0		1.052	1.196	1.505	1.810	1.950	2.090	2.314	2.73
8.0		1.041	1.169	1.456	1.770	1.935	2.060	2.270	2.64
10.0		1.037	1.152	1.417	1.732	1.922	2.050	2.240	2.58
15.0		1.030	1.125	1.350	1.660	1.890	2.030	2.200	2.48
20.0		1.026	1.108	1.308	1.598	1.859	2.010	2.170	2.40
30.0		1.021	1.089	1.256	1.528	1.809	1.990	2.140	2.35

continued

T, °K \ p, bar →	5	6	7	8	9	10	12	14	16
40.0		1,018	1,077	1.223	1,475	1,768	1,980	2,110	2,30
50,0		1.016	1.069	1.201	1.435	1,730	1,960	2.100	2,27
60.0		1,015	1.063	1.183	1.403	1,700	1,950	2.090	2,25
70.0		1,014	1,058	1.170	1,378	1.670	1,930	2,080	2,23
80.0		1,013	1,055	1.160	1,356	1,645	1,900	2.070	2.21
90,0		1,012	1,050	1.151	1,339	1.624	1.890	2.060	2,20
100.0		1,012	1,048	1.143	1,323	1,600	1.880	2,050	2.19

p, bar \ T, °K →	18	20	22	24	26	28	30	38	40
0.2	3.95	3,98	3,99	4.00	4,00				
0.4	3,90	3.97	3.98	3,99	4.00				
0.6	3.86	3,95	3.97	3.99	3.99	4,00			
0,8	3.82	3,94	3,96	3,98	3,98	3,99	4,00		
1,0	3.78	3.92	3.95	3.98	3,98	3.99	3,99	4.00	
2.0	3.62	3.85	3.95	3,97	3,98	3.99	3.99	4,00	
4.0	3,40	3.74	3.91	3.97	3.98	3,99	3,99	4,00	
6.0	3,25	3.64	3.87	3,95	3,98	3.98	3,99	4,00	
8.0	3.14	3.55	3.83	3.92	3.96	3,97	3,98	4,00	
10.0	3.07	3.49	3.79	3.90	3.96	3.97	3.98	4.00	
15.0	2.90	3.23	3.71	3.87	3.90	3.95	3,97	3,99	4.00
20.0	2.80	3.18	3,64	3.82	3.87	3,92	3.95	3,98	3.99
30,0	2,77	2.96	3.52	3.78	3.82	3.90	3.94	3,98	3.99
40.0	2,59	2.89	3.42	3,60	3,77	3.87	3,92	3,97	3.99
50.0	2.53	2,82	3.34	3,53	3,72	3,84	3.90	3.96	3.99
60,0	2.50	2,77	3.27	3.47	3,68	3.81	3.88	3,95	3.99
70,0	2.46	2.74	3.22	3.44	3,62	3,64	3,68	3.86	3,96
80,0	2,43	2.69	3.16	3.37	3.59	3.60	3,66	3.85	3,94
90.0	2,41	2,66	3.12	3,33	3,54	3,57	3,63	3.83	3.93
100,0	2.39	2,63	3.08	3.29	3.51	3,57	3,61	3.81	3.92

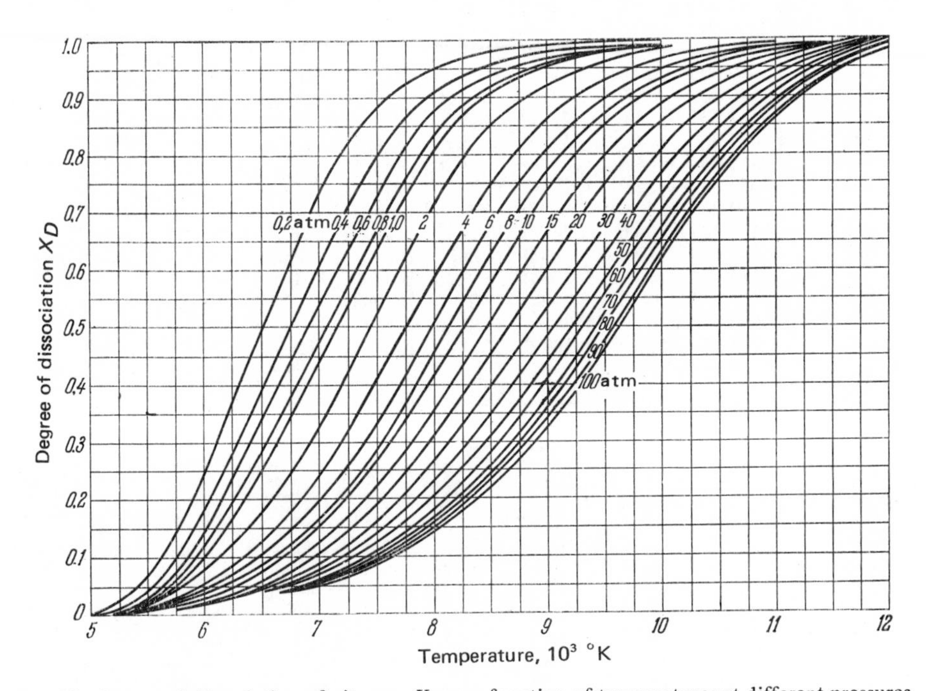

Fig. 13. Degree of dissociation of nitrogen X_D as a function of temperatures at different pressures.

Degree of dissociation of nitrogen X_D [144]

p, atm \ T, 10^3 °K →	5	6	7	8	9	10	11	12
0.2	0.0146	0.251	0.737	0,955	0.990	0.999		
0.4	0.0103	0.179	0,610	0.915	0.981	0,996		
0,6	0.0084	0,148	0.532	0.883	0.971	0.993		
0,8	0.0073	0,128	0.478	0,850	0.966	0.991		
1,0	0,0065	0.116	0.441	0,822	0.960	0.989		
2,0		0.082	0.326	0.715	0.924	0.984	0.900	
4,0		0.058	0.236	0.585	0.861	0.965	0.988	
6.0		0.050	0.197	0.505	0.810	0.950	0.985	
8,0		0.041	0.169	0,456	0.770	0.935	0,982	
10.0		0.037	0.152	0.417	0.732	0,922	0.978	
15.0		0.030	0.125	0.350	0.660	0.890	0.970	
20,0		0,026	0.108	0,308	0.598	0.859	0.960	
30,0		0,021	0.089	0.256	0.528	0,809	0.950	
40,0		0.018	0.077	0.223	0.475	0.768	0.935	0.995
50.0		0,016	0.069	0.201	0.435	0.730	0.925	0.994
60,0		0.015	0.063	0.183	0.403	0.700	0,910	0.993
70.0		0.014	0.058	0.170	0.378	0.670	0,895	0.992
80,0		0.013	0,055	0.160	0.356	0,645	0.882	0,990
90,0		0.012	0.050	0.151	0,339	0,624	0.872	0.985
100,0		0.012	0.048	0.143	0.323	0,610	0.860	0,980

Density $\rho \cdot 10^3$ (kg/m^3) of dissociated and ionized nitrogen [144]

p, atm \ T, 10^3 °K →	5	6	7	8	9	10	12	14	16
0.2	13.45	9.1	5.61	4.36	3.81	3.23	2.25	1.47	1.09
0.4	27.10	19.3	12.10	8.95	7.66	6.60	4.80	3.20	2.34
0.6	40.90	29.7	19.00	13.60	11.50	10.20	7.36	5.04	3.60
0.8	54.60	40.4	26.40	18.70	15.40	13.65	10.05	6.95	4.93
1.0	68.20	51.0	33.80	23.30	19.35	17.10	12.65	8.92	6.30
2.0	136.50	105.0	73.60	49.80	39.40	34.40	26.20	19.30	13.70
4.0	273.00	215.5	147.20	107.50	81.60	69.60	53.80	41.10	29.90
6.0	410.00	329.0	245.00	170.00	125.60	105.00	82.00	63.50	47.10
8.0	546.00	438.0	334.00	234.50	172.00	141.00	110.50	86.00	64.60
10.0	682.00	550.0	422.00	301.00	219.00	177.00	138.60	108.80	82.70
15.0	1025.00	834.0	652.00	475.00	344.00	272.00	210.00	166.50	129.00
20.0	1365.00	1106.0	885.00	654.00	474.00	367.50	283.00	225.00	177.50
30.0	2050.00	1685.0	1375.00	1020.00	750.00	570.00	431.00	344.00	274.00
40.0	2730.00	2240.0	1810.00	1400.00	1030.00	775.00	575.00	462.00	372.00
50.0	3410.00	2800.0	2278.00	1780.00	1320.00	990.00	726.00	581.00	470.00
60.0	4100.00	3370.0	2650.00	2165.00	1620.00	1205.00	879.00	700.00	570.00
70.0	4790.00	3940.0	3220.00	2555.00	1935.00	1431.00	1031.00	822.00	671.00
80.0	5460.00	4500.0	3700.00	2940.00	2240.00	1660.00	1200.00	940.00	772.00
90.0	6150.00	5060.0	4180.00	3330.00	2550.00	1890.00	1355.00	1065.00	875.00
100.0	6830.00	5620.0	4650.00	3740.00	2865.00	2120.00	1515.00	1188.00	975.00

p, atm \ T, 10^3 °K →	18	20	22	24	26	28	30	35	40
0.2	0.95	0.86	0.78	0.72	0.66	0.61	0.57	0.49	0.43
0.4	1.95	1.72	1.56	1.43	1.32	1.22	1.14	0.97	0.85
0.6	2.94	2.58	2.34	2.13	1.97	1.83	1.71	1.46	1.28
0.8	3.98	3.47	3.15	2.86	2.64	2.44	2.28	1.95	1.68
1.0	5.01	4.36	3.93	3.57	3.30	3.06	2.84	2.44	2.13
2.0	10.45	8.71	7.86	7.16	6.61	6.10	5.70	4.90	4.26
4.0	22.40	18.30	15.90	14.32	13.20	12.20	11.38	9.75	8.52
6.0	35.10	28.22	24.10	21.65	19.85	18.45	17.10	14.65	12.80
8.0	48.50	38.50	32.40	29.00	26.55	24.50	22.80	19.55	17.05
10.0	61.70	48.80	41.00	36.45	33.10	30.75	28.40	24.35	21.35

continued

p, atm \ T, 10^3 °K →	18	20	22	24	26	28	30	35	40
15.0	98.20	79.50	63.00	55.30	51.00	46.40	43.10	36.80	32.10
20.0	135.50	107.50	85.30	74.50	68.60	62.20	57.00	49.00	42.60
30.0	206.00	173.00	132.80	113.20	103.00	94.10	87.00	73.60	64.00
40.0	293.50	236.50	181.50	158.00	139.50	126.10	116.50	98.60	85.50
50.0	375.00	302.00	232.50	201.50	176.50	159.00	145.80	123.10	106.80
60.0	456.00	370.00	284.00	246.00	220.00	191.50	176.00	148.00	129.00
70.0	540.00	436.00	338.00	290.00	254.00	235.00	217.00	177.00	150.50
80.0	626.00	508.00	392.00	338.00	292.00	271.00	249.00	203.00	173.00
90.0	709.00	578.00	448.00	384.00	333.50	308.00	282.00	229.00	196.00
100.0	795.00	648.00	504.00	432.00	374.00	342.00	315.00	256.00	218.00

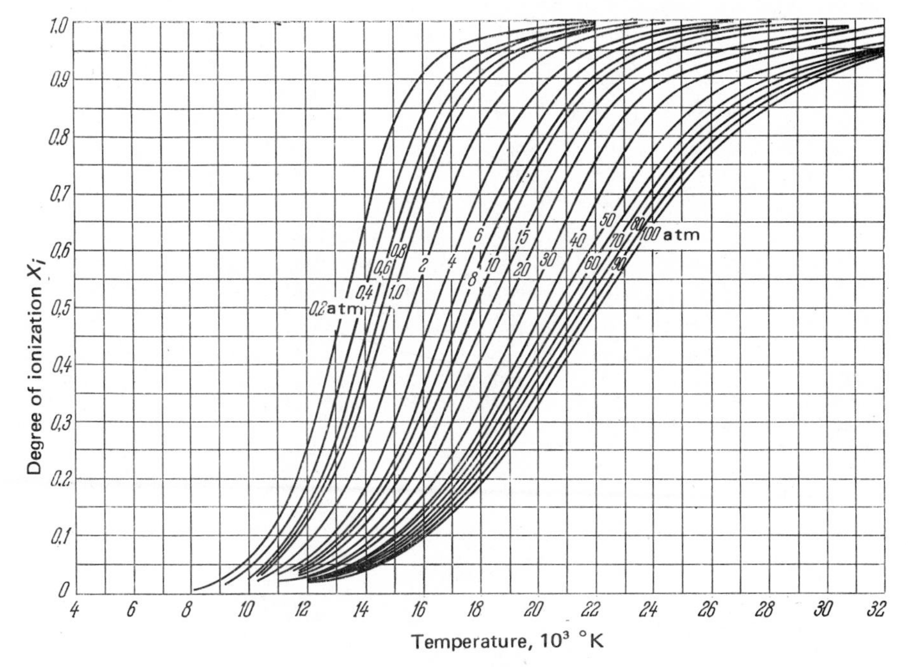

Fig. 14. Degree of ionization X_i as a function of temperature at different pressures.

Degree of ionization X_i of nitrogen at different temperatures and pressures [144]

T, °K \ p bar →	10	12	14	15	16	18	20	22
0.2	0.056	0.265	0.659	0.820	0.991	0.975	0.996	0.999
0.4	0.039	0.189	0.525	0.712	0.825	0.950	0.987	0.999
0.6	0.032	0.157	0.450	0.640	0.780	0.930	0.985	0.999
0.8	0.028	0.136	0.401	0.577	0.730	0.910	0.976	0.999
1.0	0.025	0.122	0.364	0.544	0.690	0.890	0.970	0.988
2.0	0.018	0.086	0.268	0.415	0.560	0.810	0.960	0.976
4.0		0.061	0.192	0.307	0.430	0.700	0.925	0.955
6.0		0.050	0.157	0.225	0.364	0.625	0.870	0.935
8.0		0.042	0.137	0.222	0.320	0.570	0.820	0.915
10.0	0.08	0.039	0.122	0.200	0.290	0.526	0.775	0.896
15.0		0.032	0.102	0.164	0.240	0.450	0.745	0.856

continued

$T\cdot 10^3$ °K → / p, atm	10	12	14	15	16	18	20	22
20,0		0,028	0,087	0.143	0.201	0.400	0.675	0.820
30,0		0.023	0,071	0.117	0.173	0.336	0.540	0.760
40,0		0,019	0.062	0,103	0.150	0.296	0.480	0,680
50,0		0,017	0,055	0.091	0.134	0.266	0,444	0.600
60,0		0,016	0.051	0,083	0.123	0,251	0,410	0,570
70,0		0,015	0,047	0.077	0,114	0.232	0.384	0.550
80,0		0,014	0.044	0.072	0,107	0.218	0.364	0,530
90,0		0,013	0.041	0.068	0,101	0.204	0.346	0.510
100,0	0,002	0,012	0,039	0.063	0.095	0.195	0.220	0.500

$T\cdot 10^3$ °K → / p, atm	24	25	26	28	30	35	40	
0,2	0,999	1.000	0,999	1.000	0,999	0.999		
0,4	0.999	0.999	0.999	1,000	0,999	0.999	0.999	
0,6	0.999	0,999	0.999	0.999	0.999	0,999	0.999	
0,8	0,998	0,999	0,999	0,999	0.999	0.999	0.999	
1.0	0.996	0.997	0,998	0.998	0.999	0.999	0.999	
2,0	0,992	0.992	0.993	0.997	0.998	0.999	0.999	
4.0	0.986	0.985	0.988	0.994	0.996	0.999	0.999	
6,0	0.975	0.973	0.980	0,990	0,994	0.999	0.999	
8.0	0.962	0.970	0.974	0.986	0.991	0.999	0.999	
10,0	0.950	0.960	0.965	0.981	0.989	0.998	0.999	
15,0	0.936	0.946	0.950	0.975	0.984	0,996	0.998	
20,0	0.910	0,938	0.938	0.962	0,978	0,991	0.997	
30,0	0,890	0,904	0.930	0.950	0.970	0.989	0,996	
40.0	0,852	0.875	0.885	0.935	0.960	0.985	0.995	
50.0	0.765	0.854	0,872	0.920	0,950	0,981	0.994	
60.0	0.738	0.830	0,840	0.905	0.940	0.978	0.993	
70.0	0.712	0,808	0.820	0,890	0.931	0,974	0.991	
80.0	0,688	0,788	0.800	0.880	0,925	0.970	0.989	
90.0	0,665	0.777	0,786	0.865	0,915	0.967	0.987	
100.0	0.645	0.757	0.770	0.855	0.905	0.964	0,985	

Enthalpy $I\cdot 10^4$ (cal/mole of N_2) of dissociated and ionized nitrogen [144]

T, °K → / p, atm	5	6	7	8	9	10	12	14	16
0,2	4,50	10,34	23,51	30.40	31,10	35,12	57,54	91.45	121,68
0.4	4.39	9,17	20.52	28.85	31,94	32.97	51.57	81.13	108.53
0.6	4.38	8,53	18,68	28.14	31.57	33,68	49,05	75,14	104.93
0,8	4.32	8,05	17.24	27.44	31,26	33,68	47.44	71,30	101.03
1.0	4,29	7.7	16,42	26,85	31.15	33,52	46,37	68,44	97,78
2,0		6.91	12,69	24,27	30,54	33,54	43,60	60,89	87,28
4,0		6,43	11.37	21.02	29,07	33,10	41,65	54,88	76,84
6,0		6,22	11,05	19.14	27.79	32,67	40.75	52,12	71,58
8,0		6,01	10,66	17.89	26,81	32.39	40.08	50,54	68.04
10,0		5,92	10,45	17,01	25,84	31.97	39,83	49.37	63,64
15.0		5,78	9,56	15,32	25,16	31.21	39,27	47,81	61,63
20.0		5.66	9,05	14,32	22,51	30,39	38,93	46.63	58,52
30.0		5,57	8,64	13,04	20,83	29,09	38,52	45,39	57.29
40,0		5,48	8,24	12,24	19,49	28,11	38,13	44,63	54,44
50,0		5,43	8,02	11.74	18,54	27,14	37.95	44.08	53,16
60,0		5,40	7,87	11,28	17,75	26,32	37,90	43,64	52.26
70.0		5,36	7,73	11,00	17.14	25,62	37.79	43.46	51,60
80,0		5,33	7,64	10,77	16,62	25,02	37,66	43,22	51,04
90.0		5,30	7,50	10,53	16.14	24,48	37,56	42,98	50,56
100,0		5.29	7,42	10,32	15,71	24,05	37,49	42.82	50,12

continued

T. 10^3 °K → / p. atm	18	20	22	24	26	28	30	35	40
0.2	127.46	131.24	135.45	139.72	143.92	148.28	152.50	162.94	173.58
0.4	122.85	130.26	135.38	139.65	143.88	148.28	152.50	162.94	173.58
0.6	121.16	130.21	135.24	139.56	143.77	148.24	152.50	162.94	173.58
0.8	119.51	129.36	135.11	139.45	143.71	148.18	152.46	162.92	173.56
1.0	117.86	128.85	134.26	139.26	143.56	147.96	152.30	162.86	173.56
2.0	111.48	128.13	133.36	139.01	143.26	147.84	152.22	162.84	173.54
4.0	102.26	125.31	131.51	138.56	142.91	147.68	152.12	162.76	173.50
6.0	96.16	121.02	129.91	137.71	142.21	147.48	151.90	162.72	173.44
8.0	91.76	117.06	128.16	137.31	141.56	147.13	151.76	162.42	173.36
10.0	88.16	113.96	126.56	136.91	140.86	146.68	151.56	162.32	173.30
15.0	81.86	111.51	123.86	134.16	139.56	146.18	151.26	162.30	173.24
20.0	77.82	105.31	119.96	131.96	138.26	145.18	150.56	162.04	173.18
30.0	71.85	94.56	114.96	130.16	137.26	143.78	149.95	161.72	173.12
40.0	69.24	89.66	108.36	126.26	133.76	142.53	148.86	161.32	173.06
50.0	66.86	86.46	101.86	119.26	131.36	141.18	147.46	160.81	173.00
60.0	65.64	83.76	99.26	116.86	128.66	139.78	147.16	160.22	172.92
70.0	64.03	81.56	97.46	114.71	126.86	138.38	145.26	159.72	172.86
80.0	62.93	79.75	95.66	110.40	125.06	136.63	144.56	159.22	172.70
90.0	61.76	78.36	94.06	110.42	123.76	135.18	143.52	158.92	172.54
100.0	61.04	76.86	93.06	108.81	120.26	134.18	142.46	158.62	171.30

Entropy S (cal/mole · deg) of dissociated and ionized nitrogen [144]

T. 10^3 °K → / p. atm	5	6	7	8	9	10	12	14	16	18	20	22	24	26	28	30	35
0.2	65	88	107	119	121	130	149	176	189	199	204	207	208	209	209	209	210
0.4	62	81	98	112	115	122	136	160	179	187	193	196	198	199	199	200	200
0.6	57	78	96	108	112	114	130	150	170	179	185	189	191	192	193	193	194
0.8	55	76	91	105	109	112	124	142	164	176	179	183	185	186	187	189	192
1.0	52	74	89	102	108	110	121	138	158	170	174	178	180	182	183	185	188
2.0		68	84	95	101	105	113	128	144	157	164	168	169	170	172	174	177
4.0		64	74	86	95	99	106	115	129	142	149	156	158	160	162	164	166
6.0		60	71	81	91	95	102	110	121	134	142	148	152	154	156	158	160
8.0		57	69	78	87	93	99	107	117	129	136	142	148	149	150	152	154
10.0		55	67	76	85	91	97	104	113	125	134	139	143	146	147	148	150
15.0		53	65	72	81	88	92	99	107	117	128	130	134	138	140	141	145
20.0		52	63	70	78	85	90	98	103	112	122	127	132	133	134	136	140
30.0		51	61	68	75	81	85	92	97	104	114	120	126	126	130	132	133
40.0		50	59	66	72	77	82	88	94	100	107	115	119	122	123	125	127
50.0		50	57	63	70	76	81	85	91	98	102	111	115	119	120	122	122
60.0		49	56	61	67	74	79	84	89	96	101	109	113	116	118	119	119
70.0		48	55	60	65	70	77	82	88	94	100	107	110	114	115	116	118
80.0		48	54	59	65	69	75	81	85	91	98	100	107	110	112	112	113
90.0		47	53	58	63	67	73	79	84	90	96	101	105	106	108	110	112
100.0		46	52	56	62	66	72	77	83	88	93	100	103	105	106	107	108

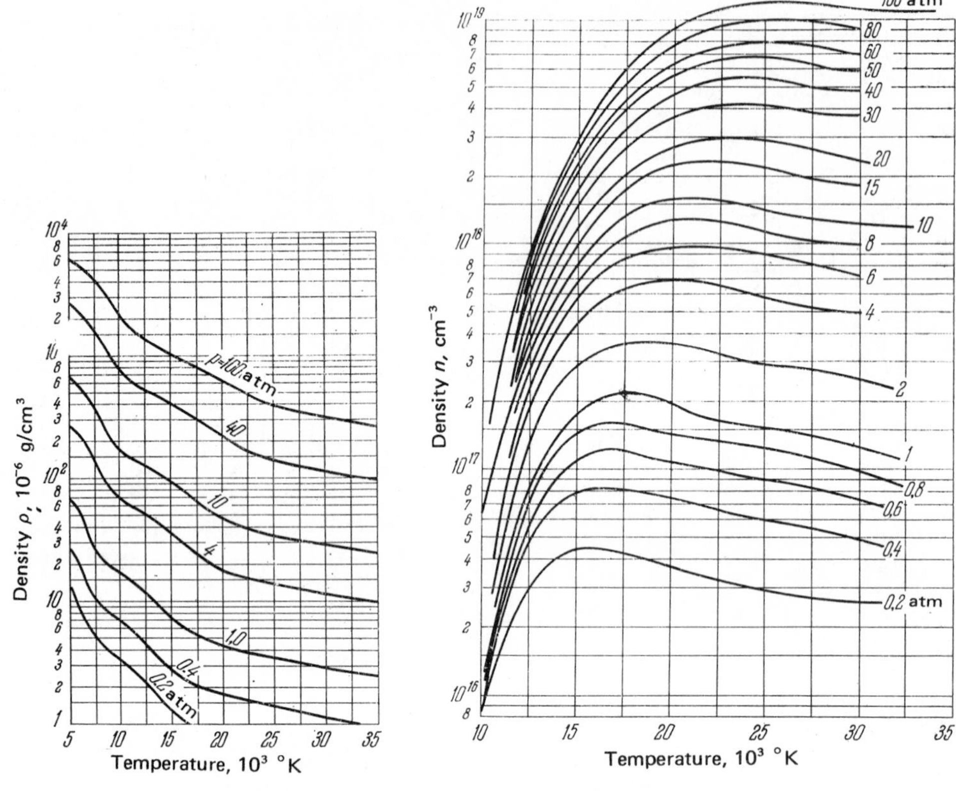

Fig. 15. Density of ionized nitrogen as a function of temperature at different pressures.

Fig. 16. Electron (ion) density in ionized nitrogen as a function of temperature at different pressures.

Electron density $n_e \cdot 10^{17}$ (cm^{-3}) in ionized nitrogen [144]

T. 10³ °K → / p. atm	10	12	14	16	18	20	22	24	26	28	30
0.2	0.079	0.26	0.42	0.44	0.4	0.4	0.3	0.3	0.3	0.3	0,2
0.4	0.093	0.39	0,73	0,83	0,8	0.7	0.7	0,6	0.6	0.5	0.5
0.6	0.105	0.50	0,98	1.21	1.2	1.1	1.0	0.9	0.9	0.8	0,7
0.8	0.119	0.59	1.62	1.55	1.6	1.4	1.3	1.2	1.1	1.1	1,0
1.0	0.128	0,66	1,39	2,19	2.2	1,8	1,7	1.5	1,4	1.3	1,2
2		0.95	2,32	3.30	3.6	3.5	3.3	3.0	2.9	2,6	2,5
4		1,42	3,39	5.50	6.8	7.0	6,5	6.1	5,6	5,2	4.9
6		1.76	4.38	7.58	9,4	10.0	9.7	9.1	8.4	8.0	7,4
8		1,97	5.17	8,96	12.0	12.9	12,8	12,0	11.1	10,4	9,9
10		2.62	5.62	10.30	14.9	15.7	15.8	14,9	13.9	13.2	12.2
15		2,79	7.16	13.40	19,1	21,4	23.2	21.8	21.0	19,5	18.6
20		3.32	8.40	15.30	23.3	27,9	30.0	29,3	27.7	25,9	23.9
30		4,14	10.50	20.00	31,2	37.0	43.6	42,6	40.4	38,5	36,3
40		4.58	12.20	24.00	37.4	46.2	56.5	54.6	53.0	50.6	48,0
50		5.13	13.80	26,40	43.6	55.4	67,0	66.3	65.5	63.0	58,2
60		5.30	15.25	29.50	49,2	61.4	78.0	78,1	79,1	74.6	71.0
70		6.14	16.55	33.00	53,1	68.3	88.5	89.0	89,1	86.6	82,6
80		6.40	17.90	35,60	59.0	76.2	98,2	99.6	100.6	98.0	94.4
90		7.15	18.60	38,10	62,1	82.0	108.0	110.0	111.5	109.0	105,5
100		7.35	19.70	40.00	67.0	88.6	112.2	120.0	123.0	118,0	117.0

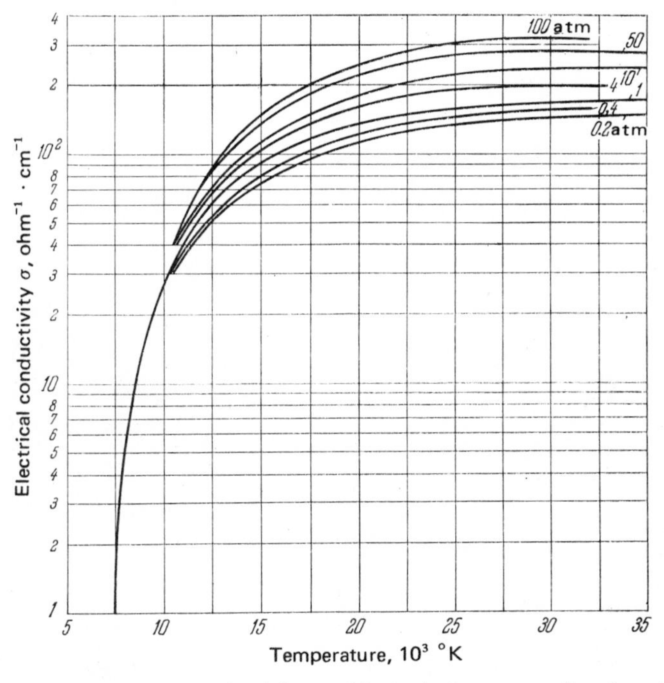

Fig. 17. Electrical conductivity σ of ionized nitrogen as a function of temperature.

Electrical conductivity σ (ohm^{-1} cm^{-1}) of ionized nitrogen [144]

p, atm \ T, 10^3 °K →	12	14	16	18	20	22	24	26	28	30	35
0.2	49.4	65.4	84.6	99.4	114.8	125.8	131.0	137.0	145.5	149.0	
0.4	51.6	69.0	91.5	107.5	122.5	134.8	140.0	146.5	152.0	156.0	
0.6	52.9	72.5	95.5	112.3	128.5	140.0	146.0	152.0	160.0	163.0	
0.8	54.2	77.4	99.1	115.5	133.0	145.0	150.0	157.0	162.5	166.5	
1	55.0	80.0	103.0	121.0	136.0	148.0	154.0	160.0	166.0	170.0	173.0
2	57.5	81.1	109.0	131.8	147.6	160.0	166.0	173.0	179.0	182.0	
4	61.1	86.0	117.2	141.0	162.0	175.0	181.5	188.0	192.5	197.0	
6	63.0	88.5	124.3	148.0	174.0	185.0	191.0	197.0	203.5	207.0	
8	64.8	91.2	127.0	150.0	177.2	192.5	197.0	204.0	210.0	214.0	
10	66.8	92.6	130.0	158.0	184.0	199.3	206.5	212.0	218.0	220.0	
15	67.5	96.5	137.0	166.0	193.0	212.0	216.0	225.0	232.0	234.0	
20	69.0	99.1	140.0	172.2	209.0	221.0	228.0	235.5	240.0	242.5	
30	69.6	102.5	146.2	182.5	215.0	236.0	244.0	250.0	254.0	256.0	
40	71.8	107.5	152.5	190.0	222.0	248.0	254.0	261.0	266.0	272.0	
50	74.6	109.0	155.5	195.0	230.0	256.0	264.0	274.0	276.0	279.0	
60	75.2	111.0	159.5	201.0	236.0	270.0	278.0	286.0	282.0	286.0	
70	77.5	112.5	163.0	205.0	241.0	273.5	281.0	291.0	290.0	294.0	
80	77.5	113.2	166.0	209.0	243.0	277.0	286.0	296.0	298.0	301.0	
90	79.8	115.5	167.8	212.0	246.0	280.0	292.0	302.0	306.0	305.5	
100	84.1	116.6	169.0	215.5	256.0	284.0	295.0	306.0	310.0	313.0	

Sound velocity u (m/s) in nitrogen [50]

T, °K \ p, atm →	1	10	40	70	100
100	201.5				
110	212.3				
120	222.1				
130	231.1				
140	240.2				
150	243.0	243.3			
160	257.1	252.7			
170	265.2	261.8			
180	273.3	270.6	265.2		
190	280.9	278.7	275.6	284.1	
200	288.1	286.7	286.1	293.8	316.7
210	295.2	294.5	295.2	302.9	323.5
220	302.2	301.9	303.6	311.3	330.2
230	309.0	309.0	311.7	319.8	337.0
240	315.7	316.1	319.4	327.5	343.7
250	322.1	322.8	326.7	335.3	347.1
260	328.5	329.5	332.3	342.3	353.8
270	334.9	335.9	341.3	349.8	360.5
280	341.3	342.4	348.1	356.5	368.0
290	347.1	348.8	354.8	363.2	374.0
300	353.1	354.5	361.2	369.6	380.4
320	364.6	366.3	373.3	382.4	392.9
340	375.7	377.7	385.1	394.2	404.3
360	386.8	388.8	396.6	405.7	415.8
380	397.3	399.3	407.4	416.5	426.6
400	407.4	409.7	417.8	426.9	437.4
420	417.5	419.8	427.9	437.3	447.1
440	426.9	429.3	437.7	447.1	456.9
460	436.7	438.7	447.5	456.6	466.3
480	445.5	448.1	456.6	465.7	475.4
500	454.6	456.9	465.7	474.8	484.2
520	463.3	465.6	474.4	483.5	492.6
540	471.7	474.4	482.9	492.0	501.1
560	480.2	482.5	491.3	500.0	509.5
580	488.2	490.6	499.4	508.1	517.2
600	496.3	498.7	507.1	515.9	525.0
620	504.1	506.4	515.2	523.6	532.8
640	511.5	514.2	522.6	631.4	540.1
660	518.9	521.6	530.0	538.8	547.6
680	526.3	529.0	537.4	545.9	554.6
700	533.7	536.4	544.5	552.9	561.7
720	540.8	543.2	551.6	560.0	568.4
740	547.9	550.3	558.7	567.8	575.2
760	555.0	557.3	565.4	573.8	581.9
780	561.7	564.1	572.1	580.2	588.3
800	568.4	570.8	578.6	586.6	594.7
900	600.8	602.8	610.6	618.3	626.1
1000	631.1	633.5	640.6	648.3	655.4
1100	660.1	662.1	669.2	676.3	683.7
1200	687.7	689.7	696.8	703.6	710.6
1300	714.3	716.3	722.8	729.5	736.9
1400	740.0	741.6	748.4	754.8	761.9
1500	764.6	766.9	772.7	779.0	785.4
1600	788.8	790.5	796.6	802.6	808.7
1700	812.1	813.7	819.5	825.9	831.6
1800	835.0	836.6	842.4	847.8	853.5
1900	856.9	858.9	864.3	870.0	875.4
2000	878.8	880.5	885.9	891.3	896.3
2100	900.0	901.4	906.8	911.8	917.2
2200	920.2	921.9	927.0	932.0	937.1
2300	940.8	942.1	947.2	951.9	957.0
2400	960.7	962.0	969.7	971.8	976.5
2500	979.9	981.2	986.3	990.3	995.4
2600	999.1	1000.4	1005.1	1009.2	1013.9
2700	1017.6	1019.0	1023.7	1028.1	1032.4
2800	1035.8	1037.1	1041.5	1046.3	1050.3
2900	1053.7	1055.0	1059.4	1063.8	1068.2
3000	1071.5	1072.5	1076.9	1081.3	1085.7

Viscosity η (N · s/m² of nitrogen gas at $p = 1$ bar [60]

T, °K	$\eta \cdot 10^7$	T, °K	$\eta \cdot 10^7$	T, °K	$\eta \cdot 10^7$	T, °K	$\eta \cdot 10^7$	T, °K	$\eta \cdot 10^7$
200	129.0	400	221.0	900	375.5	1300	466.5	1750	552.0
250	155.1	500	257.9	1000	400.0	1400	486.7	1800	560.7
273.1	166.3	600	291.1	1100	423.3	1500	506.2	1900	577.7
298.1	177.9	700	321.4	1200	445.4	1600	525.0	2000	594.4
300	178.8	800	349.4	1250	456.0	1700	543.2	2500	671.4

Viscosity $\eta \cdot 10^7$ (N · s/m²) of nitrogen at different temperatures and pressures [141, 142]

T, °K \ p, bar →	1	10	20	30	40	50	60	70	80
65	2633	2677	2728	2777	2826	2876	2927	2978	3027
70	2113	2154	2197	2244	2290	2336	2383	2429	2475
75	1677	1713	1753	1793	1832	1875	1914	1957	1998
80	55.2	1366	1400	1433	1467	1501	1537	1573	1609
85	58.6	1111	1136	1164	1192	1219	1248	1278	1308
90	62.0	932.6	952.8	973.7	995.1	1018	1040	1063	1087
95	65.4	809.3	826.6	842.9	860.2	877.7	895.1	913.5	931.9

continued

T, °K \ p, bar →	1	10	20	30	40	50	60	70	80
100	68.8	713.0	729.7	745.9	761.6	777.2	792.2	807.6	822.9
105	72.2	78.3	639.7	658.4	676.0	692.9	708.9	724.2	739.2
110	75.6	81.1	551.7	572.8	592.5	611.2	629.4	646.9	663.6
115	78.9	84.0	462.6	490.2	514.0	535.4	555.3	573.7	591.0
120	82.1	86.8	95.3	397.4	433.5	461.2	484.9	504.1	525.5
125	85.2	89.6	96.8	115.5	336.9	381.0	413.5	440.7	463.3
130	88.3	92.5	98.8	110.7	180.5	294.5	342.4	376.3	403.3
135	91.4	95.4	101.0	110.3	131.4	199.8	268.6	313.1	346.2
140	94.5	98.3	102.8	111.2	125.0	155.1	206.8	254.4	292.3
150	100.6	104.1	108.5	114.5	123.2	136.5	157.0	184.7	214.7
160	106.6	109.8	113.8	118.6	125.2	134.0	146.0	161.4	180.0
170	112.4	115.4	118.9	123.2	128.6	135.3	143.7	154.2	166.6
180	118.1	120.9	124.1	127.9	132.5	138.0	144.6	152.5	161.6
190	123.7	126.3	129.3	132.7	136.7	141.5	146.9	153.2	160.4
200	129.2	131.6	134.4	137.6	141.1	145.2	149.9	155.3	161.2
210	134.6	136.9	139.5	142.4	145.6	149.3	153.4	158.0	163.2
220	139.9	142.1	144.5	147.2	150.2	153.5	157.2	161.3	165.7
230	145.0	147.1	149.4	151.9	154.6	157.7	161.1	164.7	168.7
240	150.0	152.0	154.2	156.6	159.1	161.9	165.0	168.3	171.9
250	154.9	156.8	158.9	161.2	163.5	166.1	168.9	172.0	175.3
260	159.7	161.5	163.5	165.7	167.9	170.3	172.9	175.8	178.8
270	164.4	166.2	168.0	170.1	172.2	174.5	177.0	179.6	182.4
280	169.1	170.8	172.6	174.5	176.5	178.7	181.0	183.5	186.1
290	173.7	175.3	177.1	178.9	180.8	182.9	185.0	187.4	189.8
300	178.2	179.7	181.5	183.2	185.0	187.0	189.0	191.2	193.5
310	182.6	184.1	185.8	187.4	189.2	191.0	193.0	195.0	197.2
320	187.0	188.5	190.0	191.6	193.4	195.1	197.0	198.9	201.0
330	191.3	192.8	194.2	195.8	197.5	199.1	200.9	202.8	204.7
340	195.6	197.1	198.5	200.0	201.5	203.2	204.8	206.7	208.5
350	200.0	201.4	202.8	204.2	205.6	207.3	208.7	210.6	212.4
400	220.4	221.6	222.8	224.0	225.3	226.7	228.0	229.4	230.8
450	239.6	240.6	241.7	242.8	243.9	245.1	246.3	247.4	248.7
500	257.7	258.6	259.6	260.6	261.5	262.6	263.6	264.7	265.8
550	274.7	275.6	276.4	277.4	278.2	279.1	280.0	281.0	281.9
600	290.8	291.6	292.4	293.2	294.0	294.8	295.7	296.5	297.4
650	306.2	306.9	307.7	308.4	309.1	309.9	310.7	311.4	312.2
700	321.0	321.7	322.4	323.0	323.7	324.4	325.1	325.8	326.6
800	349.1	349.7	350.3	350.9	351.4	352.1	352.7	353.3	353.9
900	375.3	375.8	376.3	376.9	377.4	377.9	378.5	379.0	379.5
1000	399.9	400.4	400.8	401.3	401.8	402.3	402.7	403.2	403.7
1100	423.2	423.6	424.0	424.5	424.9	425.3	425.8	426.2	426.7
1200	445.3	445.7	446.1	446.5	446.9	447.3	447.6	448.1	448.5
1300	466.2	466.6	466.9	467.3	467.7	468.0	468.4	468.7	469.1

T, °K \ p, bar →	90	100	125	150	175	200	250	300	350
70	2523	2568	2687	2808	2927	3047	3288	3533	
75	2041	2084	2191	2301	2411	2523	2747	2979	3212
80	1645	1682	1777	1872	1971	2071	2279	2491	2709
85	1338	1369	1448	1530	1614	1702	1884	2075	2272
90	1111	1136	1200	1267	1338	1412	1568	1733	1908
95	950.7	970.0	1020	1075	1131	1191	1321	1462	1613
100	838.6	854.2	894.9	937.6	982.5	1030	1135	1253	1381
105	753.9	768.1	803.4	839.5	876.3	915.0	999.2	1094	1200
110	679.4	694.8	730.8	764.4	797.2	830.5	900.2	977.0	1064
115	607.8	624.3	663.6	699.3	732.5	764.0	825.5	890.2	961.2
120	543.7	560.8	600.5	637.6	673.0	705.6	765.5	823.2	883.9
125	483.6	502.3	544.5	582.1	616.7	650.7	712.7	768.6	823.3
130	427.0	447.9	493.1	532.3	567.7	600.7	663.1	720.4	772.7
135	373.0	397.0	442.7	486.3	522.9	556.3	617.2	674.8	725.9
140	322.9	348.7	401.2	443.8	481.1	515.4	576.5	632.5	682.8

continued

T, °K \ p, bar →	90	100	125	150	175	200	250	300	350
150	243.4	269.6	324.8	369.4	408.2	442.5	503.2	557.6	606.4
160	200.4	221.1	269.8	312.6	350.3	383.6	442.7	495.9	543.7
170	180.5	195.8	234.7	271.9	306.6	338.2	394.6	445.0	491.4
180	171.9	183.2	213.9	245.4	275.5	304.5	357.3	404.9	448.8
190	168.5	177.4	202.0	228.1	254.3	279.7	328.0	375.7	414.0
200	167.8	175.0	195.1	217.3	239.7	262.4	306.0	347.0	385.8
210	168.8	174.8	191.8	210.5	230.1	250.0	239.1	326.8	363.2
220	175.8	179.9	191.2	203.8	217.3	241.3	276.7	311.4	344.7
230	173.0	177.6	190.3	204.5	219.8	235.4	267.3	299.0	330.0
240	175.8	179.9	191.2	203.8	217.3	231.4	260.4	289.5	318.2
250	178.8	182.5	192.7	204.0	216.1	228.8	255.2	282.0	308.7
260	181.9	185.4	194.6	204.8	215.9	227.4	251.7	276.4	301.2
270	185.2	188.4	196.9	206.2	216.3	226.9	249.2	272.2	295.2
280	188.7	191.7	199.5	208.1	217.4	227.1	247.7	269.1	290.5
290	192.3	195.0	202.3	210.3	218.8	227.9	237.2	266.9	287.0
300	195.9	198.4	205.2	212.6	220.6	228.9	246.6	265.4	284.2
310	199.5	201.8	208.2	215.1	222.6	230.4	247.0	264.4	282.2
320	203.2	205.3	211.3	217.8	224.8	232.1	247.7	264.1	280.9
330	206.8	208.9	214.5	220.6	227.1	234.1	248.7	264.2	280.2
340	210.5	212.6	217.8	223.6	229.7	236.3	250.1	264.7	279.8
350	214.2	216.2	221.2	226.8	232.6	238.7	251.8	265.6	280.0
400	232.4	233.9	238.0	242.3	247.0	251.8	261.6	273.0	284.3
450	249.9	251.3	254.6	258.3	262.1	266.1	274.4	283.4	292.8
500	266.9	268.0	270.9	274.0	277.3	280.6	287.7	295.3	303.3
550	282.9	283.9	286.4	289.2	292.0	294.9	301.1	307.6	314.5
600	298.2	299.1	301.4	303.8	306.4	308.9	314.4	320.1	326.1
650	313.0	313.8	315.9	318.0	320.3	322.6	327.4	332.6	337.9
700	327.3	328.1	329.9	331.8	333.9	336.0	340.4	345.0	349.8
800	354.6	355.2	356.8	358.5	360.2	361.9	365.6	369.5	373.5
900	380.1	380.7	382.1	383.5	385.0	386.5	389.7	393.0	396.4
1000	404.2	404.7	406.0	407.3	408.5	409.9	412.7	415.6	418.5
1100	427.1	427.6	428.7	429.9	431.0	432.2	434.6	437.2	439.8
1200	448.9	449.3	450.3	451.4	452.4	453.5	455.7	458.0	460.4
1300	469.5	469.9	470.8	471.8	472.8	473.7	475.8	477.8	480.0

T, °K \ p, bar →	400	450	500	600	700	800	900	1000
75	3445	3678	3914					
80	2928	3151	3376					
85	2475	2685	2896					
90	2092	2283	2478					
95	1774	1945	2121					
100	1520	1668	1826					
105	1317	1445	1581					
110	1161	1268	1386					
115	1041	1131	1230					
120	950.3	1025	1108					
125	880.0	942.7	1012					
130	824.1	878.2	937.0					
135	775.0	826.4	877.4					
140	731.1	779.4	826.7					
150	654.4	700.0	743.0	827.1				
160	589.5	633.1	674.9	755.0	831.6			
170	535.4	576.1	616.7	693.6	767.1	837.4		
180	490.3	529.2	567.5	640.1	711.1	778.9	844.3	
190	452.9	490.6	526.3	596.3	622.7	727.5	790.5	854.5
200	422.7	458.4	492.6	558.4	622.0	683.2	743.5	805.0
210	397.5	431.3	463.8	526.0	586.7	645.1	702.6	760.6
220	377.3	408.5	439.6	498.7	556.2	611.8	667.1	721.1
230	360.2	390.1	418.8	475.0	529.5	582.7	635.6	687.1
240	346.4	374.3	401.5	454.7	506.4	557.0	607.4	657.3

continued

T, °K \ p, bar →	400	450	500	600	700	800	900	1000
250	335.3	361.0	386.9	437.1	486.5	534.4	582.3	630.6
260	325.9	350.1	374.5	422.0	469.1	514.8	560.5	606.7
270	318.2	341.2	364.1	409.1	453.9	497.6	541.4	585.3
280	312.1	333.7	355.4	398.2	440.6	482.5	524.5	566.1
290	307.3	327.6	348.1	388.7	429.1	469.0	509.3	548.9
300	303.5	322.6	342.0	380.5	419.0	457.0	495.6	533.6
310	300.4	318.6	337.0	373.4	410.1	446.5	483.4	520.0
320	298.0	315.3	332.8	367.5	402.4	437.4	472.5	507.8
330	296.3	312.7	329.3	362.5	395.8	429.5	462.9	496.9
340	295.2	310.8	326.6	358.3	390.1	422.5	454.6	487.2
350	294.7	309.5	324.7	355.0	385.5	416.3	447.6	478.5
400	296.1	308.6	320.9	345.0	370.1	395.4	421.2	447.1
450	302.5	312.5	322.6	343.3	364.5	386.0	407.6	430.1
500	311.5	319.9	328.6	346.5	364.5	383.1	401.9	420.9
550	321.6	328.9	336.4	352.0	367.9	384.2	400.8	417.6
600	332.3	338.8	345.5	359.0	373.3	387.7	402.6	418.0
650	343.5	349.3	355.2	367.4	380.1	393.1	406.4	420.8
700	354.8	360.0	365.4	376.2	387.8	399.7	411.8	424.1
800	377.6	381.9	386.3	395.5	405.0	414.9	425.2	435.7
900	399.9	403.6	407.3	415.2	423.3	431.8	440.5	449.5
1000	421.6	424.7	428.1	434.9	441.9	449.4	456.9	464.7
1100	442.6	445.3	448.2	454.2	460.5	467.0	473.7	480.7
1200	462.8	465.3	467.9	473.2	478.8	484.5	490.6	496.8
1300	481.9	484.4	486.7	491.6	496.6	501.8	507.2	512.8

Viscosity $\eta \cdot 10^7$ ($N \cdot s/m^2$) of dissociated nitrogen [353]

T, °K \ p, bar →	0.001	0.01	0.1	1	10	100	T, °K \ p, bar →	0.001	0.01	0.1	1	10	100
3000	920	920	920	920	920	920	4600	1303	1292	1291	1290	1290	1290
3200	967	967	967	967	967	967	4800	1358	1341	1337	1336	1335	1335
3400	1014	1014	1014	1014	1014	1014	5000	1419	1389	1383	1381	1381	1381
3600	1061	1061	1061	1061	1061	1061	5200	1486	1436	1428	1427	1427	1427
3800	1108	1107	1107	1106	1106	1106	5400	1553	1493	1474	1473	1473	1473
4000	1155	1153	1153	1153	1153	1153	5600	1615	1553	1520	1518	1519	1519
4200	1203	1200	1199	1199	1198	1198	5800	1671	1617	1568	1562	1564	1565
4400	1252	1246	1245	1244	1244	1244	6000	1723	1682	1618	1607	1610	1612

Thermal conductivity $\lambda \cdot 10^3$ (W/m · deg) of nitrogen in nitrogen liquid and gas [15]

T, °K \ p, bar →	1	10	20	30	40	50	60
80	7.82	138	139	140	141	142	143
90	8.63	113	114		116		119
100	9.58	95.2	97.4		99.3		102
110	10.4	11.9	78.3		83.5		87.2
120	11.3	12.5	14.7	63.2	68.4		73.1
130	12.0	13.3	14.9				57.0
140	13.0	14.1	15.4	17.4			
150	13.9	14.9	16.0	17.6	19.7		
160	14.8	15.7	16.7	18.0	19.6	21.8	
170	15.7	16.5	17.4	18.5	19.9	21.6	23.6
180	16.6	17.3	18.1	19.1	20.3	21.2	23.3
190	17.5	18.1	18.8	19.7	20.8	22.6	23.3
200	18.3	18.9	19.6	20.4	21.3	22.4	23.6
220	20.0	20.5	21.1	21.8	22.5	23.4	24.3
240	21.4	22.0	22.5	23.2	23.8	24.5	25.3

continued

p, bar → / T, °K	1	10	20	30	40	50	60
260	22.9	23.5	23.9	24.5	25.0	25.7	26.4
280	24.4	24.9	25.3	25.8	26.3	26.9	27.5
300	25.9	26.2	26.6	27.1	27.5	28.0	28.6
320	27.3		27.9		28.8		29.7
350	29.3		29.9		30.6		31.4
400	32.7		33.0		33.6		34.3
450	35.8		36.0		36.6		37.2
500	38.9		38.0		39.5		40.0
550	41.7		41.8		42.3		42.8
600	44.6		44.8		45.2		45.6
650	47.2		47.3		47.7		48.1
700	49.9		50.2		50.4		50.6
750	52.4		52.6		52.8		53.0
800	54.8		55.2		55.5		55.7
850	57.2		57.5		57.7		57.9
900	59.7		60.0		60.2		60.4
950	62.2		62.4		62.6		62.8
1000	64.7		64.9		65.1		65.3
1100	70.0		70.2		70.4		70.6
1200	75.8		76.0				76.4
1300	81.0		81.2				81.6
1400	87.0		87.2				87.4

p, bar → / T, °K	70	80	90	100	150	200	250
80		144	—	146	154	162	167
90		121	—	123	132	140	146
100		105	—	107	114	119	124
110		90.0	—	93.2	99.1	105	110
120		77.3	—	80.4	87.2	94.3	100
130		65.4	—	69.3	79.4	87.5	93.4
140		—	—		69.3	78.4	84.2
150		—	—		60.5	69.4	76.3
160		—	—		52.8	62.3	70.2
170	25.9	28.6	31.2	34.1	47.3	56.2	64.4
180	25.0	27.2	29.3	32.0	43.2	52.4	59.3
190	24.9	26.5	28.3	30.2	40.4	48.3	55.5
200	24.9	26.3	27.8	29.4	38.5	45.2	52.4
220	25.4	26.4	28.2	29.2	35.4	42.1	48.3
240	26.0	27.0	28.4	29.0	34.3	40.2	45.1
260	27.0	28.0	28.7	29.5	33.9	38.5	43.5
280	28.0	28.8	29.5	30.2	34.0	37.4	41.7
300	29.2	29.7	30.3	31.0	34.4	37.6	40.7
320		30.8		31.9	35.2	37.9	40.7
350		32.3		33.3	36.1	39.0	42.2
400		35.1		35.9	38.0	39.9	43.0
450		37.8		38.2	40.3	42.3	44.4
500		40.6		41.2	43.2	44.6	46.0
550		43.2		43.8	45.4	47.3	48.4
600		46.0		46.3	47.5	48.9	50.1
650		48.5		48.8	49.8	51.3	52.5
700		50.8		51.2	52.4	53.6	54.6
750		53.3		53.6	54.8	55.8	56.9
800		56.0			56.6	57.6	58.8
850		58.2			59.8	60.6	61.5
900		60.6			61.8	62.9	63.7
950		63.0			64.2	65.1	66.0
1000		65.5			66.6	67.5	
1100		70.8			71.0	71.9	
1200		76.6			76.6	77.8	
1300		81.8			82.2	82.9	
1400		87.6			87.7	88.5	

continued

T, °K \ p, bar →	300	350	400	450	500	550	600
80	171	175	179	183	188	192	197
90	151	157	163	169	174	179	183
100	130	137	144	150	156	162	168
110	116	122	128	133	139	145	151
120	105	110	115	119	123	127	133
130	99.6	101	105	110	114	118	122
140	90.5	95.4	100	103	106	110	114
150	82.4	88.2	93.6	97.3	101	105	109
160	76.3	81.4	86.1	91.2	95.4	99.3	103
170	70.5	76.4	81.2	86.3	89.5	93.4	97.3
180	65.4	71.6	76.4	80.5	84.5	88.3	92.1
190	61.3	67.2	71.4	76.5	80.4	84.2	88.4
200	58.1	63.3	68.2	72.7	76.5	80.3	83.6
220	53.4	58.5	62.4	66.6	70.3	74.6	77.5
240	50.2	54.1	58.3	62.4	66.5	69.7	72.6
260	47.4	51.6	55.5	59.4	62.7	65.3	69.4
280	45.6	49.4	52.8	55.7	59.7	61.0	65.8
300	44.8	47.7	51.8	54.9	57.8	59.6	62.7
320	43.6	47.5	50.3	53.1	56.2	59.3	61.2
350	43.8	46.7	49.8	52.2	54.7	57.2	59.3
400	44.8	47.1	48.9	51.8	54.2	55.8	57.9
450	46.2	48.3	50.2	52.4	54.3	56.3	57.5
500	47.6	49.6	51.3	53.2	55.2	56.5	58.0
550	49.5	50.5	52.7	53.8	55.4	56.8	58.8
600	51.8	53.4	54.4	55.6	57.1	58.4	59.6
650	53.7	54.9	56.1	57.3	58.5	59.7	61.0
700	55.6	56.8	57.9	58.8	59.9	61.2	62.5
750	58.0	58.8	60.0	60.9	62.0	62.9	64.0
800	60.0	60.9	62.0	63.0	63.9	65.0	66.1
850	62.0	62.9	63.8	64.9	65.8	66.9	67.8
900	64.6	65.5	66.4	67.3	68.2	69.3	70.2
950	66.9	67.8	68.7	69.6	70.5	71.4	72.3
1000	69.2		71.1		72.2		74.2
1100	73.2		74.4		75.3		76.4
1200	78.6		79.5		80.2		81.3
1300	83.8		84.9		85.8		86.6
1400	89.4		90.4		91.3		92.1

Thermal conductivity $\lambda \cdot 10^3$ (W/m · deg) of dissociated nitrogen [353]

T, °K \ p, bar →	0.001	0.01	0.1	1	10	100
2000	126	126	126	126	126	126
2200	138	138	138	138	138	138
2400	149	149	149	149	149	149
2600	160	159	159	159	159	159
2800	170	170	170	170	170	170
3000	189	183	181	180	180	180
3200	219	207	193	191	190	190
3400	278	224	207	202	200	200
3600	397	269	228	215	211	210
3800	629	349	260	232	223	220
4000	1053	494	312	255	236	230

T, °K \ p, bar →	0.001	0.01	0.1	1	10	100
4200	1753	736	396	288	253	242
4400	2800	1122	530	337	275	256
4600	4152	1697	732	409	305	272
4800	5493	2491	1026	512	345	291
5000	6142	3476	1434	657	398	315
5200	5569	4518	1971	854	470	346
5400	4084	5322	2633	1113	564	384
5600	2619	5523	3382	1443	685	432
5800	1639	4962	4126	1848	838	491
6000	1100	3903	4719	2323	1027	563

Thermal conductivity λ of saturated liquid nitrogen [15]

T, °K	90	95	100	105	110	115	120
$\lambda \cdot 10^3$, W/m · deg	112	104	95.5	88.0	80.2	70.4	62.8

Surface tension σ of nitrogen [16]

T, °K	68	70	75	77.3	80	85	90
$\sigma \cdot 10^3$, N/m	11.00	10.53	9.39	8.85	8.27	7.20	6.16

AMMONIA (NH_3)

Molecular weight 17.032

$t_{boil} = -33.4$ °C at 760 mm Hg; $t_{melt} = -77.7$ °C; $t_{cr} = 132.4$ °C;
$p_{cr} = 112.9$ bar; $\rho_{cr} = 235$ kg/m³

Thermodynamic properties of saturated ammonia [51]: v (cm³/g), i (kJ/kg) and s (kJ/kg · deg)

T, °K	p, bar	v'	v''	i'	i''	s'	s''
195.42	0.06076			613.1	2087	4.206	11.748
200	0.08666	1.372	11 140	632.7	2103	4.307	11.657
210	0.1779	1.394	5 686.8	676.2	2124	4.518	11.413
220	0.3391	1.417	3 115.9	720.0	2144	4.720	11.195
230	0.6061	1.441	1 813.9	764.2	2162	4.916	10.993
240	1.0258	1.467	1 110.0	809.0	2177	5.103	10.804
250	1.6536	1.495	709.72	854.0	2192	5.288	10.642
260	2.559	1.524	471.41	899.5	2207	5.465	10.492
270	3.819	1.556	323.2	945.7	2219	5.637	10.354
280	5.518	1.589	227.9	992.1	2230	5.804	10.226
290	7.753	1.626	164.6	1039.6	2240	5.968	10.106
300	10.624	1.667	121.3	1087.3	2246	6.128	9.993
310	14.249	1.711	90.71	1135.7	2251	6.286	9.884
320	18.66	1.760	68.93	1185.1	2255	6.440	9.776
330	24.22	1.815	52.85	1235.7	2255	6.593	9.680
340	30.82	1.878	40.87	1288.1	2250	6.743	9.577
350	38.70	1.952	31.73	1341.9	2241	6.893	9.459
360	48.03	2.039	24.62	1398.2	2225	7.043	9.341
370	58.91	2.148	19.02	1457.5	2202	7.195	9.208
380	71.54	2.292	14.50	1517.7	2162	7.360	9.046
390	86.06	2.502	10.72	1591.4	2099	7.537	8.847
400	102.8	2.903	7.310	1675.3	1982	7.638	8.525
405.6	113.0	4.255	4.255	1825.2	1825	8.122	8.122

Thermodynamic properties of ammonia at different temperatures and pressures [51]: v (cm³/g), i (kJ/kg) and s (kJ/kg · deg)

T, °K	v	i	s	v''	i	s
		p=1 bar			p=5 bar	
300	1450.6	2309	11.31	277.2	2287	10.48
320	1550.8	2351	11.44	299.7	2333	10.63
340	1650.5	2394	11.57	321.2	2379	10.77
360	1749.6	2439	11.70	342.2	2426	10.90
380	1848.5	2485	11.82	363.0	2473	11.03
400	1947.2	2531	11.93	383.5	2521	11.15
420	2045.7	2577	12.05	403.9	2568	11.27
440	2144.1	2624	12.16	424.1	2616	11.38
460	2242.3	2671	12.26	444.3	2664	11.49
480	2340.5	2719	12.36	464.3	2713	11.60

continued

T,°K	v	i	s	v	i	s
500	2438.6	2768	12.47	484.3	2762	11.70
520	2536.6	2818	12.56	504.2	2813	11.79
540	2634.7	2868	12.66	524.1	2864	11.89
560	2696.9	2920	12.75	543.9	2916	11.99
580	2830.6	2971	12.84	563.7	2968	12.08
		$p=10$ bar			$p=15$ bar	
300	129.8	2255	10.04			
320	142.9	2306	10.21	90.07	2276	9.94
340	155.1	2358	10.36	99.11	2336	10.11
360	166.5	2409	10.51	107.7	2391	10.27
380	177.6	2459	10.65	115.6	2444	10.42
400	188.4	2508	10.78	123.1	2496	10.55
420	198.9	2557	10.91	130.5	2546	10.68
440	209.4	2606	11.03	137.8	2596	10.80
460	219.8	2655	11.14	144.9	2646	10.91
480	230.0	2705	11.24	151.9	2697	11.02
500	240.3	2756	11.34	158.9	2749	11.12
520	250.5	2807	11.44	165.8	2801	11.22
540	260.6	2858	11.54	172.6	2853	11.32
560	270.6	2911	11.63	179.5	2906	11.42
580	280.6	2963	11.73	186.2	2959	11.51
		$p=20$ bar			$p=25$ bar	
310	1.71	1135	6.28			
320	1.76	1185	6.44			
340	71.16	2312	9.92	54.03	2285	9.75
360	77.03	2373	10.10	60.30	2352	9.94
380	84.43	2429	10.25	65.82	2413	10.11
400	90.48	2483	10.39	70.92	2470	10.26
420	96.29	2534	10.53	75.80	2523	10.40
440	101.98	2586	10.65	80.50	2575	10.53
460	107.50	2637	10.78	85.02	2628	10.64
480	112.90	2689	10.88	89.42	2681	10.75
500	118.25	2742	10.98	93.65	2734	10.86
520	123.59	2794	11.08	98.05	2788	10.96
540	128.82	2848	11.18	102.34	2842	11.06
560	133.98	2901	11.28	106.56	2896	11.16
580	139.09	2955	11.38	110.79	2950	11.26
		$p=30$ bar			$p=40$ bar	
310	1.70	1136	6.28	1.70	1136	6.27
320	1.76	1185	6.43	1.75	1186	6.42
330	1.81	1235	6.59	1.80	1235	6.58
340	41.93	2256	9.60	1.87	1287	6.73
350				1.95	1341	6.88
360	48.19	2331	9.80	32.69	2276	9.54
380	53.23	2396	9.98	37.40	2358	9.76
400	57.83	2455	10.14	41.32	2424	9.94
420	62.12	2510	10.28	44.84	2484	10.10
440	66.17	2565	10.42	48.13	2543	10.24
460	70.10	2619	10.53	51.27	2600	10.37
480	73.86	2673	10.65	54.29	2656	10.48
500	77.56	2727	10.75	57.20	2713	10.59
520	81.14	2782	10.86	60.06	2769	10.70
540	84.72	2836	10.96	62.88	2825	10.80
560	88.30	2891	11.06	65.64	2881	10.91
580	91.83	2946	11.16	68.28	2937	11.01
		$p=50$ bar			$p=60$ bar	
310	1.69	1136	6.26	1.69	1137	6.26
320	1.74	1186	6.42	1.74	1186	6.41
330	1.80	1235	6.57	1.79	1235	6.57

continued

T,°K	v	i	s	v	i	s
340	1.86	1286	6.72	1.85	1286	6.72
350	1.94	1339	6.88	1.93	1338	6.87
360	2.04	1397	7.04	2.03	1395	7.03
370				2.14	1456	7.21
380	27.59	2315	9.56	21.07	2264	9.36
400	31.32	2391	9.77	24.59	2354	9.60
420	34.46	2458	9.94	27.62	2430	9.80
440	37.33	2520	10.09	30.24	2496	9.96
460	40.02	2580	10.22	32.64	2560	10.10
480	42.57	2639	10.34	34.86	2622	10.23
500	45.02	2698	10.46	37.04	2683	10.35
520	47.40	2756	10.57	39.06	2742	10.46
540	49.72	2814	10.68	41.06	2802	10.58
560	51.99	2871	10.79	43.03	2860	10.68
580	54.20	2928	10.89	44.94	2919	10.79
		$p=70$ bar			$p=80$ bar	
310	1.68	1137	6.26	1.68	1138	6.25
320	1.73	1186	6.41	1.73	1186	6.41
330	1.78	1235	6.56	1.78	1235	6.55
340	1.84	1285	6.71	1.84	1285	6.70
350	1.91	1338	6.86	1.91	1336	6.85
360	2.01	1393	7.02	2.00	1391	7.01
370	2.12	1453	7.19	2.11	1450	7.18
380	15.39	2184	9.11	2.26	1516	7.35
400	19.63	2313	9.46	15.74	2263	9.28
420	22.49	2400	9.67	18.59	2368	9.54
440	24.99	2472	9.84	21.00	2447	9.72
460	27.24	2539	9.98	23.10	2518	9.88
480	29.28	2604	10.12	24.99	2586	10.03
500	31.18	2667	10.25	26.76	2652	10.16
520	32.98	2729	10.37	28.43	2716	10.29
540	34.69	2790	10.48	30.05	2778	10.40
560	36.44	2850	10.59	31.59	2840	10.52
580	38.10	2910	10.70	33.08	2900	10.63
		$p=90$ bar			$p=100$ bar	
310	1.68	1138	6.25	1.68	1138	6.24
320	1.73	1187	6.40	1.72	1187	6.40
340	1.77	1235	6.55	1.77	1235	6.54
340	1.83	1285	6.70	1.83	1285	6.69
350	1.90	1336	6.85	1.89	1335	6.84
360	1.98	1390	7.00	1.97	1388	6.99
370	2.10	1447	7.16	2.08	1445	7.15
380	2.24	1511	7.33	2.22	1507	7.32
390	2.47	1588	7.52	2.42	1581	7.50
400	12.65	2195	9.07	8.65	2064	8.73
420	15.79	2333	9.41	13.29	2292	9.28
440	17.95	2420	9.62	15.48	2390	9.51
460	19.93	2496	9.78	17.40	2473	9.70
480	21.70	2568	9.94	19.10	2549	9.86
500	23.35	2636	10.08	20.66	2619	10.01
520	24.90	2702	10.21	22.10	2688	10.14
540	26.37	2766	10.33	23.47	2754	10.26
560	27.78	2829	10.44	24.78	2819	10.38
580	29.15	2891	10.56	26.05	2881	10.49
		$p=120$ bar			$p=140$ bar	
310	1.67	1139	6.24	1.67	1140	6.23
320	1.71	1187	6.39	1.71	1188	6.38
330	1.76	1236	6.53	1.76	1236	6.52
340	1.81	1284	6.68	1.81	1284	6.67
350	1.88	1334	6.82	1.87	1333	6.81

continued

T, °K	v	i	s	v	i	s
360	1.96	1386	6.97	1.94	1384	6.96
370	2.05	1441	7.13	2.03	1438	7.10
380	2.18	1500	7.29	2.14	1495	7.26
390	2.34	1570	7.46	2.28	1560	7.42
400	2.66	1661	7.68	2.51	1638	7.62
420	9.29	2191	9.00	5.37	1994	8.50
440	11.77	2322	9.30	8.78	2239	9.08
460	13.67	2422	9.53	10.75	2366	9.36
480	15.17	2508	9.71	12.25	2466	9.57
500	16.55	2586	9.87	13.56	2551	9.75
520	17.84	2659	10.01	14.75	2629	9.89
540	19.08	2729	10.14	15.88	2701	10.03
560	20.25	2795	10.26	16.94	2769	10.15
		$p=160$ bar			$p=180$ bar	
310	1.66	1141	6.23	1.66	1142	6.21
320	1.70	1188	6.37	1.70	1189	6.36
330	1.75	1236	6.52	1.74	1236	6.51
340	1.80	1284	6.66	1.79	1284	6.65
350	1.86	1333	6.80	1.84	1332	6.79
360	1.93	1383	6.94	1.91	1382	6.93
370	2.01	1435	7.08	1.98	1433	7.07
380	2.11	1491	7.23	2.08	1487	7.21
390	2.23	1553	7.39	2.18	1546	7.36
400	2.40	1623	7.57	2.32	1612	7.53
420	3.43	1833	8.09	2.88	1773	7.92
440	6.27	2138	8.80	4.44	2023	8.52
460	8.54	2302	9.18	6.77	2237	8.99
480	10.06	2421	9.43	8.32	2373	9.29
500	11.31	2513	9.62	9.58	2474	9.51
520	12.44	2595	9.78	10.66	2561	9.67
540	13.49	2669	9.92	11.64	2638	9.82
560	14.48	2738	10.05	12.57	2708	9.95
		$p=200$ bar			$p=220$ bar	
310	1.66	1143	6.21	1.65	1144	6.20
320	1.69	1190	6.35	1.68	1190	6.35
330	1.73	1237	6.50	1.73	1237	6.49
340	1.78	1284	6.64	1.77	1284	6.63
350	1.83	1332	6.78	1.83	1332	6.77
360	1.90	1381	6.91	1.88	1380	6.90
370	1.96	1431	7.05	1.95	1430	7.04
380	2.05	1484	7.19	2.03	1482	7.17
390	2.15	1541	7.34	2.12	1537	7.31
400	2.27	1603	7.49	2.23	1596	7.46
420	2.69	1747	7.83	2.58	1730	7.78
440	3.72	1952	8.33	3.31	1905	8.20
460	5.45	2171	8.81	4.56	2109	8.64
480	6.96	2323	9.16	5.92	2273	9.04
500	8.23	2435	9.40	7.13	2395	9.29
520	9.25	2527	9.57	8.12	2494	9.47
540	10.19	2607	9.72	9.02	2578	9.63
560	11.07	2680	9.86	9.85	2653	9.77
		$p=240$ bar			$p=260$ bar	
310	1.64	1145	6.19	1.64	1146	6.19
320	1.68	1191	6.34	1.67	1192	6.33
330	1.72	1238	6.48	1.71	1238	6.47
340	1.77	1284	6.62	1.76	1285	6.61
350	1.81	1332	6.76	1.81	1332	6.74
360	1.87	1380	6.89	1.86	1379	6.88
370	1.94	1429	7.02	1.92	1428	7.01
380	2.01	1480	7.15	1.99	1479	7.14
390	2.10	1534	7.29	2.08	1532	7.27
400	2.20	1591	7.43	2.17	1587	7.41

continued

T, °K	v	i	s	v	i	s
420	2.50	1717	7.74	2.43	1707	7.70
440	3.05	1872	8.10	2.85	1847	8.03
460	3.97	2058	8.52	2.99	2018	8.41
480	5.14	2225	8.91	4.55	2182	8.80
500	6.25	2356	9.18	5.55	2319	9.08
520	7.20	2462	9.38	6.44	2431	9.30
540	8.06	2549	9.55	7.27	2522	9.47
560	8.85	2627	9.69	8.01	2603	9.62
		$p=280$ bar			$p=300$ bar	
310	1.64	1147	6.18	1.63	1148	6.18
320	1.67	1193	6.33	1.67	1194	6.32
330	1.71	1239	6.47	1.70	1239	6.46
340	1.75	1285	6.60	1.74	1286	6.59
350	1.80	1332	6.73	1.79	1332	6.72
360	1.85	1379	6.86	1.84	1379	6.85
370	1.91	1428	6.99	1.90	1427	6.98
380	1.98	1478	7.12	1.96	1476	7.11
390	2.05	1529	7.25	2.04	1527	7.24
400	2.14	1583	7.39	2.12	1580	7.37
420	2.38	1699	7.67	2.34	1693	7.65
440	2.73	1831	7.98	2.63	1818	7.94
460	3.32	1988	8.34	3.12	1964	8.28
480	4.12	2146	8.70	3.80	2116	8.61
500	5.00	2286	8.99	4.56	2255	8.91
520	5.82	2401	9.22	5.31	2373	9.14
540	6.60	2496	9.40	6.04	2472	9.33
560	7.31	2579	9.55	6.72	2556	9.49
		$p=320$ bar			$p=340$ bar	
310	1.63	1149	6.17	1.63	1151	6.16
320	1.66	1195	6.32	1.66	1196	6.31
330	1.70	1240	6.45	1.69	1241	6.44
340	1.74	1286	6.58	1.73	1286	6.58
350	1.78	1332	6.71	1.77	1332	6.70
360	1.83	1379	6.84	1.82	1378	6.83
370	1.88	1426	6.97	1.87	1426	6.96
380	1.95	1475	7.09	1.94	1474	7.08
390	2.02	1526	7.22	2.01	1524	7.21
400	2.10	1578	7.35	2.08	1575	7.33
420	2.29	1688	7.63	2.26	1684	7.61
440	2.55	1808	7.91	2.50	1800	7.89
460	2.98	1945	8.23	2.86	1931	8.19
480	3.55	2091	8.55	3.35	2069	8.50
500	4.22	2227	8.84	3.95	2203	8.77
520	4.89	2347	9.07	4.55	2323	9.00
540	5.57	2448	9.26	5.18	2426	9.20
560	6.22	2535	9.42	5.78	2514	9.37
		$p=360$ bar			$p=380$ bar	
310	1.62	1152	6.16	1.61	1154	6.15
320	1.65	1197	6.30	1.64	1198	6.29
330	1.68	1242	6.44	1.68	1243	6.43
340	1.73	1287	6.57	1.71	1288	6.56
350	1.77	1332	6.69	1.76	1333	6.69
360	1.81	1378	6.82	1.80	1378	6.81
370	1.87	1425	6.95	1.86	1425	6.94
380	1.92	1473	7.07	1.91	1473	7.06
390	1.99	1523	7.20	1.98	1522	7.18
400	2.07	1573	7.32	2.04	1572	7.31
420	2.24	1680	7.59	2.21	1677	7.58
440	2.45	1794	7.86	2.41	1789	7.84
460	2.76	1919	8.16	2.69	1909	8.12
480	3.19	2050	8.44	3.06	2035	8.40

continued

T, °K	v	i	s	v	i	s
500	3.72	2181	8.71	3.53	2162	8.66
520	4.27	2301	8.94	4.04	2280	8.89
540	4.82	2405	9.14	4.56	2385	9.09
560	5.41	2493	9.31	5.08	2474	9.26
		p=400 bar			p=450 bar	
310	1.61	1156	6.15	1.60	1160	6.13
320	1.64	1200	6.29	1.63	1203	6.27
330	1.67	1244	6.42	1.66	1247	6.41
340	1.71	1288	6.55	1.70	1291	6.53
350	1.75	1333	6.68	1.74	1335	6.66
360	1.80	1379	6.80	1.78	1379	6.78
370	1.84	1425	6.93	1.83	1425	6.90
380	1.90	1472	7.04	1.87	1471	7.02
390	1.96	1520	7.17	1.93	1518	7.14
400	2.02	1570	7.30	1.99	1567	7.27
420	2.18	1674	7.56	2.12	1668	7.53
440	2.38	1784	7.82	2.30	1774	7.78
460	2.62	1900	8.09	2.50	1885	8.03
480	2.94	2022	8.36	2.75	1999	8.28
500	3.34	2146	8.62	3.07	2114	8.52
520	3.80	2262	8.84	3.44	2225	8.74
540	4.27	2366	9.05	3.83	2327	8.94
560	4.76	2456	9.21	4.24	2417	9.10
		p=500 bar			p=550 bar	
310	1.59	1164	6.12	1.58	1168	6.11
320	1.62	1207	6.26	1.61	1210	6.24
330	1.65	1250	6.39	1.64	1252	6.37
340	1.68	1293	6.51	1.67	1295	6.50
350	1.72	1336	6.64	1.71	1338	6.62
360	1.76	1380	6.76	1.74	1381	6.74
370	1.81	1425	6.88	1.78	1426	6.86
380	1.86	1470	6.99	1.83	1471	6.97
390	1.91	1517	7.12	1.88	1516	7.09
400	1.96	1565	7.24	1.94	1564	7.21
420	2.08	1664	7.49	2.04	1662	7.46
440	2.23	1768	7.74	2.17	1764	7.70
460	2.40	1875	7.98	2.32	1867	7.94
480	2.63	1983	8.22	2.52	1971	8.16
500	2.87	2091	8.44	2.72	2074	8.38
520	3.16	2196	8.65	2.97	2173	8.57
540	3.49	2294	8.84	3.24	2267	8.76
560	3.83	2385	9.00	3.53	2358	8.92
		p=600 bar			p=700 bar	
310	1.57	1172	6.09	1.56	1180	6.07
320	1.60	1214	6.23	1.58	1221	6.20
330	1.63	1255	6.36	1.61	1262	6.33
340	1.66	1297	6.48	1.64	1303	6.45
350	1.70	1340	6.60	1.67	1344	6.57
360	1.73	1383	6.72	1.71	1386	6.68
370	1.77	1426	6.84	1.74	1429	6.80
380	1.81	1471	6.95	1.78	1472	6.91
390	1.86	1516	7.07	1.83	1517	7.03
400	1.91	1563	7.19	1.87	1564	7.14
420	2.01	1660	7.43	1.96	1659	7.38
440	2.12	1761	7.67	2.05	1757	7.61
460	2.27	1862	7.90	2.16	1854	7.83
480	2.43	1962	8.12	2.30	1950	8.04
500	2.61	2060	8.32	2.44	2042	8.23
520	2.82	2156	8.52	2.61	2132	8.41
540	3.05	2248	8.69	2.79	2220	8.58
560	3.31	2336	8.85	2.98	2305	8.74

continued

T,°K	v	i	s	v	i	s
		p=800 bar			p=900 bar	
310	1,54	1189	6.04	1,53	1198	6,02
320	1,57	1229	6,17	1,55	1237	6.15
330	1,59	1268	6.30	1.57	1276	6,27
340	1,62	1309	6.42	1.60	1315	6.39
350	1,65	1349	6.53	1,63	1355	6.50
360	1.68	1391	6.64	1,66	1396	6,62
370	1,71	1432	6.76	1,69	1437	6.73
380	1,75	1475	6,87	1.73	1479	6,84
390	1,79	1519	6,99	1,76	1523	6.95
400	1,83	1566	7,10	1,80	1569	7,06
420	1,91	1660	7.34	1.87	1662	7,30
440	2,00	1756	7,56	1.95	1758	7,52
460	2,09	1852	7.78	2.03	1851	7.72
480	2,20	1944	7.98	2,12	1940	7,92
500	2.32	2032	8,16	2.24	2025	8,10
520	2,46	2118	8,34	2,35	2108	8,27
540	2,60	2202	8,50	2,47	2189	8,43
560	2,76	2283	8,65	2,61	2269	7,58
		p=1000 bar			p=1100 bar	
310	1,52	1208	6,00	1.51	1218	5,99
320	1,54	1246	6,13	1.53	1256	6.11
330	1,56	1284	6,25	1,54	1294	6,22
340	1,58	1323	6,36	1,57	1331	6,34
350	1,61	1362	6,47	1,59	1369	6,45
360	1,64	1402	6.59	1,62	1408	6.56
370	1,67	1442	6,70	1,65	1448	6.67
380	1.70	1484	6,81	1.68	1490	6.78
390	1.74	1527	6,92	1,71	1532	6.89
400	1.77	1572	7.03	1.74	1576	7,00
420	1,84	1666	7,26	1,80	1670	7,23
440	1,91	1760	7,48	1,87	1764	7,45
460	1.98	1852	7.68	1,94	1853	7,65
480	2,07	1938	7,87	2,01	1937	7,83
500	2,16	2021	8,05	2,10	2019	8,01
520	2.26	2102	8,22	2.19	2099	8,17
540	2,37	2181	8,37	2.28	2177	8,32
560	2,48	2260	8,52	2,38	2255	8,46

Heat capacity c_p (kJ/kg · deg) of ammonia [51]

p, bar → / T, °K	1	5	10	15	20	25	30	40
300	2,158	2,51	3,10					
310					4,87		4.84	4,82
320	2,170	2.38	2,92	3.24	4.99		4,97	4.94
330							5,11	5,09
340	2.192	2.34	2,58	2.88	3,24	3,74	4,50	5.31
350								5,63
360	2,221	2.34	2,51	2,70	2.92	3,15	3.44	4,35
380	2.254	2,34	2,48	2,61	2,75	2,92	3,10	3,61
400	2,287	2.36	2,46	2,56	2,65	2,78	2,92	3,22
420	2,322	2.38	2,46	2,53	2,63	2,73	2.83	3,05
440	2,357	2,41	2,46	2,53	2,61	2,68	2,75	2,90
460	2,393	2.43	2,48	2.56	2,61	2,65	2.70	2,83
480	2,430	2,46	2,51	2,56	2,61	2,65	2,70	2,80
500	2,467	2,51	2,53	2,58	2,63	2,65	2,70	2,80
520	2,504	2,53	2,58	2,61	2,65	2,68	2.73	2,80
540	2,540	2,58	2,61	2,65	2,68	2,70	2,73	2,80
560	2,577	2,63	2,65	2,68	2,70	2,73	2,75	2,80
580	2,613	2,65	2,68	2,70	2,73	2,75	2,78	2,80

continued

T, °K \ p, bar →	50	60	70	80	90	100	120	140
310	4.77	4.74	4.72	4.70	4.70	4.67	4.67	4.65
320	4.89	4.87	4.84	4.82	4.82	4.79	4.77	4.74
330	5.04	5.01	4.99	4.97	4.94	4.92	4.87	4.84
340	5.26	5.21	5.19	5.14	5.11	5.06	4.99	4.94
350	5.56	5.48	5.43	5.36	5.31	5.26	5.16	5.09
360	5.97	5.85	5.75	5.65	5.58	5.53	5.41	5.28
370		6.49	6.29	6.12	6.00	5.90	5.75	5.60
380	4.33	5.51	10.64	7.03	6.76	6.51	6.27	6.05
390					8.48	7.84	7.18	6.76
400	3.66	4.20	4.92	6.56	10.55	29.89	9.76	8.14
420	3.29	3.64	4.03	4.57	5.21	6.05	8.41	33.85
440	3.07	3.27	3.52	3.81	4.15	4.57	5.58	7.18
460	2.95	3.10	3.24	3.44	3.66	3.93	4.57	5.51
480	2.92	3.02	3.15	3.27	3.42	3.59	3.98	4.55
500	2.90	3.00	3.10	3.20	3.29	3.39	3.61	3.88
520	2.88	2.95	3.05	3.12	3.20	3.27	3.44	3.61
540	2.88	2.92	3.00	3.05	3.12	3.20	3.32	3.44
560	2.85	2.90	2.95	3.00	3.05	3.10	3.20	3.29
580	2.85	2.88	2.92	2.95	3.00	3.02		

T, °K \ p, bar →	160	180	200	220	240	260	280	300
310	4.62	4.60	4.57	4.55	4.52	4.50	4.47	4.45
320	4.70	4.67	4.65	4.62	4.60	4.55	4.52	4.50
330	4.79	4.74	4.72	4.70	4.67	4.62	4.60	4.57
340	4.89	4.84	4.82	4.77	4.74	4.70	4.67	4.65
350	5.01	4.97	4.92	4.87	4.82	4.77	4.74	4.72
360	5.19	5.11	5.04	4.99	4.92	4.87	4.84	4.79
370	5.48	5.36	5.24	5.14	5.06	5.01	4.94	4.89
380	5.85	5.65	5.48	5.36	5.26	5.16	5.09	5.01
390	6.42	6.12	5.85	5.63	5.48	5.36	5.26	5.19
400	7.25	6.76	6.37	6.07	5.83	5.60	5.46	5.36
420	15.12	9.73	8.26	7.40	6.91	6.37	6.07	5.88
440	10.30	13.25	11.21	9.54	8.46	7.69	7.15	6.76
460	6.78	8.36	9.73	10.28	9.73	8.92	8.23	7.64
480	5.14	5.70	6.32	6.91	7.35	7.62	7.55	7.35
500	4.20	4.52	4.89	5.31	5.70	6.05	6.29	6.46
520	3.81	4.01	4.23	4.45	4.70	4.97	5.24	5.46
540	3.54	3.69	3.86	3.98	4.13	4.30	4.50	4.67
560	3.39	3.49	3.56	3.69	3.79	3.88	3.98	4.08

T, °K \ p, bar →	320	340	360	380	400	450	500	550
310	4.42	4.40	4.38	4.35	4.35	4.30	4.25	4.20
320	4.47	4.45	4.42	4.40	4.40	4.35	4.28	4.23
330	4.55	4.52	4.50	4.47	4.45	4.40	4.33	4.28
340	4.60	4.57	4.55	4.52	4.50	4.45	4.38	4.33
350	4.67	4.65	4.62	4.60	4.57	4.50	4.42	4.38
360	4.74	4.72	4.70	4.67	4.65	4.57	4.50	4.42
370	4.84	4.82	4.77	4.74	4.72	4.65	4.57	4.47
380	4.97	4.92	4.87	4.84	4.82	4.72	4.65	4.55
390	5.11	5.04	4.99	4.94	4.92	4.79	4.72	4.62
400	5.28	5.21	5.11	5.06	5.04	4.92	4.82	4.72
420	5.70	5.60	5.51	5.41	5.33	5.16	5.04	4.92
440	6.46	6.22	6.02	5.85	5.70	5.43	5.24	5.09
460	7.18	6.78	6.46	6.19	6.00	5.68	5.43	5.24
480	7.08	6.81	6.56	6.34	6.15	5.83	5.51	5.24
500	6.44	6.34	6.19	6.05	5.95	5.65	5.41	5.14
520	5.58	5.58	5.56	5.51	5.48	5.31	5.11	4.92
540	4.77	4.84	4.87	4.87	4.87	4.79	4.72	4.60
560	4.15	4.23	4.25	4.25	4.25	4.23	4.23	4.20

continued

p, bar \ t, °C →	600	700	800	900	1000	1100		
310	4.15	4.06	3.98	3.88	3.83	3.76		
320	4.18	4.08	4.01	3.91	3.86	3.79		
330	4.23	4.13	4.03	3.96	3.91	3.81		
340	4.28	4.15	4.08	3.98	3.93	3.83		
350	4.33	4.20	4.10	4.03	3.98	3.88		
360	4.38	4.25	4.15	4.06	4.01	3.91		
370	4.42	4.30	4.20	4.10	4.06	3.96		
380	4.50	4.35	4.25	4.15	4.08	4.01		
390	4.55	4.42	4.30	4.20	4.13	4.03		
400	4.65	4.50	4.38	4.25	4.15	4.06		
420	4.82	4.65	4.47	4.33	4.20	4.08		
440	4.97	4.74	4.52	4.35	4.23	4.10		
460	5.06	4.77	4.55	4.35	4.23	4.10		
480	5.01	4.74	4.50	4.30	4.20	4.08		
500	4.92	4.65	4.42	4.28	4.15	4.03		
520	4.74	4.50	4.33	4.18	4.08	3.98		
540	4.47	4.33	4.18	4.06	3.98	3.93		
560		4.08	4.01		3.88	3.86		

Viscosity $\eta \cdot 10^5$ ($N \cdot s/m^2$) of ammonia liquid and gas [145]

T, °K \ p, bar →	30	40	50	60	70	80	90	100
1	1.07	1.10	1.13	1.16	1.19	1.22	1.25	1.28
5	1.07	1.10	1.13	1.16	1.19	1.22	1.25	1.29
10			1.14	1.17	1.20	1.23	1.26	1.29
20	13.61				1.21	1.24	1.27	1.30
30	13.73	12.60				1.25	1.28	1.31
40	13.82	12.69	11.57	10.48		1.28	1.30	1.33
50	13.90	12.77	11.65	10.56	9.47	8.39	1.34	1.35
60	13.98	12.85	11.73	10.64	9.56	8.51	7.42	1.38
70	14.06	12.93	11.81	10.72	9.65	8.61	7.55	6.50
80	14.15	13.00	11.88	10.81	9.74	8.70	7.67	6.64
90	14.23	13.08	11.96	10.89	9.84	8.80	7.78	6.80
100	14.32	13.17	12.05	10.98	9.93	8.91	7.91	6.95
110	14.39	13.25	12.13	11.06	10.03	9.00	8.00	7.07
120	14.46	13.32	12.21	11.13	10.10	9.09	8.12	7.20
130	14.50	13.39	12.29	11.22	10.15	9.19	8.22	7.34
140	14.58	13.46	12.36	11.30	10.26	9.28	8.32	7.45
150	14.66	13.54	12.44	11.37	10.35	9.38	8.44	7.57
160	14.71	13.61	12.50	11.43	10.42	9.47	8.54	7.69
170	14.78	13.68	12.58	11.51	10.50	9.55	8.64	7.80
180	14.84	13.72	12.63	11.57	10.57	9.63	8.75	7.92
190	14.93	13.81	12.71	11.64	10.65	9.72	8.84	8.02
200	15.01	13.91	12.80	11.73	10.73	9.79	8.93	8.13
210	15.06	13.96	12.86	11.81	10.81	9.88	9.01	8.22
220	15.14	14.02	12.91	11.86	10.87	9.96	9.09	8.32
230	15.22	14.09	12.97	11.92	10.94	10.04	9.19	8.41
240	15.30	14.17	13.07	12.01	11.02	10.12	9.28	8.50
250	15.38	14.26	13.16	12.10	11.11	10.20	9.36	8.59
300	15.76	14.65	13.55	12.49	11.51	10.59	9.74	8.97
350	16.05	14.97	13.88	12.84	11.86	10.96	10.11	9.34
400	16.35	15.30	14.25	13.22	12.24	11.32	10.49	9.71
450	16.65	15.62	14.57	13.55	12.57	11.66	10.83	10.06
500	16.96	15.93	14.88	13.86	12.88	11.97	11.15	10.37
550	17.24	16.22	15.17	14.15	13.17	12.26	11.44	10.66
600	17.50	16.48	15.43	14.42	13.44	12.53	11.71	10.93
650	17.74	16.72	15.67	14.67	13.69	12.78	11.96	11.18

continued

p, bar \ t, °C →	30	40	50	60	70	80	90	100
700	17.97	16.95	15.90	14.90	13.92	13.01	12.20	11.43
750	18.16	17.15	16.10	15.10	14.12	13.21	12.41	11.63
800	18.31	17.30	16.25	15.25	14.28	13.37	12.57	11.79

p, bar \ t, °C →	110	120	130	140	150	160	170	180
1	1.32	1.36	1.39	1.43	1.46	1.50	1.53	1.57
5	1.32	1.36	1.39	1.43	1.46	1.50	1.53	1.57
10	1.33	1.36	1.40	1.44	1.47	1.50	1.54	1.58
20	1.34	1.38	1.42	1.45	1.48	1.51	1.55	1.59
30	1.35	1.39	1.43	1.47	1.50	1.53	1.56	1.60
40	1.37	1.41	1.45	1.48	1.52	1.55	1.58	1.62
50	1.39	1.43	1.47	1.51	1.54	1.56	1.60	1.63
60	1.41	1.45	1.49	1.52	1.56	1.59	1.62	1.65
70		1.49	1.52	1.55	1.60	1.63	1.66	1.69
80	5.68	1.54	1.57	1.58	1.62	1.64	1.67	1.70
90	5.75		1.62	1.64	1.66	1.68	1.71	1.74
100	6.03	5.07	1.70	1.70	1.70	1.71	1.74	1.76
110	6.26	5.30	2.04	1.86	1.74	1.75	1.77	1.79
120	6.41	5.50	4.15	2.20	1.84	1.79	1.80	1.83
130	6.55	5.69	4.57	2.90	2.04	1.85	1.86	1.88
140	6.68	5.85	4.85	3.56	2.29	1.94	1.92	1.93
150	6.81	6.01	5.07	3.94	2.68	2.09	2.03	2.00
160	6.96	6.16	5.24	4.22	3.18	2.31	2.19	2.12
170	7.07	6.30	5.40	4.40	3.51	2.61	2.37	2.23
180	7.18	6.42	5.56	4.63	3.77	2.92	2.55	2.35
190	7.29	6.55	5.70	4.81	3.98	3.18	2.71	2.45
200	7.40	6.66	5.83	4.96	4.16	3.40	2.87	2.57
210	7.51	6.77	5.96	5.11	4.35	3.61	3.08	2.74
220	7.60	6.88	6.08	5.26	4.51	3.79	3.28	2.92
230	7.71	6.98	6.19	5.40	4.65	3.97	3.45	3.06
240	7.80	7.07	6.30	5.52	4.79	4.13	3.62	3.22
250	7.88	7.16	6.40	5.63	4.92	4.28	3.76	3.35
300	8.27	7.57	6.86	6.16	5.50	4.92	4.42	3.98
350	8.65	7.95	7.26	6.58	6.00	5.46	4.97	4.53
400	8.99	8.28	7.60	6.95	6.40	5.90	5.43	5.00
450	9.34	8.61	7.96	7.34	6.77	6.27	5.81	5.39
500	9.64	8.81	8.26	7.64	7.06	6.59	6.15	5.74
550	9.93	9.19	8.50	7.89	7.33	6.85	6.42	6.04
600	10.20	9.46	8.77	8.14	7.57	7.09	6.67	6.29
650	10.45	9.71	9.02	8.39	7.82	7.32	6.90	6.53
700	10.69	9.97	9.29	8.64	8.06	7.57	7.16	6.79
750	10.91	10.20	9.50	8.85	8.28	7.81	7.39	7.03
800	11.07	10.37	9.17	9.02	8.45	7.98	7.56	7.22

p, bar \ t, °C →	190	200	210	220	230	240	250
1	1.60	1.64	1.67	1.71	1.74	1.78	1.81
5	1.61	1.64	1.68	1.71	1.75	1.78	1.82
10	1.61	1.65	1.69	1.72	1.75	1.79	1.82
20	1.62	1.66	1.70	1.73	1.76	1.80	1.83
30	1.64	1.67	1.71	1.74	1.77	1.81	1.84
40	1.65	1.69	1.72	1.75	1.78	1.82	1.85
50	1.66	1.69	1.72	1.76	1.79	1.82	1.86
60	1.68	1.72	1.75	1.78	1.81	1.85	1.87
70	1.70	1.73	1.77	1.80	1.83	1.86	1.89
80	1.72	1.75	1.78	1.81	1.85	1.88	1.91
90	1.76	1.77	1.80	1.83	1.86	1.89	1.92
100	1.79	1.81	1.84	1.87	1.90	1.93	1.94

continued

p, bar \ t, °C →	190	200	210	220	230	240	250
110	1.82	1.85	1.88	1.90	1.92	1.94	1.96
120	1.85	1.88	1.91	1.92	1.94	1.96	1.98
130	1.90	1.92	1.94	1.95	1.97	1.99	2.01
140	1.93	1.94	1.96	1.98	2.00	2.02	2.03
150	1.99	1.99	2.00	2.01	2.03	2.05	2.05
160	2.07	2.04	2.05	2.06	2.06	2.08	2.09
170	2.15	2.10	2.11	2.11	2.11	2.11	2.11
180	2.23	2.17	2.16	2.16	2.15	2.15	2.14
190	2.30	2.23	2.21	2.20	2.19	2.19	2.17
200	2.39	2.30	2.25	2.22	2.22	2.22	2.21
210	2.52	2.39	2.31	2.26	2.24	2.24	2.24
220	2.66	2.48	2.37	2.31	2.28	2.28	2.28
230	2.78	2.58	2.45	2.37	2.33	2.32	2.32
240	2.90	2.68	2.54	2.45	2.40	2.37	2.37
250	3.03	2.79	2.64	2.54	2.48	2.43	2.42
300	3.63	3.35	3.14	2.98	2.87	2.77	2.68
350	4.16	3.86	3.63	3.43	3.26	3.12	2.97
400	4.62	4.30	4.04	3.82	3.62	3.44	3.29
450	5.02	4.70	4.42	4.18	3.97	3.77	3.62
500	5.38	5.05	4.78	4.52	4.29	4.08	3.88
550	5.70	5.36	5.07	4.80	4.58	4.38	4.17
600	5.95	5.64	5.36	5.09	4.85	4.64	4.45
650	6.20	5.91	5.61	5.35	5.11	4.91	4.72
700	6.46	6.15	5.88	5.62	5.38	5.18	4.97
750	6.69	6.38	6.09	5.83	5.58	5.36	5.16
800	6.88	6.57	6.27	6.01	5.74	5.52	5.33

Viscosity η ($N \cdot s/m^2$) of saturated ammonia [145]

t, °C	$\eta' \cdot 10^5$	$\eta'' \cdot 10^5$	t, °C	$\eta' \cdot 10^5$	$\eta'' \cdot 10^5$
30	13.600	1.075	100	6.400	1.395
40	12.480	1.115	110	5.600	1.470
50	11.350	1.155	120	4.840	1.625
60	10.300	1.200	125	4.370	1.760
70	9.220	1.245	130	3.730	2.020
80	8.260	1.290	131.5	3.310	2.250
90	7.320	1.335	132.4	2.610	2.610

Thermal conductivity of ammonia at low temperatures and $p = 1$ bar [15]

T, °K	200	210	220	230	240	250	260	270	280	290	300
$\lambda \cdot 10^3$, W/m · deg	15.3	16.2	17.0	17.8	18.6	19.6	20.6	21.6	22.6	23.6	24.7

Thermal conductivity $\lambda \cdot 10^3$ (W/m · deg) of ammonia [15]

T, °K \ p, bar →	1	10	20	30	40	50	60
300	24.7	30.0	474	476	478	480	482
310	26.0	30.6	454	457	458	462	464
320	27.2	31.0	434	435	437	440	442
330	28.2	31.6	36.0	408	416	417	418
340	29.3	32.2	36.1	41.0	390	393	397
350	30.4	33.1	36.3	40.5	367	368	370

continued

T, °K / p, bar →	1	10	20	30	40	50	60
360	31.6	34.0	36.5	40.0	45.0	340	343
370	32.8	34.7	36.7	40.2	44.4	51.0	315
380	34.0	35.4	37.4	40.8	44.0	50.0	58.0
390	35.2	37.0	39.0	42.5	44.4	50.0	56.2
400	37.0	38.4	41.1	43.3	44.8	49.5	54.3
420	40.4	41.2	42.9	44.1	47.0	49.3	52.4
440	43.5	44.1	45.3	46.2	48.4	49.1	50.8
460	46.3	47.3	48.2	49.0	49.8	51.6	52.6
480	49.2	50.1	50.9	51.9	53.0	54.1	55.2
500	52.5	54.5	55.4	56.2	56.9	57.8	58.6
550	59.4	63.3	64.1	64.9	65.8	67.2	67.4
600	67.0	71.2	72.1	73.0	73.8	74.4	75.2

T, °K / p, bar →	70	80	90	100	150	200	250
300	484	485	486	488	493	500	506
310	466	466	469	470	477	484	490
320	444	445	448	450	456	463	470
330	420	423	425	427	436	444	452
340	398	400	402	404	416	423	430
350	372	375	377	381	391	402	411
360	346	348	352	354	367	379	388
370	318	321	325	328	345	357	370
380	67.4	293	297	302	320	335	348
390	63.4	76.3	262	273	296	314	327
400	61.2	70.4	83.0	110	269	292	307
420	55.9	61.2	66.9	75.1		244	265
440	53.8	57.2	61.4	65.2		183	219
460	55.3	57.4	60.5	63.0	84.5	133	173
480	56.0	58.2	60.8	62.5	76.4	97.3	127
500	59.4	60.2	61.1	63.3	73.2	94.5	123
550	68.2	67.1	68.9	69.7	71.6	85.4	105
600	75.9	76.6	77.4	78.2	79.0	79.8	82.1

T, °K / p, bar →	300	350	400	450	500	550	600
300	513	520	527	534	540	546	553
310	496	502	509	515	521	527	533
320	477	484	491	498	505	509	514
330	459	466	473	479	484	493	498
340	438	447	454	461	468	474	480
350	419	427	435	442	449	455	461
360	398	408	418	424	431	438	445
370	380	388	398	406	414	422	427
380	359	370	380	388	395	403	410
390	340	352	362	370	377	384	391
400	321	334	344	352	360	368	374
420	282	295	308	319	328	338	345
440	240	258	273	286	298	310	320
460	199	220	238	256	273	286	296
480	162	182	204	228	252	263	273
500	156	179	203	222	240	252	263
550	128	149	166	186	204	216	228
600	91	110	134	151	168	178	187

continued

T, °K \ p, bar →	650	700	750	800	850	900	1000
300	557	562	567	572	576	580	587
310	538	546	551	556	558	562	573
320	521	531	534	538	543	551	558
330	505	512	515	521	527	534	543
340	486	493	499	505	512	519	527
350	468	476	480	486	493	499	512
360	451	455	464	471	478	484	493
370	435	438	447	453	458	464	478
380	417	424	433	437	443	451	462
390	400	406	414	422	426	435	445
400	384	391	398	405	412	418	433
420	354	363	369	375	384	390	403
440	329	337	345	351	358	364	375
460	304	313	322	328	335	342	354
480	282	291	299	305	313	321	333

Thermal conductivity λ of saturated liquid ammonia [15]

T, °K	300	305	310	315	320	325	330	335	340	345	350	355	360	365	370	375	380
$\lambda \cdot 10^3$, W/m · deg	470	457	445	435	424	413	403	391	379	369	356	345	335	325	315	305	289

Chapter 6

OXYGEN

Molecular weight 32.000

$T_{boil} = 90.18$ °K at 760 mm Hg; $T_{melt} = 54.35$ °K; $T_{cr} = 154.77$ °K;
$p_{cr} = 50.9$ bar; $\rho_{cr} = 405$ kg/m^3

Thermodynamic properties of saturated oxygen [141, 142]:
v (dm^3/kg), c_p (kJ/kg · deg), i and r (kJ/kg) and s (kJ/kg · deg)

T, °K	p, bar	v'	v''	c_p'	i'	i''	r	s'	s''
54.35	0.001500	0.7762	93 979		−189.8	48.9	238.7	2.156	6.548
55	0.001831	0.7777	77 922		−188.9	49.5	238.4	2.172	6.507
56	0.002467	0.7800	58 873		−187.3	50.4	237.7	2.200	6.445
57	0.003287	0.7824	44 960		−185.8	51.2	237.0	2.228	6.386
58	0.004334	0.7848	34 685		−184.2	52.1	236.3	2.256	6.330
59	0.005658	0.7872	27 018		−182.6	53.0	235.6	2.283	6.276
60	0.007317	0.7896	21 239		−181.1	53.8	234.9	2.308	6.223
61	0.009378	0.7921	16 841		−179.5	54.7	234.2	2.334	6.173
62	0.01192	0.7945	13 465		−178.0	55.5	233.5	2.359	6.125
63	0.01502	0.7971	10 850		−176.4	56.4	232.8	2.384	6.079
64	0.01879	0.7997	8 808		−174.8	57.3	232.1	2.409	6.035
65	0.02333	0.8023	7 201		−173.3	58.1	231.4	2.432	5.992
66	0.02877	0.8049	5 928		−171.7	59.0	230.7	2.456	5.951
67	0.03523	0.8075	4 911		−170.2	59.8	230.0	2.478	5.911
68	0.04288	0.8101	4 094		−168.6	60.7	229.3	2.500	5.873
69	0.05186	0.8128	3 433		−167.1	61.5	228.6	2.523	5.836
70	0.06236	0.8155	2 894		−165.5	62.4	227.9	2.545	5.801
71	0.07457	0.8182	2 453		−164.0	63.2	227.2	2.567	5.767
72	0.08869	0.8210	2 090		−162.4	64.1	226.6	2.588	5.734
73	0.1049	0.8238	1 790		−160.8	64.9	225.7	2.610	5.702
74	0.1236	0.8267	1 540		−159.2	65.8	225.0	2.631	5.672
75	0.1448	0.8296	1 330	1.570	−157.6	66.6	224.2	2.653	5.642
76	0.1690	0.8326	1 154	1.574	−156.0	67.4	223.4	2.675	5.614
77	0.1963	0.8357	1 006	1.578	−154.4	68.3	222.7	2.695	5.587
78	0.2271	0.8388	879.8	1.582	−152.9	69.1	222.0	2.714	5.560
79	0.2616	0.8420	772.5	1.585	−151.3	70.0	221.3	2.734	5.535
80	0.3003	0.8452	680.7	1.589	−149.7	70.8	220.5	2.754	5.510
81	0.3435	0.8484	601.9	1.592	−148.1	71.6	219.7	2.774	5.486
82	0.3914	0.8517	533.9	1.596	−146.5	72.4	218.9	2.794	5.463
83	0.4445	0.8550	475.1	1.600	−144.8	73.3	218.1	2.812	5.440
84	0.5031	0.8584	424.1	1.603	−143.3	74.1	217.4	2.830	5.418
85	0.5677	0.8618	379.7	1.607	−141.7	74.9	216.6	2.849	5.397
86	0.6386	0.8653	340.9	1.610	−140.1	75.7	215.8	2.868	5.377
87	0.7163	0.8688	306.8	1.614	−138.5	76.5	215.0	2.886	5.357
88	0.8012	0.8724	276.9	1.617	−136.9	77.3	214.2	2.903	5.337
89	0.8937	0.8761	250.5	1.621	−135.3	78.0	213.3	2.922	5.319
90	0.9943	0.8798	227.1	1.625	−133.7	78.8	212.5	2.940	5.301
90.18	1.013	0.8805	223.2	1.626	−133.4	78.9	212.3	2.943	5.297
91	1.103	0.8836	206.4	1.629	−132.0	79.6	211.5	2.958	5.283
92	1.221	0.8874	188.0	1.633	−130.4	80.3	210.7	2.976	5.266
93	1.349	0.8913	171.6	1.637	−128.7	81.0	209.7	2.994	5.249

continued

T, °K	p, bar	v'	v''	c_p'	i'	i''	r	s'	s''
94	1.486	0.8952	157.0	1.641	−127.0	81.7	208.7	3.012	5.232
95	1.634	0.8993	143.9	1.645	−125.4	82.4	207.8	3.045	5.216
96	1.793	0.9033	132.1	1.650	−123.8	83.1	206.9	3.045	5.200
97	1.963	0.9074	121.5	1.655	−122.1	83.8	205.9	3.062	5.185
98	2.145	0.9116	111.9	1.660	−120.4	84.5	204.9	3.079	5.170
99	2.339	0.9160	103.3	1.666	−118.8	85.1	203.9	3.096	5.155
100	2.546	0.9204	95.46	1.672	−117.1	85.7	202.8	3.113	5.141
101	2.767	0.9249	88.37	1.678	−115.4	86.3	201.7	3.130	5.127
102	3.002	0.9295	81.92	1.685	−113.7	86.9	200.6	3.146	5.113
103	3.251	0.9342	76.05	1.692	−112.0	87.5	199.5	3.162	5.099
104	3.515	0.9389	70.70	1.699	−110.3	88.0	198.3	3.179	5.086
105	3.794	0.9437	65.81	1.706	−108.6	88.5	197.1	3.196	5.073
106	4.090	0.9486	61.33	1.714	−106.9	89.0	195.9	3.212	5.060
107	4.402	0.9536	57.23	1.723	−105.2	89.5	194.7	3.227	5.047
108	4.731	0.9587	53.47	1.732	−103.4	90.0	193.4	3.243	5.034
109	5.078	0.9640	50.00	1.742	−101.7	90.4	192.1	3.260	5.022
110	5.443	0.9695	46.81	1.752	−99.9	90.8	190.7	3.276	5.009
111	5.826	0.9750	43.87	1.763	−98.2	91.2	189.4	3.291	4.997
112	6.229	0.9806	41.15	1.775	−96.4	91.6	188.0	3.307	4.985
113	6.652	0.9864	38.64	1.787	−94.6	91.9	186.5	3.323	4.973
114	7.095	0.9923	36.31	1.800	−92.7	92.3	185.0	3.339	4.961
115	7.559	0.9984	34.15	1.814	−90.9	92.6	183.5	3.354	4.950
116	8.045	1.005	32.15	1.829	−89.0	92.9	181.9	3.370	4.938
117	8.558	1.005	30.29	1.844	−87.2	93.1	180.3	3.386	4.927
118	9.083	1.018	28.55	1.860	−85.4	93.3	178.7	3.401	4.915
119	9.637	1.024	26.93	1.877	−83.5	93.5	177.0	3.417	4.904
120	10.21	1.031	25.42	1.896	−81.6	93.6	175.2	3.432	4.892
121	10.82	1.038	24.01	1.915	−79.7	93.7	173.4	3.448	4.881
122	11.44	1.045	22.69	1.935	−77.8	93.8	171.6	3.463	4.870
123	12.10	1.053	21.45	1.957	−75.8	93.9	169.7	3.478	4.859
124	12.78	1.061	20.30	1.980	−73.8	93.9	167.7	3.495	4.847
125	13.48	1.070	19.21	2.004	−71.8	93.9	165.7	3.510	4.836
126	14.22	1.078	18.19	2.030	−69.8	93.9	163.7	3.526	4.825
127	14.98	1.087	17.23	2.057	−67.7	93.8	161.5	3.541	4.813
128	15.77	1.096	16.32	2.086	−65.6	93.7	159.3	3.557	4.802
129	16.59	1.106	15.47	2.116	−63.6	93.5	157.1	3.573	4.791
130	17.44	1.116	14.67	2.148	−61.5	93.3	154.8	3.588	4.779
131	18.33	1.126	13.91	2.182	−59.4	93.1	152.5	3.604	4.768
132	19.24	1.136	13.19	2.218	−57.8	92.8	150.1	3.619	4.756
133	20.19	1.147	12.51	2.256	−55.1	92.5	147.6	3.634	4.744
134	21.17	1.158	11.86	2.297	−52.9	92.1	145.0	3.650	4.732
135	22.19	1.170	11.25	2.341	−50.6	91.6	142.2	3.667	4.720
136	23.24	1.182	10.67	2.388	−48.3	91.1	139.4	3.683	4.708
137	24.33	1.195	10.12	2.439	−46.0	90.5	136.5	3.700	4.696
138	25.45	1.208	9.593	2.495	−43.7	89.9	133.6	3.715	4.683
139	26.61	1.222	9.092	2.558	−41.3	89.2	130.5	3.731	4.670
140	27.82	1.237	8.612	2.629	−38.9	88.4	127.3	3.748	4.657
141	29.06	1.253	8.154	2.710	−36.4	87.5	123.9	3.764	4.643
142	30.34	1.271	7.716	2.802	−33.6	86.5	120.3	3.782	4.629
143	31.67	1.290	7.295	2.904	−31.2	85.4	116.6	3.799	4.614
144	33.04	1.310	6.890	3.017	−28.6	84.2	112.8	3.816	4.599
145	34.45	1.332	6.499	3.141	−25.9	82.9	108.9	3.833	4.583
146	35.91	1.356	6.122	3.276	−23.2	81.4	104.6	3.851	4.567
147	37.41	1.383	5.756	3.422	−20.4	79.8	100.1	3.868	4.549
148	38.97	1.413	5.400	3.579	−17.5	77.8	95.3	3.886	4.530
149	40.57	1.447	5.051	3.747	−14.3	75.6	89.9	3.906	4.510
150	42.23	1.487	4.705		−10.8	73.1	83.9	3.928	4.487
151	43.93	1.535	4.361		−6.8	70.2	77.0	3.953	4.463
152	45.69	1.595	4.020		−2.2	66.7	68.9	3.983	4.436
153	47.51	1.672	3.678		3.2	62.5	59.3	4.017	4.404
154	49.39	1.795	3.285		10.6	56.7	46.1	4.063	4.362
154.77	50.87	2.464	2.464		35.2	35.2	0	4.219	4.219

Thermodynamic properties of oxygen liquid and gas [141, 142]:
v (dm^3/kg), c_p (kJ/kg · deg), i (kJ/kg) and s (kJ/kg · deg)

T, °K	v	c_p	i	s	v	c_p	i	s
	p=1 bar				p=2 bar			
75	0.8295	1.568	−157.6	2.653				
80	0.8451	1.589	−149.7	2.754				
85	0.8618	1.607	−141.7	2.849				
90	0.8798	1.625	−133.7	2.940				
95	239.7	0.994	83.9	5.354				
100	253.5	0.962	88.8	5.404	123.4	1.018	86.8	5.211
105	267.0	0.947	93.5	5.451	130.5	0.984	91.8	5.260
110	280.5	0.937	98.2	5.496	137.5	0.965	96.7	5.305
115	294.0	0.931	102.9	5.536	144.5	0.955	101.5	5.347
120	307.4	0.928	107.6	5.576	151.4	0.948	106.3	5.388
125	320.7	0.926	112.2	5.614	158.2	0.944	111.0	5.427
130	334.0	0.925	116.8	5.650	165.0	0.941	115.7	5.464
135	347.2	0.924	121.4	5.685	171.8	0.938	120.4	5.499
140	360.5	0.922	126.1	5.719	178.6	0.936	125.0	5.533
145	373.8	0.921	130.7	5.751	185.3	0.934	129.7	5.566
150	386.9	0.921	135.3	5.782	192.0	0.932	134.4	5.598
155	400.1	0.920	139.9	5.812	198.7	0.930	139.0	5.629
160	413.2	0.919	144.5	5.841	205.4	0.928	143.7	5.658
165	426.4	0.918	149.1	5.869	212.0	0.927	148.3	5.686
170	439.5	0.918	153.6	5.897	218.7	0.926	153.0	5.714
180	465.8	0.917	162.8	5.949	231.9	0.923	162.2	5.767
190	492.0	0.916	172.0	5.999	245.1	0.921	171.4	5.817
200	518.1	0.915	181.1	6.046	258.3	0.920	180.6	5.864
210	544.3	0.915	190.3	6.091	271.5	0.919	189.8	5.909
220	570.4	0.914	199.4	6.133	284.6	0.918	199.0	5.952
230	596.5	0.914	208.6	6.174	297.7	0.918	208.2	5.992
240	622.6	0.915	217.7	6.213	310.8	0.918	217.4	6.031
250	648.7	0.915	226.9	6.250	323.9	0.918	226.5	6.069
260	674.8	0.916	236.0	6.286	337.0	0.918	235.7	6.105
270	700.9	0.916	245.2	6.321	350.1	0.918	244.9	6.140
280	726.9	0.917	254.4	6.354	363.2	0.919	254.1	6.173
290	753.0	0.919	263.5	6.386	376.2	0.920	263.3	6.205
300	779.0	0.920	272.7	6.417	389.3	0.921	272.5	6.236
310	805.1	0.921	281.9	6.447	402.3	0.922	281.7	6.267
320	831.1	0.923	291.1	6.476	415.4	0.924	290.9	6.296
330	857.2	0.925	300.4	6.505	428.4	0.926	300.2	6.324
340	883.2	0.927	309.6	6.533	441.5	0.928	309.5	6.352
350	909.2	0.929	318.9	6.560	454.5	0.930	318.8	6.379
375	974.3	0.935	342.2	6.624	487.1	0.936	342.1	6.443
400	1039	0.942	365.7	6.685	519.6	0.942	365.6	6.504
425	1114	0.949	389.3	6.742	552.2	0.949	389.2	6.561
450	1169	0.956	413.1	6.796	584.7	0.957	413.0	6.616
475	1234	0.964	437.1	6.848	617.3	0.965	437.1	6.668
500	1299	0.972	461.3	6.898	649.8	0.973	461.3	6.718
550	1429	0.988	510.3	6.991	714.9	0.988	510.3	6.811
600	1559	1.003	560.1	7.078	779.9	1.003	560.1	6.898
650	1689	1.018	610.6	7.159	844.9	1.018	610.6	6.979
700	1819	1.031	661.9	7.235	909.3	1.031	661.8	7.055
750	1949	1.043	713.7	7.306	974.9	1.043	713.7	7.126
800	2079	1.054	766.2	7.374	1040	1.055	766.2	7.194
850	2209	1.065	819.2	7.438	1105	1.065	819.2	7.258
900	2339	1.074	872.6	7.499	1170	1.074	872.6	7.319
950	2469	1.082	926.5	7.558	1235	1.082	926.6	7.377
1000	2599	1.090	980.8	7.614	1300	1.090	980.9	7.433
1050	2729	1.097	1035.5	7.667	1365	1.097	1035.6	7.487
1100	2859	1.103	1090.5	7.718	1430	1.104	1090.6	7.538
1150	2989	1.109	1145.9	7.767	1495	1.110	1145.9	7.587
1200	3119	1.115	1201.5	7.814	1560	1.115	1201.5	7.634
1250	3248	1.120	1257.4	7.860	1625	1.120	1257.4	7.680
1300	3378	1.125	1313.5	7.904	1690	1.125	1313.5	7.724

continued

T, °K	v	c_p	i	s	v	c_p	i	s
	$p=3$ bar				$p=4$ bar			
105	84.94	1.024	90.0	5.143				
110	89.82	0.996	95.1	5.190	65.90	1.029	93.4	5.105
115	94.61	0.980	100.0	5.234	69.64	1.007	98.5	5.150
120	99.35	0.970	104.9	5.275	73.31	0.992	103.5	5.193
125	104.0	0.963	109.7	5.314	76.94	0.983	108.4	5.234
130	108.7	0.958	114.5	5.352	80.53	0.975	113.3	5.272
135	113.3	0.953	119.3	5.388	84.07	0.969	118.2	5.308
140	117.9	0.950	124.0	5.423	87.58	0.964	123.0	5.343
145	122.5	0.946	128.8	5.456	91.07	0.960	127.8	5.377
150	127.0	0.943	133.5	5.488	94.54	0.956	132.6	5.410
155	131.6	0.941	138.2	5.519	97.99	0.952	137.4	5.441
160	136.1	0.938	142.9	5.549	101.4	0.948	142.1	5.471
165	140.6	0.936	147.6	5.578	104.8	0.945	146.8	5.500
170	145.0	0.934	152.2	5.606	108.2	0.942	151.5	5.528
180	154.0	0.930	161.6	5.659	115.0	0.937	160.9	5.582
190	162.9	0.927	170.9	5.709	121.7	0.933	170.3	5.632
200	171.7	0.925	180.2	5.757	128.4	0.930	179.6	5.680
210	180.5	0.923	189.4	5.802	135.1	0.928	188.9	5.726
220	189.3	0.922	198.6	5.845	141.7	0.926	198.2	5.769
230	198.1	0.921	207.8	5.886	148.3	0.924	207.4	5.810
240	206.9	0.920	217.0	5.925	154.9	0.923	216.6	5.849
250	215.7	0.920	226.2	5.963	161.5	0.923	225.9	5.887
260	224.4	0.920	235.4	5.999	168.1	0.922	235.1	5.923
270	233.2	0.920	244.6	6.033	174.7	0.922	244.3	5.958
280	241.9	0.921	253.8	6.066	181.3	0.923	253.5	5.991
290	250.6	0.922	263.0	6.099	187.9	0.923	262.8	6.024
300	259.4	0.923	272.3	6.130	194.4	0.924	272.0	6.055
310	268.1	0.924	281.5	6.161	201.0	0.925	281.3	6.085
320	276.8	0.926	290.7	6.190	207.5	0.927	290.5	6.114
330	285.5	0.927	300.0	6.218	214.1	0.928	299.8	6.143
340	294.2	0.929	309.3	6.246	220.6	0.930	309.1	6.171
350	302.9	0.931	318.6	6.273	227.2	0.932	318.4	6.198
375	324.7	0.937	341.9	6.338	243.5	0.938	341.8	6.262
400	346.4	0.943	365.4	6.399	259.8	0.944	365.3	6.323
425	368.2	0.950	389.1	6.456	276.1	0.951	389.0	6.381
450	389.9	0.957	412.9	6.510	292.4	0.958	412.8	6.435
475	411.6	0.965	437.0	6.562	308.7	0.966	436.9	6.487
500	433.3	0.973	461.2	6.612	325.0	0.974	461.1	6.537
550	476.7	0.989	510.3	6.705	357.6	0.989	510.2	6.631
600	520.0	1.004	560.1	6.792	390.1	1.004	560.0	6.717
650	563.4	1.018	610.6	6.873	422.7	1.018	610.6	6.798
700	606.8	1.031	661.8	6.949	455.2	1.032	661.8	6.874
750	650.1	1.044	713.7	7.021	487.7	1.044	713.7	6.946
800	693.4	1.055	766.2	7.089	520.2	1.055	766.2	7.013
850	736.8	1.065	819.2	7.153	552.7	1.065	819.3	7.078
900	780.1	1.074	872.7	7.214	585.2	1.074	872.7	7.139
950	823.4	1.082	926.6	7.272	617.7	1.083	926.6	7.197
1000	866.7	1.090	980.9	7.328	650.2	1.090	980.9	7.253
1050	910.1	1.097	1035.6	7.381	682.7	1.097	1035.6	7.307
1100	953.4	1.104	1090.6	7.432	715.2	1.104	1090.7	7.358
1150	996.7	1.110	1146.0	7.481	747.7	1.110	1146.0	7.407
1200	1040	1.115	1201.6	7.528	780.2	1.115	1201.6	7.454
1250	1083	1.120	1257.5	7.574	812.7	1.120	1257.5	7.500
1300	1126	1.125	1313.6	7.618	845.2	1.125	1313.7	7.544
	$p=5$ bar				$p=6$ bar			
75	0.8290	1.567	−157.3	2.652				
80	0.8445	1.588	−149.4	2.752				
85	0.8611	1.605	−141.4	2.847				
90	0.8791	1.623	−133.5	2.938				
95	0.8686	1.643	−125.2	3.028				
100	0.9199	1.669	−117.0	3.112				

continued

T, °K	v	c_p	i	s	v	c_p	i	s
105	0.9434	1.704	−108.5	3.195				
110	51.51	1.066	91.6	5.036				
115	54.62	1.036	96.9	5.083	44.57	1.069	95.2	5.026
120	57.66	1.017	102.0	5.127	47.20	1.044	100.5	5.071
125	60.65	1.004	107.1	5.168	49.77	1.027	105.7	5.113
130	63.59	0.994	112.1	5.207	52.29	1.014	110.8	5.153
135	66.50	0.986	117.0	5.244	54.77	1.004	115.8	5.191
140	69.37	0.979	121.9	5.280	57.22	0.995	120.8	5.228
145	72.22	0.973	126.8	5.314	59.64	0.988	125.8	5.263
150	75.04	0.968	131.7	5.347	62.03	0.981	130.7	5.296
155	77.84	0.963	136.5	5.379	64.40	0.975	135.6	5.328
160	80.62	0.958	141.3	5.410	66.75	0.969	140.5	5.359
165	83.38	0.954	146.1	5.439	69.08	0.964	145.3	5.388
170	86.13	0.951	150.8	5.467	71.40	0.960	150.1	5.417
180	91.60	0.944	160.3	5.522	76.00	0.952	159.7	5.472
190	97.02	0.939	169.7	5.573	80.56	0.945	169.2	5.523
200	102.4	0.935	179.1	5.621	85.09	0.940	178.6	5.571
210	107.8	0.932	188.4	5.666	89.59	0.936	188.0	5.617
220	113.1	0.929	197.7	5.709	94.07	0.933	197.3	5.661
230	118.4	0.927	207.0	5.750	98.53	0.931	206.6	5.702
240	123.8	0.926	216.3	5.790	103.0	0.929	215.9	5.742
250	129.1	0.925	225.5	5.828	107.4	0.928	225.2	5.780
260	134.3	0.925	234.8	5.864	111.8	0.927	234.5	5.816
270	139.6	0.924	244.0	5.899	116.2	0.926	243.7	5.851
280	144.9	0.925	253.3	5.933	120.7	0.926	253.0	5.885
290	150.2	0.925	262.5	5.965	125.1	0.927	262.3	5.917
300	155.4	0.926	271.8	5.996	129.5	0.927	271.5	5.948
310	160.7	0.927	281.0	6.026	133.9	0.928	280.8	5.978
320	165.9	0.928	290.3	6.056	138.2	0.929	290.1	6.008
330	171.2	0.930	299.6	6.085	142.6	0.931	299.4	6.037
340	176.4	0.931	308.9	6.113	147.0	0.932	308.7	6.065
350	181.7	0.933	318.2	6.140	151.4	0.934	318.1	6.092
375	194.8	0.938	341.6	6.204	162.3	0.939	341.5	6.156
400	207.9	0.945	365.2	6.265	173.2	0.945	365.0	6.217
425	220.9	0.950	388.9	6.323	184.1	0.952	388.7	6.275
450	234.0	0.959	412.7	6.377	195.0	0.959	412.6	6.330
475	247.0	0.966	436.8	6.429	205.9	0.967	436.7	6.382
500	260.1	0.974	461.1	6.479	216.8	0.975	461.0	6.431
550	286.1	0.989	510.2	6.572	238.5	0.990	510.1	6.525
600	312.2	1.004	560.0	6.659	260.2	1.005	560.0	6.612
650	338.2	1.019	610.6	6.740	281.9	1.019	610.6	6.693
700	364.3	1.032	661.8	6.816	303.6	1.032	661.8	6.769
750	390.3	1.044	713.7	6.888	325.3	1.044	713.7	6.840
800	416.3	1.055	766.2	6.956	347.0	1.055	766.2	6.908
850	442.3	1.065	819.2	7.020	368.7	1.065	819.3	6.972
900	468.3	1.074	872.7	7.081	390.4	1.074	872.8	7.033
950	494.3	1.083	926.7	7.139	412.0	1.083	926.7	7.092
1000	520.3	1.090	981.0	7.195	433.7	1.090	981.0	7.148
1050	546.3	1.097	1035.7	7.249	455.4	1.097	1035.7	7.201
1100	572.3	1.104	1090.7	7.300	477.0	1.104	1090.8	7.252
1150	598.3	1.110	1146.1	7.349	498.7	1.110	1146.1	7.301
1200	624.3	1.115	1201.7	7.396	520.3	1.115	1201.7	7.348
1250	650.3	1.120	1257.6	7.442	542.0	1.120	1257.6	7.394
1300	676.3	1.125	1313.7	7.486	563.7	1.125	1313.8	7.438
	$p=8$ bar				$p=10$ bar			
75					0.8284	1.566	−157.0	2.650
80					0.8439	1.586	−149.1	2.751
85					0.8604	1.603	−141.2	2.846
90					0.8782	1.620	−133.2	2.937
95					0.8976	1.640	−125.0	3.026
100					0.9187	1.665	−116.7	3.110
105					0.9419	1.699	−108.3	3.193
110					0.9678	1.745	− 99.7	3.273

continued

T, °K	v	c_p	i	s	v	c_p	i	s
115					0.9973	1.809	− 90.8	3.352
120	34.06	1.107	97.4	4.978	26.09	1.186	94.0	4.900
125	36.13	1.080	102.9	5.023	27.88	1.143	99.8	4.948
130	38.13	1.060	108.2	5.065	29.59	1.112	105.5	4.992
135	40.09	1.043	113.4	5.104	31.24	1.088	111.0	5.034
140	42.01	1.030	118.6	5.142	32.86	1.069	116.3	5.073
145	43.90	1.018	123.8	5.178	34.43	1.052	121.6	5.110
150	45.76	1.008	128.8	5.212	35.97	1.038	126.9	5.145
155	47.59	0.999	133.8	5.245	37.49	1.026	132.0	5.179
160	49.40	0.991	138.8	5.277	38.99	1.015	137.1	5.211
165	51.20	0.984	143.8	5.307	40.46	1.005	142.2	5.242
170	52.98	0.978	148.7	5.336	41.92	0.997	147.2	5.272
180	56.50	0.967	158.4	5.392	44.80	0.982	157.1	5.329
190	59.98	0.958	168.0	5.444	47.63	0.971	166.8	5.382
200	63.43	0.951	177.5	5.493	50.43	0.962	176.5	5.431
210	66.85	0.945	187.0	5.539	53.20	0.954	186.1	5.478
220	70.25	0.941	196.4	5.583	55.95	0.949	195.6	5.522
230	73.63	0.937	205.8	5.625	58.98	0.944	205.1	5.564
240	76.99	0.935	215.2	5.665	61.40	0.941	214.5	5.604
250	80.34	0.933	224.5	5.703	64.11	0.938	223.9	5.643
260	83.69	0.931	233.9	5.739	66.80	0.936	233.2	5.680
270	87.02	0.931	243.2	5.774	69.48	0.935	242.6	5.715
280	90.35	0.930	252.5	5.808	72.16	0.934	251.9	5.749
290	93.67	0.930	261.8	5.841	74.83	0.933	261.3	5.781
300	96.98	0.930	271.1	5.872	77.49	0.933	270.6	5.813
310	100.3	0.931	280.4	5.903	80.15	0.934	280.0	5.844
320	103.6	0.932	289.7	5.933	82.81	0.934	289.3	5.874
330	106.9	0.933	299.0	5.961	85.46	0.936	298.6	5.902
340	110.2	0.934	308.4	5.989	88.11	0.937	308.0	5.930
350	113.5	0.936	317.7	6.016	90.75	0.938	317.4	5.957
375	121.7	0.941	341.2	6.081	97.35	0.943	340.9	6.022
400	129.9	0.947	364.8	6.142	103.9	0.946	354.5	6.083
425	138.1	0.954	388.5	6.200	110.5	0.955	388.3	6.141
450	146.3	0.961	412.5	6.254	117.1	0.962	412.3	6.196
475	154.5	0.968	436.6	6.306	123.6	0.969	436.4	6.248
500	162.6	0.975	460.8	6.356	130.2	0.976	460.7	6.298
550	179.0	0.990	510.0	6.450	143.2	0.991	509.9	6.392
600	195.3	1.005	559.9	6.537	156.3	1.006	559.8	6.479
650	211.6	1.019	610.5	6.618	169.3	1.020	610.5	6.560
700	227.8	1.033	661.8	6.694	182.4	1.033	661.8	6.635
750	244.1	1.045	713.7	6.765	195.4	1.045	713.8	6.707
800	260.4	1.056	766.3	6.833	208.4	1.056	766.3	6.775
850	276.7	1.066	819.3	6.898	221.4	1.066	819.3	6.839
900	292.9	1.075	872.8	6.959	234.5	1.075	872.8	6.900
950	309.2	1.083	926.7	7.017	247.5	1.083	926.8	6.959
1000	325.4	1.091	981.1	7.073	260.5	1.091	981.2	7.015
1050	341.7	1.098	1035.8	7.126	273.5	1.098	1035.9	7.068
1100	357.9	1.104	1090.8	7.177	286.5	1.104	1090.9	7.119
1150	374.2	1.110	1146.2	7.226	299.5	1.110	1146.3	7.169
1200	390.4	1.115	1201.8	7.274	312.5	1.116	1201.9	7.216
1250	406.7	1.120	1257.7	7.320	325.5	1.121	1257.8	7.261
1300	422.9	1.125	1313.9	7.364	338.5	1.125	1314.0	7.305
		$p=15$ bar				$p=20$ bar		
75	0.8278	1.565	−156.7	2.649	0.8272	1.563	−156.4	2.647
80	0.8432	1.584	−148.8	2.749	0.8425	1.582	−148.5	2.748
85	0.8596	1.601	−140.9	2.844	0.8589	1.599	−140.6	2.842
90	0.8774	1.618	−132.9	2.935	0.8765	1.615	−132.7	2.933
95	0.8966	1.637	−124.7	3.024	0.8956	1.633	−124.4	3.022
100	0.9175	1.661	−116.5	3.107	0.9163	1.657	−116.3	3.105
105	0.9405	1.693	−108.1	3.191	0.9405	1.688	−107.9	3.188
110	0.9661	1.738	− 99.6	3.271	0.9661	1.731	− 99.4	3.268
115	0.9950	1.799	− 90.7	3.349	0.9950	1.788	− 90.6	3.346
120	1.0285	1.881	− 81.5	3.428	1.0285	1.866	− 81.4	3.425

continued

T, °K	v	c_p	i	s	v	c_p	i	s
125	1.0685	1.997	− 71.8	3.509	1.0685	1.973	− 71.8	3.504
130	18.02	1.296	97.7	4.844	1.1128	2.127	− 61.6	3.585
135	19.33	1.238	104.0	4.892	13.17	1.493	95.9	4.772
140	20.56	1.191	110.1	4.936	14.28	1.377	103.0	4.824
145	21.74	1.155	116.0	4.977	15.30	1.299	109.7	4.871
150	22.88	1.126	121.7	5.016	16.26	1.241	116.0	4.914
155	23.99	1.102	127.3	5.052	17.18	1.197	122.1	4.954
160	25.07	1.081	132.7	5.087	18.06	1.162	128.0	4.991
165	26.12	1.064	138.1	5.120	18.92	1.133	138.8	5.026
170	27.15	1.049	143.4	5.151	19.75	1.109	139.4	5.060
180	29.16	1.024	153.8	5.210	21.36	1.071	150.3	5.122
190	31.30	1.005	163.9	5.265	22.91	1.042	160.8	5.179
200	33.25	0.990	173.8	5.317	24.42	1.020	171.1	5.232
210	35.17	0.978	183.7	5.365	25.91	1.003	181.2	5.281
220	37.06	0.969	193.4	5.410	27.36	0.990	191.2	5.328
230	38.94	0.961	203.1	5.453	28.80	0.979	201.1	5.372
240	40.79	0.956	212.6	5.494	30.22	0.971	210.8	5.413
250	42.64	0.951	222.1	5.533	31.62	0.965	220.5	5.452
260	44.47	0.947	231.7	5.570	32.02	0.960	230.1	5.490
270	46.30	0.945	241.2	5.606	34.41	0.956	239.7	5.526
280	48.12	0.943	250.6	5.640	35.78	0.953	249.2	5.561
290	49.93	0.942	260.0	5.673	37.15	0.951	258.7	5.595
300	51.74	0.941	269.4	5.705	38.52	0.949	268.2	5.627
310	53.54	0.940	278.8	5.736	39.88	0.948	277.7	5.658
320	55.54	0.941	288.2	5.766	41.24	0.948	287.2	5.688
330	57.13	0.941	297.7	5.795	42.59	0.948	296.7	5.717
340	58.92	0.942	307.1	5.823	43.94	0.948	306.2	5.745
350	60.71	0.943	316.5	5.850	45.29	0.949	315.6	5.773
375	65.16	0.947	340.2	5.915	48.63	0.952	339.4	5.838
400	69.60	0.952	363.8	5.976	51.96	0.956	363.2	5.900
425	74.02	0.958	387.7	6.034	55.29	0.961	387.2	5.958
450	78.43	0.964	411.8	6.089	58.60	0.967	411.3	6.013
475	82.84	0.971	436.0	6.142	61.90	0.974	435.6	6.066
500	87.24	0.978	460.3	6.192	65.20	0.981	460.0	6.116
550	96.02	0.993	509.6	6.286	71.78	0.995	509.4	6.210
600	104.8	1.007	559.6	6.373	78.35	1.009	559.5	6.297
650	113.5	1.021	610.4	6.454	84.90	1.022	610.3	6.379
700	123.3	1.034	661.8	6.530	91.44	1.035	661.7	6.455
750	131.0	1.046	713.8	6.602	97.97	1.047	713.8	6.526
800	139.7	1.056	766.3	6.670	104.5	1.057	766.4	6.594
850	148.4	1.066	819.4	6.734	111.0	1.067	819.5	6.659
900	157.2	1.075	872.9	6.795	117.5	1.076	873.1	6.720
950	165.9	1.083	926.9	6.853	124.1	1.084	927.1	6.778
1000	174.6	1.091	981.3	6.919	130.6	1.092	981.5	6.834
1050	183.3	1.098	1036.0	6.963	137.1	1.099	1036.2	6.888
1100	192.0	1.104	1091.1	7.014	143.6	1.105	1091.3	6.939
1150	200.7	1.110	1146.5	7.063	150.1	1.111	1146.7	6.988
1200	209.5	1.116	1202.1	7.111	156.6	1.116	1202.4	7.035
1250	218.2	1.121	1258.0	7.156	163.1	1.121	1258.8	7.081
1300	226.9	1.126	1314.2	7.200	169.6	1.126	1314.5	7.125
	$p=25$ bar				$p=30$ bar			
75	0.8266	1.562	−156.1	2.646	0.8260	1.561	−155.7	2.644
80	0.8419	1.581	−148.2	2.746	0.8412	1.579	−148.0	2.745
85	0.8582	1.596	−140.3	2.841	0.8575	1.594	−140.0	2.839
90	0.8757	1.613	−132.4	2.931	0.8749	1.610	−132.1	2.929
95	0.8946	1.630	−124.2	3.020	0.8937	1.627	−123.9	3.018
100	0.9152	1.653	−116.0	3.103	0.9141	1.649	−115.8	3.101
105	0.9377	1.683	−107.7	3.186	0.9364	1.678	−107.5	3.183
110	0.9627	1.724	− 99.2	3.265	0.9610	1.717	− 99.0	3.263
115	0.9907	1.779	− 90.4	3.343	0.9887	1.770	− 90.2	3.340
120	1.0229	1.852	− 81.4	3.421	1.0202	1.839	− 81.3	3.418
125	1.0608	1.952	− 71.8	3.500	1.0572	1.932	− 71.8	3.496
130	1.1072	2.091	− 61.7	3.580	1.1021	2.058	− 61.8	3.575

continued

T, °K	v	c_p	i	s	v	c_p	i	s
135	1.1675	2.305	− 50.8	3.663	1.1593	2.243	− 51.2	3.656
140	10.33	1.710	94.4	4.719	1.2389	2.564	− 39.2	3.744
145	11.32	1.520	102.4	4.775	8.528	1.927	93.6	4.680
150	12.22	1.403	109.7	4.825	9.437	1.652	102.5	4.740
155	13.05	1.323	116.5	4.869	10.23	1.497	110.3	4.792
160	13.83	1.263	123.0	4.910	10.96	1.394	117.5	4.838
165	14.57	1.217	129.2	4.948	11.64	1.320	124.3	4.879
170	15.29	1.179	135.2	4.984	12.29	1.264	130.7	4.918
180	16.65	1.123	146.7	5.050	13.51	1.183	142.9	4.988
190	17.96	1.083	157.7	5.109	14.65	1.128	154.5	5.050
200	19.22	1.053	168.4	5.164	15.74	1.088	165.6	5.107
210	20.44	1.030	178.8	5.215	16.80	1.058	176.3	5.159
220	21.64	1.012	189.0	5.262	17.83	1.035	186.7	5.208
230	22.82	0.998	199.0	5.307	18.83	1.018	197.0	5.253
240	23.98	0.987	209.0	5.350	19.82	1.004	207.1	5.296
250	25.13	0.979	218.8	5.390	20.80	0.993	217.1	5.337
260	26.26	0.972	228.5	5.428	21.76	0.985	227.0	5.376
270	27.39	0.967	238.2	5.464	22.71	0.978	236.8	5.413
280	28.51	0.962	247.9	5.499	23.66	0.972	246.5	5.448
290	29.62	0.959	257.5	5.533	24.60	0.968	256.2	5.482
300	30.73	0.957	267.1	5.566	25.53	0.965	265.9	5.515
310	31.83	0.955	276.6	5.597	26.46	0.963	275.5	5.547
320	32.92	0.954	286.2	5.627	27.38	0.961	285.1	5.578
330	31.01	0.954	295.7	5.657	28.30	0.960	294.7	5.607
340	35.10	0.954	305.2	5.685	29.22	0.959	304.3	5.635
350	36.19	0.954	314.8	5.713	30.13	0.959	313.9	5.663
375	38.89	0.956	338.7	5.779	32.39	0.960	337.9	5.729
400	41.57	0.960	362.6	5.841	34.64	0.963	362.0	5.791
425	44.24	0.965	386.6	5.899	36.88	0.968	386.1	5.850
450	46.90	0.970	410.8	5.954	39.11	0.973	410.4	5.905
475	49.56	0.976	435.2	6.007	41.33	0.979	434.8	5.958
500	52.21	0.983	459.7	6.057	43.55	0.986	459.3	6.009
550	57.49	0.997	509.1	6.152	47.96	0.999	508.9	6.104
600	62.76	1.011	559.3	6.239	52.36	1.012	559.2	6.191
650	68.01	1.024	610.2	6.320	56.75	1.025	610.1	6.272
700	73.25	1.036	661.7	6.396	61.12	1.037	661.6	6.348
750	78.48	1.048	713.8	6.468	65.49	1.049	713.8	6.420
800	83.71	1.058	766.4	6.536	69.85	1.059	766.5	6.488
850	88.93	1.068	819.6	6.601	74.21	1.068	819.7	6.553
900	94.15	1.077	873.2	6.662	78.56	1.077	873.3	6.614
950	99.37	1.085	927.2	6.720	82.91	1.085	927.4	6.673
1000	104.6	1.092	981.7	6.776	87.26	1.092	981.8	6.729
1050	109.8	1.099	1036.5	6.830	91.61	1.099	1036.6	6.782
1100	115.0	1.105	1091.6	6.881	95.95	1.105	1091.8	6.833
1150	120.2	1.111	1147.0	6.930	100.3	1.111	1147.2	6.882
1200	125.4	1.116	1202.7	6.977	104.6	1.117	1202.9	6.930
1250	130.6	1.121	1258.6	7.023	109.0	1.122	1258.8	6.976
1300	135.8	1.126	1314.8	7.067	113.3	1.126	1315.0	7.020
	$p=35$ bar				$p=40$ bar			
75	0.8255	1.560	−155.5	2.643	0.8249	1.558	−155.2	2.641
80	0.8406	1.577	−147.7	2.743	0.8400	1.576	−147.4	2.741
85	0.8567	1.592	−139.7	2.837	0.8560	1.590	−139.5	2.836
90	0.8741	1.608	−131.8	2.928	0.8733	1.605	−131.6	2.926
95	0.8927	1.624	−123.6	3.016	0.8918	1.621	−123.4	3.014
100	0.9130	1.645	−115.5	3.099	0.9119	1.641	−115.2	3.097
105	0.9350	1.673	−107.2	3.181	0.9337	1.668	−107.0	3.179
110	0.9594	1.711	− 98.8	3.260	0.9578	1.705	− 98.6	3.258
115	0.9866	1.761	− 90.1	3.337	0.9847	1.753	− 89.9	3.334
120	1.0176	1.827	− 81.2	3.415	1.0151	1.815	− 81.0	3.411
125	1.0537	1.913	− 71.8	3.492	1.0504	1.896	− 71.7	3.486
130	1.0971	2.028	− 61.9	3.570	1.0925	2.001	− 62.0	3.565
135	1.1517	2.190	− 51.4	3.650	1.1447	2.144	− 51.7	3.644

continued

T, °K	v	c_p	i	s	v	c_p	i	s
140	1.2254	2.456	− 39.9	3.734	1.2135	2.377	− 40.5	3.726
145	1.3402	3.190	− 26.1	3.831	1.3143	2.918	− 27.4	3.817
150	7.330	2.105	93.6	4.653	5.537	3.309	81.4	4.551
155	8.159	1.759	103.1	4.716	6.516	2.213	94.6	4.637
160	8.877	1.572	111.5	4.769	7.266	1.830	104.5	4.700
165	9.528	1.451	119.1	4.815	7.913	1.624	113.1	4.753
170	10.13	1.366	126.1	4.857	8.497	1.493	120.9	4.800
180	11.25	1.251	139.0	4.932	9.549	1.330	134.9	4.880
190	12.28	1.177	151.2	4.997	10.50	1.232	147.7	4.949
200	13.26	1.126	162.7	5.056	11.39	1.167	159.7	5.011
210	14.19	1.088	173.7	5.110	12.24	1.120	171.1	5.066
220	15.10	1.060	184.4	5.160	13.06	1.085	182.1	5.117
230	15.99	1.038	194.9	5.207	13.86	1.059	192.8	5.165
240	16.86	1.021	205.2	5.251	14.63	1.039	203.3	5.210
250	17.71	1.008	215.4	5.292	15.39	1.023	213.6	5.252
260	18.55	0.997	225.4	5.331	16.14	1.010	223.8	5.292
270	19.38	0.989	235.3	5.368	16.88	1.000	233.9	5.330
280	20.20	0.982	245.2	5.404	17.61	0.992	243.8	5.366
290	21.01	0.977	255.0	5.439	18.33	0.986	253.7	5.401
300	21.82	0.973	264.7	5.472	19.04	0.981	263.5	5.434
310	22.63	0.970	274.4	5.504	19.75	0.977	273.3	5.466
320	23.43	0.968	284.1	5.534	20.46	0.974	283.1	5.497
330	24.22	0.966	293.8	5.564	21.16	0.972	292.8	5.527
340	25.01	0.965	303.5	5.593	21.86	0.970	302.5	5.556
350	25.80	0.964	313.1	5.621	22.55	0.969	312.2	5.584
375	27.75	0.965	337.2	5.688	24.28	0.969	336.4	5.651
400	29.70	0.967	361.3	5.750	25.99	0.971	360.7	5.714
425	31.63	0.971	385.5	5.809	27.68	0.974	385.0	5.773
450	33.55	0.976	409.8	5.864	29.37	0.979	409.4	5.828
475	35.46	0.982	434.3	5.917	31.05	0.984	433.9	5.881
500	37.36	0.988	459.0	5.967	32.72	0.990	458.6	5.932
550	41.16	1.000	508.7	6.062	36.05	1.002	508.4	6.027
600	44.94	1.013	559.0	6.150	39.37	1.015	558.8	6.115
650	48.70	1.026	610.0	6.232	42.67	1.027	609.9	6.197
700	52.46	1.038	661.6	6.308	45.96	1.039	661.6	6.273
750	56.21	1.049	713.8	6.380	49.25	1.050	713.8	6.345
800	59.95	1.060	766.6	6.448	52.53	1.060	766.6	6.413
850	63.69	1.069	819.8	6.513	55.80	1.069	819.9	6.478
900	67.43	1.078	873.4	6.574	59.07	1.078	873.6	6.539
950	71.16	1.086	927.5	6.633	62.34	1.086	927.7	6.598
1000	74.89	1.093	982.0	6.689	65.61	1.093	982.2	6.654
1050	78.62	1.100	1036.8	6.742	68.87	1.100	1037.0	6.707
1100	82.34	1.106	1092.0	6.793	72.13	1.106	1092.2	6.758
1150	86.06	1.112	1147.4	6.842	75.39	1.112	1147.6	6.807
1200	89.78	1.117	1203.1	6.890	78.65	1.117	1203.3	6.855
1250	93.50	1.122	1259.1	6.936	81.90	1.122	1259.3	6.901
1300	97.22	1.127	1315.3	6.980	85.15	1.127	1315.6	6.945
	$p = 45$ bar				$p = 50$ bar			
75	0.8243	1.557	−154.9	2.640	0.8238	1.556	− 154.5	2.638
80	0.8393	1.574	−147.1	2.740	0.8387	1.572	− 146.7	2.738
85	0.8553	1.588	−139.2	2.834	0.8546	1.587	− 138.9	2.832
90	0.8723	1.603	−131.2	2.924	0.8717	1.601	− 131.0	2.922
95	0.8909	1.618	−123.1	3.012	0.8900	1.616	− 122.8	3.010
100	0.9108	1.638	−115.0	3.095	0.9097	1.635	− 114.7	3.093
105	0.9325	1.664	−106.8	3.176	0.9312	1.659	− 106.6	3.174
110	0.9568	1.699	− 98.4	3.225	0.9547	1.693	− 98.2	3.253
115	0.9827	1.745	− 89.8	3.332	0.9809	1.737	− 89.6	3.329
120	1.0121	1.804	− 80.9	3.408	1.0103	1.793	− 80.8	3.405
125	1.0472	1.880	− 71.7	3.484	1.0441	1.864	− 71.6	3.481
130	1.0880	1.976	− 62.0	3.561	1.0838	1.954	− 62.1	3.556
135	1.1382	2.103	− 51.9	3.638	1.1321	2.067	− 52.1	3.632

continued

T, °K	v	c_p	i	s	v	c_p	i	s
140	1.2028	2.310	− 41.0	3.718	1.1932	2.253	− 41.3	3.711
145	1.2935	2.734	− 28.5	3.805	1.2761	2.596	− 29.4	3.795
150	1.4436	3.596	− 13.0	3.911	1.4026	3.251	− 15.0	3.892
155	5.096	3.244	83.3	4.546	3.577	9.846	63.1	4.401
160	5.955	2.244	96.5	4.630	4.822	3.025	86.5	4.551
165	6.626	1.864	106.7	4.692	5.560	2.215	99.3	4.629
170	7.206	1.654	115.4	4.744	6.155	1.865	109.4	4.689
180	8.220	1.422	130.7	4.832	7.150	1.530	126.2	4.785
190	9.118	1.293	144.2	4.905	8.007	1.361	140.5	4.863
200	9.946	1.211	156.7	4.969	8.787	1.259	153.6	4.930
210	10.73	1.154	168.5	5.027	9.515	1.189	165.8	4.990
220	11.48	1.112	179.8	5.079	10.21	1.140	177.5	5.044
230	12.20	1.081	190.8	5.128	10.88	1.103	188.7	5.094
240	12.90	1.057	201.5	5.173	11.52	1.075	199.6	5.140
250	13.59	1.038	211.9	5.215	12.15	1.054	210.2	5.183
260	14.27	1.023	222.2	5.257	12.77	1.037	220.6	5.224
270	14.93	1.011	232.4	5.295	13.38	1.023	230.9	5.263
280	15.59	1.002	242.5	5.332	13.98	1.013	241.1	5.300
290	16.24	0.995	252.5	5.367	14.57	1.004	251.2	5.336
300	16.88	0.989	262.4	5.401	15.16	0.997	261.2	5.370
310	17.52	0.984	272.2	5.433	15.74	0.992	271.1	5.403
320	18.15	0.981	282.0	5.464	16.31	0.987	281.0	5.434
330	18.78	0.978	291.8	5.494	16.88	0.984	290.9	5.464
340	19.41	0.976	301.6	5.523	17.45	0.982	300.7	5.493
350	20.03	0.975	311.4	5.551	18.01	0.980	310.5	5.522
375	21.57	0.973	335.7	5.618	19.41	0.978	335.0	5.589
400	23.10	0.975	360.1	5.681	20.80	0.978	359.4	5.652
425	24.62	0.977	384.5	5.741	22.17	0.981	383.9	5.712
450	26.12	0.982	408.9	5.797	23.53	0.984	408.5	5.768
475	27.62	0.987	433.5	5.850	24.88	0.989	433.2	5.821
500	29.12	0.992	458.3	5.900	26.23	0.994	457.9	5.872
550	32.09	1.004	508.2	5.995	28.91	1.006	507.9	5.967
600	35.04	1.017	558.7	6.083	31.58	1.018	558.6	6.055
650	37.98	1.029	609.8	6.165	34.23	1.030	609.7	6.137
700	40.91	1.040	661.5	6.242	36.87	1.041	661.5	6.214
750	43.84	1.051	713.8	6.314	39.51	1.052	713.8	6.286
800	46.76	1.061	766.6	6.382	42.14	1.062	766.7	6.354
850	49.67	1.070	819.9	6.447	44.76	1.071	820.0	6.419
900	52.58	1.079	873.7	6.508	47.38	1.079	873.8	6.481
950	55.49	1.087	927.8	6.567	50.00	1.087	928.0	6.539
1000	58.39	1.094	982.3	6.623	52.62	1.094	982.5	6.595
1050	61.29	1.100	1037.2	6.677	55.23	1.101	1037.4	6.649
1100	64.19	1.106	1092.4	6.728	57.84	1.107	1092.6	6.700
1150	67.09	1.112	1147.9	6.777	60.45	1.113	1148.1	6.749
1200	69.98	1.117	1203.6	6.824	63.06	1.118	1203.8	6.797
1250	72.88	1.122	1259.6	6.870	65.66	1.123	1259.8	6.843
1300	75.78	1.127	1315.7	6.914	68.26	1.127	1316.1	6.887
	$p=60$ bar				$p=80$ bar			
75	0.8226	1.554	−153.9	2.635	0.8205	1.549	−152.8	2.630
80	0.8375	1.569	−146.2	2.735	0.8351	1.564	−145.0	2.729
85	0.8533	1.583	−138.3	2.829	0.8506	1.575	−137.4	2.823
90	0.8701	1.596	−130.5	2.919	0.8671	1.588	−129.3	2.912
95	0.8882	1.610	−122.4	3.006	0.8848	1.600	−121.3	2.999
100	0.9077	1.628	−114.3	3.089	0.9037	1.616	−113.3	3.081
105	0.9287	1.651	−106.1	3.170	0.9240	1.636	−105.1	3.161
110	0.9518	1.682	− 97.8	3.248	0.9462	1.662	− 96.9	3.238
115	0.9772	1.722	− 89.2	3.323	0.9704	1.697	− 88.5	3.313
120	1.006	1.773	− 80.5	3.399	0.9972	1.739	− 79.9	3.387
125	1.038	1.837	− 71.5	3.474	1.027	1.790	− 71.1	3.460
130	1.076	1.913	− 62.1	3.548	1.062	1.848	− 62.0	3.532
135	1.121	2.006	− 52.3	3.622	1.102	1.912	− 52.6	3.604
140	1.176	2.159	− 42.0	3.698	1.149	2.017	− 42.9	3.675

continued

T, °K	v	c_p	i	s	v	c_p	i	s
145	1.248	2.404	− 30.8	3.777	1.206	2.174	− 32.5	3.748
150	1.374	2.825	− 17.8	3.865	1.279	2.412	− 21.0	3.826
155	1.533	4.791	2.5	4.009	1.375	2.777	− 7.2	3.921
160	2.581	11.705	48.5	4.290	1.543	3.648	10.1	4.034
165	3.823	3.772	80.1	4.484	1.871	4.951	31.9	4.170
170	4.520	2.553	95.3	4.575	2.413	4.780	57.0	4.311
180	5.531	1.809	116.4	4.696	3.481	2.716	93.3	4.519
190	6.339	1.522	132.9	4.785	4.259	1.960	116.1	4.642
200	7.050	1.366	147.2	4.859	4.894	1.631	133.8	4.733
210	7.701	1.267	160.4	4.923	5.453	1.448	149.1	4.808
220	8.312	1.200	172.7	4.981	5.963	1.333	163.0	4.873
230	8.895	1.151	184.4	5.033	6.441	1.254	175.9	4.930
240	9.457	1.114	195.7	5.081	6.896	1.197	188.1	4.982
250	10.00	1.086	206.7	5.126	7.332	1.154	199.9	5.030
260	10.53	1.064	217.5	5.168	7.755	1.121	211.3	5.075
270	11.05	1.047	228.0	5.208	8.166	1.096	222.4	5.117
280	11.56	1.033	238.4	5.246	8.568	1.076	233.2	5.156
290	12.07	1.022	248.7	5.282	8.963	1.059	243.9	5.193
300	12.57	1.013	258.9	5.316	9.351	1.046	254.4	5.229
310	13.06	1.006	269.0	5.349	9.733	1.036	264.8	5.263
320	13.55	1.001	279.0	5.381	10.11	1.027	275.1	5.296
330	14.03	0.997	289.0	5.412	10.49	1.020	285.3	5.328
340	14.51	0.993	299.0	5.441	10.86	1.015	295.5	5.358
350	14.99	0.989	308.9	5.470	11.22	1.010	305.7	5.387
375	16.17	0.986	333.6	5.538	12.13	1.003	330.8	5.456
400	17.34	0.986	358.2	5.602	13.02	1.000	355.8	5.521
425	18.49	0.987	382.9	5.662	13.90	0.999	380.8	5.582
450	19.63	0.990	407.6	5.718	14.77	1.001	405.8	5.639
475	20.77	0.994	432.4	5.772	15.64	1.003	430.9	5.693
500	21.90	0.999	457.3	5.823	16.50	1.007	456.0	5.745
550	24.15	1.009	507.5	5.919	18.20	1.016	506.5	5.841
600	26.38	1.021	558.2	6.007	19.89	1.026	557.6	5.930
650	28.60	1.032	609.5	6.089	21.56	1.037	609.2	6.013
700	30.81	1.043	661.4	6.166	23.23	1.047	661.3	6.090
750	33.01	1.054	713.9	6.238	24.89	1.057	713.9	6.162
800	35.21	1.064	766.8	6.306	26.55	1.066	767.0	6.231
850	37.40	1.073	820.2	6.371	28.20	1.075	820.6	6.296
900	39.59	1.081	874.0	6.433	29.84	1.083	874.5	6.357
950	41.77	1.088	928.3	6.492	31.48	1.090	928.8	6.416
1000	43.95	1.095	982.9	6.548	33.12	1.097	983.5	6.472
1050	46.13	1.102	1037.8	6.602	34.76	1.103	1038.5	6.526
1100	48.31	1.108	1093.0	6.653	36.40	1.109	1093.8	6.578
1150	50.49	1.113	1148.5	6.702	38.04	1.114	1149.4	6.627
1200	52.67	1.118	1204.3	6.749	39.67	1.119	1205.2	6.674
1250	54.84	1.123	1260.3	6.795	41.30	1.124	1261.3	6.720
1300	57.01	1.128	1316.6	6.839	42.93	1.129	1317.7	6.764
	$p = 100$ bar				$p = 150$ bar			
75	0.8184	1.545	−151.6	2.624	0.8134	1.536	−148.5	2.610
80	0.8324	1.558	−143.8	2.723	0.8274	1.546	−140.8	2.709
85	0.8481	1.569	−136.0	2.816	0.8420	1.555	−133.1	2.801
90	0.8642	1.580	−128.1	2.905	0.8575	1.563	−125.3	2.889
95	0.8815	1.591	−120.2	2.992	0.8738	1.571	−117.4	2.974
100	0.8999	1.604	−112.2	3.073	0.8911	1.581	−109.6	3.056
105	0.9196	1.622	−104.2	3.153	0.9095	1.593	−101.6	3.133
110	0.9409	1.645	− 96.0	3.229	0.9290	1.609	− 93.7	3.208
115	0.9641	1.674	− 87.7	3.303	0.9500	1.630	− 85.6	3.280
120	0.9895	1.710	− 79.3	3.376	0.9727	1.654	− 77.4	3.351
125	1.0178	1.751	− 70.6	3.448	0.9973	1.680	− 69.0	3.420
130	1.0495	1.797	− 61.7	3.518	1.024	1.707	− 60.5	3.487
135	1.0857	1.846	− 52.6	3.587	1.054	1.737	− 52.0	3.553
140	1.1274	1.920	− 43.3	3.656	1.087	1.772	− 43.3	3.617
145	1.1762	2.029	− 33.5	3.725	1.124	1.817	− 34.3	3.680
150	1.2348	2.177	− 22.9	3.796	1.165	1.871	− 24.8	3.744

continued

T, °K	v	c_p	i	s	v	c_p	i	s
155	1.3070	2.365	−11.1	3.874	1.213	1.938	−15.0	3.808
160	1.4044	2.569	2.3	3.961	1.268	2.014	−4.6	3.872
165	1.545	3.094	17.1	4.055	1.331	2.106	6.2	3.940
170	1.759	3.560	34.0	4.152	1.408	2.216	17.7	4.008
180	2.388	3.299	69.4	4.354	1.614	2.493	41.4	4.146
190	3.060	2.462	98.1	4.509	1.892	2.472	66.5	4.282
200	3.636	1.942	119.8	4.621	2.210	2.262	90.3	4.404
210	4.135	1.654	137.7	4.708	2.538	2.013	111.6	4.508
220	4.583	1.480	153.3	4.781	2.858	1.792	130.6	4.596
230	4.996	1.364	167.5	4.844	3.161	1.619	147.6	4.672
240	5.384	1.283	180.7	4.900	3.448	1.490	163.2	4.738
250	5.754	1.224	193.2	4.951	3.720	1.394	177.6	4.797
260	6.109	1.179	205.2	4.998	3.979	1.320	191.1	4.850
270	6.454	1.145	216.8	5.042	4.229	1.264	204.0	4.899
280	6.789	1.118	228.1	5.083	4.471	1.220	216.4	4.944
290	7.117	1.096	239.2	5.122	4.705	1.185	228.4	4.986
300	7.438	1.079	250.1	5.159	4.934	1.157	240.1	5.026
310	7.754	1.065	260.8	5.194	5.158	1.134	251.6	5.063
320	8.065	1.053	271.4	5.228	5.378	1.115	262.8	5.099
330	8.372	1.044	281.9	5.260	5.594	1.100	273.9	5.133
340	8.676	1.036	292.3	5.291	5.807	1.087	284.8	5.166
350	8.976	1.030	302.6	5.321	6.016	1.076	295.6	5.197
375	9.717	1.019	328.2	5.392	6.531	1.057	322.3	5.271
400	10.44	1.013	353.6	5.458	7.033	1.045	348.6	5.339
425	11.16	1.011	378.9	5.519	7.526	1.038	374.6	5.402
450	11.87	1.011	404.1	5.576	8.011	1.034	400.5	5.461
475	12.57	1.012	429.4	5.631	8.490	1.033	426.3	5.517
500	13.26	1.015	454.8	5.683	8.964	1.034	452.2	5.570
550	14.64	1.023	505.7	5.780	9.899	1.038	503.9	5.668
600	16.00	1.032	557.1	5.870	10.82	1.044	555.9	5.759
650	17.35	1.041	608.9	5.953	11.73	1.052	608.3	5.843
700	18.69	1.051	661.2	6.030	12.64	1.060	661.1	5.921
750	20.02	1.060	714.0	6.103	13.54	1.068	714.4	5.995
800	21.35	1.069	767.2	6.172	14.43	1.076	768.0	6.064
850	22.68	1.077	820.9	6.237	15.32	1.083	822.0	6.129
900	24.00	1.085	875.0	6.299	16.21	1.090	876.3	6.191
950	25.32	1.092	929.4	6.358	17.09	1.097	930.9	6.250
1000	26.64	1.099	984.2	6.414	17.97	1.103	985.9	6.307
1050	27.95	1.105	1039.3	6.468	18.25	1.108	1041.2	6.361
1100	29.26	1.110	1094.7	6.519	19.73	1.113	1096.8	6.412
1150	30.57	1.115	1150.3	6.568	20.61	1.118	1152.6	6.462
1200	31.88	1.120	1206.2	6.616	21.49	1.123	1208.6	6.510
1250	33.18	1.125	1262.3	6.662	22.36	1.127	1264.8	6.556
1300	34.48	1.129	1318.7	6.706	23.23	1.132	1321.3	6.600
		$p=200$ bar				$p=300$ bar		
75	0.8088	1.529	−145.5	2.597	0.8004	1.518	−139.4	2.571
80	0.8223	1.536	−137.8	2.695	0.8133	1.520	−131.8	2.668
85	0.8365	1.542	−130.1	2.786	0.8266	1.523	−124.2	2.758
90	0.8513	1.548	−122.5	2.873	0.8403	1.526	−116.6	2.844
95	0.8669	1.554	−114.7	2.958	0.8546	1.529	−108.9	2.927
100	0.8832	1.560	−106.9	3.037	0.8695	1.533	−101.3	3.005
105	0.9005	1.570	−99.1	3.115	0.8849	1.537	−93.6	3.081
110	0.9186	1.582	−91.2	3.189	0.9010	1.543	−86.0	3.154
115	0.9379	1.596	−83.2	3.259	0.9178	1.550	−78.2	3.222
120	0.9585	1.613	−75.2	3.329	0.9354	1.558	−70.4	3.290
125	0.9805	1.631	−67.1	3.396	0.9539	1.567	−62.6	3.354
130	1.0042	1.647	−58.9	3.461	0.9733	1.574	−54.7	3.417
135	1.0298	1.664	−50.6	3.524	0.9938	1.580	−46.9	3.477
140	1.0576	1.684	−42.3	3.585	1.0153	1.587	−39.0	3.535
145	1.0876	1.708	−33.9	3.645	1.0381	1.596	−31.0	3.591
150	1.1206	1.736	−25.0	3.705	1.0623	1.605	−22.8	3.646
155	1.1573	1.767	−15.6	3.764	1.0883	1.616	−13.9	3.701
160	1.1985	1.802	−6.2	3.823	1.1166	1.632	−5.1	3.754

continued

T, °K	v	c_p	i	s	v	c_p	i	s
165	1.244	1.844	3.7	3.881	1.148	1.651	3.4	3.807
170	1.293	1.895	13.3	3.940	1.180	1.674	11.7	3.859
180	1.413	2.032	32.8	4.056	1.251	1.725	28.3	3.958
190	1.565	2.128	53.7	4.169	1.330	1.770	45.7	4.053
200	1.726	2.095	74.5	4.278	1.421	1.796	63.6	4.144
210	1.946	1.983	95.3	4.378	1.522	1.783	81.5	4.232
220	2.155	1.850	114.5	4.467	1.631	1.737	99.1	4.314
230	2.366	1.720	132.3	4.546	1.746	1.674	116.4	4.390
240	2.576	1.605	148.9	4.617	1.865	1.605	132.6	4.459
250	2.781	1.506	164.5	4.681	1.986	1.540	148.3	4.523
260	2.981	1.425	179.1	4.738	2.107	1.480	163.4	4.583
270	3.175	1.359	193.0	4.791	2.229	1.426	177.9	4.637
280	3.364	1.305	206.3	4.839	2.350	1.379	191.9	4.688
290	3.547	1.260	219.1	4.884	2.471	1.338	205.5	4.736
300	3.726	1.224	231.5	4.926	2.591	1.302	218.7	4.781
310	3.901	1.195	243.6	4.966	2.709	1.271	231.6	4.823
320	4.073	1.170	255.5	5.003	2.826	1.224	244.2	4.863
330	4.241	1.149	267.1	5.039	2.942	1.220	256.6	4.901
340	4.406	1.132	278.5	5.073	3.056	1.199	268.6	4.937
350	4.569	1.118	289.7	5.106	3.168	1.181	280.5	4.972
375	4.968	1.091	317.3	5.182	3.444	1.146	309.5	5.052
400	5.355	1.074	344.3	5.252	3.713	1.121	337.9	5.125
425	5.734	1.063	371.0	5.316	3.975	1.104	365.7	5.192
450	6.106	1.056	397.5	5.377	4.232	1.092	393.1	5.255
475	6.473	1.052	423.8	5.434	4.484	1.084	420.3	5.314
500	6.835	1.050	450.1	5.488	4.732	1.079	447.4	5.369
550	7.547	1.051	502.6	5.588	5.219	1.074	501.2	5.472
600	8.248	1.055	555.2	5.679	5.696	1.075	554.9	5.565
650	8.940	1.061	608.1	5.764	6.166	1.077	608.7	5.651
700	9.625	1.068	661.4	5.843	6.629	1.082	662.6	5.731
750	10.30	1.075	715.0	5.917	7.088	1.087	716.8	5.806
800	10.98	1.082	768.9	5.986	7.544	1.092	771.3	5.877
850	11.65	1.089	823.1	6.052	7.996	1.098	826.1	5.943
900	12.32	1.095	877.7	6.115	8.446	1.103	881.1	6.006
950	12.99	1.101	932.6	6.174	8.893	1.108	936.4	6.066
1000	13.65	1.106	987.8	6.231	9.339	1.113	991.9	6.123
1050	14.31	1.111	1043.2	6.285	9.784	1.118	1047.6	6.177
1100	14.97	1.116	1098.9	6.337	10.23	1.122	1103.6	6.229
1150	15.63	1.121	1154.9	6.386	10.67	1.126	1159.8	6.279
1200	16.29	1.125	1211.0	6.434	11.11	1.130	1216.2	6.327
1250	16.95	1.129	1267.4	6.480	11.55	1.134	1272.8	6.373
1300	17.61	1.134	1324.0	6.524	11.99	1.137	1329.5	6.418
		p=400 bar				p=500 bar		
75	0.7930	1.510	−133.3	2.546	0.7863	1.505	−127.2	2.522
80	0.8052	1.508	−125.7	2.642	0.7980	1.500	−119.7	2.618
85	0.8178	1.508	−118.2	2.732	0.8100	1.498	−112.2	2.707
90	0.8308	1.510	−110.8	2.817	0.8222	1.498	−104.8	2.791
95	0.8441	1.511	−103.1	2.899	0.8347	1.499	− 97.2	2.873
100	0.8578	1.513	− 95.6	2.976	0.8475	1.499	− 89.7	2.950
105	0.8719	1.515	− 88.0	3.051	0.8606	1.500	− 82.2	3.024
110	0.8864	1.517	− 80.4	3,122	0.8739	1.501	− 74.7	3.094
115	0.9014	1.521	− 72.8	3.190	0.8876	1.502	− 67.2	3.161
120	0.9169	1.524	− 65.2	3.256	0.9015	1.503	− 59.7	3.226
125	0.9330	1.528	− 57.6	3.319	0.9159	1.504	− 52.2	3.288
130	0.9497	1.531	− 49.9	3.380	0.9306	1.505	− 44.6	3.348
135	0.9670	1.533	− 42.3	3.438	0.9458	1.506	− 37.1	3.406
140	0.9850	1.536	− 34.6	3.495	0.9613	1.508	− 29.6	3.461
145	1.0036	1.539	− 26.9	3.549	0.9772	1.511	− 22.1	3.514
150	1.0230	1.543	− 19.1	3.601	0.9936	1.515	− 14.5	3.565
155	1.0434	1.548	− 10.9	3.652	1.0102	1.520	− 6.7	3.615
160	1.0652	1.557	− 2.8	3.703	1.0280	1.526	1.0	3.663
165	1.089	1.567	5.8	3.753	1.047	1.534	8.6	3.710
170	1.115	1.580	13.2	3.801	1.068	1.543	16.2	3.755

continued

T, °K	v	c_p	i	s	v	c_p	i	s
180	1.168	1.609	28.9	3.895	1.112	1.564	31.3	3.845
190	1.225	1.638	45.1	3.983	1.159	1.581	46.9	3.929
200	1.287	1.652	61.6	4.067	1.208	1.587	62.8	4.011
210	1.354	1.645	78.0	4.147	1.259	1.574	78.6	4.088
220	1.425	1.623	94.4	4.223	1.312	1.550	94.2	4.161
230	1.500	1.589	110.5	4.295	1.367	1.522	109.6	4.229
240	1.579	1.548	126.2	4.362	1.425	1.491	124.7	4.293
250	1.660	1.504	141.4	4.424	1.485	1.460	139.4	4.353
260	1.743	1.461	156.2	4.482	1.547	1.428	153.8	4.410
270	1.827	1.420	170.6	4.536	1.610	1.397	168.0	4.463
280	1.912	1.382	184.6	4.587	1.674	1.367	181.8	4.513
290	1.997	1.348	198.3	4.635	1.739	1.340	195.3	4.561
300	2.083	1.318	211.6	4.680	1.804	1.315	208.6	4.606
310	2.163	1.292	224.6	4.723	1.869	1.292	221.6	4.649
320	2.253	1.269	237.5	4.763	1.935	1.272	234.4	4.689
330	2.338	1.248	250.1	4.802	2.001	1.254	247.0	4.728
340	2.422	1.229	262.4	4.839	2.067	1.238	259.5	4.765
350	2.506	1.213	274.7	4.875	2.132	1.224	271.8	4.801
375	2.713	1.179	304.5	4.957	2.295	1.194	302.0	4.885
400	2.917	1.154	333.7	5.033	2.456	1.171	331.6	4.961
425	3.117	1.135	362.3	5.102	2.615	1.153	360.7	5.031
450	3.313	1.121	390.5	5.166	2.773	1.139	389.3	5.097
475	3.506	1.110	418.3	5.226	2.929	1.129	417.6	5.158
500	3.696	1.103	446.0	5.283	3.083	1.121	445.7	5.216
550	4.069	1.094	500.9	5.388	3.385	1.111	501.5	5.322
600	4.433	1.091	555.5	5.483	3.680	1.106	556.9	5.418
650	4.791	1.092	610.1	5.570	3.970	1.104	612.1	5.507
700	5.143	1.094	664.7	5.651	4.255	1.105	667.4	5.589
750	5.491	1.098	719.5	5.727	4.536	1.107	722.7	5.665
800	5.836	1.102	774.5	5.798	4.815	1.110	778.1	5.736
850	6.178	1.106	829.7	5.865	5.091	1.113	833.7	5.804
900	6.518	1.110	885.1	5.928	5.365	1.117	889.4	5.868
950	6.856	1.114	940.7	5.988	5.637	1.120	945.4	5.928
1000	7.192	1.118	996.5	6.045	5.908	1.124	1001.5	5.985
1050	7.527	1.122	1052.5	6.100	6.177	1.127	1057.8	6.040
1100	7.861	1.126	1108.7	6.153	6.445	1.130	1114.2	6.093
1150	8.194	1.130	1165.1	6.203	6.712	1.134	1170.8	6.143
1200	8.526	1.133	1221.7	6.251	6.979	1.137	1227.5	6.191
1250	8.857	1.137	1278.5	6.297	7.245	1.140	1284.4	6.238
1300	9.187	1.140	1335.4	6.342	7.510	1.143	1341.5	6.283
		$p=600$ bar				$p=700$ bar		
155	0.9809		−0.6	3.593				
160	0.9971	1.339	6.1	3.635	0.9738	1.275	11.0	3.604
165	1.014	1.374	12.9	3.677	0.9885	1.315	17.5	3.644
170	1.032	1.424	19.9	3.718	1.004	1.374	24.2	3.684
180	1.071	1.510	34.6	3.802	1.037	1.478	38.5	3.766
190	1.111	1.551	49.9	3.885	1.072	1.531	53.6	3.847
200	1.152	1.556	65.5	3.965	1.109	1.540	69.0	3.926
210	1.194	1.539	81.0	4.041	1.146	1.522	84.3	4.001
220	1.237	1.511	96.2	4.112	1.183	1.492	99.4	4.072
230	1.282	1.480	111.2	4.178	1.221	1.457	114.1	4.137
240	1.328	1.450	125.8	4.240	1.259	1.424	128.5	4.198
250	1.375	1.421	140.2	4.299	1.299	1.394	142.6	4.256
260	1.424	1.394	154.3	4.354	1.339	1.367	156.4	4.310
270	1.474	1.369	168.1	4.406	1.380	1.344	170.0	4.361
280	1.525	1.346	181.7	4.456	1.422	1.324	183.3	4.409
290	1.576	1.324	195.0	4.503	1.465	1.306	196.4	4.455
300	1.628	1.304	208.1	4.548	1.508	1.289	209.4	4.499
310	1.681	1.286	221.1	4.590	1.552	1.274	222.2	4.541
320	1.734	1.269	233.9	4.630	1.596	1.261	234.9	4.581
330	1.788	1.253	246.5	4.669	1.640	1.248	247.5	4.620
340	1.841	1.239	258.9	4.706	1.685	1.236	259.9	4.657
350	1.894	1.226	271.2	4.742	1.730	1.226	272.2	4.693

continued

T, °K	v	c_p	i	s	v	c_p	i	s
375	2.027	1.200	301.5	4.826	1.842	1.203	302.6	4.777
400	2.160	1.179	331.3	4.902	1.955	1.184	332.4	4.854
425	2.292	1.163	360.6	4.973	2.066	1.169	361.8	4.925
450	2.423	1.151	389.5	5.039	2.177	1.158	390.9	4.992
475	2.552	1.141	418.1	5.101	2.287	1.149	419.7	5.054
500	2.680	1.133	446.5	5.160	2.397	1.141	448.3	5.113
550	2.932	1.123	502.9	5.267	2.613	1.132	505.1	5.221
600	3.180	1.117	558.9	5.365	2.826	1.126	561.5	5.319
650	3.424	1.115	614.7	5.454	3.036	1.123	617.8	5.409
700	3.664	1.115	670.5	5.537	3.243	1.123	673.9	5.492
750	3.901	1.116	726.2	5.614	3.447	1.123	730.1	5.570
800	4.135	1.118	782.0	5.686	3.649	1.124	786.2	5.643
850	4.367	1.120	838.0	5.753	3.849	1.126	842.5	5.711
900	4.597	1.123	894.1	5.817	4.048	1.128	898.9	5.775
950	4.825	1.126	950.3	5.878	4.245	1.131	955.4	5.836
1000	5.052	1.129	1006.6	5.936	4.441	1.133	1012.0	5.894
1050	5.278	1.132	1063.1	5.991	4.636	1.136	1068.7	5.949
1100	5.503	1.135	1119.8	6.044	4.829	1.138	1125.5	6.002
1150	5.726	1.137	1176.6	6.095	5.022	1.141	1182.5	6.053
1200	5.949	1.140	1233.5	6.144	5.214	1.144	1239.6	6.102
1250	6.171	1.143	1290.6	6.190	5.405	1.146	1296.8	6.149
1300	6.393	1.146	1347.8	6.234	5.596	1.149	1354.2	6.194
		p=800 bar				p=900 bar		
170	0.9811	1.320	29.1	3.654				
180	1.010	1.441	42.9	3.733	0.9876	1.400	47.8	3.704
190	1.041	1.512	57.8	3.814	1.015	1.487	62.3	3.783
200	1.074	1.530	73.0	3.892	1.044	1.518	77.3	3.861
210	1.107	1.515	88.2	3.966	1.074	1.510	92.5	3.935
220	1.140	1.483	103.2	4.036	1.104	1.481	107.5	4.004
230	1.173	1.446	117.9	4.101	1.134	1.443	122.1	4.069
240	1.207	1.410	132.2	4.162	1.165	1.404	136.3	4.130
250	1.242	1.377	146.1	4.219	1.195	1.369	150.2	4.186
260	1.275	1.349	159.7	4.272	1.226	1.338	163.7	4.239
270	1.311	1.325	173.1	4.322	1.257	1.312	177.0	4.289
280	1.346	1.305	186.2	4.370	1.288	1.291	190.0	4.337
290	1.383	1.288	199.2	4.416	1.319	1.274	202.8	4.382
300	1.419	1.274	212.0	4.459	1.351	1.260	215.5	4.425
310	1.456	1.261	224.7	4.501	1.384	1.249	228.0	4.466
320	1.494	1.250	237.2	4.541	1.417	1.239	240.4	4.505
330	1.532	1.240	249.7	4.579	1.450	1.230	252.8	4.543
340	1.570	1.231	262.0	4.616	1.483	1.223	265.1	4.580
350	1.609	1.222	274.3	4.651	1.517	1.216	277.3	4.615
375	1.706	1.202	304.6	4.735	1.602	1.201	307.5	4.699
400	1.803	1.187	334.4	4.812	1.687	1.188	337.3	4.776
425	1.900	1.173	363.9	4.884	1.773	1.176	366.8	4.847
450	1.996	1.162	393.1	4.951	1.858	1.166	396.1	4.914
475	2.092	1.154	422.1	5.013	1.943	1.158	425.2	4.977
500	2.188	1.147	450.8	5.072	2.027	1.152	454.1	5.036
550	2.376	1.138	508.0	5.181	2.194	1.143	511.4	5.146
600	2.562	1.133	564.8	5.280	2.359	1.137	568.4	5.245
650	2.746	1.130	621.3	5.370	2.522	1.135	625.2	5.336
700	2.927	1.129	677.7	5.454	2.683	1.134	681.9	5.420
750	3.107	1.129	734.2	5.532	2.843	1.134	738.6	5.498
800	3.285	1.130	790.7	5.605	3.001	1.135	795.3	5.571
850	3.461	1.132	847.2	5.673	3.158	1.136	852.1	5.640
900	3.636	1.133	903.8	5.738	3.314	1.138	909.0	5.705
950	3.809	1.135	960.5	5.800	3.469	1.140	965.9	5.767
1000	3.981	1.138	1017.4	5.858	3.623	1.141	1022.9	5.825
1050	4.152	1.140	1074.3	5.913	3.776	1.143	1080.0	5.881
1100	4.323	1.142	1131.3	5.966	3.928	1.146	1137.2	5.934
1150	4.493	1.144	1188.5	6.017	4.080	1.148	1194.5	5.985

continued

T, °K	v	c_p	i	s	v	c_p	i	s
1200	4.662	1.147	1245.8	6.066	4.231	1.150	1251.9	6.034
1250	4.830	1.149	1303.2	6.113	4.381	1.152	1309.5	6.081
1300	4.997	1.151	1360.7	6.158	4.531	1.154	1367.2	6.126

T, °K	v	c_p	i	s	T, °K	v	c_p	i	s
				p=1000 bar					
180	0.9689	1.356	53.1	3.680	425	1.672	1.177	370.4	4.815
190	0.9933	1.456	67.2	3.756	450	1.748	1.169	399.7	4.882
200	1.020	1.502	82.0	3.832	475	1.824	1.162	428.8	4.945
210	1.047	1.504	97.1	3.906	500	1.899	1.156	457.8	5.005
220	1.074	1.479	112.0	3.975	550	2.049	1.147	515.3	5.115
230	1.101	1.442	126.6	4.040	600	2.197	1.141	572.5	5.214
240	1.129	1.403	140.9	4.101	650	2.343	1.139	629.5	5.305
250	1.157	1.366	154.7	4.157	700	2.488	1.138	686.4	5.389
260	1.185	1.333	168.2	4.210	750	2.632	1.138	743.3	5.468
270	1.213	1.305	181.4	4.260	800	2.775	1.139	800.2	5.541
280	1.241	1.282	194.3	4.307	850	2.916	1.140	857.2	5.610
290	1.269	1.264	207.0	4.352	900	3.057	1.141	914.2	5.675
300	1.297	1.250	219.6	4.394	950	3.197	1.143	971.3	5.737
310	1.326	1.238	232.1	4.435	1000	3.336	1.145	1028.5	5.796
320	1.355	1.229	244.4	4.474	1050	3.474	1.147	1085.7	5.852
330	1.384	1.221	256.6	4.511	1100	3.612	1.149	1143.1	5.905
340	1.414	1.215	268.8	4.548	1150	3.749	1.150	1200.6	5.956
350	1.444	1.209	280.9	4.584	1200	3.885	1.152	1258.2	6.005
375	1.519	1.197	311.0	4.666	1250	4.021	1.154	1315.8	6.052
400	1.595	1.187	340.8	4.743	1300	4.156	1.156	1373.5	6.098

Specific volume v (m³/kg) of dissociated oxygen at high temperatures [143] (c.f. p.600)

p, bar \ T, °K →	1250	1500	1750	2000
0.1	32.48	38.98	45.47	52.02
0.2	16.24	19.49	22.74	26.00
0.4	8.121	9.745	11.37	13.00
0.6	5.414	6.497	7.578	8.666
1	3.849	3.898	4.547	5.199
2	1.625	1.950	2.274	2.600
4	0.8128	0.9752	1.137	1.300
6	0.5421	0.6500	0.7587	0.8671
10	0.3256	0.3906	0.4556	0.5206
20	0.1532	0.1856	0.2282	0.2607
40	0.09197	0.09825	0.1145	0.1308
60	0.05491	0.06578	0.07658	0.08747
100	0.03326	0.03979	0.04623	0.05282
200	0.01702	0.02031	0.02358	0.02683
300	0.01161	0.01381	0.01599	0.01817
500	0.007880	0.008511	0.009926	0.01124
1000	0.004025	0.004703	0.005367	0.006030

p, bar \ T, °K →	2200	2400	2600	2800	3000
0.1	57.41	63.22	70.04	78.97	91.68
0.2	28.67	31.48	51.01	38.58	43.87
0.4	14.32	15.70	17.20	18.97	21.33
0.6	9.545	10.45	11.43	12.55	13.94

continued

p, bar \ T, °K →	2200	2400	2600	2800	3000
1	6.725	6.264	6.836	7.474	8.231
2	2.862	3.128	3.407	3.708	4.104
4	1.431	1.563	1.700	1.844	2.005
6	0.9541	1.042	1.132	1.227	1.330
10	0.5727	0.6253	0.6789	0.7346	0.7942
20	0.2868	0.3130	0.3395	0.3667	0.3955
40	0.1438	0.1569	0.1869	0.1834	0.1975
60	0.09615	0.1078	0.1136	0.1225	0.1317
100	0.05803	0.06325	0.06850	0.07381	0.07925
200	0.02944	0.03205	0.03466	0.03730	0.03998
300	0.01991	0.02165	0.02339	0.02610	0.02692
500	0.01228	0.01333	0.01437	0.01542	0.01650
1000	0.006555	0.007077	0.007597	0.008123	0.008650

p, bar \ T, °K →	3200	3400	3600	3800	4000
0.1	110.0	133.8	159.6	182.0	199.6
0.2	51.30	61.45	73.70	86.00	96.25
0.4	24.20	28.44	33.81	40.05	45.78
0.6	15.77	18.23	21.03	25.40	29.43
1	9.206	10.48	12.16	14.26	16.60
2	4.474	5.006	5.695	6.569	7.617
4	2.191	2.419	2.703	3.062	3.507
6	1.447	1.587	1.759	1.972	2.239
10	0.8595	0.9373	1.029	1.141	1.278
20	0.4262	0.4613	0.5069	0.5489	0.6058
40	0.2123	0.2283	0.2463	0.2670	0.2910
60	0.1414	0.1517	0.1631	0.1759	0.1906
100	0.08490	0.09088	0.09734	0.1045	0.1125
200	0.04272	0.04562	0.04866	0.05195	0.05555
300	0.02874	0.03062	0.03260	0.03470	0.03698
500	0.01759	0.01867	0.01982	0.02103	0.02234
1000	0.009184	0.009719	0.01029	0.01087	0.01147

p, bar \ T, °K →	4200	4400	4600	4800	5000
0.1	213.8	226.2	237.2	248.6	259.3
0.2	105.0	112.0	118.1	123.9	129.4
0.4	50.80	54.93	58.43	61.52	64.44
0.6	33.00	36.03	38.55	40.75	42.80
1	18.91	20.98	22.72	24.17	25.48
2	8.760	9.881	10.86	11.78	12.52
4	4.021	4.577	5.147	5.626	6.069
6	2.555	2.903	3.269	3.619	3.943
10	1.444	1.635	1.845	2.059	2.266
20	0.6741	0.7520	0.8462	0.9471	1.051
40	0.3195	0.3528	0.3914	0.4352	0.4829
60	0.2077	0.2277	0.2508	0.2772	0.3070
100	0.1216	0.1322	0.1443	0.1581	0.1738
200	0.05955	0.06405	0.06945	0.07500	0.08138
300	0.03913	0.04225	0.04535	0.04882	0.05272
500	0.02372	0.02524	0.02692	0.02877	0.03078
1000	0.01212	0.01281	0.01356	0.01438	0.01386

p, bar \ T, °K →	5200	5400	5600	5800	6000
0.1	269.9	280.4	290.8	301.3	311.7
0.2	134.8	140.1	145.4	150.6	155.8
0.4	67.22	69.93	72.60	75.24	77.87

continued

p, bar \ T, °K →	5200	5400	5600	5800	6000
0.6	44.70	46.55	48.35	50.13	51.89
1	26.80	27.84	28.95	30.03	31.10
2	13.19	13.81	14.39	14.96	15.51
4	6.459	6.808	7.125	7.430	7.712
6	4.225	4.478	4.703	4.920	5.110
10	2.453	2.623	2.773	2.915	3.039
20	1.150	1.248	1.336	1.419	1.490
40	0.5328	0.5828	0.6310	0.6764	0.7185
60	0.3381	0.3707	0.4031	0.4350	0.4648
100	0.1908	0.2091	0.2282	0.2473	0.2661
200	0.08864	0.09575	0.1051	0.1141	0.1253
300	0.05706	0.06143	0.06683	0.07262	0.08210
500	0.03312	0.03564	0.03839	0.04137	0.04455
1000	0.01622	0.01727	0.01843	0.01968	0.02103

Enthalpy i (kJ/kg) of dissociated oxygen at high temperatures and different pressures [143]

p, bar \ T, °K →	1250	1500	1750	2000	2200	2400	2600	2800	3000
0.1	1257	1540	1814	2139	2428	2819	3431	4459	6163
0.2	1257	1540	1815	2134	2408	2754	3259	4059	5351
0.4	1257	1540	1816	2130	2393	2709	3137	3776	4767
0.6	1257	1540	1817	2129	2387	2689	3083	3650	4506
1	1257	1540	1818	2127	2381	2669	3029	3523	4243
2	1257	1540	1819	2126	2375	2649	2974	3396	3978
4	1257	1541	1820	2125	2370	2634	2936	3306	3791
6	1257	1541	1820	2124	2368	2628	2919	3266	3708
10	1257	1541	1820	2124	2367	2622	2902	3227	3625
20	1258	1542	1820	2124	2366	2617	2886	3186	3542
40	1259	1543	1821	2126	2366	2614	2877	3159	3484
60	1260	1545	1825	2127	2367	2614	2873	3150	3459
100	1262	1548	1831	2130	2370	2615	2870	3140	3436
200	1268	1556	1836	2138	2377	2621	2873	3136	3415
300	1273	1664	1845	2145	2385	2629	2879	3140	3416
500	1285	1579	1872	2161	2401	2643	2894	3151	3422
1000	1315	1618	1915	2199	2441	2685	2934	3188	3452

p, bar \ T, °K →	3200	3400	3600	3800	4000	4200	4400	4600	4800	5000
0.1	8763	12116	15439	17906	19418	20314	20891	21315	21667	21982
0.2	7346	10124	13352	16287	18749	19734	20567	21132	21559	21917
0.4	6283	8464	11262	14266	16870	18921	19976	20784	21352	21790
0.6	5799	7669	10151	13014	15756	17927	19448	20458	21194	21667
1	5307	6841	8926	11489	14215	16660	18542	19853	20775	21427
2	4807	5981	7591	9668	12103	14616	16864	18640	19941	20879
4	4452	5362	6598	8219	10222	12496	14812	16906	18618	19926
6	4294	5085	6148	7541	9301	11345	13560	15714	17603	19136
10	4095	4806	5691	6843	8299	10222	12051	14139	16136	17893
20	3987	4525	5285	6126	7256	8640	10270	12093	14004	15869
40	3865	4328	4900	5614	6497	7577	8865	10354	12004	13742
60	3816	4241	4756	5386	6158	7094	8211	9513	10982	12576
100	3770	4156	4612	5159	5817	6605	7541	8634	9882	11269
200	3728	4075	4473	4936	5478	6114	6859	7722	8712	9826
300	3714	4044	4416	4841	5332	5900	6558	7316	8181	9156
500	3709	4034	4368	4755	5194	5694	6264	6913	7648	8472
1000	3729	4022	4345	4695	5081	5512	5993	6531	7001	7712

continued

p, bar \ T, °K →	5200	5400	5600	5800	6000
0.1	22280	22569	22852	23135	23416
0.2	22240	22542	22836	23123	23408
0.4	22160	22490	22802	23100	23392
0.6	22081	22440	22768	23076	23374
1	21927	22339	22700	23030	23342
2	21567	22095	22533	22915	23260
4	20901	21638	22217	22692	23102
6	20319	21220	21918	22479	22948
10	19296	20477	21370	22077	22653

p, bar \ T, °K →	5200	5400	5600	5800	6000
20	17871	19023	20222	21195	21385
40	15474	17103	18561	19815	20869
60	14230	15861	17110	18774	19976
100	12759	14299	15827	17283	18619
200	11055	12375	13758	15156	16793
300	10240	11417	12672	13975	14359
500	9394	10402	11489	12643	13841
1000	8541	9353	10235	11181	12183

Entropy s (kJ/kg · deg) of dissociated oxygen at high temperatures and different pressures [143]

p, bar \ T, °K →	1250	1500	1750	2000	2200	2400	2600	2800	3000
0.1	8.457	8.663	8.840	9.007	9.114	9.314	9.558	9.938	10.52
0.2	8.277	8.483	8.660	8.824	8.954	9.105	9.306	9.602	10.05
0.4	8.097	8.303	8.480	8.642	8.767	8.904	9.075	9.311	9.652
0.6	7.991	8.198	8.373	8.536	8.659	8.790	8.947	9.156	9.451
1	7.859	8.065	8.240	8.402	8.524	8.648	8.792	8.975	9.223
2	7.679	7.885	8.064	8.221	8.340	8.459	8.589	8.745	8.946
4	7.499	7.705	7.883	8.040	8.158	8.272	8.393	8.530	8.697
6	7.394	7.600	7.778	7.935	8.051	8.164	8.280	8.409	8.561
10	7.262	7.467	7.646	7.802	7.918	8.029	8.140	8.261	8.398
20	7.080	7.287	7.465	7.622	7.736	7.846	7.953	8.062	8.187
40	6.900	7.106	7.281	7.441	7.556	7.663	7.768	7.870	7.985
60	6.795	7.001	7.179	7.336	7.450	7.557	7.660	7.763	7.870
100	6.660	6.868	7.046	7.203	7.317	7.424	7.526	7.626	7.728
200	6.479	6.688	6.865	7.022	7.136	7.242	7.343	7.441	7.536
300	6.370	6.582	6.760	6.916	7.030	7.136	7.237	7.333	7.428
500	6.233	6.448	6.625	6.782	6.897	7.003	7.103	7.198	7.291
1000	6.043	6.254	6.440	6.599	6.714	6.821	6.921	7.015	7.106

p, bar \ T, °K →	3200	3400	3600	3800	4000	4200	4400	4600	4800	5000
0.1	11.36	12.38	13.33	14.00	14.38	14.60	14.74	14.83	14.91	14.97
0.2	10.69	11.53	12.45	13.26	14.05	14.12	14.31	14.44	14.53	14.60
0.4	10.14	10.80	11.60	12.41	13.08	13.54	13.82	14.00	14.13	14.22
0.6	9.868	10.43	11.14	12.20	12.62	13.15	13.51	13.73	13.90	13.98
1	9.565	10.03	10.62	11.32	12.02	12.61	13.05	13.34	13.54	13.67
2	9.212	9.568	10.03	10.59	11.21	11.82	12.35	12.74	13.02	13.21
4	8.910	9.185	9.538	9.976	10.49	11.04	11.58	12.05	12.41	12.68
6	8.750	8.989	9.293	9.669	10.13	10.62	11.13	11.61	12.01	12.33
10	8.480	8.765	9.018	9.329	9.702	10.13	10.59	11.06	11.48	11.84
20	8.327	8.493	8.788	8.936	9.226	9.563	9.942	10.35	10.75	11.14
40	8.108	8.248	8.412	8.576	8.831	9.094	9.393	9.724	10.08	10.43
60	7.985	8.114	8.261	8.431	8.629	8.857	9.117	9.406	9.718	10.04
100	7.835	7.952	8.082	8.230	8.398	8.591	8.808	9.051	9.317	9.600
200	7.638	7.743	7.857	7.982	8.120	8.276	8.449	8.641	8.851	9.040
300	7.525	7.625	7.731	7.846	7.972	8.110	8.263	8.431	8.615	8.814
500	7.384	7.485	7.578	7.682	7.795	7.917	8.049	8.194	8.315	8.521
1000	7.196	7.279	7.367	7.472	7.571	7.676	7.788	7.907	8.041	8.180

continued

p, bar \ T, °K →	5200	5400	5600	5800	6000
0.1	15.03	15.08	15.14	15.18	15.23
0.2	14.66	14.72	14.77	14.82	14.87
0.4	14.29	14.35	14.41	14.46	14.51
0.6	14.06	14.13	14.19	14.25	14.30
1	13.77	13.85	13.91	13.97	14.02
2	13.35	13.45	13.53	13.59	13.65
4	12.87	13.01	13.12	13.20	13.27
6	12.56	12.73	12.86	12.96	13.04
10	12.12	12.34	12.50	12.63	12.72
20	11.67	11.74	12.02	12.13	12.26
40	10.77	11.08	11.34	11.56	11.74
60	10.37	10.68	10.78	11.20	11.40
100	9.892	10.18	10.46	10.72	10.94
200	9.319	9.569	9.820	10.06	10.46
300	9.028	9.249	9.477	9.706	9.929
500	8.699	8.889	9.086	9.289	9.492
1000	8.317	8.470	8.630	8.796	8.966

Speed of sound u (m/s) in oxygen [50]

T, °K \ p, atm →	1	10	40	70	100
100					
120	207.5				
140	224.5				
160	240.5	233.9			
180	255.3	250.9	235.8		
200	269.5	266.3	257.8	255.6	
220	282.7	280.8	275.8	275.8	286.8
240	295.3	294.0	291.8	293.1	301.0
260	307.3	306.6	306.3	308.5	314.8
280	318.6	315.8	319.5	322.7	328.0
300	329.6	329.9	332.1	335.6	340.9
320	340.3	340.9	343.8	347.9	353.2
340	350.7	351.3	354.8	359.2	364.9
360	360.5	361.4	365.5	370.2	375.9
380	369.9	371.2	375.6	380.6	386.3
400	379.0	380.3	385.0	390.4	406.1
420	387.8	389.4	394.5	400.1	396.3
440	396.7	398.2	403.6	409.3	415.2
460	405.2	406.4	412.1	417.8	424.1
480	413.3	414.9	420.6	426.6	432.6
500	421.5	423.1	428.8	434.8	441.1
520	429.1	430.9	436.6	442.9	449.2
540	437.0	438.5	444.5	450.5	457.1
560	444.2	446.1	452.1	458.4	464.7
580	451.8	453.3	459.6	465.6	472.2
600	459.0	460.6	466.9	472.8	479.5
620	465.9	467.8	474.1	480.1	486.7
640	472.8	474.7	481.0	487.3	493.6
660	479.8	481.7	487.6	493.9	500.6
680	486.7	488.6	494.6	500.9	507.2
700	493.3	495.2	501.2	507.5	513.8
720	499.9	501.8	507.8	514.1	520.4
740	506.5	508.4	514.4	520.4	527.0
760	512.8	514.7	520.7	527.0	533.3
780	519.1	521.0	527.0	533.0	539.3
800	525.4	527.3	533.3	539.3	545.6
900	555.6	557.2	563.2	569.2	575.5
1000	584.3	586.2	591.9	597.5	603.5
1100	611.7	613.3	618.9	624.6	630.3
1200	637.8	639.4	645.1	650.4	655.8
1300	663.0	664.3	669.9	675.0	680.6
1400	687.2	688.5	693.9	698.9	704.2
1500	710.5	712.1	716.8	721.9	727.2
1600	733.2	734.5	739.2	744.2	748.9
1700	754.9	756.2	760.9	765.6	770.4
1800	776.0	777.3	782.0	786.4	791.4
1900	796.5	798.1	802.5	806.9	811.3
2000	816.3	817.6	822.0	826.7	831.1
2100	835.8	837.1	841.5	845.6	850.0
2200	855.0	856.3	860.4	864.5	868.6
2300	873.6	874.6	878.7	882.7	886.8
2400	891.6	892.8	896.6	900.7	904.8
2500	909.2	910.4	914.2	918.0	922.1
2600	926.5	927.8	931.5	935.3	939.1
2700	943.2	944.5	948.2	952.0	955.8
2800	959.9	961.1	964.6	968.4	972.2
2900	976.2	977.2	980.9	984.4	987.9
3000	992.3	993.6	997.0	1000	1004

Viscosity η ($N \cdot s/m^2$) of oxygen gas at $p = 1$ bar [60]

T, °K	$\eta \cdot 10^7$	T, °K	$\eta \cdot 10^7$	T, °K	$\eta \cdot 10^7$	T, °K	$\eta \cdot 10^7$	T, °K	$\eta \cdot 10^7$
200	147.1	400	258.1	900	447.0	1300	558.4	1750	663.0
250	178.3	500	303.2	1000	477.0	1400	583.2	1800	673.7
271.1	191.8	600	343.7	1100	505.5	1500	607.0	1900	694.4
298.1	205.9	700	380.8	1200	532.6	1600	630.0	2000	714.8
300	207.0	800	415.0	1250	545.6	1700	652.2		

Viscosity $\eta \cdot 10^7$ (N · s/m²) of oxygen at different temperatures and pressures [141, 142]

T, °K \ p, bar →	1	10	20	30	40	50	60	70	80
75	3038	3081	3131	3179	3229	3279	3328	3378	3430
80	2536	2569	2607	2644	2682	2721	2759	2801	2841
85	2162	2189	2218	2247	2277	2307	2338	2368	2399
90	1882	1903	1927	1950	1973	1998	2022	2047	2071
95	72.1	1684	1704	1723	1743	1763	1783	1803	1824
100	76.4	1507	1525	1542	1560	1578	1595	1613	1630
105	80.5	1355	1372	1389	1406	1423	1439	1456	1472
110	84.6	1216	1234	1252	1268	1285	1302	1318	1334
115	88.6	1086	1105	1123	1141	1158	1175	1191	1208
120	92.6	97.9	986.3	1004	1022	1040	1057	1074	1091
125	96.5	101.4	881.5	899.5	916.9	934.3	951.1	967.9	984.3
130	100.3	104.9	787.8	807.5	825.8	843.4	860.0	876.1	892.0
135	104.0	108.3	115.9	715.0	737.4	757.8	777.1	794.9	811.9
140	107.7	111.8	118.5	616.0	645.6	671.2	694.0	714.9	734.3
145	111.3	115.2	121.2	131.7	546.5	581.3	610.0	635.3	657.9
150	114.8	118.5	124.0	132.8	150.9	484.3	523.5	555.0	581.9
155	118.2	121.8	126.8	134.4	147.2	185.7	417.8	467.7	506.4
160	121.6	125.0	129.7	136.5	146.7	165.3	232.4	355.3	416.8
165	124.9	128.2	132.6	138.7	140.5	163.4	192.0	263.9	324.0
170	128.2	131.4	135.5	141.1	142.4	159.5	176.0	204.4	252.2
180	134.7	137.6	141.4	146.2	147.3	160.4	170.9	185.0	204.4
190	141.1	143.8	147.3	151.5	152.6	163.3	171.2	181.0	193.1
200	147.5	150.1	153.2	157.1	158.1	167.2	173.7	181.3	190.3
210	153.8	156.2	159.2	162.7	163.6	171.6	177.1	183.5	190.7
220	160.1	162.4	165.2	168.4	169.3	176.4	181.2	186.7	192.8
230	166.3	168.5	171.1	174.1	175.0	181.4	185.7	190.5	195.8
240	172.5	174.6	177.0	179.8	180.7	186.5	190.4	194.7	199.5
250	178.6	180.6	182.8	185.5	186.4	191.7	195.2	199.2	203.5
260	184.5	186.4	188.5	191.0	191.9	196.8	200.0	203.7	207.6
270	190.2	192.1	194.1	196.5	197.3	201.9	204.9	208.2	211.8
280	195.9	197.7	199.6	201.9	202.7	207.0	209.8	212.9	216.2
290	201.6	203.3	205.2	207.3	208.1	212.1	214.8	217.7	220.8
300	207.2	208.8	210.7	212.7	213.5	217.2	219.8	222.5	225.4
310	212.7	214.2	216.0	218.0	218.8	222.3	224.7	227.3	230.0
320	218.0	219.5	221.2	223.1	223.9	227.2	229.5	231.9	234.5
330	223.2	224.7	226.3	228.1	228.9	232.0	234.2	236.5	239.0
340	228.4	229.8	231.4	233.1	233.9	236.9	239.0	241.2	243.5
350	233.5	234.8	236.4	238.0	238.8	241.7	243.7	245.8	248.0
400	258.2	259.4	260.7	262.1	262.8	265.1	266.8	268.4	270.2
450	281.4	282.5	283.6	284.8	285.5	287.4	288.8	290.2	291.7
500	303.3	304.3	305.3	306.3	307.0	308.6	309.8	311.1	312.4
550	324.0	324.9	325.8	326.7	327.4	328.8	329.8	331.0	332.1
600	343.7	344.5	345.3	346.2	346.8	348.0	349.0	350.0	351.0
700	380.8	381.4	382.2	382.9	383.4	384.4	385.2	386.0	386.9
800	415.2	415.8	416.4	417.0	417.5	418.3	419.0	419.7	420.4
900	447.2	447.7	448.3	448.8	449.2	449.9	450.6	451.1	451.8
1000	477.0	477.5	477.9	478.4	478.8	479.5	480.0	480.5	481.1
1100	505.5	505.9	506.3	506.8	507.2	507.7	508.2	508.7	509.2
1200	532.5	533.0	533.3	533.7	534.1	534.6	535.1	535.5	535.9
1300	558.4	558.8	559.1	559.5	559.8	560.3	560.7	561.1	561.5

T, °K \ p, bar →	90	100	125	150	175	200	250	300	350
75	3482	3532	3664	3800	3939	4077	4368	4668	4979
80	2879	2921	3024	3127	3236	3345	3574	3812	4061
85	2431	2463	2544	2626	2711	2798	2976	3165	3365
90	2096	2121	2185	2251	2318	2386	2529	2681	2838
95	1844	1862	1916	1970	2024	2080	2195	2316	2443
100	1648	1666	1710	1755	1800	1846	1942	2041	2145

continued

T, °K \ p, bar →	90	100	125	150	175	200	250	300	350
105	1488	1504	1545	1584	1624	1665	1746	1830	1917
110	1350	1365	1404	1441	1478	1516	1589	1663	1738
115	1223	1240	1278	1315	1352	1388	1457	1525	1594
120	1107	1123	1163	1201	1237	1273	1341	1408	1472
125	1001	1017	1056	1094	1131	1168	1236	1302	1365
130	907.8	923.1	961.3	998.5	1035	1071	1140	1205	1268
135	827.9	843.2	879.8	915.2	949.8	984.1	1051	1117	1179
140	752.4	769.5	808.7	844.3	877.5	909.8	973.5	1037	1098
145	678.6	697.8	741.2	779.6	814.4	846.5	906.8	966.2	1025
150	606.1	627.7	675.7	717.2	754.3	788.4	849.3	905.4	961.2
155	534.3	559.6	612.4	657.0	696.5	732.2	795.7	852.0	904.8
160	458.2	490.0	552.1	599.5	640.9	678.1	744.1	802.2	854.7
165	377.2	417.2	492.2	545.0	589.0	628.1	695.3	754.8	807.0
170	305.1	350.8	435.1	494.3	541.5	582.1	650.1	709.9	762.0
180	230.2	260.8	337.5	401.8	454.1	497.7	570.1	630.0	682.8
190	207.9	225.7	279.1	333.5	383.4	427.1	501.6	562.3	615.9
200	200.8	212.8	249.7	291.8	333.8	373.5	444.9	505.5	559.3
210	198.9	208.0	235.4	267.7	302.0	336.1	400.7	458.4	510.6
220	199.6	207.0	228.7	254.3	282.2	311.0	367.9	421.1	470.8
230	201.6	207.9	225.9	246.8	270.0	294.5	344.0	392.3	438.2
240	204.5	210.0	225.5	243.1	262.8	283.7	327.1	370.4	412.6
250	208.0	212.9	226.4	241.8	258.7	276.8	315.1	354.0	392.4
260	211.7	216.2	228.3	241.8	256.7	272.6	306.6	341.7	376.7
270	215.6	219.7	230.6	242.8	256.0	270.2	300.5	332.3	364.4
280	219.7	223.5	233.4	244.5	256.5	269.2	296.6	325.5	354.8
290	224.0	227.5	236.7	246.8	257.7	269.4	294.3	320.7	347.7
300	228.4	231.6	240.2	249.5	259.5	270.2	293.1	317.3	342.3
310	232.8	235.8	243.8	252.5	261.8	271.7	292.8	315.1	338.3
320	237.2	240.0	247.5	255.6	264.3	273.4	293.0	313.7	335.4
330	241.5	244.2	251.3	258.9	267.0	275.5	293.8	313.1	333.3
340	245.9	248.4	255.1	262.3	269.9	278.0	295.0	313.2	332.1
350	250.3	252.7	259.0	265.8	273.0	280.6	296.7	313.7	331.6
400	272.1	274.0	278.9	284.5	290.1	296.0	308.5	320.9	335.2
450	293.3	294.9	299.1	303.6	308.2	313.1	323.2	333.9	345.0
500	313.7	315.1	318.7	322.5	326.5	330.6	339.2	348.2	357.5
550	333.2	334.5	337.6	340.9	344.4	347.9	355.4	363.2	371.2
600	352.0	353.1	355.9	358.9	361.9	365.0	371.6	378.5	385.5
700	387.7	388.6	390.9	393.3	395.8	398.3	403.7	409.2	414.9
800	421.2	421.9	423.8	425.8	427.9	430.1	434.5	439.2	444.0
900	452.4	453.1	454.7	456.4	458.2	460.1	463.9	467.9	472.0
1000	481.6	482.2	483.7	485.2	486.8	488.4	491.8	495.2	498.8
1100	509.7	510.2	511.5	512.8	514.2	515.7	518.6	521.7	524.9
1200	536.4	536.9	538.0	539.2	540.5	541.8	544.5	547.2	550.1
1300	561.9	562.3	563.4	564.5	565.6	566.8	569.2	571.7	574.3

T, °K \ p, bar →	400	450	500	600	700	800	900	1000
75	5299							
80	4320	4585	4862					
85	3572	3787	4008					
90	3004	3178	3360					
95	2576	2717	2866					
100	2254	2368	2489					
105	2007	2103	2202					
110	1816	1896	1981					
115	1664	1734	1807					
120	1536	1601	1666					
125	1437	1488	1548					
130	1329	1388	1447					
135	1240	1299	1356					
140	1159	1217	1273					

continued

T, °K \ p, bar →	400	450	500	600	700	800	900	1000
145	1084	1142	1198					
150	1017	1073	1128					
155	957.8	1013	1066					
160	905.2	956.3	1008					
165	857.5	906.3	954.0					
170	812.7	860.6	906.1					
180	733.4	779.8	822.2					
190	655.3							
200	607.0	651.4						
210	557.2	600.5	640.7					
220	515.7	558.3	597.2	670.4				
230	481.1	521.9	560.1	630.5				
240	452.8	491.4	528.1	596.2	661.3			
250	429.9	466.2	501.0	566.5	629.2	684.7		
260	411.3	445.2	478.0	540.7	601.1	655.4		
270	396.4	427.7	458.6	518.3	576.5	629.0	680.0	
280	384.4	413.6	442.5	499.3	554.8	605.3	654.8	703.1
290	375.0	402.4	429.4	483.1	535.8	584.2	632.7	678.9
300	367.7	393.3	418.6	469.2	519.5	565.9	612.8	657.3
310	362.0	385.9	409.6	457.4	505.1	549.9	594.7	638.0
320	357.5	379.8	402.2	447.3	492.7	535.9	578.5	620.6
330	354.1	375.0	396.2	438.6	481.9	523.3	564.3	605.1
340	351.6	371.3	391.3	431.4	472.6	512.1	551.7	591.0
350	349.9	368.6	387.3	425.5	464.5	502.4	540.0	578.1
400	349.3	363.8	378.4	408.5	439.3	469.9	501.0	532.3
450	356.4	368.1	380.1	404.6	429.8	454.9	480.8	506.9
500	367.1	376.9	386.9	407.5	428.8	450.2	472.1	494.3
550	379.5	388.0	396.6	414.4	432.7	451.2	470.2	489.4
600	392.9	400.3	407.9	423.5	439.6	455.9	472.6	489.5
700	420.8	426.8	432.9	445.4	458.3	471.4	484.9	498.5
800	448.9	453.9	459.0	469.4	480.2	491.2	502.4	513.8
900	476.2	480.5	484.9	493.9	503.2	512.5	522.1	531.9
1000	515.4	519.0	522.6	530.0	526.1	534.3	542.7	551.2
1100	528.2	531.6	534.9	541.9	549.1	556.4	563.9	571.5
1200	553.0	556.1	559.1	565.3	571.8	578.4	585.1	591.9
1300	577.0	579.6	582.5	588.2	594.0	600.0	606.1	612.2

Viscosity $\eta \cdot 10^7$ ($N \cdot s/m^2$) of dissociated oxygen [353]

T, °K \ p, bar →	0.001	0.01	0.1	1	10	100	T, °K \ p, bar →	0.001	0.01	0.1	1	10	100
2000	737	736	735	735	735	735	4200	1320	1321	1332	1386	1384	1294
2200	791	786	784	783	783	783	4400	1368	1369	1375	1418	1458	1365
2400	859	840	833	830	829	829	4600	1416	1416	1420	1451	1519	1447
2600	939	906	886	878	876	875	4800	1463	1463	1466	1487	1565	1528
2800	1001	986	948	929	922	920	5000	1510	1510	1512	1526	1601	1607
3000	1039	1061	1024	986	970	965	5200	1557	1557	1558	1568	1632	1680
3200	1080	1109	1106	1053	1023	1011	5400	1603	1603	1604	1611	1663	1744
3400	1126	1144	1176	1130	1081	1059	5600	1649	1649	1650	1655	1696	1797
3600	1174	1183	1223	1213	1146	1110	5800	1695	1695	1696	1696	1731	1841
3800	1223	1228	1257	1288	1221	1165	6000	1741	1740	1741	1744	1768	1878
4000	1272	1274	1292	1346	1302	1226							

Thermal conductivity $\lambda \cdot 10^3$ (W/m · deg) of oxygen liquid and gas [15]

T, °K \ p, bar →	1	10	20	30	40	50	60
80	161	162	163		164		165
90	147	148	149		150		151
100	9.25	134	135		136		138
110	10.2	120	121		123		125
120	11.0	12.2	108		100		110
130	11.9	13.0	95.9		97.4		99.6
140	12.8	13.7	15.4	80.6	83.5	85.4	87.6
150	13.8	14.7	16.0	18.2	21.0	65.3	72.2
160	14.7	15.5	16.7	18.4	20.9	25.1	
170	15.6	16.4	17.4	18.8	20.7	23.0	
180	16.6	17.2	18.1	19.3	21.0	22.8	
190	17.4	18.0	18.9	19.9	21.3	22.9	24.8
200	18.3	18.9	19.7	20.6	21.8	23.0	24.7
220	20.0		21.2		22.9		25.2
240	21.7		22.8		24.2		25.4
260	23.4		24.3		25.6		27.2
280	25.0		25.8		27.0		28.4
300	26.8		27.4		28.4		29.6
350	29.6		30.8		31.6		32.6
400	33.0		34.0		35.0		36.0
450	36.3		37.3		38.2		39.3
500	41.2		41.4		41.8		42.7
550	44.1		44.4		44.9		
600	47.3				47.8		
650	50.0				51.4		
700	52.8				53.6		
750	56.2				57.1		
800	58.9				59.8		
850	62.1						
900	64.9						
950	68.1						
1000	71.0						
1100	75.8						
1200	81.9						
1300	87.1						
1400	92.3						

T, °K \ p, bar →	70	80	90	100	150	200	250
80		166		167	170	172	175
90		152		154	157	159	162
100		140		142	144	147	150
110		126		128	131	135	138
120		111		113	115	117	121
130		100		102	106	109	113
140	89.5	91.3	93.8	95.6	99.4	104	108
150	74.4	77.3	79.1	81.2	89.3	95.2	100
160		61.2	63.3	68.4	79.2	87.4	93.3
170					69.3	78.5	84.4
180					59.2	70.4	77.3
190	27.0	29.8	32.8	36.0	55.3	58.2	70.4
200	26.6	28.6	30.9	33.4	46.2	57.4	64.6
220		28.0		31.3	40.3	48.2	56.0
240		28.4		30.9	38.8	45.3	51.0
260		29.0		31.0	36.8	42.6	48.2
280		30.0		32.0	36.6	41.6	46.4
300		31.0		32.6	36.8	41.2	45.5
350		33.6		34.8	38.0	40.7	44.8
400		37.0		38.0	40.4	43.1	46.0
450		40.2		40.8	43.0	45.3	47.7

continued

T, °K \ p, bar →	70	80	90	100	150	200	250
500		43.6		44.3	46.0	47.8	49.7
550		45.8		46.6	48.2	50.0	51.8
600		48.7		49.2	50.8	52.4	54.0
650		52.3		52.7	53.8	55.2	56.7
700				54.8	56.0	57.2	58.6
750				58.3	58.3	60.1	60.9
800				61.3	62.3	63.2	64.4
850				63.8	64.8	65.9	67.1
900				66.2	67.0	68.1	69.1
950				69.3	70.5	71.3	72.1
1000				71.8	72.6	73.4	74.2
1100				76.6	77.6	78.1	78.9
1200				82.6	83.1	83.6	84.1
1300				87.9	88.5	89.0	89.5
1400				92.8	93.3	93.8	94.3

T, °K \ p, bar →	300	350	400	450	500	550	600
80	177	179	181	183	185	187	189
90	164	166	168	170	172	174	176
100	153	155	157	159	161	163	165
110	141	143	146	149	152	155	157
120	125	128	132	135	137	140	143
130	116	120	124	127	130	133	135
140	112	115	118	121	124	127	130
150	105	108	111	114	117	120	123
160	98.1	103	107	111	114	119	122
170	90.2	95.3	99.2	103	108	111	115
180	83.4	88.5	93.4	97.3	101	105	108
190	77.2	82.1	87.4	91.2	95.4	98.3	102
200	71.3	76.4	81.5	86.3	89.5	93.4	97.5
220	62.2	68.5	72.4	77.1	81.6	84.7	87.6
240	57.4	62.3	66.5	70.6	74.4	78.3	81.8
260	53.3	58.1	62.4	66.6	69.7	73.4	76.5
280	51.2	55.4	59.0	62.1	66.4	69.3	72.7
300	50.0	53.2	57.1	60.3	63.0	66.2	69.4
350	48.5	51.4	54.2	57.3	59.1	62.7	64.5
400	48.1	51.3	54.4	56.5	58.4	60.6	63.7
450	50.3	52.1	54.5	57.3	59.5	61.4	62.3
500	52.4	54.3	56.6	58.3	60.2	61.5	63.4
550	54.2	55.1	57.3	59.4	61.2	62.3	64.4
600	56.1	57.2	59.3	60.4	62.5	63.3	65.5
650	58.3	59.1	61.4	62.5	64.6	65.4	66.4
700	60.4	61.4	63.3	64.5	65.4	67.3	68.2
750	62.3	63.1	65.2	66.1	67.2	68.3	69.3
800	66.3	67.3	68.2	69.1	70.1	71.0	72.1
850	68.2	69.3	70.1	71.1	72.3	73.2	74.1
900	70.2	71.0	71.9	72.8	73.9	74.8	75.9
950	72.9	73.7	74.6	75.4	76.2	77.0	77.8
1000	75.0	76.8	77.6	78.4	79.2	80.0	80.8
1100	79.6	80.4	81.1	81.9	82.6	83.3	84.1
1200	84.7	85.2	85.7	86.3	86.8	87.4	88.0
1300	90.0	90.5	91.0	91.6	92.1	92.6	93.1
1400	94.8	95.3	95.9	96.4	96.9	97.3	97.8

Thermal conductivity $\lambda \cdot 10^3$ (W/m · deg) of dissociated oxygen [353]

T, °K \ p, bar →	0.001	0.01	0.1	1	10	100	T, °K \ p, bar →	0.001	0.01	0.1	1	10	100
1600	110	106	104	104	104	104	4000	259	343	1019	2750	2065	939
1800	158	128	119	115	115	114	4200	265	303	650	2210	2410	1185
2000	338	192	146	131	126	125	4400	273	292	471	1599	2586	1451
2200	894	382	213	159	142	137	4600	283	293	388	1119	2535	1718
2400	2147	850	374	218	167	152	4800	293	298	352	804	2279	1961
2600	3728	1764	712	335	212	172	5000	304	307	337	616	1913	2148
2800	3530	3001	1310	550	288	203	5200	314	316	335	508	1538	2255
3000	1734	3620	2163	904	414	251	5400	326	327	338	448	1219	2266
3200	715	2742	3003	1415	607	321	5600	337	338	345	416	975	2185
3400	383	1466	3247	2040	878	420	5800	348	349	354	401	801	2030
3600	287	748	2624	2627	1231	554	6000	360	360	363	396	682	1831
3800	262	453	1695	2924	1644	727							

Thermal conductivity of saturated liquid oxygen [15]

T, °K	90	95	100	105	110	115	120	125	130	135	140	145	150
$\lambda \cdot 10^3$, W/m · deg	148	142	135	129	122	115	109	102	95.1	88.6	82.0	72.8	65.3

Chapter 7

SULFUR DIOXIDE

Molecular weight 64.066

$t_{boil} = -10.0\ °C$ at 760 mm Hg; $t_{melt} = -75.3\ °C$;
$t_{cr} = 157.5\ °C$; $p_{cr} = 78.8$ bar; $\rho_{cr} = 525\ kg/m^3$

Saturated vapor pressure of sulfur dioxide at low temperatures [115]

t, °C	−69.7	−60.5	−54.6	−46.9	−35.4	−23.0	−10.0
p, mm Hg	20	40	60	100	200	400	760

Thermodynamic properties of saturated sulfur dioxide [34]:
ρ (kg/m³) and r (kJ/kg)

t, °C	P, atm	ϱ'	ϱ''	r	t, °C	P, atm	ϱ'	ϱ''	r
10	2.27		6.61		95	24.70	1134	68.5	266.1
20	3.26		9.30		100	27.41	1113	76.8	257.8
30	4.56		12.7		105	30.34	1091	86.2	248.6
40	6.22		17.2		110	33.50	1068	96.9	238.6
50	8.48	1297	23.4	313.2	115	36.92	1043	109.1	227.5
55	9.68	1280	26.7	310.2	120	40.59	1017	123.2	215.4
60	11.01	1263	30.3	306.6	130	48.77	956.6	158.9	187.1
65	12.47	1246	34.2	302.5	140	58.15	880.5	210.7	151.1
70	14.08	1229	38.6	297.9	150	68.84	769.1	298.0	99.9
75	15.85	1211	43.4	292.8	155	74.73	672.1	383.1	57.9
80	17.79	1193	48.7	287.1	157		593.3	457.1	
85	19.90	1174	54.6	280.8	157.5	77.81	525	525	0
90	22.20	1155	61.2	273.8					

Thermophysical properties of sulfur dioxide gas at $p = 1$ atm [42]: ρ (kg/m³), c_p (kJ/kg · deg), η (N · s/m²) and λ (W/m · deg)

t, °C	0	100	200	300	400	500	600	700	800	900	1000
ϱ	2.926	2.140	1.690	1.395	1.187	1.033	0.916	0.892	0.743	0.681	0.626
c_p	0.607	0.662	0.712	0.754	0.783	0.808	0.825	0.837	0.850	0.858	0.867
$\eta \cdot 10^7$	1.16	1.61	2.00	2.38	2.75	3.13	3.45	3.75	4.03	4.29	4.53
$\lambda \cdot 10^2$	0.84	1.23	1.66	2.12	2.58	3.07	3.58	4.10	4.63	5.19	5.76

Compressibility factor z of sulfur dioxide [341]

p, atm \ t, °C →	10	20	30	40	50	75	100	125	150
0.5	0.9889	0.9903	0.9917	0.9928					
1	0.9775	0.9806	0.9835	0.9855	0.9871	0.9902	0.9925	0.9938	0.9951
2	0.9531	0.9607	0.9667	0.9709	0.9742	0.9804	0.9894	0.9877	0.9901
3		0.9392	0.9495	0.9560	0.9611	0.9706	0.9773	0.9815	0.9852
4			0.9313	0.9406	0.9478	0.9606	0.9696	0.9752	0.9802
5				0.9248	0.9344	0.9505	0.9619	0.9690	0.9752
6				0.9080	0.9207	0.9403	0.9540	0.9627	0.9702
7					0.9065	0.9298	0.9460	0.9564	0.9652
8					0.8906	0.9191	0.9379	0.9500	0.9601
10						0.8968	0.9213	0.9371	0.9500
12						0.8731	0.9042	0.9240	0.9398
14						0.8470	0.8865	0.9106	0.9294
16							0.8682	0.8970	0.9188
18							0.8492	0.8830	0.9081
20							0.8292	0.8687	0.8973
25							0.7728	0.8310	0.8692
30								0.7902	0.8394
35									
40								0.6905	0.7737
45									
50									0.6981
55									
60									0.6002

p, atm \ t, °C →	157.5	175	200	225	250
1	0.9953	0.9961	0.9967	0.9973	0.9973
2	0.9906	0.9922	0.9934	0.9946	0.9954
5	0.9765	0.9804	0.9836	0.9864	0.9884
10	0.9528	0.9605	0.9671	0.9728	0.9769
15	0.9286	0.9399	0.9504	0.9592	0.9653
20	0.9037	0.9185	0.9334	0.9454	0.9538
25	0.8655	0.8963	0.9157	0.9315	0.9422
30	0.8507	0.8732	0.8976	0.9173	0.9306
35	0.8222	0.8492	0.8791	0.9030	0.9191
40	0.7916	0.8243	0.8602	0.8883	0.9075
45	0.7588	0.7983	0.8407	0.8734	0.8958
50	0.7241	0.7713	0.8208	0.8583	0.8840
55	0.6858	0.7429	0.8004	0.8429	0.8719
60	0.6435	0.7133	0.7795	0.8273	0.8597
65	0.5960	0.6820	0.7580	0.8115	0.8476
70	0.5359	0.6492	0.7360	0.7956	0.8353
75	0.4473	0.6127	0.7134	0.7794	0.8231
80	0.2062	0.5721	0.6900	0.7628	0.8107
85	0.1992	0.5255	0.6660	0.7464	0.7984
90	0.2050	0.4718	0.6412	0.7294	0.7860
95	0.2093	0.4093	0.6156	0.7123	0.7737
100	0.2145	0.3470	0.5891	0.6952	0.7612
110	0.2310	0.2922	0.5339	0.6607	0.7365
120	0.2477	0.2849	0.4810	0.6264	0.7121
130	0.2564	0.2910	0.4371	0.5939	0.6887
140	0.2684	0.2984	0.4120	0.5643	0.6670
150	0.2869	0.3102	0.3985	0.5395	0.6461
160	0.3104	0.3276	0.3927	0.5198	0.6274
170	0.3224	0.3403	0.3952	0.5060	0.6116
180	0.3340	0.3510	0.4011	0.4976	0.5993
190	0.3478	0.3633	0.4090	0.4944	0.5894
200	0.3631	0.3766	0.4182	0.4947	0.5818
210	0.3789	0.3925	0.4272	0.4973	0.5772
220	0.3946	0.4069	0.4370	0.5014	0.5755
230	0.4089	0.4206	0.4485	0.5076	0.5764

continued

p, atm \ t, °C →	157.5	175	200	225	250
240	0.4224	0.4345	0.4598	0.5154	0.5785
250	0.4362	0.4477	0.4711	0.5235	0.5822
260	0.4519	0.4612	0.4837	0.5324	0.5871
270	0.4659	0.4746	0.4954	0.5421	0.5930
280	0.4799	0.4839	0.5077	0.5524	0.5997
290	0.4941	0.5032	0.5209	0.5627	0.6074
300	0.5068	0.5170	0.5342	0.5740	0.6148
310	0.5230	0.5298	0.5488	0.5844	0.6224
315	0.5307	0.5362	0.5565	0.5891	0.6260

Chapter 8

HALOGENS

FLUORINE (F_2)

Molecular weight 38.000

$T_{boil} = 85.2$ °K at 760 mm Hg; $T_{melt} = 53$ °K; $T_{cr} = 144$ °K;
$p_{cr} = 53.2$ bar; $\rho_{cr} = 535$ kg/m³

Thermodynamic properties of saturated fluorine [147]:
v (dm³/kg), r and i (kJ/kg) and s (kJ/kg · deg)

T, °K	p, bar	v′	v″	i′	i″	r	s′	s″
95.0	2.775	0.6968	69.41	−342.5	−164.2	178.3	2.314	4.190
97.5	3.465	0.7072	56.32	−338.1	−163.2	174.9	2.362	4.156
100.0	4.282	0.7181	46.05	−333.8	−162.4	171.4	2.408	4.122
102.5	5.236	0.7295	37.98	−329.4	−161.7	167.7	2.454	4.090
105.0	6.340	0.7414	31.56	−324.9	−161.1	163.8	2.498	4.058
107.5	7.602	0.7541	26.42	−320.6	−160.8	159.8	2.541	4.028
110.0	9.029	0.7675	22.29	−316.1	−160.5	155.6	2.583	3.998
112.5	10.63	0.7818	18.92	−311.6	−160.5	151.1	2.626	3.969
115.0	12.41	0.7972	16.18	−307.0	−160.6	146.4	2.668	3.941
117.5	14.39	0.8138	13.88	−302.2	−160.9	141.3	2.710	3.912
120.0	16.59	0.8319	11.94	−297.4	−161.5	135.9	2.751	3.884
122.5	19.03	0.8518	10.29	−292.4	−162.3	130.1	2.792	3.854
125.0	21.73	0.8739	8.878	−287.3	−163.5	123.8	2.834	3.824
127.5	24.70	0.8990	7.660	−282.0	−165.0	117.0	2.875	3.793
130.0	27.98	0.9278	6.596	−276.5	−166.9	109.6	2.916	3.760
132.5	31.59	0.9619	5.657	−270.9	−169.5	101.4	2.958	3.723
135.0	35.57	1.0039	4.814	−264.7	−172.8	91.9	3.002	3.683
137.5	39.93	1.0593	4.051	−257.4	−177.2	80.2	3.053	3.637
140.0	44.69	1.1526	3.345	−248.7	−183.2	65.5	3.113	3.581
142.5	49.87	1.3351	2.640	−236.8	−192.4	44.4	3.193	3.505
144.0	53.25	1.8727	1.8727	−210.0	−210.0	0	3.376	3.376

Saturated vapor pressure of fluorine at low temperatures [115]

p, mm Hg	1	2	10	20	40	60	100	200	400	760
T, °K	50.1	56.3	59.1	62.2	65.5	67.6	70.5	74.9	80.0	85.2

Thermodynamic properties of fluorine at different temperatures and pressures [147]:
v (dm³/kg), i (kJ/kg) and s (kJ/kg · deg)

T, °K	v	i	s	v	i	s	v	i	s
		p=1 bar			p=2 bar			p=4 bar	
100	214.1	−157.2	4.477	104.6	−158.7	4.315	49.69	−161.9	4.141
110	236.8	−149.2	4.552	116.4	−150.5	4.393	56.17	−153.1	4.225
120	259.4	−141.4	4.620	128.1	−142.4	4.463	62.38	−144.6	4.299
130	281.8	−133.6	4.683	139.6	−134.5	4.527	68.41	−136.3	4.365

continued

T, °K	v	i	s	v	i	s	v	i	s
140	304.1	−125.8	4.741	150.9	−126.5	4.585	74.33	−128.1	4.426
150	326.3	−118.0	4.795	162.2	−118.6	4.640	80.16	−120.0	4.482
160	348.5	−110.1	4.845	173.5	−110.8	4.691	85.93	−111.9	4.534
170	370.6	−102.4	4.892	184.6	−102.9	4.738	91.65	−103.9	4.582
180	392.7	− 94.59	4.937	195.8	− 95.04	4.783	97.33	− 95.96	4.628
190	414.8	− 86.76	4.979	206.9	− 87.17	4.826	103.0	− 87.99	4.671
200	436.8	− 78.91	5.019	218.0	− 79.28	4.866	108.6	− 80.01	4.712
220	480.8	− 63.13	5.095	240.1	− 63.43	4.942	119.8	− 64.03	4.788
240	524.8	− 47.23	5.164	262.2	− 47.47	5.011	130.9	− 47.97	4.858
260	568.7	− 31.17	5.228	284.2	− 31.38	5.076	142.0	− 31.79	4.923
280	612.6	− 14.96	5.288	306.3	− 15.13	5.136	153.1	− 15.47	4.983
300	656.4	1.427	5.345	328.2	1.284	5.192	164.1	0.9992	5.040
320	700.3	17.99	5.398	350.2	17.88	5.246	175.2	17.64	5.093
340	744.1	34.75	5.449	372.2	34.65	5.297	186.2	34.45	5.144
360	788.0	51.69	5.497	394.1	51.61	5.345	197.2	51.44	5.193
380	831.8	68.81	5.544	416.1	68.75	5.392	208.2	68.61	5.239
400	875.6	86.12	5.588	438.1	86.06	5.436	219.2	85.95	5.284
450	985.1	130.1	5.691	492.8	130.1	5.540	246.6	130.0	5.388
500	1094.6	174.9	5.786	547.6	174.9	5.634	274.1	174.9	5.482
	p=6 bar			p=8 bar			p=10 bar		
100	0.7177	−333.6	0.7773	0.7773	−337.7	2.406	0.7169	−333.6	2.406
110	35.98	−155.9	4.118	25.80	−158.9	4.035	0.7672	−316.1	2.583
120	40.43	−146.8	4.197	29.41	−149.2	4.120	22.76	−151.7	4.056
130	44.67	−138.1	4.266	32.78	−140.1	4.193	25.62	−142.1	4.133
140	48.78	−129.7	4.329	35.99	−131.3	4.258	28.31	−133.0	4.200
150	52.80	−121.4	4.386	39.11	−121.7	4.317	30.89	−124.2	4.261
160	56.75	−113.1	4.439	42.15	−114.3	4.371	33.39	−115.6	4.316
170	60.65	−105.0	4.489	45.14	−106.0	4.421	35.84	−107.1	4.368
180	64.50	− 96.89	4.535	48.09	− 97.82	4.468	38.24	−98.76	4.415
190	68.33	− 88.81	4.579	51.01	− 89.64	4.512	40.62	−90.48	4.460
200	72.13	− 80.75	4.620	53.90	− 81.49	4.554	42.96	−82.24	4.502
220	79.68	− 64.63	4.697	59.63	− 65.23	4.632	47.59	−65.83	4.581
240	87.17	− 48.46	4.767	65.29	− 48.95	4.703	52.17	−49.44	4.652
260	94.62	− 32.20	4.832	70.92	− 32.60	4.768	56.70	−33.01	4.718
280	102.0	− 15.81	4.893	76.52	− 16.15	4.829	61.21	−16.49	4.779
300	109.4	0.7150	4.950	82.10	0.4315	4.886	65.69	0.1488	4.836
320	116.8	17.40	5.004	87.66	17.16	4.940	70.16	16.93	4.890
340	124.2	34.25	5.055	93.20	34.05	4.991	74.61	33.86	4.942
360	131.6	51.28	5.104	98.74	51.11	5.040	79.05	50.95	4.991
380	138.9	68.47	5.150	104.3	68.34	5.087	83.48	68.20	5.037
400	146.3	85.84	5.195	109.8	85.73	5.131	87.91	85.62	5.082
450	164.6	129.9	5.299	123.6	129.9	5.235	98.95	129.8	5.186
500	182.9	174.9	5.393	137.3	174.8	5.330	110.0	174.8	5.281
	p=20 bar			p=30 bar			p=40 bar		
100	0.7148	−333.4	2.401	0.7128	−333.1	2.397	0.7108	−332.8	2.393
110	0.7639	−316.0	2.577	0.7607	−315.5	2.572	0.7577	−315.6	2.566
120	0.8298	−297.4	2.748	0.8240	−297.5	2.740	0.8185	−297.6	2.733
130	11.09	−153.8	3.914	0.9247	−276.7	2.914	0.9108	−277.5	2.900
140	12.84	−142.2	4.000	7.519	−153.4	3.849	4.576	−169.6	3.691
150	14.40	−131.7	4.072	8.831	−140.3	3.940	5.968	−150.4	3.824
160	15.85	−122.0	4.135	9.965	−128.9	4.013	6.994	−136.5	3.914
170	17.22	−112.6	4.192	11.00	−118.4	4.077	7.878	−124.6	3.986
180	18.54	−103.6	4.243	11.97	−108.6	4.133	8.683	−113.7	4.048
190	19.83	− 94.71	4.291	12.90	− 99.05	4.185	9.436	−103.5	4.104
200	21.08	− 85.99	4.336	13.80	− 89.81	4.232	10.15	− 93.69	4.154
220	23.53	− 68.84	4.418	15.52	− 71.87	4.318	11.51	− 74.91	4.243
240	25.92	− 51.90	4.492	17.18	− 54.35	4.394	12.81	− 56.79	4.322
260	28.27	− 35.04	4.559	18.79	− 37.05	4.463	14.06	− 39.04	4.393
280	30.85	− 18.17	4.622	20.38	− 19.83	4.527	15.28	− 21.48	4.458
300	32.88	− 12.53	4.680	21.94	− 2.635	4.586	16.48	− 3.997	4.519
320	35.15	15.76	4.735	23.49	14.61	4.642	17.66	13.48	4.575
340	37.42	32.88	4.787	25.02	31.93	4.694	18.83	30.99	4.628

continued

T, °K	v	i	s	v	i	s	v	i	s
360	39.67	50.14	4.836	26.55	49.35	4.744	19.98	48.57	4.678
380	41.91	67.54	4.883	28.06	66.89	4.792	21.13	66.25	4.726
400	44.15	85.08	4.928	29.57	84.56	4.837	22.28	84.04	4.772
450	49.72	129.5	5.033	33.31	129.3	4.942	25.11	129.0	4.878
500	55.27	164.7	5.128	37.03	174.6	5.038	27.92	174.5	4.974
	$p=50$ bar			$p=60$ bar			$p=70$ bar		
100	0.7089	−332.5	2.388	0.7071	−332.2	2.384	0.7053	−331.9	2.380
110	0.7548	−315.5	2.561	0.7520	−315.3	2.556	0.7493	−315.0	2.551
120	0.8135	−297.6	2.726	0.8087	−297.6	2.720	0.8043	−297.6	2.713
130	0.8991	−278.1	2.889	0.8890	−278.6	2.878	0.8800	−279.0	2.868
140	1.092	−252.0	3.085	1.042	−255.3	3.054	1.010	−257.4	3.032
150	4.147	−163.1	3.706	2.745	−181.8	3.558	1.578	−213.2	3.335
160	5.182	−145.0	3.823	3.943	−154.8	3.734	3.027	−166.1	3.641
170	5.995	−131.2	3.907	4.732	−138.2	3.834	3.824	−145.8	3.765
180	6.707	−119.1	3.976	5.390	−124.7	3.911	4.449	−130.5	3.852
190	7.360	−108.1	4.036	5.977	−112.7	3.976	4.992	−117.5	3.923
200	7.972	−97.62	4.089	6.520	−101.6	4.033	5.486	−105.6	3.983
220	9.117	−77.95	4.183	7.522	−80.98	4.132	6.385	−84.02	4.086
240	10.19	−59.21	4.265	8.451	−61.62	4.216	7.210	−64.01	4.174
260	11.22	−41.01	4.337	9.336	−42.96	4.291	7.990	−44.89	4.250
280	12.22	−23.10	4.404	10.19	−24.70	4.358	8.738	−26.27	4.319
300	13.20	−5.338	4.465	11.02	−6.658	4.421	9.464	−7.957	4.382
320	14.16	12.36	4.522	11.84	11.27	4.478	10.17	10.20	4.441
340	15.11	30.07	4.576	12.64	29.16	4.533	10.87	28.27	4.496
360	16.05	47.81	4.627	13.43	47.07	4.584	11.56	46.34	4.547
380	16.98	65.63	4.675	14.21	65.02	4.632	12.23	64.43	4.596
400	17.90	83.54	4.721	14.99	83.05	4.679	12.91	82.57	4.643
450	20.19	128.7	4.827	16.91	128.5	4.786	14.56	128.2	4.750
500	22.45	174.4	4.923	18.80	174.4	4.882	16.20	174.3	4.847
	$p=80$ bar			$p=100$ bar			$p=200$ bar		
100	0.7035	−331.6	2.376	0.7001	−331.0	2.368	0.6850	−327.7	2.332
110	0.7467	−314.8	2.546	0.7418	−314.4	2.537	0.7208	−311.6	2.496
120	0.8000	−297.5	2.707	0.7922	−297.3	2.695	0.7616	−295.5	2.646
130	0.8718	−279.3	2.860	0.8577	−279.7	2.843	0.8094	−279.4	2.781
140	0.9868	−258.8	3.014	0.9531	−260.7	2.987	0.8672	−263.5	2.902
150	1.293	−225.8	3.241	1.128	−234.9	3.165	0.9393	−244.5	3.034
160	2.317	−179.6	3.540	1.533	−203.2	3.370	1.032	−226.2	3.152
170	3.139	−153.9	3.697	2.193	−171.4	3.563	1.151	−207.5	3.266
180	3.744	−136.6	3.796	2.765	−149.1	3.690	1.297	−188.9	3.372
190	4.255	−122.3	3.873	3.232	−132.2	3.782	1.464	−170.8	3.470
200	4.713	−109.7	3.938	3.639	−117.8	3.856	1.652	−153.3	3.559
220	5.535	−87.04	4.046	4.352	−93.03	3.974	2.062	−120.7	3.715
240	6.282	−66.38	4.136	4.987	−71.04	4.070	2.447	−92.54	3.838
260	6.982	−46.79	4.214	5.575	−50.52	4.152	2.798	−67.63	3.937
280	7.650	−27.83	4.284	6.132	−30.86	4.225	3.123	−44.71	4.022
300	8.297	−9.235	4.348	6.667	−11.73	4.291	3.429	−23.05	4.097
320	8.927	9.141	4.408	7.186	7.085	4.351	3.721	−2.196	4.164
340	9.545	27.40	4.463	7.692	25.71	4.408	4.001	18.11	4.226
360	10.15	45.62	4.515	8.189	44.24	4.461	4.274	38.04	4.283
380	10.75	63.85	4.564	8.678	62.72	4.511	4.540	57.73	4.336
400	11.35	82.10	4.611	9.161	81.20	4.558	4.800	77.26	4.386
450	12.81	128.0	4.719	10.35	127.5	4.667	5.431	125.7	4.500
500	14.25	174.2	4.817	11.51	174.1	4.765	6.044	173.8	4.602
	$p=300$ bar			$p=400$ bar			$p=500$ bar		
100	0.6723	−324.1	2.300	0.6613	−320.4	2.271	0.6516	−316.6	2.243
110	0.7043	−308.4	2.460	0.6905	−304.9	2.428	0.6787	−301.2	2.400
120	0.7394	−292.8	2.606	0.7218	−289.7	2.571	0.7072	−286.2	2.540
130	0.7786	−277.5	2.735	0.7557	−274.8	2.696	0.7374	−271.7	2.663
140	0.8229	−262.7	2.848	0.7927	−260.6	2.805	0.7698	−257.9	2.769
150	0.8736	−245.3	2.968	0.8334	−244.0	2.920	0.8045	−241.7	2.881
160	0.9321	−229.2	3.072	0.8783	−228.8	3.019	0.8418	−227.0	2.976

continued

T, °K	v	i	s	v	i	s	v	i	s
170	0.9994	−213.1	3.170	0.9275	−213.7	3.110	0.8878	−212.5	3.064
180	1.076	−197.1	3.261	0.9814	−198.9	3.195	0.9244	−198.3	3.145
190	1.161	−181.4	3.346	1.040	−184.3	3.274	0.9696	−184.3	3.221
200	1.254	−166.1	3.425	1.102	−169.9	3.347	1.017	−170.5	3.291
220	1.457	−136.6	3.565	1.236	−142.1	3.480	1.119	−143.7	3.419
240	1.680	−108.4	3.688	1.381	−115.4	3.596	1.227	−117.8	3.532
260	1.916	− 81.49	3.796	1.533	− 89.63	3.699	1.340	− 92.72	3.632
280	2.147	− 56.30	3.889	1.694	− 64.48	3.792	1.457	− 68.25	3.723
300	2.368	− 32.61	3.971	1.858	− 40.02	3.877	1.578	− 44.29	3.806
320	2.579	− 10.06	4.044	2.020	− 16.42	3.953	1.702	− 20.68	3.882
340	2.781	11.68	4.110	2.178	6.375	4.022	1.827	2.526	3.952
360	2.976	32.85	4.170	2.331	28.52	4.085	1.951	25.24	4.017
380	3.165	53.59	4.226	2.480	50.16	4.144	2.073	47.50	4.077
400	3.349	74.04	4.279	2.625	71.40	4.198	2.192	69.36	4.133
450	3.793	124.3	4.397	2.973	123.3	4.321	2.480	122.7	4.259
500	4.220	173.9	4.502	3.305	174.2	4.428	2.755	174.7	4.368

Molar fraction of F_2 in dissociated fluorine [148]

T, °K \ p, bar →	0.1	0.2	0.4	0.6	0.8	1	2
600	0.9996	0.9997	0.9998	0.9998	0.9998	0.9999	0.9999
700	0.9956	0.9969	0.9978	0.9982	0.9984	0.9986	0.9990
800	0.9746	0.9820	0.9872	0.9895	0.9909	0.9919	0.9943
900	0.9037	0.9309	0.9506	0.9595	0.9648	0.9685	0.9776
1000	0.7384	0.8066	0.8589	0.8832	0.8980	0.9082	0.9342
1100	0.4797	0.5914	0.6883	0.7367	0.7673	0.7890	0.8455
1200	0.2313	0.3405	0.4587	0.5265	0.5725	0.6064	0.7008
1300	0.0900	0.1552	0.2468	0.3103	0.3583	0.3963	0.5139
1400	0.0338	0.0635	0.1137	0.1550	0.1899	0.2201	0.3274
1500	0.0135	0.0264	0.0502	0.0719	0.0918	0.1101	0.1848
1600	0.0059	0.0117	0.0230	0.0337	0.0440	0.0538	0.0979
1700	0.0028	0.0057	0.0112	0.0166	0.0219	0.0271	0.0516
1800	0.0015	0.0029	0.0059	0.0087	0.0116	0.0144	0.0280
1900	0.0008	0.0016	0.0033	0.0049	0.0065	0.0081	0.0159
2000	0.0005	0.0010	0.0019	0.0029	0.0038	0.0048	0.0095
2200	0.0002	0.0004	0.0008	0.0011	0.0015	0.0019	0.0038
2400	0.0001	0.0002	0.0004	0.0005	0.0007	0.0009	0.0018
2600	0.0001	0.0001	0.0002	0.0003	0.0004	0.0005	0.0009
2800	0.0000	0.0000	0.0001	0.0002	0.0002	0.0003	0.0005
3000	0.0000	0.0000	0.0001	0.0001	0.0001	0.0002	0.0003
3500	0.0000	0.0000	0.0000	0.0000	0.0000	0.0001	0.0001
4000	0.0000	0.0000	0.0000	0.0000	0.0000	0.0000	0.0001
5000	0.0000	0.0000	0.0000	0.0000	0.0000	0.0000	0.0000
6000	0.0000	0.0000	0.0000	0.0000	0.0000	0.0000	0.0000

T, °K \ p, bar →	4	6	8	10	20	40	60
600	0.9999	0.9999	0.9999	1.0000	1.0000	1.0000	1.0000
700	0.9993	0.9994	0.9995	0.9996	0.9997	0.9998	0.9998
800	0.9959	0.9967	0.9971	0.9974	0.9982	0.9987	0.9989
900	0.9841	0.9870	0.9887	0.9899	0.9929	0.9949	0.9959
1000	0.9530	0.9615	0.9665	0.9700	0.9787	0.9849	0.9877
1100	0.8880	0.9076	0.9194	0.9276	0.9483	0.9631	0.9698
1200	0.7772	0.8138	0.8365	0.8524	0.8932	0.9232	0.9368
1300	0.6219	0.6777	0.7136	0.7392	0.8073	0.8593	0.8835
1400	0.4453	0.5135	0.5600	0.5945	0.6909	0.7692	0.8069
1500	0.2847	0.3512	0.4002	0.4384	0.5537	0.6562	0.7083
1600	0.1570	0.2197	0.2602	0.2971	0.4135	0.5302	0.5938
1700	0.0941	0.1302	0.1613	0.1887	0.2894	0.4052	0.4743

continued

T, °K \ p, bar →	4	6	8	10	20	40	60
1800	0.0532	0.0759	0.0903	0.1159	0.1930	0.2946	0.3616
1900	0.0308	0.0449	0.0582	0.0709	0.1255	0.2065	0.2653
2000	0.0186	0.0274	0.0358	0.0440	0.0813	0.1418	0.1895
2200	0.0076	0.0112	0.0149	0.0185	0.0357	0.0667	0.0942
2400	0.0035	0.0053	0.0070	0.0087	0.0172	0.0332	0.0482
2600	0.0018	0.0028	0.0037	0.0046	0.0091	0.0179	0.0263
2800	0.0011	0.0016	0.0021	0.0026	0.0052	0.0099	0.0154
3000	0.0006	0.0010	0.0013	0.0016	0.0032	0.0065	0.0096
3500	0.0002	0.0004	0.0005	0.0006	0.0012	0.0025	0.0037
4000	0.0001	0.0002	0.0002	0.0003	0.0006	0.0012	0.0018
5000	0.0000	0.0001	0.0001	0.0001	0.0002	0.0004	0.0006
6000	0.0000	0.0000	0.0000	0.0001	0.0001	0.0002	0.0003

T, °K \ p, bar →	80	100	200	300	400	500
600	1.0000	1.0000	1.0000	1.0000	1.0000	1.0000
700	0.9998	0.9999	0.9999	0.9999	0.9999	0.9999
800	0.9991	0.9992	0.9994	0.9995	0.9996	0.9996
900	0.9964	0.9968	0.9977	0.9981	0.9984	0.9986
1000	0.9893	0.9904	0.9932	0.9944	0.9952	0.9957
1100	0.9738	0.9765	0.9833	0.9863	0.9881	0.9893
1200	0.9450	0.9506	0.9647	0.9711	0.9748	0.9774
1300	0.8982	0.9084	0.9342	0.9458	0.9528	0.9576
1400	0.8303	0.8467	0.8887	0.9079	0.9195	0.9275
1500	0.7414	0.7649	0.8268	0.8558	0.8735	0.8858
1600	0.6358	0.6664	0.7493	0.7894	0.8143	0.8317
1700	0.5221	0.5579	0.6593	0.7106	0.7431	0.7661
1800	0.4106	0.4487	0.5625	0.6231	0.6626	0.6911
1900	0.3109	0.3478	0.4653	0.5321	0.5770	0.6101
2000	0.2287	0.2616	0.3742	0.4429	0.4909	0.5271
2200	0.1188	0.1410	0.2272	0.2881	0.3344	0.3713
2400	0.0624	0.0757	0.1327	0.1781	0.2155	0.2471
2600	0.0348	0.0424	0.0782	0.1092	0.1363	0.1604
2800	0.0203	0.0251	0.0478	0.0644	0.0872	0.1046
3000	0.0127	0.0158	0.0306	0.0444	0.0574	0.0697
3500	0.0049	0.0061	0.0121	0.0179	0.0235	0.0290
4000	0.0024	0.0030	0.0060	0.0089	0.0117	0.0145
5000	0.0009	0.0011	0.0022	0.0033	0.0043	0.0050
6000	0.0004	0.0006	0.0011	0.0017	0.0022	0.0028

Thermodynamic properties of dissociated fluorine [148]: v (m³/kg), c_p (kJ/kg · deg), i* (kJ/kg) and s (kJ/kg · deg)

T,°K	v	c_p	i	s	v	c_p	i	s
	p=0.1 bar				p=0.2 bar			
600	13.13	0.957	500.2	6.4566	6.566	0.948	500.0	6.3044
700	15.35	1.164	602.6	6.6140	7.671	1.100	599.8	6.4581
800	17.73	1.960	743.8	6.8016	8.833	1.665	727.6	6.6280
900	20.69	4.232	1 003.7	7.1056	10.20	3.259	939.7	6.8764
1000	25.17	9.284	1 536	7.6628	12.11	6.829	1 347	7.3030
1100	32.65	17.27	2 521	8.6216	15.17	13.23	2 104	8.0381
1200	42.93	19.52	3 831	9.7795	19.69	18.55	3 245	9.0443
1300	52.65	12.11	4 877	10.6347	24.81	15.62	4 415	9.9988
1400	59.85	5.667	5 435	11.0575	29.08	8.667	5 193	10.5879
1500	65.44	2.867	5 721	11.2572	32.30	4.346	5 609	10.8812
1600	70.34	1.822	5 899	11.3746	34.96	2.476	5 848	11.0375
1700	74.18	1.395	5 975	11.3396	36.99	1.676	5 951	11.0230

*Due to different base level of calculations, these values of i are higher by 232.3 kJ/kg than those given on pp. 506-509.

continued

T, °K	v	c_p	i	s	v	c_p	i	s
1800	78.66	1.240	6 098	11.4095	39.27	1.374	6 085	11.0997
1900	83.08	1.171	6 214	11.4723	41.51	1.239	6 206	11.1655
2000	87.48	1.138	6 327	11.5303	43.72	1.175	6 323	11.2251
2200	96.26	1.113	6 550	11.6365	48.12	1.125	6 548	11.3325
2400	105.0	1.105	6 770	11.7326	52.51	1.109	6 770	11.4290
2600	113.8	1.101	6 991	11.8208	56.89	1.103	6 990	11.5173
2800	122.5	1.099	7 211	11.9022	61.26	1.100	7 210	11.5988
3000	131.3	1.098	7 430	11.9780	65.64	1.099	7 430	11.6748
3500	153.2	1.096	7 979	12.1471	76.58	1.096	7 979	11.8347
4000	175.0	1.096	8 527	12.2934	87.52	1.096	8 527	11.9901
5000	218.8	1.096	9 623	12.5380	109.4	1.096	9 623	12.2347
6000	262.6	1.099	10 718	12.7377	131.3	1.099	10 718	12.4343
		$p=0.4$ bar				$p=0.6$ bar		
600	3.283	0.942	499.8	6.1524	2.189	0.940	499.7	6.0635
700	3.834	1.055	597.8	6.3034	2.556	1.035	597.8	6.2133
800	4.405	1.458	716.1	6.4607	2.933	1.366	711.0	6.3651
900	5.049	2.580	894.4	6.6697	3.351	2.281	874.3	6.5566
1000	5.886	5.084	1 212	7.0025	3.874	4.315	1 152	6.8474
1100	7.143	9.820	1 788	7.5607	4.628	8.212	1 644	7.3234
1200	9.036	15.55	2 711	8.3733	5.753	13.49	2 442	8.0263
1300	11.48	17.06	3 849	9.2997	7.277	16.64	3 504	8.8889
1400	13.87	12.11	4 813	10.0287	8.910	13.78	4 526	9.6613
1500	15.78	6.679	5 411	10.4500	10.30	8.396	5 237	10.1628
1600	17.29	3.652	5 750	10.6733	11.40	4.673	5 658	10.4402
1700	18.39	2.209	5 902	10.6938	12.20	2.707	5 856	10.4913
1800	19.58	1.635	6 059	10.7834	13.02	1.887	6 034	10.5935
1900	20.72	1.374	6 192	10.8554	13.79	1.505	6 178	10.6712
2000	21.84	1.248	6 314	10.9179	14.55	1.320	6 306	10.7367
2200	24.05	1.150	6 544	11.0278	16.03	1.174	6 541	10.8490
2400	26.25	1.119	6 768	11.1251	17.50	1.129	6 767	10.9471
2600	28.44	1.108	6 989	11.2140	18.96	1.112	6 989	11.0360
2800	30.63	1.103	7 210	11.2954	20.42	1.105	7 209	11.1178
3000	32.82	1.100	7 430	11.3712	21.88	1.101	7 430	11.1939
3500	38.29	1.097	7 979	11.5406	25.53	1.097	7 978	11.3629
4000	43.76	1.096	8 527	11.6868	29.17	1.096	8 527	11.5093
5000	54.70	1.096	9 623	11.9313	36.47	1.096	9 623	11.7539
6000	65.64	1.099	10 718	12.1310	43.76	1.099	10 718	11.9536
		$p=0.8$ bar				$p=1.0$ bar		
600	1.641	0.938	499.6	6.0004	1.313	0.937	499.6	5.9515
700	1.917	1.023	596.4	6.1495	1.533	1.015	596.1	6.1001
800	2.199	1.311	708.0	6.2981	1.758	1.274	705.9	6.2464
900	2.506	2.104	862.3	6.4791	2.002	1.983	854.2	6.4204
1000	2.883	3.858	1 116	6.7449	2.294	3.548	1 091	6.6690
1100	3.410	7.237	1 556	7.1709	2.695	6.567	1 496	7.0606
1200	4.187	12.07	2 274	7.8020	3.278	11.02	2 156	7.6401
1300	5.262	15.89	3 265	8.6067	4.094	15.11	3 087	8.3961
1400	6.483	14.60	4 299	9.3874	5.056	14.95	4 114	9.1706
1500	7.583	9.678	5 085	9.9411	5.964	10.64	4 949	9.7589
1600	8.466	5.562	5 572	10.2627	6.708	6.340	5 492	10.1169
1700	9.100	3.173	5 811	10.3413	7.244	3.608	5 767	10.2293
1800	9.734	2.130	6 009	10.4550	7.766	2.365	5 985	10.3451
1900	10.33	1.634	6 164	10.5386	8.249	1.761	6 150	10.4343
2000	10.90	1.391	6 297	10.6070	8.711	1.461	6 289	10.5056
2200	12.02	1.199	6 538	10.7217	9.610	1.223	6 534	10.6227
2400	13.12	1.139	6 765	10.8206	10.49	1.149	6 763	10.7224
2600	14.22	1.117	6 988	10.9098	11.37	1.121	6 987	10.8119
2800	15.31	1.107	7 209	10.9917	12.25	1.109	7 209	10.8939
3000	16.41	1.102	7 429	11.0677	13.13	1.103	7 429	10.9700
3500	19.15	1.098	7 978	11.2370	15.32	1.098	7 978	11.1393
4000	21.88	1.096	8 527	11.3834	17.50	1.097	8 526	11.2857
5000	27.35	1.096	9 623	11.6280	21.88	1.096	9 623	11.5303
6000	32.82	1.099	10 718	11.8277	26.26	1.099	10 718	11.7300

continued

T, °K	v	c_p	i	s	v	c_p	i	s
	$p=2$ bar				$p=4$ bar			
600	0.6569	0.935	499.5	5.7996	0.3287	0.933	499.3	5.6476
700	0.7668	0.994	595.2	5.9470	0.3836	0.980	594.5	5.7942
800	0.8784	1.182	700.8	6.0878	0.4391	1.116	697.2	5.9311
900	0.9965	1.684	833.9	6.2641	0.4970	1.474	819.6	6.0749
1000	1.132	2.784	1 030	6.4501	0.5609	2.249	987.0	6.2507
1100	1.306	4.902	1 347	6.7553	0.6386	3.731	1 240	6.4944
1200	1.547	8.211	1 852	7.1989	0.7405	6.097	1 630	6.8364
1300	1.886	12.183	2 595	7.8011	0.8799	9.302	2 206	7.3031
1400	2.321	14.500	3 523	8.5004	1.065	12.36	2 977	7.8826
1500	2.791	12.93	4 440	9.1449	1.286	13.32	3 854	8.4979
1600	3.217	9.036	5 149	9.6123	1.512	11.32	4 665	9.0318
1700	3.538	5.407	5 567	9.0106	1.701	7.706	5 241	9.3354
1800	3.832	3.424	5 870	9.9838	1.871	5.074	5 665	9.5778
1900	4.093	2.357	6 082	10.0983	2.017	3.391	5 956	9.7358
2000	4.336	1.800	6 248	10.1839	2.149	2.422	6 170	9.8454
2200	4.796	1.343	6 518	10.3126	2.389	1.574	6 485	9.9959
2400	5.243	1.197	6 756	10.4162	2.617	1.292	6 740	10.1071
2600	5.684	1.143	6 983	10.5072	2.840	1.186	6 775	10.2011
2800	6.124	1.120	7 206	10.5899	3.061	1.142	7 202	10.2851
3000	6.563	1.109	7 428	10 6662	3.281	1.121	7 425	10.3621
3500	7.658	1.100	7 978	10.8359	3.829	1.103	7 977	10.5323
4000	8.752	1.097	8 526	10.9824	4.376	1.099	8 526	10.6789
5000	10.94	1.096	9 623	11.2270	5.471	1.096	9 623	10.9236
6000	13.13	1.099	10 718	11.4267	6.565	1.099	10 718	11.1233
	$p=6$ bar				$p=8$ bar			
600	0.2193	0.932	499.2	5.5585	0.1646	0.931	499.2	5.4953
700	0.2559	0.974	594.3	5.7049	0.1921	0.970	594.1	5.6415
800	0.2929	1.087	695.6	5.8400	0.2198	1.070	694.6	5.7757
900	0.3311	1.381	813.3	5.9784	0.2482	1.326	809.5	5.9108
1000	0.3726	2.014	767.9	6.1408	0.2789	1.874	956.6	6.0653
1100	0.4216	3.218	1 193	6.3571	0.3144	2.913	1 164	6.2651
1200	0.4839	5.147	1 530	6.5530	0.3586	4.580	1 471	6.5333
1300	0.5671	7.856	2 026	7.0537	0.4166	6.959	1 916	6.8932
1400	0.6778	10.825	2 701	7.5608	0.4932	9.739	2 526	7.3516
1500	0.8146	12.64	3 512	8.1296	0.5895	11.88	3 281	7.8808
1600	0.9640	11.98	4 332	8.6694	0.6986	12.06	4 086	8.4100
1700	1.098	9.001	4 984	9.0245	0.8015	9.747	4 775	8.7913
1800	1.221	6.273	5 487	9.3123	0.8985	7.157	5 331	9.1099
1900	1.327	4.249	5 841	9.5038	0.9828	4.965	5 734	9.3280
2000	1.421	2.978	6 096	9.6347	1.057	3.475	6 025	9.4773
2200	1.587	1.794	6 453	9.8055	1.186	2.005	6 422	9.6669
2400	1.742	1.385	6 725	9.9240	1.304	1.476	6 710	9.7926
2600	1.892	1.230	6 967	10.0209	1.418	1.272	6 959	9.8924
2800	2.040	1.164	7 197	10.1062	1.529	1.186	7 193	9.9789
3000	2.187	1.133	7 422	10.1838	1.640	1.145	7 419	10.0571
3500	2.552	1.107	7 976	10.3546	1.914	1.110	7 975	10.2284
4000	2.917	1.100	8 526	10.5014	2.188	1.101	8 525	10.3754
5000	3.647	1.096	9 622	10.7462	2.735	1.097	9 622	10.6203
6000	4.377	1.099	10 718	10.9459	3.283	1.099	10 718	10.8200
	$p=10$ bar				$p=20$ bar			
600	0.1317	0.931	499.1	5.4462	0.06610	0.929	498.8	5.2932
700	0.1538	0.967	594.0	5.5923	0.07716	0.960	593.6	5.4394
800	0.1759	1.058	694.0	5.7258	0.08824	1.029	692.5	5.5713
900	0.1986	1.289	807.0	5.8587	0.09951	1.195	800.8	5.6988
1000	0.2229	1.779	948.8	6.0078	0.1113	1.544	929.9	5.8344
1100	0.2506	2.706	1 145	6.1965	0.1243	2.197	1 098	5.9954
1200	0.2845	4.193	1 430	6.4463	0.1396	3.240	1 328	6.1972
1300	0.3284	6.335	1 840	6.7772	0.1584	4.763	1 650	6.4569
1400	0.3861	8.933	2 404	7.2002	0.1824	6.743	2 088	6.7854
1500	0.4591	11.19	3 112	7.6967	0.2127	8.886	2 655	7.1817
1600	0.5437	11.91	3 895	8.2107	0.2496	10.51	3 328	7.6235

continued

T, °K	v	c_p	i	s	v	c_p	i	s
1700	0.6266	10.17	4 600	8.6052	0.2893	10.45	4 021	8.0189
1800	0.7066	7.816	5 194	8.9449	0.3309	9.331	4 682	8.3971
1900	0.7772	5.567	5 636	9.1844	0.3701	7.448	5 236	8.6965
2000	0.8390	3.922	5 958	9.3498	0.4054	5.577	5 666	8.9177
2200	0.9459	2.206	6 391	9.5569	0.4655	3.090	6 247	9.1956
2400	1.042	1.565	6 695	9.6894	0.5169	1.982	6 623	9.3594
2600	1.133	1.314	6 951	9.7920	0.5644	1.517	6 912	9.4755
2800	1.223	1.207	7 188	9.8798	0.6101	1.313	7 166	9.5695
3000	1.311	1.157	7 411	9.9587	0.6549	1.216	7 403	9.6513
3500	1.531	1.113	7 974	10.1305	0.7655	1.131	7 969	9.8259
4000	1.751	1.102	8 525	10.2776	0.8753	1.109	8 523	9.9738
5000	2.188	1.097	9 622	10.5226	1.094	1.099	9 622	10.2191
6000	2.626	1.099	10 718	10.6851	1.313	1.100	10 718	10.4190
		$p=40$ bar				$p=60$ bar		
600	0.03329	0.927	498.2	5.1389	0.02236	0.925	497.7	5.0477
700	0.03886	0.955	593.3	5.2856	0.02610	0.953	593.2	5.1950
800	0.04443	1.009	691.6	5.4168	0.02983	0.999	691.4	5.3261
900	0.05005	1.130	796.8	5.5406	0.03359	1.101	795.4	5.4485
1000	0.05586	1.379	916.9	5.6670	0.03744	1.298	911.6	5.5708
1100	0.06209	1.840	1 065	5.8085	0.04151	1.684	1 051	5.7039
1200	0.06909	2.573	1 257	5.9768	0.04601	2.281	1 226	5.8574
1300	0.07738	3.646	1 515	6.1846	0.05120	3.154	1 455	6.0420
1400	0.08753	5.081	1 858	6.4416	0.05741	4.330	1 756	6.2665
1500	0.1001	6.790	2 303	6.7521	0.06500	5.772	2 141	6.5357
1600	0.1156	8.488	2 849	7.1100	0.07426	7.320	2 619	6.8480
1700	0.1332	9.360	3 459	7.4618	0.08496	8.386	3 166	7.1653
1800	0.1529	9.523	4 102	7.8297	0.09722	9.034	3 768	7.5095
1900	0.1731	8.680	4 709	8.1581	0.1103	9.831	4 370	7.8351
2000	0.1924	7.230	5 234	8.4273	0.1234	7.886	4 924	8.1194
2200	0.2263	4.382	5 999	8.7932	0.1473	5.249	5 791	8.5340
2400	0.2548	2.698	6 489	9.0069	0.1677	3.285	6 367	8.7851
2600	0.2801	1.892	6 838	9.1470	0.1854	2.227	6 768	8.9457
2800	0.3038	1.514	7 122	9.2524	0.2018	1.702	7 080	9.0618
3000	0.3267	1.329	7 376	9.3401	0.2173	1.438	7 350	9.1549
3500	0.3826	1.164	7 960	9.5201	0.2549	1.198	7 950	9.3402
4000	0.4377	1.122	8 519	9.6695	0.2918	1.135	8 515	9.4910
5000	0.5473	1.102	9 621	9.9155	0.3650	1.105	9 621	9.7379
6000	0.6568	1.101	10 718	10.1155	0.4380	1.102	10 719	9.9380
		$p=80$ bar				$p=100$ bar		
600	0.01689	0.924	497.2	4.9822	0.01362	0.922	493.1	4.9310
700	0.01973	0.951	593.2	5.1303	0.01590	0.950	593.2	5.0797
800	0.02254	0.994	691.4	5.2615	0.01816	0.990	691.6	5.2111
900	0.02536	1.084	794.8	5.3831	0.02043	1.072	794.6	5.3324
1000	0.02824	1.311	908.8	5.5032	0.02273	1.323	907.1	5.4509
1100	0.03126	1.241	1 043	5.6312	0.02513	1.528	1 037	5.5756
1200	0.03456	2.108	1 208	5.7759	0.02773	1.991	1 196	5.7143
1300	0.03830	2.863	1 420	5.9468	0.03065	2.665	1 397	5.8759
1400	0.04272	3.881	1 695	6.1517	0.03404	3.576	1 653	6.0673
1500	0.04804	5.147	2 044	6.3955	0.03809	4.716	1 978	6.2936
1600	0.05447	6.557	2 477	6.6786	0.04295	6.013	2 379	6.5558
1700	0.06193	7.654	2 979	6.9707	0.04859	7.092	2 847	6.8288
1800	0.07061	8.505	3 544	7.2934	0.05519	8.033	3 381	7.1337
1900	0.08007	8.776	4 128	7.6093	0.06249	8.429	3 945	7.4386
2000	0.08980	8.122	4 688	7.8966	0.07014	8.163	4 501	7.7240
2200	0.1083	5.843	5 615	8.3393	0.08510	6.256	5 462	8.1828
2400	0.1243	3.768	6 265	8.6189	0.09832	4.170	6 154	8.4844
2600	0.1381	2.529	6 701	8.7973	0.1098	2.801	6 637	8.6784
2800	0.1508	1.879	7 040	8.9231	0.1202	2.046	7 000	8.8131
3000	0.1627	1.543	7 325	9.0215	0.1299	1.644	7 300	8.9164
3500	0.1911	1.231	7 941	9.2118	0.1528	1.263	7 932	9.1118
4000	0.2189	1.148	8 511	9.3642	0.1751	1.160	8 507	9.2655
5000	0.2738	1.108	9 620	9.6117	0.2191	1.111	9 620	9.5138
6000	0.3286	1.103	10 719	9.8121	0.2630	1.104	10 719	9.7143

continued

T, °K	v	c_p	i	s	v	c_p	i	s
	p=200 bar				p=300 bar			
600	0.007090	0.916	495.6	4.7676	0.004928	0.910	495.5	4.6682
700	0.008267	0.945	593.9	4.9197	0.005731	0.942	595.5	4.8232
800	0.009424	0.980	693.3	5.0527	0.006516	0.976	695.9	4.9578
900	0.01057	1.044	795.9	5.1736	0.007292	1.032	798.7	5.0792
1000	0.01173	1.362	905.3	5.2889	0.008069	1.439	907.1	5.1937
1100	0.01292	1.375	1 027	5.4026	0.008860	1.309	1 026	5.3073
1200	0.01417	1.704	1 170	5.5300	0.009685	1.580	1 161	5.4256
1300	0.01553	2.180	1 342	5.6684	0.01057	1.970	1 321	5.5541
1400	0.01706	2.823	1 554	5.8266	0.01154	2.495	1 513	5.6978
1500	0.01883	3.637	1 815	6.0087	0.01264	3.162	1 747	5.8602
1600	0.02089	4.600	2 134	6.2168	0.01391	3.959	2 028	6.0436
1700	0.02326	5.508	2 509	6.4504	0.01534	4.739	2 357	6.2372
1800	0.02604	6.466	2 944	6.6854	0.01702	5.609	2 741	6.4565
1900	0.02919	7.215	3 426	6.9459	0.01892	6.365	3 171	6.6891
2000	0.03264	7.594	3 934	7.2063	0.02103	6.940	3 635	6.9272
2200	0.03997	7.028	4 923	7.6781	0.02568	7.034	4 590	7.3822
2400	0.04706	5.394	5 745	8.0363	0.03044	5.925	5 451	7.7573
2600	0.05343	3.821	6 361	8.2832	0.03488	4.460	6 139	8.0329
2800	0.05912	2.742	6 820	8.4536	0.03889	3.265	6 664	8.2279
3000	0.06433	2.092	7 182	8.5784	0.04254	2.465	7 075	8.3697
3500	0.07627	1.417	7 887	8.7966	0.05076	1.560	7 845	8.6079
4000	0.08759	1.222	8 489	8.9573	0.05842	1.282	8 470	8.7752
5000	0.1097	1.126	9 617	9.2093	0.07326	1.141	9 614	9.0307
6000	0.1317	1.109	10 721	9.4106	0.08791	1.114	10 722	9.2328
	p=400 bar				p=500 bar			
600	0.003853	0.905	496.2	4.5954	0.003211	0.901	497.5	4.5374
700	0.004467	0.939	597.6	4.7529	0.003710	0.937	600.1	4.6973
800	0.005065	0.973	699.0	4.8891	0.004195	0.972	702.4	4.8349
900	0.005654	1.026	802.3	5.0113	0.004671	1.022	806.2	4.9579
1000	0.006241	1.494	910.3	5.1255	0.005144	1.547	914.2	5.0721
1100	0.006836	1.271	1 027	5.2375	0.005622	1.244	1 030	5.1833
1200	0.007451	1.507	1 159	5.3524	0.006113	1.459	1 159	5.2960
1300	0.008104	1.847	1 311	5.4752	0.006630	1.765	1 307	5.4150
1400	0.008814	2.303	1 492	5.6103	0.007189	2.174	1 480	5.5444
1500	0.009606	2.881	1 709	5.7611	0.007805	2.692	1 685	5.6873
1600	0.01051	3.576	1 967	5.9297	0.008497	3.316	1 928	5.8458
1700	0.01152	4.258	2 268	6.1073	0.009270	3.945	2 210	6.0124
1800	0.01269	5.061	2 619	6.3078	0.01016	4.675	2 538	6.1996
1900	0.01401	5.811	3 014	6.5214	0.01116	5.388	2 907	6.3995
2000	0.01549	6.417	3 445	6.7426	0.01228	6.005	3 313	6.6077
2200	0.01881	6.853	4 359	7.1779	0.01483	6.630	4 188	7.0247
2400	0.02233	6.149	5 227	7.5559	0.01758	6.225	5 050	7.3999
2600	0.02572	4.872	5 955	7.8476	0.02031	5.141	5 801	7.7006
2800	0.02884	3.663	6 528	8.0600	0.02286	3.971	6 408	7.9256
3000	0.03168	2.776	6 978	8.2154	0.02519	3.038	6 889	8.0919
3500	0.03802	1.692	7 804	8.4712	0.03038	1.814	7 766	8.3633
4000	0.04384	1.339	8 453	8.6447	0.03509	1.394	8 436	8.5426
5000	0.05502	1.155	9 611	8.9036	0.04408	1.170	9 609	8.8048
6000	0.06603	1.118	10 724	9.1065	0.05290	1.123	10 726	9.0085

Viscosity $\eta \cdot 10^6$ $(N \cdot s/m^2)$ of molecular fluorine gas at different temperatures and pressures [352, 360]

T, °K \ p, bar →	1	10	20	40	60	80	100
90	7.67						
100	8.60						
150	12.9						
200	16.4	16.9	17.3	17.9	18.5	19.0	19.5

continued

T, °K \ p, bar →	1	10	20	40	60	80	100
225	18.5	19.0	19.4	20.4	21.3	22.3	23.2
250	20.4	20.8	21.3	22.2	23.3	24.4	25.6
275	22.2	22.5	22.9	23.8	24.7	25.7	26.8
300	24.0	24.3	24.7	25.5	26.3	27.2	28.1
325	25.3	25.8	26.1	26.8	27.5	28.3	29.1
350	27.0	27.3	27.6	28.2	28.8	29.5	30.2
375	28.5	28.8	29.0	29.6	30.2	30.8	31.4
400	30.0	30.2	30.5	31.0	31.5	32.1	32.7
450	32.7	32.9	33.1	33.6	34.0	34.5	35.0
500	35.2	35.4	35.6	35.9	36.3	36.7	37.2
550	37.8	38.0	38.1	38.4	38.8	39.1	39.5
600	40.3	40.4	40.6	40.9	41.2	41.5	41.8
650	42.6	42.7	42.8	43.1	43.4	43.6	43.9
700	44.8	44.9	45.0	45.2	45.5	45.7	46.0
750	47.0	47.1	47.2	47.4	47.6	47.8	48.1
800	49.1	49.2	49.3	49.5	49.6	49.8	50.0
850	51.3	51.4	51.5	51.6	51.8	52.0	52.2
900	53.3	53.4	53.4	53.6	53.7	53.9	54.1

Viscosity $\eta \cdot 10^6$ ($N \cdot s/m^2$) of dissociated fluorine at high temperatures [148]

T, °K \ p, bar →	1	10	100	T, °K \ p, bar →	1	10	100
1000	58.7	57.8	57.5	2400	130	130	128
1200	71.6	67.4	65.8	2600	137	137	137
1400	85.7	79.6	75.0	2800	143	143	143
1600	95.5	92.1	85.5	3000	152	152	152
1800	104	102	95.6	4000	185	185	185
2000	114	114	109	5000	217	217	217
2200	122	122	120	6000	247	247	247

Viscosity η of liquid fluorine [149]

T, °K	69.2	73.2	75.3	78.2	80.9	83.2
$\eta \cdot 10^3$, $N \cdot s/m^2$	0.414	0.349	0.328	0.299	0.275	0.257

Thermal conductivity of fluorine gas at $p \leqslant 1$ bar [360]

T, °K	100	150	200	250	273	300	350	400	450	500	550	600	650	700
$\lambda \cdot 10^4$, W/m · deg	86.3	134	182	228	248	269	308	345	381	416	451	488	524	559

Surface tension of fluorine [149]

T, °K	69.2	71.2	73.2	75.3	76.4	78.2	81.0
$\sigma \cdot 10^3$, N/m	17.9	17.4	16.7	16.2	15.9	15.4	14.6

CHLORINE (Cl_2)

Molecular weight 70.914

$t_{boil} = -34.04$ °C at 760 mm Hg; $t_{melt} = -100.5$ °C; $t_{cr} = 144$ °C;

$p_{cr} = 77.1$ bar; $\rho_{cr} = 573$ kg/m³

Thermodynamic properties of saturated chlorine [150]: v (dm³/kg), i and r (kJ/kg) and s (kJ/kg · deg)

t, °C	p, bar	v′	v″	i′	i″	r	s′	s″
−90	0.0360	0.5867	5993	182.46	501.45	319.0	1.56879	3.31025
−78.89	0.0827	0.5961	2733	193.76	506.27	312.5	1.62866	3.23728
−67.78	0.173	0.6061	1378	204.86	511.08	306.2	1.68410	3.17523
−56.67	0.333	0.6165	755.4	215.75	515.90	300.1	1.73580	3.12210
−45.56	0.593	0.6276	443.5	226.55	520.59	294.0	1.78441	3.07621
−34.44	0.996	0.6394	275.7	237.31	525.19	287.9	1.83043	0.03635
−34.04	1.013	0.6398	271.3	237.68	525.36	287.7	1.83202	3.03501
−23.33	1.580	0.6519	179.7	248.07	529.63	281.6	1.87426	3.00135
−12.22	2.411	0.6652	122.0	258.83	533.90	275.1	1.91617	2.97037
− 1.11	3.535	0.6796	85.67	269.63	537.92	268.3	1.95645	2.94269
10.0	5.014	0.6949	61.88	280.52	541.69	261.2	1.99530	2.91766
21.11	6.909	0.7116	45.78	291.53	545.08	253.5	2.03294	2.89471
32.22	9.279	0.7298	34.55	302.62	548.14	245.5	2.06949	2.87340
43.33	12.207	0.7498	26.51	313.97	550.73	236.8	2.10525	2.85326
54.44	15.752	0.7718	20.61	325.57	552.78	227.2	2.14038	2.83396
65.56	19.997	0.7965	16.19	337.50	554.21	216.7	2.17521	2.81499
76.67	25.011	0.8245	12.81	349.93	554.83	204.9	2.21013	2.79594
87.78	30.886	0.8571	10.18	363.00	554.58	191.6	2.24551	2.77622
98.89	37.694	0.8958	8.08	376.98	553.03	176.0	2.28210	2.75521
110.00	45.544	0.9438	6.38	392.30	549.77	157.5	2.32074	2.73168
121.11	54.520	1.008	4.95	409.68	543.91	134.2	2.36316	2.70363
132.22	64.751	1.107	3.68	430.82	533.15	102.3	2.41319	2.66569
137.78	70.363	1.192	3.040	444.22	523.43	79.2	2.44488	2.63726
143.33	76.340	1.427	2.135	467.25	499.78	32.5	2.49789	2.57639
144.00	77.089	1.745	1.745	483.16	483.16	0.00	2.53645	2.53645

Thermodynamic properties of chlorine at different temperatures and pressures [150]: v (dm³/kg), i (kJ/kg) and s (kJ/kg · deg)

t, °C	v	i	s	v	i	s
	p = 0.069 bar			p = 1.034 bar		
−78.89	3296.2	506.31	3.2593			
−73.33	3390.9	508.78	3.2718			
−67.78	3485.6	511.25	3.2841			
−62.22	3580.3	513.78	3.2961			
−56.67	3674.9	516.27	3.3078			
−51.11	3769.6	518.79	3.3193			
−45.56	3864.3	521.30	3.3305			
−40.00	3958.9	523.85	3.3415			
−34.44	4053.6	526.41	3.3523			
−28.89	4148.2	528.96	3.3629	271.70	527.70	3.0425
−23.33	4242.8	531.51	3.3733	278.68	530.38	3.0531
−17.78	4337.4	534.11	3.3835	284.63	532.94	3.0634
−12.22	4432.1	536.66	3.3935	291.08	535.58	3.0735
−6.67	4526.6	539.26	3.4033	297.52	538.17	3.0834
−1.11	4621.2	541.86	3.4130	303.96	540.81	3.0932
4.44	4715.8	544.45	3.4225	310.39	543.45	3.1028
10.00	4810.4	547.09	3.4318	316.81	546.08	3.1122
15.56	4905.0	549.68	3.4410	323.23	548.72	3.1215
21.11	4999.5	552.36	3.4500	329.65	551.40	3.1306
26.67	5094.1	555.00	3.4589	336.06	554.04	3.1396
32.22	5188.7	557.64	3.4677	342.47	556.72	3.1484
37.78	5283.3	560.28	3.4763	348.87	559.40	3.1571

continued

t, °C	v	i	s	v	i	s
43.33	5377.8	562.96	3.4848	355.26	562.12	3.1656
48.89	5472.4	565.64	3.4932	361.66	564.76	3.1741
54.44	5566.9	568.32	3.5014	368.04	567.48	3.1824
60.00	5661.5	571.00	3.5095	374.43	570.20	3.1905
65.56	5756.0	573.68	3.5175	380.82	572.88	3.1986
71.11	5850.6	576.40	3.5254	387.20	575.60	3.2066
82.22	6039.6	581.80	3.5409	399.95	581.04	3.2222
93.33	6228.7	587.24	3.5560	412.69	596.53	3.2373
104.44	6417.6	592.72	3.5707	425.42	592.01	3.2521
115.56	6606.7	598.17	3.5850	438.15	597.54	3.2665
126.67	6795.9	603.69	3.5990	450.87	603.07	3.2805
137.78	6985.1	609.22	3.6126	463.58	608.59	3.2942
148.89	7173.6	614.75	3.6259	476.27	614.16	3.3075
160.00	7362.7	620.32	3.6389	488.97	619.73	3.3205
171.11	7551.9	625.88	3.6516	501.66	625.34	3.3333
182.22	7741.1	631.45	3.6640	514.36	630.91	3.3458
193.33	7930.2	637.06	3.6761	527.03	636.52	3.3579
204.44	8118.8	642.63	3.6880	533.41	642.30	3.3698
215.56	8307.9	648.28	3.6996	552.39	647.78	3.3815
226.67	8497.1	653.89	3.7110	565.05	653.43	3.3929
237.78	8686.2	659.50	3.7221	577.72	659.13	3.4041
248.89	8874.8	665.16	3.7330	590.39	664.74	3.4150
260.00	9063.9	670.81	3.7437	603.05	670.39	3.4257
271.11	9253.1	676.42	3.7542	615.70	676.04	3.4362
282.22	9441.6	682.07	3.7644	628.34	681.69	3.4465
		$p=2.068$ bar			$p=4.136$ bar	
−12.22	143.12	534.32	2.9894			
− 6.67	146.42	537.00	2.9995			
− 1.11	149.71	539.64	3.0093			
4.44	153.00	542.32	3.0191	74.221	539.97	2.9326
10.00	156.28	545.00	3.0286	75.937	542.69	2.9424
15.56	159.56	547.68	3.0380	77.648	545.46	2.9519
21.11	162.82	550.35	3.0472	79.346	548.18	2.9614
26.67	166.09	553.03	3.0562	81.044	550.94	2.9706
32.22	169.35	555.71	3.0652	82.736	553.66	2.9797
37.78	172.61	558.44	3.0739	84.428	556.47	2.9887
43.33	175.86	561.16	3.0825	86.107	559.19	2.9975
48.89	179.10	563.88	3.0910	87.786	561.95	3.0061
54.44	182.34	566.56	3.0994	89.459	564.72	3.0146
60.00	185.58	569.32	3.1076	91.126	567.48	3.0230
65.56	188.82	572.04	3.1158	92.793	570.28	3.0312
71.11	192.06	574.76	3.1238	94.460	573.05	3.0394
76.67	195.29	577.48	3.1317	96.114	575.81	3.0474
82.22	198.51	580.25	3.1395	97.775	578.57	3.0553
87.78	201.74	582.97	3.1471	99.429	581.38	3.0631
93.33	204.96	585.91	3.1547	101.08	584.18	3.0707
98.89	208.18	588.50	3.1622	102.72	586.95	3.0783
104.44	211.40	591.26	3.1696	104.37	589.75	3.0858
110.00	214.61	594.02	3.1769	106.01	592.56	3.0931
115.56	217.83	596.79	3.1840	107.66	595.36	3.1004
121.11	221.04	599.59	3.1911	109.29	598.17	3.1075
126.67	224.25	602.35	3.1981	110.93	600.97	3.1146
132.22	227.46	605.16	3.2050	112.56	603.78	3.1216
137.78	230.66	607.96	3.2119	114.20	606.58	3.1285
143.33	233.87	610.73	3.2186	115.83	609.43	3.1353
148.89	237.07	613.53	3.2253	117.46	612.24	3.1420
154.44	240.27	616.34	3.2319	119.09	615.08	3.1486
160.00	243.47	619.14	3.2384	120.71	617.89	3.1552
165.56	246.67	621.91	3.2448	122.33	620.73	3.1617
171.11	249.87	624.75	3.2513	123.96	623.54	3.1681
176.67	253.06	627.56	3.2575	125.58	626.39	3.1744
182.22	256.25	630.36	3.2636	127.20	629.19	3.1807
187.78	259.45	633.17	3.2698	128.82	632.04	3.1869

continued

t, °C	v	i	s	v	i	s
193.33	262.64	636.02	3.2759	130.44	634.76	3.1930
198.89	265.83	638.82	3.2819	132.06	637.73	3.1990
204.44	269.02	641.63	3.2878	133.68	640.54	3.2050
210.00	272.21	644.47	3.2937	135.29	643.39	3.2109
215.56	275.40	447.28	3.2995	136.90	646.23	3.2168
221.11	278.58	650.13	3.3053	138.51	649.08	3.2226
226.67	281.77	652.93	3.3110	140.12	651.93	3.2283
237.78	288.14	658.58	3.3221	143.35	657.62	3.2396
248.89	294.51	664.28	3.3331	146.57	663.31	3.2506
260.00	300.87	669.93	3.3438	149.78	669.01	3.2614
271.11	307.23	675.58	3.3544	152.99	674.70	3.2719
282.22	313.59	681.23	3.3647	156.21	680.40	3.2823
		$p=6.893$ bar			$p=10.34$ bar	
21.11	45.861	545.12	2.8949			
26.67	46.941	547.97	2.9045			
32.22	48.015	550.82	2.9139			
37.78	49.081	553.62	2.9231	31.317	549.85	2.8677
43.33	50.143	556.47	2.9321	32.077	552.82	2.8772
48.89	51.198	559.31	2.9410	32.830	555.76	2.8864
54.44	52.250	562.08	2.9497	33.577	558.73	2.8955
60.00	53.296	564.97	2.9583	34.318	561.66	2.9043
71.11	55.376	570.66	2.9751	35.784	567.52	2.9216
82.22	57.441	576.35	2.9913	37.233	573.34	2.9383
93.33	59.493	582.01	3.0070	38.665	579.20	2.9545
104.44	61.533	587.70	3.0223	40.085	585.02	2.9702
115.56	63.564	593.40	3.0372	41.492	590.84	2.9853
126.67	65.581	599.09	3.0516	42.889	596.66	3.0000
137.78	67.597	604.78	3.0657	44.276	602.44	3.0144
148.89	69.601	610.52	3.0794	45.655	608.26	3.0283
160.00	71.599	616.21	3.0927	47.027	614.08	3.0419
171.11	73.590	621.91	3.1058	48.392	619.90	3.0551
182.22	75.575	627.64	3.1185	49.750	625.68	3.0680
193.33	77.554	633.38	3.1309	51.102	631.45	3.0806
204.44	79.527	639.12	3.1431	52.450	637.27	3.0929
215,56	81.500	644.85	3.1550	53.793	643.05	3.1049
226.67	83.466	650.59	3.1666	55.132	648.87	3.1166
237.78	85.433	656.32	3.1779	56.467	654.65	3.1281
248.89	87.387	662.06	3.1890	57.798	660.43	3.1393
260.00	89.347	667.75	3.1999	59.125	666.24	3.1503
271.11	91.301	673.35	3.2105	60.450	672.02	3.1610
282.22	93.249	679.22	3.2209	61.771	677.80	3.1715
		$p=13.79$ bar			$p=17.23$ bar	
48.89	23.568	551.95	2.8448			
54.44	24.171	555.04	2.8543			
60.00	24.767	558.10	2.8636	18.975	554.25	2.8295
71.11	25.939	564.21	2.8815	19.983	560.61	2.8484
82.22	27.088	570.24	2.8988	20.963	566.89	2.8663
93.33	28.219	576.23	2.9154	21.920	573.13	2.8836
104.44	29.334	582.22	2.9315	22.858	579.29	2.9001
115.56	30.434	588.16	2.9471	23.779	585.40	2.9161
126.67	31.523	594.15	2.9621	24.687	591.51	2.9316
137.78	32.602	600.05	2.9768	25.583	597.54	2.9465
148.89	33.670	605.96	2.9910	26.468	603.61	2.9610
160.00	34.731	611.86	3.0048	27.344	609.60	2.9751
171.11	35.784	617.76	3.0282	28.212	615.58	2.9887
182.22	36.831	623.67	3.0313	29.073	621.57	3.0020
193.33	37.871	629.53	3.0440	29.927	627.56	3.0150
204.44	38.906	635.39	3.0565	30.775	633.50	3.0276
215.56	39.936	641.29	3.0686	31.618	639.45	3.0399
226.67	40.961	647.15	3.0805	32.456	645.35	3.0159
237.78	41.982	652.97	3.0921	33.289	651.30	3.0636
248.89	42.999	658.83	3.1034	34.119	657.20	3.0750

continued

t,°C	v	i	s	v	i	s
260.00	44.013	664.70	3.1145	34.945	663.10	3.0862
271.11	45.024	670.52	3.1253	35.767	668.97	3.0971
282.22	46.031	676.34	3.1359	36.586	674.87	3.1079
		p=20.67 bar			p=27.57 bar	
71.11	15.963	556.72	2.8192			
76.67	16.406	560.07	2.8287			
82.22	16.842	563.33	2.8381	11.570	555.21	2.7880
87.78	17.262	566.60	2.8471	11.949	558.85	2.7983
93.33	17.691	569.78	2.8560	12.317	562.41	2.8081
98.89	18.107	573.00	2.8647	12.675	565.97	2.8177
104.44	18.517	576.19	2.8732	13.025	569.40	2.8270
110.00	18.922	579.37	2.8815	13.367	572.88	2.8360
115.56	19.324	582.51	2.8897	13.703	576.27	2.8448
121.11	19.721	585.65	2.8977	14.033	579.62	2.8533
126.67	20.115	588.79	2.9056	14.358	582.93	2.8617
137.78	20.891	594.99	2.9209	14.995	589.54	2.8779
148.89	21.657	601.14	2.9357	15.616	596.03	2.8935
160.00	22.412	607.25	2.9500	16.225	602.44	2.9085
171.11	23.157	613.41	2.9640	16.822	608.80	2.9230
182.22	23.895	619.48	2.9775	17.410	615.08	2.9370
193.33	24.626	625.55	2.9906	17.989	621.36	2.9506
204.44	25.351	631.54	3.0034	18.562	627.56	2.9638
215.56	26.069	637.57	3.0159	19.127	633.80	2.9766
226.67	26.783	643.59	3.0280	19.687	639.95	2.9891
237.78	27.492	649.58	3.0399	20.241	646.06	3.0013
248.89	28.197	655.57	3.0514	20.791	652.18	3.0131
260.00	28.898	661.51	3.0627	21.337	658.29	3.0246
271.11	29.595	667.46	3.0737	21.878	664.32	3.0359
282.22	30.289	673.36	3.0845	22.416	670.39	3.0469
		p=34.43 bar			p=41.36 bar	
98.89	9.2986	557.64	2.7751			
104.44	9.6308	561.58	2.7857	7.2292	551.86	2.7446
110.00	9.9498	565.43	2.7958	7.5613	556.47	2.7568
115.56	10.259	569.15	2.8055	7.8728	560.86	2.7681
121.11	10.558	572.88	2.8149	8.1681	565.09	2.7789
126.67	10.851	576.48	2.8240	8.4509	569.11	2.7891
132.22				8.7224	573.09	2.7990
137.78	11.416	583.56	2.8415	8.9859	576.94	2.8084
143.33				9.2412	580.71	2.8175
148.89	11.960	590.46	2.8581	9.4903	584.44	2.8263
154.44				9.7338	588.08	2.8349
160.00	12.488	597.25	2.8739	9.9716	591.68	2.8433
165.56				10.206	595.24	2.8514
171.11	13.001	603.90	2.8891	10.435	598.71	2.8594
176.67				10.661	602.19	2.8672
182.22	13.503	610.52	2.9038	10.884	605.66	2.8747
193.33	13.995	617.01	2.9179	11.321	612.44	2.8895
204.44	14.478	623.46	2.9316	11.748	619.14	2.9037
215.56	14.954	629.82	2.9448	12.165	625.76	2.9174
226.67	15.423	636.18	2.9576	12.575	632.29	2.9306
237.78	15.886	642.51	2.9701	12.979	638.78	2.9435
248.89	16.344	648.74	2.9822	13.376	645.23	2.9559
260.00	16.797	654.98	2.9940	13.769	651.59	2.9680
271.11	17.246	661.18	3.0055	14.157	657.91	2.9798
282.22	17.691	667.33	3.0167	14.541	664.19	2.9912
		p=55.15 bar			p=68.93 bar	
126.67	5.1865	549.27	2.7163			
132.22	5.5036	555.13	2.7309			
137.78	5.7883	560.49	2.7439	3.3723	530.59	2.6558
143.33	6.0510	565.43	2.7559	3.8331	541.86	2.6831
148.89	6.2971	570.12	2.7671	4.1689	549.89	2.7023
154.44	6.5300	574.55	2.7776	4.4505	556.59	2.7182

continued

t, °C	v	i	s	v	i	s
160.00	6.7535	578.91	2.7876	4.7002	562.58	2.7320
165.56	6.9676	583.05	2.7972	4.9283	568.06	2.7445
171.11	7.1748	587.11	2.8064	5.1407	573.13	2.7561
176.67	7.3759	591.09	2.8153	5.3409	578.03	2.7669
182.22	7.5713	594.99	2.8239	5.5314	582.64	2.7771
193.33	7.9489	602.56	2.8403	5.8899	591.43	2.7962
204.44	8.3123	609.93	2.8559	6.2254	599.72	2.8138
215.56	8.6631	617.09	2.8708	6.5437	607.67	2.8303
226.67	9.0040	624.13	2.8850	6.8483	615.38	2.8458
237.78	9.3361	631.08	2.8987	7.1418	622.87	2.8606
248.89	9.6613	637.90	2.9119	7.4258	630.16	2.8748
260.00	9.9797	644.60	2.9247	7.7030	637.31	2.8883
271.11	10.293	651.26	2.9370	7.9727	644.35	2.9014
282.22	10.601	657.83	2.9490	8.2374	651.26	2.9140
		$p=77.09$ bar			$p=82.71$ bar	
148.89	3.0113	529.21	2.6463	1.7822	488.01	2.5454
154.44	3.4288	541.10	2.6744	2.7021	524.65	2.6317
160.00	3.7394	549.73	2.6943	3.1202	538.05	2.6629
165.56	4.0006	556.84	2.7107	3.4274	547.42	2.6844
171.11	4.2320	563.17	2.7249	3.6834	555.09	2.7017
176.67	4.4432	568.86	2.7377	3.9087	561.74	2.7167
182.22	4.6396	574.22	2.7496	4.1134	567.77	2.7300
187.78	4.8245	579.24	2.7606	4.3030	573.34	2.7422
193.33	5.0002	584.06	2.7709	4.4809	578.57	2.7535
198.89	5.1683	588.71	2.7808	4.6497	583.56	2.7641
204.44	5.3302	593.14	2.7902	4.8109	588.33	2.7741
210.00	5.4867	597.50	2.7992	4.9658	592.93	2.7837
215.56	5.6385	601.73	2.8079	5.1153	597.37	2.7929
221.11	5.7863	605.83	2.8163	5.2602	601.73	2.8017
226.67	5.9304	609.89	2.8244	5.4011	605.96	2.8102
237.78	6.2093	617.76	2.8400	5.6725	614.12	2.8264
243.33	6.3445	621.61	2.8475	5.8037	618.10	2.8341
248.89	6.4781	625.38	2.8548	5.9325	622.03	2.8417
254.44	6.6086	629.15	2.8619	6.0588	625.88	2.8490
260.00	6.7378	632.83	2.8689	6.1830	629.69	2.8562
265.56	6.8652	636.52	2.8757	6.3052	633.42	2.8632
271.11	6.9907	640.12	2.8824	6.4257	637.15	2.8701
276.67	7.1143	643.72	2.8890	6.5449	640.83	2.8768
282.22	7.2366	647.28	2.8955	6.6623	644.47	2.8834

$p=96.50$ bar

t, °C	v	i	s	t, °C	v	i	s
154.44	1.3342	465.49	2.4875	221.11	4.2254	591.01	2.7668
160.00	1.7116	491.28	2.5474	226.67	4.3613	595.78	2.7764
165.56	2.1554	513.76	2.5990	237.78	4.6200	604.87	2.7944
171.11	2.5142	529.00	2.6335	243.33	4.7438	609.22	2.8029
176.67	2.7999	540.14	2.6584	248.89	4.8645	613.49	2.8111
182.22	3.0402	549.06	2.6782	254.44	4.9825	617.64	2.8191
187.78	3.2513	556.72	2.6948	260.00	5.0979	621.74	2.8268
193.33	3.4420	563.50	2.7095	265.56	5.2111	625.80	2.8343
198.89	3.6177	569.70	2.7227	271.11	5.3222	629.74	2.8416
204.44	3.7819	575.48	2.7349	276.67	5.4314	633.63	2.8488
210.00	3.9368	580.92	2.7462	282.22	5.5389	637.52	2.8557
215.56	4.0843	586.07	2.7568				

Thermal conductivity of chlorine gas at $p \leqslant 1$ bar [360]

T, °K	200	250	273	300	350	400	450	500	550	600	650	700
$\lambda \cdot 10^4$, W/m · deg	53.6	71.2	78.7	88.3	106	124	142	158	173	188	202	215

Chapter 9

MONOATOMIC GASES

HELIUM (He)

Atomic weight 4.003

$t_{boil} = -268.94$ °C at 760 mm Hg; $t_{melt} = -267.96$ °C;
$p_{cr} = 2.29$ bar; $\rho_{cr} = 69.3$ kg/m³; λ-point at 2.18 °K

Saturated vapor pressure (mm Hg) of helium [16]

T, °K	p	T, °K	p	T, °K	p	T, °K	p	T, °K	p
1.0	0.12	2.0	23.8	3.0	183	3.8	503	4.6	1080
1.2	0.62	2.2	41	3.2	243	4.0	619	4.8	1270
1.4	2.1	2.4	64	3.4	316	4.2	753	5.0	1490
1.6	5.7	2.6	94	3.6	402	4.4	900	5.2	1720
1.8	12.5	2.8	134						

Thermodynamic properties of helium at low temperatures [151]: ρ (kg/m³), i (kJ/kg) and s (kJ/kg · deg) For the base level of calculations it was assumed that at 273.15 °K $i^0 = 1428.3$ kJ/kg and $s^0 = 29.65$ kJ/kg · deg at 273.15 °K and $p = 1$ bar.

T, °K	ρ	i	s	ρ	i	s
	$p=0.1$ bar			$p=1$ bar		
18	0.2675	103.1	20.30	2.6846	102.6	15.50
20	0.2407	113.5	20.85	2.4117	113.0	16.05
25	0.1927	139.5	22.01	1.9260	139.1	17.21
30	0.1604	165.5	22.96	1.6031	165.2	18.16
35	0.1375	191.5	23.76	1.3733	191.2	18.97
40	0.1203	217.4	24.45	1.2013	217.3	19.66
45	0.1069	243.4	25.06	1.0676	243.3	20.28
50	0.09624	269.4	25.61	0.9609	269.3	20.82
55	0.08748	295.3	26.11	0.8735	295.4	21.32
60	0.08019	321.3	26.56	0.8008	321.4	21.77
65	0.07402	347.3	26.97	0.7392	347.4	22.19
70	0.06874	373.3	27.36	0.6864	371.4	22.57
75	0.06416	399.2	27.72	0.6407	399.4	22.96
80	0.06014	425.2	28.05	0.6007	425.3	23.27
85	0.05661	451.2	28.37	0.5654	451.3	23.58
90	0.05346	477.1	28.66	0.5340	477.3	23.88
95	0.05064	503.1	28.95	0.5060	503.3	24.16
100	0.04812	529.1	29.21	0.4807	529.3	24.43
110	0.04375	581.0	29.71	0.4371	581.2	24.92
120	0.04009	633.0	30.16	0.4006	633.1	25.37
130	0.03701	684.9	30.57	0.3698	685.1	25.79
140	0.03437	736.8	30.96	0.3435	737.0	26.18
150	0.03208	788.8	31.32	0.3206	789.0	26.53
160	0.03007	840.7	31.65	0.3006	840.9	26.87
170	0.02831	892.6	31.97	0.2829	892.8	27.18
180	0.02674	944.6	32.26	0.2672	944.8	27.48

continued

T, °K	ϱ	i	s	ϱ	i	s
190	0.02533	996.5	32.55	0.2531	996.7	27.76
200	0.02405	1048.4	32.81	0.2404	1048.6	28.03
220	0.02187	1152.3	33.31	0.2186	1152.5	28.52
240	0.02005	1256.2	33.76	0.2004	1256.4	28.97
260	0.01851	1360.1	34.17	0.1850	1360.3	29.39
280	0.01718	1463.9	34.56	0.1717	1464.1	29.78
300	0.01604	1567.8	34.92	0.1604	1568.0	30.13
		$p=2$ bar			$p=3$ bar	
18	5.3856	102.1	14.04	8.0975	101.6	13.18
20	4.8342	112.6	14.59	7.2601	112.1	13.73
25	3.8514	138.7	15.76	5.7742	138.4	14.90
30	3.2027	164.9	16.71	4.7975	164.6	15.86
35	2.7422	191.0	17.52	4.1060	190.9	16.67
40	2.3982	217.2	18.22	3.5901	217.1	17.37
45	2.1313	243.3	18.83	3.1903	243.2	17.98
50	1.9180	269.3	19.38	2.8712	269.3	18.53
55	1.7438	295.4	19.88	2.6104	295.5	19.03
60	1.5986	321.4	20.33	2.3933	321.5	19.49
65	1.4758	347.5	20.75	2.2096	347.6	19.90
70	1.3696	373.5	21.13	2.0523	373.6	20.29
75	1.2794	399.5	21.49	1.9159	399.7	20.65
80	1.1995	425.5	21.83	1.7966	425.7	20.98
85	1.1292	451.5	22.14	1.6911	451.7	20.30
90	1.0666	477.5	22.44	1.5976	477.7	21.60
95	1.0105	503.5	22.72	1.5138	503.7	21.88
100	0.9602	529.5	22.99	1.4383	529.7	21.14
110	0.8730	581.4	23.48	1.3080	581.7	22.64
120	0.8004	633.4	23.93	1.1993	633.6	23.09
130	0.7390	685.3	24.35	1.1073	685.6	23.51
140	0.6863	737.3	24.74	1.0284	737.5	23.89
150	0.6406	789.2	25.09	0.9600	789.5	24.25
160	0.6006	841.1	25.43	0.9002	841.4	24.59
170	0.5654	893.1	25.74	0.8473	893.3	24.90
180	0.5340	945.0	26.04	0.8004	945.3	25.20
190	0.5059	997.0	26.32	0.7583	997.2	25.48
200	0.4806	1048.9	26.59	0.7204	1049.1	25.75
220	0.4370	1152.8	27.08	0.6551	1153.0	26.24
240	0.4006	1257.1	27.53	0.6006	1256.9	26.69
260	0.3699	1360.5	27.95	0.5544	1360.8	27.11
280	0.3434	1464.4	28.34	0.5149	1464.6	27.49
300	0.3206	1568.2	28.69	0.4803	1568.5	27.85
		$p=4$ bar			$p=6$ bar	
18	10.817	101.1	12.56	16.260	100.2	11.68
20	9.6876	111.7	13.11	14.537	110.8	12.24
25	7.6926	138.0	14.29	11.512	137.4	13.42
30	6.3867	164.4	15.25	9.5457	163.9	14.39
35	5.4642	190.7	16.06	8.1621	190.4	15.20
40	4.7769	217.0	16.76	7.1340	216.8	15.91
45	4.2448	243.2	17.38	6.3392	243.1	16.53
50	3.8202	269.4	17.93	5.7058	269.4	17.08
55	3.4735	295.5	18.43	5.1886	295.7	17.58
60	3.1848	321.6	18.89	4.7581	321.9	18.04
65	2.9407	347.7	19.30	4.3942	348.0	18.46
70	2.7314	373.8	19.69	4.0823	374.1	18.85
75	2.5502	399.9	20.05	3.8121	400.2	19.21
80	2.3915	425.9	20.39	3.5755	426.3	19.54
85	2.2515	451.9	20.70	3.3667	452.3	19.86
90	2.1269	477.9	21.00	3.1809	478.4	20.16
95	2.0155	503.9	21.28	3.0147	504.4	20.44
100	1.9147	529.9	21.55	2.8650	530.4	20.70
110	1.7418	581.9	22.04	2.6063	582.4	21.20
120	1.5973	633.9	22.49	2.3904	634.4	21.65

continued

T, °K	ϱ	i	s	ϱ	i	s
130	1.4749	685.8	22.91	2.2076	686.3	22.07
140	1.3699	737.8	23.29	2.0508	738.3	22.45
150	1.2779	789.7	23.65	1.9148	790.2	22.81
160	1.1992	841.7	23.99	1.7957	842.2	23.15
170	1.1289	893.6	24.30	1.6905	894.1	23.46
180	1.0663	945.5	24.60	1.5970	946.1	23.76
190	1.0103	997.5	24.88	1.5133	998.0	24.04
200	0.9600	1049.4	25.15	1.4380	1049.9	24.31
220	0.8729	1153.3	25.64	1.3077	1153.8	24.80
240	0.8003	1257.1	26.09	1.1990	1257.7	25.25
260	0.7389	1361.0	26.51	1.1071	1361.6	25.67
280	0.6862	1464.9	26.90	1.0283	1465.4	26.05
300	0.6415	1568.8	27.25	0.9599	1569.3	26.41
		$p=8$ bar			$p=10$ bar	
18	21.693	99.4	11.04	27.088	98.6	10.54
20	19.364	110.1	11.60	24.153	109.4	11.11
25	15.302	136.8	12.80	19.054	136.3	12.31
30	12.676	163.5	13.77	15.773	163.1	13.29
35	10.834	190.1	14.59	13.478	189.9	14.11
40	9.4683	216.7	15.30	11.779	216.6	14.83
45	8.4822	243.1	15.92	10.468	243.1	15.45
50	7.5741	269.5	16.48	9.4249	269.6	16.01
55	6.8888	295.8	16.98	8.5739	296.0	16.51
60	6.3185	322.1	17.44	7.8658	322.3	16.97
65	5.8365	348.3	17.86	7.2671	348.6	17.39
70	5.4232	374.5	18.25	6.7540	374.8	17.78
75	5.0651	400.6	18.61	6.3091	401.0	18.14
80	4.7515	426.7	18.94	5.9196	427.1	18.48
85	4.4748	452.8	19.26	5.5757	453.2	18.79
90	4.2285	478.8	19.56	5.2697	479.3	19.09
95	4.0081	504.9	19.84	4.9957	505.4	19.37
100	3.8096	530.9	20.11	4.7490	531.4	19.64
110	3.4664	582.9	20.60	4.3220	583.4	20.14
120	3.1799	634.9	21.05	3.9657	635.4	20.59
130	2.9372	686.9	21.47	3.6637	687.4	21.01
140	2.7290	738.8	21.85	3.4044	739.4	21.39
150	2.5483	790.8	22.21	3.1794	791.3	21.75
160	2.3900	842.7	22.55	2.9823	843.3	22.08
170	2.2504	894.7	22.86	2.8083	895.2	22.40
180	2.1260	946.6	23.16	2.6545	947.2	22.70
190	2.0148	998.5	23.44	2.5148	999.1	22.98
200	1.9156	1050.5	23.71	2.3898	1051.0	23.24
220	1.7414	1154.4	24.20	2.1739	1154.9	23.74
240	1.5969	1258.2	24.65	1.9938	1258.8	24.19
260	1.4746	1362.1	25.07	1.8412	1362.7	24.61
280	1.3697	1466.0	25.45	1.7103	1466.5	24.99
300	1.2787	1569.8	25.81	1.5968	1570.4	25.35
		$p=15$ bar			$p=20$ bar	
18	40.299	97.0	9.620	52.920	95.7	8.950
20	35.872	107.9	10.19	47.097	106.8	9.532
25	28.236	135.2	11.41	37.078	134.4	10.76
30	23.356	162.4	12.40	30.686	161.9	11.76
35	19.957	189.5	13.24	26.240	189.3	12.61
40	17.447	216.5	13.96	22.956	216.5	13.34
45	15.514	243.3	14.59	20.427	243.5	13.97
50	13.975	270.0	15.15	18.415	270.4	14.54
55	12.721	296.6	15.66	16.773	297.2	15.05
60	11.676	323.0	16.12	15.406	323.8	15.51
65	10.794	349.4	16.54	14.250	350.3	15.94
70	10.037	375.8	16.93	13.258	376.7	16.33
75	9.3803	420.0	17.29	12.397	403.1	16.69
80	8.8052	428.2	17.63	11.642	429.4	17.03

continued

T, °K	ϱ	i	s	ϱ	i	s
85	8.2970	454.4	17.95	10.975	455.6	17.35
90	7.8448	480.5	18.25	10.380	481.8	17.65
95	7.4395	506.6	18.53	9.8477	507.9	17.93
100	7.0744	532.7	18.80	9.3673	534.0	18.20
110	6.4421	584.8	19.29	8.5352	586.1	18.70
120	5.9139	636.8	19.75	7.8392	638.2	19.15
130	5.4658	688.8	20.16	7.2484	690.2	19.57
140	5.0810	740.8	20.55	6.7405	742.2	19.95
150	4.7468	792.7	20.91	6.2992	794.2	20.31
160	4.4539	844.7	21.24	5.9122	846.1	20.64
170	4.1950	896.6	21.56	5.5700	898.1	20.96
180	3.9645	948.6	21.85	5.2653	950.0	21.26
190	3.7581	1000.5	22.13	4.9922	1001.9	21.54
200	3.5722	1052.5	22.40	4.7459	1053.9	21.80
220	3.2504	1156.3	22.90	4.3198	1157.8	22.30
240	2.9818	1260.2	23.35	3.9640	1261.6	22.75
260	2.7542	1364.1	23.76	3.6623	1365.5	23.17
280	2.5590	1467.9	24.15	3.4033	1468.4	23.55
300	2.3895	1571.8	24.51	3.1784	1573.3	23.91
		$p=30$ bar			$p=40$ bar	
18	75.815	94.0	7.987	95.265	93.3	7.296
20	67.672	105.3	8.571	85.522	104.7	7.898
25	53.568	133.4	9.837	68.372	133.3	9.172
30	44.508	161.5	10.86	57.172	161.7	10.20
35	38.173	189.3	11.71	49.256	189.9	11.07
40	33.481	216.9	12.45	43.347	217.8	11.82
45	30.055	244.4	13.10	38.756	245.5	12.47
50	26.863	271.5	13.67	35.078	272.9	13.05
55	24.598	298.5	14.19	32.060	300.2	13.57
60	22.626	325.4	14.66	29.535	327.3	14.04
65	20.954	352.1	15.08	27.389	354.1	14.47
70	19.517	378.7	15.48	25.542	380.9	14.87
75	18.268	405.2	15.84	23.932	407.5	15.24
80	17.172	431.6	16.18	22.518	434.0	15.58
85	16.202	457.9	16.50	21.263	460.4	15.90
90	15.336	484.2	16.80	20.143	486.8	16.20
95	14.559	510.4	17.09	19.136	513.0	16.49
100	13.859	536.5	17.35	18.226	539.2	16.75
110	12.642	588.8	17.85	16.645	591.5	17.25
120	11.622	640.9	18.31	15.318	643.7	17.71
130	10.755	692.9	18.72	14.187	695.8	18.12
140	10.009	745.0	19.11	13.213	747.8	18.51
150	9.3602	796.9	19.47	12.363	799.8	18.87
160	8.7902	848.9	19.80	11.617	851.8	19.20
170	8.2855	900.9	20.12	10.956	903.8	19.52
180	7.8357	952.8	20.41	10.366	955.7	19.82
190	7.4324	1004.8	20.69	9.8359	1007.7	20.10
200	7.0683	1056.7	20.96	9.3577	1059.6	20.36
220	6.4379	1160.6	21.46	8.5278	1163.5	20.86
240	5.9107	1264.4	21.91	7.8342	1267.4	21.31
260	5.4633	1368.3	22.32	7.2444	1371.3	21.73
280	5.0788	1472.2	22.71	6.7373	1475.1	22.11
300	4.7450	1576.1	23.07	6.2965	1579.0	22.47
		$p=60$ bar			$p=80$ bar	
18	124.93	93.8	6.325	145.70	96.4	5.651
20	113.74	105.5	6.938	134.43	108.2	6.270
25	93.213	134.5	8.235	112.86	137.5	7.579
30	79.194	163.4	9.289	97.441	166.7	8.643
35	68.986	192.1	10.17	85.851	195.6	9.536
40	61.202	220.4	10.93	76.789	224.2	10.30
45	55.058	248.5	11.59	69.546	252.6	10.97
50	50.078	276.4	12.18	63.478	280.8	11.56

continued

T, °K	ϱ	i	s	ϱ	i	s
55	45.952	304.0	12.70	58.582	308.5	12.09
60	42.474	331.3	13.18	54.334	336.0	12.57
65	39.500	358.5	13.62	50.675	363.2	13.00
70	36.926	385.5	14.02	47.489	390.3	13.41
75	34.673	412.3	14.38	44.688	417.3	13.78
80	32.676	438.9	14.73	42.204	444.1	14.12
85	30.917	465.5	15.05	39.987	470.7	14.45
90	29.333	491.9	15.35	37.996	497.3	14.75
95	27.906	518.2	15.64	36.194	523.6	15.04
100	26.612	544.5	15.91	34.549	550.0	15.31
110	24.357	597.0	16.41	31.699	602.5	15.81
120	22.457	649.2	16.86	29.279	654.9	16.26
130	20.834	701.4	17.28	27.205	707.1	16.68
140	19.430	753.5	17.67	25.406	759.2	17.07
150	18.203	805.5	18.03	23.831	811.3	17.43
160	17.094	857.5	18.36	22.441	863.3	17.76
170	16.164	909.5	18.68	21.204	915.3	18.08
180	15.307	961.5	18.97	20.097	967.3	18.38
190	14.537	1013.4	19.25	19.099	1019.3	18.66
200	13.840	1065.4	19.52	18.196	1071.2	18.92
220	12.629	1169.3	20.02	16.624	1175.1	19.42
240	11.613	1273.1	20.47	15.303	1279.0	19.87
260	10.749	1377.0	20.88	14.176	1382.9	20.35
280	10.003	1480.9	21.27	13.203	1486.8	20.67
300	9.3550	1584.7	21.63	12.355	1590.6	20.03

T, °K	ϱ	i	s	T, °K	ϱ	i	s
			$p = 100$ bar				
18	161.06	100.2	5.143	100	42.101	555.7	14.84
20	151.31	112.0	5.765	110	38.696	608.3	15.34
25	128.73	141.5	7.080	120	35.805	660.8	15.80
30	112.75	170.8	8.149	130	33.317	713.0	16.22
35	100.38	199.9	9.047	140	31.156	765.1	16.60
40	90.518	228.7	9.816	150	29.258	817.2	16.96
45	82.466	257.2	10.48	160	27.579	869.3	17.30
50	75.761	285.3	11.08	170	26.083	921.3	17.61
55	70.089	313.3	11.61	180	24.740	973.3	17.91
60	65.224	340.9	12.09	190	23.530	1025.3	18.19
65	61.004	368.3	12.53	200	22.434	1077.2	18.46
70	57.306	395.5	12.94	220	20.519	1181.1	18.95
75	54.040	422.6	13.31	240	18.906	1285.0	19.41
80	51.130	449.4	13.65	260	17.529	1388.9	19.82
85	48.523	476.2	13.98	280	16.339	1492.8	20.21
90	46.172	502.8	14.28	300	15.300	1596.7	20.57
95	44.042	529.3	14.57				

Thermodynamic properties of helium at high temperatures [152]: ρ (kg/m³), i (kJ/kg) and s (kJ/kg · deg)
(Heat capacity of helium gas between 0 and 1000 °C and 1 to 200 bar can be considered constant and equal to 5.192 kJ/kg · deg. The values of at 273.15 °K $i^0 = 0$ and $s^0 = 0$ were taken at $T = 273.15$ °K and $p = 1$ bar.)

t, °C	ϱ	i	s	ϱ	i	s
		$p = 1$ bar			$p = 5$ bar	
0	0.17615	0.32720	0.011607	0.87893	1.6360	−3.3427
10	0.16993	52.257	0.18672	0.84798	53.564	−3.1560
20	0.16414	104.19	0.36695	0.81913	105.49	−2.9758
30	0.15873	156.12	0.54114	0.79218	157.42	−2.8016
40	0.15366	208.05	0.70968	0.76694	209.35	−2.6330

continued

t, °C	ϱ	i	s	ϱ	i	s
60	0.14444	311.90	1.0312	0.72101	313.21	−2.3115
80	0.13627	415.76	1.3339	0.68027	417.06	−2.0088
100	0.12896	519.62	1.6200	0.64388	520.92	−1.7227
120	0.12241	623.48	1.8911	0.61119	624.78	−1.4516
140	0.11648	727.34	2.1488	0.58166	728.63	−1.1939
160	0.11111	831.20	2.3943	0.055485	832.49	−0.94847
180	0.10620	935.06	2.6287	0.053040	936.34	−0.71407
200	0.10172	1038.9	2.8530	0.50802	1040.2	−0.48979
220	0.097593	1142.8	3.0680	0.48745	1144.1	−0.27481
240	0.093791	1246.6	3.2744	0.46848	1247.9	−0.06836
260	0.090274	1350.5	3.4730	0.40593	1351.8	0.13018
280	0.087010	1454.4	3.6642	0.43465	1455.6	0.32141
300	0.083975	1558.2	3.8487	0.41950	1559.5	0.50585
320	0.081144	1662.1	4.0268	0.40537	1663.3	0.68397
340	0.078498	1765.9	4.1990	0.39217	1767.2	0.85617
360	0.076019	1869.8	4.3657	0.37980	1871.0	1.0228
380	0.073692	1973.6	4.5272	0.36818	1974.9	1.1843
400	0.071503	2077.5	4.6838	0.35725	2078.8	1.3410
420	0.069440	2181.4	4.8358	0.34696	2182.6	1.4930
440	0.067493	2285.2	4.9836	0.33724	2286.5	1.6407
460	0.065652	2389.1	5.1272	0.32804	2390.3	1.7843
480	0.063909	2492.9	5.2670	0.31934	2494.2	1.9241
500	0.062256	2596.8	5.4031	0.31109	2598.0	2.0602
550	0.058475	2856.4	5.7285	0.29221	2857.7	2.3856
600	0.055128	3116.1	6.0347	0.27549	3117.3	2.6918
650	0.052142	3375.7	6.3239	0.26058	3376.9	2.9810
700	0.049463	3635.4	6.5978	0.24720	3636.6	3.2549
750	0.047047	3895.0	6.8580	0.23513	3896.2	3.5151
800	0.044855	4154.7	7.1057	0.22418	4155.9	3.7628
850	0.042858	4414.3	7.3422	0.21421	4415.5	3.9993
900	0.041032	4674.0	7.5684	0.20508	4675.1	4.2255
950	0.039355	4933.6	7.7852	0.19671	4934.8	4.4422
1000	0.037809	5193.3	7.9932	0.18898	5194.4	4.6503
1100	0.035056	5712.6	8.3859	0.17224	5713.7	5.0429
1200	0.032677	6231.9	8.7509	0.16334	6233.0	5.4079
1300	0.030600	6751.2	9.0920	0.15296	6752.3	5.7490
1400	0.028771	7270.5	9.4120	0.14382	7271.5	6.0690
1600	0.025699	8309.1	9.9984	0.12847	8310.1	6.6553
1800	0.023220	9347.6	10.525	0.11608	9348.7	7.1821
2000	0.021177	10386	11.003	0.10587	10387	7.6604
2200	0.019465	11425	11.441	0.097311	11426	8.0983
2400	0.018009	12463	11.845	0.090032	12464	8.5021
2600	0.016755	13502	12.220	0.083766	13503	8.8768
2800	0.015665	14541	12.569	0.078316	14541	9.2262
3000	0.014707	15579	12.897	0.073531	15580	9.5537
		$p = 10$ bar			$p = 20$ bar	
0	1.7533	3.2720	−4.7820	3.4886	6.5440	−6.2206
10	1.6917	55.199	−4.5952	3.3667	58.468	−6.0339
20	1.6343	107.13	−4.4150	3.2531	110.39	−5.8537
30	1.5807	159.05	−4.2408	3.1469	162.32	−5.6795
40	1.5305	210.98	−4.0723	3.0474	214.24	−5.5110
60	1.4390	314.83	−3.7508	2.8662	318.09	−5.1896
80	1.3579	418.69	−3.4481	2.7053	424.93	−4.8868
100	1.2854	522.54	−3.1620	2.5615	525.78	−4.6008
120	1.2203	626.39	−2.8909	2.4322	629.62	−4.3297
140	1.1614	730.24	−2.6333	2.3153	733.47	−4.0721
160	1.1080	834.10	−2.3878	2.2092	837.32	−3.8266
180	1.0593	937.95	−2.1534	2.1123	941.16	−3.5922
200	1.01463	1041.8	−1.9291	2.0236	1045.0	−3.3680
220	0.97361	1145.7	−1.7141	1.9421	1148.8	−3.1530
240	0.93577	1249.6	−1.5077	1.8668	1252.7	−2.9466
260	0.90077	1353.4	−1.3092	1.7972	1356.5	−2.7481
280	0.86829	1457.2	−1.1180	1.7326	1460.4	−2.5569

continued

t, °C	ϱ	i	s	ϱ	i	s
300	0.83807	1 561.1	−0.93353	1.6724	1 564.2	−2.3725
320	0.80989	1 664.9	−0.75542	1.6163	1 668.1	−2.1944
340	0.78353	1 768.8	−0.58322	1.5639	1 771.9	−2.0222
360	0.75884	1 872.6	−0.41655	1.5147	1 875.7	−1.8555
380	0.73566	1 976.5	−0.25506	1.4685	1 979.6	−1.6940
400	0.71385	2 080.3	−0.098445	1.4251	2 083.4	−1.5374
420	0.69330	2 184.2	0.05358	1.3841	2 187.3	−1.3854
440	0.67390	2 288.0	0.20129	1.3455	2 291.1	−1.2377
460	0.65558	2 391.9	0.34491	1.3089	2 395.0	−1.0341
480	0.63818	2 495.7	0.48466	1.2743	2 498.8	−0.95438
500	0.62170	2 599.6	0.62076	1.2415	2 602.6	−0.81831
550	0.58400	2 859.3	0.94615	1.1663	2 862.3	−0.49294
600	0.55062	3 118.8	1.2523	1.0998	3 121.9	−0.18676
650	0.52084	3 378.5	1.5415	1.0404	3 381.5	0.10236
700	0.49412	3 638.1	1.8154	0.98710	3 641.1	0.37623
750	0.47001	3 897.7	2.0756	0.93899	3 900.7	0.63637
800	0.44814	4 157.3	2.3233	0.89536	4 160.3	0.88410
850	0.42821	4 417.0	2.5598	0.85560	4 419.9	1.1205
900	0.40998	4 676.6	2.7859	0.81922	4 679.5	1.3467
950	0.39324	4 936.2	3.0027	0.78583	4 939.1	1.5634
1000	0.37782	5 195.8	3.2107	0.75502	5 188.7	1.7714
1100	0.35033	5 715.1	3.6033	0.70014	5 717.9	2.1640
1200	0.32657	6 234.4	3.9683	0.65270	6 237.1	2.5290
1300	0.30583	6 753.6	4.3094	0.61128	6 756.3	2.8700
1400	0.28756	7 272.9	4.6294	0.57480	7 275.6	3.1900
1600	0.25688	8 311.4	5.2157	0.51351	8 314.0	3.7763
1800	0.23211	9 349.9	5.7425	0.46403	9 352.5	4.3030
2000	0.21170	10 388	6.2207	0.42325	10 391	4.7812
2200	0.19459	11 427	6.6586	0.38905	11 429	5.2191
2400	0.18094	12 465	7.0624	0.36000	12 568	5.6229
2600	0.16751	13 504	7.4371	0.33493	13 506	5.9975
2800	0.15661	14 543	7.7865	0.31314	14 545	6.3469
3000	0.14705	15 581	8.1139	0.29403	15 583	6.6743
		$p=30$ bar			$p=40$ bar	
0	5.2062	9.8160	−7.0617	6.9064	13.088	−7.6581
10	5.0253	61.737	−6.8750	6.6677	65.006	−7.4715
20	4.8566	113.66	−6.6948	6.4450	116.92	−7.2913
30	4.6988	165.68	−6.5207	6.2367	168.34	−7.1171
40	4.5510	217.50	−6.3521	6.0415	220.76	−6.9486
60	4.2816	321.34	−6.0307	5.6855	324.59	−6.6272
80	4.0423	425.18	−5.7280	5.3691	428.43	−6.3245
100	3.8283	529.02	−5.4420	5.0860	532.26	−6.0385
120	3.6358	632.86	−5.1709	4.8313	636.09	−5.7675
140	3.4618	736.70	−4.9133	4.6009	739.92	−5.5099
160	3.3036	840.53	−4.6679	4.3914	843.75	−5.2644
180	3.1593	944.37	−4.4335	4.2002	947.58	−5.0301
200	3.0271	1 048.2	−4.2093	4.0250	1 051.4	−4.8059
220	2.9054	1 152.0	−3.9943	3.8637	1 155.2	−4.5970
240	2.7932	1 255.9	−3.7879	3.7149	1 259.1	−4.3846
260	2.6893	1 359.7	−3.5894	3.5772	1 362.9	−4.1861
280	2.5929	1 463.5	−3.3982	3.4492	1 466.7	−3.9949
300	2.5031	1 567.4	−3.2138	3.3301	1 570.5	−3.8105
320	2.4193	1 671.2	−3.0357	3.2190	1 674.4	−3.6324
340	2.3410	1 775.1	−2.8636	3.1150	1 778.2	−3.4603
360	2.2676	1 878.9	−2.6969	3.0175	1 882.0	−3.2936
380	2.1986	1 982.7	−2.5355	2.9260	1 985.8	−3.1322
400	2.1338	2 086.6	−2.3789	2.8398	2 089.7	−2.9756
420	2.0726	2 190.4	−2.2269	2.7586	2 193.5	−2.8236
440	2.0148	2 294.2	−2.0792	2.6819	2 297.3	−2.6760
460	1.9602	2 398.1	−1.9356	2.6093	2 401.1	−2.5324
480	1.9084	2 501.9	−1.7958	2.5405	2 505.0	−2.3927
500	1.8594	2 685.7	−1.6598	2.4753	2 608.8	−2.2566
550	1.7470	2 865.3	−1.3344	2.3260	2 868.4	−1.9313

continued

t, °C	ϱ	i	s	ϱ	i	s
600	1.6475	3 124.9	−1.0283	2.1937	3 127.9	−1.6252
650	1.5587	3 384.5	−0.73920	2.0757	3 387.5	−1.3361
700	1.4789	3 644.1	−0.46556	1.9696	3 647.0	−1.0623
750	1.4070	3 903.6	−0.20524	1.8739	3 906.6	−0.80218
800	1.3417	4 163.2	0.042471	1.7871	4 166.2	−0.55449
850	1.2822	4 422.8	0.27890	1.7079	4 425.7	−0.31809
900	1.2277	4 682.4	0.50502	1.6355	4 685.3	−0.091982
950	1.1778	4 942.0	0.72171	1.5689	4 944.8	0.12469
1000	1.1316	5 201.6	0.92971	1.5076	5 204.4	0.33267
1100	1.0494	5 270.7	1.3223	1.3982	5 723.5	0.72521
1200	0.97839	6 239.9	1.6872	1.3036	6 242.7	1.0901
1300	0.91636	6 759.1	2.0282	1.2211	6 761.9	1.4311
1400	0.86171	7 278.3	2.3482	1.1484	7 280.9	1.7510
1600	0.76989	8 316.6	2.9344	1.0260	8 319.2	2.3372
1800	0.69575	9 355.0	3.4611	0.92728	9 357.5	2.8639
2000	0.63464	10 393	3.9393	0.84587	10 396	3.3420
2200	0.58339	11 432	4.3771	0.77759	11 434	3.7798
2400	0.53979	12 470	4.7809	0.71951	12 472	4.1835
2600	0.50226	13 509	5.1555	0.66951	13 511	4.5581
2800	0.46961	14 547	5.5049	0.62600	14 549	4.9075
3000	0.44094	15 585	5.8323	0.58780	15 588	5.2349
		$p=60$ bar			$p=80$ bar	
0	10.256	19.632	−8.4981	13.540	26.176	−9.0933
10	9.9053	71.544	−8.3114	13.082	78.082	−8.9067
20	9.5779	123.46	−8.1312	12.654	129.99	−8.7265
30	9.2714	175.37	−7.9571	12.252	181.89	−8.5524
40	8.9839	227.28	−7.7886	11.876	233.80	−8.3840
60	8.4593	331.10	−7.4672	11.189	337.61	−8.0626
80	7.9925	434.92	−7.1646	10.577	441.41	−7.7600
100	7.5746	538.74	−6.8786	10.028	545.22	−7.4741
120	7.1982	642.56	−6.6076	9.5336	649.02	−7.2031
140	6.8574	746.37	−6.3500	9.0854	752.82	−6.9456
160	6.5474	850.19	−6.1047	8.6776	856.62	−6.7002
180	6.2642	954.00	−5.8704	8.3047	960.42	−6.4660
200	6.0045	1 057.8	−5.6462	7.9625	1 064.2	−6.2418
220	5.7654	1 161.6	−5.4313	7.6474	1 165.0	−6.0269
240	5.5447	1 265.4	−5.2249	7.3563	1 271.8	−5.8206
260	5.3402	1 369.2	−5.0265	7.0865	1 375.6	−5.6222
280	5.1502	1 473.1	−4.8353	6.8358	1 479.4	−5.4311
300	4.9733	1 576.9	−4.6509	6.6023	1 503.2	−5.2467
320	4.8082	1 680.7	−4.4729	6.3841	1 627.0	−5.0687
340	4.6536	1 784.5	−4.3008	6.1799	1 790.8	−4.8966
360	4.5087	1 888.3	−4.1342	5.9883	1 894.6	−4.7301
380	4.3725	1 992.1	−3.9728	5.8083	1 998.4	−4.5687
400	4.2443	2 095.9	−3.8162	5.6387	2 102.2	−4.4121
420	4.1234	2 199.7	−3.6642	5.4788	2 205.9	−4.2602
440	4.0092	2 303.5	−3.5166	5.3277	2 309.7	−4.1126
460	3.9012	2 407.3	−3.3730	5.1847	2 413.5	−3.9690
480	3.7988	2 511.1	−3.2333	5.0491	2 517.3	−3.8294
500	3.7016	2 615.0	−3.0973	4.9205	2 621.1	−3.6934
550	3.4792	2 874.5	−2.7721	4.6258	2 880.6	−3.3682
600	3.2819	3 134	−2.4660	4.3644	3 140.0	−3.0621
650	3.1058	3 393.5	−2.1770	4.1310	3 399.5	−2.7731
700	2.9477	3 653.0	−1.9032	3.9212	3 659.0	−2.4995
750	2.8048	3 912.5	−1.6431	3.7317	3 918.5	−2.2394
800	2.6752	4 172.0	−1.3655	3,5597	4 177.9	−1.9918
850	2.5570	4 431.6	−1.1591	3.4028	4 437.4	−1.7555
900	2.4488	4 691.1	−0.93307	3.2591	4 696.9	−1.5295
950	2.3493	4 950.6	−0.71644	3.1271	4 956,3	−1.3129
1000	2.2577	5 210.1	−0.50849	3.0053	5 215.8	−1.1050
1100	2.0942	5 729.1	−0.11602	2.7882	5 731.8	−0.71258
1200	1.9528	6 248.2	0.24885	2.6003	6 263.7	−0.34777
1300	1.8293	6 767.2	0,58975	2.4361	6 772.8	−0.00693

continued

t, °C	ϱ	i	s	ϱ	i	s
1400	1.7206	7 286.3	0.90964	2.2914	7 291.7	0.31291
1600	1.5375	8 324.4	1.4957	2.0481	8 329.7	0.89892
1800	1.3887	9 362.6	2.0223	1.8514	9 367.7	1.4254
2000	1.2679	10 401	2.5004	1.6892	10 406	1.9034
2200	1.1656	11 439	2.9381	1.5531	11 444	2.3413
2400	1.0786	12 477	3.3418	1.4373	12 482	2.7448
2600	1.0037	13 515	3.7164	1.3376	13 520	3.4930
2800	0.93854	14 554	4.0657	1.2508	14 558	3.4686
3000	0.88130	15 592	4.3930	1.1746	15 596	3.7959
		$p = 100$ bar			$p = 120$ bar	
0	16.761	32.720	−9.5545	19.922	39.264	−9.9309
10	16.200	84.620	−9.3679	19.261	91.158	−9.7443
20	15.675	136.52	−9.1878	18.643	105.72	−9.5642
30	15.183	188.42	−9.0137	18.063	194.94	−9.3902
40	14.721	240.32	−8.8453	17.518	246.84	−9.2217
60	13.876	344.11	−8.5240	16.522	350.62	−8.9005
80	13.123	447.91	−8.2214	15.632	454.40	−8.5980
100	14.448	551.70	−7.9355	14.835	558.18	−8.3121
120	11.838	655.49	−7.6646	14.113	661.95	−8.0412
140	11.286	759.27	−7.4071	13.459	765.72	−7.7837
160	10.783	863.06	−7.1617	12.863	869.50	−7.5385
180	10.322	966.84	−6.9275	12.317	973.27	−7.3043
200	9.8996	1 070.6	−6.7034	11.816	1 077.0	−7.0802
220	9.5102	1 174.4	−6.4886	11.354	1 180.8	−6.8654
240	9.1503	1 278.2	−6.2823	10.927	1 284.6	−6.6591
260	8.8166	1 382.0	−6.0839	10.530	1 388.3	−6.4607
280	8.5063	1 485.7	−5.8928	10.162	1 492.1	−6.2697
300	8.2172	1 589.5	−5.7085	9.8182	1 595.8	−6.0854
320	7.9470	1 693.3	−5.5305	9.4970	1 699.7	−5.9075
340	7.6940	1 797.1	−5.3584	9.1961	1 803.4	−5.7354
360	7.4566	1 900.8	−5.1919	8.9137	1 907.1	−5.5690
380	7.2334	2 004.6	−5.0305	8.6481	2 010.9	−5.4976
400	7.0232	2 108.4	−4.8740	8.3978	2 114.6	−5.2511
420	6.8248	2 212.2	−4.7221	8.1617	2 218.4	−5.0992
440	6.6373	2 315.9	−4.5745	7.9383	2 322.1	−4.9516
460	6.4599	2 419.7	−4.4310	7.7269	2 426.0	−4.8081
480	6.2917	2 523.5	−4.2913	7.5265	2 530.0	−4.6685
500	6.1320	2 627.3	−4.1554	7.3361	2 633.4	−4.5326
550	5.7660	2 886.7	−3.8302	6.8999	2 892.8	−4.2075
600	5.4413	3 146.1	−3.5242	6.5125	3 152.2	−3.9016
650	5.1511	3 405.5	−3.2853	6.1663	3 411.6	−3.6127
700	4.8903	3 665.0	−2.9617	5.8551	3 670.9	−3.3391
750	4.6547	3 924.4	−2.7017	5.5736	3 930.3	−3.0791
800	4.4406	4 183.8	−2.4541	5.3180	4 189.7	−2.8316
850	4.2454	4 443.2	−2.2178	5.0848	4 449.1	−2.5954
900	4.0666	4 702.7	−1.9919	4.8711	4 708.5	−2.3694
950	3.9022	4 962.1	−1.7753	4.6747	4 967.8	−2.1530
1000	3.7506	5 221.5	−1.5674	4.4935	5 227.2	−1.9451
1100	3.4801	5 740.4	−1.1751	4.1701	5 746.0	−1.5528
1200	3.2460	6 259.2	−0.81034	3.8901	6 264.8	−1.1882
1300	3.0414	6 778.2	−0.46955	3.6453	6 783.6	−0.84737
1400	2.8611	7 297.0	−0.14976	3.4295	7 302.4	−0.52763
1600	2.5576	8 334.9	0.43616	3.0663	8 340.1	−0.058205
1800	2.3124	9 372.7	0.96261	2.7725	9 377.8	0.58457
2000	2.1100	10 411	1.4405	2.5301	10 415	1.0624
2200	1.9402	11 449	1.8782	2.3267	11 453	1.5000
2400	1.7956	12 486	2.2818	2.1535	12 491	1.9036
2600	1.6712	13 524	2.6562	2.0043	13 530	2.2780
2800	1.5627	14 563	3.0055	1.8744	14 567	2.6272
3000	1.4675	15 601	3.3328	1.7603	15 805	2.9544

continued

t, °C	ϱ	i	s	ϱ	i	s
		p=140 bar			p=160 bar	
0	23.026	45.808	−10.249	26.073	52.352	−10.524
10	22.269	97.697	−10.062	25.224	104.23	−10.337
20	21.560	149.58	− 9.8822	24.429	156.12	−10.157
30	20.896	201.47	− 9.7081	23.683	208.00	− 9.9832
40	20.271	253.36	− 9.5397	22.981	259.88	− 9.8149
60	19.128	357.13	− 9.2185	21.695	363.63	− 9.4937
80	18.106	460.89	− 8.9160	20.545	467.39	− 9.1912
100	17.188	564.66	− 8.6302	19.511	571.14	− 8.9055
120	16.359	668.42	− 8.3593	18.577	674.88	− 8.6346
140	15.606	772.18	− 8.1019	17.727	778.63	− 8.3772
160	14.919	875.93	− 7.8567	16.953	882.37	− 8.1320
180	14.291	979.69	− 7.6225	16.242	986.11	− 7.8979
200	13.713	1 083.4	− 7.3984	15.589	1 089.8	− 7.6738
220	13.180	1 187.2	− 7.1837	14.987	1 193.6	− 7.4591
240	12.686	1 290.9	− 6.9774	14.429	1 297.3	− 7.2529
260	12.229	1 394.7	− 6.7791	13.911	1 401.0	− 7.0546
280	11.803	1 498.4	− 6.5881	13.429	1 504.8	− 6.8636
300	11.406	1 602.2	− 6.4038	12.980	1 608.5	− 6.6794
320	11.034	1 705.9	− 6.2259	12.559	1 712.2	− 6.5015
340	10.686	1 809.7	− 6.0539	12.165	1 815.9	− 6.3295
360	10.360	1 913.4	− 5.8874	11.795	1 919.7	− 6.1631
380	10.052	2 017.1	− 5.7261	11.446	2 023.4	− 6.0018
400	9.7627	2 120.9	− 5.5696	11.118	2 127.1	− 5.8454
420	9.4893	2 224.6	− 5.4178	10.808	2 230.8	− 5.6935
440	9.2307	2 328.3	− 5.2702	10.515	2 334.5	− 5.5460
460	8.9862	2 432.1	− 5.1268	10.237	2 438.3	− 5.4026
480	8.7536	2 535.8	− 4.9872	9.9732	2 542.0	− 5.2630
500	8.5331	2 639.6	− 4.8512	9.7229	2 645.7	− 5.1271
550	8.0274	2 899.0	− 4.5262	9.1487	2 905.0	− 4.8021
600	7.5782	3 158.2	− 4.2203	8.6385	3 164.3	− 4.4963
650	7.1766	3 417.6	− 3.9315	8.1821	3 423.6	− 4.2075
700	6.8154	3 676.9	− 3.6579	7.7714	3 682.9	− 3.9340
750	6.4887	3 936.2	− 3.3981	7.3999	3 942.2	− 3.6742
800	6.1919	4 195.6	− 3.1506	7.0623	4 201.5	− 3.4267
850	5.9210	4 454.9	− 2.9144	6.7541	4 460.8	− 3.1906
900	5.6728	4 714.3	− 2.6885	6.4716	4 720.0	− 2.9648
950	5.4445	4 973.6	− 2.4720	6.2118	4 979.3	− 2.7482
1000	5.2339	5 232.9	− 2.2642	5.9720	5 238.7	− 2.5405
1100	4.8580	5 751.6	− 1.8720	5.5439	5 757.3	− 2.1483
1200	4.5324	6 270.3	− 1.5073	5.1730	6 275.9	− 1.7838
1300	4.2476	6 789.1	− 1.1667	4.8486	6 794.5	− 1.4431
1400	3.9965	7 308.8	− 0.84698	4.5623	7 313.2	− 1.1236
1600	3.5738	8 345.3	− 0.26124	4.0804	8 350.5	− 0.53785
1800	3.2319	9 382.9	0.26506	3.6905	9 387.9	− 0.011627
2000	2.9496	10 420	0.74287	3.3685	10 425	0.46613
2200	2.7127	11 454	1.1804	3.0982	11 463	0.90358
2400	2.5109	12 496	1.5839	2.8679	12 500	1.3070
2600	2.3371	13 534	1.9583	2.6695	13 538	1.6814
2800	2.1857	14 571	2.3075	2.4968	14 576	2.0305
3000	2.0528	15 609	2.6346	2.3450	15 614	2.3577
		p=180 bar			p=200 bar	
0	29.068	58.896	−10.766	32.013	65.440	−10.983
10	28.130	110.77	−10.580	30.989	117.31	−10.796
20	27.251	162.65	−10.400	30.028	169.18	−10.616
30	26.426	214.52	−10.226	29.126	221.05	−10.442
40	25.649	266.40	−10.057	28.277	272.92	−10.274
60	24.225	370.14	− 9.7361	26.719	376.65	− 9.9528
80	22.951	473.88	− 9.4337	25.324	480.37	− 9.6504
100	21.804	577.62	− 9.1480	24.068	584.09	− 9.3648
120	20.767	681.35	− 8.8772	22.930	687.81	− 9.0940
140	19.824	785.08	− 8.6199	21.896	791.53	− 8.8367
160	18.963	888.80	− 8.3747	20.951	895.24	− 8.5915

continued

t, C°	ϱ	i	s	ϱ	i	s
180	18.173	992.53	−8.1406	20.084	998.95	−8.3575
200	17.448	1 096.2	−7.9167	19.286	1 102.7	−8.1335
220	16.776	1 200.0	−7.7019	18.549	1 206.4	−7.9188
240	16.156	1 303.7	−7.4957	17.866	1 310.1	−7.7127
260	15.579	1 407.4	−7.2975	17.232	1 413.8	−7.5145
280	15.042	1 511.1	−7.1065	16.641	1 517.4	−7.3935
300	14.541	1 614.8	−6.9223	16.089	1 621.1	−7.1394
320	14.072	1 718.5	−6.7444	15.573	1 724.0	−6.9615
340	13.632	1 822.2	−6.5725	15.088	1 776.7	−6.7897
360	13.219	1 925.9	−6.4060	14.633	1 880.4	−6.6232
380	12.831	2 029.6	−6.2448	14.205	1 984.1	−6.4620
400	12.464	2 133.4	−6.0884	13.799	2 139.6	−6.3056
420	12.118	2 237.1	−5.9366	13.419	2 243.3	−6.1538
440	11.790	2 340.8	−5.7891	13.057	2 347.0	−6.0063
460	11.480	2 444.5	−5.6457	12.715	2 450.6	−5.8629
480	11.185	2 548.2	−5.5061	12.390	2 554.3	−5.7234
500	10.906	2 651.9	−5.3702	12.081	2 658.0	−5.5875
550	10.264	2 911.1	−5.0453	11.373	2 917.2	−5.2627
600	9.6933	3 170.4	−4.7395	10.743	3 176.4	−4.9570
650	9.1827	3 429.6	−4.4508	10.178	3 435.6	−4.6683
700	8.7231	3 688.8	−4.1773	9.6706	3 694.8	−4.3949
750	8.3073	3 948.2	−3.9175	9.2108	3 954.0	−4.1351
800	7.9292	4 207.3	−3.6702	8.7927	4 213.2	−3.8878
850	7.5840	4 466.6	−3.4340	8.4109	4 472.4	−3.6517
900	7.2676	4 725.8	−3.2082	8.0608	4 731.6	−3.4259
950	6.9765	4 985.1	−2.9918	7.7386	4 990.8	−3.2095
1000	6.7077	5 244.4	−2.7841	7.4411	5 250.1	−3.0018
1100	6.2279	5 762.9	−2.3920	6.9097	5 768.5	−2.6098
1200	5.8119	6 281.4	−2.0275	6.4491	6 287.0	−2.2454
1300	5.4479	6 800.0	−1.6869	6.0459	6 815.4	−1.9048
1400	5.1268	7 318.5	−1.3673	5.6901	7 323.9	−1.5853
1600	4.5860	8 355.7	−0.78174	5.0907	8 360.9	−0.99983
1800	4.1483	9 393.0	−0.25560	4.6054	9 398.1	−0.47377
2000	3.7868	10 430	0.22208	4.2045	10 435	0.00385
2200	3.4831	11 468	0.65949	3.8676	11 472	0.44120
2400	3.2245	12 505	1.0629	3.5807	12 510	0.84455
2600	3.0016	13 543	1.4372	3.3334	13 547	1.2188
2800	2.8076	14 580	1.7864	3.1180	14 585	1.5679
3000	2.6369	15 618	2.1134	2.9287	15 622	1.8950

Heat capacity c_s (kJ/kg · deg) of saturated liquid helium [16]

T, °K	c_s	T, °K	c_s	T, °K	c_s	T, °K	c_s	T, °K	c_s
1.8	2.81	2.10	7.51	2.4	2.38	3.4	2.97	4.4	5.11
1.85	3.26	2.15	9.35	2.6	2.27	3.6	3.26	4.6	5.94
1.9	3.79	2.17	12.6	2.8	2.34	3.8	3.60	4.8	7.53
2.0	5.18	2.2	3.98	3.0	2.49	4.0	3.99	5.0	11.5
2.05	6.16	2.3	2.64	3.2	2.69	4.2	4.48	5.05	13.5

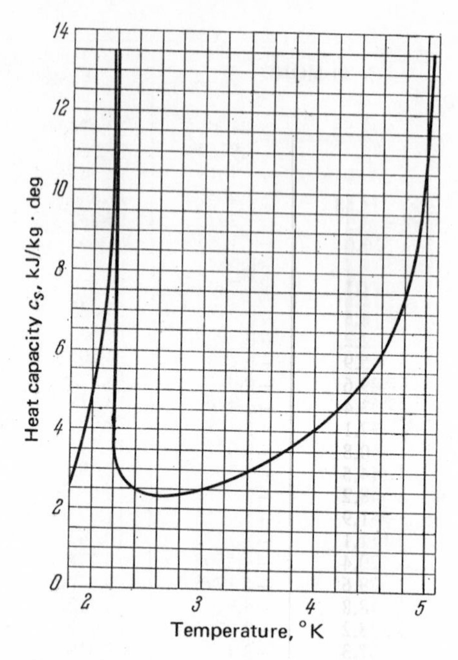

Fig. 18. Heat capacity c_s of saturated liquid helium as a function of temperature.

Heat capacity c_v (kJ/kg · deg) of helium at low temperatures and different pressures [16]

T, °K \ p, atm →	3	5	10	20	40	60	80	100
3		1.859	1.708	1.582	1.331			
4	2.324	2.234	2.110	1.943	1.737	1.600	1.499	1.444
5	2.600	2.529	2.407	2.252	2.064	1.922	1,817	1,733
6	3.123	2.780	2.621	2.483	2.311	2.190	2.097	2.010
6.5	3.144							
7	3.086	3.010	2.801	2.650	2.512	2.403	2.324	
8	3.090	3.056	2.926	2.780	2.654	2.566	2.495	
10	3.094	3.081	3.023	2.935	2.847	2.793	2.738	
12	3.098	3.098	3.065	3.018	2.981	2.930	2.923	
16	3.102		3.107	3.098	3.081	3.056	3.056	
20			3.140	3.148	3.161	3.174	3.182	

Heat capacity c_p (kJ/kg · deg) of helium at low temperatures and different pressures [16]

T, °K \ p, atm →	3	5	6	10	15	30	50	70
6	12.18			4.94	4.06	3.22	2.80	2.57
6.5	8.96	14.23	9.42	5.65	4,56			
7	7.70	11.85	11.89	6.40	5,02	3.77	3.10	2.97
8	6.49	8.21	9.08	8.08	5.90	4.27	3.64	3.31
9	6.11	6.99	7.45	8.21	6.70	4.77	3.81	3.64
10	5.86	6.40	6.74	7.58	7.16	5.23	4.40	3.98
12		5.95	6.11	6.66	6,87	5,86	4.94	4.52
14		5.71	5.82	6.15	6,36	6.15	5.36	4.94
16		5.61	5.65	5,86	6,07	6.20	5.71	5.11
18		5.53	5.57	5.69	5.90	6.11	5.90	5.53
20			5.48	5.61	5.78	6.03	5.99	5.71

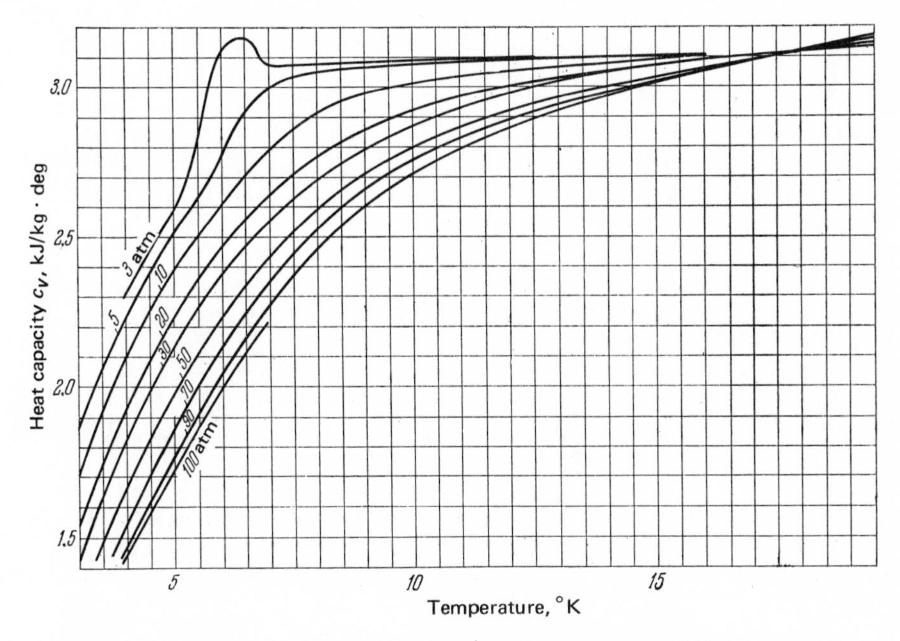

Fig. 19. Heat capacity c_v of helium as a function of temperature at different pressures.

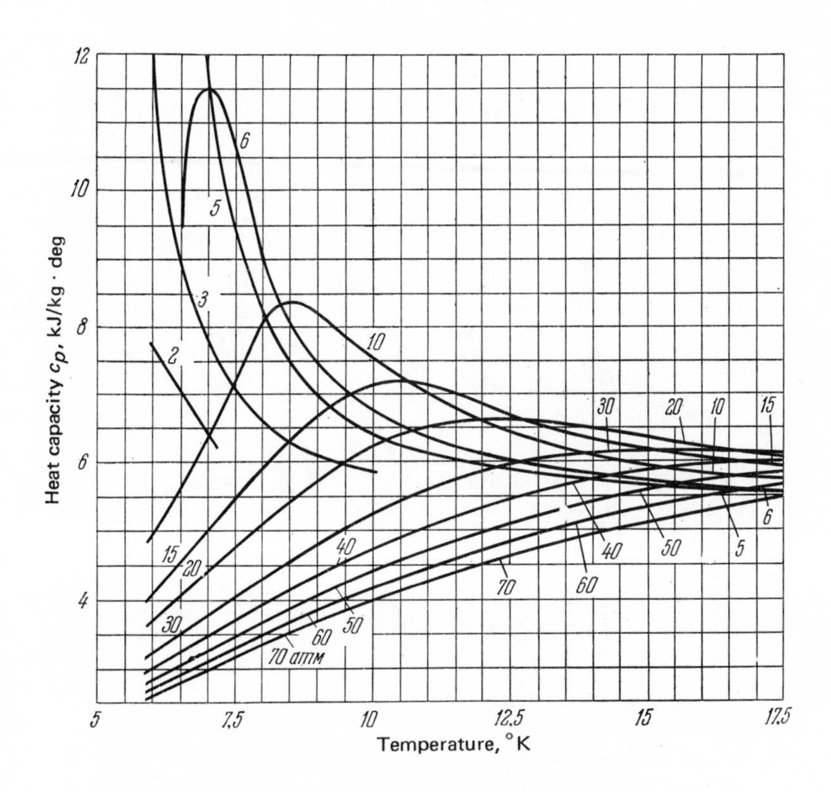

Fig. 20. Heat capacity c_p of helium as a function of temperature at different pressures.

Latent heat of vaporization r (kJ/kg) of liquid helium [16]

T, °K	r	T, °K	r	T, °K	r	T, °K	r	T, °K	r
2.2	22.8	3.0	23.7	3.8	22.7	4.6	18.0	5.15	6.70
2.4	23.1	3.2	23.6	4.0	21.9	4.8	15.6	5.18	4.00
2.6	23.3	3.4	23.5	4.2	20.9	5.0	12.0		
2.8	23.5	3.6	23.2	4.4	19.7	5.1	8.99		

Density ρ of liquid helium [16]

T, °K	2.2	2.3	2.4	2.6	2.8	3.0	3.2	3.4	3.6	3.8	4.0	4.2	4.4	4.6	4.8	5.0	5.15	5.18
kg/m³	147	146	146	144	143	141	139	137	134	132	129	125	122	117	111	101	87	79

Density ρ (kg/m³) and compressibility factor z of helium at high pressures [152]

p, atm	p, bar	ϱ	z	p, atm	p, bar	ϱ	z
	$t=-70$ °C				$t=50$ °C		
100	101.3	22.406	1.0714	100	101.3	14.452	1.0443
200	202.6	42.037	1.1421	200	202.6	27.756	1.0875
400	405 3	75.223	1.2768	400	405.3	51,555	1.1711
600	607.9	102.17	1.4100	600	607.9	72.513	1.2489
800	810.6	125.07	1.5359	800	810.6	90.912	1.3283
				1000	1013	107.49	1.4040
	$t=-50$ °C				$t=100$ °C		
100	101.3	20.512	1.0654	100	101.3	12.601	1.0372
200	202.6	34.266	1.1952	200	202.6	24.345	1.0737
400	405.3	62.181	1.1376	400	405.3	45.663	1.1451
600	607.9	85.437	1.4383	600	607.9	64.693	1.2123
800	810.6	105.50	1.5531	800	810.6	81.682	1.2803
900	911.9	114.60	1.6085	1000	1013	97.196	1.3446
	$t=0$ °C				$t=200$ °C		
100	101.3	16.959	1.0528	100	101.3	10.024	1.0283
200	202.6	32.340	1.1042	200	202.6	19.522	1.0560
400	405.3	59.368	1.2032	400	405.3	37.225	1.1078
600	607.9	82.351	1.3010	600	607.9	53.137	1.1640
800	810.6	102.55	1.3951	800	810.6	68.049	1.2120
1000	1013	120.26	1.4846	1000	1013	81.522	1.2643

Viscosity η (N · s/m²) of helium gas at $p = 1$ bar [16, 45, 152, 154]

T, °K	$\eta \cdot 10^7$	T, °K	$\eta \cdot 10^7$	T, °K	$\eta \cdot 10^7$	T, °K	$\eta \cdot 10^7$
14.4	28.5	80	84.2	373.16	229.2	1373.16	554.5
20	35.0	90	91.2	473.16	268.8	1473.16	581.9
25	40.0	100	97.7	573.16	305.8	1573.16	608.7
30	44.7	125	112.9	673.16	341.0	1673.16	635.1
35	49.3	150	127.4	773.16	374.5	1773.16	660.8
40	53.6	175	141.0	873.16	406.9	1873.16	686.2
45	57.8	200	153.5	973.16	438.1	1973.16	711.1
50	61.8	225	164.9	1073.16	468.4	2073.16	735.7
60	69.6	250	175.8	1173.16	497.8	2173.16	759.9
70	77.0	273.16	186.0	1273.16	526.4	2273.16	783.8

Viscosity $\eta \cdot 10^7$ (N · s/m²) of helium at different temperatures and pressures [45, 47, 48, 152, 380, 381 and 385]

p, bar \ T, °K →	77.36	157.16	194.66	273.16	373.16	473.16	773.16	1273.16
1	82.0	131.0	150.5	186.0	229.2	268.8	374.5	526.4
50	83.9	132.7	151.0	186.2				
100	88.5	134.6	151.6	186.4	229.9	269.3		
200	100.9	135.0	153.8	187.3	231.2	270.0	375.0	526.5
300	112.0	138.0	156.7	190.7	233.2	271.8		
400	129.8		161.0	193.1	235.2	273.2		
500	150.0	155.0	169.0	197.5	237.2	274.3	377.0	528.0
600				200.4	238.7	275.3		
700				204.0				
800				207.3	241.2	276.8		

Viscosity η of liquid helium [16]

T, °K	2.186	2.2	2.3	2.4	2.6	2.8	3.0	3.2	3.4	3.6	3.8	4.0
$\eta \cdot 10^6$, N · s/m²	2.78	2.89	3.26	3.50	3.73	3.78	3.76	3.74	3.70	3.67	3.63	3.60

Thermal conductivity η (W/m · deg) of helium at $p = 1$ bar [15]

T, °K	$\lambda \cdot 10^3$	T, °K	$\lambda \cdot 10^3$	T° K,	$\lambda \cdot 10^3$	T, °K	$\lambda \cdot 10^3$
70	57.9	210	120	350	166	850	317
80	63.2	220	124	360	170	900	330
90	67.6	230	127	370	173	950	342
100	72.0	240	130	380	176	1000	354
110	76.4	250	134	390	181	1100	379
120	81.6	260	138	400	184	1200	405
130	86.0	270	142	450	201	1300	430
140	90.5	280	145	500	218	1400	455
150	94.5	290	148	550	235	1500	479
160	98.8	300	151	600	250	1600	502
170	103	310	154	650	264	1700	523
180	107	320	157	700	278	1800	543
190	111	330	160	750	291	1900	562
200	115	340	163	800	304	2000	579

Thermal conductivity λ of helium at high temperatures and $p = 1$ bar [361]

T, °K	2500	3000	3500	4000	4500	5000	5500	6000
$\lambda \cdot 10^3$, W/m · deg	657	745	826	907	970	1050	1180	1200

Thermal conductivity of liquid helium [16]

T, °K	2.3	2.4	2.6	2.8	3.0	3.5	4.0	4.2
$\lambda \cdot 10^3$, W/m · deg	18.1	18.5	19.5	20.5	21.4	23.8	26.2	27.1

Thermal conductivity $\lambda \cdot 10^3$ (W/m · deg) of helium at different temperatures and pressures [15]

p, bar → / T, °K	1	50	100	150	200	250	300	p, bar → / T, °K	1	50	100	150	200	250	300
270	142	144	147	150	153	156	159	650	264	265	266	267	269	271	273
280	145	148	151	153	156	159	162	700	278	279	280	281	282	283	285
290	148	151	153	156	159	161	164	750	291	292	293	294	295	296	297
300	151	154	158	158	161	164	167	800	304	305	306	307	308	309	311
310	154	157	160	162	165	167	170	850	317	318	319	320	321	322	323
320	157	160	162	164	167	169	172	900	330	331	331	332	333	334	335
330	160	162	165	167	170	172	175	950	342	343	344	345	345	346	347
340	163	165	167	169	172	174	177	1000	354	355	356	357	357	358	359
350	166	168	170	172	174	176	179	1100	379	380	381	381	382	383	384
400	184	186	188	180	182	184	188	1200	405	406	406	407	408	408	409
450	201	203	205	207	209	211	213	1300	430	430	431	431	432	433	434
500	218	220	221	223	224	226	228	1400	455	455	456	456	457	457	458
550	235	236	238	239	240	242	244	1500	479	479	480	480	481	482	483
600	250	251	252	254	255	257	259								

NEON (Ne)

Atomic weight 20.183

$T_{boil} = 27.09$ °K at 760 mm Hg; $T_{melt} = 24.5$ °K;
$T_{cr} = 44.4$ °K; $p_{cr} = 26.54$ bar; $\rho_{cr} = 483$ kg/m³

Thermodynamic properties of saturated neon [155]:
ρ (kg/m³), i (kJ/kg) and s (kJ/kg · deg)

T, °K	p, bar	ϱ'	ϱ''	i'	i''	s'	s''
25	0.51033	1240.2	5.1019	0.90	89.57	0.0346	3.5816
26	0.71841	1223.7	6.9708	2.83	90.35	0.1099	3.4758
27	0.98545	1206.4	9.3109	4.83	91.06	0.1844	3.3780
28	1.3210	1188.5	12.195	6.89	91.69	0.2582	3.2868
29	1.7351	1170.0	15.702	9.00	92.23	0.3311	3.2011
30	2.2381	1150.8	19.923	11.16	92.67	0.4031	3.1199
31	2.8402	1131.0	24.958	13.38	93.00	0.4741	3.0424
32	3.5526	1110.3	30.926	15.65	93.20	0.5441	2.9677
33	4.3860	1088.8	37.965	17.96	93.27	0.6131	2.8952
34	5.3518	1066.4	46.243	20.33	93.19	0.6809	2.8240
35	6.4618	1042.8	55.961	22.74	92.94	0.7477	2.7536
36	7.7282	1018.0	67.368	25.19	92.50	0.8135	2.6832
37	9.1637	991.56	80.773	27.70	91.85	0.8784	2.6122
38	10.7820	963.19	96.567	30.28	90.97	0.9426	2.5399
39	12.597	932.35	115.26	32.93	89.83	1.0065	2.4655
40	14.625	898.22	137.55	35.69	88.38	1.0710	2.3882
41	16.882	859.44	164.51	38.67	86.58	1.1382	2.3066
42	19.387	813.38	198.16	42.05	84.28	1.2124	2.2179
43	22.157	753.63	243.45	46.32	81.13	1.3044	2.1140
44	25.217	650.96	322.40	53.39	75.51	1.4569	1.9597
44,4	26.54	483.0	483.0				

Thermodynamic properties of neon at different temperatures and pressures [155]:
ρ (kg/m³), i (kJ/kg) and s (kJ/kg · deg)

T, °K	ϱ	i	s	ϱ	i	s
	$p=0.1$ bar			$p=1$ bar		
25	0.97611	90.08	4.2640	1240.6	0.92	0.0341
30	0.81193	95.24	4.4522	8.4153	94.24	3.4844
35	0.69514	100.41	4.6114	7.1209	99.57	3.6485
40	0.60779	105.57	4.7492	6.1819	104.86	3.7967

continued

T, °K	ϱ	i	s	ϱ	i	s
45	0.53999	110.73	4.8708	5.4668	110.12	3.9137
50	0.48583	115.89	4.9795	4.9029	115.37	4.0242
55	0.44165	121.05	5.0778	4.4462	120.59	4.1237
60	0.40469	126.20	5.1675	4.0684	125.80	4.2144
70	0.34679	136.51	5.3264	3.4790	136.19	4.3746
80	0.30341	146.82	5.4640	3.0399	146.56	4.5133
90	0.26967	157.12	5.5854	2.6998	156.91	4.6351
100	0.24268	167.43	5.6939	2.4284	167.26	4.7440
110	0.22062	177.33	5.7921	2.2069	177.59	4.8427
120	0.20223	188.03	5.8817	2.0224	187.92	4.9323
130	0.18667	198.34	5.9642	1.8665	198.24	5.0750
140	0.17333	208.64	6.0405	1.7329	208.56	5.0914
150	0.16178	218.94	6.1116	1.6173	218.87	5.1626
160	0.15166	229.24	6.1781	1.5160	229.18	5.2291
170	0.14274	239.54	6.2405	1.4268	239.50	5.2915
180	0.13481	249.84	6.2994	1.3474	249.81	5.3505
190	0.12772	260.14	6.3551	1.2766	260.12	5.4062
200	0.12133	270.44	6.4079	1.2127	270.42	5.4591
220	0.11030	291.04	6.5061	1.1024	291.04	5.5573
240	0.10111	311.65	6.5957	1.0105	311.65	5.6469
260	0.093330	332.25	6.6781	0.93283	332.26	5.7294
280	0.086663	352.85	6.7544	0.86620	352.86	5.8058
300	0.080886	373.45	6.8255	0.80847	373.47	5.8768
		$p=2$ bar			$p=3$ bar	
25	1241.3	0.98	0.0330	1242.0	1.03	0.0319
30	17.851	92.99	3.1731	1151.6	11.20	0.4020
35	14.853	98.59	3.3455	22.689	97.51	3.1591
40	12.776	104.04	3.4914	19.306	103.19	3.3109
45	11.235	109.44	3.6184	16.871	108.73	3.4413
50	10.039	114.78	3.7309	15.016	114.17	3.5561
55	9.0801	120.07	3.8319	13.546	119.56	3.6587
60	8.2933	125.35	3.9238	12.349	124.91	3.7517
70	7.0751	135.85	4.0854	10.511	135.42	3.9149
80	6.1735	146.29	4.2248	9.1583	146.00	4.0553
90	5.4780	156.69	4.3474	8.1196	156.46	4.1784
100	4.9246	167.07	4.4568	7.2953	166.89	4.2882
110	4.4735	177.43	4.5556	6.6245	177.29	4.3872
120	4.0986	187.79	4.6456	6.0677	187.67	4.4776
130	3.7819	198.13	4.7284	5.5978	198.02	4.5605
140	3.5108	208.47	4.8050	5.1959	208.38	4.6372
150	3.2762	218.80	4.8763	4.8482	218.72	4.7086
160	3.0710	229.12	4.9429	4.5448	229.06	4.7753
170	2.8901	239.45	5.0055	4.2763	239.40	4.8380
180	2.7293	249.77	5.0645	4.0384	249.73	4.8970
190	2.5855	260.09	5.1203	3.8255	260.06	4.9529
200	2.4562	270.40	5.1732	3.6340	270.38	5.0058
220	2.2328	291.03	5.2715	3.3035	291.02	5.1042
240	2.0467	311.65	5.3612	3.0282	311.65	5.1939
260	1.8893	332.27	5.4437	2.7954	332.28	5.2765
280	1.7544	352.88	5.5200	2.5957	352.90	5.3529
300	1.6375	373.50	5.5911	2.4228	373.52	5.4240
		$p=4$ bar			$p=6$ bar	
25	1242.8	1.09	0.0310	1241.1	1.20	0.0288
30	1152.5	11.24	0.4005	1154.4	11.32	0.3975
35	31.317	96.35	3.0195	51.018	93.65	2.7995
40	26.303	102.31	3.1787	41.349	100.41	2.9805
45	22.829	108.01	3.3131	35.312	106.52	3.1245
50	20.234	113.57	3.4303	31.011	112.34	3.2472
55	18.204	119.05	3.5346	27.737	118.00	3.3550
60	16.563	124.45	3.6287	25.138	123.56	3.4517
70	14.063	135.15	3.7936	21.239	134.45	3.6197

continued

T, °K	ϱ	i	s	ϱ	i	s
80	12.237	145.72	3.9348	18.430	145.17	3.7629
90	10.839	156.23	4.0586	16.298	155.79	3.8879
100	9.7335	166.70	4.1688	14.619	166.33	3.9991
110	8.8352	177.13	4.2682	13.260	176.82	4.0991
120	8.0906	187.54	4.3587	12.136	187.28	4.1900
130	7.4627	197.92	4.4418	11.191	197.71	4.2734
140	6.9261	208.29	4.5187	10.383	208.12	4.3506
150	6.4620	218.65	4.5902	9.6858	218.51	4.4223
160	6.0564	229.00	4.6570	9.0768	228.88	4.4893
170	5.6991	239.35	4.7197	8.5404	239.25	4.5521
180	5.3817	249.69	4.7788	8.0643	249.61	4.6113
190	5.0979	260.03	4.8347	7.6389	259.97	4.6673
200	4.8427	270.36	4.8877	7.2561	270.31	4.7204
220	4.4023	291.01	4.9861	6.5959	290.99	4.8189
240	4.0353	311.65	5.0759	6.0462	311.66	4.9087
260	3.7250	332.29	5.1585	5.5812	332.31	4.9913
280	3.4591	352.92	5.2349	5.1829	352.96	5.0678
300	3.2286	373.55	5.3060	4.8377	373.60	5.1390
		$p=8$ bar			$p=10$ bar	
25	1245.6	1.30	0.0267	1247.0	1.41	0.0246
30	1156.3	11.41	0.3946	1158.2	11.49	0.3916
35	1045.3	22.76	0.7440	1048.4	22.79	0.7394
40	58.02	98.29	2.8252	78.18	95.89	2.6901
45	48.58	104.94	2.9821	63.67	103.28	2.8645
50	42.273	111.08	3.1113	54.052	109.78	3.0016
55	37.572	116.95	3.2231	47.720	115.87	3.1178
60	33.912	122.65	3.3224	42.886	121.74	3.2198
70	28.509	133.76	3.4937	35.873	133.07	3.3944
80	24.670	144.62	3.6388	30.957	144.08	3.5416
90	21.780	155.34	3.7651	27.285	154.91	3.6692
100	19.515	165.97	3.8771	24.423	165.61	3.7820
110	17.690	176.53	3.9777	22.122	176.23	3.8831
120	16.182	187.03	4.0691	20.227	186.79	3.9750
130	14.916	197.50	4.1529	18.639	197.30	4.0591
140	13.837	207.95	4.2302	17.286	207.78	4.1367
150	12.905	218.37	4.3021	16.119	218.23	4.2088
160	12.092	228.78	4.3693	15.102	228.66	4.2761
170	11.376	239.16	4.4323	14.207	239.07	4.3392
180	10.742	249.54	4.4916	13.413	249.47	4.3986
190	10.174	259.91	4.5476	12.705	259.85	4.4548
200	9.6643	270.27	4.6008	12.067	270.23	4.5080
220	8.7847	290.98	4.6995	10.969	290.96	4.6068
240	8.0525	311.66	4.7894	10.055	311.67	4.6969
260	7.4334	332.34	4.8722	9.2814	332.36	4.7797
280	6.9029	353.00	4.9487	8.6193	353.04	4.8563
300	6.4434	373.65	5.0199	8.0458	373.70	4.9275
		$p=15$ bar			$p=20$ bar	
25	1250.5	1.68	0.0195	1253.7	1.96	0.0145
30	1162.6	11.70	0.3844	1167.0	11.93	0.3775
35	1053.1	22.87	0.7282	1062.6	22.96	0.7177
40	868.0	35.63	1.0689	917.4	35.21	1.0441
45	104.0	98.61	2.6229	157.4	92.80	2.4074
50	86.055	106.36	2.7875	122.2	102.65	2.6154
55	74.518	113.14	2.9168	103.51	110.32	2.7617
60	66.205	119.45	3.0267	90.798	117.15	2.8807
70	52.699	131.36	3.2103	74.000	129.68	3.0740
80	46.863	142.74	3.3624	63.014	141.44	3.2310
90	41.140	153.83	3.4930	55.110	152.79	3.3646
100	36.731	164.73	3.6078	49.086	163.88	3.4816
110	33.215	175.50	3.7105	44.319	174.80	3.5848
120	30.336	186.18	3.8034	40.434	185.60	3.6797

continued

T, °K	ϱ	i	s	ϱ	i	s
130	27.931	196.80	3.8884	37.201	196.32	3.7654
140	25.889	207.37	3.9666	34.464	206.96	3.8443
150	24.132	217.88	4.0392	32.112	217.56	3.9174
160	22.602	228.38	4.1070	30.069	228.11	3.9856
170	21.259	234.85	4.1704	28.276	238.63	4.0492
180	20.068	249.29	4.2301	26.689	249.12	4.1092
190	19.006	259.71	4.2864	25.274	259.59	4.1658
200	18.052	270.13	4.3398	24.004	270.05	4.2194
220	16.408	290.93	4.4389	21.816	290.89	4.3188
240	15.040	311.69	4.5292	19.998	311.70	4.4093
260	13.884	332.42	4.6122	18.461	332.48	4.4925
280	12.894	353.13	4.6885	17.147	353.23	4.5694
300	12.036	373.83	4.7603	16.008	373.95	4.6408
		$p=25$ bar			$p=30$ bar	
25	1257.1	2.23	0.0094			
30	1171.2	12.15	0.3706	1175.3	12.37	0.3639
35	1069.2	23.08	0.7075	1074.6	23.21	0.6978
40	932.6	34.90	1.0229	945.7	34.69	1.0041
45	243.0	84.21	2.1580	609.0	58.38	1.5178
50	164.2	98.53	2.4622	215.2	93.76	2.3133
55	134.97	107.39	2.6313	168.9	104.31	2.5150
60	116.69	114.83	2.7610	143.96	112.49	2.6575
70	93.818	128.03	2.9646	114.09	126.41	2.8723
80	79.379	140.16	3.1268	95.929	138.93	3.0397
90	69.171	151.77	3.2635	83.308	150.79	3.1793
100	61.476	163.05	3.3823	73.886	162.25	3.3002
110	55.423	174.12	3.4878	66.521	173.46	3.4070
120	50.516	185.04	3.5829	60.577	184.49	3.5030
130	46.445	195.85	3.6694	55.660	195.40	3.5902
140	43.007	206.58	3.7489	51.517	206.20	3.6704
150	40.059	217.24	3.8225	47.971	216.93	3.7443
160	37.502	227.85	3.8909	44.899	227.60	3.8132
170	35.260	236.42	3.9550	42.208	238.22	3.8776
180	33.277	248.96	4.0152	39.830	248.80	3.9380
190	31.509	259.47	4.0720	37.712	259.35	3.9950
200	29.924	269.96	4.1258	35.813	269.87	4.0490
220	27.196	290.86	4.2255	32.546	290.84	4.1489
240	24.929	311.73	4.3163	29.834	311.75	4.2399
260	23.015	332.54	4.3996	27.545	332.60	4.3234
280	21.377	353.33	4.4766	25.586	353.41	4.4005
300	19.958	374.08	4.5482	23.889	374.20	4.4722
		$p=40$ bar			$p=60$ bar	
30	1183.0	12.84	0.3509	1197.3	13.77	0.3264
35	1086.9	23.49	0.6794	1107.2	24.14	0.6661
40	967.7	34.43	0.9718	1002.1	34.38	0.9197
45	773.4	49.62	1.3213	865.5	46.36	1.2003
50	375.7	80.51	1.9770	655.3	63.67	1.5638
55	249.6	97.42	2.3014	454.4	82.57	1.9245
60	203.25	107.63	2.4791	342.7	97.65	2.1771
70	155.92	123.22	2.7202	244.5	116.92	2.4849
80	129.48	136.55	2.8984	197.92	132.06	2.6874
90	111.73	148.91	3.0440	168.79	145.44	2.8452
100	98.722	160.73	3.1686	148.19	157.95	2.9771
110	88.668	172.22	3.2780	132.58	169.95	3.0914
120	80.615	183.46	3.3759	120.24	181.59	3.1928
130	73.991	194.55	3.4646	110.18	193.00	3.2841
140	68.430	205.50	3.5458	101.78	204.23	3.3673
150	63.686	216.35	3.6206	94.649	215.31	3.4437
160	59.584	227.13	3.6902	88.505	226.29	3.5145
170	55.999	237.84	3.7551	83.149	237.18	3.5805
180	52.834	248.51	3.8161	78.433	248.00	3.6423

continued

T, °K	ϱ	i	s	ϱ	i	s
190	50.019	259.13	3.8735	74.244	258.75	3.7005
200	47.496	269.72	3.9278	70.497	269.46	3.7554
220	43.163	290.80	4.0282	64.065	290.76	3.8570
240	39.568	311.80	4.1196	58.738	311.93	3.9490
260	36.535	332.73	4.2034	54.248	333.02	4.0334
280	33.940	353.61	4.2808	50.408	354.02	4.1112
300	31.694	374.46	4.3527	47.085	374.97	4.1835
		$p=80$ bar			$p=100$ bar	
30	1210.3	14.75	0.3034	1222.2	15.74	0.2816
35	1124.8	24.90	0.6164	1140.4	25.71	0.5891
40	1029.4	34.65	0.8774	1051.2	35.13	0.8412
45	915.4	45.36	1.1282	955.4	45.09	1.0748
50	770.6	58.54	1.4055	841.8	56.59	1.3167
55	606.2	74.14	1.7027	702.5	69.85	1.5696
60	478.9	88.46	1.9521	582.5	83.17	1.8011
70	337.03	110.85	2.2987	423.4	105.82	2.1513
80	267.22	127.82	2.5159	335.1	123.98	2.3944
90	225.58	142.28	2.6962	281.3	139.38	2.5759
100	197.00	155.47	2.8353	244.8	153.23	2.7219
110	175.73	167.94	2.9542	218.0	166.17	2.8453
120	159.08	179.97	3.0588	197.1	178.53	2.9529
130	145.61	191.67	3.1525	180.3	190.51	3.0487
140	134.42	203.14	3.2375	166.4	202.20	3.1354
150	124.94	214.43	3.3154	154.6	213.69	3.2146
160	116.80	225.59	3.3874	144.6	225,00	3.2877
170	109.72	236.63	3.4543	135.8	236.19	3.3555
180	103.49	247.59	3.5169	128.1	247.27	3.4188
190	97.957	258.46	3.5757	121.2	258.26	3.4782
200	93.015	269.29	3.6313	115.1	269.19	3.5342
220	84.542	290.78	3.7336	104.7	290.85	3.6374
240	77.530	312.11	3.8265	96.02	312.33	3.7309
260	71.623	333.32	3.9114	88.73	333.66	3.8162
280	66.573	354.45	3.9897	82.50	354.89	3.8949
300	62.203	375.49	4.0623	77.07	376.03	3.9679
		$p=120$ bar			$p=140$ bar	
30	1233.3	16.75	0.2610	1243.4	17.77	0.2412
35	1154.4	26.57	0.5640	1167.3	27.47	0.5404
40	1070.5	35.73	0.8090	1087.5	36.42	0.7800
45	978.9	45.20	1.0311	1002.8	45.53	0.9936
50	877.3	55.76	1.2535	911.9	55.49	1.2032
55	767.0	67.63	1.4795	814.2	66.48	1.4126
60	659.6	79.92	1.6934	718.1	77.93	1.6119
70	498.1	102.15	2.0369	560.8	99.57	1.9460
80	398.7	120.77	2.2859	455.9	118.27	2.1960
90	335.0	136.82	2.4552	385.2	134.68	2.3896
100	291.3	151.22	2.6270	335.3	149.49	2.5357
110	259.0	164.58	2.7544	298.4	163.21	2.6765
120	234.0	177.27	2.8648	269.7	176.18	2.7894
130	214.0	189.51	2.9627	246.6	188.65	2.8892
140	197.5	201.40	3.0509	227.6	200.74	2.9787
150	183.5	213.06	3.1314	211.6	212.56	3.0603
160	171.6	224.53	3.2053	197.9	224.15	3.1352
170	161.2	235.85	3.2740	185.9	255.59	3.2045
180	152.1	247.04	3.3379	175.4	246.89	3.2691
190	144.0	256.14	3.3980	166.2	258.08	3.3296
200	136.8	269.14	3.4544	157.9	269.18	3.3865
220	124.4	290.97	3.5584	143.7	291.14	3.4912
240	114.1	312.58	3.6524	131.9	312.87	3.5857
260	105.5	334.03	3.7382	122.0	334.42	3.6720
280	98.89	355.34	3.8172	113.5	355.84	3.7513
300	92.52	376.59	3.8905	106.2	377.16	3.8249

continued

T, °K	ϱ	i	s	ϱ	i	s
	$p=160$ bar			$p=180$ bar		
30	1253.1	18.70	0.2223	1262.2	19.85	0.2041
35	1179.2	28.40	0.5182	1190.1	29.35	0.4972
40	1102.7	37.18	0.7533	1116.5	37.98	0.7285
45	1022.7	46.01	0.9605	1040.6	46.61	0.9306
50	938.6	55.54	1.1611	962.0	55.81	1.1244
55	851.1	65.93	1.3590	881.4	65.77	1.3141
60	764.1	76.76	1.5475	801.5	76.12	1.4943
70	613.8	97.75	1.8715	658.9	96.51	1.8088
80	506.6	116.40	2.1207	551.6	115.04	2.0564
90	431.6	132.98	2.3162	473.6	131.68	2.2527
100	377.0	148.05	2.4751	415.9	146.91	2.4132
110	336.0	162.04	2.6085	371.7	161.10	2.5485
120	304.0	175.26	2.7235	336.7	174.51	2.6652
130	278.2	187.92	2.8250	308.6	187.35	2.7681
140	256.9	200.20	2.9158	285.2	199.77	2.8600
150	238.9	212.15	2.9983	265.4	211.86	2.9434
160	223.5	223.88	3.0740	248.4	223.70	3.0198
170	210.1	235.43	3.1440	233.6	235.34	3.0905
180	198.4	246.82	3.2091	220.7	246.82	3.1561
190	187.9	258.09	3.2701	209.1	258.17	3.2174
200	178.6	269.26	3.3275	198.8	269.41	3.2751
220	162.6	291.37	3.4327	181.1	291.63	3.3809
240	149.4	313.20	3.5278	166.5	313.58	3.4764
260	138.2	334.85	3.6144	154.1	335.31	3.5635
280	128.6	356.36	3.6941	143.5	356.90	3.6434
300	120.3	377.74	3.7678	134.3	378.35	3.7174

T, °K	ϱ	i	s	T, °K	ϱ	i	s
			$p=200$ bar				
30	1270.8	20.90	0.1264	130	337.7	186.91	2.7170
35	1200.5	30.32	0.4771	140	312.4	199.46	2.8100
40	1129.2	38.84	0.7052	150	290.6	211.66	2.8942
45	1056.6	47.28	0.9032	160	272.5	223.61	2.9712
50	982.4	56.23	1.0917	170	256.5	235.34	3.0423
55	907.2	65.86	1.2751	180	242.3	246.90	3.1085
60	832.8	75.85	1.4490	190	229.8	258.32	3.1702
70	697.5	95.70	1.7551	200	218.6	269.62	3.2282
80	591.4	114.05	2.0005	220	199.3	291.95	3.3347
90	512.1	130.72	2.1970	240	183.3	313.99	3.4305
100	452.0	146.05	2.3585	260	169.7	335.81	3.5178
110	405.3	160.37	2.4950	280	158.2	357.46	3.5980
120	368.0	173.93	2.6131	300	148.1	378.98	3.6722

Note: Thermodynamic tables for neon at high pressures at temperatures from 0 to 150 °C are given in Ref. [365].

Viscosity η (N · s/m²) of neon gas at $p \leqslant 1$ bar [16, 49, 52, 363, 364]

T, °K	$\eta \cdot 10^7$	T, °K	$\eta \cdot 10^7$	T, °K	$\eta \cdot 10^7$	T, °K	$\eta \cdot 10^7$	T, °K	$\eta \cdot 10^7$
20	33.2	73	115	223	260	600	506	1200	790
25	42.1	93	140	273	298	700	558	1300	832
30	50.1	113	161	293	313	800	608	1400	873
40	66.5	133	182	300	318	900	656	1500	913
50	81.5	153	200	400	388	1000	702	1600	952
53	86.5	173	218	500	450	1100	746		

Viscosity $\eta \cdot 10^7$ (N · s/m²) of neon at different temperatures and pressures [362]

p, bar \ t, °C →	25	50	75	p, bar \ t, °C →	25	50	75
1	317	334	352	1000	426	433	441
100	322	339	356	1100	439	446	453
200	330	346	362	1200	453	459	464
300	340	354	368	1300	468	472	476
400	351	364	377	1400	481	484	487
500	362	374	387	1500	494	497	499
600	375	385	398	1600		509	511
700	387	397	408	1700			522
800	400	409	420	1800			534
900	413	421	430				

Viscosity $\eta \cdot 10^7$ (N · s/m²) of neon at low temperatures*

T, °K \ p, bar →	1	10	20	60	100	T, °K \ p, bar →	1	10	20	60	100
40	67	72				160	207	208	209	213	219
50	82	86	92			180	224	225	226	229	234
60	97	100	103	146		200	241	242	243	245	248
70	111	113	116	139	181	220	257	258	259	261	264
80	124	126	128	144	171	240	273	274	275	277	280
90	137	138	140	152	172	260	288	289	290	292	294
100	149	150	152	162	176	280	303	304	304	306	309
120	169	170	171	178	188	300	318	319	319	321	323
140	188	189	190	195	203						

*The values of η at different temperatures and pressures were recalculated by the author from experimental data [362] from $(\eta - \eta_1) = f(\rho)$. The values of η_1 at $p = 1$ bar were taken from Refs [52, 363] and the values of density ρ were taken from pp. 536-541 of the present handbook.

Viscosity η of liquid neon [379]

T, °K	25.09	27.10	27.70	28.10	28.83	31.40	34.50	38.90	44.13
$\eta \cdot 10^7$, N · s/m²	1600	1240	1210	1150	1080	860	670	500	270

Thermal conductivity λ (W/m · deg) of neon gas at $p = 1$ bar [377]

T, °K	$\lambda \cdot 10^4$	T, °K	$\lambda \cdot 10^4$	T, °K	$\lambda \cdot 10^4$	T, °K	$\lambda \cdot 10^4$
90	205	400	598	750	928	1050	1166
125	266	450	649	800	971	1100	1202
175	338	500	698	850	1012	1150	1236
225	403	550	747	900	1052	1200	1269
273	464	600	794	950	1091	1250	1302
300	494	650	839	1000	1129	1300	1333
350	547	700	884				

Thermal conductivity λ (W/m · deg) of neon gas at different temperatures and pressures [156]

p, bar \ t, °C →	25	50	75	p, bar \ t, °C →	25	50	75
1	0.0488	0.0516	0.0542	900	0.0753	0.0768	0.0774
100	0.0516	0.0543	0.0566	1000	0.0784	0.0795	0.0801
200	0.0545	0.0569	0.0591	1200	0.0844	0.0850	0.0854
300	0.0574	0.0596	0.0615	1400	0.0904	0.0905	0.0907
400	0.0603	0.0624	0.0642	1500	0.0932	0.0933	0.0933
500	0.0633	0.0653	0.0668	1600	0.0960	0.0960	0.0959
600	0.0663	0.0682	0.0694	1800	0.1017	0.1015	0.1012
700	0.0693	0.0710	0.0721	2000	0.1072	0.1074	0.1065
800	0.0723	0.0739	0.0748	2500	0.1215	0.1213	0.1196

Thermal conductivity λ of liquid neon [157]

T, °K	25	26	27	28	29	30
λ, W/m · deg	0.117	0.115	0.113	0.112	0.108	0.092

Surface tension σ of neon [16]

T, °K	24	25	26	27	28
$\sigma \cdot 10^3$, N/m	5.90	5.50	5.15	4.80	4.45

ARGON (Ar)

Atomic weight 39.944

$T_{boil} = 87.29$ °K at 760 mm Hg; $T_{melt} = 83.78$ °K;

$T_{cr} = 150.86$ °K; $p_{cr} = 50.0$ bar; $\rho_{cr} = 536$ kg/m³

Thermodynamic properties of saturated argon [141, 142]: v (dm³/kg), i and r (kJ/kg), s and c_p (kJ/kg · deg)

T, °K	p, bar	v'	v''	i'	i''	r	s'	s''	c_p'
83.78	0.6875	0.7068	246.9	−119.6	42.2	161.8	1.352	3.283	0.975
84	0.7052	0.7075	241.2	−119.4	42.3	161.7	1.354	3.279	0.977
85	0.7898	0.7106	217.4	−118.4	42.7	161.1	1.366	3.261	0.984
86	0.8821	0.7138	196.5	−117.4	43.0	160.4	1.377	3.243	0.991
87	0.9825	0.7171	178.0	−116.4	43.4	159.8	1.388	3.225	0.999
87.29	1.013	0.7180	173.0	−116.1	43.5	159.6	1.392	3.220	1.001
88	1.091	0.7204	161.6	−115.4	43.8	159.2	1.399	3.208	1.007
89	1.209	0.7237	147.1	−114.4	44.1	158.5	1.411	3.192	1.015
90	1.337	0.7270	134.2	−113.4	44.5	157.9	1.422	3.176	1.023
91	1.474	0.7303	122.6	−112.4	44.8	157.2	1.433	3.160	1.031
92	1.622	0.7337	112.3	−111.3	45.1	156.4	1.444	3.144	1.039
93	1.781	0.7372	103.0	−110.3	45.4	155.7	1.455	3.129	1.047
94	1.952	0.7408	94.72	−109.2	45.7	154.9	1.466	3.114	1.055
95	2.134	0.7444	87.23	−108.1	46.0	154.1	1.478	3.100	1.063
96	2.329	0.7480	80.46	−107.0	46.3	153.3	1.489	3.086	1.071
97	2.537	0.7517	74.35	−106.0	46.3	152.5	1.500	3.072	1.079
98	2.758	0.7555	68.81	−104.9	46.8	151.7	1.510	3.058	1.087
99	2.993	0.7593	63.77	−103.8	47.1	150.9	1.521	3.045	1.095
100	3.243	0.7632	59.19	−102.7	47.3	150.0	1.532	3.032	1.103
101	3.507	0.7672	55.02	−101.6	47.5	149.4	1.543	3.019	1.111
102	3.787	0.7713	51.21	−100.4	47.7	148.1	1.554	3.006	1.120
103	4.084	0.7754	47.72	−99.3	47.9	147.2	1.565	2.994	1.129
104	4.397	0.7796	44.53	−98.2	48.1	146.3	1.575	2.981	1.138

continued

T, °K	p, bar	v′	v″	i′	i″	r	s′	s″	c_p′
105	4.727	0.7838	41.60	−97.0	48.2	145.2	1.586	2.969	1.147
106	5.074	0.7881	38.91	−95.8	48.4	144.2	1.597	2.958	1.157
107	5.440	0.7925	36.43	−94.7	48.5	143.2	1.608	2.946	1.167
108	5.825	0.7970	34.14	−93.5	48.6	142.1	1.618	2.934	1.177
109	6.229	0.8017	32.03	−92.3	48.7	141.0	1.629	2.923	1.188
110	6.652	0.8066	30.08	−91.1	48.8	139.9	1.640	2.912	1.199
111	7.097	0.8116	28.27	−89.9	48.9	138.8	1.651	2.901	1.210
112	7.562	0.8166	26.59	−88.7	48.9	137.6	1.661	2.890	1.222
113	8.048	0.8217	25.03	−87.4	49.0	136.4	1.672	2.879	1.235
114	8.557	0.8270	23.59	−86.2	49.0	135.2	1.682	2.868	1.248
115	9.088	0.8325	22.24	−84.9	49.0	133.9	1.693	2.857	1.261
116	9.643	0.8382	20.98	−83.6	49.0	132.6	1.704	2.847	1.275
117	10.22	0.8440	19.81	−82.3	49.0	131.3	1.714	2.836	1.290
118	10.82	0.8499	18.71	−81.0	48.8	129.8	1.725	2.826	1.306
119	11.45	0.8560	17.69	−79.7	48.8	128.5	1.735	2.815	1.323
120	12.11	0.8624	16.73	−78.4	48.6	127.0	1.746	2.805	1.340
121	12.79	0.8690	15.83	−77.1	48.5	125.6	1.757	2.795	1.358
122	13.49	0.8758	14.98	−75.7	48.3	124.0	1.768	2.784	1.377
123	14.23	0.8828	14.19	−74.3	48.1	122.4	1.779	2.774	1.398
124	14.99	0.8900	13.44	−72.9	47.9	120.8	1.790	2.764	1.420
125	15.78	0.8975	12.74	−71.4	47.7	119.1	1.800	2.753	1.444
126	16.60	0.9053	12.07	−70.0	47.4	117.4	1.811	2.743	1.469
127	17.45	0.9134	11.45	−68.5	47.1	115.6	1.823	2.733	1.495
128	18.33	0.9218	10.85	−67.0	46.7	113.7	1.834	2.722	1.523
129	19.25	0.9306	10.29	−65.5	46.3	111.8	1.845	2.712	1.554
130	20.20	0.9399	9.759	−64.0	45.9	109.9	1.856	2.701	1.587
131	21.18	0.9495	9.254	−62.4	45.4	107.8	1.867	2.690	1.622
132	22.19	0.9595	8.776	−60.9	44.9	105.8	1.868	2.679	1.659
133	23.24	0.9701	8.320	−59.3	44.3	103.6	1.889	2.668	1.700
134	24.32	0.9812	7.887	−57.6	43.7	101.3	1.901	2.657	1.744
135	25.45	0.9929	7.473	−55.9	43.0	98.9	1.913	2.646	1.792
136	26.31	1.005	7.078	−54.2	42.3	96.5	1.924	2.634	1.844
137	27.80	1.017	6.701	−52.5	41.5	94.0	1.936	2.622	1.900
138	29.04	1.031	6.339	−50.8	40.6	91.4	1.948	2.609	1.960
139	30.32	1.046	5.992	−49.0	39.6	88.6	1.960	2.597	2.022
140	31.64	1.062	5.658	−47.1	38.5	85.6	1.972	2.583	2.086
141	33.00	1.080	5.336	−45.3	37.4	82.7	1.983	2.570	2.153
142	34.41	1.099	5.025	−43.5	36.0	79.5	1.994	2.555	2.222
143	35.86	1.121	4.724	−41.7	34.6	76.3	2.006	2.540	2.294
144	37.36	1.145	4.428	−39.8	32.9	72.7	2.019	2.524	2.368
145	38.90	1.173	4.133	−37.6	31.2	68.8	2.033	2.507	2.445
146	40.50	1.205	3.843	−35.2	28.9	64.1	2.049	2.488	
147	42.14	1.245	3.547	−32.4	26.3	58.7	2.067	2.466	
148	43.83	1.293	3.240	−29.0	23.1	52.1	2.088	2.440	
149	45.58	1.358	2.907	−24.7	18.9	43.6	2.115	2.408	
150	47.39	1.464	2.525	−18.3	12.8	31.1	2.157	2.364	
150.86	48.98	1.867	1.867	−2.4	−2.4	0	2.261	2.261	

Thermodynamic properties of argon liquid and gas [141, 142]:
v (dm³/kg), i (kJ/kg), s and c_p (kJ/kg · deg)

T, °K	v	i	s	c_p	v	i	s	c_p
	p=1 bar				p=2 bar			
85	0.7105	−118.4	1.365	0.984				
90	181.4	45.1	3.240	0.562				
95	192.4	47.4	3.271	0.555	93.46	46.2	3.115	0.594
100	203.4	50.6	3.299	0.550	99.21	49.2	3.145	0.581
105	214.2	53.4	3.326	0.546	104.9	52.1	3.173	0.571
110	225.0	56.1	3.351	0.543	110.5	54.9	3.200	0.564
115	235.7	58.8	3.375	0.538	116.0	57.7	3.225	0.558
120	246.4	61.5	3.398	0.536	121.5	60.5	3.248	0.553

continued

T, °K	v	i	s	c_p	v	i	s	c_p
125	257.1	64.2	3.420	0.534	127.0	63.3	3.271	0.548
130	267.7	66.8	3.441	0.532	132.4	66.0	3.293	0.545
135	278.3	69.5	3.461	0.531	137.8	68.7	3.313	0.542
140	288.9	72.1	3.480	0.530	143.2	71.4	3.332	0.540
145	299.5	74.8	3.499	0.529	148.5	74.1	3.351	0.538
150	310.1	77.4	3.516	0.528	153.9	76.8	3.369	0.536
155	320.6	80.0	3.534	0.527	159.3	79.5	3.387	0.535
160	331.1	82.7	3.551	0.527	164.6	82.1	3.404	0.533
170	352.2	88.0	3.582	0.526	175.2	87.4	3.436	0.531
180	373.2	93.2	3.612	0.525	185.8	92.7	3.466	0.529
190	394.1	98.4	3.641	0.524	196.4	98.0	3.495	0.528
200	415.1	103.7	3.668	0.524	207.0	103.3	3.522	0.527
210	436.0	108.9	3.693	0.523	217.5	108.6	3.548	0.526
220	456.9	114.2	3.718	0.523	228.0	113.8	3.572	0.526
230	477.8	119.4	3.741	0.523	238.5	119.1	3.596	0.525
240	498.8	124.6	3.763	0.522	249.0	124.3	3.618	0.524
250	519.7	129.8	3.784	0.522	259.5	129.6	3.639	0.524
260	540.6	135.1	3.805	0.522	270.0	134.8	3.660	0.524
270	561.4	140.3	3.824	0.522	280.4	140.0	3.680	0.523
280	582.3	145.5	3.844	0.522	290.9	145.3	3.699	0.523
290	603.2	150.7	3.862	0.522	301.4	150.5	3.717	0.523
300	624.1	155.9	3.880	0.522	311.8	155.7	3.735	0.523
310	644.9	161.1	3.897	0.521	322.3	161.0	3.752	0.523
320	665.8	166.3	3.913	0.521	332.7	166.2	3.768	0.522
330	686.6	171.6	3.929	0.521	343.2	171.4	3.784	0.522
340	707.5	176.8	3.945	0.521	353.6	176.6	3.800	0.522
350	728.3	182.0	3.960	0.521	364.1	181.8	3.815	0.522
375	780.5	195.0	3.996	0.521	390.2	194.9	3.851	0.522
400	832.6	208.0	4.029	0.521	416.3	207.9	3.885	0.521
425	884.7	221.1	4.061	0.521	442.4	221.0	3.916	0.521
450	936.7	234.1	4.091	0.521	468.4	234.0	3.946	0.521
475	988.8	247.1	4.119	0.521	494.5	247.0	3.975	0.521
500	1041	260.1	4.146	0.521	520.5	260.0	4.001	0.52'
550	1145	286.2	4.195	0.521	572.6	286.1	4.051	0.521
600	1249	312.2	4.241	0.521	624.7	312.2	4.096	0.521
650	1353	338.2	4.282	0.521	676.8	338.2	4.138	0.521
700	1457	364.2	4.321	0.521	728.9	364.3	4.177	0.521
750	1561	390.3	4.357	0.520	780.9	390.3	4.212	0.521
800	1666	416.3	4.390	0.520	833.0	416.3	4.246	0.521
850	1770	442.3	4.422	0.520	885.1	442.3	4.278	0.521
900	1874	468.3	4.452	0.520	937.1	468.4	4.307	0.521
950	1978	494.4	4.480	0.520	989.2	494.4	4.335	0.520
1000	2082	520.4	4.507	0.520	1041	520.4	4.362	0.520
1050	2186	546.4	4.532	0.520	1093	546.4	4.388	0.520
1100	2290	572.4	4.556	0.520	1145	572.5	4.412	0.520
1150	2394	598.5	4.579	0.520	1197	598.5	4.435	0.520
1200	2498	624.5	4.601	0.520	1249	624.5	4.457	0.520
1250	2602	650.5	4.623	0.520	1301	650.5	4.478	0.520
1300	2706	676.5	4.643	0.520	1353	676.5	4.499	0.520
		$p=3$ bar				$p=4$ bar		
100	64.42	47.7	3.050	0.617				
105	68.35	50.7	3.080	0.601	50.07	49.3	3.011	0.633
110	72.25	53.7	3.108	0.588	53.10	52.4	3.040	0.615
115	76.07	56.6	3.134	0.578	56.07	55.4	3.067	0.600
120	79.85	59.5	3.158	0.570	58.99	58.4	3.092	0.589
125	83.58	62.3	3.181	0.564	61.87	61.3	3.116	0.580
130	87.29	65.1	3.203	0.558	64.72	64.2	3.139	0.572
135	90.97	67.9	3.224	0.554	67.53	67.1	3.160	0.566
140	94.63	70.7	3.244	0.550	70.33	69.9	3.181	0.561
145	98.27	73.4	3.264	0.547	73.10	72.7	3.200	0.557
150	101.9	76.1	3.282	0.544	75.86	75.5	3.219	0.553
155	105.5	78.8	3.300	0.542	78.60	78.3	3.237	0.550
160	109.1	81.5	3.317	0.540	81.33	81.0	3.254	0.547

continued

T, °K	v	i	s	c_p	v	i	s	c_p
170	116.3	86.9	3.350	0.537	86.76	86.4	3.288	0.542
180	123.4	92.3	3.380	0.534	91.16	91.8	3.319	0.539
190	130.5	97.6	3.409	0.532	97.53	97.2	3.348	0.536
200	137.6	102.9	3.436	0.531	102.9	102.5	3.375	0.534
210	144.6	108.2	3.462	0.529	108.2	107.9	3.401	0.532
220	151.7	113.5	3.487	0.528	113.5	113.2	3.426	0.531
230	158.7	118.8	3.510	0.527	118.8	118.5	3.449	0.530
240	165.7	124.1	3.533	0.527	124.1	123.8	3.472	0.529
250	172.8	129.3	3.554	0.526	129.4	129.1	3.494	0.528
260	179.8	134.6	3.575	0.525	134.7	134.3	3.514	0.527
270	186.8	139.8	3.594	0.525	139.9	139.6	3.534	0.526
280	193.8	145.1	3.614	0.524	145.2	144.8	3.553	0.526
290	200.8	150.3	3.632	0.524	150.5	150.1	3.572	0.525
300	207.8	155.6	3.650	0.524	155.7	155.4	3.590	0.525
310	214.8	160.8	3.667	0.524	161.0	160.6	3.607	0.525
320	221.8	166.0	3.684	0.523	166.2	165.8	3.623	0.524
330	228.7	171.2	3.700	0.523	171.5	171.1	3.639	0.524
340	235.7	176.5	3.715	0.523	176.7	176.3	3.655	0.524
350	242.7	181.7	3.730	0.523	182.0	181.6	3.670	0.523
375	260.1	194.8	3.766	0.523	195.0	194.6	3.706	0.523
400	277.5	207.8	3.800	0.522	208.1	207.7	3.740	0.523
425	294.9	220.9	3.832	0.522	221.2	220.8	3.772	0.522
450	312.3	233.9	3.862	0.522	234.2	233.8	3.802	0.522
475	329.7	247.0	3.890	0.521	247.3	246.9	3.830	0.522
500	374.1	260.0	3.917	0.521	260.3	260.0	3.857	0.522
550	381.8	286.1	3.966	0.521	286.4	286.0	3.906	0.521
600	416.6	312.1	4.012	0.521	312.5	312.1	3.952	0.521
650	451.3	338.2	4.053	0.521	338.6	338.1	3.994	0.521
700	486.0	364.2	4.092	0.521	364.6	364.2	4.032	0.521
750	520.8	390.3	4.128	0.521	390.7	390.3	4.068	0.521
800	555.5	416.3	4.161	0.521	416.7	416.3	4.120	0.521
850	590.2	442.3	4.193	0.521	442.7	442.3	4.133	0.521
900	624.9	468.4	4.223	0.521	468.8	468.4	4.163	0.521
950	659.6	494.4	4.251	0.521	494.8	494.4	4.191	0.521
1000	694.3	520.4	4.278	0.521	520.9	520.4	4.218	0.521
1050	729.0	546.5	4.303	0.521	546.9	456.5	4.243	0.521
1100	763.7	572.5	4.327	0.520	572.9	572.5	4.267	0.521
1150	798.4	598.5	4.351	0.520	598.9	598.5	4.291	0.521
1200	833.1	624.5	4.373	0.520	625.0	624.6	4.313	0.521
1250	867.8	650.6	4.394	0.520	651.0	650.5	4.334	0.520
1300	902.5	676.6	4.414	0.520	677.0	676.6	4.354	0.520
	$p=5$ bar				$p=6$ bar			
85	0.7100	−118.2	1.364	0.983				
90	0.7263	−113.2	1.420	1.022				
95	0.7438	−108.0	1.477	1.061				
100	0.7627	−102.6	1.532	1.102				
105	0.7837	−97.0	1.586	1.147				
110	41.59	51.1	2.986	0.644	33.88	49.7	2.939	0.677
115	44.05	54.3	3.014	0.624	36.01	53.1	2.969	0.651
120	46.46	57.4	3.040	0.609	38.09	56.3	2.996	0.631
125	48.83	60.4	3.065	0.597	40.12	59.4	3.021	0.615
130	51.16	63.3	3.088	0.587	42.11	62.4	3.045	0.602
135	53.46	66.2	3.110	0.579	44.07	65.4	3.068	0.592
140	55.74	69.1	3.131	0.572	46.01	68.3	3.089	0.584
145	58.00	72.0	3.151	0.566	47.92	71.2	3.109	0.577
150	60.24	74.8	3.170	0.562	49.82	71.1	3.129	0.571
155	62.46	77.6	3.188	0.558	51.70	76.9	3.147	0.566
160	64.67	80.4	3.206	0.554	53.57	79.8	3.165	0.561
170	69.07	85.9	3.239	0.548	57.27	85.3	3.199	0.554
180	73.42	91.4	3.270	0.544	60.93	90.8	3.231	0.549
190	77.75	96.8	3.299	0.540	64.57	96.3	3.260	0.544
200	82.06	102.2	3.327	0.538	68.18	101.7	3.288	0.541
210	86.35	107.6	3.353	0.535	71.78	107.1	3.314	0.538
220	90.63	112.9	3.378	0.533	75.36	112.5	3.339	0.536

continued

T, °K	v	i	s	c_p	v	i	s	c_p
230	94.89	118.2	3.402	0.532	78.93	117.9	3.363	0.534
240	99.14	123.5	3.425	0.531	82.49	123.2	3.386	0.533
250	103.4	128.8	3.446	0.530	86.04	128.5	3.408	0.532
260	107.6	134.1	3.467	0.529	89.59	133.8	3.428	0.530
270	111.8	139.4	3.487	0.528	93.12	139.1	3.448	0.529
280	116.1	144.6	3.506	0.527	96.65	144.4	3.468	0.529
290	120.3	149.9	3.525	0.527	100.2	149.7	3.486	0.528
300	124.5	155.2	3.543	0.526	103.7	155.0	3.504	0.527
310	128.7	160.4	3.560	0.526	107.2	160.2	3.521	0.527
320	132.9	165.7	3.577	0.525	110.7	165.5	3.538	0.526
330	137.1	170.9	3.593	0.525	114.2	170.8	3.554	0.526
340	141.3	176.2	3.608	0.525	117.7	176.0	3.570	0.525
350	145.5	181.4	3.623	0.524	121.2	181.3	3.585	0.525
375	156.0	194.5	3.660	0.524	130.0	194.4	3.621	0.524
400	166.5	207.6	3.693	0.523	138.7	207.5	3.655	0.524
425	177.0	220.7	3.725	0.523	147.5	220.6	3.687	0.523
450	187.4	233.8	3.755	0.523	156.2	233.7	3.717	0.523
475	197.9	246.8	3.783	0.522	164.9	246.7	3.745	0.523
500	208.3	259.9	3.810	0.522	173.6	259.8	3.772	0.522
550	229.2	286.0	3.860	0.522	191.0	285.9	3.822	0.522
600	250.1	312.1	3.905	0.521	208.4	312.0	3.867	0.522
650	270.9	338.1	3.947	0.521	225.8	338.1	3.909	0.521
700	291.8	364.2	3.986	0.521	243.2	364.2	3.948	0.521
750	312.6	390.3	4.022	0.521	260.6	390.3	3.984	0.521
800	333.4	416.3	4.055	0.521	277.9	416.3	4.017	0.521
850	354.3	442.4	4.087	0.521	295.3	442.4	4.049	0.521
900	375.1	468.4	4.114	0.521	312.7	468.4	4.079	0.521
950	395.9	494.4	4.145	0.521	330.0	494.4	4.107	0.521
1000	416.7	520.5	4.172	0.521	347.4	520.5	4.134	0.521
1050	437.6	546.5	4.197	0.521	364.8	546.5	4.159	0.521
1100	458.4	572.5	4.221	0.521	382.1	572.6	4.183	0.521
1150	479.3	598.6	4.244	0.521	399.5	598.6	4.206	0.521
1200	500.1	624.6	4.266	0.521	416.7	624.6	4.228	0.521
1250	520.9	650.6	4.288	0.521	434.2	650.6	4.250	0.521
1300	541.7	676.7	4.308	0.521	451.5	676.7	4.270	0.521
		$p = 8$ bar				$p = 10$ bar		
85					0.7093	−118.0	1.363	0.982
90					0.7255	−113.0	1.419	1.020
95					0.7428	−107.8	1.475	1.058
100					0.7615	−120.4	1.530	1.098
105					0.7822	−96.8	1.584	1.142
110					0.8054	−91.0	1.639	1.194
115	25.91	50.5	2.893	0.713	0.8321	−84.9	1.692	1.259
120	27.58	54.0	2.923	0.680	21.22	51.5	2.862	0.741
125	29.20	57.3	2.950	0.656	22.61	55.1	2.891	0.704
130	30.78	60.5	2.975	0.637	23.95	58.5	2.918	0.676
135	32.32	63.7	2.999	0.621	25.24	61.9	2.943	0.654
140	33.83	66.8	3.021	0.609	26.50	65.1	2.967	0.636
145	35.32	69.8	3.042	0.598	27.74	68.2	2.989	0.622
150	36.78	72.7	3.063	0.590	28.95	71.3	3.010	0.611
155	38.24	75.7	3.082	0.583	30.15	74.3	3.030	0.601
160	39.67	78.6	3.100	0.576	31.33	77.2	3.049	0.592
170	42.51	84.3	3.135	0.566	33.65	83.2	3.084	0.579
180	45.31	89.9	3.167	0.559	35.94	88.9	3.117	0.570
190	48.09	95.4	3.197	0.553	38.20	94.6	3.147	0.562
200	50.84	101.0	3.225	0.548	40.43	100.2	3.176	0.556
210	53.57	106.4	3.252	0.545	42.64	105.7	3.203	0.551
220	56.28	111.8	3.277	0.542	44.83	111.2	3.229	0.547
230	58.99	117.3	3.301	0.539	47.02	116.6	3.253	0.544
240	61.68	122.6	3.324	0.537	49.19	122.1	3.276	0.541
250	64.36	128.0	3.346	0.535	51.35	127.5	3.298	0.539
260	67.04	133.4	3.367	0.534	53.51	132.9	3.319	0.537
270	69.71	138.7	3.387	0.533	55.66	138.2	3.340	0.536

continued

T, °K	v	i	s	c_p	v	i	s	c_p
280	72.37	144.0	3.406	0.531	57.80	143.6	3.359	0.534
290	75.03	149.3	3.425	0.530	59.94	148.9	3.378	0.533
300	77.68	154.6	3.443	0.530	62.07	154.3	3.396	0.532
310	80.33	159.9	3.460	0.529	64.20	159.6	3.413	0.531
320	82.98	165.2	3.477	0.528	66.33	164.9	3.430	0.530
330	85.62	170.5	3.493	0.528	68.45	170.2	3.446	0.530
340	88.26	175.7	3.509	0.527	70.57	175.5	3.462	0.528
350	90.90	181.0	3.524	0.527	72.69	180.7	3.477	0.528
375	97.48	194.2	3.560	0.526	77.97	193.9	3.514	0.527
400	104.1	207.3	3.595	0.525	83.24	207.1	3.548	0.526
425	110.6	220.4	3.627	0.524	88.51	220.2	3.580	0.525
450	117.2	233.5	3.657	0.524	93.76	233.4	3.610	0.525
475	123.7	246.6	3.685	0.523	99.00	246.5	3.638	0.524
500	130.3	259.7	3.712	0.523	104.2	259.6	3.665	0.524
550	143.3	285.8	3.762	0.523	114.7	285.7	3.715	0.523
600	156.0	312.0	3.807	0.522	125.2	311.9	3.760	0.523
650	169.4	338.1	3.849	0.522	135.6	338.0	3.802	0.522
700	182.5	364.2	3.888	0.521	146.1	364.2	3.841	0.522
750	195.5	390.3	3.924	0.521	156.5	390.3	3.877	0.522
800	208.6	416.3	3.957	0.521	166.9	416.3	3.911	0.521
850	221.6	442.4	3.989	0.521	177.4	442.4	3.942	0.521
900	234.6	468.4	4.019	0.521	187.8	468.5	3.972	0.521
950	247.6	494.5	4.047	0.521	198.2	494.5	4.000	0.521
1000	260.7	520.5	4.073	0.521	208.6	520.6	4.027	0.521
1050	273.7	546.6	4.098	0.521	219.1	546.6	4.052	0.521
1100	286.7	572.6	4.123	0.521	229.5	572.7	4.077	0.521
1150	299.7	598.6	4.146	0.521	239.9	598.7	4.100	0.521
1200	312.8	624.7	4.168	0.521	250.3	624.7	4.122	0.521
1250	325.8	650.7	4.190	0.521	260.7	650.8	4.143	0.521
1300	338.8	676.8	4.210	0.521	271.1	676.8	4.164	0.521
	$p=15$ bar				$p=20$ bar			
85	0.7085	−117.8	1.361	0.981	0.7079	−117.6	1.359	0.977
90	0.7247	−112.8	1.417	1.019	0.7238	−112.6	1.415	1.017
95	0.7418	−107.6	1.474	1.056	0.7408	−107.4	1.472	1.053
100	0.7603	−102.3	1.528	1.094	0.7591	−102.1	1.526	1.090
105	0.7807	− 96.7	1.581	1.137	0.7792	− 96.5	1.579	1.132
110	0.8035	− 90.9	1.636	1.186	0.8017	− 90.7	1.634	1.179
115	0.8297	− 84.8	1.689	1.248	0.8273	− 84.7	1.686	1.238
120	0.8605	− 78.4	1.745	1.330	0.8574	− 78.3	1.741	1.315
125	13.65	49.2	2.770	0.884	0.8937	− 71.5	1.797	1.423
130	14.71	53.0	2.803	0.809	9.906	46.2	2.705	1.060
135	15.71	57.0	2.883	0.760	10.88	51.2	2.742	0.929
140	16.67	60.7	2.860	0.722	11.67	55.6	2.774	0.847
145	17.58	64.2	2.884	0.693	12.45	59.7	2.803	0.790
150	18.47	67.6	2.907	0.671	13.19	63.5	2.829	0.749
155	19.34	70.9	2.928	0.653	13.90	67.2	2.853	0.718
160	20.19	74.1	2.948	0.637	14.58	70.7	2.875	0.695
170	21.84	80.3	2.986	0.614	15.90	77.4	2.916	0.656
180	23.43	86.3	3.021	0.598	17.17	83.8	2.953	0.630
190	25.12	92.4	3.055	0.580	18.40	90.0	2.986	0.611
200	26.67	98.2	3.085	0.572	19.60	96.1	3.018	0.597
210	28.20	103.8	3.113	0.568	20.78	102.0	3.046	0.586
220	29.70	109.5	3.139	0.562	21.94	107.8	3.073	0.577
230	31.20	115.1	3.163	0.554	23.08	113.6	3.099	0.570
240	32.69	120.7	3.188	0.550	24.22	119.2	3.123	0.564
250	34.16	126.2	3.210	0.547	25.34	124.8	3.146	0.559
260	35.64	131.6	3.231	0.544	26.46	130.4	3.168	0.555
270	37.10	137.1	3.250	0.543	27.56	135.9	3.189	0.552
280	38.55	142.5	3.243	0.541	28.67	141.4	3.209	0.549
290	40.00	147.9	3.292	0.540	29.76	146.9	3.228	0.546
300	41.45	153.3	3.310	0.538	30.86	152.4	3.246	0.544
310	42.89	185.6	3.327	0.537	31.95	157.8	3.264	0.542

continued

T, °K	v	i	s	c_p	v	i	s	c_p
320	44.33	164.0	3.344	0.535	33.03	163.2	3.281	0.540
330	45.76	169.4	3.360	0.534	34.11	168.6	3.298	0.538
340	47.20	174.7	3.376	0.533	35.19	174.0	3.314	0.537
350	48.63	180.1	3.392	0.532	36.27	179.4	3.330	0.536
375	52.18	193.3	3.428	0.531	38.95	192.8	3.367	0.534
400	56.00	206.6	3.462	0.529	41.62	206.1	3.401	0.532
425	59.29	219.8	3.495	0.528	44.28	219.4	3.433	0.530
450	62.82	232.9	3.541	0.527	46.93	232.6	3.463	0.529
475	66.35	246.1	3.570	0.526	49.57	245.8	3.492	0.528
500	69.86	259.2	3.581	0.525	52.21	259.0	3.519	0.527
550	76.89	285.5	3.631	0.524	57.48	285.3	3.569	0.526
600	83.91	311.7	3.676	0.523	62.73	311.6	3.615	0.525
650	90.82	337.9	3.718	0.523	67.97	337.8	3.657	0.524
700	97.91	364.1	3.757	0.522	73.21	364.0	3.696	0.523
750	104.9	390.2	3.793	0.522	78.44	390.2	3.732	0.523
800	111.9	416.3	3.826	0.522	83.67	416.4	3.766	0.522
850	118.9	442.4	3.858	0.522	88.90	442.5	3.798	0.522
900	125.9	468.5	3.888	0.522	94.12	468.6	3.828	0.522
950	132.9	494.6	3.916	0.521	99.34	494.7	3.856	0.522
1000	139.9	520.7	3.943	0.521	104.6	520.8	3.883	0.522
1050	146.8	546.8	3.968	0.521	109.8	546.8	3.908	0.522
1100	153.8	572.8	3.993	0.521	115.0	572.9	3.932	0.521
1150	160.8	598.9	4.016	0.521	120.2	599.0	3.955	0.521
1200	167.7	624.9	4.038	0.521	125.4	625.0	3.977	0.521
1250	174.8	651.0	4.059	0.521	130.6	651.1	3.998	0.521
1300	181.7	677.0	4.080	0.521	135.8	677.2	4.019	0.521
		$p=25$ bar				$p=30$ bar		
85	0.7072	−117.4	1.358	0.979	0.7065	−117.1	1.356	0.978
90	0.7230	−112.4	1.413	1.015	0.7222	−112.2	1.412	1.013
95	0.7398	−107.2	1.470	1.051	0.7389	−107.0	1.468	1.048
100	0.7579	−101.9	1.524	1.087	0.7568	−101.7	1.522	1.084
105	0.7778	− 96.3	1.577	1.127	0.7764	− 96.2	1.575	1.122
110	0.7999	− 90.6	1.631	1.173	0.7982	− 90.4	1.629	1.166
115	0.8251	− 84.6	1.684	1.229	0.8229	− 84.5	1.681	1.220
120	0.8544	− 78.3	1.738	1.301	0.8515	− 78.2	1.735	1.287
125	0.8896	− 71.6	1.793	1.400	0.8856	− 71.6	1.789	1.378
130	0.9338	− 64.2	1.851	1.547	0.9279	− 64.4	1.846	1.510
135	7.707	43.8	2.654	1.276	0.9840	− 56.3	1.907	1.723
140	8.551	49.6	2.696	1.055	6.307	41.8	2.614	1.509
145	9.290	54.5	2.731	0.934	7.094	48.4	2.660	1.171
150	9.965	59.0	2.761	0.856	7.761	53.9	2.697	1.014
155	10.60	63.1	2.788	0.801	8.360	58.7	2.729	0.915
160	11.20	67.0	2.813	0.760	8.915	63.1	2.757	0.847
170	12.33	74.3	2.857	0.704	9.938	71.1	2.805	0.761
180	13.40	81.2	2.896	0.666	10.89	78.4	2.847	0.707
190	14.43	87.7	2.931	0.640	11.78	85.3	2.884	0.671
200	15.43	94.0	2.964	0.620	12.65	91.8	2.918	0.645
210	16.40	100.1	2.994	0.605	13.49	98.2	2.949	0.625
220	17.36	106.1	3.021	0.593	14.30	104.4	2.978	0.610
230	18.30	112.0	3.048	0.584	15.11	110.4	3.004	0.598
240	19.22	117.8	3.072	0.576	15.90	116.3	3.030	0.589
250	20.14	123.5	3.096	0.570	16.68	122.2	3.054	0.581
260	21.05	129.2	3.118	0.565	17.45	127.9	3.076	0.574
270	21.95	134.8	3.139	0.560	18.21	133.7	3.098	0.569
280	22.84	140.4	3.159	0.556	18.96	139.3	3.118	0.564
290	23.73	145.9	3.179	0.553	19.71	144.9	3.138	0.560
300	24.62	151.4	3.198	0.550	20.46	150.5	3.157	0.556
310	25.50	156.9	3.216	0.548	21.20	156.1	3.175	0.553
320	26.38	162.4	3.233	0.546	21.94	161.6	3.193	0.550
330	27.25	167.9	3.250	0.544	22.68	167.1	3.210	0.548
340	28.12	173.3	3.266	0.542	23.41	172.6	3.226	0.546
350	28.99	178.7	3.282	0.540	24.14	178.0	3.242	0.544

continued

T, °K	v	i	s	c_p	v	i	s	c_p
375	31.15	192.2	3.319	0,537	25,95	191.5	3.279	0,541
400	33.30	205,6	3,353	0,535	27,75	205,0	3,314	0,538
425	35,44	219,0	3,385	0,533	29,54	218,5	3,347	0,535
450	37,57	232,3	3,416	0,531	31,32	232,0	3,378	0,533
475	39,69	245,6	3,445	0,529	33,10	245,3	3,407	0,531
500	41,81	258,8	3,472	0,528	34,87	258,5	3,434	0,529
550	46,03	285,2	3,522	0,527	38,40	284,9	3,484	0,528
600	50,24	311,5	3,568	0,526	41,92	311,3	3,530	0,527
650	54,45	337,8	3,610	0,525	45,43	337,7	3,572	0,526
700	58,64	364,0	3,649	0,524	48,93	364,0	3,611	0,525
750	62,83	390,2	3,685	0,523	52,43	390,2	3,647	0,524
800	67,02	416,4	3,719	0,523	55,92	416,4	3,681	0,524
850	71,21	442,6	3,751	0,523	59,41	442,6	3,713	0,523
900	75,39	468,7	3,781	0,522	62,90	468,7	3,743	0,523
950	79,57	494,8	3,809	0,522	66,39	494,8	3,771	0,523
1000	83,75	520,9	3,836	0,522	69,87	521,0	3,798	0,522
1050	87,93	547,0	3,861	0,522	73,25	547,1	3,823	0,522
1100	92,10	573,0	3,885	0,522	76,83	573,2	3,847	0,522
1150	96,27	599,1	3,909	0,521	80,31	599,3	3,871	0,522
1200	100,4	625,2	3,931	0,521	83,79	625,4	3,893	0,522
1250	104,6	651,3	3,952	0,521	87,27	651,4	3,914	0,521
1300	108,8	677,3	3,973	0,521	90,75	677,5	3,935	0,521
		$p=35$ bar				$p=40$ bar		
85	0,7058	−116,9	1,355	0,977	0,7052	−116,7	1,353	0,976
90	0,7214	−111,9	1,410	1,012	0,7206	−111,7	1,409	1,010
95	0,7379	−106,8	1,467	1,046	0,7370	−106,6	1,465	1,043
100	0,7557	−101,5	1,520	1,080	0,7546	−101,3	1,518	1,077
105	0,7750	−96,0	1,573	1,118	0,7737	−95,8	1,571	1,113
110	0,7965	−90,3	1,627	1,160	0,7948	−90,2	1,625	1,154
115	0,8207	−84,4	1,678	1,210	0,8187	−84,3	1,676	1,203
120	0,8487	−78,2	1,732	1,275	0,8460	−78,1	1,729	1,263
125	0,8818	−71,6	1,785	1,359	0,8782	−71,6	1,782	1,341
130	0,9224	−64,5	1,841	1,478	0,9173	−64,7	1,837	1,449
135	0,9751	−56,7	1,901	1,661	0,9671	−57,0	1,895	1,609
140	1,0502	−47,7	1,965	1,988	1,0357	−48,4	1,957	1,872
145	5,386	40,5	2,584	1,707	1,1436	−37,9	2,030	2,380
150	6,116	47,8	2,634	1,276	4,777	40,1	2,564	1,812
155	6,720	53,6	2,672	1,078	5,440	47,8	2,615	1,339
160	7,258	58,7	2,704	0,963	5,985	53,9	2,653	1,124
170	8,216	67,6	2,758	0,829	6,913	63,9	2,714	0,913
180	9,083	75,5	2,803	0,754	7,724	72,4	2,763	0,808
190	9,892	82,8	2,843	0,705	8,469	80,2	2,805	0,744
200	10,66	89,6	2,878	0,672	9,171	87,4	2,842	0,701
210	11,40	96,2	2,910	0,647	9,843	94,2	2,875	0,670
220	12,12	102,6	2,940	0,628	10,49	100,8	2,906	0,647
230	12,83	108,8	2,967	0,613	11,12	107,2	2,934	0,629
240	13,52	114,9	2,993	0,601	11,74	113,4	2,961	0,615
250	14,20	120,8	3,018	0,592	12,35	119,5	2,986	0,603
260	14,87	126,7	3,041	0,586	12,94	125,5	3,009	0,594
270	15,54	132,5	3,062	0,577	13,53	131,4	3,031	0,586
280	16,19	138,3	3,083	0,572	14,12	137,2	3,053	0,579
290	16,84	144,0	3,103	0,567	41,69	143,0	3,073	0,574
300	17,49	149,6	3,122	0,563	15,26	148,7	3,092	0,569
310	18,13	155,2	3,141	0,559	15,83	154,4	3,111	0,565
320	18,77	160,8	3,159	0,556	16,40	160,0	3,129	0,561
330	19,41	166,3	3,176	0,553	16,96	165,6	3,146	0,558
340	20,04	171,8	3,192	0,550	17,52	171,2	3,162	0,555
350	20,67	177,3	3,208	0,547	18,07	176,7	3,178	0,553
375	22,24	191,0	3,245	0,544	19,45	190,4	3,215	0,547
400	23,79	204,6	3,280	0,541	20,82	204,0	3,250	0,543
425	25,33	218,1	3,313	0,538	22,18	217,6	3,283	0,540
450	26,87	231,5	3,344	0,535	23,53	231,2	3,314	0,537

continued

T, °K	v	i	s	c_p	v	i	s	c_p
475	28.40	244.9	3.373	0.533	24.87	244.6	3.344	0.535
500	29.92	258.2	3.400	0.531	26.20	258.0	3.372	0.533
550	32.95	284.8	3.451	0.529	28.86	284.6	3.423	0.531
600	35.97	311.2	3.497	0.527	31.51	311.1	3.469	0.529
650	38.99	337.6	3.539	0.526	34.15	337.5	3.512	0.527
700	42.00	363.9	3.578	0.525	36.79	363.9	3.552	0.526
750	45.00	390.2	3.614	0.525	39.42	390.2	3.588	0.525
800	48.00	416.4	3.648	0.524	42.05	416.5	3.621	0.524
850	50.99	442.6	3.680	0.524	44.67	442.7	3.652	0.524
900	53.98	468.8	3.700	0.523	47.29	468.9	3.682	0.524
950	56.97	495.0	3.739	0.523	49.91	495.1	3.711	0.523
1000	59.96	521.1	3.766	0.523	52.53	521.2	3.738	0.523
1050	62.95	547.2	3.791	0.522	55.15	547.3	3.763	0.523
1100	65.94	573.3	3.815	0.522	57.76	573.4	3.787	0.522
1150	68.92	599.4	3.838	0.522	60.37	599.5	3.810	0.522
1200	71.90	625.5	3.860	0.522	62.98	625.6	3.833	0.522
1250	74.88	651.6	3.882	0.522	65.59	651.7	3.854	0.522
1300	77.86	677.7	3.903	0.522	68.20	677.8	3.875	0.522
		$p=45$ bar				$p=50$ bar		
85	0.7045	−116.5	1.352	0.975				
90	0.7199	−111.5	1.407	1.009	0.7191	−111.3	1.406	1.007
95	0.7361	−106.4	1.463	1.041	0.7352	−106.2	1.462	1.039
100	0.7535	−101.1	1.516	1.074	0.7524	−100.9	1.515	1.071
105	0.7724	−95.7	1.569	1.109	0.7711	−95.5	1.567	1.105
110	0.7932	−90.0	1.622	1.148	0.7916	−89.8	1.620	1.143
115	0.8166	−84.2	1.673	1.195	0.8147	−84.0	1.671	1.187
120	0.8434	−78.0	1.726	1.252	0.8409	−78.0	1.729	1.241
125	0.8747	−71.6	1.778	1.325	0.8714	−71.6	1.774	1.310
130	0.9124	−64.7	1.832	1.423	0.9078	−64.8	1.828	1.400
135	0.9598	−57.3	1.889	1.564	0.9530	−57.5	1.884	1.525
140	1.0231	−49.0	1.949	1.782	1.0120	−49.5	1.941	1.709
145	1.1169	−39.2	2.017	2.153	1.0955	−40.3	2.006	1.992
150	3.516	28.3	2.472	3.738	1.3155	−20.0	2.292	2.390
155	4.374	40.5	2.552	1.813	3.410	30.8	2.477	2.957
160	4.962	48.3	2.602	1.362	4.103	41.6	2.547	1.745
170	5.888	59.9	2.672	1.019	5.056	55.6	2.631	1.152
180	6.663	69.3	2.726	0.870	5.810	66.0	2.690	0.943
190	7.361	77.5	2.770	0.786	6.474	74.8	2.738	0.833
200	8.011	85.1	2.809	0.732	7.084	82.8	2.779	0.765
210	8.629	92.2	2.844	0.694	7.658	90.2	2.815	0.720
220	9.222	99.0	2.876	0.666	8.207	97.2	2.848	0.686
230	9.797	105.6	2.905	0.645	8.737	103.9	2.877	0.662
240	10.36	111.9	2.932	0.628	9.252	110.5	2.905	0.642
250	10.91	118.2	2.957	0.615	9.755	116.8	2.931	0.627
260	11.45	124.2	2.981	0.604	10.25	123.0	2.955	0.614
270	11.98	130.2	3.004	0.595	10.73	129.1	2.978	0.604
280	12.50	136.1	3.025	0.587	11.21	135.1	3.000	0.595
290	13.02	142.0	3.046	0.581	11.68	141.0	3.021	0.588
300	13.54	147.8	3.065	0.575	12.15	146.8	3.041	0.582
310	14.05	153.5	3.084	0.571	12.62	152.6	3.060	0.577
320	14.56	159.2	3.102	0.566	13.08	158.4	3.078	0.572
330	15.06	164.8	3.119	0.563	13.54	164.1	3.095	0.568
340	15.56	170.4	3.136	0.560	13.99	169.8	3.112	0.564
350	16.05	176.0	3.152	0.557	14.44	175.4	3.128	0.561
375	17.29	189.8	3.189	0.551	15.56	189.3	3.167	0.554
400	18.51	203.6	3.224	0.546	16.66	203.1	3.203	0.549
425	19.72	217.2	3.258	0.542	17.76	216.7	3.236	0.545
450	20.93	230.7	3.290	0.539	18.85	230.3	3.267	0.542
475	22.13	244.2	3.320	0.537	19.93	243.8	3.296	0.539
500	23.31	257.6	3.347	0.535	21.00	257.3	3.324	0.536
550	25.69	284.3	3.397	0.533	23.14	284.0	3.375	0.533
600	28.05	310.8	3.444	0.531	25.27	310.7	3.422	0.531
650	30.40	337.3	3.487	0.529	27.39	337.3	3.465	0.529

continued

T, °K	v	i	s	c_p	v	i	s	c_p
700	32.74	363.8	3.526	0.527	29.51	363.8	3.504	0.527
750	35.08	390.2	3.562	0.526	31.62	390.2	3.540	0.526
800	37.42	416.5	3.596	0.525	33.72	416.5	3.574	0.525
850	39.76	442.7	3.628	0.524	35.82	442.8	3.606	0.525
900	42.09	468.9	3.658	0.524	37.92	469.0	3.636	0.524
950	44.42	495.1	3.686	0.524	40.02	495.2	3.664	0.524
1000	46.75	521.3	3.713	0.523	42.12	521.4	3.691	0.524
1050	49.08	547.5	3.738	0.523	44.22	547.6	3.716	0.523
1100	51.40	573.6	3.762	0.523	46.31	573.8	3.740	0.523
1150	53.72	599.7	3.786	0.522	48.40	599.9	3.764	0.523
1200	56.04	625.8	3.808	0.522	50.49	626.0	3.786	0.522
1250	58.36	651.9	3.829	0.522	52.58	652.1	3.807	0.522
1300	60.68	678.0	3.850	0.522	54.67	678.2	3.828	0.522
		$p = 60$ bar				$p = 80$ bar		
90	0.7176	-110.9	1.403	1.004	0.7147	-110.0	1.396	0.999
95	0.7334	-105.8	1.458	1.035	0.7300	-104.9	1.452	1.027
100	0.7503	-100.5	1.511	1.065	0.7462	-99.7	1.504	1.055
105	0.7685	-95.1	1.563	1.097	0.7637	-94.4	1.556	1.083
110	0.7886	-89.5	1.616	1.133	0.7828	-88.9	1.608	1.144
115	0.8109	-83.8	1.666	1.174	0.8038	-83.2	1.657	1.149
120	0.8361	-77.8	1.718	1.222	0.8272	-77.4	1.707	1.189
125	0.8651	-71.5	1.769	1.282	0.8538	-71.3	1.757	1.237
130	0.8993	-64.9	1.820	1.359	0.8844	-65.0	1.806	1.295
135	0.9407	-57.9	1.874	1.461	0.9204	-58.3	1.857	1.366
140	0.9931	-50.3	1.929	1.599	0.9636	-51.3	1.907	1.454
145	1.062	-41.8	1.988	1.794	1.017	-43.8	1.960	1.572
150	1.185	-30.2	2.069	2.134	1.085	-35.4	2.017	1.746
155	1.513	-10.8	2.193	6.742	1.188	-25.0	2.085	2.216
160	2.652	23.3	2.410	3.803	1.374	-12.2	2.166	2.975
170	3.778	45.8	2.548	1.546	2.161	21.2	2.368	2.851
180	4.522	58.8	2.622	1.125	2.910	42.6	2.492	1.658
190	5.141	69.1	2.677	0.943	3.483	56.8	2.568	1.227
200	5.693	78.0	2.733	0.841	3.968	67.9	2.625	1.021
210	6.204	86.0	2.762	0.775	4.402	77.5	2.672	0.902
220	6.688	93.5	2.797	0.730	4.803	86.1	2.712	0.826
230	7.150	100.7	2.829	0.697	5.180	94.1	2.747	0.772
240	7.597	107.5	2.858	0.671	5.541	101.6	2.780	0.732
250	8.031	114.1	2.885	0.651	5.889	108.8	2.809	0.702
260	8.455	120.5	2.910	0.635	6.226	115.6	2.836	0.679
270	8.871	126.8	2.934	0.622	6.554	122.3	2.861	0.660
280	9.280	133.0	2.956	0.611	6.876	128.8	2.885	0.644
290	9.684	139.0	2.978	0.602	7.191	135.2	2.907	0.631
300	10.08	145.0	2.998	0.595	7.502	141.5	2.928	0.620
310	10.48	150.9	3.017	0.588	7.808	147.6	2.948	0.611
320	10.87	156.8	3.036	0.582	8.111	153.7	2.967	0.603
330	11.26	162.6	3.054	0.577	8.410	159.7	2.986	0.596
340	11.64	168.3	3.071	0.573	8.707	165.6	3.004	0.590
350	12.02	174.0	3.087	0.569	9.001	171.5	3.021	0.584
375	12.96	188.1	3.126	0.561	9.726	186.0	3.061	0.575
400	13.90	202.1	3.162	0.555	10.44	200.2	3.098	0.566
425	14.82	215.9	3.196	0.550	11.15	214.3	3.132	0.559
450	15.73	229.6	3.228	0.546	11.84	228.2	3.164	0.554
475	16.62	243.2	3.257	0.542	12.53	242.0	3.194	0.549
500	17.54	256.8	3.284	0.538	13.21	255.7	3.222	0.545
550	19.33	283.7	3.335	0.535	14.57	282.9	3.273	0.540
600	21.11	310.4	3.382	0.532	15.92	309.9	3.320	0.536
650	22.88	337.1	3.425	0.530	17.26	336.7	3.363	0.533
700	24.65	363.7	3.465	0.529	18.59	363.4	3.403	0.531
750	26.41	390.2	3.502	0.528	19.92	390.0	3.440	0.529
800	28.17	416.6	3.536	0.527	21.24	416.5	3.475	0.528
850	29.93	442.9	3.567	0.526	22.56	443.0	3.507	0.527
900	31.68	469.2	3.597	0.525	23.88	469.4	3.537	0.526
950	33.43	495.4	3.626	0.524	25.20	495.8	3.565	0.526

continued

T, °K	v	i	s	c_p	v	i	s	c_p
1000	35.18	521.6	3.653	0.524	26.52	522.1	3.592	0.525
1050	36.93	547.8	3.678	0.524	27.83	548.3	3.618	0.525
1100	38.68	574.0	3.702	0.523	29.14	574.5	3.642	0.524
1150	40.42	600.2	3.726	0.523	30.45	600.7	3.665	0.524
1200	42.16	626.3	3.748	0.523	31.76	626.9	3.688	0.524
1250	43.90	652.4	3.769	0.523	33.07	653.1	3.709	0.523
1300	45.64	678.5	3.790	0.522	34.38	679.2	3.730	0.523
	$p = 100$ bar				$p = 150$ bar			
90	0.7119	−109.1	1.391	0.995	0.7053	−106.8	1.377	0.985
95	0.7267	−104.0	1.446	1.020	0.7192	−101.8	1.431	1.006
100	0.7424	−98.9	1.498	1.046	0.7337	−96.7	1.482	1.026
105	0.7592	−93.6	1.549	1.071	0.7490	−91.6	1.532	1.046
110	0.7774	−88.2	1.600	1.098	0.7654	−86.3	1.582	1.066
115	0.7973	−82.6	1.648	1.128	0.7831	−80.9	1.629	1.087
120	0.8193	−76.9	1.698	1.162	0.8022	−75.4	1.676	1.110
125	0.8439	−71.0	1.746	1.210	0.8232	−69.8	1.722	1.136
130	0.8717	−64.8	1.794	1.246	0.8463	−64.0	1.767	1.163
135	0.9037	−58.5	1.843	1.300	0.8719	−58.1	1.812	1.193
140	0.9411	−51.8	1.890	1.361	0.9005	−52.1	1.855	1.225
145	0.9853	−44.9	1.939	1.438	0.9327	−45.9	1.898	1.258
150	1.0384	−37.4	1.989	1.542	0.9688	−39.6	1.942	1.295
155	1.107	−29.1	2.044	1.708	1.010	−33.0	1.986	1.335
160	1.202	−19.9	2.102	1.954	1.058	−26.0	2.029	1.397
170	1.526	2.4	2.237	2.459	1.181	−11.4	2.117	1.528
180	2.035	26.0	2.372	2.097	1.350	4.4	2.208	1.621
190	2.533	44.0	2.469	1.539	1.567	20.6	2.295	1.599
200	2.964	57.6	2.539	1.223	1.815	35.9	2.374	1.459
210	3.346	68.8	2.594	1.042	2.069	49.7	2.441	1.286
220	3.694	78.7	2.640	0.928	2.314	61.7	2.497	1.138
230	4.018	87.5	2.679	0.851	2.548	72.5	2.545	1.024
240	4.325	95.8	2.714	0.796	2.771	82.3	2.587	0.939
250	4.619	103.5	2.746	0.755	2.984	91.4	2.624	0.874
260	4.902	110.9	2.775	0.723	3.188	99.8	2.657	0.824
270	5.177	117.8	2.802	0.697	3.386	107.9	2.688	0.784
280	5.445	124.8	2.827	0.677	3.578	115.6	2.715	0.753
290	5.707	131.5	2.850	0.660	3.765	123.0	2.741	0.727
300	5.964	138.0	2.872	0.646	3.947	130.1	2.765	0.705
310	6.217	144.4	2.893	0.634	4.126	137.1	2.788	0.687
320	6.467	150.7	2.913	0.624	4.302	143.9	2.810	0.672
330	6.713	156.9	2.932	0.615	4.475	150.5	2.831	0.658
340	6.956	163.0	2.950	0.608	4.646	157.0	2.850	0.647
350	7.197	169.1	2.967	0.601	4.815	163.5	2.868	0.637
375	7.790	183.9	3.009	0.587	5.228	179.1	2.911	0.617
400	8.372	198.4	3.048	0.577	5.632	194.4	2.951	0.602
425	8.945	212.7	3.083	0.569	6.028	209.3	2.988	0.590
450	9.510	226.9	3.116	0.562	6.416	223.9	3.022	0.581
475	10.07	240.9	3.146	0.556	6.798	238.3	3.053	0.573
500	10.62	254.8	3.174	0.552	7.175	252.6	3.082	0.566
550	11.72	282.2	3.226	0.545	7.919	280.9	3.135	0.556
600	12.80	309.5	3.274	0.540	8.653	308.8	3.183	0.549
650	13.88	336.7	3.317	0.537	9.381	336.3	3.227	0.544
700	14.95	363.6	3.356	0.534	10.10	363.6	3.268	0.540
750	16.02	390.3	3.393	0.532	10.82	390.6	3.306	0.537
800	17.08	416.9	3.427	0.530	11.54	417.4	3.341	0.535
850	18.14	443.4	3.459	0.529	12.25	444.1	3.374	0.533
900	19.20	469.8	3.490	0.528	12.96	470.7	3.404	0.531
950	20.26	496.2	3.518	0.527	13.67	497.2	3.432	0.530
1000	21.31	522.5	3.545	0.526	14.38	523.7	3.459	0.529
1050	22.36	548.8	3.571	0.526	15.09	550.1	3.485	0.528
1100	23.41	575.1	3.595	0.525	15.79	576.5	3.510	0.527
1150	24.46	601.3	3.619	0.525	16.49	602.9	3.534	0.527

continued

T, °K	v	i	s	c_p	v	i	s	c_p
1200	25.51	627.5	3.641	0.524	17.19	609.2	3.556	0.526
1250	26.56	653.7	3.662	0.524	17.89	655.5	3.577	0.526
1300	27.61	679.9	3.683	0.524	18.59	681.7	3.598	0.525
		$p=200$ bar				$p=300$ bar		
90	0.6993	−104.5	1.363	0.978				
95	0.7123	−99.5	1.417	0.995	0.7003	−94.8	1.392	0.979
100	0.7258	−94.5	1.468	1.011	0.7123	−89.9	1.442	0.989
105	0.7400	−89.4	1.517	1.026	0.7247	−85.0	1.490	0.998
110	0.7550	−84.3	1.566	1.042	0.7377	−79.9	1.537	1.007
115	0.7710	−79.0	1.611	1.057	0.7513	−74.9	1.581	1.015
120	0.7882	−73.7	1.657	1.074	0.7657	−69.8	1.625	1.024
125	0.8066	−68.3	1.701	1.091	0.7808	−64.7	1.667	1.032
130	0.8266	−62.8	1.744	1.109	0.7970	−59.5	1.708	1.041
135	0.8484	−57.2	1.788	1.128	0.8140	−54.2	1.748	1.049
140	0.8720	−51.5	1.828	1.147	0.8322	−49.0	1.785	1.058
145	0.8979	−45.7	1.868	1.165	0.8515	−43.7	1.822	1.065
150	0.9263	−39.8	1.908	1.184	0.8721	−38.4	1.858	1.073
155	0.9573	−33.9	1.947	1.207	0.8942	−33.0	1.893	1.080
160	0.9913	−27.8	1.985	1.231	0.9174	−27.7	1.928	1.080
170	1.071	−15.3	2.061	1.282	0.9676	−16.7	1.994	1.099
180	1.170	−2.3	2.136	1.326	1.024	−5.8	2.056	1.109
190	1.290	11.1	2.208	1.344	1.089	5.3	2.116	1.116
200	1.430	24.4	2.277	1.324	1.160	16.4	2.174	1.113
210	1.584	37.4	2.340	1.266	1.238	27.4	2.228	1.100
220	1.749	49.7	2.397	1.184	1.321	38.3	2.278	1.079
230	1.912	61.1	2.448	1.098	1.410	49.1	2.326	1.049
240	2.075	71.7	2.493	1.019	1.502	59.4	2.370	1.014
250	2.235	81.5	2.533	0.951	1.597	69.4	2.410	0.975
260	2.390	90.7	2.569	0.895	1.692	78.9	2.448	0.937
270	2.542	99.4	2.602	0.849	1.788	88.1	2.482	0.900
280	2.690	107.7	2.632	0.811	1.883	96.9	2.514	0.865
290	2.835	115.7	2.660	0.780	1.978	105.4	2.544	0.835
300	2.976	123.4	2.686	0.754	2.071	113.6	2.572	0.807
310	3.115	130.8	2.710	0.731	2.164	121.6	2.598	0.783
320	3.251	138.0	2.733	0.712	2.256	129.3	2.623	0.762
330	3.385	145.0	2.755	0.695	2.347	136.8	2.646	0.743
340	3.517	151.9	2.776	0.681	2.436	144.2	2.668	0.726
350	3.648	158.7	2.795	0.669	2.525	151.4	2.689	0.711
375	3.967	175.0	2.840	0.643	2.744	168.7	2.736	0.680
400	4.279	190.7	2.881	0.624	2.957	185.4	2.780	0.657
425	4.585	206.2	2.919	0.609	3.167	201.8	2.820	0.639
450	4.883	221.5	2.954	0.597	3.373	217.8	2.857	0.624
475	5.175	236.6	2.987	0.588	3.574	233.5	2.892	0.612
500	5.464	251.4	3.018	0.580	3.772	249.0	2.924	0.602
550	6.031	280.3	3.073	0.566	4.159	279.0	2.981	0.585
600	6.589	308.7	3.122	0.557	4.539	308.4	3.031	0.572
650	7.140	336.6	3.166	0.550	4.912	337.1	3.076	0.562
700	7.686	364.0	3.207	0.545	5.281	365.0	3.118	0.555
750	8.229	391.1	3.244	0.541	5.647	392.6	3.156	0.549
800	8.768	418.1	3.279	0.538	6.011	419.9	3.191	0.545
850	9.305	445.0	3.312	0.536	6.372	447.1	3.224	0.542
900	9.841	471.7	3.342	0.534	6.732	474.2	3.255	0.539
950	10.36	498.4	3.371	0.532	7.090	501.1	3.284	0.537
1000	10.91	525.0	3.398	0.531	7.448	527.9	3.312	0.535
1050	11.44	551.5	3.424	0.530	7.804	554.6	3.338	0.534
1100	11.97	578.0	3.449	0.529	8.160	581.3	3.363	0.533
1150	12.50	604.4	3.473	0.528	8.515	607.9	3.386	0.532
1200	13.03	630.8	3.495	0.528	8.869	634.4	3.409	0.531
1250	13.56	657.2	3.516	0.527	9.223	660.9	3.431	0.530
1300	14.08	683.6	3.537	0.527	9.576	687.4	3.451	0.529

continued

T, °K	v	i	s	c_p	v	i	s	c_p
	$p=400$ bar				$p=500$ bar			
95	0.6900	−90.0	1.370	0.968				
100	0.7009	−85.2	1.419	0.974	0.6910	−80.3	1.398	0.963
105	0.7120	−80.3	1.466	0.978	0.7011	−75.5	1.444	0.964
110	0.7236	−75.4	1.512	0.983	0.7116	−70.7	1.490	0.965
115	0.7356	−70.5	1.555	0.987	0.7224	−65.8	1.532	0.966
120	0.7481	−65.5	1.598	0.991	0.7335	−61.0	1.573	0.967
125	0.7611	−60.6	1.638	0.995	0.7451	−56.2	1.613	0.969
130	0.7748	−55.6	1.677	0.999	0.7572	−51.3	1.651	0.969
135	0.7892	−50.6	1.716	1.002	0.7697	−46.5	1.688	0.970
140	0.8042	−45.6	1.751	1.006	0.7827	−41.6	1.723	0.971
145	0.8200	−40.5	1.786	1.009	0.7963	−36.7	1.756	0.972
150	0.8366	−35.5	1.821	1.012	0.8103	−31.9	1.790	0.973
155	0.8542	−30.5	1.854	1.015	0.8249	−27.0	1.822	0.973
160	0.8723	−25.3	1.886	1.017	0.8401	−22.1	1.853	0.973
170	0.9107	−15.1	1.948	1.021	0.8720	−12.3	1.912	0.971
180	0.9520	− 5.1	2.005	1.020	0.9051	− 2.7	1.967	0.969
190	0.9971	5.1	2.060	1.019	0.9405	7.0	2.019	0.965
200	1.046	15.3	2.113	1.016	0.9780	16.6	2.069	0.962
210	1.098	25.4	2.162	1.008	1.018	26.2	2.116	0.955
220	1.153	35.4	2.209	0.994	1.059	35.7	2.160	0.943
230	1.212	45.3	2.252	0.978	1.103	45.0	2.201	0.930
240	1.272	55.0	2.294	0.959	1.148	54.3	2.241	0.916
250	1.335	64.5	2.333	0.937	1.195	63.4	2.278	0.901
260	1.400	73.7	2.369	0.914	1.243	72.3	2.313	0.885
270	1.465	82.8	2.403	0.890	1.292	81.0	2.346	0.868
280	1.532	91.5	2.435	0.866	1.342	89.6	2.377	0.850
290	1.599	100.1	2.465	0.843	1.392	98.1	2.406	0.833
300	1.666	108.4	2.493	0.821	1.443	106.3	2.434	0.816
310	1.733	116.5	2.520	0.800	1.494	114.4	2.461	0.799
320	1.800	124.4	2.545	0.781	1.546	122.3	2.486	0.783
330	1.866	132.1	2.568	0.763	1.597	130.0	2.510	0.768
340	1.932	139.8	2.591	0.747	1.649	137.6	2.533	0.754
350	1.998	147.1	2.612	0.732	1.700	145.1	2.554	0.740
375	2.161	165.0	2.662	0.701	1.828	163.2	2.604	0.711
400	2.322	182.2	2.707	0.677	1.955	180.8	2.650	0.688
425	2.480	199.1	2.748	0.657	2.080	198.0	2.692	0.669
450	2.636	215.6	2.786	0.641	2.204	214.9	2.730	0.653
475	2.789	231.9	2.821	0.628	2.326	231.4	2.766	0.639
500	2.940	247.9	2.854	0.617	2.448	247.6	2.800	0.628
550	3.236	278.7	2.913	0.599	2.688	279.2	2.860	0.610
600	3.525	308.8	2.966	0.584	2.922	310.0	2.913	0.595
650	3.808	338.2	3.012	0.572	3.151	339.9	2.961	0.582
700	4.088	366.8	3.054	0.563	3.377	368.8	3.004	0.571
750	4.365	394.6	3.093	0.556	3.600	397.2	3.044	0.563
800	4.640	422.2	3.129	0.551	3.822	425.1	3.080	0.557
850	4.912	449.7	3.162	0.547	4.041	452.8	3.113	0.552
900	5.183	477.1	3.193	0.544	4.259	480.3	3.144	0.547
950	5.454	504.3	3.222	0.541	4.476	507.6	3.174	0.544
1000	5.723	531.3	3.250	0.539	4.692	534.8	3.202	0.542
1050	5.992	558.2	3.276	0.537	4.908	561.8	3.228	0.540
1100	6.260	584.9	3.301	0.535	5.123	588.7	3.253	0.538
1150	6.527	611.6	3.325	0.534	5.337	615.6	3.277	0.536
1200	6.794	638.3	3.348	0.533	5.551	642.4	3.300	0.535
1250	7.060	664.9	3.370	0.532	5.765	669.1	3.322	0.534
1300	7.326	691.5	3.390	0.531	5.978	695.7	3.343	0.533
	$p=600$ bar				$p=700$ bar			
180	0.8709	0.6	1.936	0.930				
190	0.9003	9.9	1.986	0.930	0.8696	13.4	1.958	0.907
200	0.9312	19.2	2.034	0.927	0.8961	22.4	2.005	0.903
210	0.9636	28.4	2.079	0.920	0.9236	31.4	2.049	0.896
220	0.9973	37.6	2.122	0.910	0.9520	40.4	2.090	0.887
230	1.032	46.6	2.162	0.899	0.9814	49.2	2.129	0.876

continued

T, °K	v	i	s	c_p	v	i	s	c_p
240	1.068	55.5	2.200	0.886	1.012	57.9	2.166	0.865
250	1.105	64.3	2.236	0.873	1.042	66.5	2.201	0.853
260	1.143	73.0	2.270	0.860	1.074	74.9	2.235	0.841
270	1.182	81.5	2.302	0.846	1.106	83.3	2.266	0.829
280	1.222	89.9	2.332	0.832	1.139	91.5	2.296	0.817
290	1.262	98.2	2.361	0.819	1.173	99.6	2.324	0.805
300	1.303	106.3	2.389	0.805	1.206	107.6	2.352	0.794
310	1.344	114.3	2.415	0.791	1.240	115.5	2.377	0.782
320	1.385	122.1	2.440	0.778	1.275	123.3	2.402	0.771
330	1.427	129.8	2.464	0.765	1.310	130.9	2.426	0.760
340	1.469	134.4	2.486	0.753	1.345	138.5	2.448	0.749
350	1.511	144.9	2.508	0.742	1.380	145.9	2.470	0.739
375	1.615	163.2	2.558	0.715	1.468	164.1	2.520	0.716
400	1.718	180.9	2.603	0.693	1.556	181.9	2.565	0.695
425	1.820	198.2	2.646	0.674	1.642	199.4	2.608	0.677
450	1.921	215.2	2.685	0.658	1.728	216.5	2.647	0.662
475	2.022	232.0	2.721	0.645	1.813	233.4	2.684	0.649
500	2.123	248.5	2.755	0.634	1.898	250.0	2.718	0.638
550	2.324	280.5	2.816	0.616	2.068	282.3	2.779	0.622
600	2.521	311.7	2.870	0.602	2.237	313.7	2.834	0.608
650	2.715	342.0	2.919	0.589	2.404	344.3	2.884	0.596
700	2.905	371.3	2.963	0.578	2.569	374.0	2.928	0.585
750	3.093	400.0	3.003	0.569	2.731	403.0	2.968	0.575
800	3.279	428.3	3.033	0.562	2.892	431.6	3.005	0.567
850	3.463	456.2	3.073	0.556	3.051	460.0	3.039	0.561
900	3.645	483.9	3.105	0.551	3.208	487.8	3.071	0.556
950	3.826	511.3	3.135	0.548	3.364	515.3	3.101	0.551
1000	4.007	538.6	3.163	0.545	3.519	542.7	3.129	0.547
1050	4.188	565.8	3.189	0.542	3.674	570.0	3.156	0.544
1100	4.367	592.9	3.214	0.540	3.828	597.2	3.181	0.542
1150	4.546	619.8	3.238	0.538	3.982	624.2	3.205	0.540
1200	4.725	646.7	3.261	0.536	4.136	651.2	3.228	0.538
1250	4.903	673.5	3.283	0.535	4.289	678.1	3.250	0.537
1300	5.081	700.2	3.304	0.534	4.441	704.9	3.271	0.536
		$p=800$ bar				$p=900$ bar		
200	0.8682	26.2	1.979	0.885				
210	0.8922	35.0	2.022	0.878				
220	0.9169	43.8	2.063	0.870	0.8886	47.6	2.040	0.856
230	0.9424	52.4	2.102	0.860	0.9111	56.1	2.077	0.847
240	0.9684	61.0	2.138	0.849	0.9341	64.6	2.113	0.837
250	0.9950	69.4	2.172	0.837	0.9575	72.9	2.147	0.826
260	1.022	77.7	2.205	0.826	0.9814	81.1	2.179	0.815
270	1.050	85.9	2.236	0.815	1.006	89.2	2.210	0.804
280	1.078	94.0	2.265	0.804	1.030	97.2	2.239	0.794
290	1.106	102.0	2.293	0.793	1.055	105.0	2.267	0.784
300	1.135	109.9	2.320	0.783	1.080	112.8	2.293	0.774
310	1.164	117.7	2.346	0.773	1.106	120.5	2.318	0.765
320	1.194	125.4	2.370	0.763	1.132	128.1	2.342	0.756
330	1.224	132.9	2.393	0.754	1.158	135.6	2.366	0.747
340	1.254	140.4	2.416	0.744	1.184	143.0	2.388	0.739
350	1.284	147.8	2.437	0.735	1.210	150.4	2.409	0.731
375	1.359	166.0	2.487	0.714	1.276	168.7	2.459	0.712
400	1.434	183.8	2.533	0.695	1.343	186.4	2.505	0.694
425	1.509	201.2	2.575	0.679	1.409	203.8	2.548	0.678
450	1.583	218.4	2.615	0.665	1.475	220.9	2.587	0.664
475	1.656	235.3	2.651	0.653	1.541	237.7	2.624	0.653
500	1.729	251.9	2.685	0.642	1.606	254.3	2.658	0.643
550	1.876	284.3	2.746	0.626	1.736	286.7	2.719	0.628
600	2.022	315.9	2.801	0.613	1.865	318.4	2.774	0.615
650	2.168	346.7	2.851	0.601	1.994	349.4	2.824	0.605
700	2.316	376.8	2.897	0.591	2.122	379.7	2.870	0.596
750	2.460	406.2	2.938	0.581	2.249	409.4	2.911	0.587
800	2.602	435.0	2.975	0.572	2.375	438.5	2.948	0.578

continued

T, °K	v	i	s	c_p	v	i	s	c_p
850	2.742	463.5	3.010	0.565	2.501	467.2	2.983	0.570
900	2.880	491.6	3.042	0.559	2.625	495.5	3.016	0.563
950	3.018	519.4	3.072	0.554	2.748	523.5	3.046	0.558
1000	3.155	547.0	3.100	0.550	2.871	551.3	3.074	0.553
1050	3.291	574.4	3.127	0.547	2.992	578.9	3.101	0.549
1100	3.426	601.7	3.152	0.544	3.113	606.3	3.127	0.546
1150	3.561	628.8	3.176	0.542	3.233	633.5	3.151	0.544
1200	3.695	655.9	3.199	0.540	3.353	660.6	3.174	0.542
1250	3.829	682.8	3.221	0.538	3.472	687.7	3.196	0.540
1300	3.963	709.7	3.243	0.537	3.591	714.6	3.217	0.538

T, °K	v	i	s	c_p	T, °K	v	i	s	c_p
				$p = 1000$ bar					
230	0.8852	60.2	2.056	0.837	500	1.505	257.1	2.633	0.643
240	0.9058	68.5	2.091	0.827	550	1.620	289.5	2.695	0.629
250	0.9268	76.7	2.125	0.816	600	1.735	321.1	2.750	0.617
260	0.9481	84.8	2.157	0.806	650	1.850	352.1	2.800	0.608
270	0.9698	92.8	2.187	0.796	700	1.965	382.5	2.845	0.599
280	0.9917	100.7	2.216	0.786	750	2.080	412.5	2.886	0.591
290	1.014	108.5	2.243	0.776	800	2.195	442.0	2.924	0.583
300	1.036	116.2	2.269	0.767	850	2.309	471.0	2.959	0.575
310	1.059	123.9	2.294	0.758	900	2.422	499.5	2.992	0.568
320	1.082	131.4	2.318	0.750	950	2.534	527.7	3.023	0.562
330	1.105	138.8	2.341	0.742	1000	2.644	555.7	3.051	0.556
340	1.128	146.2	2.363	0.734	1050	2.753	583.4	3.078	0.552
350	1.151	153.5	2.384	0.726	1100	2.862	610.9	3.104	0.549
375	1.211	171.5	2.434	0.709	1150	2.971	638.3	3.128	0.546
400	1.270	189.2	2.480	0.693	1200	3.079	665.5	3.151	0.543
425	1.329	206.6	2.522	0.678	1250	3.187	692.6	3.174	0.541
450	1.388	223.7	2.561	0.665	1300	3.295	719.6	3.195	0.539
475	1.447	240.5	2.598	0.653					

Speed of sound u (m/s) in argon [50]

p, atm → / T, °K	0.01	1	10	40	70	100	p, atm → / T, °K	0,01	1	10	40	70	100
100	186.3	184.1					540	432.9	433.2	434.7	440.9	447.0	453.8
120	204.1	202.9					560	440.9	440.9	442.7	448.9	455.0	461.8
140	220.4	219.5					580	448.6	448.6	450.4	456.6	463.0	469.5
160	235.5	235.2					600	456.3	456.3	458.1	464.3	470.7	477.2
180	249.1	249.7	246.3				620	463.1	463.1	465.8	471.1	478.1	484.6
200	263.5	263.2	261.7				640	471.4	471.4	473.2	479.4	485.5	491.1
220	276.2	276.2	275.2				660	478.4	478.7	480.3	486.4	492.9	499.4
240	288.5	288.5	288.2	289.4	292.5	301.7	680	485.8	485.8	487.7	493.5	499.7	506.1
260	300.5	300.5	300.5	301.7	307.9	314.0	700	492.9	492.9	494.8	500.6	506.8	513.2
280	311.6	311.6	312.2	314.0	320.2	326.3	720	499.7	499.7	501.8	507.7	513.8	520.0
300	322.6	322.6	323.6	326.3	332.5	338.7	740	506.8	506.8	508.6	514.8	520.6	526.8
320	333.1	333.1	334.3	338.7	344.8	350.1	760	513.5	513.5	515.4	521.2	527.4	533.5
340	343.6	343.6	344.8	350.1	357.1	363.3	780	520.3	520.3	522.2	528.0	534.2	540.0
360	353.4	353.4	354.7	360.2	366.4	372.5	800	526.8	527.1	528.6	534.5	540.3	546.5
380	362.1	363.3	364.5	369.4	375.6	381.8	900	558.8	559.1	560.6	566.5	572.0	577.9
400	372.5	372.5	374.1	379.3	384.8	391.0	1000	588.1	589.3	590.8	596.4	601.9	607.1
420	381.8	381.8	383.6	389.2	395.3	403.3	1100	617.9	617.9	619.4	624.7	629.9	635.5
440	390.7	391.0	392.5	398.4	404.5	412.5	1200	645.3	645.3	646.8	646.8	657.3	662.2
460	399.6	399.6	401.5	407.3	413.5	420.6	1300	671.5	671.8	673.0	678.2	683.2	688.1
480	408.2	408.2	410.1	415.9	422.4	429.2	1400	697.0	697.0	698.6	703.2	708.1	713.0
500	416.6	416.9	418.4	424.6	430.7	437.8	1500	721.4	721.7	722.9	727.5	732.1	737.1
520	424.9	424.9	426.7	432.6	439.0	445.8	1600	745.1	745.4	746.6	751.2	755.5	760.1

continued

p, atm → T, °K	0.01	1	10	40	70	100	p, atm → T, °K	0.01	1	10	40	70	100
1700	768.2	768.2	769.4	774.0	778.0	782.3	2400	912.5	912.5	913.8	917.2	921.2	924.6
1800	790.3	790.3	791.5	795.9	800.2	804.5	2500	931.3	931.3	932.6	935.9	939.6	943.3
1900	811.9	812.2	813.4	817.4	821.4	825.7	2600	949.8	949.8	951.0	954.4	957.8	961.5
2000	833.1	833.1	834.3	838.3	842.3	846.4	2700	967.1	967.1	969.2	972.3	975.7	979.4
2100	853.7	853.7	854.1	858.1	862.7	866.7	2800	985.5	985.8	986.7	989.8	993.5	996.9
2200	873.8	873.8	874.1	878.7	882.7	886.4	2900	1003	1003	1004	1007	1011	1014
2300	893.5	893.5	894.7	898.4	902.1	905.5	3000	1020	1020	1021	1024	1028	1031

Viscosity $\eta \cdot 10^7$ (N · s/m²) of argon gas and liquid [49, 141, 142, 363, 364, 366, 425]

p, bar → T, °K	1	10	20	30	40	50	60	70	80
85	2798	2840	2888	2936	2985				
90	74.5	2388	2427	2467	2507	2548	2589	2631	2673
95	78.8	2046	2080	2115	2149	2184	2219	2254	2291
100	83.0	1777	1808	1839	1869	1900	1931	1962	1993
105	87.2	1553	1582	1611	1639	1668	1697	1725	1754
110	91.3	1356	1385	1413	1441	1469	1496	1524	1551
115	95.4	1175	1205	1234	1262	1290	1318	1345	1372
120	99.4	105.7	1040	1070	1098	1127	1151	1182	1209
125	103.4	109.4	897.3	925.3	953.3	980.6	1008	1035	1062
130	107.4	112.9	123.1	809.5	834.2	859.0	883.8	908.7	933.6
135	111.4	116.6	125.4	713.1	740.2	764.6	787.1	809.0	830.6
140	115.3	120.2	128.1	143.2	645.2	676.2	703.3	727.6	749.9
145	119.2	123.9	131.0	143.1	539.5	582.9	617.6	647.1	673.4
150	123.1	127.6	134.1	144.4	163.6	434.5	511.0	560.8	597.7
155	126.9	131.2	137.3	146.3	160.9	191.8	360.2	455.2	509.3
160	130.7	134.8	140.5	148.6	160.6	180.7	224.6	333.4	416.0
170	138.1	141.9	146.9	153.7	162.9	175.6	194.2	222.9	266.9
180	145.4	148.9	153.5	159.4	166.8	176.5	189.1	205.5	227.1
190	152.7	156.0	160.2	165.4	171.8	179.7	189.4	201.2	215.7
200	159.9	163.0	166.9	171.5	177.2	183.9	191.9	201.3	212.2
210	167.0	169.9	173.5	177.8	182.8	188.7	195.5	203.4	212.3
220	174.1	176.9	180.2	184.1	188.7	193.9	199.9	206.7	214.3
230	181.2	183.8	187.0	190.6	194.8	199.5	204.9	210.9	217.5
240	188.2	190.7	193.7	197.1	200.9	205.3	210.1	215.5	221.4
250	195.1	197.5	200.3	203.5	207.1	211.1	215.5	220.4	225.7
260	201.8	204.1	206.7	209.8	213.1	216.8	220.9	225.4	230.2
270	208.3	210.5	213.0	215.9	219.0	222.5	226.3	230.4	234.8
280	214.6	216.7	219.1	221.9	224.8	228.1	231.6	235.5	239.5
290	220.9	222.9	225.2	227.8	230.6	233.7	237.0	240.6	244.4
300	227.1	229.1	231.3	233.7	236.4	239.3	242.4	245.8	249.4
310	233.3	235.2	237.3	239.7	242.2	244.9	247.9	251.1	254.5
320	239.4	241.2	243.2	245.5	247.9	250.5	253.4	256.3	259.6
330	245.3	247.1	249.0	251.2	253.4	255.9	258.6	261.5	264.6
340	251.1	252.8	254.6	256.6	258.6	261.0	263.3	266.7	269.6
350	259.2	260.6	262.2	263.9	265.7	267.6	269.6	274.1	276.9
400	289.1	290.3	291.7	293.2	294.7	296.4	298.1	301.6	303.8
450	316.2	317.3	318.6	319.8	321.2	322.6	324.1	327.0	328.8
500	341.6	342.6	343.7	344.9	346.1	347.3	348.7	351.0	352.6
550	365.5	366.5	367.4	368.5	369.6	370.7	371.9	373.9	375.3
600	389.1	390.0	390.9	391.8	392.8	393.9	394.9	396.7	397.9
650	411.5	412.3	413.1	414.0	414.9	415.9	416.8	418.4	419.5
700	433.1	433.9	434.6	435.4	436.3	437.2	438.0	439.5	440.5
750	454.0	454.7	455.4	456.2	457.0	457.8	458.6	459.9	460.8
800	474.4	475.1	475.8	476.6	477.4	478.2	479.0	479.9	480.7
850	494.3	495.0	495.7	496.4	497.1	497.8	498.6	499.4	500.2
900	513.8	514.4	515.1	515.7	516.4	517.1	517.8	518.6	518.7

continued

T, °K \ p, bar →	1	10	20	30	40	50	60	70	80
1000	551.4	552.0	552.5	553.1	553.7	554.4	555.0	555.7	556.3
1100	587.7	588.2	588.7	589.3	589.8	590.4	590.9	591.5	592.1
1200	622.7	623.2	623.7	624.1	624.6	625.1	625.7	626.2	626.7
1300	656.7	657.1	657.6	658.0	658.5	658.9	659.4	659.9	660.4

T, °K \ p, bar →	90	100	125	150	175	200	250	300	350
90	2716	2759	2870	2983	3100	3219	3469		
95	2326	2364	2456	2551	2649	2751	2960	3182	3416
100	2024	2057	2137	2218	2303	2387	2566	2755	2954
105	1782	1810	1882	1954	2028	2102	2256	2418	2588
110	1578	1604	1671	1738	1804	1871	2007	2148	2296
115	1399	1425	1489	1552	1615	1677	1801	1928	2058
120	1236	1262	1326	1388	1449	1509	1626	1742	1860
125	1088	1114	1178	1239	1299	1358	1471	1582	1692
130	958.5	983.0	1045	1105	1164	1221	1332	1440	1544
135	852.5	874.4	930.2	986.5	1042	1098	1206	1310	1412
140	770.8	790.3	838.6	887.7	938.3	989.7	1093	1194	1292
145	697.0	718.9	767.6	811.1	854.7	899.8	993.6	1090	1184
150	625.0	649.7	703.2	747.0	789.7	828.8	910.6	997.5	1087
155	547.2	579.0	640.0	688.3	730.1	768.6	843.9	919.3	1000
160	467.7	507.1	579.6	634.2	678.0	720.0	791.8	857.1	927.3
170	321.3	371.5	463.8	529.3	582.4	627.1	701.8	765.4	825.0
180	254.7	287.3	371.6	440.9	496.9	544.8	623.8	690.3	747.0
190	233.0	253.3	313.5	374.9	429.2	476.8	556.7	622.9	682.3
200	225.0	239.5	282.6	331.5	379.6	423.8	501.4	567.0	625.1
210	222.4	233.7	266.8	305.1	345.4	384.9	457.3	520.3	577.2
220	222.7	232.0	258.7	289.8	323.2	357.3	422.8	482.8	536.7
230	224.7	232.6	255.1	280.9	309.1	338.4	397.2	452.4	503.8
240	227.7	234.6	254.0	276.1	300.2	325.7	377.8	428.6	476.4
250	231.4	237.5	254.6	273.9	294.9	317.2	363.7	409.8	454.5
260	235.4	240.9	256.2	273.3	292.0	311.8	353.3	395.5	436.9
270	239.6	244.6	258.5	273.9	290.6	308.4	345.9	384.5	422.8
280	243.9	248.5	261.2	275.2	290.4	305.9	337.0	369.5	402.5
290	248.5	252.8	264.3	277.3	291.2	305.9	337.0	369.5	402.5
300	253.2	257.3	267.9	279.9	292.6	306.2	334.9	364.9	395.7
310	258.0	261.8	271.8	282.9	294.7	307.3	333.8	361.8	390.4
320	262.9	266.4	275.9	286.2	297.2	308.9	333.7	359.8	386.4
330	267.8	271.0	280.0	289.7	300.0	310.9	334.1	358.5	383.5
340	272.6	275.7	284.2	293.3	303.0	313.3	335.0	357.9	381.5
350	279.7	282.7	290.7	299.3	308.5	318.2	338.7	360.3	382.6
400	306.1	308.5	314.8	321.5	328.7	336.2	352.1	368.9	386.3
450	330.7	332.7	337.9	343.5	349.4	355.5	368.5	382.1	397.4
500	354.3	356.0	360.4	365.2	370.2	375.4	386.3	397.8	409.8
550	376.8	378.2	382.2	386.3	390.6	395.1	404.6	414.5	424.9
600	399.2	400.5	404.0	407.7	411.5	415.4	423.8	532.5	441.6
650	420.7	421.9	425.0	428.3	431.7	435.2	442.7	449.5	458.6
700	441.5	442.6	445.4	448.4	451.5	454.7	461.4	468.5	475.8
750	461.8	462.8	465.3	468.1	470.9	473.8	479.9	486.3	492.9
800	481.6	482.6	484.9	487.4	490.0	492.7	498.3	504.1	510.3
850	501.0	501.9	504.1	506.4	508.8	511.3	516.4	522.0	527.5
900	520.1	520.9	523.0	525.1	527.3	529.6	534.4	539.5	544.7
1000	557.0	557.7	559.5	561.4	563.3	565.3	569.5	573.9	578.4
1100	592.7	593.4	594.0	596.6	598.3	600.0	603.8	607.7	611.8
1200	627.3	627.9	629.3	630.8	632.3	633.9	637.2	641.7	644.3
1300	660.9	661.4	662.7	664.1	665.5	666.9	669.9	673.1	676.3

continued

T, °K \ p, bar →	400	450	500	600	700	800	900	1000
95	3665	3925						
100	3164	3386	3619					
105	2768	2958	3158					
110	2451	2613	2785					
115	2193	2335	2484					
120	1981	2107	2237					
125	1802	1916	2031					
130	1648	1752	1858					
135	1511	1609	1708					
140	1388	1483	1576					
145	1277	1367	1457					
150	1175	1263	1350					
155	1083	1168	1252					
160	1004	1084	1162					
170	887.5	950.2	1016					
180	802.3	855.0	908.0	976.9				
190	734.7	783.3	828.6	911.9	987.6			
200	667.3	726.4	770.7	853.7	928.8	998.6		
210	628.3	676.2	719.8	801.7	876.1	945.1		
220	586.7	632.9	675.7	755.9	828.9	897.0	960.8	
230	551.4	596.2	637.6	715.8	786.6	853.6	916.4	976.2
240	521.9	564.6	604.9	680.5	749.1	814.8	876.3	935.0
250	497.3	537.8	576.3	649.6	716.4	780.2	840.1	897.6
260	476.8	515.4	552.1	622.6	687.6	749.2	807.5	863.5
270	460.1	496.5	531.4	598.8	661.9	721.3	778.1	832.6
280	446.4	480.6	513.8	578.0	638.9	696.5	751.7	804.6
290	435.1	467.4	499.0	560.0	618.5	674.4	728.0	779.4
300	426.0	456.6	486.5	544.6	600.8	654.6	706.5	756.6
310	418.9	447.8	476.1	531.5	585.3	637.0	687.1	735.8
320	413.4	440.5	467.4	520.2	571.5	621.3	669.6	716.9
330	409.0	434.5	460.0	510.3	559.3	607.3	654.0	699.8
340	405.6	429.7	453.9	501.8	548.8	594.9	640.1	684.6
350	405.4	428.2	451.3	496.9	542.1	586.4	630.2	673.4
400	404.1	422.2	440.3	477.3	514.2	551.2	587.7	623.9
450	410.9	425.8	441.1	472.2	502.9	534.4	564.9	595.9
500	422.1	434.7	447.6	474.1	501.6	528.3	553.7	582.3
550	435.5	446.4	457.5	480.4	504.2	528.2	550.9	576.1
600	451.0	460.6	470.4	490.4	511.2	532.7	553.1	576.0
650	467.0	475.5	484.3	502.1	521.5	539.6	558.7	579.0
700	483.3	491.0	498.9	515.1	531.6	548.6	566.1	584.2
750	499.9	506.9	514.1	528.8	544.8	559.2	575.1	591.1
800	516.6	523.0	529.6	543.1	556.9	571.0	585.5	600.2
850	533.3	539.3	545.4	557.8	570.6	583.6	597.0	610.4
900	550.1	555.6	561.3	572.8	584.7	596.8	609.1	621.6
1000	583.2	588.0	592.9	603.1	613.4	624.0	634.8	645.8
1100	615.9	620.2	624.5	633.5	642.7	652.2	661.7	671.5
1200	648.0	651.9	655.8	663.8	682.1	680.6	689.2	697.9
1300	679.7	683.1	686.7	693.9	701.5	709.2	717.0	724.9

Viscosity η (N · s/m²) of argon at $p = 1$ bar [366, 425]

T, °K	$\eta \cdot 10^7$	T, °K	$\eta \cdot 10^7$	T, °K	$\eta \cdot 10^7$	T, °K	$\eta \cdot 10^7$	T, °K	$\eta \cdot 10^7$
1000	560.0	1250	651.2	1500	733.4	1750	808.4	2000	878.4
1100	598.0	1300	667.9	1600	763.5	1800	822.9	2100	905.5
1200	633.7	1400	700.9	1700	793.6	1900	850.8		

Viscosity $\eta \cdot 10^7$ (N · s/m²) of ionized argon [158, 366, 425]*

T, °K \ p, kg/cm² →	1	10^{-1}	10^{-2}	10^{-3}	10^{-4}
2	878	878	878	878	878
3	1140	1140	1140	1140	1140
4	1390	1390	1390	1390	1390
5	1630	1630	1630	1630	1630
6	1880	1880	1880	1880	1880
7	2120	2120	2110	2030	1837
8	2380	2340	2190	1855	1452
9	2590	2380	1991	1349	623
10	2710	2170	1537	710	144
11	2645	1750	888	203	35.7
12	2305	1219	377	62.3	31.4
13	1805	722	156	48.1	33.2
14	1264	353	89.0	48.7	34.3
15	850	205	79.2	49.7	33.2
16	597	155	79.9	49.5	14.4
17	389	134	78.5	42.6	7.21
18	290	132	67.0	21.1	6.65
19	241	128	49.5	13.8	6.80
20	233	116	33.6	11.8	6.92
21	232	90.0	25.4	10.9	7.21
22	223	68.9	20.2	10.8	6.72
23	208	52.7	18.6	10.7	5.68
24	184	43.3	18.2	10.4	4.46
25	152	36.7	17.9	9.33	3.70
26	123	33.1	17.4	7.63	3.44
28	87.6	31.1	15.1	5.55	3.49
30	72.8	28.6	11.6	4.95	4.10

*The values of η from 2000 to 5000 °K were obtained by graphic interpolation of data.

Thermal conductivity λ (W/m · deg) of argon at $p = 1$ bar [15]

T, °K	$\lambda \cdot 10^3$	T, °K	$\lambda \cdot 10^3$	T, °K	$\lambda \cdot 10^3$	T, °K	$\lambda \cdot 10^3$
90	6.00	250	15.2	460	24.8	1050	45.0
100	6.60	260	15.7	480	25.7	1100	46.3
110	7.20	270	16.2	500	26.6	1150	47.6
120	7.80	280	16.7	520	27.5	1200	48.9
130	8.40	290	17.2	540	28.3	1250	50.2
140	9.00	300	17.7	560	29.1	1300	51.4
150	9.60	310	18.2	580	29.9	1350	52.6
160	10.3	320	18.6	600	30.7	1400	53.7
170	10.9	330	19.2	650	32.4	1500	56.0
180	11.5	340	19.6	700	34.1	1600	58.3
190	12.0	350	20.0	750	35.8	1700	60.5
200	12.6	360	20.5	800	37.4	1800	62.6
210	13.1	380	21.3	850	39.1	1900	64.7
220	13.6	400	22.2	900	40.6	2000	66.7
230	14.1	420	23.0	950	42.2		
240	14.7	440	23.9	1000	43.6		

Thermal conductivity of argon at high temperatures and $p = 1$ bar [15, 361]

$T \cdot 10^{-3}$, °K	1500	2000	2500	3000	3500	4000	4500	5000
$\lambda \cdot 10^3$, W/m · deg	56	68	80	91	102	110	118	131

Thermal conductivity $\lambda \cdot 10^3$ (W/m · deg) of argon liquid and gas [15]

p, bar → / T, °K	1	10	20	30	40	50	60
90	6.00	121	122	123	124		125
100	6.60	109	110	111	112		113
110	7.20	96.2	97.1	98.2	99.3		110
120	7.80	9.07	86.4	87.4	88.5	89.4	90.5
130	8.40	9.50		73.4	74.3	75.9	77.6
140	9.00	10.1	11.3	13.0	61.2	62.8	64.3
150	9.60	10.4	11.5	13.0	14.3		48.6
160	10.3	10.8	11.7	13.1	14.5	17.3	
170	10.9	11.5	12.3	13.3	14.6		
180	11.5	12.0	12.7	13.6	14.7	15.9	17.7
190	12.0	12.5	13.2	14.0	14.9	16.0	17.3
200	12.6	13.0	13.6	14.4	15.2	16.1	17.2
220	13.6	14.1	14.6	15.2	15.9	16.6	17.5
240	14.7	15.1	15.1	16.1	16.6	17.3	18.0
260	15.7	16.1	16.5	17.0	17.4	18.0	18.6
280	16.7	17.1	17.4	17.9	18.3	18.8	19.3
300	17.7	18.0	18.4	18.8	19.2	19.6	20.1
320	18.6		19.3		20.0	20.4	20.8
350	20.0		20.7		21.3	21.6	22.0
400	22.2		22.9		23.4	23.7	24.0
450	24.6		25.0		25.5	25.7	26.0
500	26.6		27.0		27.4	27.6	27.8
550	28.6		29.0		29.4	29.6	29.8
600	30.7		30.9		31.2	31.4	31.6
650	32.4		32.7		33.0	33.1	33.3
700	34.1		34.4		34.6	34.7	34.9
750	35.8				36.3	36.4	36.6
800	37.4				38.0	38.2	38.4
850	39.1				39.5	39.6	39.7
900	40.6				40.9	41.0	41.2
950	42.0				42.4	42.5	42.6
1000	43.6					43.9	
1100	46.3					46.5	
1200	48.9					47.2	
1300	51.4					52.0	
1400	53.7					54.2	

p, bar → / T, °K	70	80	90	100	150	200	250
90		126		127	129	132	135
100		114	115	116	118	122	125
110	101	102	103	104	107	110	114
120	91.4	92.3	93.3	94.4	98.3	102	106
130	78.8	80.0	81.0	82.0	86.5	90.8	94.9
140	66.4	69.2	70.7	72.3	78.4	81.9	86.7
150	52.6	56.8	59.6	62.2	69.3	74.4	80.0
160			45.1	49.3	59.4	65.6	70.9
170					50.8	58.5	64.2
180	19.8	22.4	25.6	29.2	43.5	52.0	58.2
190	18.9	20.7	22.8	25.2	37.5	46.5	53.0
200	18.5	20.0	21.5	23.3	33.3	42.1	48.6
220	18.4	19.4	20.5	21.7	28.5	35.7	41.8
240	18.7	19.5	20.4	21.3	26.4	32.1	37.3
260	19.2	19.9	20.6	21.4	25.5	29.4	34.2
280	19.9	20.5	21.0	21.7	25.1	28.9	32.9
300	20.6	21.1	21.6	21.1	25.2	28.4	31.9
320		21.7		22.7	25.3	28.2	31.2
350		22.8		23.6	25.9	28.4	31.0
400		24.7		25.4	27.2	29.3	31.2
450		26.6		27.1	28.7	30.3	32.0

continued

T, °K \ p, bar →	70	80	90	100	150	200	250
500		28.3		28.8	30.1	31.9	33.2
550		30.2		30.6	31.8	33.2	34.5
600		31.9		32.3	33.4	34.5	35.8
650		33.6		33.9	34.9	35.8	36.8
700		35.3		35.8	36.5	37.4	38.3
750		36.9		37.2	38.0	38.8	39.7
800		38.7		38.8	39.4	40.1	41.0
850		40.0		40.2	40.8	41.6	42.3
900		41.0		41.7	42.3	43.0	43.7
950		42.8		43.0	43.7	44.3	45.0
1000				44.4	45.0	45.8	46.4
1100				47.0	48.1	48.2	48.7
1200				49.7	50.2	50.7	51.1
1300				52.5	52.7	53.0	53.3
1400				54.4	54.7	55.1	55.4

T, °K \ p, bar →	300	350	400	450	500	550	600
90							
100	128	130	132	134	136	138	140
110	117	119	121	123	125	128	131
120	108	111	113	115	117	120	123
130	98.0	102	106	109	111	114	117
140	90.8	94.2	97.9	101	104	108	110
150	84.1	87.2	91.0	93.9	96.8	100	103
160	75.3	79.2	83.0	87.2	91.0	94.3	97.2
170	69.0	73.2	76.9	80.4	83.4	86.8	88.4
180	63.3	67.6	71.5	75.2	78.2	81.5	83.2
190	58.2	62.7	66.8	70.3	73.6	76.8	79.8
200	54.0	58.5	62.4	66.4	69.3	72.5	75.6
220	47.0	51.4	55.3	59.0	62.3	65.4	68.3
240	42.1	46.2	50.1	53.5	56.8	60.2	62.6
260	38.5	42.2	45.8	49.1	52.3	55.0	57.8
280	36.6	40.1	43.3	46.4	49.2	51.9	54.5
300	35.2	38.3	41.2	44.1	46.9	49.3	51.8
320	34.3	37.1	40.0	42.4	45.0	47.2	49.6
350	33.6	36.0	38.3	40.8	43.0	45.2	47.4
400	33.3	35.4	37.5	39.4	41.3	43.3	45.0
450	33.9	35.6	37.3	39.1	40.9	42.4	44.0
500	34.6	36.3	37.9	39.3	40.7	42.1	43.6
550	35.6	37.2	38.4	39.9	41.1	42.4	43.5
600	36.8	38.1	39.3	40.5	41.6	42.7	43.6
650	37.9	38.8	39.9	40.8	41.7	43.1	43.7
700	39.3	40.2	41.2	42.2	43.3	44.2	45.2
750	40.6	41.6	42.4	43.0	43.8	44.6	45.8
800	41.8	42.6	43.5	44.4	45.2	46.1	46.8
850	43.1	43.9	44.7	45.5	46.2	47.1	47.9
900	44.7	45.2	45.9	46.6	47.3	48.0	48.9
950	45.6	46.3	46.9	47.6	48.3	48.9	49.5
1000	47.0	47.7	48.3	48.9	49.6	50.2	51.0
1100	49.3	49.8	50.4	50.9	51.5	52.0	52.6
1200	51.5	51.9	52.4	52.8	53.3	53.7	54.2
1300	53.6	53.9	54.2	54.6	54.9	55.4	56.8
1400	55.6	55.9	56.2	56.5	56.8	57.3	57.6

Thermal conductivity of saturated liquid argon [15]

T, °K	90	95	100	105	110	115	120	125	130	135	140	145	150
$\lambda \cdot 10^3$, W/m · deg	121	114	108	102	97.2	91.0	85.5	78.6	71.5	65.1	58.2	48.3	38.0

Thermal conductivity λ (kcal/m ·hr · deg) of ionized argon at high temperatures [15, 158]*

p, kg/cm² → $T \cdot 10^{-3}$, °K	1	10^{-1}	10^{-2}	10^{-3}	10^{-4}	p, kg/cm² → $T \cdot 10^{-3}$, °K	1	10^{-1}	10^{-2}	10^{-3}	10^{-4}
2	0.058	0.058	0.058	0.058	0.058	16	1.59	0.840	0.596	0.452	0.301
3	0.077	0.077	0.077	0.077	0.077	17	1.58	0.924	0.667	0.481	0.318
4	0.095	0.095	0.095	0.095	0.095	18	1.66	0.998	0.740	0.509	0.350
5	0.111	0.111	0.111	0.112	0.121	19	1.83	1.10	0.800	0.565	0.396
6	0.126	0.127	0.134	0.150	0.192	20	1.95	1.19	0.840	0.622	0.452
7	0.175	0.184	0.201	0.244	0.362	21	2.11	1.27	0.876	0.651	0.470
8	0.250	0.272	0.292	0.444	1.07	22	2.33	1.38	0.933	0.721	0.487
9	0.353	0.388	0.530	0.943	1.31	23	2.56	1.48	1.00	0.763	0.516
10	0.485	0.573	0.917	1.25	0.550	24	2.78	1.63	1.09	0.806	0.558
11	0.676	0.818	1.190	0.600	0.221	25	2.97	1.78	1.19	0.827	0.587
12	0.95	1.18	0.900	0.360	0.220	26	3.14	1.95	1.26	0.848	0.637
13	1.18	1.19	0.585	0.324	0.251	28	3.42	2.26	1.40	0.890	0.720
14	1.41	0.933	0.524	0.361	0.276	30	3.76	2.54	1.59	1.0	0.820
15	1.53	0.844	0.552	0.403	0.286						

*Values of λ between 2000 and 5000 °K obtained by graphic interpolation of data.

Surface tension of argon [16]

T, °K	84	85	86	87	88	89	90
$\sigma \cdot 10^3$, N/m	11.46	11.30	11.15	11.00	10.84	10.69	10.53

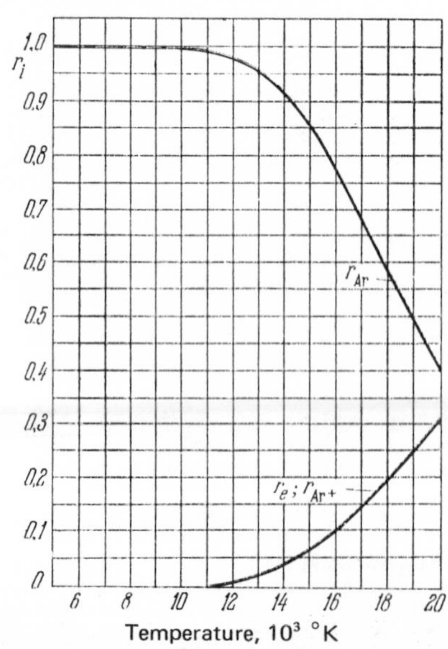

Fig. 21. Volume fractions r_i of ionized argon as a function of temperature at $p = 10^2$ kg/cm².

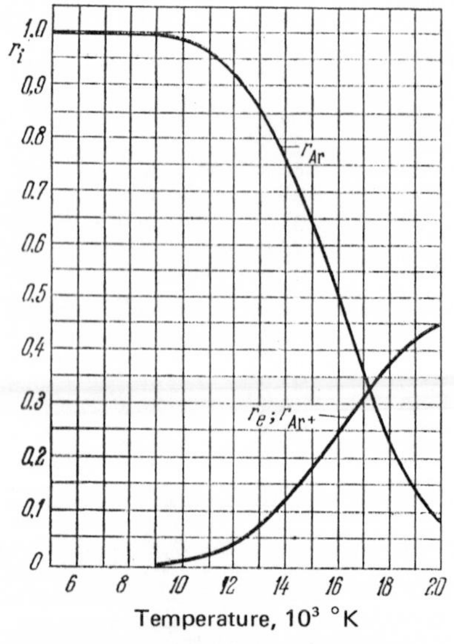

Fig. 22. Volume fractions r_i of ionized argon as a function of temperature at $p = 10$ kg/cm².

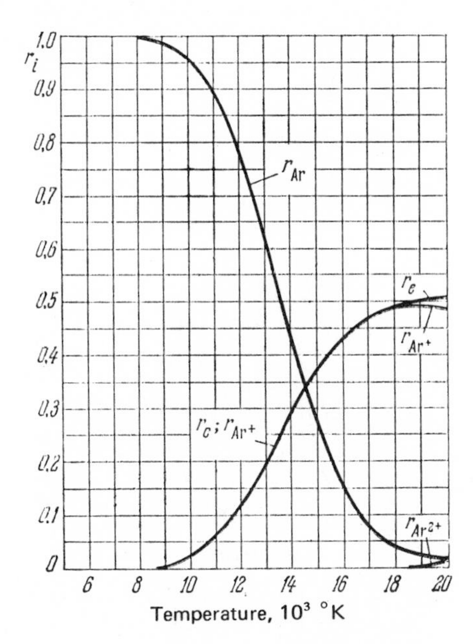

Fig. 23. Volume fractions r_i of ionized argon as a function of temperature at $p = 1$ kg/cm².

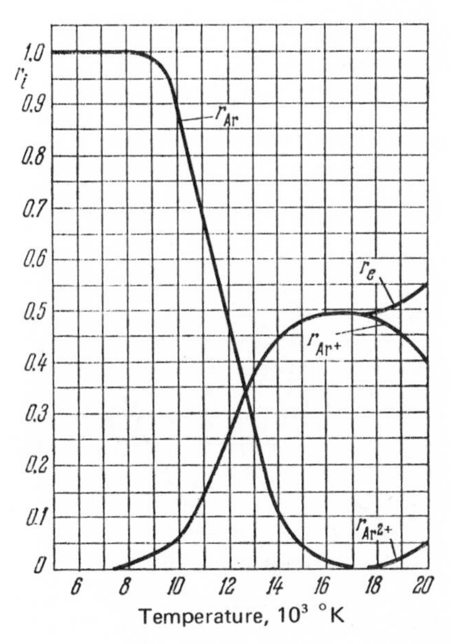

Fig. 24. Volume fractions r_i of ionized argon as a function of temperature at $p = 10^{-1}$ kg/cm².

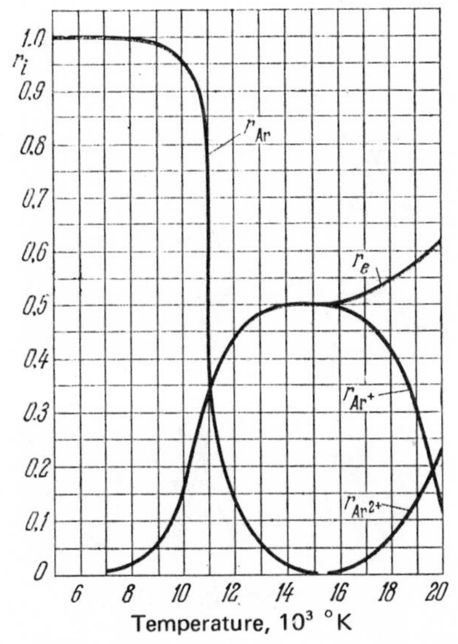

Fig. 25. Volume fractions r_i of ionized argon as a function of temperature at $p = 10^{-2}$ kg/cm².

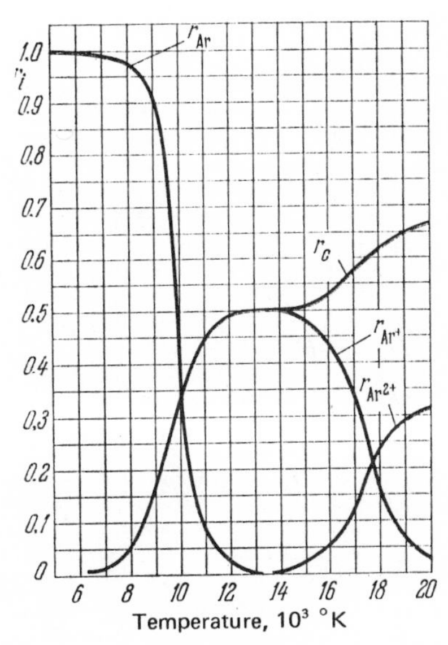

Fig. 26. Volume fractions r_i of ionized argon as a function of temperature at $p = 10^{-3}$ kg/cm².

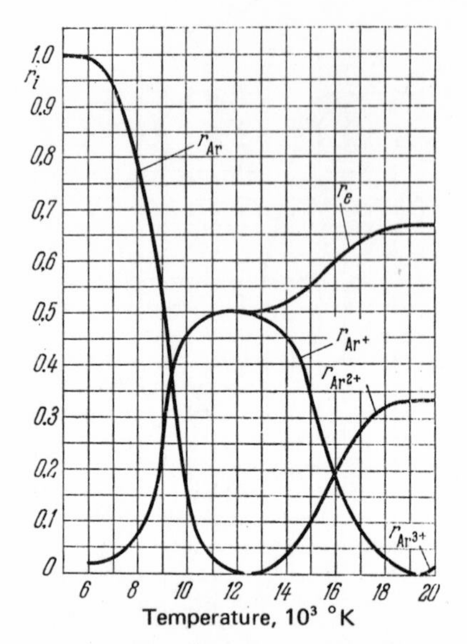

Fig. 27. Volume fractions r_i of ionized argon as a function of temperature at $p = 10^{-4}$ kg/cm².

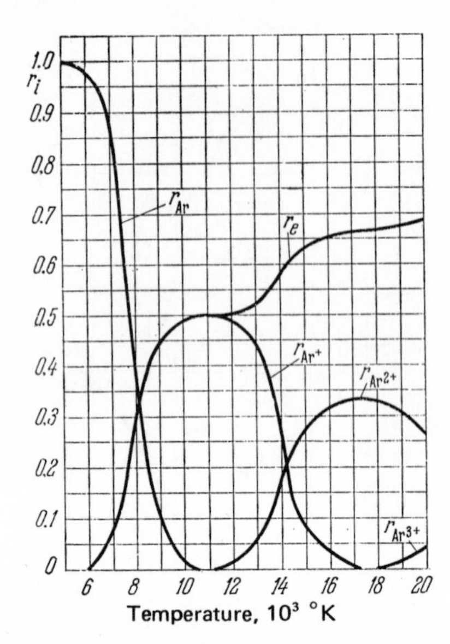

Fig. 28. Volume fractions r_i f ionized argon as a function of temperature at $p = 10^{-5}$ kg/cm².

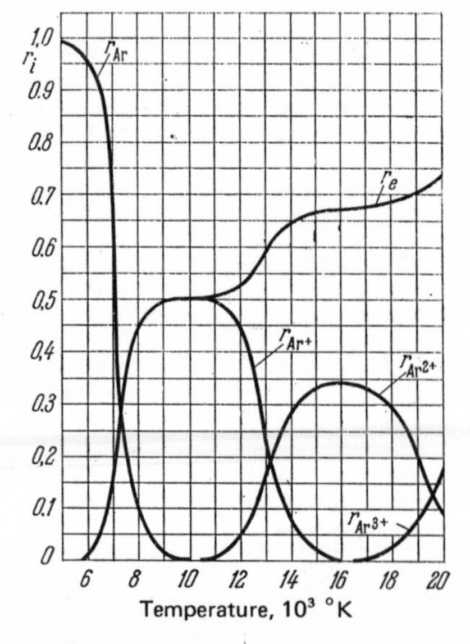

Fig. 29. Volume fractions r_i of ionized argon as a function of temperature at $p = 10^{-6}$ kg/cm².

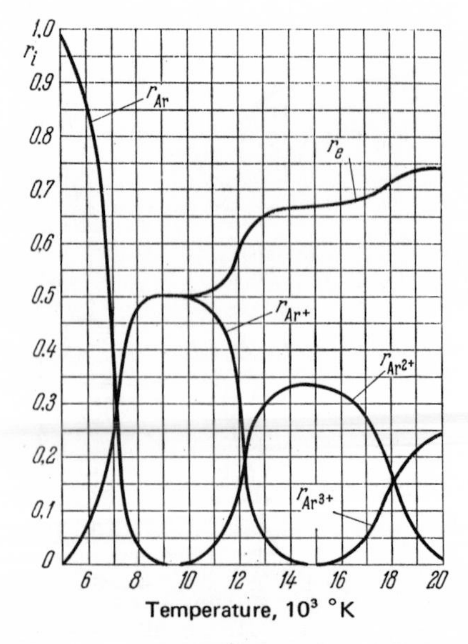

Fig. 30. Volume fractions r_i of ionized argon as a function of temperature at $p = 10^{-7}$ kg/cm².

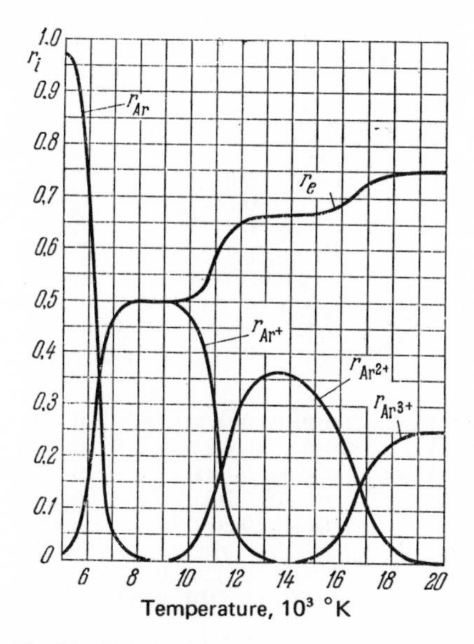

Fig. 31. Volume fractions r_i of ionized argon as a function of temperature at $p = 10^{-8}$ kg/cm².

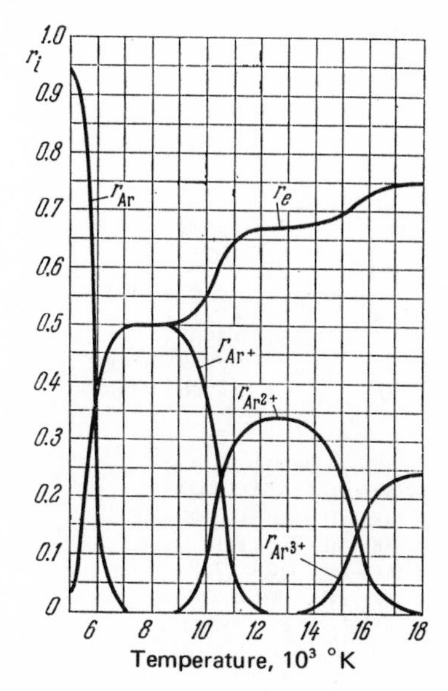

Fig. 32. Volume fractions r_i of ionized argon as a function of temperature at $p = 10^{-9}$ kg/cm².

Volume fractions r_i of ionized argon [30]

T, °K → r_i	r_{Ar}	r_{Ar^+}	$r_{Ar^{2+}}$	$r_{Ar^{3+}}$	r_e	T, °K → r_i	r_{rA}	r_{Ar^+}	$r_{Ar^{2+}}$	$r_{Ar^{3+}}$	r_e
					$p=10^{-8}$ kg/cm²						
5 000	0.9812	0.0094			0.0094	13 000		0.0047	0.3302		0.6651
6 000	0.6410	0.1795			0.1795	14 000			0.3312	0.0016	0.6672
7 000	0.0352	0.4824			0.4824	15 000			0.3248	0.0064	0.6688
8 000	0.0010	0.4995			0.4995	16 000			0.2504	0.0622	0.6874
9 000		0.4988	0.0008		0.5004	17 000			0.1116	0.1663	0.7221
10 000		0.4811	0.0126		0.5063	18 000			0.0260	0.2305	0.7435
11 000		0.2816	0.1456		0.5728	19 000			0.0076	0.2443	0.7481
12 000		0.0437	0.3042		0.6521	20 000			0.0000	0.2500	0.7500
					$p=10^{-7}$ kg/cm²						
5 000	0.9950	0.0025			0.0025	13 000		0.0470	0.3020		0.6510
6 000	0.8650	0.0675			0.0675	14 000		0.0080	0.3280		0.6640
7 000	0.2754	0.3623			0.3623	15 000		0.0017	0.3314	0.0006	0.6663
8 000	0.0110	0.4945			0.4945	16 000			0.3240	0.0070	0.6690
9 000	0.0004	0.4997			0.4997	17 000			0.2760	0.0430	0.6810
10 000		0.4982	0.0012		0.5006	18 000			0.1520	0.1360	0.7120
11 000		0.4580	0.0280		0.5142	19 000			0.0548	0.2089	0.7363
12 000		0.2333	0.1778		0.5889	20 000			0.0144	0.2392	0.7464
					$p=10^{-6}$ kg/cm²						
5 000	0.9980	0.0010			0.0010	13 000		0.2420	0.1720		0.5860
6 000	0.9524	0.0238			0.0238	14 000		0.0650	0.2900		0.6450
7 000	0.5924	0.2038			0.2038	15 000		0.0140	0.3240		0.6620
8 000	0.0900	0.4550			0.4550	16 000		0.0036	0.3300	0.0014	0.6650
9 000	0.0060	0.4970			0.4970	17 000		0.0015	0.3250	0.0055	0.6680
10 000	0.0007	0.4995	0.0001		0.4997	18 000			0.2960	0.0280	0.6760
11 000	0.0002	0.4954	0.0030		0.5014	19 000			0.2156	0.0883	0.6961
12 000		0.4442	0.0372		0.5186	20 000			0.1020	0.1735	0.7245

continued

r_i / T, K	r_{Ar}	r_{Ar^+}	$r_{Ar^{2+}}$	$r_{Ar^{3+}}$	r_e	r_i / T, °K	r_{Ar}	r_{Ar^+}	$r_{Ar^{2+}}$	$r_{Ar^{3+}}$	r_e
					$p=10^{-5}$ kg/cm²						
5 000	1.000					13 000		0.4457	0.0362		0.5181
6 000	0.9852	0.0074			0.0074	14 000		0.2810	0.1460		0.5730
7 000	0.8558	0.0721			0.0721	15 000		0.1058	0.2628		0.6314
8 000	0.3960	0.3020			0.3020	16 000		0.0311	0.3126		0.6563
9 000	0.0576	0.4712			0.4712	17 000		0.0134	0.3244		0.6622
10 000	0.0066	0.4967			0.4967	18 000		0.0020	0.3280	0.0030	0.6670
11 000	0.0010	0.4989	0.0004		0.4997	19 000		0.0015	0.3150	0.0130	0.6705
12 000		0.4940	0.0040		0.5020	20 000			0.2720	0.0460	0.6820
					$p=10^{-4}$ kg/cm²						
5 000	1.0000					13 000		0.4970	0.0020		0.5010
6 000	0.9952	0.0024			0.0024	14 000		0.4610	0.0260		0.5130
7 000	0.9520	0.0240			0.0240	15 000		0.3500	0.1000		0.5500
8 000	0.7380	0.1310			0.1310	16 000		0.1880	0.2080		0.6040
9 000	0.3040	0.3480			0.3480	17 000		0.1040	0.2640		0.6320
10 000	0.0600	0.4700			0.4700	18 000		0.0230	0.3180		0.6590
11 000	0.0080	0.4960			0.4960	19 000		0.0075	0.3250	0.0010	0.6640
12 000	0.0020	0.4990			0.4990	20 000		0.0025	0.3230	0.0065	0.6680
					$p=10^{-3}$ kg/cm²						
5 000	1.0000					13 000	0.0044	0.4972	0.0004		0.4980
6 000	0.9970	0.0015			0.0015	14 000	0.0015	0.4949	0.0029		0.5007
7 000	0.9848	0.0076			0.0076	15 000	0.0042	0.4760	0.0146		0.5052
8 000	0.9080	0.0460			0.0460	16 000		0.4250	0.0500		0.5250
9 000	0.6780	0.1610			0.1610	17 000		0.3500	0.1000		0.5500
10 000	0.3190	0.3405			0.3405	18 000		0.1520	0.2320		0.6160
11 000	0.0780	0.4610			0.4610	19 000		0.0620	0.2920		0.6460
12 000	0.0170	0.4915			0.4915	20 000		0.0285	0.3110	0.0025	0.6580
					$p=10^{-2}$ kg/cm²						
5 000	1.0000					13 000	0.0420	0.4790			0.4790
6 000	1.0000					14 000	0.0150	0.4925			0.4925
7 000	0.9950	0.0020			0.0020	15 000	0.0055	0.4950	0.0015		0.4980
8 000	0.9604	0.0153			0.0153	16 000	0.0019	0.4893	0.0065		0.5023
9 000	0.8780	0.0610			0.0610	17 000	0.0012	0.4772	0.0148		0.5068
10 000	0.6716	0.1642			0.1642	18 000	0.0005	0.3880	0.0745		0.5370
11 000	0.3670	0.3165			0.3165	19 000	0.0002	0.2986	0.1342		0.5670
12 000	0.1400	0.4300			0.4300	20 000		0.1760	0.2160		0.6080
					$p=10^{-1}$ kg/cm²						
5 000	1.0000					13 000	0.2580	0.3710			0.3710
6 000	1.0000					14 000	0.1090	0.4455			0.4455
7 000	0.9980	0.0010			0.0010	15 000	0.0428	0.4786			0.4786
8 000	0.9900	0.0050			0.0050	16 000	0.0192	0.4895	0.0006		0.4907
9 000	0.9590	0.0205			0.0205	17 000	0.0085	0.4935	0.0015		0.4965
10 000	0.8858	0.0571			0.0571	18 000	0.0037	0.4845	0.0091		0.5027
11 000	0.7230	0.1385			0.1385	19 000	0.0020	0.4603	0.0258		0.5119
12 000	0.4720	0.2640			0.2640	20 000	0.0010	0.4143	0.0568		0.5279
					$p=1$ kg/cm²						
5 000	1.0000					13 000	0.6380	0.1810			0.1810
6 000	1.0000					14 000	0.4330	0.2835			0.2835
7 000	0.9990	0.0005			0.0005	15 000	0.2484	0.3758			0.3758
8 000	0.9960	0.0020			0.0020	16 000	0.1440	0.4280			0.4280
9 000	0.9880	0.0060			0.0060	17 000	0.0740	0.4630			0.4630
10 000	0.9600	0.0200			0.0200	18 000	0.0372	0.4796	0.0012		0.4820
11 000	0.8990	0.0505			0.0505	19 000	0.0197	0.4858	0.0029		0.4916
12 000	0.7896	0.1052			0.1052	20 000	0.0105	0.4835	0.0075		0.4985
					$p=10$ kg/cm²						
5 000	1.0000					13 000	0.8584	0.0708			0.0708
6 000	1.0000					14 000	0.7640	0.1180			0.1180
7 000	1.0000					15 000	0.6310	0.1845			0.1845

continued

T, °K ↓ r_i →	r_{Ar}	r_{Ar^+}	$r_{Ar^{2+}}$	$r_{Ar^{3+}}$	r_e	T, °K ↓ r_i →	r_{Ar}	r_{Ar^+}	$r_{Ar^{2+}}$	$r_{Ar^{3+}}$	r_e
8 000	0.9990	0.0005			0.0005	16 000	0.5080	0.2460			0.2460
9 000	0.9950	0.0025			0.0025	17 000	0.3580	0.3210			0.3210
10 000	0.9882	0.0059			0.0059	18 000	0.2326	0.2837			0.3837
11 000	0.9660	0.0170			0.0170	19 000	0.1500	0.4250			0.4250
12 000	0.9260	0.0370			0.0370	20 000	0.0940	0.4530			0.4530
					$p = 100$ kg/cm²						
5 000	1.0000					13 000	0.9550	0.0225			0.0225
6 000	1.0000					14 000	0.9150	0.0425			0.0425
7 000	1.0000					15 000	0.8580	0.0710			0.0710
8 000	0.9998	0.0001			0.0001	16 000	0.7966	0.1017			0.1017
9 000	0.9990	0.0005			0.0005	17 000	0.7062	0.1469			0.1469
10 000	0.9946	0.0027			0.0027	18 000	0.5958	0.2021			0.2021
11 000	0.9900	0.0050			0.0050	19 000	0.4910	0.2545			0.2545
12 000	0.9756	0.0122			0.0122	20 000	0.4112	0.2944			0.2944

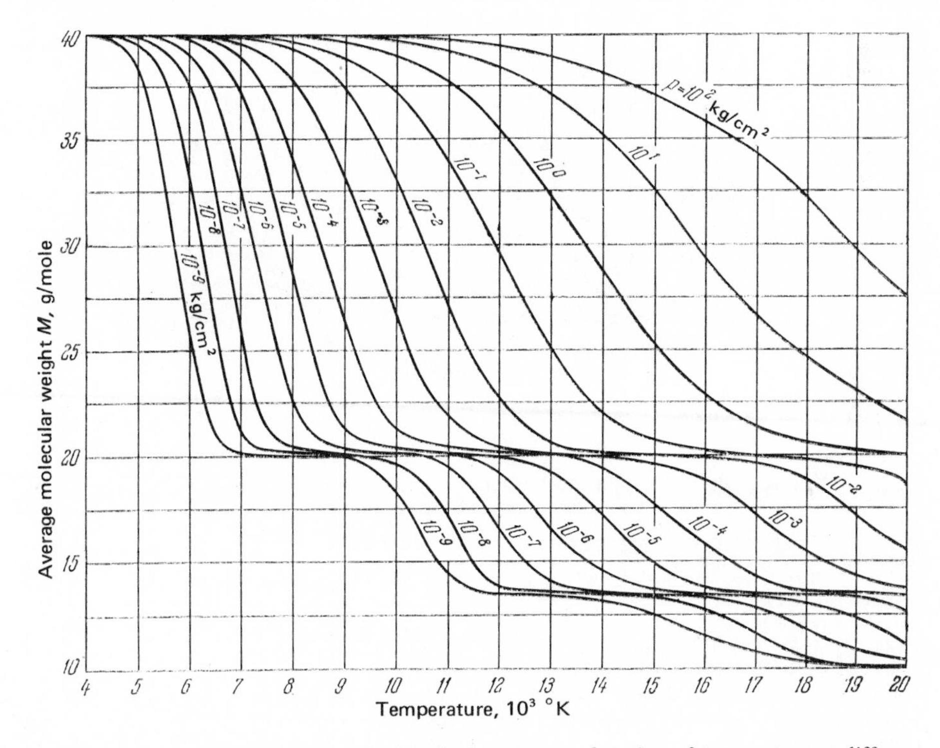

Fig. 33. Average molecular weight M of ionized argon as a function of temperature at different pressures.

Average molecular weight M of ionized argon [30]

T, °K ↓ p, kg/cm² →	10^{-9}	10^{-8}	10^{-7}	10^{-6}	10^{-5}	10^{-4}	10^{-3}	10^{-2}	10^{-1}	1	10	100
5 000	38.80	39.50	39.78	39.92	39.94	39.94	39.94	39.94	39.94	39.94	39.94	39.94
6 000	25.10	32.40	37.40	39.14	39.71	39.94	39.94	39.94	39.94	39.94	39.94	39.94
7 000	20.00	20.57	25.20	32.00	36.92	39.00	39.64	39.85	39.94	39.94	39.94	39.94
8 000	20.00	20.00	20.14	21.78	27.71	33.92	38.00	39.28	39.71	39.85	39.94	39.94
9 000	19.81	19.98	20.00	20.14	21.00	25.85	33.07	37.57	39.00	39.70	39.94	39.94

continued

p, kg/cm² → / T, °K	10^{-9}	10^{-8}	10^{-7}	10^{-6}	10^{-5}	10^{-4}	10^{-3}	10^{-2}	10^{-1}	1	10	100
10 000	18.25	19.33	20.00	20.00	20.14	21.14	26.28	33.00	37.35	39.10	39.71	39.94
11 000	14.20	17.00	19.40	19.85	20.00	20.28	21.57	27.20	34.28	37.98	39.28	39.90
12 000	13.40	13.71	16.40	19.14	19.85	20.14	20.28	22.71	29.57	35.57	38.50	39.50
13 000	13.30	13.42	13.92	16.57	19.14	19.98	20.00	20.50	25.14	32.35	37.40	38.86
14 000	13.20	13.27	13.40	14.57	17.14	19.35	19.85	20.20	22.20	28.85	35.50	38.42
15 000	12.40	13.28	13.28	13.50	14.85	17.71	19.64	20.00	20.71	25.14	32.85	37.20
16 000	11.50	12.56	13.20	13.40	13.78	15.78	18.85	19.85	20.28	22.85	29.40	35.85
17 000	10.85	11.57	12.71	13.28	13.50	14.71	17.12	19.71	20.07	21.50	26.71	34.57
18 000	10.20	10.28	11.57	12.92	13.35	13.57	15.50	18.85	19.85	20.71	24.71	32.57
19 000	10.00	10.28	10.57	12.14	13.14	13.40	14.28	17.20	19.55	20.30	23.28	29.80
20 000	10.00	10.00	10.20	11.00	12.71	13.28	13.71	15.57	18.85	20.00	21.85	27.64

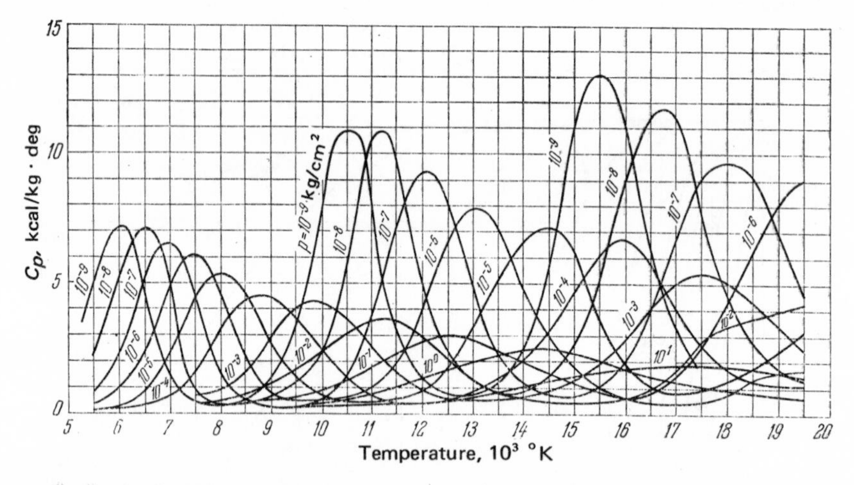

Fig. 34. Heat capacity c_p of ionized argon as a function of temperature at different pressures.

Heat capacity c_p (kcal/kg · deg) of ionized argon at different temperatures and pressures [30]

p, kg/cm² → / T, °K	10^{-9}	10^{-8}	10^{-7}	10^{-6}	10^{-5}	10^{-4}	10^{-3}	10^{-2}	10^{-1}	1	10
5 000	1.50	0.65	0.20	0.18	0.14	0.124	0.124	0.124	0.124	0.124	0.124
500	5.30	2.40	0.90	0.30	0.20	0.15	0.143	0.138	0.129	0.124	0.124
6 000	7.30	5.00	2.40	0.92	0.35	0.20	0.172	0.157	0.135	0.124	0.124
500	4.30	7.10	5.35	2.40	0.81	0.325	0.202	0.190	0.148	0.124	0.124
7 000	1.25	4.20	6.37	4.88	2.30	0.60	0.243	0.236	0.178	0.124	0.124
500	0.37	0.80	4.26	5.98	4.26	1.60	0.600	0.310	0.201	0.124	0.124
8 000	0.23	0.19	1.42	4.50	5.20	3.15	0.720	0.400	0.246	0.124	0.124
500	0.45	0.22	0.35	1.93	4.40	4.20	1.450	0.600	0.308	0.132	0.124
9 000	1.23	0.53	0.15	0.70	2.57	4.30	2.800	1.010	0.394	0.153	0.124
500	3.30	1.02	0.18	0.31	1.25	3.55	3.900	1.600	0.519	0.201	0.124
10 000	7.50	2.05	0.42	0.27	0.60	2.40	4.130	2.230	0.713	0.290	0.140
500	10.83	5.60	1.30	0.48	0.30	1.15	3.560	2.900	1.100	0.428	0.158
11 000	8.40	10.15	3.40	0.82	0.30	0.52	2.500	3.400	1.690	0.631	0.187
500	3.25	9.70	6.90	1.63	0.40	0.32	1.420	3.400	2.200	0.900	0.230
12 000	1.32	5.10	9.17	3.70	0.66	0.30	0.790	2.860	2.641	1.187	0.292
500	0.58	2.40	8.36	6.27	1.45	0.40	0.510	2.010	2.880	1.495	0.383
13 000	0.60	1.26	5.05	7.80	3.10	0.70	0.400	1.250	2.790	1.790	0.518
500	0.98	0.68	2.30	7.20	4.90	1.20	0.400	0.720	2.333	2.070	0.700
14 000	2.26	0.70	1.16	5.05	6.40	1.90	0.500	0.:00	1.911	2.330	0.96

continued

p, kg/cm² → / T, °K	10^{-9}	10^{-8}	10^{-7}	10^{-6}	10^{-5}	10^{-4}	10^{-3}	10^{-2}	10^{-1}	1	10
500	5.15	1.25	0.70	3.10	7.10	3.00	0.790	0.400	1.500	2.400	1.109
15 000	10.15	2.33	0.62	1.80	6.40	4.41	1.120	0.370	1.095	2.276	1.295
500	13.03	4.70	0.92	1.02	3.90	5.92	1.810	0.390	0.799	1.975	1.467
16 000	11.50	8.35	1.83	0.60	1.90	6.68	2.800	0.510	0.600	1.628	1.616
500	6.70	11.15	3.67	0.83	1.00	5.80	3.900	0.720	0.490	1.335	1.718
17 000	3.50	11.50	6.25	1.62	0.80	4.00	4.900	1.630	0.440	1.142	1.77
500	1.72	8.23	8.85	2.65	0.89	2.65	5.320	2.600	4.480	1.000	1.772
18 000	1.15	4.80	9.65	4.19	1.25	1.60	5.10	3.29	0.69	0.89	1.71
500	0.40	2.75	9.20	6.00	1.75	1.10	4.30	3.70	1.20	0.78	1.61
19 000		1.65	7.00	7.99	2.25	1.05	1.85	3.95	1.55	0.620	1.48
500		1.19	4.40	9.00	3.15	1.01	1.68	4.10	1.61	0.57	1.20
20 000		0.82	3.30	8.30	4.50	1.10	1.65	3.98	1.32	0.49	1.10

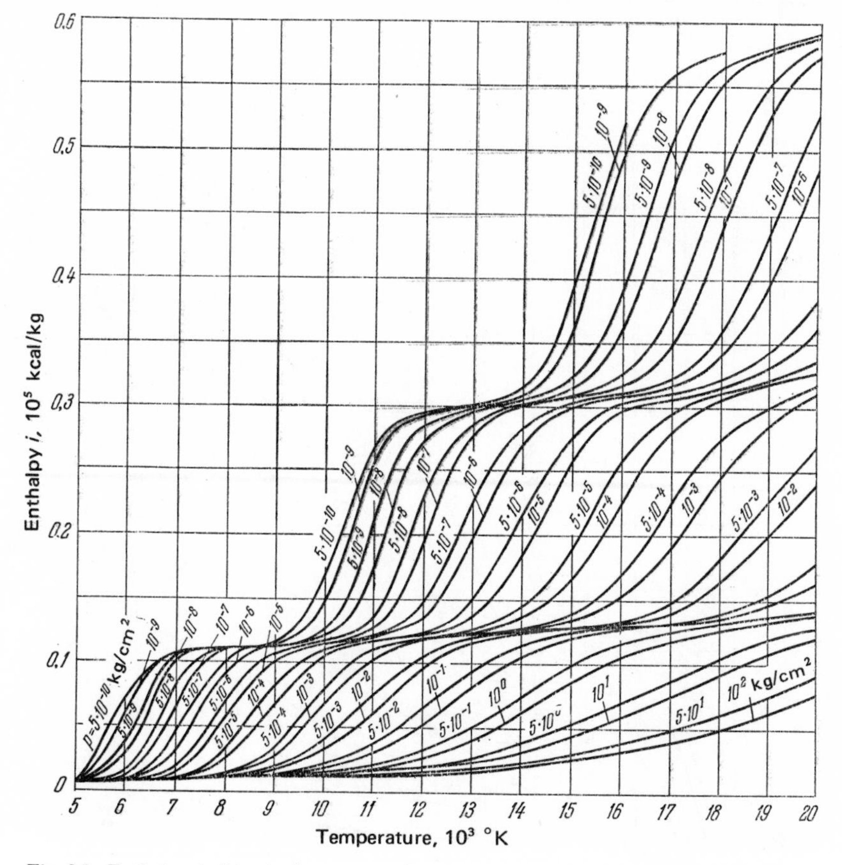

Fig. 35. Enthalpy i of ionized argon as a function of temperature at different pressures.

Enthalpy i (kcal/kg) of ionized argon at different temperatures and presssures [30]

p, kg/cm² → / T, °K	10^{-9}	10^{-8}	10^{-7}	10^{-6}	10^{-5}	10^{-4}	10^{-3}	10^{-2}	10^{-1}	1	10	100
5000	876.3	658.2	578.1	576.1	600.3	600.3	600.3	600.3	600.3	600.3	600.3	600.3
6000	6614.0	3025.0	1417.0	945.3	780.7	747.0	730.0	725.4	725.4	725.4	725.4	725.4
7000	10200	10210	6587.0	3406	1598	1100	955.2	880.0	850.4	850.4	850.4	850.4

continued

p, kg/cm² → T, °K	10^{-9}	10^{-8}	10^{-7}	10^{-6}	10^{-5}	10^{-4}	10^{-3}	10^{-2}	10^{-1}	1	10	100
8 000	11 050	10 800	10 600	9 412	5 813	2 535	1 421	1 095	1 007	960.0	950.5	950.5
9 000	11 510	11 310	11 300	11 170	10 290	6 692	3 305	1 840	1 272	1 134	1 101	1 101
10 000	14 900	12 210	11 600	11 500	11 420	10 450	6 621	3 333	1 820	1 400	1 259	1 251
11 000	25 920	17 820	12 730	11 890	11 800	11 590	10 200	6 213	3 034	1 843	1 502	1 429
12 000	29 250	27 720	19 690	13 480	12 290	11 920	11 740	9 511	5 073	2 727	1 890	1 570
13 000	30 740	29 930	27 660	19 070	13 790	12 410	12 250	11 610	7 955	4 019	2 299	1 827
14 000	31 800	30 590	30 000	26 630	18 490	13 410	12 700	12 330	10 450	5 962	3 164	2 212
15 000	36 530	31 900	30 870	29 930	24 710	16 830	13 340	12 800	11 850	8 274	4 323	2 634
16 000	46 090	35 990	31 820	30 890	28 880	22 430	15 070	13 250	12 720	12 400	5 782	3 180
17 000	52 160	44 940	35 250	31 780	30 670	26 510	18 170	13 850	13 150	11 810	7 525	3 876
18 000	56 600	52 000	43 990	34 210	31 910	30 800	24 520	16 390	13 900	12 800	9 227	6 097
19 000	58 500	56 710	53 170	39 950	33 330	31 940	28 710	20 120	14 680	13 600	9 880	6 275
20 000	59 100	59 100	57 250	49 360	36 580	32 980	32 220	24 410	16 390	14 100	12 080	7 634

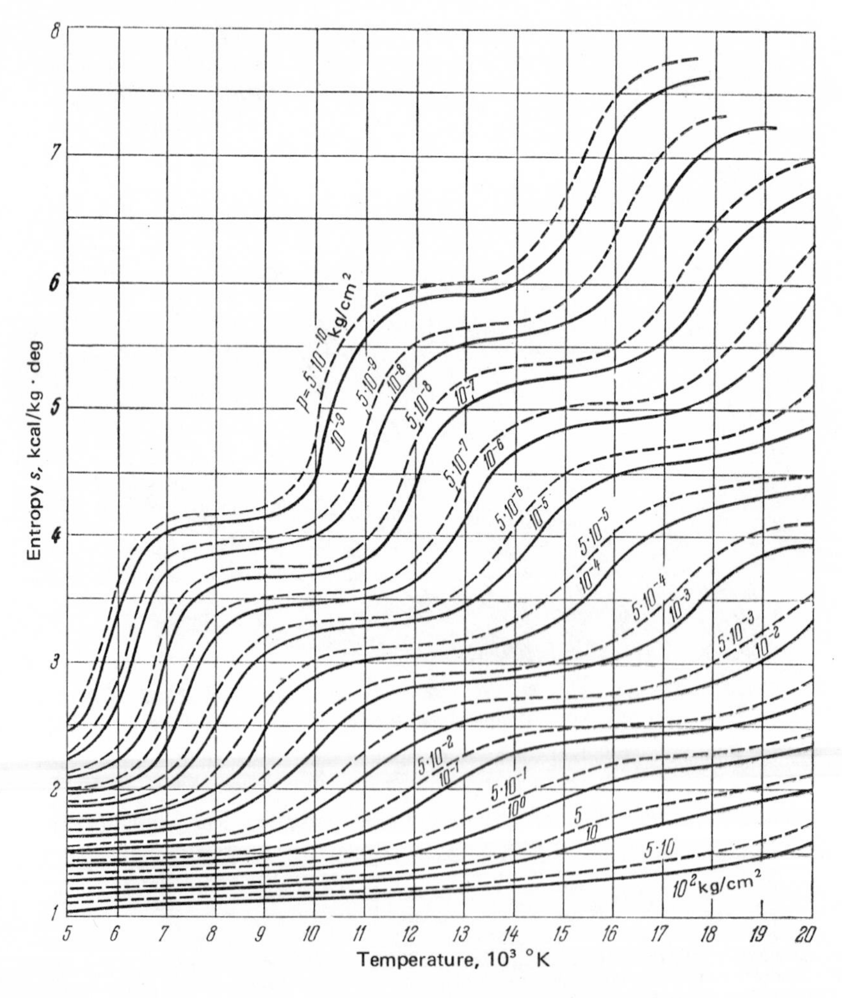

Fig. 36. Entropy s of ionized argon as a function of temperature at different pressures.

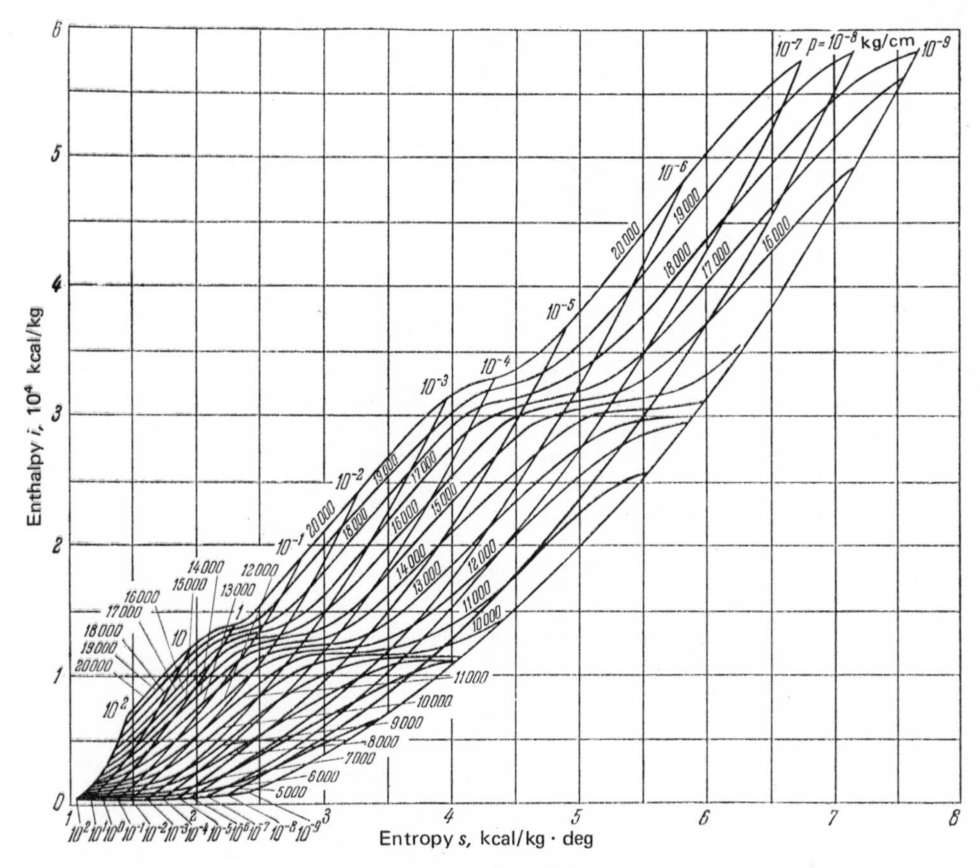

Fig. 37. An i–s diagram for argon

Entropy s (kcal/kg · deg) of ionized argon at different temperatures and pressures [30]

p, kg/cm² / T, °K	10^{-9}	10^{-8}	10^{-7}	10^{-6}	10^{-5}	10^{-4}	10^{-3}	10^{-2}	10^{-1}	1	10	100
5 000	2.36	2.21	2.08	1.96	1.85	1.74	1.62	1.50	1.39	1.28	1.16	1.05
6 000	3.36	2.66	2.22	2.02	1.88	1.76	1.64	1.53	1.41	1.30	1.18	1.07
7 000	4.04	3.69	3.06	2.39	2.01	1.81	1.67	1.56	1.43	1.32	1.21	1.10
8 000	4.08	3.84	3.60	3.21	2.52	2.00	1.75	1.57	1.44	1.33	1.23	1.12
9 000	4.13	3.89	3.66	3.42	3.07	2.48	1.96	1.67	1.48	1.34	1.24	1.13
10 000	4.44	3.98	3.68	3.46	3.22	2.89	2.30	1.82	1.55	1.38	1.26	1.14
11 000	5.56	4.50	3.80	3.48	3.26	3.00	2.66	2.13	1.68	1.43	1.28	1.16
12 000	5.87	5.32	4.38	3.63	3.29	3.04	2.79	2.29	1.85	1.50	1.32	1.17
13 000	5.90	5.54	5.02	4.13	3.42	3.08	2.84	2.34	2.09	1.60	1.35	1.19
14 000	5.97	5.58	5.22	4.66	3.76	3.16	2.85	2.62	2.27	1.74	1.41	1.22
15 000	6.34	5.64	5.26	4.87	4.23	3.37	2.91	2.64	2.36	1.91	1.49	1.25
16 000	7.16	5.96	5.32	4.93	4.49	3.75	3.03	2.67	2.41	2.06	1.62	1.29
17 000	7.58	6.60	5.54	4.97	4.58	3.99	3.19	2.71	2.44	2.13	1.70	1.33
18 000	7.66	7.12	6.08	5.12	4.65	4.24	3.57	2.82	2.46	2.18	1.80	1.39
19 000	7.72	7.26	6.54	5.44	4.73	4.32	3.84	3.00	2.54	2.24	1.88	1.44
20 000	7.76	7.30	6.79	5.89	4.89	4.38	3.91	3.30	2.68	2.34	1.99	1.56

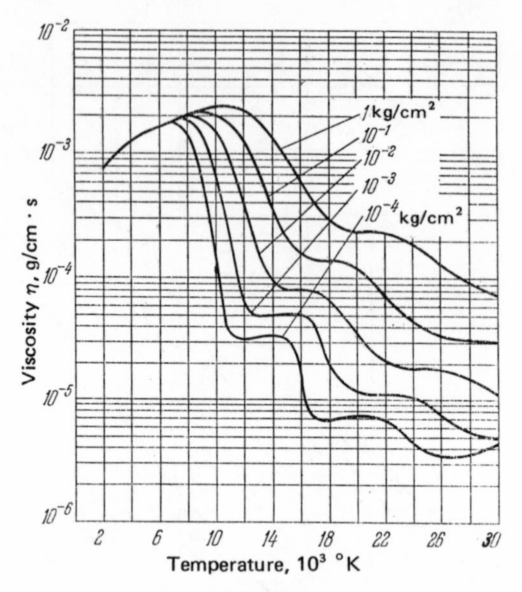

Fig. 38. Viscosity η of ionized argon as a function of temperature at different pressures.

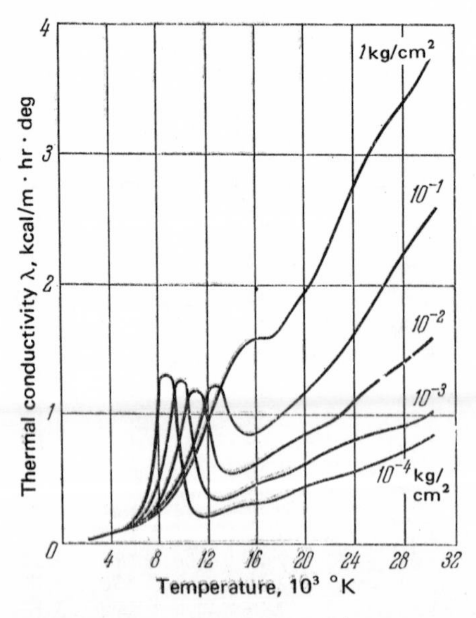

Fig. 39. Thermal conductivity of ionized argon as a function of temperature and different pressures.

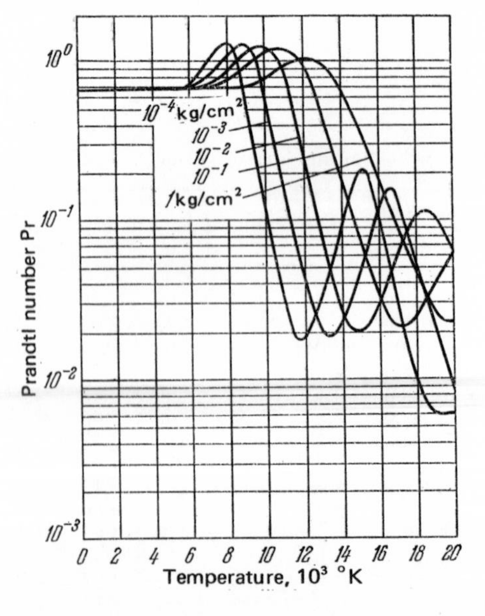

Fig. 40. Prandtl number of ionized argon as a function of temperature at different pressures.

KRYPTON (Kr)

Atomic weight 83.8

T_{boil} = 119.78 °K at 760 mmm Hg; T_{melt} = 115.76 °K;
T_{cr} = 209.4 °K; p_{cr} = 54.9 bar; ρ_{cr} = 911 kg/m³

Thermodynamic properties of saturated krypton [398] : ρ (kg/m³) and r (kJ/kg)

T, °K	p, bar	ρ′	ρ″	r	T, °K	p, bar	ρ′	ρ″	r
115.76	0.7292	2452	6.52	109.6	164	12.25	2032	91.21	86,2
116	0.7442	2450	6.64	109.5	166	13.29	2011	98.89	84,9
118	0.8785	2434	7.73	108.7	168	14.38	1990	107.1	83.6
120	1.031	2418	8.95	107.9	170	15.54	1968	115.8	82.3
122	1.202	2402	10.31	107.1	172	16.76	1945	125.1	80.9
124	1.395	2386	11.82	106.2	174	18.06	1922	135.1	79.4
126	1.610	2370	13.49	105.3	176	19.42	1897	145.9	77.8
128	1.849	2355	15.33	104.4	178	20.85	1872	157.5	76.2
130	2.114	2339	17.35	103.5	180	22.36	1846	169.9	74.5
132	2.406	2322	19.56	102.6	182	23.95	1819	183.3	72.6
134	2.728	2305	21.97	101.7	184	25.62	1791	197.8	70.7
136	3.080	2288	24.59	100.7	186	27.37	1762	213.6	68.6
138	3.465	2271	27.43	99.8	188	29.20	1731	231.0	66.3
140	3.884	2254	30.50	98.9	190	31.12	1699	250.2	63.7
142	4.339	2237	33.82	97.9	192	33.14	1666	271.6	60.9
144	4.832	2220	37.40	97.0	194	35.25	1631	295.3	58.0
146	5.364	2203	41.25	96.0	196	37.45	1593	321.4	54.9
148	5.938	2185	45.38	95.1	198	39.76	1553	350.5	51.5
150	6.556	2167	49.81	94.1	200	42.17	1508	383.9	47.8
152	7.218	2149	54.56	93.1	202	44.68	1456	423.9	43.4
154	7.928	2130	59.66	92.1	204	47.31	1395	474.2	38.1
156	8.687	2111	65.13	91.0	206	50.05	1317	540.1	31.5
158	9.497	2092	71.00	89.9	208	52.91	1209	632.5	22.9
160	10.36	2073	77.29	88.7	209.39	54.97	911.0	911.0	0

Thermodynamic properties of krypton at different temperatures and pressures [159]: ρ (kg/m³), i (kJ/kg), s and c_p (kJ/kg · deg)

p, bar	ρ	i	s	c_p	ρ	i	s	c_p
	T=250 °K				T=260 °K			
1	4.045	195.0	1.9135	0.2499	3.889	197.5	1.9231	0.2498
2	8.121	194.8	1.8439	0.2519	7.802	197.3	1.8537	0.2515
3	12.12	194.5	1.8030	0.2539	11.74	197.0	1.8128	0.2533
4	16.36	194.2	1.7737	0.2559	15.70	196.8	1.7835	0.2551
5	20.52	193.9	1.7508	0.2580	19.70	196.5	1.7607	0.2569
10	41.83	192.5	1.6781	0.2687	40.04	195.2	1.6885	0.2664
20	87.07	189.6	1.6011	0.2934	82.91	194.2	1.6124	0.2877
30	136.4	186.4	1.5521	0.3232	129.0	189.6	1.5644	0.3128
40	190.6	183.1	1.5139	0.3600	179.0	186.6	1.5275	0.3426
50	250.8	179.5	1.4813	0.4062	233.4	183.4	1.4965	0.3784
60	318.5	175.6	1.4516	0.4655	292.9	180.0	1.4688	0.4216
70	395.2	171.4	1.4236	0.5423	358.3	176.5	1.4433	0.4739
80	482.8	166.9	1.3963	0.6412	430.4	172.7	1.4191	0.5363
90	582.5	162.0	1.3694	0.7620	509.5	168.8	1.3959	0.6086
100	693.0	157.0	1.3431	0.8894	595.2	164.8	1.3734	0.6866
150	1168	139.3	1.2507	0.8776	1023	147.9	1.2842	0.8311
200	1395	133.2	1.2109	0.6953	1283	140.2	1.2380	0.6951
300	1622	129.6	1.1701	0.5663	1543	135.2	1.1921	0.5617
400	1756	129.3	1.1452	0.5163	1692	134.4	1.1651	0.5086
500	1853	130.2	1.1267	0.4890	1797	135.0	1.1455	0.4800
600	1929	131.7	1.1117	0.4714	1878	136.4	1.1299	0.4618
800	2046	135.9	1.0881	0.4491	2003	140.3	1.1053	0.4393
1000	2136	140.8	1.0694	0.4348	2097	145.0	1.0861	0.4252

continued

p, bar	ϱ	i	s	c_p	ϱ	i	s	c_p
	$T=270$ °K				$T=280$ °K			
1	3.743	200.0	1.9324	0.2496	3.808	202.5	1.9415	0.2494
2	7.508	199.8	1.8631	0.2512	7.235	202.3	1.8722	0.2508
3	11.29	199.6	1.8222	0.2527	10.88	202.1	1.8314	0.2523
4	15.10	199.3	1.7931	0.2543	14.54	201.9	1.8023	0.2537
5	18.93	199.1	1.7703	0.2560	18.22	201.6	1.7786	0.2552
10	38.41	197.8	1.6984	0.2644	36.92	200.5	1.7079	0.2628
20	79.19	195.3	1.6231	0.2831	75.82	198.1	1.6333	0.2793
30	122 6	192.7	1.5759	0.3046	116.9	195.7	1.5868	0.2979
40	169.0	189.9	1.5401	0.3294	160.4	193.1	1.5518	0.3189
50	218.8	187.1	1.5103	0.3581	206.5	190.6	1.5230	0.3427
60	272.4	184.1	1.4841	0.3915	255.5	187.9	1.4978	0.3695
70	330.1	181.0	1.4602	0.4301	307.6	185.1	1.4752	0.3996
80	392.3	177.8	1.4380	0.4742	362.7	182.3	1.4544	0.4330
90	459.0	174.4	1.4170	0.5434	421.1	179.4	1.4349	1.4692
100	530.0	171.1	1.3970	0.5760	482.3	176.5	1.4166	0.5075
150	902.9	155.8	1.3140	0.7457	807.9	162.8	1.3395	0.6604
200	1176	147.1	1.2640	0.6809	1077	153.7	1.2882	0.6527
300	1465	140.8	1.2131	0.5574	1389	146.4	1.2333	0.5518
400	1628	139.4	1.1841	0.5028	1566	144.5	1.2023	0.4979
500	1741	139.8	1.1634	0.4733	1687	144.5	1.1805	0.4680
600	1828	141.0	1.1471	0.4547	1779	145.5	1.1634	0.4491
800	1960	144.7	1.1217	0.4319	1918	149.0	1.1372	0.4262
1000	2059	149.3	1.1019	0.4181	2022	153.4	1.1170	0.4126
	$T=290$ °K				$T=300$ °K			
1	3.483	205.0	1.9502	0.2493	3.366	207.5	1.9587	0.2492
2	6.982	204.8	1.8810	0.2506	6.746	207.3	1.8895	0.2504
3	10.50	204.6	1.8402	0.2519	10.14	207.1	1.8488	0.2516
4	14.03	204.4	1.8112	0.2532	13.55	206.9	1.8198	0.2527
5	17.57	204.2	1.7885	0.2545	16.97	206.7	1.7972	0.2539
10	35.55	203.1	1.7171	0.2614	34.28	205.7	1.7260	0.2601
20	72.77	200.9	1.6430	0.2761	69.98	203.6	1.6523	0.2733
30	111.8	198.6	1.5972	0.2924	107.2	201.5	1.6071	0.2878
40	152.8	196.3	1.5629	0.3105	146.0	199.4	1.5733	0.3036
50	195.9	193.9	1.5348	0.3306	186.5	197.2	1.5458	0.3209
60	241.2	191.5	1.5105	0.3528	228.8	194.9	1.5223	0.3396
70	288.8	189.0	1.4888	0.3771	272.9	192.7	1.5014	0.3598
80	338.8	186.4	1.4691	0.4035	318.7	190.4	1.4824	0.3814
90	391.0	183.9	1.4507	0.4316	366.2	188.0	1.4649	0.4041
100	445.3	181.3	1.4335	0.4611	415.4	185.7	1.4486	0.4276
150	733.5	169.0	1.3614	0.5904	674.3	174.6	1.3805	0.5359
200	990.5	160.1	1.3105	0.6160	915.4	166.1	1.3308	0.5773
300	1316	151.9	1.2525	0.5440	1247	157.3	1.2708	0.5336
400	1504	149.4	1.2197	0.4930	1454	154.3	1.2363	0.4877
500	1633	149.2	1.1968	0.4633	1581	153.8	1.2125	0.4590
600	1731	150.0	1.1791	0.4444	1684	154.4	1.1942	0.4402
800	1877	153.2	1.1521	0.4216	1836	157.4	1.1664	0.4176
1000	1985	157.5	1.1314	0.4081	1949	161.6	1.1452	0.4043
	$T=350$ °K				$T=400$ °K			
1	2.883	220.0	1.9975	0.2488	2.521	232.4	2.0310	0.2486
2	5.772	219.8	1.9284	0.2496	5.046	232.3	1.9620	0.2491
3	8.669	219.7	1.8879	0.2504	7.574	232.2	1.9216	0.2497
4	11.57	219.5	1.8590	0.2512	10.10	232.0	1.8928	0.2502
5	14.48	219.3	1.8366	0.2519	12.64	231.9	1.8704	0.2508
10	29.13	218.6	1.7662	0.2560	25.36	231.3	1.8005	0.2536
20	58.92	217.1	1.6941	0.2643	51.04	230.1	1.7294	0.2594
30	89.38	215.5	1.6506	0.2730	77.04	228.9	1.6868	0.2653
40	120.5	214.0	1.6187	0.2821	103.3	227.8	1.6559	0.2713
50	152.3	212.4	1.5932	0.2917	129.9	226.6	1.6315	0.2774
60	184.7	210.8	1.5718	0.3015	156.7	225.4	1.6110	0.2837
70	217.7	209.3	1.5531	0.3117	183.8	224.3	1.5931	0.2900
80	251.3	207.7	1.5364	0.3221	211.0	223.1	1.5773	0.2964

continued

p, bar	ϱ	i	s	c_p	ϱ	i	s	c_p
90	285.5	206.2	1.5213	0.3327	238.5	222.0	1.5639	0.3028
100	320.1	204.6	1.5075	0.3434	266.0	220.8	1.5511	0.3092
150	496.9	197.3	1.4509	0.3950	404.8	215.5	1.4999	0.3399
200	671.0	190.9	1.4082	0.4345	541.3	210.7	1.4615	0.3662
300	968.8	182.2	1.3482	0.4609	790.0	203.5	1.4057	0.3978
400	1186	177.8	1.3094	0.4504	993.4	199.2	1.3669	0.4062
500	1345	176.1	1.2819	0.4343	1155	197.1	1.3392	0.4037
600	1467	175.9	1.2610	0.4206	1284	196.4	1.3160	0.3977
800	1646	177.8	1.2299	0.4014	1481	197.5	1.2828	0.3855
1000	1778	181.4	1.2068	0.3896	1626	200.6	1.2583	0.3763
		$T=450$ °K				$T=500$ °K		
1	2.240	244.8	2.0603	0,2484	2.016	257.2	2.0863	0.2483
2	4.483	244.7	1.9913	0.2489	4.033	257.2	2.0174	0.2487
3	6.726	244.6	1.9509	0.2493	6.050	257.1	1.9770	0.2490
4	8.972	244.5	1.9222	0.2497	8.068	257.0	1.9483	0.2493
5	11.22	244.4	1.8999	0.2501	10.09	256.9	1.9260	0.2496
10	22.48	244.0	1.8303	0.2522	20.19	256.9	1.8566	0.2512
20	45.10	243.0	1.7597	0.2564	40.44	255.8	1.7864	0.2544
30	67.86	242.1	1.7178	0.2606	60.73	255.0	1.7449	0.2577
40	90.75	241.2	1.6875	0.2650	81.07	254.3	1.7150	0.2609
50	113.7	240.2	1.6636	0.2693	101.4	253.6	1.6915	0.2641
60	136.8	239.3	1.6438	0.2737	121.8	252.8	1.6721	0.2674
70	160.0	238.4	1.6268	0.2780	142.2	252.1	1.6555	0.2706
80	183.2	237.5	1.6119	0.2824	162.6	251.4	1.6409	0.2738
90	206.5	236.7	1.5985	0.2868	182.9	250.7	1.6280	0.2770
100	229.8	235.8	1.5864	0.2911	203.3	250.1	1.6162	0.2802
150	345.9	231.7	1.5382	0.3119	304.1	246.9	1.5699	0.2953
200	459.7	228.1	1.5023	0.3302	402.5	244.0	1.5357	0.3089
300	671.5	222.3	1.4500	0.3566	587.6	239.5	1.4859	0.3300
400	854.7	218.6	1.4125	0.3697	752.4	236.4	1.4498	0.3430
500	1008	216.5	1.3840	0.3741	895.6	234.6	1.4219	0.3498
600	1137	215.7	1.3614	0.3739	1019	233.8	1 3995	0.3527
800	1339	216.4	1.3272	0.3689	1220	234.4	1.3650	0.3527
1000	1492	219.1	1.3018	0.3630	1376	236.9	1.3392	0.3500
		$T=600$ °K				$T=700$ °K		
1	1.680	282.1	2.1311	0.2482	1.440	306.9	2.1691	0.2482
2	3.359	282.0	2.0622	0.2484	2.879	306.9	2.1003	0.2483
3	5.039	282.0	2.0219	0.2486	4.318	306.8	2.0600	0.2485
4	6.718	281.9	1.9932	0.2489	5.756	306.8	2.0314	0.2486
5	8.397	281.9	1.9710	0.2491	7.194	306.7	2.0092	0.2487
10	16.79	281.6	1.9018	0.2501	14.38	306.6	1.9401	0.2495
20	33.56	281.1	1.8321	0.2521	28.71	306.3	1.8707	0.2509
30	50.30	280.6	1.7910	0.2542	42.99	305.9	1.8299	0.2523
40	67.01	280.1	1.7616	0.2562	57.22	305.6	1.8007	0.2537
50	83.68	279.7	1.7386	0.2582	71.39	305.3	1.7780	0.2550
60	100.3	279.2	1.7196	0.2602	85.51	305.0	1.7593	0.2564
70	116.9	278.7	1.7035	0.2622	99.57	304.7	1.7434	0.2578
80	133.4	278.3	1.6894	0.2642	113.6	304.4	1.7295	0.2591
90	149.9	277.8	1.6769	0.2661	127.5	304.1	1.7173	0.2604
100	166.3	277.4	1.6656	0.2680	141.4	303.9	1.7063	0.2617
150	247.3	275.4	1.6215	0.2772	209.7	302.6	1.6679	0.2679
200	326.0	273.6	1.5893	0.2856	276.0	301.5	1.6321	0.2736
300	475.3	270.7	1.5425	0.2995	402.4	299.8	1.5872	0.2835
400	612.0	268.8	1.5086	0.3097	519.6	298.8	1.5546	0.2911
500	735.4	267.4	1.4820	0.3167	627.4	298.4	1.5291	0.2970
600	846.1	267.4	1.4603	0.3212	726.2	298.4	1.5081	0.3013
800	1034	268.3	1.4264	0.3258	899.8	299.9	1.4749	0.3068
1000	1188	270.7	1.4004	0.3272	1045	302.5	1.4493	0.3096
		$T=800$ °K				$T=900$ °K		
1	1.260	331.7	2.2024	0.2481	1.120	356.5	2.2320	0.2481
2	2.519	331.7	2.1336	0.2482	2.239	356.5	2.1632	0.2482
3	3.777	331.7	2.0933	0.2483	3.357	356.5	2.1229	0.2483

continued

p, bar	ϱ	i	s	c_p	ϱ	i	s	c_p
4	5.035	331.6	2.0647	0.2485	4.475	356.5	2.0943	0.2484
5	6.293	331.6	2.0426	0.2486	5.593	356.5	2.0721	0.2484
10	12.57	331.5	1.9736	0.2491	11.17	356.4	2.0032	0.2488
20	25.09	331.3	1.9043	0.2501	22.30	356.3	1.9341	0.2496
30	37.56	331.1	1.8636	0.2511	33.37	356.2	1.8935	0.2504
40	49.97	330.9	1.8346	0.2522	44.38	356.1	1.8646	0.2512
50	62.33	330.7	1.8120	0.2532	55.35	356.0	1.8421	0.2519
60	74.63	330.5	1.7935	0.2541	66.26	355.9	1.8237	0.2527
70	86.87	330.3	1.7778	0.2551	77.12	355.8	1.8080	0.2534
80	99.05	330.2	1.7641	0.2561	87.92	355.7	1.7945	0.2542
90	111.2	330.0	1.7520	0.2570	98.67	355.6	1.7824	0.2549
100	123.2	329.8	1.7411	0.2580	109.3	355.5	1.7716	0.2556
150	182.6	329.1	1.6988	0.2625	162.0	355.2	1.7298	0.2590
200	240.2	328.5	1.6683	0.2667	213.1	354.9	1.6998	0.2622
300	350.4	327.7	1.6245	0.2740	311.1	354.7	1.6568	0.2679
400	453.4	327.3	1.5929	0.2799	403.2	354.9	1.6257	0.2726
500	549.3	327.4	1.5680	0.2847	489.7	355.4	1.6014	0.2765
600	638.2	327.9	1.5475	0.2884	570.6	356.3	1.5813	0.2797
800	797.2	329.8	1.5161	0.2936	717.2	358.7	1.5494	0.2844
1000	934.3	332.8	1.4899	0.2968	845.8	362.0	1.5246	0.2875
		$T=1000\,°K$				$T=1100\,°K$		
1	1.008	381.3	2.2584	0.2481	0.9161	406.1	2.2823	0.2481
2	2.015	381.3	2.1896	0.2482	1.832	406.1	2.2135	0.2481
3	3.021	381.3	2.1494	0.2482	2.747	406.1	2.1732	0.2482
4	4.028	381.3	2.1208	0.2483	3.662	406.1	2.1447	0.2482
5	5.033	381.3	2.0986	0 2483	4.576	401.1	2.1225	0.2483
10	10.05	381.3	2.0297	0.2487	9.141	406.1	2.0536	0.2489
20	20.06	381.2	1.9607	0.2493	18.24	406.1	1.9846	0.2490
30	30.02	381.2	1.9202	0.2499	27.29	406.2	1.9441	0.2495
40	39.93	381.2	1.8913	0.2505	36.30	406.2	1.9154	0.2500
50	49.79	381.1	1.8689	0.2511	45.27	406.2	1.8930	0.2505
60	56.61	381.1	1.8506	0.2517	54.19	406.2	1.8747	0.2510
70	69.37	381.1	1.8350	0.2523	63.07	406.2	1.8592	0.2515
80	79.09	381.0	1.8215	0.2529	71.90	406.3	1.8457	0.2519
90	88.75	381.0	1.8095	0.2534	80.69	406.3	1.8338	0.2524
100	98.37	381.0	1.7988	0.2540	89.43	406.3	1.8231	0.2528
150	145.7	380.9	1.7573	0.2567	132.5	406.5	1.7819	0.2550
200	191.8	381.0	1.7275	0.2592	174.5	406.8	1.7523	0.2571
300	280.2	381.3	1.6851	0.2637	255.2	407.5	1.7102	0.2608
400	363.7	381.9	1.6545	0.2676	331.7	408.5	1.6800	0.2640
500	442.5	382.8	1.6305	0.2709	404.2	409.7	1.6563	0.2668
600	516.8	383.9	1.6108	0.2736	472.8	411.0	1.6368	0.2691
800	652.7	386.8	1.5794	0.2777	599.4	414.3	1.6058	0.2728
1000	773.4	390.4	1.5549	0.2807	713.1	418.2	1.5816	0.2755
		$T=1200\,°K$				$T=1300\,°K$		
1	0.8397	430.9	2.3038	0.2481	0.7751	455.8	2.3235	0.2481
2	1.679	430.9	2.2351	0.2481	1.550	455.8	2.2547	0.2481
3	2.518	431.0	2.1948	0.2482	2.324	455.8	2.2144	0.2481
4	3.356	431.0	2.1662	0.2482	3.098	455.8	2.1859	0.2482
5	4.195	431.0	2.1441	0.2482	3.872	455.8	2.1637	0.2482
10	8.379	431.0	2.0752	0.2484	7.735	455.8	2.0949	0.2484
20	16.72	431.0	2.0063	0.2489	15.43	455.9	2.0259	0.2487
30	25.02	431.1	1.9658	0.2493	23.10	456.0	1.9855	0.2491
40	33.28	431.2	1.9371	0.2497	30.73	456.1	1.9568	0.2494
50	41.50	431.2	1.9148	0.2501	38.32	456.2	1.9345	0.2497
60	49.68	431.3	1.8965	0.2505	45.87	456.3	1.9163	0.2501
70	57.82	431.3	1.8810	0.2509	53.40	456.4	1.9009	0,2504
80	65.93	431.4	1.8676	0.2512	60.88	456.5	1.8874	0.2507
90	73.99	431.5	1.8557	0.2516	68.33	456.6	1.8756	0.2510
100	82.01	431.6	1.8451	0.2520	75.75	456.7	1.8650	0.2514
150	121.5	432.0	1.8040	0.2538	112.3	457.3	1.8240	0.2529
200	160.1	432.4	1.7746	0.2555	148.0	457.9	1.7948	0.2543

continued

p, bar	ϱ	i	s	c_p	ϱ	i	s	c_p
300	239.4	433.5	1.7328	0.2586	216.9	459.3	1.7532	0.2570
400	305.1	434.7	1.7028	0.2613	282.6	460.8	1.7234	0.2593
500	372.2	436.2	1.6794	0.2637	345.2	462.4	1.7001	0.2613
600	436.1	437.8	1.6601	0.2657	405.0	464.2	1.6810	0.2631
800	554.6	441.4	1.6293	0.2690	516.4	468.1	1.6505	0.2661
1000	662.0	445.5	1.6053	0.2715	618.1	472.5	1.6267	0.2683

Viscosity of krypton gas at $p = 1$ bar [49, 363, 364]

T, °K	293.2	300	400	500	600	700	800	900	1000	1100	1200	1300	1400	1500	1600
$\eta \cdot 10^7$, N · s/m	251	256	331	397	457	512	547	598	646	693	738	782	824	865	905

Thermal conductivity λ (W/m · deg) of krypton gas at $p = 1$ bar [377]

T, °K	$\lambda \cdot 10^4$	T, °K	$\lambda \cdot 10^4$	T, °K	$\lambda \cdot 10^4$	T, °K	$\lambda \cdot 10^4$
125	42.0	400	124	700	196	1000	258
175	58.5	450	137	750	207	1050	267
225	72.0	500	149	800	218	1100	275
273	88.5	550	162	850	228	1150	284
300	97	600	174	900	238	1200	292
350	111	650	185	950	248	1300	307

Thermal conductivity of saturated krypton [368]

T, °K	120	130	140	150	160	170	180	190	195	200
$\lambda' \cdot 10^3$, W/m · deg	90.5	83.9	77.3	70.8	64.2	57.6	51.0	44.4	40.8	36.6
$\lambda'' \cdot 10^3$, W/m · deg	4.06	4.52	5.01	5.54	6.2	7.0	7.9	9.3	10.1	11.2

Thermal conductivity λ (W/m · deg) of krypton at different temperatures and pressures [15, 378]

T, °K	p, bar	$\lambda \cdot 10^3$	T, °K	p, bar	$\lambda \cdot 10^3$	T, °K	p, bar	$\lambda \cdot 10^3$
125.46	25.5	88.0	150.35	304.7	85.7	200.30	203.3	54.3
125.46	50.9	88.9	150.32	406	90.0	200.28	304	60.9
125.45	101	91.2	150.32	507.3	93.6	200.29	406	66.3
125.45	202.7	95.2	175.34	25.8	54.2	200.28	506.6	71.0
125.45	303.3	98.7	175.34	51.7	56.5	235.43	50.3	10.7
125.47	306.7	99.0	175.34	100.8	60.4	235.44	76.2	17.0
125.54	337.7	102.7	175.32	203.3	67.2	235.46	101.3	27.5
125.62	407.7	131	175.34	305.7	72.7	235.45	131.5	32.2
125.60	507.3	133	175.26	406.7	77.6	235.47	202.7	39.6
150.35	25.8	71.1	175.25	506.6	82.0	235.46	306.7	47.2
150.35	50.6	73.7	200.26	51.1	41.2	235.47	405	52.9
150.35	101.5	75.7	200.28	101.5	46.2	235.50	505.3	58.1
150.35	204	81.0						

XENON (Xe)

Atomic weight 131.3
$T_{boil} = 160.05$ °K at 760 mm Hg; $T_{melt} = 161.3$ °K;
$T_{cr} = 289.7$ °K; $p_{cr} = 58.3$ bar; $\rho_{cr} = 1110$ kg/m³

Thermodynamic properties of saturated xenon [398]: ρ (kg/m³) and r (kJ/kg)

T, °K	p, bar	ϱ′	ϱ″	r	T, °K	p, bar	ϱ′	ϱ″	r
161.36	0.8159	2985	8.20	96.98	226	12.58	2485	105.5	77.42
162	0.8480	2980	8.50	96.76	228	13.35	2467	111.9	76.63
164	0.9546	2964	9.47	96.29	230	14.15	2449	118.6	75.80
166	1.071	2948	10.53	95.80	232	14.99	2431	125.7	74.92
168	1.199	2932	11.68	95.30	234	15.87	2411	133.3	73.99
170	1.337	2917	12.90	94.79	236	16.78	2391	141.2	73.00
172	1.488	2902	14.23	94.27	238	17.72	2372	149.6	71.96
174	1.651	2886	15.66	93.74	240	18.71	2352	158.5	70.88
176	1.827	2871	17.19	93.20	242	19.73	2330	167.9	69.75
178	2.017	2857	18.83	92.65	244	20.79	2308	177.8	68.59
180	2.222	2841	20.59	92.09	246	21.90	2286	188.3	67.38
182	2.442	2826	22.47	91.52	248	23.04	2263	199.3	66.18
184	2.678	2812	24.47	90.95	250	24.23	2241	210.9	64.92
186	2.930	2797	26.59	90.38	252	25.46	2217	223.1	63.65
188	3.200	2782	28.84	89.81	254	26.74	2197	235.9	62.38
190	3.487	2768	31.24	89.24	256	28.06	2173	249.4	61.07
192	3.794	2753	33.78	88.66	258	29.43	2148	263.8	59.68
194	4.119	2738	36.47	88.07	260	30.84	2120	279.3	58.18
196	4.465	2725	39.32	87.48	262	32.31	2093	296.0	56.57
198	4.832	2710	42.34	86.88	264	33.82	2062	314.0	54.85
200	5.220	2695	45.51	86.27	266	35.39	2035	333.4	53.06
202	5.631	2680	48.86	85.65	268	37.00	2002	354.3	51.16
204	6.064	2664	52.40	85.01	270	38.68	1970	376.8	49.18
206	6.522	2650	56.13	84.37	272	40.40	1934	401.1	47.10
208	7.004	2635	60.05	83.72	274	42.18	1895	427.6	44.88
210	7.511	2620	64.17	83.07	276	44.01	1855	456.9	42.49
212	8.045	2605	68.50	82.41	278	45.91	1812	489.8	39.87
214	8.605	2589	73.05	81.74	280	47.87	1764	527.4	36.95
216	9.194	2573	77.83	81.05	282	49.88	1711	571.1	33.68
218	9.810	2557	82.85	80.35	284	51.96	1650	622.7	29.96
220	10.46	2540	88.12	79.63	286	54.10	1573	686.0	25.56
222	11.13	2522	93.65	78.90	288	56.31	1475	783.1	19.33
224	11.84	2503	99.45	78.17	289.74	58.28	1100	1100	0

Thermodynamic properties of xenon [159]: ρ (kg/m³), i (kJ/kg), s and c_p (kJ/kg · deg)

p, bar	ϱ	i	s	c_p	ϱ	i	s	c_p
	T=290 °K				T=300 °K			
1	5.476	166.6	1.2871	0.1601	5.290	168.2	1.2925	0.1599
2	11.01	166.3	1.2426	0.1620	10.63	167.9	1.2480	0.1616
3	16.61	166.0	1.2162	0.1639	16.03	167.6	1.2217	0.1633
4	22.28	165.7	1.1973	0.1660	21.49	167.4	1.2029	0.1651
5	28.02	165.4	1.1825	0.1680	27.01	167.1	1.1881	0.1669
10	57.81	163.8	1.1349	0.1796	55.54	165.6	1.1409	0.1771
20	124.2	160.2	1.0825	0.2111	118.3	162.3	1.0895	0.2037
30	203.8	156.0	1.0462	0.2620	191.3	158.5	1.0548	0.2436
40	306.1	150.7	1.0142	0.3581	280.2	154.0	1.0254	0.3089
50	459.2	143.3	0.9793	0.6189	397.0	148.4	0.9966	0.4347
60	1526	108.3	0.8530	2.0774	576.5	140.5	0.9632	0.7753
70	1714	104.1	0.8366	0.9089	1040	124.0	0.9036	3.4863
80	1805	102.3	0.8285	0.7076	1518	111.3	0.8588	1.2124
90	1868	101.2	0.8227	0.6145	1658	108.2	0.8464	0.8188
100	1918	100.4	0.8181	0.5588	1744	106.5	0.8387	0.6740
150	2081	98.36	0.8025	0.4408	1971	102.9	0.8178	0.4640
200	2184	97.68	0.7921	0.3960	2096	101.7	0.8056	0.4034

continued

p, bar	ϱ	i	s	c_p	ϱ	i	s	c_p
300	2325	97.80	0.7772	0.3558	2257	101.3	0.7892	0.3538
400	2426	98.79	0.7662	0.3367	2368	102.1	0.7774	0.3314
500	2505	100.2	0.7571	0.3256	2453	103.4	0.7680	0.3184
600	2572	101.9	0.7494	0.3184	2524	105.0	0.7600	0.3100
800	2680	105.8	0.7365	0.3100	2638	108.8	0.7468	0.2999
1000	2767	110.0	0.7258	0.3056	2730	113.0	0.7359	0.2942
		T=310 °K				T=320 °K		
1	5.117	169.8	1.2978	0.1598	4.956	171.4	1.3028	0.1596
2	10.28	169.6	1.2533	0.1613	9.953	171.2	1.2584	0.1610
3	15.50	169.3	1.2271	0.1628	14.99	170.9	1.2322	0.1624
4	20.76	169.0	1.2083	0.1644	20.08	170.6	1.2135	0.1638
5	26.07	168.7	1.1936	0.1660	25.20	170.4	1.1988	0.1653
10	53.46	167.4	1.1466	0.1750	51.55	169.1	1.1522	0.1733
20	113.0	164.3	1.0960	0.1978	108.3	166.3	1.1022	0.1930
30	180.8	160.9	1.0625	0.2301	171.8	163.1	1.0696	0.2198
40	260.4	157.0	1.0350	0.2783	244.4	159.6	1.0434	0.2572
50	357.9	152.3	1.0094	0.3565	329.6	155.6	1.0200	0.3119
60	485.8	146.6	0.9832	0.5004	433.2	151.0	0.9972	0.3966
70	673.4	139.0	0.9529	0.8219	565.4	145.5	0.9736	0.5360
80	989.0	128.1	0.9140	1.5373	742.3	138.8	0.9479	0.7690
90	1332	118.6	0.8803	1.2855	975.3	131.1	0.9201	1.0489
100	1512	114.2	0.8641	0.8935	1214	124.2	0.8959	1.0497
150	1851	107.7	0.8335	0.4960	1719	112.8	0.8498	0.5347
200	2004	105.8	0.8190	0.4143	1908	110.0	0.8323	0.4276
300	2188	104.9	0.8008	0.3542	2118	108.4	0.8121	0.3562
400	2309	105.4	0.7882	0.3284	2250	108.7	0.7986	0.3271
500	2401	106.6	0.7783	0.3138	2350	109.7	0.7882	0.3108
600	2477	108.1	0.7700	0.3043	2430	111.1	0.7796	0.3004
800	2598	111.8	0.7564	0.2928	2557	114.7	0.7656	0.2877
1000	2693	115.9	0.7454	0.2860	2657	118.8	0.7543	0.2801
		T=330 °K				T=340 °K		
1	4.804	173.0	1.3077	0.1595	4.661	174.6	1.3125	0.1594
2	9.664	172.8	1.2634	0.1607	9.354	174.4	1.2682	0.1605
3	14.52	172.5	1.2372	0.1620	14.08	174.2	1.2421	0.1617
4	19.44	172.3	1.2185	0.1633	18.84	173.9	1.2234	0.1629
5	24.39	172.0	1.2039	0.1646	23.64	173.7	1.2088	0.1653
10	49.79	170.8	1.1575	0.1718	48.15	172.5	1.1626	0.1705
20	104.0	168.2	1.1081	0.1891	100.2	170.0	1.1137	0.1859
30	163.9	165.3	1.0763	0.2118	156.9	167.4	1.0825	0.2053
40	230.9	162.1	1.0511	0.2419	219.4	164.5	1.0582	0.2302
50	307.3	158.6	1.0291	0.2829	289.2	161.3	1.0372	0.2624
60	396.3	154.7	1.0085	0.3403	368.0	157.9	1.0181	0.3046
70	502.3	150.2	0.9882	0.4223	458.2	154.1	0.9998	0.3601
80	631.3	145.2	0.9675	0.5388	562.6	150.0	0.9818	0.4321
90	788.5	139.5	0.9461	0.6882	683.3	145.5	0.9639	0.5205
100	969.2	133.7	0.9251	0.8194	820.0	140.8	0.9462	0.6140
150	1575	118.4	0.8669	0.5725	1427	124.2	0.8843	0.5927
200	1807	114.3	0.8457	0.4417	1704	118.8	0.8591	0.4542
300	2046	112.0	0.8231	0.3589	1974	115.6	0.8339	0.3619
400	2191	112.0	0.8087	0.3267	2132	115.2	0.8185	0.3269
500	2298	112.8	0.7978	0.3091	2246	115.9	0.8070	0.3080
600	2383	114.1	0.7888	0.2978	2337	117.1	0.7977	0.2960
800	2516	117.5	0.7745	0.2841	2476	120.4	0.7829	0.2815
1000	2620	121.5	0.7629	0.2759	2585	124.3	0.7712	0.2729
		T=350 °K				T=400 °K		
1	4.526	176.2	1.3172	0.1593	3.956	184.2	1.3386	0.1590
2	9.082	176.0	1.2729	0.1603	7.929	184.0	1.2944	0.1597
3	13.66	175.8	1.2468	0.1614	11.92	183.8	1.2684	0.1604
4	18.28	175.6	1.2281	0.1625	15.92	183.6	1.2499	0.1612
5	22.93	175.3	1.2136	0.1636	19.95	183.5	1.2355	0.1619
10	46.63	174.2	1.1676	0.1694	40.33	182.6	1.1901	0.1658

continued

p, bar	ϱ	i	s	c_p	ϱ	i	s	c_p
20	96.62	171.9	1.1191	0.1831	82.45	180.8	1.1430	0.1743
30	150.6	169.4	1.0884	0.2000	126.5	178.9	1.1141	0.1839
40	209.4	166.7	1.0647	0.2210	172.7	177.0	1.0924	0.1948
50	273.8	163.9	1.0446	0.2472	221.1	175.1	1.0747	0.2071
60	345.1	160.8	1.0265	0.2799	271.9	173.0	1.0594	0.2207
70	424.6	157.5	1.0096	0.3206	325.2	171.0	1.0458	0.2358
80	513.7	154.0	0.9934	0.3705	381.2	168.8	1.0334	0.2522
90	613.4	150.2	0.9776	0.4294	439.6	166.6	1.0219	0.2698
100	723.8	146.3	0.9622	0.4935	500.6	164.4	1.0111	0.2883
150	1283	130.1	0.9015	0.5812	830.4	153.8	0.9652	0.3747
200	1589	123.4	0.8724	0.4624	1141	145.6	0.9319	0.4020
300	1902	119.2	0.8444	0.3646	1550	137.5	0.8933	0.3596
400	2073	118.5	0.8280	0.3272	1785	134.8	0.8717	0.3244
500	2195	119.0	0.8159	0.3073	1945	134.3	0.8569	0.3034
600	2290	120.0	0.8063	0.2947	2065	134.7	0.8455	0.2899
800	2437	123.2	0.7911	0.2796	2244	137.0	0.8281	0.2738
1000	2749	127.0	0.7790	0.2707	2376	140.4	0.8149	0.2646
		T=450 °K				T=500 °K		
1	3.514	192.1	1.3573	0.1588	3.161	200.0	1.3741	0.1587
2	7.038	192.0	1.3132	0.1593	6.329	199.9	1.3300	0.1591
3	10.57	191.8	1.2873	0.1599	9.503	199.8	1.3042	0.1595
4	14.12	191.7	1.2689	0.1604	12.68	199.7	1.2858	0.1599
5	17.67	191.5	1.2445	0.1609	15.87	199.6	1.2715	0.1603
10	35.60	190.8	1.2095	0.1637	31.89	199.0	1.2267	0.1624
20	72.21	189.4	1.1633	0.1700	64.38	197.8	1.1810	0.1667
30	109.9	187.9	1.1353	0.1759	97.47	196.6	1.1536	0.1713
40	148.6	186.4	1.1147	0.1828	131.2	195.4	1.1335	0.1761
50	188.5	185.0	1.0981	0.1902	165.4	194.4	1.1176	0.1811
60	229.4	183.4	1.0840	0.1980	200.2	193.0	1.1042	0.1863
70	271.4	181.9	1.0717	0.2062	235.6	191.8	1.0926	0.1917
80	314.5	180.4	1.0607	0.2148	271.4	190.6	1.0823	0.1972
90	358.6	178.8	1.0507	0.2238	307.7	189.4	1.0730	0.2027
100	403.6	177.3	1.0414	0.2330	344.4	188.2	1.0645	0.2084
150	638.8	169.8	1.0030	0.2785	532.2	182.5	1.0299	0.2365
200	874.2	163.2	0.9737	0.3115	720.2	177.4	1.0036	0.2602
300	1263	154.6	0.9338	0.3230	1058	169.8	0.9657	0.2833
400	1528	150.7	0.9092	0.3076	1320	165.5	0.9404	0.2834
500	1715	149.2	0.8922	0.2928	1518	163.4	0.9222	0.2768
600	1857	149.0	0.8793	0.2817	1671	162.8	0.9084	0.2698
800	2064	150.5	0.8601	0.2673	1899	163.7	0.8878	0.2589
1000	2215	153.4	0.8485	0.2589	2066	166.2	0.8727	0.2519
		T=600 °K				T=700 °K		
1	2.633	215.9	1.4028	0.1586	2.257	213.8	1.4272	0.1585
2	5.268	215.8	1.3588	0.1588	4.513	231.7	1.3832	0.1587
3	7.906	215.7	1.3330	0.1591	6.771	231.6	1.3575	0.1588
4	10.55	215.6	1.3147	0.1594	9.029	231.6	1.3392	0.1590
5	13.19	215.6	1.3005	0.1596	11.29	231.5	1.3249	0.1592
10	26.43	215.1	1.2560	0.1609	22.59	231.2	1.2807	0.1601
20	53.08	214.3	1.2110	0.1636	45.24	230.6	1.2360	0.1620
30	79.92	213.4	1.1842	0.1664	67.94	230.0	1.2095	0.1638
40	106.9	212.6	1.1648	0.1692	90.68	229.4	1.1905	0.1657
50	134.1	211.8	1.1496	0.1720	113.4	228.8	1.1756	0.1675
60	161.5	211.0	1.1369	0.1748	136.2	228.2	1.1633	0.1694
70	188.9	210.2	1.1260	0.1777	159.0	227.6	1.1528	0.1712
80	216.5	209.4	1.1164	0.1806	181.8	227.0	1.1436	0.1731
90	244.2	208.6	1.1079	0.1835	204.5	226.5	1.1354	0.1749
100	271.9	207.8	1.1001	0.1864	227.3	225.9	1.1279	0.1767
150	411.0	204.1	1.0692	0.2007	340.2	223.3	1.0987	0.1855
200	548.4	200.7	1.0460	0.2135	451.0	221.0	1.0772	0.1936
300	807.1	195.2	1.0121	0.2323	661.8	217.1	1.0457	0.2068
400	1032	191.6	0.9879	0.2414	852.6	214.3	1.0229	0.2154
500	1220	189.4	0.9696	0.2441	1021	212.6	1.0051	0.2202

continued

p, bar	ϱ	i	s	c_p	ϱ	i	s	c_p
600	1378	188.4	0.9551	0.2438	1168	211.7	0.9909	0.2226
800	1623	188.7	0.9333	0.2402	1410	211.8	0.9689	0.2234
1000	1808	190.6	0.9171	0.2363	1600	213.5	0.9524	0.2223
	$T=800$ °K				$T=900$ °K			
1	1.974	247.6	1.4484	0.1584	1.754	263.4	1.4672	0.1584
2	3.948	247.6	1.4044	0.1586	3.509	263.4	1.4232	0.1585
3	5.922	247.5	1.3787	0.1587	5.262	263.4	1.3975	0.1586
4	7.896	247.4	1.3604	0.1588	7.016	263.3	1.3792	0.1587
5	9.870	247.4	1.3462	0.1590	8.769	263.3	1.3651	0.1588
10	19.74	247.2	1.3020	0.1596	17.53	263.1	1.3209	0.1593
20	39.47	246.7	1.2576	0.1610	35.02	262.8	1.2766	0.1604
30	59.19	246.2	1.2313	0.1623	52.47	262.4	1.2505	0.1614
40	78.88	245.8	1.2125	0.1636	69.88	262.1	1.2318	0.1624
50	98.55	245.4	1.1978	0.1650	87.24	261.8	1.2173	0.1633
60	118.2	244.9	1.1857	0.1663	104.5	261.5	1.2053	0.1643
70	137.8	244.5	1.1754	0.1676	121.8	261.2	1.1951	0.1653
80	157.3	244.1	1.1664	0.1689	139.0	260.8	1.1863	0.1662
90	176.8	243.7	1.1584	0.1701	156.1	260.6	1.1784	0.1672
100	196.2	243.3	1.1512	0.1714	173.2	260.3	1.1713	0.1681
150	292.4	241.4	1.1229	0.1775	257.4	258.9	1.1437	0.1726
200	386.4	239.7	1.1023	0.1831	339.5	257.7	1.1236	0.1768
300	565.8	237.0	1.0724	0.1926	496.7	255.8	1.0946	0.1840
400	731.1	235.0	1.0505	0.1997	643.0	254.4	1.0736	0.1896
500	881.1	233.8	1.0335	0.2044	777.7	253.6	10.570	0.1938
600	1016	233.2	1.0195	0.2074	900.9	253.4	1.0435	0.1968
800	1245	233.5	0.9978	0.2103	1116	254.0	1.0221	0.2003
1000	1432	235.2	0.9813	0.2108	1296	255.8	1.0057	0.2018
	$T=1000$ °K				$T=1100$ °K			
1	1.579	279.3	1.4840	0.1584	1.435	295.1	1.4993	0.1584
2	3.157	279.2	1.4401	0.1585	2.870	295.1	1.4552	0.1584
3	4.735	279.2	1.4143	0.1586	4.305	295.1	1.4295	0.1585
4	6.313	279.2	1.3961	0.1586	5.738	295.1	1.4113	0.1586
5	7.890	279.2	1.3819	0.1587	7.172	285.0	1.3971	0.1586
10	15.77	279.0	1.3379	0.1591	14.33	294.9	1.3531	0.1590
20	31.49	278.8	1.2936	0.1599	28.61	294.8	1.3089	0.1596
30	47.16	278.5	1.2676	0.1607	42.83	294.6	1.2830	0.1602
40	62.77	278.3	1.2490	0.1615	57.00	294.4	1.2645	0.1608
50	78.32	278.0	1.2346	0.1622	71.10	294.2	1.2501	0.1615
60	93.82	277.8	1.2227	0.1630	85.15	294.1	1.2383	0.1621
70	109.2	277.6	1.2126	0.1638	99.14	293.9	1.2282	0.1627
80	124.6	277.4	1.2038	0.1645	113.1	293.8	1.2195	0.1633
90	139.9	277.2	1.1960	0.1652	126.9	293.6	1.2118	0.1638
100	155.2	277.0	1.1890	0.1660	140.7	293.5	1.2049	0.1644
150	230.4	276.0	1.1618	0.1694	208.8	292.8	1.1779	0.1672
200	303.6	275.2	1.1422	0.1726	275.1	292.3	1.1586	0.1698
300	444.0	273.9	1.1138	0.1783	402.3	291.5	1.1307	0.1743
400	575.6	273.0	1.0933	0.1829	522.1	291.1	1.1106	0.1781
500	698.0	272.6	1.0772	0.1865	634.3	291.0	1.0948	0.1812
600	811.2	272.6	1.0639	0.1892	739.0	291.3	1.0818	0.1836
800	1012	273.6	1.0429	0.1928	927.5	292.6	1.0611	0.1870
1000	1185	275.6	1.0267	0.1947	1091	294.8	1.0451	0.1891
	$T=1200$ °K				$T=1300$ °K			
1	1.316	311.0	1.5129	0.1584	1.214	326.8	1.5255	0.1584
2	2.631	311.0	1.4690	0.1584	2.428	326.8	1.4816	0.1584
3	3.946	311.0	1.4433	0.1585	3.642	326.8	1.4559	0.1584
4	5.260	311.0	1.4251	0.1585	4.855	326.8	1.4376	0.1585
5	6.573	311.0	1.4109	0.1586	6.068	326.8	1.4235	0.1585
10	13.13	310.8	1.3669	0.1588	12.12	326.7	1.3795	0.1588
20	26.21	310.7	1.3228	0.1594	24.19	326.6	1.3354	0.1592
30	39.24	310.6	1.2969	0.1599	36.21	326.6	1.3096	0.1596
40	52.21	310.5	1.2784	0.1604	48.18	326.5	1.2911	0.1600

continued

p, bar	ϱ	i	s	c_p	ϱ	i	s	c_p
50	65.12	310.4	1.2641	0.1609	60.09	326.4	1.2768	0.1605
60	77.98	310.2	1.2523	0.1614	71.95	326.4	1.2651	0.1609
70	90.78	310.1	1.2423	0.1619	83.75	326.3	1.2552	0.1613
80	103.5	310.0	1.2337	0.1624	95.50	326.2	1.2465	0.1617
90	116.2	310.0	1.2260	0.1628	107.2	326.2	1.2389	0.1621
100	128.8	309.9	1.2191	0.1633	118.8	326.1	1.2320	0.1625
150	191.0	309.4	1.1924	0.1656	176.2	326.0	1.2055	0.1644
200	251.7	309.1	1.1732	0.1677	232.2	325.8	1.1865	0.1661
300	368.3	308.8	1.1458	0.1714	339.9	325.8	1.1593	0.1693
400	478.4	308.7	1.1259	0.1746	442.0	326.0	1.1397	0.1720
500	582.2	308.9	1.1110	0.1773	538.5	326.5	1.1243	0.1743
600	679.6	309.4	1.0975	0.1794	629.6	327.2	1.1116	0.1762
800	856.6	311.1	1.0772	0.1826	796.4	329.1	1.0915	0.1791
1000	1012	313.5	1.0613	0.1847	944.9	331.7	1.0758	0.1811

Viscosity η ($N \cdot s/m^2$) of xenon gas at $p = 1$ bar [49]

T, °K	$\eta \cdot 10^7$	T, °K	$\eta \cdot 10^7$	T, °K	$\eta \cdot 10^7$	T, °K	$\eta \cdot 10^7$	T, °K	$\eta \cdot 10^7$
293.2	228	500	375	800	547	1100	693	1400	824
300	233	600	436	900	598	1200	738	1500	865
400	308	700	493	1000	646	1300	782	1600	905

Viscosity $\eta \cdot 10^7$ ($N \cdot s/m^2$) of xenon gas at different temperatures and pressures [367]

t, °C \ p, bar →	100	200	300	400	500	600	700	800
50	543	978	1276	1472	1680	1868	2048	2192
100	388	680	941	1136	1315	1488	1643	1800
150	388	544	739	923	1087	1235	1367	1479
200	409	528	668	792	925	1052	1168	1272

Thermal conductivity of saturated xenon [368]

T, °K	170	180	190	200	210	220	230	240	250	260
$\lambda' \cdot 10^3$, W/m · deg	70	66	62	58	54	50	46	42	38	34
$\lambda'' \cdot 10^3$, W/m · deg	3.4	3.7	4.1	4.4	4.8	5.1	5.5	6.0	6.6	7.3

Thermal conductivity λ (W/m · deg) of xenon gas at $p = 1$ bar [377]

T, °K	$\lambda \cdot 10^4$	T, °K	$\lambda \cdot 10^4$	T, °K	$\lambda \cdot 10^4$	T, °K	$\lambda \cdot 10^4$
175	33.4	450	83	750	128	1050	169
225	43.3	500	90	800	135	1100	176
273	52	550	98	850	142	1150	182
300	58	600	106	900	149	1200	188
350	67	650	113	950	156	1250	194
400	75	700	121	1000	163	1300	200

Thermal conductivity $\lambda \cdot 10^3$ (W/m · deg) of xenon at different temperatures and pressures [378]

T, °K	p, bar	$\lambda \cdot 10^3$	T, °K	p, bar	$\lambda \cdot 10^3$	T, °K	p, bar	$\lambda \cdot 10$
170.24	51.1	70.5	190.41	204	68.3	210.16	405.3	68.5
170.24	98.7	71.9	190.42	305.7	71.5	210.16	506	71.2
170.24	203.7	74.8	190.41	406	74.3	235.08	26	45.7
170.30	304.3	106.5	190.41	501.4	76.7	235.05	52.07	46.3
170.29	314	108	210.20	26	54.8	235.06	101.5	49.0
170.30	406.3	107.5	210.20	51.9	55.6	235.02	197.8	53.9
170.30	504.5	167.7	210.21	96.6	57.6	235.03	304.3	57.7
190.44	24.8	62.1	210.23	201.4	61.8	235.03	405.7	61.2
190.43	53.6	63.1	210.22	304	65.4	235.04	501.1	64.3
190.42	95.4	64.7						

PART II

MIXTURES

Chapter 10

AIR

Molecular weight 28.96

Thermodynamic properties of saturated air [141, 142]: boiling pressure p_{boil} and condensation pressure p_{cond} (bar), v (dm³/kg), i (kJ/kg), s and c_p (kJ/kg · deg)

T, °K	p_{boil}	p_{cond}	v'	v''	i'	i''	s'	s''	c_p'
64	0.1234	0.07115	1.060	2570	−151.4	63.6	2.641	6.080	
65	0.1468	0.08613	1.065	2154	−149.6	64.6	2.669	6.040	
66	0.1737	0.1036	1.070	1816	−147.8	65.5	2.696	6.002	
67	0.2045	0.1239	1.075	1540	−146.0	66.4	2.722	5.965	
68	0.2394	0.1474	1.080	1313	−144.2	67.4	2.747	5.929	
69	0.2789	0.1744	1.085	1125	−142.4	68.3	2.772	5.895	
70	0.3234	0.2052	1.090	968.4	−140.6	69.2	2.797	5.862	
71	0.3734	0.2403	1.095	837.6	−138.8	70.1	2.822	5.830	
72	0.4292	0.2801	1.101	727.5	−137.1	71.0	2.847	5.799	
73	0.4913	0.3250	1.107	634.6	−135.3	71.9	2.871	5.769	
74	0.5603	0.3755	1.113	555.7	−133.5	72.8	2.895	5.740	
75	0.6366	0.4321	1.119	488.4	−131.7	73.7	2.918	5.712	1.843
76	0.7207	0.4953	1.125	430.9	−129.9	74.5	2.941	5.685	1.849
77	0.8131	0.5656	1.131	381.4	−128.1	75.4	2.964	5.659	1.855
78	0.9145	0.6435	1.136	338.7	−126.3	76.2	2.988	5.634	1.861
79	1.025	0.7296	1.142	301.7	−124.4	77.0	3.011	5.609	1.867
80	1.146	0.8245	1.148	269.6	−122.6	77.8	3.034	5.585	1.873
81	1.277	0.9289	1.154	241.6	−120.7	78.6	3.056	5.562	1.879
82	1.420	1.043	1.160	217.1	−118.8	79.4	3.079	5.540	1.885
83	1.574	1.168	1.167	195.5	−116.9	80.1	3.101	5.518	1.891
84	1.741	1.305	1.173	176.5	−115.0	80.9	3.123	5.496	1.898
85	1.920	1.453	1.180	159.8	−113.1	81.6	3.145	5.475	1.905
86	2.114	1.614	1.187	145.0	−111.2	82.3	3.167	5.454	1.912
87	2.321	1.788	1.194	131.8	−109.3	82.9	3.188	5.434	1.919
88	2.544	1.976	1.201	120.1	−107.4	83.6	3.209	5.414	1.927
89	2.782	2.179	1.208	109.6	−105.4	84.2	3.230	5.395	1.935
90	3.036	2.397	1.216	100.2	−103.5	84.8	3.251	5.376	1.944
91	3.307	2.632	1.223	91.83	−101.5	85.4	3.272	5.358	1.953
92	3.596	2.884	1.231	84.28	−99.5	85.9	3.293	5.340	1.962
93	3.903	3.153	1.239	77.47	−97.5	86.5	3.314	5.322	1.972
94	4.229	3.441	1.247	71.32	−95.5	87.0	3.335	5.304	1.982
95	4.574	3.748	1.256	65.75	−93.5	87.4	3.356	5.287	1.992
96	4.940	4.075	1.265	60.70	−91.5	87.9	3.376	5.270	2.003
97	5.327	4.423	1.274	56.12	−89.5	88.3	3.396	5.253	2.015
98	5.736	4.792	1.283	51.95	−87.5	88.7	3.416	5.236	2.027
99	6.167	5.184	1.292	48.14	−85.4	89.0	3.436	5.220	2.040
100	6.621	5.599	1.302	44.67	−83.3	89.3	3.456	5.204	2.053
101	7.099	6.039	1.312	41.49	−81.3	89.6	3.475	5.188	2.067
102	7.602	6.504	1.322	38.57	−79.2	89.8	3.495	5.172	2.082
103	8.130	6.994	1.333	35.89	−77.1	90.0	3.514	5.156	2.099
104	8.684	7.511	1.344	33.43	−75.0	90.1	3.534	5.140	2.117
105	9.265	8.056	1.355	31.16	−72.8	90.2	3.553	5.124	2.137

continued

T, °K	p_{boil}	p_{cond}	v'	v''	i'	i''	s'	s''	c'_p
106	9.873	8.629	1.367	29.07	−70.7	90.3	3.572	5.108	2.159
107	10.51	9.231	1.379	27.14	−68.6	90.3	3.591	5.093	2.182
108	11.17	9.863	1.391	25.35	−66.4	90.3	3.611	5.077	2.207
109	11.87	10.53	1.404	23.69	−64.1	90.2	3.630	5.061	2.234
110	12.59	11.22	1.418	22.15	−61.9	90.1	3.649	5.045	2.264
111	13.35	11.95	1.432	20.72	−59.6	89.9	3.668	5.029	2.297
112	14.13	12.71	1.447	19.39	−57.3	89.6	3.688	5.013	2.334
113	14.95	13.51	1.462	18.15	−55.0	89.3	3.707	4.997	2.376
114	15.80	14.34	1.478	17.00	−52.6	88.9	3.727	4.981	2.423
115	16.68	15.21	1.495	15.92	−50.3	88.4	3.747	4.964	2.477
116	17.60	16.12	1.513	14.91	−47.9	87.8	3.767	4.947	2.540
117	18.55	17.07	1.532	13.96	−45.4	87.2	3.787	4.930	2.613
118	19.54	18.05	1.552	13.07	−42.8	86.5	3.808	4.913	2.697
119	20.56	19.07	1.573	12.24	−40.2	85.7	3.829	4.895	2.795
120	21.61	20.14	1.596	11.45	−37.5	84.8	3.850	4.877	2.916
121	22.70	21.25	1.622	10.71	−34.7	83.8	3.872	4.858	3.070
122	23.83	22.40	1.650	10.01	−31.8	82.6	3.894	4.838	3.275
123	24.99	23.60	1.681	9.343	−28.7	81.3	3.918	4.818	3.555
124	26.19	24.85	1.717	8.714	−25.5	79.8	3.943	4.797	3.965
125	27.43	26.14	1.757	8.115	−22.0	78.2	3.969	4.776	4.585
126	28.70	27.48	1.802	7.543	−18.3	76.4	3.997	4.753	
127	30.01	28.86	1.852	6.996	−14.2	74.3	4.027	4.728	
128	31.36	30.31	1.911	6.470	− 9.8	71.9	4.060	4.702	
129	32.74	31.78	1.983	5.960	− 5.0	69.2	4.096	4.675	
130	34.16	33.32	2.075	5.425	0.4	66.1	4.136	4.644	
131	35.62	34.91	2.206	4.858	7.6	62.3	4.191	4.609	
132	37.12	36.56	2.450	4.202	19.3	55.5	4.280	4.558	
132.55		37.69		3.196		37.4		4.410	

Thermodynamic properties of air in gaseous and liquid states [141, 142]:
v (dm³/kg), i (kJ/kg), s and c_p (kJ/kg · deg)

T, °K	v	i	s	c_p	v	i	s	c_p
	p=1 bar				p=2 bar			
75	1.1192	−131.7	2.918	1.843				
85	236.0	82.7	5.591	1.052				
90	251.2	87.9	5.650	1.044	121.7	85.7	5.435	1.095
95	266.2	91.3	5.706	1.037	129.7	91.1	5.494	1.079
100	281.2	98.3	5.759	1.032	137.5	96.5	5.549	1.067
105	296.1	103.4	5.810	1.028	145.3	101.8	5.601	1.058
110	310.9	108.6	5.858	1.025	152.9	107.1	5.650	1.050
115	325.6	113.7	5.903	1.022	160.5	112.3	5.697	1.044
120	340.3	118.8	5.946	1.020	168.1	117.5	5.741	1.039
125	355.0	123.9	5.988	1.018	175.6	122.7	5.783	1.035
130	369.7	129.0	6.028	1.016	183.0	127.9	5.823	1.031
135	384.8	134.0	6.066	1.015	190.5	133.1	5.862	1.028
140	398.9	139.1	6.103	1.014	197.9	138.2	5.900	1.026
145	413.4	144.2	6.139	1.013	205.3	143.3	5.936	1.024
150	428.0	149.2	6.173	1.012	212.7	148.4	5.970	1.022
160	457.0	159.3	6.238	1.010	227.4	158.6	6.036	1.019
170	486.0	169.4	6.299	1.009	242.0	168.8	6.098	1.016
180	515.0	179.5	6.357	1.008	256.6	178.9	6.156	1.014
190	543.9	189.6	6.412	1.008	271.2	189.1	6.211	1.013
200	572.8	199.7	6.463	1.007	285.7	199.2	6.263	1.011
210	601.7	209.7	6.512	1.006	300.2	209.3	6.312	1.010
220	630.5	119.8	6.559	1.006	314.8	219.4	6.359	1.010
230	659.4	229.9	6.604	1.006	329.2	229.5	6.404	1.009
240	688.2	239.9	6.647	1.006	343.7	239.6	6.447	1.009
250	717.0	250.0	6.688	1.006	358.2	249.7	6.488	1.008
260	745.8	260.0	6.727	1.006	372.6	259.7	6.527	1.008
270	774.6	270.1	6.765	1.006	387.1	269.8	6.565	1.008

continued

T, °K	v	i	s	c_p	v	i	s	c_p
280	803.4	280.2	6.802	1.006	401.5	279.9	6.602	1.008
290	832.2	290.2	6.837	1.006	415.9	290.0	6.637	1.008
300	861.0	300.3	6.871	1.007	430.4	300.1	6.671	1.008
310	889.8	310.4	6.904	1.007	444.8	310.1	6.705	1.008
320	918.5	320.4	6.936	1.007	459.2	320.2	6.737	1.009
330	947.3	330.5	6.967	1.008	473.6	330.3	6.768	1.009
340	976.0	340.6	6.997	1.009	488.0	340.4	6.798	1.010
350	1005	350.7	7.026	1.009	502.4	350.5	6.827	1.010
375	1077	375.9	7.096	1.012	538.4	375.8	6.897	1.012
400	1148	401.2	7.161	1.014	574.4	401.1	6.962	1.015
425	1220	426.7	7.223	1.017	610.4	426.6	7.024	1.018
450	1292	452.1	7.282	1.021	646.3	452.1	7.083	1.022
475	1364	477.7	7.337	1.025	682.3	477.7	7.138	1.026
500	1436	503.4	7.389	1.030	718.2	503.4	7.190	1.031
550	1580	555.2	7.488	1.040	790.1	555.1	7.289	1.041
600	1723	607.5	7.579	1.051	861.9	607.4	7.380	1.052
650	1867	660.3	7.664	1.063	933.7	660.3	7.465	1.063
700	2010	713.8	7.743	1.075	1006	713.8	7.544	1.075
750	2154	767.9	7.817	1.087	1077	767.9	7.618	1.087
800	2297	822.5	7.888	1.099	1149	822.5	7.689	1.099
850	2441	877.7	7.955	1.110	1221	877.8	7.756	1.110
900	2585	933.5	8.019	1.121	1293	933.6	7.820	1.121
950	2728	989.8	8.080	1.131	1365	989.9	7.881	1.132
1000	2872	1046.8	8.138	1.141	1436	1046.7	7.939	1.142
1050	3015	1103.9	8.194	1.150	1505	1104.0	7.995	1.151
1100	3159	1161.7	8.248	1.159	1580	1161.8	8.049	1.159
1150	3302	1219.9	8.299	1.167	1652	1220.0	8.100	1.167
1200	3446	1278.4	8.349	1.175	1723	1278.5	8.150	1.175
1250	3590	1337.3	8.397	1.182	1795	1337.4	8.198	1.182
1300	3733	1396.6	8.444	1.189	1867	1396.6	8.245	1.189
		$p=3$ bar				$p=4$ bar		
95	84.05	89.1	5.363	1.129				
100	89.54	94.7	5.420	1.108	65.46	92.7	5.324	1.155
105	94.92	100.2	5.474	1.091	69.69	98.4	5.380	1.129
110	100.2	105.6	5.524	1.078	73.81	104.0	5.432	1.110
115	105.4	110.9	5.572	1.068	77.85	109.5	5.481	1.095
120	110.6	116.2	5.617	1.060	81.84	115.0	5.527	1.082
125	115.7	121.5	5.660	1.053	85.78	120.4	5.571	1.072
130	120.8	126.8	5.701	1.047	89.68	125.7	5.613	1.064
135	125.9	132.0	5.741	1.042	93.54	131.0	5.653	1.057
140	130.9	137.2	5.779	1.038	97.38	136.3	5.691	1.052
145	135.9	142.4	5.815	1.035	101.2	141.5	5.728	1.047
150	140.9	147.6	5.850	1.031	105.0	146.7	5.764	1.042
160	150.8	157.9	5.917	1.027	112.5	157.1	5.831	1.036
170	160.7	168.1	5.979	1.023	120.0	167.4	5.893	1.030
180	170.5	178.3	6.037	1.020	127.4	177.7	5.952	1.026
190	180.3	188.5	6.092	1.018	134.8	188.0	6.007	1.023
200	190.0	198.7	6.144	1.016	142.2	198.2	6.060	1.020
210	199.8	208.8	6.194	1.014	149.5	208.4	6.110	1.018
220	209.5	219.0	6.241	1.013	156.9	218.6	6.157	1.017
230	219.2	229.1	6.286	1.012	164.2	228.7	6.202	1.015
240	228.9	239.2	6.329	1.011	171.5	238.9	6.245	1.014
250	238.6	249.3	6.370	1.011	178.8	249.0	6.286	1.013
260	248.2	259.4	6.410	1.010	186.0	259.1	6.326	1.013
270	257.9	269.5	6.448	1.010	193.3	269.3	6.364	1.012
280	267.5	279.6	6.485	1.010	200.6	279.4	6.401	1.012
290	277.2	289.7	6.520	1.010	207.8	289.5	6.437	1.011
300	286.8	299.8	6.554	1.010	215.1	299.6	6.471	1.011
310	296.5	309.9	6.588	1.010	222.3	309.7	6.504	1.011
320	306.1	320.0	6.620	1.010	229.5	319.8	6.536	1.011
330	315.7	330.1	6.651	1.010	236.8	329.9	6.568	1.012
340	325.3	340.2	6.681	1.011	244.0	340.1	6.598	1.012
350	335.0	350.3	6.710	1.012	251.2	350.2	6.627	1.013

continued

T, °K	v	i	s	c_p	v	i	s	c_p
375	359.0	375.6	6.780	0.013	269.3	375.5	6.697	1.014
400	383.0	401.0	6.845	1.016	287.3	400.9	6.763	1.017
425	407.0	426.5	6.907	1.019	305.3	426.4	6.825	1.020
450	431.0	452.0	6.965	1.023	323.3	451.9	6.883	1.023
475	455.0	477.6	7.021	1.027	341.3	474.5	6.938	1.027
500	479.0	503.3	7.074	1.031	359.3	503.2	6.991	1.031
550	526.9	555.1	7.172	1.041	395.3	555.1	7.090	1.041
600	574.8	607.4	7.263	1.052	431.3	607.4	7.181	1.052
650	622.7	660.3	7.348	1.064	467.2	660.3	7.266	1.064
700	670.6	713.8	7.427	1.076	503.2	713.8	7.345	1.076
750	718.5	767.9	7.502	1.088	539.1	767.9	7.419	1.088
800	766.4	822.6	7.573	1.099	575.0	822.6	7.490	1.099
850	814.3	877.8	7.640	1.110	610.9	877.8	7.557	1.111
900	862.2	933.6	7.703	1.121	646.9	933.6	7.621	1.122
950	910.0	989.9	7.764	1.132	682.8	990.0	7.682	1.132
1000	957.9	1046.8	7.822	1.142	718.7	1046.8	7.740	1.142
1050	1006	1104.1	7.878	1.151	754.6	1104.1	7.796	1.151
1100	1054	1161.8	7.932	1.159	790.5	1161.8	7.850	1.159
1150	1101	1220.0	7.984	1.167	826.4	1220.0	7.901	1.167
1200	1149	1278.6	8.034	1.175	862.3	1278.6	7.951	1.175
1250	1197	1337.5	8.082	1.182	898.2	1337.5	7.999	1.182
1300	1245	1396.7	8.128	1.189	934.1	1396.8	8.046	1.189
		$p=5$ bar				$p=6$ bar		
75	1.1183	−131.4	2.916	1.840				
80	1.1470	−122.3	3.031	1.868				
85	1.1790	−112.9	3.143	1.901				
90	1.2150	−103.3	3.250	1.941				
95	1.2559	− 93.5	3.356	1.991				
100	50.93	90.6	5.246	1.212				
105	54.98	96.6	5.304	1.174	44.30	94.6	5.239	1.226
110	57.92	102.4	5.358	1.145	47.30	100.7	5.295	1.186
115	61.28	108.0	5.408	1.124	50.20	106.5	5.347	1.156
120	64.57	113.6	5.455	1.107	53.03	112.2	5.395	1.134
125	67.80	119.1	5.500	1.093	55.80	117.8	5.441	1.116
130	70.99	124.5	5.543	1.082	58.52	123.4	5.485	1.101
135	74.14	129.9	5.584	1.073	61.20	128.9	5.526	1.090
140	77.27	135.3	5.623	1.065	63.85	134.3	5.565	1.080
145	80.37	140.6	5.660	1.059	66.48	139.7	5.603	1.072
150	83.44	145.9	5.696	1.053	69.08	145.0	5.639	1.065
160	89.54	156.4	5.763	1.045	74.23	155.6	5.708	1.054
170	95.59	166.8	5.826	1.038	79.32	166.1	5.772	1.045
180	101.6	177.1	5.885	1.033	84.36	176.5	5.831	1.039
190	107.6	187.4	5.941	1.028	89.37	186.9	5.887	1.034
200	113.5	197.7	5.994	1.025	94.35	197.2	5.940	1.030
210	119.4	207.9	6.044	1.022	99.30	207.5	5.990	1.027
220	125.3	218.1	6.092	1.020	104.2	217.7	6.038	1.024
230	131.2	228.3	6.137	1.018	109.2	228.0	6.083	1.022
240	137.0	238.5	6.180	1.017	114.1	238.2	6.126	1.020
250	142.9	248.7	6.222	1.016	119.0	248.4	6.168	1.018
260	148.7	258.8	6.262	1.015	123.8	258.5	6.208	1.017
270	154.5	269.0	6.300	1.014	128.7	268.7	6.246	1.016
280	160.4	279.1	6.337	1.013	133.6	278.9	6.283	1.015
290	166.2	289.2	6.372	1.013	138.4	289.0	6.319	1.015
300	172.0	299.4	6.406	1.013	143.3	299.2	6.354	1.014
310	177.8	309.5	6.440	1.013	148.2	309.3	6.387	1.014
320	183.6	319.6	6.472	1.013	153.0	319.4	6.419	1.014
330	189.4	329.8	6.503	1.013	157.8	329.6	6.450	1.014
340	195.2	339.9	6.533	1.013	162.7	339.7	6.480	1.014
350	201.0	350.0	6.563	1.014	167.5	349.9	6.510	1.015
375	215.5	375.4	6.633	1.015	179.6	375.3	6.580	1.016
400	229.9	400.8	6.698	1.017	191.6	400.7	6.645	1.018
425	244.3	426.3	6.760	1.020	203.7	426.2	6.707	1.021
450	258.8	451.8	6.818	1.024	215.7	451.8	6.766	1.024
475	273.2	477.4	6.874	1.028	227.7	477.4	6.822	1.028

continued

T, °K	v	i	s	c_p	v	i	s	c_p
500	287.6	503.2	6.927	1.032	239.7	503.1	6.874	1.032
550	316.4	555.0	7.025	1.042	263.7	555.0	6.973	1.042
600	345.2	607.4	7.116	1.053	287.7	607.4	7.064	1.053
650	373.9	660.3	7.201	1.064	311.7	660.3	7.149	1.064
700	402.7	713.8	7.280	1.076	335.7	713.8	7.228	1.076
750	431.4	767.9	7.355	1.088	359.7	767.9	7.303	1.088
800	460.2	822.6	7.426	1.100	383.6	822.6	7.373	1.100
850	488.9	877.9	7.493	1.111	407.6	877.9	7.440	1.111
900	517.7	933.7	7.557	1.122	431.5	933.7	7.504	1.122
950	546.4	990.0	7.618	1.132	455.5	990.1	7.565	1.132
1000	575.1	1046.9	7.676	1.142	479.4	1046.9	7.623	1.142
1050	603.9	1104.2	7.732	1.151	503.4	1104.2	7.679	1.151
1100	632.6	1161.9	7.785	1.159	527.8	1162.0	7.733	1.159
1150	661.3	1220.1	7.837	1.167	551.8	1220.2	7.785	1.167
1200	690.0	1278.7	7.887	1.175	575.2	1278.8	7.835	1.175
1250	718.8	1337.6	7.935	1.182	599.2	1337.7	7.883	1.182
1300	747.5	1396.9	7.982	1.189	623.1	1396.9	7.929	1.189
		$p=8$ bar				$p=10$ bar		
75					1.1171	−131.1	2.913	1.836
80					1.1456	−122.0	3.028	1.863
85					1.1773	−112.6	3.139	1.894
90					1.2128	−103.1	3.246	1.932
95					1.2531	− 93.3	3.351	1.979
100					1.2995	− 83.2	3.452	2.041
105	31.43	90.4	5.127	1.361	1.3544	− 72.8	3.552	2.133
110	33.93	97.0	5.188	1.285	25.78	92.9	5.097	1.422
115	36.29	103.3	5.244	1.233	27.87	99.7	5.158	1.332
120	38.56	109.3	5.296	1.195	29.83	106.2	5.214	1.270
125	40.76	115.2	5.344	1.166	31.70	112.5	5.264	1.226
130	42.91	121.0	5.389	1.144	33.51	118.5	5.311	1.193
135	45.01	126.7	5.432	1.126	35.27	124.4	5.356	1.167
140	47.07	132.3	5.473	1.111	36.99	130.2	5.398	1.146
145	49.11	137.8	5.512	1.099	38.67	135.9	5.438	1.129
150	51.12	143.3	5.549	1.089	40.33	141.5	5.476	1.115
160	55.08	154.1	5.619	1.073	43.58	152.5	5.548	1.093
170	58.98	164.7	5.683	1.061	46.77	163.4	5.614	1.077
180	62.83	175.3	5.743	1.052	49.91	174.1	5.675	1.065
190	66.64	185.8	5.800	1.045	53.00	184.7	5.732	1.056
200	70.42	196.2	5.854	1.039	56.07	195.2	5.786	1.049
210	74.18	206.6	5.904	1.035	59.12	205.7	5.837	1.043
220	77.92	216.9	5.952	1.031	62.14	216.1	5.885	1.038
230	81.65	227.2	5.998	1.028	65.15	226.4	5.931	1.034
240	85.36	237.5	6.042	1.025	68.14	236.7	5.975	1.031
250	89.06	247.7	6.084	1.023	71.12	247.0	6.017	1.028
260	92.74	257.9	6.124	1.022	74.09	257.3	6.058	1.026
270	96.42	268.1	6.162	1.020	77.05	267.6	6.097	1.024
280	100.1	278.3	6.199	1.019	80.00	277.8	6.134	1.023
290	103.8	288.5	6.235	1.018	82.95	288.0	6.169	1.022
300	107.4	298.7	6.270	1.018	85.89	298.3	6.204	1.021
310	111.1	308.9	6.303	1.017	88.82	308.5	6.238	1.020
320	114.7	319.0	6.335	1.017	91.75	318.7	6.270	1.020
330	118.4	329.2	6.366	1.017	94.68	328.9	6.301	1.019
340	122.0	339.4	6.396	1.017	97.60	339.1	6.331	1.019
350	125.6	349.6	6.426	1.017	100.5	349.2	6.361	1.019
375	134.7	375.0	6.496	1.018	107.8	374.7	6.431	1.020
400	143.8	400.5	6.562	1.020	115.1	400.2	6.497	1.021
425	152.8	426.0	6.624	1.022	122.3	425.8	6.559	1.024
450	161.9	451.6	6.683	1.025	129.6	451.4	6.618	1.027
475	170.9	477.3	6.739	1.029	136.8	477.1	6.674	1.030
500	179.9	503.0	6.791	1.033	144.0	502.9	6.727	1.034
550	198.0	554.9	6.890	1.043	158.5	554.9	6.826	1.044
600	216.0	607.3	6.981	1.054	172.9	607.3	6.917	1.055
650	234.0	660.3	7.066	1.065	187.3	660.3	7.002	1.066

continued

T, °K	v	i	s	c_p	v	i	s	c_p
700	252.0	713.9	7.145	1.077	201.7	713.9	7.081	1.077
750	270.0	768.0	7.220	1.089	216.1	768.0	7.156	1.089
800	287.9	822.7	7.291	1.100	230.5	822.7	7.226	1.100
850	305.9	878.0	7.358	1.111	244.9	878.0	7.293	1.111
900	323.9	933.8	7.421	1.122	259.3	933.9	7.357	1.122
950	341.9	990.2	7.482	1.132	273.7	990.3	7.418	1.132
1000	359.8	1047.1	7.541	1.142	288.1	1047.2	7.477	1.142
1050	377.8	1104.4	7.597	1.151	302.4	1104.5	7.533	1.151
1100	395.8	1162.1	7.650	1.160	316.8	1162.2	7.536	1.160
1150	413.7	1220.3	7.702	1.168	331.2	1220.4	7.538	1.168
1200	431.7	1278.9	7.752	1.175	345.6	1279.0	7.688	1.175
1250	449.6	1337.8	7.800	1.182	359.9	1338.0	7.736	1.182
1300	467.6	1397.1	7.847	1.189	374.3	1397.2	7.783	1.189
		$p = 15$ bar				$p = 20$ bar		
75	1.1159	−130.7	2.910	1.832	1.1148	−130.4	2.907	1.828
80	1.1442	−121.6	3.025	1.858	1.1428	−121.3	3.022	1.853
85	1.1755	−112.3	3.136	1.887	1.1738	−112.0	3.138	1.881
90	1.2106	−102.8	3.243	1.924	1.2085	−102.5	3.239	1.916
95	1.2503	− 93.1	3.347	1.968	1.2475	− 92.8	3.343	1.957
100	1.2958	− 83.1	3.447	2.025	1.2922	− 82.9	3.442	2.010
105	1.3493	− 72.8	3.546	2.109	1.3443	− 72.7	3.540	2.086
110	1.4143	− 61.9	3.646	2.244	1.4071	− 62.0	3.639	2.205
115	16.26	89.0	4.972	1.767	1.4871	− 50.5	3.741	2.425
120	17.25	97.2	5.042	1.560	11.59	85.2	4.882	2.237
125	19.47	104.8	5.103	1.436	13.12	95.2	4.963	1.813
130	20.87	111.7	5.158	1.353	14.42	103.7	5.030	1.604
135	22.22	118.3	5.207	1.295	15.59	111.4	5.088	1.476
140	23.49	124.6	5.254	1.250	16.67	118.5	5.140	1.390
145	24.72	130.8	5.296	1.216	17.70	125.3	5.187	1.328
150	25.92	136.8	5.338	1.189	18.69	131.8	5.232	1.281
160	28.38	148.5	5.414	1.150	20.56	144.3	5.312	1.215
170	30.63	159.8	5.483	1.122	22.34	156.2	5.384	1.171
180	34.83	170.9	5.546	1.101	24.06	167.7	5.450	1.141
190	35.84	181.8	5.605	1.086	25.74	179.0	5.511	1.118
200	37.11	192.7	5.661	1.074	27.38	190.1	5.568	1.101
210	39.21	203.3	5.713	1.064	28.99	201.1	5.622	1.087
220	41.28	213.9	5.764	1.057	30.58	211.9	5.672	1.076
230	43.34	224.5	5.809	1.051	32.15	222.6	5.720	1.068
240	45.39	235.0	5.854	1.046	33.71	233.2	5.765	1.061
250	47.42	245.4	5.896	1.041	35.25	243.8	5.808	1.055
260	49.44	255.8	5.937	1.038	36.79	254.3	5.849	1.050
270	51.45	266.2	5.976	1.035	38.31	264.8	5.889	1.046
280	53.45	276.5	6.019	1.032	39.83	275.2	5.927	1.042
290	55.45	286.8	6.050	1.030	41.34	285.6	5.963	1.039
300	57.44	297.1	6.085	1.028	42.84	296.0	5.998	1.037
310	59.43	307.4	6.119	1.027	44.34	306.4	6.032	1.035
320	61.41	317.7	6.151	1.026	45.84	316.8	6.065	1.033
330	63.39	327.9	6.182	1.025	47.33	327.1	6.097	1.032
340	65.36	338.2	6.213	1.025	48.82	337.4	6.128	1.031
350	67.33	348.4	6.243	1.025	50.30	347.7	6.158	1.030
375	72.24	374.0	6.314	1.024	53.99	373.4	6.229	1.029
400	77.14	399.6	6.380	1.026	57.67	399.1	6.295	1.029
425	82.03	425.3	6.442	1.027	61.34	424.9	6.358	1.030
450	86.90	451.0	6.501	1.030	64.99	450.7	6.417	1.033
475	91.77	476.8	6.557	1.033	68.64	476.5	6.473	1.036
500	96.72	502.6	6.610	1.037	72.29	502.4	6.526	1.039
550	106.3	554.7	6.709	1.046	79.56	554.6	6.625	1.047
600	116.0	607.2	6.800	1.056	86.81	607.2	6.716	1.057
650	125.7	660.3	6.885	1.067	94.05	660.3	6.801	1.068
700	135.3	713.9	6.964	1.078	101.3	714.0	6.881	1.079
750	145.0	768.1	7.039	1.090	108.5	768.2	6.956	1.091
800	154.6	822.9	7.110	1.101	115.7	823.0	7.027	1.102

continued

T, °K	v	i	s	c_p	v	i	s	c_p
850	164.3	878.2	7.177	1.112	122.9	878.4	7.094	1.112
900	173.9	934.2	7.244	1.123	130.1	934.3	7.158	1.123
950	183.6	990.6	7.302	1.133	137.3	990.8	7.219	1.134
1000	193.2	1047.5	7.360	1.143	144.5	1047.7	7.277	1.143
1050	202.8	1104.8	7.416	1.152	151.7	1105.1	7.333	1.152
1100	212.5	1162.6	7.470	1.160	158.9	1162.9	7.387	1.161
1150	222.1	1220.8	7.522	1.168	166.1	1221.1	7.439	1.169
1200	231.7	1279.4	7.572	1.176	173.3	1279.7	7.489	1.176
1250	241.4	1338.3	7.620	1.183	180.5	1338.7	7.537	1.183
1300	251.0	1397.6	7.666	1.189	187.7	1398.0	7.583	1.190
		$p=25$ bar				$p=30$ bar		
75	1.1136	−130.0	2.905	1.824	1.1125	−129.7	2.902	1.820
80	1.1414	−121.0	3.019	1.849	1.1400	−120.6	3.016	1.844
85	1.1721	−111.7	3.130	1.875	1.1705	−111.4	3.126	1.870
90	1.2064	−102.2	3.236	1.908	1.2043	−102.0	3.232	1.900
95	1.2449	− 92.6	3.339	1.947	1.2422	− 92.4	3.335	1.937
100	1.2887	− 82.7	3.438	1.996	1.2853	− 82.6	3.433	1.983
105	1.3395	− 72.6	3.535	2.065	1.3349	− 72.5	3.529	2.045
110	1.4002	− 62.1	3.632	2.170	1.3936	− 62.1	3.625	2.139
115	1.4762	− 50.8	3.732	2.357	1.4661	− 51.0	3.723	2.300
120	1.5816	− 38.1	3.841	2.784	1.5631	− 38.8	3.829	2.684
125	8.944	82.2	4.815	2.772	1.7267	− 23.4	3.954	3.910
130	10.36	93.9	4.908	2.057	7.367	80.7	4.772	3.197
135	11.51	103.4	4.979	1.755	8.662	93.9	4.871	2.271
140	12.52	111.7	5.040	1.584	9.682	104.0	4.945	1.871
145	13.45	119.3	5.093	1.473	10.57	102.8	5.007	1.668
150	14.32	126.5	5.142	1.395	11.38	120.8	5.061	1.538
160	15.94	139.9	5.228	1.292	12.84	135.3	5.155	1.381
170	17.45	152.5	5.304	1.227	14.19	148.6	5.235	1.290
180	18.89	164.5	5.373	1.183	15.45	161.2	5.307	1.230
190	20.29	176.2	5.436	1.152	16.65	173.3	5.373	1.188
200	21.65	187.6	5.495	1.129	17.82	185.0	5.433	1.158
210	22.97	198.8	5.549	1.111	18.96	196.4	5.489	1.135
220	24.27	209.8	5.600	1.096	20.07	207.7	5.541	1.117
230	25.56	220.7	5.649	1.085	21.17	218.8	5.590	1.103
240	26.83	231.5	5.695	1.076	22.25	229.7	5.637	1.091
250	28.09	242.2	5.739	1.068	23.32	240.6	5.681	1.081
260	29.93	252.8	5.781	1.061	24.37	251.4	5.723	1.073
270	30.57	263.4	5.821	1.056	25.41	262.1	5.764	1.067
280	31.80	274.0	5.859	1.052	26.45	272.7	5.803	1.061
290	33.02	284.5	5.896	1.048	27.48	283.3	5.840	1.057
300	34.24	294.9	5.931	1.045	28.51	293.8	5.876	1.053
310	35.45	305.4	5.965	1.042	29.53	304.3	5.910	1.049
320	36.66	315.8	5.998	1.040	30.54	314.8	5.943	1.046
330	37.86	326.2	6.030	1.038	31.55	325.3	5.975	1.044
340	39.06	336.6	6.061	1.036	32.56	335.7	6.006	1.042
350	40.26	346.9	6.091	1.035	33.57	346.1	6.037	1.041
375	43.23	372.8	6.162	1.033	36.06	372.1	6.108	1.038
400	46.19	398.6	6.229	1.033	38.54	398.0	6.175	1.037
425	49.14	424.4	6.292	1.034	41.01	423.9	6.238	1.037
450	52.08	450.3	6.352	1.035	43.48	449.9	6.298	1.038
475	55.01	476.2	6.408	1.038	45.93	475.9	6.354	1.040
500	57.94	502.2	6.460	1.041	48.37	501.9	6.407	1.043
550	63.77	554.4	6.560	1.049	53.25	554.3	6.507	1.051
600	69.59	607.1	6.652	1.059	58.11	607.1	6.599	1.060
650	75.39	660.3	6.737	1.069	62.95	660.3	6.684	1.070
700	81.18	714.0	6.817	1.080	67.79	714.1	6.764	1.081
750	86.97	768.3	6.892	1.092	72.62	768.5	6.839	1.092
800	92.75	823.2	6.962	1.103	77.44	823.4	6.910	1.103
850	98.53	878.6	7.029	1.114	82.26	878.8	6.977	1.114
900	104.3	934.6	7.093	1.124	87.08	934.8	7.041	1.125
950	110.1	991.0	7.154	1.134	91.89	991.3	7.102	1.135

continued

T, °K	v	i	s	c_p	v	i	s	c_p
1000	115.8	1043.0	7.213	1.143	96.69	1048.2	7.160	1.144
1050	121.6	1105.4	7.260	1.152	101.5	1105.6	7.216	1.153
1100	127.4	1163.2	7.323	1.161	106.3	1163.5	7.270	1.161
1150	133.1	1221.4	7.374	1.169	111.1	1221.8	7.322	1.169
1200	138.9	1280.1	7.424	1.176	115.9	1280.4	7.372	1.177
1250	144.7	1339.1	7.472	1.183	120.7	1339.4	7.420	1.184
1300	150.4	1398.4	7.519	1.190	125.5	1398.8	7.467	1.190
		$p=35$ bar				$p=40$ bar		
75	1.1113	−129.3	2.900	1.816	1.1102	−128.9	2.897	1.813
80	1.1387	−120.3	3.014	1.839	1.1373	−120.0	3.011	1.834
85	1.1688	−111.1	3.123	1.864	1.1672	−110.8	3.120	1.858
90	1.2023	−101.7	3.228	1.893	1.2003	−101.4	3.225	1.886
95	1.2397	− 92.1	3.330	1.928	1.2371	− 91.9	3.327	1.919
100	1.2819	− 82.4	3.428	1.970	1.2787	− 82.2	3.424	1.958
105	1.3304	− 72.4	3.524	2.027	1.3261	− 72.3	3.519	2.010
110	1.3874	− 62.1	3.619	2.111	1.3814	− 62.1	3.613	2.036
115	1.4567	− 52.2	3.715	2.251	1.4479	− 51.4	3.708	2.208
120	1.5469	− 39.4	3.817	2.521	1.5325	− 39.8	3.807	2.432
125	1.6847	− 25.3	3.933	3.285	1.6536	− 26.6	3.916	2.962
130	1.995	− 0.9	4.127		1.871	− 5.8	4.080	4.821
135	6.435	81.2	4.749	3.325	4.314	59.9	4.572	8.684
140	7.572	94.8	4.849	2.324	5.883	83.6	4.745	3.193
145	8.472	105.4	4.923	1.941	6.852	97.0	4.839	2.341
150	9.255	114.5	4.985	1.723	7.638	107.7	4.912	1.966
160	10.63	130.4	5.088	1.486	8.959	125.3	5.025	1.610
170	11.85	144.6	5.174	1.359	10.10	140.5	5.117	1.437
180	12.99	157.8	5.249	1.280	11.14	154.3	5.196	1.335
190	14.06	170.3	5.317	1.227	12.12	167.3	5.266	1.268
200	15.10	182.4	5.379	1.189	13.06	179.7	5.330	1.221
210	16.10	194.1	5.436	1.160	13.96	191.8	5.389	1.186
220	17.08	205.6	5.489	1.138	14.83	203.5	5.444	1.159
230	18.04	216.9	5.539	1.120	15.69	215.0	5.495	1.139
240	18.98	228.0	5.587	1.106	16.53	226.3	5.543	1.122
250	19.91	239.0	5.632	1.095	17.35	237.4	5.589	1.108
260	20.82	249.9	5.675	1.085	18.17	248.5	5.632	1.097
270	21.73	260.7	5.715	1.078	18.98	259.4	5.673	1.088
280	22.63	271.5	5.754	1.071	19.77	270.2	5.712	1.081
290	23.53	282.2	5.792	1.065	20.56	281.0	5.750	1.074
300	24.42	292.8	5.828	1.061	21.35	291.7	5.786	1.068
310	25.30	303.4	5.863	1.057	22.13	302.4	5.821	1.064
320	26.18	313.9	5.897	1.053	22.91	313.0	5.855	1.060
330	27.05	324.4	5.929	1.050	23.68	323.6	5.888	1.056
340	27.92	334.9	5.960	1.048	24.45	334.1	5.919	1.053
350	28.79	345.4	5.990	1.046	25.21	344.6	5.950	1.051
375	30.94	371.5	6.062	1.042	27.11	370.8	6.022	1.047
400	33.08	397.5	6.130	1.041	28.99	397.0	6.090	1.044
425	35.21	423.5	6.193	1.040	30.85	423.1	6.153	1.044
450	37.33	449.5	6.252	1.041	32.72	449.2	6.212	1.044
475	39.44	475.6	6.308	1.043	34.57	475.3	6.269	1.046
500	41.54	501.7	6.362	1.046	36.42	501.5	6.323	1.049
550	45.73	554.1	6.462	1.053	40.10	554.0	6.423	1.055
600	49.91	607.0	6.554	1.062	43.76	606.9	6.515	1.063
650	54.07	660.3	6.639	1.072	47.41	660.3	6.600	1.073
700	58.22	714.2	6.719	1.082	51.05	714.2	6.680	1.083
750	63.37	768.6	6.794	1.093	54.68	768.7	6.755	1.094
800	66.51	823.5	6.865	1.104	58.31	823.7	6.826	1.105
850	70.65	879.0	6.932	1.115	61.93	879.2	6.894	1.116
900	74.78	935.0	6.996	1.125	65.55	935.2	6.958	1.126
950	78.90	991.5	7.057	1.135	69.17	991.8	7.019	1.136
1000	83.03	1048.5	7.116	1.144	72.78	1048.8	7.077	1.145
1050	87.15	1105.9	7.172	1.153	76.39	1106.3	7.133	1.154
1100	91.27	1163.8	7.226	1.162	80.00	1164.2	7.187	1.162
1150	95.39	1222.1	7.278	1.170	83.60	1222.5	7.239	1.170

continued

T, °K	v	i	s	c_p	v	i	s	c_p
1200	99.50	1280.8	7.328	1.177	87.20	1281.2	7.289	1.177
1250	103.6	1339.8	7.376	1.184	90.80	1340.2	7.337	1.184
1300	107.7	1399.2	7.422	1.190	94.40	1399.6	7.384	1.191
		$p=45$ bar				$p=50$ bar		
75	1.1091	−128.6	2.894	1.809	1.1080	−128.2	2.892	1.806
80	1.1360	−119.6	3.008	1.830	1.1347	−119.3	3.005	1.826
85	1.1656	−110.4	3.117	1.853	1.1640	−110.1	3.114	1.848
90	1.1983	−101.4	3.221	1.879	1.1963	−100.8	3.218	1.873
95	1.2347	− 91.6	3.323	1.910	1.2322	− 91.4	3.319	1.902
100	1.2755	− 82.0	3.420	1.946	1.2724	− 81.8	3.415	1.939
105	1.3219	− 72.1	3.514	1.994	1.3179	− 72.0	3.509	1.980
110	1.3757	− 62.0	3.607	2.063	1.3702	− 62.0	3.601	2.042
115	1.4396	− 51.5	3.701	2.170	1.4318	− 51.6	3.694	2.138
120	1.5194	− 40.2	3.798	2.360	1.5075	− 40.5	3.789	2.300
125	1.6285	− 27.5	3.902	2.758	1.6073	− 28.3	3.889	2.614
130	1.806	− 10.6	4.042	3.713	1.757	− 13.5	4.012	3.204
135	2.288	17.4	4.246	8.672	2.054	9.2	4.177	5.023
140	4.418	68.4	4.618	5.178	3.130	47.0	4.452	8.694
145	5.543	87.3	4.751	2.960	4.453	75.8	4.654	3.931
150	6.360	100.2	4.838	2.290	5.321	91.9	4.764	2.721
160	7.656	120.0	4.966	1.756	6.612	114.4	4.909	1.927
170	8.740	136.3	5.065	1.524	7.653	131.9	5.015	1.620
180	9.713	150.8	5.148	1.394	8.571	147.2	5.103	1.457
190	10.62	164.3	5.221	1.311	9.415	161.3	5.179	1.356
200	11.47	177.1	5.287	1.254	10.21	174.5	5.246	1.288
210	12.29	189.4	5.347	1.213	10.97	187.1	5.308	1.240
220	13.09	201.4	5.402	1.181	11.70	199.3	5.365	1.204
230	13.87	213.1	5.454	1.157	12.41	211.2	5.418	1.176
240	14.63	224.6	5.503	1.138	13.11	222.8	5.467	1.154
250	15.37	235.9	5.549	1.122	13.79	234.3	5.514	1.136
260	16.11	247.0	5.593	1.110	14.46	245.6	5.558	1.122
270	16.83	258.0	5.635	1.099	15.12	256.7	5.600	1.110
280	17.55	269.0	5.675	1.090	15.77	267.7	5.640	1.100
290	18.26	279.9	5.713	1.083	16.42	278.7	5.679	1.091
300	18.97	290.7	5.749	1.076	17.06	289.6	5.716	1.084
310	19.67	301.4	5.785	1.071	17.70	300.4	5.751	1.078
320	20.36	312.1	5.818	1.066	18.33	311.2	5.785	1.073
330	21.05	322.7	5.851	1.062	18.96	321.9	5.818	1.069
340	21.74	333.3	5.883	1.059	19.58	332.6	5.850	1.065
350	22.42	343.9	5.913	1.056	20.20	343.2	5.881	1.061
375	24.12	370.2	5.986	1.051	21.74	369.6	5.954	1.055
400	25.81	396.5	6.054	1.048	23.26	395.9	6.022	1.052
425	27.48	422.7	6.117	1.047	24.77	422.2	6.086	1.050
450	29.14	448.8	6.177	1.047	26.27	448.5	6.146	1.050
475	30.79	475.0	6.234	1.048	27.77	474.7	6.203	1.050
500	32.44	501.2	6.288	1.050	29.26	501.0	6.256	1.052
550	35.72	553.9	6.388	1.056	32.21	553.7	6.356	1.058
600	38.98	606.9	6.480	1.065	35.15	606.8	6.449	1.066
650	42.23	660.4	6.566	1.074	38.09	660.4	6.535	1.075
700	45.47	714.3	6.646	1.084	41.01	714.4	6.615	1.085
750	48.71	768.8	6.721	1.095	43.93	768.9	6.691	1.096
800	51.94	823.8	6.792	1.106	46.84	824.0	6.762	1.107
850	55.16	879.4	6.860	1.116	49.74	879.6	6.829	1.117
900	58.38	935.5	6.924	1.126	52.64	935.7	6.893	1.127
950	61.60	992.1	6.985	1.136	55.54	992.3	6.954	1.137
1000	64.81	1049.1	7.043	1.145	58.43	1049.4	7.013	1.146
1050	68.02	1106.6	7.099	1.154	61.32	1106.9	7.069	1.155
1100	71.23	1164.5	7.153	1.162	64.21	1164.8	7.123	1.163
1150	74.43	1222.8	7.205	1.170	67.10	1223.2	7.175	1.171
1200	77.64	1281.5	7.255	1.177	69.99	1281.9	7.225	1.178
1250	80.84	1340.6	7.303	1.184	72.87	1340.9	7.273	1.185
1300	84.04	1399.9	7.350	1.191	75.75	1400.3	7.319	1.191

continued

T, °K	v	i	s	c_p	v	i	s	c_p
	$p=60$ bar				$p=80$ bar			
75	1.106	−127.5	2.887	1.799	1.102	−126.0	2.877	1.786
80	1.132	−118.6	3.000	1.818	1.127	−117.2	2.989	1.802
85	1.161	−109.5	3.108	1.838	1.155	−108.2	3.096	1.819
90	1.192	−100.3	3.211	1.860	1.185	− 99.1	3.198	1.838
95	1.227	− 90.9	3.311	1.886	1.219	− 89.9	3.297	1.858
100	1.261	− 81.4	3.407	1.915	1.255	− 80.4	3.391	1.881
105	1.303	− 71.7	3.499	1.953	1.296	− 70.9	3.482	1.909
110	1.350	− 61.8	3.590	2.005	1.341	− 61.3	3.570	1.945
115	1.404	− 51.6	3.681	2.081	1.392	− 51.5	3.657	1.997
120	1.468	− 40.8	3.773	2.205	1.451	− 41.3	3.745	2.078
125	1.573	− 29.4	3.867	2.422	1.521	− 30.7	3.833	2.200
130	1.691	− 16.4	3.971	2.824	1.606	− 19.1	3.924	2.395
135	1.875	0.7	4.097	3.482	1.720	− 6.1	4.025	2.649
140	2.219	22.8	4.260	4.808	1.877	9.0	4.138	2.992
145	2.928	49.9	4.450	5.485	2.102	26.3	4.257	3.373
150	3.773	73.1	4.608	3.837	2.422	44.2	4.378	3.622
160	5.054	90.0	4.798	2.338	3.270	78.4	4.597	3.029
170	6.033	113.7	4.922	1.836	4.090	104.6	4.757	2.291
180	6.869	132.6	5.020	1.594	4.800	125.3	4.875	1.887
190	7.624	149.0	5.102	1.452	5.431	142.9	4.970	1.655
200	8.325	163.9	5.174	1.361	6.009	158.7	5.051	1.510
210	8.989	177.8	5.239	1.296	6.549	173.3	5.122	1.412
220	9.625	191.1	5.298	1.249	7.061	187.1	5.186	1.342
230	10.24	203.8	5.353	1.214	7.552	200.2	5.245	1.190
240	10.84	216.1	5.404	1.186	8.027	212.9	5.299	1.250
250	11.42	228.2	5.452	1.164	8.488	225.2	5.349	1.219
260	11.99	240.0	5.497	1.146	8.939	237.3	5.396	1.194
270	12.56	251.6	5.540	1.131	9.381	249.1	5.441	1.173
280	13.12	263.1	5.581	1.119	9.814	260.8	5.484	1.156
290	13.67	274.4	5.620	1.109	10.24	272.3	5.524	1.142
300	14.21	285.6	5.657	1.100	10.66	283.7	5.562	1.130
310	14.75	296.7	5.693	1.092	11.08	294.9	5.599	1.120
320	15.29	307.7	5.728	1.086	11.49	306.0	5.635	1.111
330	15.82	318.6	5.761	1.080	11.90	317.1	5.669	1.103
340	16.35	329.5	5.793	1.076	12.31	328.1	5.702	1.097
350	16.87	340.4	5.824	1.072	12.71	339.0	5.733	1.091
375	18.16	367.3	5.898	1.064	13.70	366.2	5.808	1.080
400	19.44	394.0	5.967	1.059	14.68	393.1	5.878	1.073
425	20.72	420.6	6.031	1.056	15.65	419.8	5.943	1.069
450	21.98	447.1	6.091	1.055	16.61	446.5	6.004	1.066
475	23.23	474.2	6.148	1.055	17.57	473.1	6.062	1.065
500	24.48	500.6	6.202	1.057	18.52	499.8	6.116	1.065
550	26.96	553.5	6.303	1.062	20.40	553.1	6.218	1.068
600	29.43	606.8	6.396	1.069	22.26	606.7	6.311	1.075
650	31.88	660.5	6.482	1.078	24.11	660.6	6.397	1.083
700	34.32	714.6	6.562	1.088	25.96	714.9	6.477	1.092
750	36.76	769.2	6.637	1.098	27.80	769.7	6.553	1.101
800	39.19	824.3	6.708	1.108	29.63	825.1	6.624	1.111
850	41.61	880.0	6.776	1.118	31.46	880.9	6.692	1.121
900	44.03	936.2	6.840	1.128	33.28	937.2	6.756	1.131
950	46.45	992.8	6.901	1.138	35.10	993.9	6.818	1.140
1000	48.87	1050.0	6.960	1.147	36.92	1051.1	6.877	1.149
1050	51.28	1107.5	7.016	1.156	38.73	1108.8	6.933	1.157
1100	53.69	1165.5	7.070	1.164	40.54	1166.9	6.987	1.165
1150	56.10	1223.9	7.122	1.171	42.35	1225.3	7.039	1.173
1200	58.51	1282.6	7.172	1.178	44.16	1284.1	7.089	1.180
1250	60.92	1341.7	7.220	1.185	45.97	1343.3	7.137	1.187
1300	63.32	1401.1	7.267	1.192	47.78	1402.8	7.184	1.193
	$p=100$ bar				$p=150$ bar			
75	1.0976	−124.5	2.867	1.774	1.088	−120.8	2.845	1.749
80	1.1223	−115.8	2.978	1.789	1.111	−112.2	2.954	1.758
85	1.1492	−106.9	3.085	1.803	1.136	−103.4	3.058	1.767

continued

T, °K	v	i	s	c_p	v	i	s	c_p
90	1.1784	−97.8	3.186	1.818	1.163	−94.5	3.158	1.777
95	1.2102	−88.6	3.283	1.834	1.191	−85.6	3.252	1.787
100	1.2448	−79.4	3.376	1.852	1.222	−76.6	3.342	1.798
105	1.2828	−70.1	3.465	1.873	1.255	−67.6	3.428	1.809
110	1.3247	−60.7	3.552	1.900	1.290	−58.5	3.512	1.823
115	1.3711	−51.1	3.637	1.937	1.328	−49.4	3.593	1.843
120	1.4231	−41.3	3.721	1.992	1.369	−40.1	3.673	1.870
125	1.4823	−31.1	3.805	2.062	1.414	−30.6	3.751	1.904
130	1.5514	−20.3	3.891	2.170	1.463	−20.7	3.829	1.947
135	1.636	−8.7	3.982	2.320	1.519	−10.3	3.909	1.998
140	1.744	3.9	4.076	2.506	1.583	0.5	3.988	2.059
145	1.880	17.6	4.178	2.682	1.656	11.5	4.067	2.126
150	2.053	32.8	4.271	2.832	1.740	22.8	4.144	2.183
160	2.521	61.7	4.457	2.874	1.941	45.2	4.287	2.243
170	3.092	88.8	4.622	2.508	2.188	67.7	4.423	2.227
180	3.660	111.8	4.753	2.114	2.473	89.5	4.548	2.130
190	4.187	131.5	4.860	1.836	2.777	110.1	4.659	2.984
200	4.674	148.8	4.949	1.650	3.086	129.2	4.757	1.832
210	5.130	164.6	5.026	1.522	3.391	146.8	4.843	1.699
220	5.561	179.4	5.095	1.431	3.687	163.2	4.919	1.591
230	5.973	193.4	5.157	1.363	3.973	178.7	4.988	1.504
240	6.369	206.7	5.214	1.311	4.251	193.4	5.051	1.435
250	6.753	219.6	5.266	1.271	4.521	207.4	5.108	1.379
260	7.128	232.2	5.315	1.239	4.784	221.0	5.161	1.335
270	7.493	244.4	5.362	1.213	5.041	234.2	5.211	1.298
280	7.852	256.4	5.406	1.191	5.293	247.0	5.257	1.267
290	8.204	268.3	5.447	1.173	5.540	259.5	5.301	1.242
300	8.551	279.9	5.486	1.158	5.783	271.8	5.343	1.220
310	8.894	291.4	5.524	1.146	6.022	283.9	5.383	1.202
320	9.232	302.8	5.560	1.135	6.258	295.9	5.421	1.186
330	9.567	314.1	5.595	1.125	6.491	307.7	5.457	1.173
340	9.898	325.3	5.629	1.117	6.721	319.3	5.492	1.161
350	10.23	336.5	5.661	1.110	6.950	330.9	5.525	1.151
375	11.04	364.0	5.737	1.096	7.511	359.4	5.604	1.131
400	11.84	391.3	5.807	1.087	8.062	387.5	5.677	1.117
425	12.62	418.4	5.873	1.080	8.605	415.3	5.744	1.106
450	13.40	445.3	5.935	1.076	9.140	442.9	5.807	1.099
475	14.17	472.2	5.993	1.074	9.670	470.2	5.867	1.095
500	14.94	499.0	6.048	1.073	10.19	497.5	5.922	1.092
550	16.45	552.7	6.150	1.075	11.23	552.1	6.026	1.090
600	17.97	606.6	6.244	1.080	12.26	606.6	6.121	1.093
650	19.46	660.8	6.331	1.087	13.27	661.4	6.209	1.098
700	20.95	715.3	6.412	1.096	14.27	716.5	6.291	1.105
750	22.43	770.3	6.488	1.105	15.27	771.9	6.367	1.113
800	23.90	825.8	6.559	1.114	16.26	827.8	6.439	1.121
850	25.37	881.8	6.627	1.124	17.25	884.1	6.507	1.130
900	26.83	938.2	6.691	1.133	18.24	940.8	6.572	1.139
950	28.29	994.9	6.753	1.142	19.22	997.9	6.634	1.147
1000	29.75	1052.4	6.812	1.151	20.20	1055.5	6.693	1.155
1050	31.21	1110.1	6.868	1.159	21.18	1113.5	6.750	1.163
1100	32.66	1168.2	6.922	1.167	22.15	1171.8	6.804	1.170
1150	34.11	1226.7	6.974	1.174	23.12	1230.5	6.856	1.177
1200	35.56	1285.6	7.024	1.181	24.09	1289.5	6.906	1.184
1250	37.01	1344.8	7.073	1.188	25.06	1348.9	6.955	1.190
1300	38.46	1404.4	7.120	1.194	26.03	1408.6	7.002	1.196
		$p=200$ bar				$p=300$ bar		
75	1.0791	−117.0	2.823	1.726				
80	1.1008	−108.5	2.930	1.733	1.0823	−101.0	2.888	1.694
85	1.1239	−99.9	3.038	1.740	1.1028	−92.5	2.988	1.698
90	1.1485	−91.2	3.130	1.747	1.1242	−84.0	3.083	1.703
95	1.1747	−82.4	3.224	1.753	1.1466	−75.5	3.174	1.703
100	1.2023	−73.6	3.312	1.761	1.1699	−67.0	3.260	1.713
105	1.2316	−64.8	3.396	1.767	1.1941	−58.4	3.342	1.718

continued

T, °K	v	i	s	c_p	v	i	s	c_p
110	1.2625	−55.9	3.477	1.776	1.2191	−49.8	3.421	1.724
115	1.2952	−47.0	3.556	1.789	1.2450	−41.1	3.497	1.732
120	1.3296	−38.0	3.634	1.809	1.2717	−32.4	3.572	1.740
125	1.3663	−28.9	3.709	1.831	1.2994	−23.7	3.644	1.748
130	1.4055	−19.5	3.784	1.856	1.3284	−14.9	3.714	1.757
135	1.450	−9.8	3.858	1.881	1.3590	−6.0	3.782	1.763
140	1.497	0.2	3.931	1.905	1.3921	3.1	3.849	1.769
145	1.549	10.3	4.001	1.928	1.4285	12.3	3.913	1.774
150	1.606	20.5	4.071	1.951	1.466	21.5	3.976	1.776
160	1.737	40.2	4.198	1.988	1.547	39.2	4.090	1.777
170	1.890	60.1	4.319	1.986	1.636	56.9	4.198	1.769
180	2.063	79.8	4.432	1.953	1.734	74.5	4.298	1.751
190	2.253	99.0	4.536	1.893	1.838	91.9	4.392	1.723
200	2.454	117.6	4.631	1.814	1.949	109.0	4.480	1.689
210	2.661	135.4	4.717	1.728	2.066	125.7	4.561	1.650
220	2.870	152.2	4.796	1.643	2.186	142.0	4.637	1.607
230	3.078	168.3	4.867	1.567	2.309	157.8	4.707	1.562
240	3.283	183.6	4.932	1.501	2.434	173.2	4.773	1.518
250	3.485	198.3	4.992	1.444	2.560	188.2	4.834	1.477
260	3.684	212.5	5.048	1.396	2.685	202.7	4.891	1.438
270	3.879	226.2	5.100	1.355	2.811	216.9	4.945	1.402
280	4.071	239.6	5.149	1.321	2.936	230.8	4.995	1.370
290	4.260	252.7	5.195	1.291	3.060	244.4	5.043	1.341
300	4.446	265.5	5.238	1.266	3.183	257.7	5.088	1.316
310	4.629	278.0	5.279	1.245	3.305	270.7	5.131	1.293
320	4.810	290.4	5.318	1.226	3.426	283.5	5.171	1.273
330	4.989	302.6	5.356	1.210	3.546	296.1	5.210	1.255
340	5.167	314.6	5.392	1.196	3.666	308.6	5.247	1.240
350	5.342	326.5	5.426	1.184	3.785	320.9	5.283	1.226
375	5.774	355.8	5.507	1.159	4.078	351.2	5.367	1.197
400	6.197	384.5	5.581	1.141	4.367	380.9	5.443	1.176
425	6.613	412.8	5.650	1.128	4.651	410.1	5.514	1.160
450	7.024	440.9	5.715	1.119	4.932	438.9	5.580	1.148
475	7.429	468.8	5.775	1.112	5.209	467.5	5.642	1.139
500	7.831	496.6	5.831	1.108	5.484	495.9	5.700	1.133
550	8.623	551.8	5.937	1.104	6.026	552.3	5.808	1.126
600	9.403	607.0	6.033	1.104	6.560	608.5	5.906	1.124
650	10.17	662.3	6.121	1.108	7.087	664.7	5.996	1.125
700	10.94	717.9	6.204	1.114	7.608	721.1	6.079	1.129
750	11.70	773.7	6.281	1.121	8.124	777.6	6.157	1.134
800	12.45	829.9	6.353	1.128	8.636	834.5	6.230	1.140
850	13.20	886.5	6.422	1.136	9.144	891.7	6.300	1.147
900	13.94	943.5	6.487	1.144	9.650	949.2	6.366	1.154
950	14.68	1000.9	6.549	1.152	10.15	1007.1	6.428	1.161
1000	15.42	1058.7	6.608	1.160	10.65	1065.3	6.488	1.168
1050	16.16	1116.9	6.665	1.167	11.15	1123.9	6.545	1.175
1100	16.90	1175.4	6.720	1.174	11.65	1182.8	6.600	1.181
1150	17.64	1234.3	6.772	1.181	12.14	1242.0	6.652	1.187
1200	18.37	1293.5	6.822	1.187	12.64	1301.5	6.703	1.193
1250	19.10	1353.0	6.871	1.193	13.13	1361.3	6.752	1.199
1300	19.83	1412.8	6.918	1.199	13.62	1421.4	6.799	1.204
		$p=400$ bar				$p=500$ bar		
85	1.0846	−85.0	2.949	1.669				
90	1.1037	−76.6	3.042	1.674	1.0859	−69.0	3.005	1.655
95	1.1234	−68.2	3.132	1.680	1.1035	−60.7	3.094	1.663
100	1.1436	−59.8	3.216	1.686	1.1215	−52.3	3.177	1.670
105	1.1644	−51.4	3.296	1.692	1.1399	−48.9	3.257	1.678
110	1.1857	−42.9	3.374	1.698	1.1584	−35.5	3.334	1.683
115	1.2074	−34.4	3.450	1.702	1.1772	−27.1	3.409	1.686
120	1.2295	−25.9	3.523	1.704	1.1963	−18.7	3.482	1.686
125	1.2522	−17.4	3.593	1.705	1.2157	−10.3	3.551	1.683
130	1.2756	−8.8	3.661	1.706	1.2356	−2.0	3.617	1.679
135	1.3002	−0.8	3.725	1.704	1.2563	6.2	3.681	1.673

continued

T, °K	v	i	s	c_p	v	i	s	c_p
140	1.3263	8.3	3.788	1.702	1.2781	14.4	3.743	1.667
145	1.3541	16.8	3.849	1.700	1.3012	22.7	3.802	1,660
150	1.3832	25.4	3.907	1.696	1.3250	30.9	3.860	1.651
160	1.4450	42.4	4.016	1.685	1.3750	47.4	3.966	1.644
170	1.511	59.2	4.119	1.668	1.428	63.7	4.060	1.619
180	1.580	75.8	4.214	1.654	1.484	79.8	4.151	1.598
190	1.653	92.3	4.303	1.633	1.541	95.7	4.237	1.580
200	1.730	108.5	4.386	1.607	1.601	111.4	4.317	1.557
210	1.810	124.4	4.464	1.579	1.662	126.8	4.392	1.533
220	1.892	140.1	4.537	1.550	1.725	142.0	4.463	1.509
230	1.977	155.5	4.605	1.521	1.789	157.0	4.530	1.485
240	2.063	170.5	4.669	1,490	1.855	171.7	4.593	1.461
250	2.151	185.2	4.729	1.460	1.922	186.2	4.652	1.438
260	2.240	199.7	4.786	1.431	1.990	200.5	4.708	1.415
270	2.329	213.9	4.839	1.404	2.059	214.6	4.761	1.392
280	2.419	227.8	4.890	1.378	2.128	228.4	4.811	1.371
290	2.509	241.4	4.938	1.353	2.197	242.0	4.859	1.351
300	2.599	254.8	4.983	1.331	2.267	255.4	4.905	1.331
310	2.688	268.0	5.026	1.310	2.337	268.6	4.948	1.313
320	2.777	281.0	5.067	1.292	2.406	281.6	4.989	1.297
330	2.866	293.9	5.107	1.275	2.476	294.5	5.029	1.282
340	2.955	306.6	5.145	1.260	2.546	307.3	5.067	1.268
350	3.043	319.1	5.181	1.246	2.615	319.9	5.103	1.255
375	3.262	349.9	5.266	1.217	2.788	350.9	5.189	1.227
400	3.478	380.0	5.344	1.195	2.960	381.3	5.267	1.206
425	3.692	409.7	5.416	1.179	3.131	411.2	5.340	1.189
450	3.904	439.0	5.483	1.166	3.301	440.8	5.408	1.176
475	4.115	468.0	5.546	1.156	3.469	470.1	5.471	1.167
500	4.324	496.8	5.605	1.149	3.636	499.1	5.531	1.159
550	4.737	554.0	5.714	1.141	3.968	556.8	5.641	1.151
600	5.144	611.0	5.813	1.138	4,297	614.3	5.741	1.148
650	5.546	667.8	5.904	1.138	4.622	671.7	5.833	1.148
700	5.943	724.8	5.989	1.141	4.944	729.1	5.918	1.150
750	6.337	782.0	6.068	1.146	5.263	786.7	5.997	1.154
800	6.728	839.4	6.142	1.151	5.580	844.6	6.072	1.159
850	7.115	897.1	6.212	1.157	5.894	902.7	6.143	1.165
900	7.500	955.1	6.278	1.163	6.206	961.1	6.209	1.171
950	7.883	1013.4	6.341	1.170	6.516	1019.8	6.272	1.177
1000	8.263	1072.0	6.401	1.176	6.825	1078.8	6.333	1.183
1050	8.642	1131.0	6.459	1.182	7.132	1138.1	6.391	1.189
1100	9.019	1190.3	6.514	1.188	7.437	1197.7	6.446	1.195
1150	9.394	1249.8	6.567	1.194	7.741	1257.5	6.499	1.200
1200	9.768	1309.6	6.618	1.199	8.043	1317.6	6.550	1.205
1250	10.14	1369.7	6.667	1.204	8.345	1377.9	6.599	1,210
1300	10.51	1430.0	6.714	1.209	8.646	1438.5	6.647	1.214
		p=600 bar				p=700 bar		
190	1.464	100.7	4.184	1.545				
200	1.513	116.0	2.263	1.525				
210	1.563	131.2	4,337	1.502	1.490	136.6	4.290	1.481
220	1.614	146.1	4,406	1.480	1.534	151.3	4.359	1.460
230	1.666	160.8	4.472	1.459	1.578	165.8	4.423	1.439
240	1.720	175.3	4.533	1.438	1.623	180.1	4.484	1.420
250	1.774	189.5	4.591	1.418	1.668	194,2	4.541	1.402
260	1.829	203.6	4.646	1.398	1.715	208.1	4,596	1.384
270	1.884	217.5	4.699	1.379	1.761	221.9	4.648	1.367
280	1.940	231.2	4.749	1.361	1.808	235.5	4.698	1.351
290	1.996	244.7	4.797	1.344	1.856	248.9	4.745	1.336
300	2.053	258.1	4.842	1.327	1.903	262.2	4.790	1.321
310	2.110	271.3	4.885	1.311	1.951	275.3	4.833	1.307
320	2.167	284.3	4.926	1.296	1.999	288.3	4.874	1.293
330	2.224	297.2	4.966	1.282	2.047	301.2	4.914	1.281
340	2.281	310.0	5.004	1.270	2.095	314.0	4.952	1.269
350	2.338	322.6	5.041	1.258	2.144	326.6	4.988	1.258

continued

T, °K	v	i	s	c_p	v	i	s	c_p
375	2.480	353.7	5.126	1.232	2.265	357.7	5.074	1,234
400	2.622	384.2	5.205	1.211	2.385	388.3	5.153	1.214
425	2.763	414.3	5.278	1.195	2.505	418.5	5.226	1.198
450	2.904	444.0	5.346	1.182	2.625	448.3	5.294	1.186
475	3.044	473.4	5.410	1.173	2.744	477.8	5.359	1.176
500	3.183	502.6	5.470	1.166	2.863	507.1	5.418	1.169
550	3.460	560.7	5.581	1.157	3.100	565.3	5.529	1.161
600	3.735	618.5	5.681	1.154	3.336	623.3	5.630	1.158
650	4.008	676.1	5.778	1.154	3.570	681.2	5.723	1.159
700	4.278	733.9	5.859	1.157	3.803	739.2	5.809	1.162
750	4.546	791.9	5.939	1.161	4.034	797.4	5.890	1.166
800	4.813	850.1	6.014	1.166	4.264	855.8	5.965	1.171
850	5.078	908.5	6.085	1.172	4.493	914.5	6.036	1.177
900	5.341	967.2	6.152	1.177	4.720	973.5	6.103	1.183
950	5.602	1026.2	6.216	1.183	4.946	1032.8	6.167	1.188
1000	5.862	1085.5	6.277	1.189	5.171	1092.4	6.228	1.194
1050	6.120	1145.1	6.335	1.195	5.395	1152.2	6.287	1.200
1100	6.377	1205.0	6.391	1.200	5.618	1212.3	6.343	1.205
1150	6.633	1265.1	6.444	1.205	5.839	1272.7	6.396	1.210
1200	6.888	1325.5	6.495	1.210	6.059	1333.3	6.448	1.215
1250	7.142	1386.1	6.545	1.215	6.279	1394.1	6.498	1.219
1300	7.395	1446.9	6.593	1.219	6.498	1455.2	6.546	1.223
	$p=800$ bar				$p=900$ bar			
220	1.472	157.4	4.318	1.445				
230	1.510	171.7	4.382	1.425	1.456	178.1	4.345	1.414
240	1.549	185.9	4.442	1.406	1,490	192.2	4.405	1.396
250	1.588	199.9	4.499	1.389	1.525	206.1	4.462	1.379
260	1.628	213.7	4.553	1.372	1.560	219.8	4.515	1.363
270	1.668	227.3	4.604	1.356	1.596	233.4	4.566	1.348
280	1.709	240.3	4.653	1.342	1.632	246.8	4.615	1.334
290	1.750	254.1	4.700	1.328	1.668	260.0	4.662	1.321
300	1.791	267.3	4.745	1.314	1.704	273.2	4.706	1.309
310	1.832	280.4	4.788	1.302	1.740	286.2	4,749	1.297
320	1.874	293.4	4.829	1.290	1.777	299.1	4.790	1.286
330	1.916	306.2	4.869	1.278	1.814	311.9	4.829	1,275
340	1.958	318.9	4.907	1.267	1.851	324.6	4.867	1.265
350	2.000	331.6	4.943	1.257	1.888	337.2	4.904	1.256
375	2.104	362.7	5.029	1.235	1.980	368.3	4.990	1.235
400	2.209	393.8	5.108	1.216	2.073	399.0	5.069	1.217
425	2.314	423.5	5.181	1.200	2.166	429.2	5.142	1.202
450	2.418	453.4	5.250	1.188	2.258	459.1	5.211	1.190
475	2.522	483.0	5.314	1.179	2.350	488.7	5.275	1.181
500	2.626	512.3	5.374	1.172	2.442	518.1	5.335	1.174
550	2.832	570.7	5.485	1.164	2.625	576.6	5.446	1.165
600	3.038	625.8	5.586	1.161	2.808	634.8	5.548	1.163
650	3.243	686.8	5.679	1.162	2.990	692.9	5.641	1.164
700	3.447	745.0	5.765	1.165	3.171	751.1	5.727	1.167
750	3.650	803.4	5.846	1.169	3.351	809.6	5.808	1.172
800	3.852	862.0	5.922	1.175	3.531	868.4	5.884	1.177
850	4.053	920.8	5.993	1.181	3.710	927.4	5.956	1.183
900	4.253	980.0	6.061	1.187	3.889	986.7	6.023	1.190
950	4.452	1039.5	6.125	1.192	4.067	1046.3	6.087	1.196
1000	4.651	1099.3	6.136	1.198	4.244	1106.8	6.149	1.202
1050	4.848	1159.3	6.245	1.204	4.421	1166.5	6.208	1,207
1100	5.044	1219.6	6.301	1.209	4.597	1227.0	6.268	1.212
1150	5.240	1280.2	6.355	1.214	4.772	1287.7	6.318	1.217
1200	5.435	1341.0	6.407	1.219	4.946	1348.7	6.370	1.222
1250	5.629	1402.0	6.456	1.223	5.120	1409.9	6.420	1.227
1300	5.822	1463.3	6.505	1.227	5.293	1471.4	6,468	1.231

continued

T, °K	v	i	s	c_p	T, °K	v	i	s	c_p
				p=1000 bar					
250	1.473	212.8	4.428	1.371	550	2.460	583.0	5,412	1,167
260	1.505	226.4	4.482	1.355	600	2.624	641.2	5.513	1.164
270	1.537	239.9	4.533	1.340	650	2.787	699.4	5.606	1.165
280	1.569	253.2	4.582	1.327	700	2.950	757.7	5.693	1.168
290	1.601	266.4	4.628	1.315	750	3.113	816.3	5.774	1.173
300	1.633	279.5	4.672	1.303	800	3.275	875.1	5.850	1.179
310	1.666	292.5	4.714	1.292	850	3.437	934.2	5.921	1.185
320	1.699	305.4	4.755	1.282	900	3.598	993.6	5.989	1.192
330	1.732	318.1	4.795	1.272	950	3.759	1053.3	6.054	1,198
340	1.765	330.8	4.832	1.263	1000	3.919	1113.3	6.115	1.204
350	1.798	343.4	4.869	1.254	1050	4.079	1173.7	6.174	1.210
375	1.881	374.5	4.955	1.234	1100	4.238	1234.4	6.231	1.215
400	1.964	405.1	5.034	1.217	1150	4.396	1295.3	6.285	1.220
425	2.048	435.4	5.107	1.203	1200	4.554	1356.4	6.337	1.225
450	2.131	465.3	5.176	1.192	1250	4.711	1417.8	6.387	1.230
475	2.214	495.0	5.240	1.182	1300	4.868	1479.4	6.435	1.234
500	2.296	524.4	5.300	1.175					

THERMODYNAMIC PROPERTIES OF AIR

The table for thermodynamic properties of air given below, as well as the tables for nitrogen and oxygen at high temperatures and in the dissociated state, were calculated by P. M. Kesselman and A. S. Bestuzhev taking into account the nonideal properties of the gas [143]. They have assumed the following basic composition of air (by volume): 78.08% N_2, 20.95% O_2, and the remaining-argon. Analysis of equilibrium constants and approximate calculations showed that, within the considered temperature and pressure ranges, the presence of the following components must be taken into account: N_2, O_2, NO, Ar, O and N.

The thermodynamic properties of molecular components were calculated from the equation of state with two virial coefficients $B(t)$ and $C(t)$ in accordance with the method described in Ref. [345]. The non-ideal properties of atomic components were taken into account by the second virial coefficients obtained in [375], because the concentration of atomic components is of importance only at comparatively moderate pressures, when the effect of third virial coefficients is negligibly small.

For the calculation of second virial coefficients by different methods (spectroscopic data, on the basis of δ-function model, from quantum-mechanical relationships, on the basis of the electrostatic Gell-Mann-Feynman theorem, etc) curves of the potential energy of the interaction of atoms of nitrogen and oxygen in different electronic states were obtained. The integration was carried out in the phase-space domain, where the formation of links is impossible.

The values of the thermodynamic functions of components in the ideal-gas state were taken from Ref. [346], taking 0 °K as a reference temperature.

The composition of dissociated mixture was determined by solving a system of chemical equilibrium equations at different temperatures and pressures. The non-ideal properties of the mixtures were taken into account by introducing the coefficient K_γ. The equilibrium constant was found from the ratio:

$$K_p = \frac{K_p{}^0}{K_\gamma}$$

The values of $K_p{}^0$ were taken from Ref. [346], and the values of K_γ were calculated from the equation:

$$K_\gamma = \Pi \gamma_i^{\nu_i},$$

where γ_i are the activity coefficients of components, calculated from data for virial coefficients, and ν_i are the stoichiometric reaction numbers.

The data for the virial coefficients of the components and for the compositions, were used to derive necessary expressions for the calculation of thermodynamic properties, taking both the real properties and chemical reactions into account.

Thermodynamic properties of dissociated air:
v (m³/kg), i (kJ/kg), s and c_p (kJ/kg · deg)

T, °K	v	i	s	c_p	v	i	s	c_p
		p=0.1 bar				p=0.2 bar		
1300	37.32	1 396	9.1027	1.190	18.66	1 396	8.9037	1.190
1350	38.75	1 455	9.1480	1.198	19.38	1 455	8.9490	1.198
1400	40.19	1 515	9.1919	1.207	20.09	1 515	8.9930	1.207
1450	41.62	1 575	9.2347	1.218	20.81	1 575	9.0357	1.218
1500	43.06	1 640	9.2762	1.230	21.53	1 640	9.0773	1.230
1600	45.93	1 764	9.3563	1.250	22.97	1 764	9.1573	1.249
1700	48.80	1 890	9.4327	1.271	24.40	1 890	9.2336	1.268
1800	51.67	2 017	9.5060	1.296	25.84	2 017	9.3067	1.291
1900	54.55	2 148	9.5770	1.327	27.27	2 148	9.3774	1.318
2000	57.44	2 285	9.6465	1.379	28.72	2 283	9.4482	1.362
2100	60.34	2 427	9.7155	1.454	30.16	2 422	9.5140	1.419
2200	63.27	2 577	9.7855	1.562	31.62	2 567	9.5817	1.500
2300	66.25	2 740	9.8581	1.717	33.09	2 723	9.6508	1.615
2400	69,31	2 923	9.9355	1.935	34.59	2 892	9.7227	1.775
2500	72.48	3 130	10.0202	2.228	36.14	3 079	9.7994	1.991
2600	75.81	3 371	10.1146	2.604	37.74	3 292	9.8827	2.271
2700	79.35	3 653	10.2212	3.059	39.42	3 536	9.9747	2.617
2800	83.17	3 985	10.3416	3.573	41.20	3 817	10.0770	3.024
2900	87.29	4 368	10.4762	4.097	43.10	4 142	10.1909	3.471
3000	91.75	4 802	10.6232	4.555	45.15	4 512	10.3162	3.918
3100	96.51	5 274	10.7779	4.851	47.35	4 924	10.4512	4.305
3200	101.5	5 763	10.9334	4.900	49.68	5 368	10.5924	4.563
3300	106.5	6 245	11.0814	4.676	52.11	5 830	10.7344	4.630
3400	111.5	6 692	11.2149	4.233	54.60	6 287	10.8709	4.480
3500	116.3	7 088	11.3298	3.690	57.07	6 720	10.9963	4.146
3600	120.9	7 430	11.4263	3.166	59.47	7 113	11.1071	3.707
3700	125.3	7 725	11.5069	2.738	61.79	7 461	11.2025	3.255
3800	129.4	7 982	11.5756	2.430	64.00	7 776	11.2838	2.859
3900	133.5	8 214	11.6360	2.239	66.13	8 036	11.3540	2.555
4000	137.4	8 435	11.6913	2.146	68.19	8 280	11.4159	2.349
4100	141.3	8 646	11.7440	2.138	70.19	8 509	11.4723	2.233
4200	145.2	8 863	11.7962	2.202	72.16	8 729	11.5255	2.196
4300	149.1	9 089	11.8491	2.332	74.13	8 950	11.5774	2.229
4400	153.1	9 332	11.9051	2.529	76.10	9 177	11.6291	2.325
4500	157.1	9 597	11.9648	2.793	78.09	9 417	11.6835	2.480
4600	161.3	9 893	12.0297	3.130	80.12	9 675	11.7402	2.696
4700	165.7	10 221	12.1014	3.545	82.20	9 958	11.8011	2.974
4800	170.2	10 604	12.1811	4.046	84.35	10 272	11.8672	3.319
4900	175.1	11 038	12.2704	4.638	86.59	10 624	11.9398	3.734
5000	180.2	11 536	12.3709	5.330	88.94	11 022	12.0200	4.225
5200	191.7	12 764	12.6117	7.027	94.07	11 984	12.2085	5.452
5400	205.2	14 374	12.9152	9.133	99.94	13 225	12.4477	7.025
5600	221.3	16 438	13.2903	11.543	106.8	14 816	12.7316	8.927
5800	240.4	18 993	13.7383	13.974	114.8	16 812	13.0817	11.058
6000	262.4	21 996	14.2471	15.921	124.2	19 239	13.4929	13.184
		p=0.4 bar				p=0.6 bar		
1300	9.330	1 396	8.7047	1.190	6.220	1 396	8.5884	1.190
1350	9.689	1 455	8.7500	1.198	6.460	1 455	8.6336	1.199
1400	10.05	1 515	8.7940	1.207	6.699	1 515	8.6776	1.207
1450	10.41	1 575	8.8367	1.218	6.938	1 575	8.7203	1.218
1500	10.77	1 640	8.8783	1.230	7.177	1 640	8.7619	1.230
1600	11.48	1 764	8.9583	1.248	7.656	1 764	8.8419	1.248
1700	12.20	1 890	9.0346	1.267	8.134	1 890	8.9181	1.267
1800	12.92	2 017	9.1046	1.288	8.613	2 017	8.9911	1.288
1900	13.64	2 148	9.1780	1.314	9.092	2 147	9.0614	1.311
2000	14.36	2 281	9.2463	1.349	9.571	2 280	9.1295	1.343
2100	15.08	2 418	9.3132	1.394	10.05	2 416	9.1960	1.383
2200	15.80	2 560	9.3794	1.456	10.53	2 557	9.2615	1.437
2300	16.54	2 710	9.4459	1.542	11.02	2 704	9.3269	1.510
2400	17.28	2 870	9.5139	1.661	11.51	2 860	9.3931	1.610
2500	18,03	3 049	9.5848	1.820	12.01	3 027	9.4614	1.743

continued

T, °K	v	i	s	c_p	v	i	s	c_p
2600	18.82	3 235	9.6599	2.026	12.52	3 210	9.5330	1.916
2700	19.61	3 450	9.7412	2.285	13.05	3 412	9.6092	2.133
2800	20.46	3 694	9.8398	2.597	13.60	3 638	9.6915	2.398
2900	21.35	3 971	9.9270	2.954	14.17	3 893	9.7808	2.705
3000	22.30	4 286	10.0336	3.338	14.78	4 180	9.8782	3.044
3100	23.31	4 639	10.1493	3.717	15.42	4 502	9.9837	3.395
3200	24.39	5 028	10.2727	4.048	16.11	4 859	10.0969	3.726
3300	25.53	5 445	10.4011	4.279	16.83	5 246	10.2159	3.998
3400	26.71	5 879	10.5305	4.365	17.60	5 655	10.3381	4.171
3500	27.93	6 312	10.6563	4.283	18.39	6 075	10.4599	4.209
3600	29.15	6 730	10.7740	4.049	19.19	6 492	10.5773	4.104
3700	30.35	7 119	10.8805	3.710	19.99	6 892	10.6869	3.874
3800	31.51	7 471	10.9744	3.334	20.78	7 264	10.7862	3.565
3900	32.64	7 786	11.0563	2.980	21.55	7 604	10.8745	3.232
4000	33.72	8 069	11.1279	2.687	22.30	7 911	10.9525	2.922
4100	34.77	8 326	11.1915	2.471	23.02	8 190	11.0212	2.665
4200	35.80	8 566	11.2492	2.333	23.72	8 447	11.0830	2.476
4300	36.80	8 795	11.3032	2.268	24.41	8 688	11.1398	2.357
4400	37.80	9 022	11.3553	2.268	25.08	8 920	11.1932	2.302
4500	38.79	9 251	11.4068	2.327	25.75	9 151	11.2449	2.307
4600	39.79	9 489	11.4591	2.442	26.42	9 384	11.2962	2.368
4700	40.81	9 741	11.5133	2.611	27.09	9 626	11.3488	2.480
4800	41.84	10 013	11.5705	2.843	27.77	9 881	11.4020	2.643
4900	42.90	10 310	11.6317	3.114	28.46	10 156	11.4587	2.857
5000	44.00	10 638	11.6980	3.452	29.18	10 455	11.5190	3.123
5200	46.35	11 410	11.8494	4.320	30.68	11 145	11.6543	3.821
5400	48.96	12 384	12.0329	5.461	32.33	11 999	11.8153	4.756
5600	51.93	13 614	12.2565	6.889	34.17	13 065	12.0090	5.945
5800	55.35	15 157	12.5270	8.580	36.26	14 393	12.2420	7.383
6000	59.32	17 058	12.8491	10.448	38.67	16 032	12.5195	9.029
		p=0.8 bar				p=1 bar		
1300	4.666	1 396	8.5051	1.190	3.733	1 396	8.4417	1.190
1350	4.845	1 455	8.5300	1.199	3.876	1 455	8.4870	1.199
1400	5.024	1 515	8.5950	1.207	4.020	1 515	8.5310	1.207
1450	5.204	1 575	8.6377	1.218	4.163	1 575	8.5737	1.218
1500	5.383	1 640	8.6793	1.230	4.307	1 640	8.6153	1.230
1600	5.742	1 764	8.7593	1.248	4.594	1 764	8.6952	1.248
1700	6.101	1 890	8.8355	1.267	4.881	1 890	8.7715	1.267
1800	6.460	2 017	8.9085	1.287	5.168	2 017	8.8444	1.267
1900	6.819	2 147	8.9788	1.309	5.455	2 147	8.9146	1.286
2000	7.178	2 280	9.0467	1.339	5.743	2 279	8.9825	1.307
2100	7.539	2 415	9.1129	1.376	6.031	2 415	9.0485	1.337
2200	7.900	2 555	9.1780	1.425	6.320	2 554	9.1133	1.372
2300	8.264	2 701	9.2427	1.491	6.611	2 699	9.1776	1.417
2400	8.631	2 854	9.3079	1.579	6.904	2 850	9.2421	1.478
2500	9.003	3 018	9.3747	1.697	7.200	3 011	9.3078	1.558
2600	9.383	3 195	9.4441	1.849	7.502	3 184	9.3757	1.665
2700	9.774	3 389	9.5173	2.041	7.812	3 375	9.4469	1.803
2800	10.18	3 604	9.5957	2.275	8.132	3 581	9.5225	1.978
2900	10.60	3 845	9.6802	2.550	8.464	3 812	9.6037	2.191
3000	11.04	4 116	9.7718	2.858	8.813	4 071	9.6912	2.419
3100	11.51	4 418	9.8708	3.184	9.180	4 358	9.7855	2.726
3200	12.01	4 752	9.9770	3.505	9.569	4 677	9.8867	3.032
3300	12.54	5 117	10.0893	3.788	9.980	5 026	9.9938	3.340
3400	13.02	5 507	10.2057	3.998	10.42	5 400	10.1056	3.624
3500	13.67	5 913	10.3234	4.101	10.87	5 793	10.2196	3.852
3600	14.26	6 325	10.4389	4.077	11.33	6 195	10.3323	3.994
3700	14.86	6 725	10.5489	3.930	11.81	6 594	10.4421	4.024
3800	15.46	7 106	10.6506	3.685	12.28	6 979	10.5448	3.937
3900	16.04	7 460	10.7426	3.389	12.75	7 341	10.6389	3.747
4000	16.61	7 784	10.8245	3.087	13.22	7 676	10.7237	3.490
4100	17.16	8 079	10.8973	2.817	13.66	7 983	10.7995	3.207
4200	17.70	8 349	10.9625	2.600	14.09	8 265	10.8674	2.936

continued

T, °K	v	i	s	c_p	v	i	s	c_p
4300	18.22	8 601	11.0218	2.446	14.52	8 526	10.9288	2.529
4400	18.74	8 840	11.0768	2.355	14.94	8 772	10.9855	2.411
4500	19.24	9 074	11.1293	2.323	15.35	9 010	11.0389	2.352
4600	19.75	9 307	11.1805	2.357	15.75	9 245	11.0905	2.347
4700	20.25	9 545	11.2317	2.421	16.16	9 481	11.1414	2.393
4800	20.76	9 793	11.2839	2.545	16.56	9 725	11.1927	2.488
4900	21.27	10 055	11.3380	2.717	16.97	9 980	11.2453	2.629
5000	21.80	10 338	11.3951	2.937	17.39	10 252	11.3003	2.816
5200	22.90	10 981	11.5211	3.528	18.26	10 864	11.4201	3.333
5400	24.00	11 763	11.6687	4.335	19.19	11 599	11.5587	4.049
5600	25.42	12 730	11.8443	5.372	20.21	12 498	11.7221	4.980
5800	26.90	13 928	12.0544	6.645	21.35	13 605	11.9163	6.131
6000	28.59	15 402	12.3042	8.128	22.65	14 964	12.1466	7.491
		$p=2$ bar				$p=3$ bar		
1300	1.867	1 396	8.2427	1.191	1.245	1 396	8.1264	1.191
1350	1.939	1 455	8.2880	1.199	1.293	1 456	8.1716	1.199
1400	2.010	1 515	8.3320	1.207	1.341	1 515	8.2156	1.207
1450	2.082	1 576	8.3747	1.218	1.388	1 576	8.2583	1.218
1500	2.154	1 640	8.4163	1.230	1.436	1 640	8.2999	1.230
1600	2.297	1 764	8.4963	1.248	1.532	1 764	8.3799	1.248
1700	2.441	1 890	8.5725	1.266	1.628	1 890	8.4561	1.266
1800	2.585	2 017	8.6454	1.285	1.723	2 017	8.5290	1.285
1900	2.728	2 147	8.7155	1.306	1.819	2 147	8.5990	1.305
2000	2.771	2 279	8.7831	1.331	1.914	2 278	8.6665	1.329
2100	3.016	2 413	8.8487	1.361	2.011	2 413	8.7320	1.356
2200	3.160	2 551	8.9126	1.397	2.107	2 550	8.7958	1.399
2300	3.305	2 693	8.9759	1.445	2.203	2 691	8.8584	1.430
2400	3.450	2 841	9.0387	1.507	2.300	2 836	8.9203	1.483
2500	3.597	2 995	9.1017	1.585	2.398	2 988	8.9822	1.552
2600	3.746	3 159	9.1659	1.689	2.496	3 147	9.0447	1.638
2700	3.898	3 334	9.2320	1.818	2.596	3 316	9.1085	1.746
2800	4.053	3 523	9.3008	1.976	2.698	3 497	9.1743	1.879
2900	4.213	3 730	9.3734	2.164	2.803	3 683	9.2429	2.037
3000	4.379	3 957	9.4503	2.382	2.911	3 906	9.3150	2.221
3100	4.552	4 207	9.5323	2.623	3.023	4 138	9.3911	2.429
3200	4.733	4 482	9.6196	2.881	3.140	4 292	9.4718	2.654
3300	4.924	4 783	9.7126	3.139	3.262	4 669	9.5570	2.977
3400	5.124	5 109	9.8096	3.381	3.389	4 969	9.6466	3.117
3500	5.334	5 458	9.9107	3.583	3.524	5 292	9.7400	3.325
3600	5.554	5 824	10.0138	3.724	3.604	5 633	9.8362	3.495
3700	5.781	6 200	10.1168	3.785	3.810	5 989	9.9336	3.608
3800	6.012	6 578	10.2176	3.758	3.959	6 352	10.0306	3.652
3900	6.247	6 949	10.3139	3.697	4,113	6 716	10.1252	3.621
4000	6.480	7 305	10.4042	3.470	4.267	7 074	10.2158	3.521
4100	6.710	7 642	10.4842	3.255	4.421	7 419	10.3009	3.368
4200	6.937	7 956	10.5630	3.032	4.574	7 747	10.3799	3.183
4300	7.158	8 249	10.6318	2.824	4.724	8 055	10.4525	2.990
4400	7.374	8 522	10.6947	2.651	4.871	8 345	10.5192	2.810
4500	7.586	8 780	10.7527	2.521	5.016	8 618	10.5805	2.657
4600	7.795	9 028	10.8072	2.438	5.158	8 878	10.6376	2.542
4700	8.001	9 269	10.8591	2.403	5.297	9 128	10.6914	2.468
4800	8.206	9 510	10.9098	2.414	5.436	9 373	10.7430	2.435
4900	8.411	9 754	10.9600	2.468	5.573	9 616	10.7932	2.444
5000	8.617	10 005	11.0108	2.563	5.711	9 863	10.8430	2.493
5200	9.038	10 546	11.1169	2.878	5.889	10 380	10.9444	2.705
5400	9.478	11 167	11.2339	3.356	6.277	10 955	11.0528	3.067
5600	9.948	11 900	11.3672	4.005	6.579	11 617	11.1173	3.582
5800	10.46	12 781	11.5216	4.833	6.904	12 398	11.3101	4.651
6000	11.03	13 845	11.7020	5.842	7.258	13 330	11.4668	5.088

continued

T, °K	v	i	s	c_p	v	i	s	c_p
	$p=4$ bar				$p=5$ bar			
1300	0.9340	1 396	8.0438	1.191	0.7474	1 396	7.9797	1.191
1350	0.9699	1 456	8.0891	1.200	0.7761	1 456	8.0250	1.200
1400	1.006	1 516	8.1330	1.207	0.8048	1 516	8.0689	1.208
1450	1.042	1 576	8.1757	1.218	0.8535	1 576	8.1117	1.218
1500	1.078	1 640	8.2175	1.230	0.8622	1 640	8.1532	1.230
1600	1.149	1 764	8.2973	1.248	0.9197	1 764	8.2332	1.248
1700	1.221	1 890	8.3735	1.266	0.9771	1 890	8.3094	1.266
1800	1.293	2 017	8.4463	1.285	1.034	2 017	8.3823	1.285
1900	1.365	2 147	8.5163	1.304	1.092	2 147	8.4523	1.304
2000	1.436	2 278	8.5838	1.327	1.149	2 278	8.5197	1.326
2100	1.508	2 412	8.6492	1.353	1.207	2 412	8.5850	1.351
2200	1.580	2 549	8.7128	1.383	1.264	2 549	8.6485	1.380
2300	1.653	2 689	8.7751	1.422	1.322	2 688	8.7106	1.416
2400	1.725	2 834	8.8366	1.470	1.380	2 832	8.7717	1.460
2500	1.798	2 984	8.8978	1.530	1.438	2 981	8.8324	1.516
2600	1.872	3 140	8.9592	1.607	1.497	3 136	8.8932	1.586
2700	1.946	3 306	9.0216	1.703	1.557	3 299	8.9547	1.673
2800	2.022	3 482	9.0856	1.820	1.617	3 471	9.0174	1.780
2900	2.099	3 671	9.1518	1.960	1.679	3 655	9.0820	1.907
3000	2.180	3 875	9.2210	2.123	1.742	3 853	9.1491	2.055
3100	2.262	4 096	9.2936	2.308	1.807	4 067	9.2192	2.225
3200	2.348	4 337	9.3700	2.511	1.847	4 299	9.2927	2.411
3300	2.437	4 598	9.4506	2.726	1.944	4 550	9.3699	2.611
3400	2.530	4 882	9.5351	2.942	2.017	4 821	9.4509	2.814
3500	2.628	5 187	9.6234	3.146	2.094	5 113	9.5354	3.012
3600	2.730	5 510	9.7146	3.324	2.173	5 423	9.6228	3.191
3700	2.836	5 850	9.8076	3.460	2.256	5 750	9.7123	3.338
3800	2.946	6 200	9.9011	3.540	2.342	6 089	9.8029	3.440
3900	3.058	6 556	9.9934	3.557	2.431	6 436	9.8929	3.486
4000	3.172	6 910	10.0830	3.509	2.521	6 784	9.9811	3.473
4100	3.287	7 256	10.1684	3.403	2.612	7 129	10.0661	3.404
4200	3.402	7 589	10.2488	3.256	2.703	7 464	10.1469	3.289
4300	3.515	7 906	10.3234	3.087	2.794	7 785	10.2226	3.144
4400	3.627	8 206	10.3924	2.915	2.884	8 092	10.2931	2.975
4500	3.737	8 490	10.4561	2.759	2.973	8 383	10.3585	2.823
4600	3.845	8 759	10.5153	2.629	3.060	8 659	10.4192	2.698
4700	3.951	9 017	10.5707	2.533	3.146	8 923	10.4761	2.591
4800	4.057	9 267	10.6234	2.475	3.231	9 179	10.5298	2.516
4900	4.160	9 513	10.6741	2.455	3.315	9 428	10.5812	2.477
5000	4.264	9 759	10.7238	2.473	3.398	9 675	10.6311	2.479
5200	4.472	10 266	10.8232	2.619	3.565	10 177	10.7296	2.572
5400	4.685	10 816	10.9270	2.908	3.734	10 713	10.8306	2.807
5600	4.908	11 438	11.0401	3.337	3.910	11 309	10.9390	3.176
5800	5.164	12 161	11.1668	3.912	4.095	11 992	11.0589	3.682
6000	5.399	13 013	11.3112	4.635	4.294	12 791	11.1941	4.326
	$p=6$ bar				$p=8$ bar			
1300	0.6230	1 396	7.9274	1.191	0.4675	1 396	7.8448	1.191
1350	0.6470	1 456	7.9727	1.200	0.4855	1 456	7.8901	1.200
1400	0.6709	1 516	8.0166	1.208	0.5034	1 516	7.9340	1.208
1450	0.6948	1 576	8.0593	1.218	0.5214	1 576	7.9767	1.218
1500	0.7187	1 640	8.1009	1.230	0.5393	1 641	8.0183	1.230
1600	0.7666	1 764	8.1809	1.248	0.5752	1 765	8.0983	1.248
1700	0.8144	1 890	8.2571	1.266	0.6111	1 890	8.1745	1.266
1800	0.8623	2 018	8.3299	1.285	0.6470	2 018	8.2473	1.285
1900	0.9101	2 147	8.3999	1.304	0.6829	2 147	8.3179	1.303
2000	0.9580	2 278	8.4673	1.325	0.7188	2 278	8.3846	1.324
2100	1.005	2 412	8.5325	1.349	0.7547	2 412	8.4498	1.347
2200	1.054	2 548	8.5959	1.377	0.7909	2 548	8.5131	1.374
2300	1.102	2 688	8.6579	1.411	0.8267	2 687	8.5748	1.405
2400	1.150	2 831	8.7188	1.454	0.8628	2 829	8.6354	1.444
2500	1.199	2 979	8.7791	1.506	0.8991	2 976	8.6952	1.491

continued

T, °K	v	i	s	c_p	v	i	s	c_p
2600	1.248	3 132	8.8394	1.571	0.9357	3 128	8.7548	1.549
2700	1.297	3 293	8.9002	1.652	0.9726	3 286	8.8146	1.621
2800	1.347	3 463	8.9620	1.750	1.010	3 452	8.8750	1.708
2900	1.398	3 644	9.0254	1.867	1.048	3 628	8.9367	1.812
3000	1.450	3 838	9.0909	2.005	1.087	3 815	9.0421	1.933
3100	1.504	4 046	9.1592	2.162	1.126	4 016	9.1089	2.072
3200	1.560	4 270	9.2305	2.336	1.167	4 230	9.1785	2.228
3300	1.617	4 513	9.3052	2.523	1.210	4 461	9.2513	2.396
3400	1.677	4 775	9.3834	2.716	1.253	4 710	9.3272	2.573
3500	1.740	5 057	9.4649	2.908	1.299	4 976	9.3564	2.752
3600	1.805	5 356	9.5494	3.085	1.346	5 260	9.4363	2.923
3700	1.872	5 673	9.6361	3.327	1.396	5 560	9.5186	3.077
3800	1.943	6 002	9.7240	3.351	1.447	5 875	9.6024	3.204
3900	2.015	6 341	9.8120	3.417	1.500	6 200	9.6869	3.294
4000	2.089	6 684	9.8988	3.430	1.554	6 532	9.7709	3.340
4100	2.165	7 025	9.9831	3.389	1.610	6 866	9.8535	3.337
4200	2.240	7 360	10.0638	3.300	1.666	7 198	9.9334	3.289
4300	2.316	7 684	10.1400	3.177	1.722	7 523	10.0099	3.203
4400	2.391	7 995	10.2115	3.035	1.779	7 838	10.0823	3.090
4500	2.466	8 291	10.2780	2.889	1.835	8 140	10.1503	2.963
4600	2.539	8 573	10.3400	2.754	1.890	8 430	10.2140	2.835
4700	2.611	8 843	10.3980	2.641	1.945	8 708	10.2727	2.719
4800	2.682	9 162	10.4527	2.555	1.999	8 975	10.3299	2.622
4900	2.752	9 355	10.5047	2.502	2.052	9 233	10.3832	2.552
5000	2.822	9 604	10.5550	2.482	2.105	9 486	10.4343	2.511
5200	2.862	10 104	10.6532	2.545	2.210	9 987	10.5325	2.521
5400	3.102	10 631	10.7524	2.739	2.315	10 503	10.6298	2.655
5600	3.247	11 209	10.8575	3.062	2.423	11 057	11.7306	2.911
5800	3.400	11 864	10.9725	3.515	2.535	11 675	10.8390	3.286
6000	3.562	12 623	11.1011	4.099	2.653	12 380	10.9584	3.784
		$p=10$ bar				$p=12$ bar		
1300	0.3742	1 397	7.7808	1.191	0.3120	1 397	7.7284	1.191
1350	0.3886	1 456	7.8260	1.201	0.3240	1 456	7.7737	1.201
1400	0.4029	1 516	7.8699	1.208	0.3360	1 516	7.8176	1.208
1450	0.4173	1 576	7.9127	1.219	0.3479	1 576	7.8603	1.219
1500	0.4317	1 641	7.9542	1.230	0.3599	1 641	7.9019	1.230
1600	0.4604	1 765	8.0342	1.248	0.3838	1 765	7.9818	1.248
1700	0.4891	1 890	8.1104	1.266	0.4078	1 891	8.0580	1.266
1800	0.5178	2 018	8.1833	1.284	0.4317	2 018	8.1309	1.284
1900	0.5465	2 147	8.2532	1.303	0.4556	2 147	8.2008	1.303
2000	0.5752	2 279	8.3205	1.324	0.4795	2 279	8.2682	1.323
2100	0.6040	2 412	8.3856	1.346	0.5035	2 412	8.3332	1.345
2200	0.6327	2 548	8.4488	1.371	0.5275	2 548	8.3963	1.370
2300	0.6615	2 686	8.5104	1.401	0.5515	2 686	8.4578	1.398
2400	0.6904	2 828	8.5708	1.437	0.5755	2 828	8.5180	1.432
2500	0.7195	2 974	8.6303	1.481	0.5997	2 973	8.5773	1.473
2600	0.7486	3 125	8.6894	1.534	0.6240	3 122	8.6360	1.523
2700	0.7781	3 281	8.7485	1.600	0.6484	3 278	8.6946	1.584
2800	0.8078	3 445	8.8080	1.679	0.6732	3 440	8.7535	1.658
2900	0.8380	3 618	8.8685	1.773	0.6982	3 610	8.8131	1.745
3000	0.8688	3 800	8.9305	1.884	0.7237	3 789	8.8740	1.847
3100	0.9003	3 995	8.9942	2.010	0.7497	3 980	8.9364	1.964
3200	0.9326	4 203	9.0603	2.152	0.7764	4 182	9.0008	2.096
3300	0.9559	4 426	9.1288	2.307	0.8039	4 399	9.0675	2.240
3400	1.000	4 665	9.2001	2.471	0.8322	4 631	9.1366	2.394
3500	1.036	4 920	9.2742	2.639	0.8616	4 878	9.2083	2.553
3600	1.073	5 192	9.3509	2.804	0.8920	5 141	9.2824	2.711
3700	1.112	5 480	9.4298	2.956	0.9236	5 420	9.3588	2.860
3800	1.152	5 783	9.5104	3.088	0.9564	5 713	9.4368	2.994
3900	1.193	6 097	9.5921	3.190	0.9902	6 018	9.5161	3.102
4000	1.236	6 420	9.6737	3.255	1.025	6 332	9.5957	3.180
4100	1.280	6 747	9.7545	3.278	1.061	6 653	9.6748	3.220
4200	1.324	7 074	9.8333	3.259	1.097	6 975	9.7525	3.221

continued

T, °K	v	i	s	c_p	v	i	s	c_p
4300	1.369	7 397	9.9094	3.201	1.134	7 296	9.8279	3.185
4400	1.414	7 713	9.9820	3.112	1.172	7 611	9.9004	3.116
4500	1.458	8 019	10.0508	3.003	1.209	7 918	9.9694	3.025
4600	1.503	8 314	10.1155	2.887	1.246	8 215	10.0348	2.921
4700	1.547	8 597	10.1764	2.775	1.283	8 502	10.0965	2.815
4800	1.590	8 869	10.2337	2.676	1.319	8 779	10.1547	2.716
4900	1.633	9 132	10.2880	2.596	1.355	9 046	10.2098	2.633
5000	1.676	9 389	10.3399	2.542	1.391	9 306	10.2623	2.571
5200	1.760	9 893	10.4387	2.517	1.461	9 813	10.3618	2.529
5400	1.845	10 403	10.5351	2.608	1.532	10 322	10.4578	2.581
5600	1.930	10 944	10.6533	2.816	1.603	10 853	10.5544	2.752
5800	2.019	11 537	10.7374	3.137	1.676	11 450	10.6555	3.031
6000	2.111	12 207	10.8508	3.573	1.753	12 073	10.7645	3.421
		$p=14$ bar				$p=16$ bar		
1300	0.2676	1 397	7.6842	1.191	0.2343	1 397	7.6459	1.191
1350	0.2779	1 456	7.7294	1.201	0.2433	1 457	7.6911	1.201
1400	0.2881	1 516	7.7733	1.208	0.2522	1 517	7.7350	1.208
1450	0.2984	1 577	7.8160	1.219	0.2612	1 577	7.7777	1.219
1500	0.3086	1 641	7.8576	1.230	0.2702	1 641	7.8193	1.230
1600	0.3292	1 765	7.9376	1.248	0.2881	1 765	7.8992	1.248
1700	0.3497	1 891	8.0138	1.266	0.3061	1 891	7.9754	1.266
1800	0.3702	2 018	8.0867	1.284	0.3240	2 019	8.0183	1.284
1900	0.3907	2 148	8.1566	1.303	0.3420	2 148	8.1182	1.303
2000	0.4112	2 279	8.2239	1.323	0.3599	2 279	8.1855	1.322
2100	0.4317	2 412	8.2889	1.344	0.3779	2 413	8.2505	1.344
2200	0.4523	2 548	8.3520	1.368	0.3959	2 548	8.3136	1.367
2300	0.4728	2 686	8.4134	1.396	0.4139	2 686	8.3749	1.394
2400	0.4934	2 827	8.4735	1.428	0.4319	2 826	8.4349	1.425
2500	0.5141	2 972	8.5325	1.467	0.4499	2 971	8.4938	1.463
2600	0.5349	3 121	8.5909	1.515	0.4615	3 119	8.5520	1.505
2700	0.5559	3 275	8.6492	1.572	0.4864	3 273	8.6089	1.562
2800	0.5770	3 436	8.7075	1.641	0.5049	3 432	8.6678	1.627
2900	0.5934	3 604	8.7665	1.723	0.5236	3 599	8.7263	1.705
3000	0.6202	3 781	8.8265	1.818	0.5426	3 774	8.7835	1.795
3100	0.6423	3 968	8.8878	1.928	0.5619	3 958	8.8460	1.899
3200	0.6650	4 167	8.9510	2.051	0.5816	4 154	8.9081	2.015
3300	0.6884	4 378	9.0168	2.187	0.6019	4 362	8.9712	2.144
3400	0.7126	4 604	9.0836	2.332	0.6227	4 583	9.0381	2.282
3500	0.7373	4 845	9.1534	2.484	0.6442	4 818	9.1064	2.427
3600	0.7630	5 101	9.2255	2.635	0.6665	5 068	9.1768	2.573
3700	0.7897	5 372	9.2997	2.782	0.6896	5 333	9.2492	2.715
3800	0.8173	5 657	9.3737	2.915	0.7134	5 611	9.3234	2.847
3900	0.8459	5 954	9.4559	3.027	0.7381	5 902	9.3989	2.962
4000	0.8754	6 262	9.5307	3.113	0.7636	6 203	9.4751	3.053
4100	0.9057	6 576	9.6083	3.165	0.7898	6 511	9.5513	3.114
4200	0.9366	6 893	9.6848	3.181	0.8166	6 824	9.6268	3.142
4300	0.9680	7 211	9.7595	3.162	0.8438	7 139	9.7007	3.136
4400	0.9997	7 525	9.8316	3.111	0.8713	7 451	9.7724	3.099
4500	1.031	7 832	9.9007	3.034	0.8990	7 758	9.8414	3.036
4600	1.063	8 131	9.9664	2.942	0.9267	8 057	9.9073	2.955
4700	1.095	8 420	10.0287	2.843	0.9543	8 348	9.9699	2.864
4800	1.126	8 700	10.0875	2.748	0.9818	8 630	10.0292	2.772
4900	1.157	8 970	10.1433	2.663	1.009	8 903	10.0855	2.689
5000	1.188	9 233	10.1964	2.596	1.036	9 168	10.1391	2.619
5200	1.249	9 742	10.2966	2.530	1.089	9 683	10.2400	2.540
5400	1.309	10 252	10.3924	2.565	1.142	10 191	10.3358	2.556
5600	1.370	10 777	10.4880	2.706	1.196	10 654	10.4306	2.673
5800	1.432	11 342	10.5869	2.953	1.250	11 202	10.5279	2.892
6000	1.497	11 966	10.6926	3.305	1.306	11 798	10.6311	3.214

continued

T, °K	v	i	s	c_p	v	i	s	c_p
	$p=18$ bar				$p=20$ bar			
1300	0.2084	1 397	7.6121	1.191	0.1877	1 397	7.5818	1.191
1350	0.2164	1 457	7.6573	1.201	0.1948	1 457	7.6270	1.201
1400	0.2245	1 517	7.7012	1.209	0.2020	1 517	7.6709	1.209
1450	0.2323	1 577	7.7439	1.219	0.2092	1 577	7.7132	1.219
1500	0.2403	1 642	7.7854	1.230	0.2164	1 642	7.7552	1.230
1600	0.2563	1 766	7.8654	1.249	0.2307	1 766	7.8352	1.249
1700	0.2722	1 891	7.9416	1.266	0.2451	1 891	7.9114	1.266
1800	0.2882	2 019	8.0145	1.284	0.2595	2 019	7.9842	1.284
1900	0.3041	2 148	8.0844	1.303	0.2738	2 148	8,0542	1.303
2000	0.3201	2 279	8.1517	1.322	0.2882	2 279	8.1214	1.322
2100	0.3360	2 413	8.2167	1.343	0.3025	2 413	8.1864	1.342
2200	0.3520	2 548	8.2797	1.366	0.3169	2 548	8.2494	1.365
2300	0.3680	2 686	8.3410	1.392	0.3313	2 686	8.3106	1.391
2400	0.3840	2 826	8.4008	1.423	0.3457	2 826	8.3704	1.421
2500	0.4001	2 970	8.4596	1.459	0.3602	2 970	8.4281	1.456
2600	0.4123	3 118	8.5176	1.502	0.3747	3 118	8.4870	1.497
2700	0.4325	3 271	8.5753	1.554	0.3893	3 270	8.5444	1.547
2800	0.4489	3 430	8.6329	1.616	0.4040	3 427	8.6017	1.607
2900	0.4654	3 595	8.6908	1.690	0.4189	3 591	8.6593	1.677
3000	0.4822	3 768	8.7495	1.776	0.4340	3 763	8.7175	1.759
3100	0.4993	3 950	8.8093	1.874	0.4493	3 944	8.7766	1.853
3200	0.5168	4 143	8.8706	1.985	0.4650	4 134	8.8371	1.960
3300	0.5347	4 348	8.9335	2.108	0.4810	4 336	8.8992	2.077
3400	0.5531	4 565	8.9984	2.240	0.4974	4 533	8.9631	2.204
3500	0.5720	4 796	9.0653	2.379	0.5144	4 777	9.0289	2.338
3600	0.5916	5 041	9.1343	2.520	0.5319	5 018	9.0967	2.475
3700	0.6119	5 300	9.2053	2.659	0.5500	5 272	9.1663	2.610
3800	0.6329	5 572	9.2779	2.789	0.5687	5 539	9.2379	2.738
3900	0.6546	5 857	9.3519	2.905	0.5879	5 819	9.3103	2.854
4000	0.6770	6 153	9.4267	2.999	0.6079	6 119	9.3838	2.951
4100	0.7000	6 456	9.5016	3.067	0.6284	6 408	9.4577	3.023
4200	0.7236	6 765	9.5761	3.104	0.6494	6 713	9.5311	3.068
4300	0.7476	7 076	9.6492	3.109	0.6709	7 021	9.6035	3.082
4400	0.7719	7 386	9.7205	3.084	0.6926	7 329	9.6743	3.067
4500	0.7964	7 699	9.7893	3.032	0.7146	7 634	9.7442	3.025
4600	0.8210	7 992	9.8551	2.961	0.7366	7 933	9.8086	2.963
4700	0.8455	8 284	9.9180	2.878	0.7587	8 226	9.8715	2.887
4800	0.8699	8 567	9.9776	2.791	0.7806	8 511	9.9315	2.808
4900	0.8941	8 842	10.0343	2.709	0.8025	8 787	9.9885	2.726
5000	0.9182	9 110	10.0883	2.639	0.8241	9 056	10.0429	2.655
5200	0.9658	9 627	10.1899	2.550	0.8671	9 576	10.1449	2.561
5400	1.013	10 136	10.2858	2.551	0.9096	10 086	10.2411	2.548
5600	1.060	10 654	10.3801	2.648	0.9523	10 622	10.3340	2.629
5800	1.108	11 202	10.4761	2.844	0.9955	11 144	10.4300	2.800
6000	1.158	11 798	10.5772	3.140	1.040	11 731	10.5294	3.079
	$p=25$ bar				$p=30$ bar			
1300	0.1503	1 398	7.5178	1.191	0.1255	1 398	7.4655	1.192
1350	0.1561	1 457	7.5629	1.202	0.1303	1 458	7.5106	1.202
1400	0.1618	1 517	7.6068	1.209	0.1350	1 518	7.5544	1.209
1450	0.1676	1 578	7.6495	1.219	0.1398	1 578	7.5971	1.219
1500	0.1733	1 642	7.6911	1.230	0.1446	1 643	7.6387	1.230
1600	0.1848	1 766	7.7711	1.249	0.1542	1 767	7.7187	1.249
1700	0.1963	1 892	7.8473	1.266	0.1638	1 892	7.7949	1.266
1800	0.2078	2 019	7.9202	1.284	0.1733	2 020	7.8678	1.284
1900	0.2193	2 149	7.9901	1.303	0.1829	2 149	7.9377	1.303
2000	0.2307	2 280	8.0574	1.322	0.1925	2 280	8.0050	1.322
2100	0.2422	2 413	8.1223	1.342	0.2021	2 414	8.0699	1.342
2200	0.2537	2 548	8.1852	1.364	0.2116	2 549	8.1328	1.363
2300	0.2652	2 686	8.2464	1.388	0.2212	2 686	8.1939	1.387
2400	0.2768	2 826	8.3060	1.416	0.2308	2 826	8.2534	1.413
2500	0.2883	2 969	8.3645	1.449	0.2404	2 969	8.3117	1.444
2600	0.2999	3 116	8.4220	1.488	0.2501	3 115	8.3691	1.481

continued

T, °K	v	i	s	c_p	v	i	s	c_p
2700	0,3116	3 267	8.4790	1,534	0,2598	3 265	8,4257	1.524
2800	0.3233	3 423	8.5358	1.588	0.2696	3 420	8.4820	1.575
2900	0.3352	3 585	8.5926	1.652	0,2794	3 580	8.5383	1.634
3000	0.3472	3 754	8.6498	1.727	0.2894	3 747	8.5948	1.703
3100	0.3594	3 931	8.7078	1.813	0.2995	3 921	8.6519	1.782
3200	0.3718	4 117	8.7669	1.909	0.3098	4 104	8.7099	1.872
3300	0.3845	4 313	8.8272	2.016	0.3203	4 296	8.7690	1.971
3400	0.3975	4 520	8.8891	2.132	0.3310	4 498	8.8294	2.079
3500	0.4108	4 740	8.9527	2.256	0.3420	4 712	8.8914	2.194
3600	0.4246	4 972	9.0180	2.383	0.3533	4 938	8.9548	2.314
3700	0.4388	5 216	9.0851	2.511	0.3650	5 175	9.0199	2.435
3800	0.4534	5 474	9.1538	2.634	0.3770	5 424	9.0834	2.553
3900	0.4686	5 743	9.2236	2.748	0.3894	5 685	9.1542	2.665
4000	0.4842	6 023	9.2945	2.848	0.4022	5 957	9.2230	2.766
4100	0.5002	6 312	9.3659	2.929	0.4153	6 238	9.2923	2.850
4200	0.5167	6 608	9.4372	2.986	0.4288	6 526	9.3618	2.915
4300	0.5336	6 908	9.5079	3.016	0.4426	6 820	9.4310	2.956
4400	0.5507	7 210	9.5773	3.020	0.4567	7 117	9.4992	2.973
4500	0.5680	7 512	9.6450	2.999	0.4710	7 414	9.5660	2.967
4600	0.5855	7 809	9.7105	2.956	0.4854	7 710	9.6309	2.939
4700	0.6031	8 102	9.7734	2.896	0.4999	8 001	9.6937	2.893
4800	0.6205	8 388	9.8337	2.827	0.5145	8 288	9.7540	2.835
4900	0.6381	8 668	9.8913	2.755	0.5291	8 568	9.8118	2.772
5000	0.6555	8 940	9.9463	2.687	0.5436	8 842	9.8672	2.708
5200	0.6900	9 466	10.0495	2.584	0.5724	9 373	9.9712	2.603
5400	0.7241	9 978	10.1461	2.549	0.6009	9 887	10.0683	2.554
5600	0.7582	10 491	10.2394	2.598	0.6294	10 399	10.1615	2.581
5800	0.7927	11 023	10.3327	2.736	0.6580	10 925	10.2537	2.690
6000	0.8279	11 592	10.4291	2.964	0.6872	11 481	10.3479	2.884
		p=35 bar				p=40 bar		
1300	0.1077	1 399	7.4213	1.192	0.09437	1 399	7.3829	1.192
1350	0.1118	1 458	7.4663	1.203	0.09796	1 459	7.4280	1.203
1400	0.1159	1 518	7.5102	1.209	0.1015	1 519	7.4725	1.210
1450	0.1200	1 579	7.5529	1.220	0.1051	1 579	7.5145	1.220
1500	0.1241	1 643	7.5944	1.230	0.1087	1 644	7.5560	1.230
1600	0.1323	1 767	7.6764	1.249	0.1159	1 768	7.6361	1.249
1700	0.1405	1 893	7.7506	1.267	0.1231	1 893	7.7123	1.267
1800	0.1487	2 021	7.8235	1.284	0.1303	2 021	7.7852	1.284
1900	0.1569	2 150	7.8935	1.303	0.1375	2 150	7.8551	1.303
2000	0.1651	2 281	7.9607	1.322	0.1446	2 281	7.9224	1.322
2100	0.1733	2 414	8.0256	1.341	0.1518	2 415	7.9873	1.341
2200	0.1816	2 549	8.0885	1.362	0.1590	2 550	8.0501	1.362
2300	0.1898	2 686	8.1495	1.385	0.1662	2 687	8.1110	1.384
2400	0.1980	2 826	8.2090	1.411	0.1734	2 826	8.1705	1.409
2500	0.2062	2 967	8.2672	1.440	0.1806	2 969	8.2286	1.438
2600	0.2146	3 145	8.3243	1.476	0.1878	3 114	8.2856	1.471
2700	0,2228	3 264	8,3807	1.516	0.1951	3 263	8.3418	1.510
2800	0.2312	3 418	8.4367	1.564	0.2024	3 416	8.3975	1.555
2900	0.2377	3 577	8.4925	1.620	0.2098	3 574	8.4530	1.608
3000	0.2481	3 742	8.5485	1.685	0.2172	3 738	8.5085	1.670
3100	0.2568	3 914	8.6049	1.759	0.2247	3 909	8.5644	1.740
3200	0.2655	4 094	8,6621	1.842	0.2324	4 086	8.6208	1.819
3300	0.2745	4 283	8.7202	1.935	0.2401	4 273	8.6781	1.906
3400	0.2836	4 482	8.7794	2.037	0.2481	4 468	8.7365	2.002
3500	0.2929	4 691	8.8400	2.145	0.2562	4 673	8.7960	2.105
3600	0.3025	4 911	8.9021	2.258	0.2645	4 889	8.8568	2.213
3700	0.3124	5 142	8.9655	2.374	0.2731	5 116	8.9189	2.324
3800	0.3226	5 385	9.0303	2.488	0.2819	5 354	8.9824	2.434
3900	0.3330	5 640	9.0964	2.597	0.2909	5 603	9.0470	2.540
4000	0.3438	5 905	9.1634	2.697	0.3002	5 862	9.1126	2.639
4100	0.3549	6 179	9.2311	2.783	0.3098	6 130	9.1788	2.726
4200	0.3663	6 461	9.2991	2.853	0.3197	6 406	9.2454	2.798
4300	0.3780	6 749	9.3668	2.902	0.3297	6 689	9.3120	2.853

continued

T, °K	v	i	s	c_p	v	i	s	c_p
4400	0.3899	7 041	9.4339	2.929	0.3401	6 976	9.3780	2.887
4500	0.4020	7 334	9.4998	2.933	0.3506	7 266	9.4430	2.900
4600	0.4143	7 626	9.5841	2.917	0.3612	7 556	9.5058	2.893
4700	0.4267	7 917	9.6265	2.883	0.3720	7 844	9.5688	2.869
4800	0.4391	8 203	9.6868	2.835	0.3828	8 129	9.6288	2.830
4900	0.4516	8 483	9.7477	2.780	0.3937	8 410	9.6867	2.782
5000	0.4640	8 759	9.8002	2.721	0.4045	8 685	9.7423	2.729
5200	0.4887	9 292	9.9049	2.618	0.4261	9 221	9.8478	2.630
5400	0.5132	9 809	10.0024	2.561	0.4476	9 740	9.9463	2.567
5600	0.5376	10 321	10.0954	2.571	0.4690	10 252	10.0384	2.565
5800	0.5621	10 843	10.1870	2.658	0.4904	10 771	10.1294	2.635
6000	0.5871	11 390	10.2798	2.827	0.5122	11 311	10.2210	2.782
		$p=50$ bar				$p=60$ bar		
1300	0.07571	1 400	7.3189	1.192	0.06327	1 401	7.2665	1.192
1350	0.07858	1 460	7.3639	1.204	0.06567	1 461	7.3115	1.204
1400	0.08146	1 520	7.4077	1.210	0.06806	1 521	7.3553	1.210
1450	0.08433	1 580	7.4503	1.220	0.07046	1 581	7.3979	1.220
1500	0.08721	1 645	7.4919	1.230	0.07295	1 646	7.4395	1.230
1600	0.09295	1 769	7.5719	1.249	0.07764	1 770	7.5195	1.249
1700	0.09870	1 895	7.6482	1.268	0.08243	1 896	7.5958	1.268
1800	0.1044	2 022	7.7211	1.286	0.08722	2 023	7.6687	1.286
1900	0.1102	2 151	7.7910	1.303	0.09201	2 152	7.7388	1.303
2000	0.1159	2 283	7.8583	1.322	0.09679	2 284	7.8059	1.322
2100	0.1217	2 416	7.9232	1.341	0.1016	2 417	7.8708	1.341
2200	0.1274	2 551	7.9860	1.361	0.1064	2 552	7.9336	1.360
2300	0.1332	2 688	8.0469	1.382	0.1112	2 689	7.9945	1.381
2400	0.1389	2 827	8.1062	1.406	0.1160	2 827	8.0537	1.404
2500	0.1447	2 969	8.1641	1.433	0.1207	2 969	8.1115	1.430
2600	0.1505	3 114	8.2209	1.465	0.1256	3 114	8.1682	1.460
2700	0.1563	3 262	8.2768	1.500	0.1304	3 261	8.2268	1.493
2800	0.1621	3 414	8.3321	1.542	0.1353	3 413	8.2788	1.533
2900	0.1680	3 571	8.3871	1.591	0.1401	3 568	8.3334	1.578
3000	0.1739	3 732	8.4419	1.647	0.1451	3 728	8.3877	1.630
3100	0.1799	3 900	8.4969	1.710	0.1500	3 894	8.4421	1.688
3200	0.1860	4 075	8.5524	1.782	0.1551	4 066	8.4967	1.755
3300	0.1921	4 257	8.6084	1.862	0.1602	4 245	8.5519	1.829
3400	0.1984	4 447	8.6653	1.949	0.1654	4 432	8.6076	1.910
3500	0.2048	4 647	8.7231	2.043	0.1707	4 628	8.6643	1.997
3600	0.2114	4 856	8.7821	2.142	0.1761	4 832	8.7218	2.089
3700	0.2181	5 076	8.8422	2.245	0.1816	5 046	8.7804	2.185
3800	0.2251	5 305	8.9034	2.348	0.1873	5 269	8.8399	2.282
3900	0.2322	5 545	8.9657	2.449	0.1932	5 502	8.9005	2.379
4000	0.2395	5 795	9.0290	2.545	0.1992	5 745	8.9619	2.471
4100	0.2470	6 054	9.0929	2.632	0.2053	5 996	9.0240	2.557
4200	0.2547	6 321	9.1573	2.707	0.2116	6 256	9.0866	2.634
4300	0.2626	6 595	9.2217	2.768	0.2181	6 523	9.1493	2.698
4400	0.2707	6 874	9.2859	2.812	0.2248	6 795	9.2120	2.748
4500	0.2790	7 157	9.3494	2.838	0.2315	7 072	9.2741	2.781
4600	0.2874	7 441	9.4119	2.845	0.2384	7 351	9.3355	2.798
4700	0.2958	7 725	9.4730	2.835	0.2454	7 631	9.3957	2.800
4800	0.3044	8 008	9.5325	2.811	0.2525	7 910	9.4546	2.786
4900	0.3130	8 287	9.5901	2.775	0.2595	8 188	9.5118	2.761
5000	0.3217	8 563	9.6458	2.733	0.2668	8 463	9.5672	2.727
5200	0.3389	9 100	9.7512	2.644	0.2811	9 000	9.6727	2.650
5400	0.3561	9 622	9.8497	2.578	0.2954	9 524	9.7715	2.585
5600	0.3732	10 134	9.9429	2.559	0.3096	10 037	9.8649	2.558
5800	0.3904	10 650	10.0333	2.604	0.3240	10 550	9.9549	2.585
6000	0.4077	11 181	10.1234	2.719	0.3384	11 076	10.0440	2.677

continued

T, °K	v	i	s	c_p	v	i	s	c_p
		$p=70$ bar				$p=80$ bar		
1300	0.05439	1 402	7.2223	1.192	0.04773	1 402	7.1840	1.194
1350	0.05644	1 461	7.2672	1.204	0.04952	1 463	7.2288	1.205
1400	0.05849	1 521	7.3109	1.210	0.05132	1 522	7.2725	1.210
1450	0.06055	1 582	7.3536	1.220	0.05311	1 583	7.3152	1.220
1500	0.06260	1 647	7.3951	1.230	0.05491	1 648	7.3567	1.230
1600	0.06671	1 771	7.4752	1.250	0.05851	1 772	7.4368	1.249
1700	0.07081	1 897	7.5515	1.268	0.06210	1 898	7.5131	1.269
1800	0.07492	2 024	7.6243	1.286	0.06569	2 025	7.5861	1.286
1900	0.07907	2 154	7.6944	1.304	0.06928	2 155	7.6560	1.304
2000	0.08312	2 285	7.7617	1.322	0.07287	2 285	7.7233	1.322
2100	0.08723	2 418	7.8266	1.341	0.07646	2 419	7.7882	1.340
2200	0.09133	2 552	7.8893	1.360	0.08005	2 554	7.8509	1.360
2300	0.09543	2 689	7.9502	1.380	0.08364	2 690	7.9118	1.379
2400	0.09954	2 829	8.0093	1.403	0.08724	2 829	7.9709	1.402
2500	0.1037	2 970	8.0671	1.427	0.09083	2 971	8.0286	1.426
2600	0.1078	3 114	8.1236	1.456	0.09444	3 114	8.0850	1.453
2700	0.1119	3 261	8.1791	1.488	0.09806	3 261	8.1403	1.484
2800	0.1161	3 412	8.2338	1.525	0.1017	3 411	8.1949	1.519
2900	0.1203	3 566	8.2881	1.568	0.1053	3 565	8.2489	1.559
3000	0.1245	3 725	8.3420	1.616	0.1090	3 723	8.3025	1.605
3100	0.1287	3 890	8.3959	1.672	0.1127	3 886	8.3570	1.658
3200	0.1330	4 060	8.4499	1.734	0.1164	4 055	8.4096	1.716
3300	0.1374	4 237	8.5043	1.803	0.1203	4 230	8.4634	1.782
3400	0.1418	4 421	8.5593	1.879	0.1241	4 412	8.5176	1.853
3500	0.1463	4 613	8.6149	1.960	0.1281	4 601	8.5725	1.931
3600	0.1509	4 813	8.6714	2.047	0.1321	4 798	8.6280	2.013
3700	0.1556	5 022	8.7287	2.138	0.1362	5 004	8.6843	2.099
3800	0.1604	5 241	8.7869	2.230	0.1403	5 218	8.7415	2.187
3900	0.1654	5 468	8.8461	2.322	0.1446	5 441	8.7995	2.276
4000	0.1705	5 705	8.9060	2.412	0.1490	5 673	8.8582	2.362
4100	0.1757	5 951	8.9666	2.496	0.1535	5 914	8.9176	2.445
4200	0.1810	6 204	9.0277	2.572	0.1581	6 162	8.9774	2.520
4300	0.1865	6 465	9.0891	2.638	0.1629	6 418	9.0375	2.587
4400	0.1921	6 732	9.1504	2.692	0.1677	6 679	9.0977	2.643
4500	0.1978	7 003	9.2112	2.731	0.1727	6 946	9.1576	2.686
4600	0.2036	7 267	9.2715	2.756	0.1777	7 216	9.2170	2.715
4700	0.2096	7 554	9.3311	2.765	0.1829	7 489	9.2756	2.739
4800	0.2156	7 830	9.3892	2.760	0.1881	7 762	9.3332	2.733
4900	0.2216	8 105	9.4460	2.743	0.1933	8 035	9.3894	2.723
5000	0.2277	8 378	9.5012	2.717	0.1986	8 307	9.4443	2.704
5200	0.2400	8 916	9.6065	2.651	0.2093	8 842	9.5493	2.648
5400	0.2522	9 439	9.7054	2.589	0.2200	9 366	9.6482	2.591
5600	0.2645	9 953	9.7988	2.557	0.2307	9 880	9.7417	2.556
5800	0.2767	10 466	9.8887	2.573	0.2414	10 391	9.8314	2.564
6000	0.2890	10 987	9.9770	2.648	0.2521	10 910	9.9192	2.625
		$p=90$ bar				$p=100$ bar		
1300	0.04254	1 403	7.1502	1.194	0.03840	1 404	7.1199	1.195
1350	0.04414	1 463	7.1950	1.205	0.03983	1 464	7.1647	1.205
1400	0.04573	1 523	7.2387	1.210	0.04127	1 524	7.2083	1.211
1450	0.04733	1 584	7.2813	1.220	0.04271	1 585	7.2510	1.220
1500	0.04893	1 649	7.3228	1.230	0.04415	1 650	7.2925	1.230
1600	0.05213	1 773	7.4029	1.249	0.04702	1 774	7.3726	1.250
1700	0.05533	1 899	7.4793	1.269	0.04990	1 900	7.4490	1.269
1800	0.05852	2 026	7.5522	1.288	0.05277	2 027	7.5220	1.288
1900	0.06171	2 156	7.6222	1.304	0.05565	2 157	7.5919	1.305
2000	0.06490	2 287	7.6895	1.323	0.05842	2 288	7.6593	1.323
2100	0.06809	2 420	7.7544	1.341	0.06139	2 421	7.7241	1.341
2200	0.07128	2 555	7.8171	1.360	0.06426	2 556	7.7869	1.360
2300	0.07447	2 692	7.8779	1.379	0.06713	2 693	7.8476	1.379
2400	0.07766	2 830	7.9370	1.401	0.07001	2 831	7.9067	1.400
2500	0.08086	2 971	7.9946	1.424	0.07288	2 972	7.9643	1.423
2600	0.08407	3 115	8.0509	1.450	0.07577	3 116	8.0205	1.448

continued

T, °K	v	i	s	c_p	v	i	s	c_p
2700	0.08728	3 262	8.1062	1.480	0.07866	3 262	8.0757	1.477
2800	0.09051	3 411	8.1606	1.514	0.08156	3 411	8.1299	1.510
2900	0.09375	3 564	8.2164	1.553	0.08448	3 564	8.1836	1.547
3000	0.09702	3 722	8.2678	1.597	0.08741	3 721	8.2367	1.589
3100	0.1003	3 884	8.3209	1.646	0.09037	3 882	8.2896	1.637
3200	0.1036	4 051	8.3740	1.702	0.09335	4 048	8.3424	1.690
3300	0.1070	4 225	8.4274	1.764	0.09638	4 220	8.3953	1.749
3400	0.1104	4 404	8.4810	1.832	0.09944	4 398	8.4485	1.814
3500	0.1139	4 591	8.5352	1.906	0.1026	4 583	8.5021	1.885
3600	0.1174	4 786	8.5900	1.984	0.1057	4 776	8.5562	1.960
3700	0.1210	4 988	8.6455	2.067	0.1089	4 976	8.6110	2.039
3800	0.1247	5 199	8.7018	2.151	0.1122	5 184	8.6665	2.120
3900	0.1285	5 419	8.7588	2.236	0.1156	5 400	8.7226	2.202
4000	0.1324	5 647	8.8152	2.320	0.1191	5 624	8.7795	2.284
4100	0.1363	5 883	8.8648	2.401	0.1226	5 857	8.8368	2.362
4200	0.1404	6 127	8.9335	2.476	0.1262	6 097	8.8947	2.436
4300	0.1446	6 378	8.9926	2.543	0.1300	6 344	8.9528	2.503
4400	0.1488	6 635	9.0518	2.600	0.1338	6 597	9.0111	2.562
4500	0.1532	6 898	9.1107	2.646	0.1376	6 856	9.0692	2.609
4600	0.1576	7 164	9.1693	2.679	0.1416	7 119	9.1270	2.646
4700	0.1620	7 433	9.2271	2.699	0.1456	7 385	9.1842	2.670
4800	0.1667	7 704	9.2841	2.707	0.1497	7 652	9.2406	2.682
4900	0.1714	7 970	9.3399	2.703	0.1539	7 921	9.2959	2.683
5000	0.1760	8 244	9.3944	2.689	0.1580	8 189	9.3500	2.674
5200	0.1855	8 778	9.4991	2.643	0.1665	8 720	9.4543	2.636
5400	0.1949	9 301	9.5978	2.590	0.1750	9 243	9.5529	2.588
5600	0.2045	9 815	9.6913	2.555	0.1835	9 757	9.6463	2.555
5800	0.2140	10 326	9.7909	2.557	0.1921	10 267	9.7358	2.551
6000	0.2235	10 841	9.8683	2.608	0.2007	10 780	9.8229	2.594
		p=125 bar				p=150 bar		
1300	0.03093	1 406	7.0559	1.196	0.02596	1 408	7.0036	1.197
1350	0.03208	1 466	7.1005	1.205	0.02692	1 468	7.0480	1.206
1400	0.03320	1 526	7.1431	1.212	0.02787	1 529	7.0916	1.213
1450	0.03438	1 587	7.1867	1.220	0.02883	1 589	7.1341	1.221
1500	0.03554	1 652	7.2282	1.231	0.02979	1 654	7.1757	1.231
1600	0.03784	1 776	7.3083	1.251	0.03171	1 779	7.2558	1.252
1700	0.04014	1 902	7.3848	1.271	0.03363	1 905	7.3323	1.272
1800	0.04244	2 030	7.4578	1.289	0.03555	2 033	7.4054	1.290
1900	0.04474	2 159	7.5278	1.306	0.03746	2 162	7.4754	1.307
2000	0.04703	2 291	7.5952	1.324	0.03938	2 294	7.5428	1.325
2100	0.04933	2 424	7.6600	1.341	0.04129	2 426	7.6077	1.342
2200	0.05163	2 559	7.7228	1.360	0.04321	2 561	7.6704	1.360
2300	0.05393	2 695	7.7835	1.378	0.04512	2 698	7.7311	1.378
2400	0.05622	2 834	7.8425	1.398	0.04704	2 836	7.7901	1.397
2500	0.05852	2 975	7.8999	1.420	0.04895	2 977	7.8475	1.418
2600	0.06083	3 118	7.9561	1.444	0.05087	3 120	7.9035	1.441
2700	0.06314	3 263	8.0111	1.471	0.05280	3 265	7.9584	1.467
2800	0.06546	3 412	8.0651	1.501	0.05472	3 413	8.0122	1.495
2900	0.06779	3 564	8.1154	1.536	0.05666	3 564	8.0652	1.527
3000	0.07013	3 719	8.1711	1.574	0.05861	3 719	8.1176	1.563
3100	0.07249	3 879	8.2234	1.618	0.06057	3 877	8.1695	1.604
3200	0.07486	4 043	8.2755	1.666	0.06265	4 040	8.2211	1.649
3300	0.07727	4 212	8.3276	1.720	0.06454	4 207	8.2756	1.699
3400	0.07970	4 387	8.3798	1.779	0.06656	4 380	8.3241	1.753
3500	0.08217	4 568	8.4324	1.843	0.06860	4 558	8.3758	1.813
3600	0.08468	4 756	8.4852	1.912	0.07068	4 742	8.4278	1.876
3700	0.08724	4 951	8.5386	1.984	0.07279	4 953	8.4801	1.943
3800	0.08984	5 153	8.5925	2.059	0.07494	5 131	8.5329	2.012
3900	0.09250	5 363	8.6470	2.135	0.07713	5 336	8.5861	2.084
4000	0.09523	5 580	8.7021	2.211	0.07938	5 548	8.6398	2.155
4100	0.09801	5 805	8.7576	2.285	0.08166	5 767	8.6939	2.226
4200	0.1009	6 037	8.8135	2.356	0.08400	5 993	8.7484	2.294
4300	0.1038	6 276	8.8698	2.422	0.08639	6 226	8.8031	2.358

continued

T, °K	v	i	s	c_p	v	i	s	c_p
4400	0.1068	6 522	8.9262	2.481	0.08884	6 465	8.8581	2.417
4500	0.1098	6 773	8.9825	2.532	0.09133	6 710	8.9130	2.469
4600	0.1129	7 028	9.0387	2.573	0.09388	6 959	8.9678	2.513
4700	0.1161	7 287	9.0944	2.604	0.09648	7 212	9.0222	2.547
4800	0.1193	7 549	9.1494	2.639	0.09912	7 468	9.0762	2.573
4900	0.1225	7 812	9.2037	2.634	0.1018	7 223	9.1294	2.589
5000	0.1258	8 075	9.2569	2.634	0.1045	7 986	9.1818	2.596
5200	0.1325	8 601	9.3600	2.614	0.1100	8 505	9.2836	2.589
5400	0.1393	9 120	9.4580	2.578	0.1156	9 021	9.3809	2.564
5600	0.1461	9 633	9.5512	2.547	0.1212	9 277	9.4738	2.538
5800	0.1529	10 141	9.6404	2.539	0.1269	10 038	9.5627	2.529
6000	0.1597	10 631	9.7269	2.568	0.1326	10 545	9.6487	2.549
		$p=200$ bar				$p=250$ bar		
1300	0.01974	1 413	6.9210	1.200	0.01601	1 417	6.8570	1.202
1350	0.02046	1 473	6.9652	1.206	0.01658	1 477	6.9009	1.208
1400	0.02118	1 533	7.0086	1.214	0.01716	1 538	6.9441	1.216
1450	0.02190	1 594	7.0511	1.222	0.01773	1 599	6.9866	1.224
1500	0.02262	1 659	7.0926	1.232	0.01831	1 664	7.0281	1.234
1600	0.02406	1 783	7.1728	1.254	0.01946	1 789	7.1084	1.256
1700	0.02550	1 910	7.2494	1.274	0.02062	1 915	7.1850	1.276
1800	0.02694	2 038	7.3226	1.292	0.02177	2 043	7.2583	1.294
1900	0.02837	2 168	7.3927	1.309	0.02290	2 173	7.3285	1.311
2000	0.02981	2 299	7.4601	1.326	0.02407	2 304	7.3960	1.328
2100	0.03124	2 432	7.5251	1.343	0.02521	2 438	7.4610	1.344
2200	0.03268	2 567	7.5878	1.360	0.02636	2 573	7.5237	1.361
2300	0.03411	2 703	7.6485	1.378	0.02759	2 709	7.5844	1.378
2400	0.03555	2 842	7.7074	1.396	0.02866	2 847	7.6433	1.396
2500	0.03699	2 982	7.7647	1.415	0.02980	2 988	7.7006	1.414
2600	0.03842	3 125	7.8206	1.437	0.03095	3 130	7.7564	1.435
2700	0.03986	3 270	7.8753	1.461	0.03211	3 274	7.8109	1.457
2800	0.04131	3 417	7.9288	1.487	0.03326	3 421	7.8642	1.481
2900	0.04276	3 567	7.9817	1.516	0.03442	3 570	7.9167	1.508
3000	0.04422	3 720	8.0334	1.548	0.03558	3 723	7.9683	1.537
3100	0.04568	3 876	8.0847	1.584	0.03675	3 878	8.0192	1.570
3200	0.04716	4 037	8.1356	1.624	0.03793	4 037	8.0696	1.607
3300	0.04864	4 201	8.1863	1.668	0.03911	4 199	8.1197	1.647
3400	0.05015	4 371	8.2368	1.716	0.04031	4 366	8.1696	1.691
3500	0.05167	4 545	8.2874	1.769	0.04152	4 538	8.2193	1.738
3600	0.05321	4 725	8.3380	1.825	0.04274	4 714	8.2690	1.789
3700	0.05477	4 910	8.3888	1.884	0.04398	4 896	8.3188	1.843
3800	0.05635	5 102	8.4399	1.946	0.04524	5 083	8.3687	1.899
3900	0.05798	5 300	8.4913	2.010	0.04652	5 276	8.4188	1.958
4000	0.05963	5 504	8.5430	2.074	0.04782	5 475	8.4692	2.018
4100	0.06131	5 715	8.5951	2.139	0.04915	5 680	8.5198	2.077
4200	0.06303	5 932	8.6474	2.202	0.05050	5 891	8.5706	2.137
4300	0.06478	6 155	8.6999	2.263	0.05187	6 108	8.6216	2.194
4400	0.06657	6 385	8.7527	2.320	0.05328	6 309	8.6727	2.249
4500	0.06840	6 620	8.8055	2.372	0.05472	6 558	8.7279	2.300
4600	0.07026	6 859	8.8582	2.418	0.05618	6 790	8.7750	2.346
4700	0.07216	7 103	8.9106	2.457	0.05767	7 027	8.8259	2.387
4800	0.07409	7 351	8.9627	2.488	0.05919	7 268	8.8756	2.421
4900	0.07605	7 601	9.0143	2.512	0.06073	7 511	8.9268	2.449
5000	0.07804	7 854	9.0663	2.528	0.06229	7 758	8.9766	2.470
5200	0.08210	8 361	9.1648	2.540	0.06548	8 255	9.0741	2.492
5400	0.08623	8 868	9.2606	2.532	0.06874	8 755	9.1684	2.498
5600	0.09040	9 373	9.3525	2.516	0.07205	9 254	9.2592	2.492
5800	0.09462	9 876	9.4406	2.508	0.07539	9 752	9.3468	2.488
6000	0.09886	10 379	9.5258	2.521	0.07876	10 251	9.4311	2.498

continued

T, °K	v	i	s	c_p	v	i	s	c_p
	$p=300$ bar				$p=400$ bar			
1300	0.01352	1 421	6.8047	1.204	0.01041	1 430	6.7220	1.209
1350	0.01400	1 482	6.8483	1.210	0.01076	1 491	6.7651	1.215
1400	0.01448	1 542	6.8914	1.217	0.01112	1 552	6.8079	1.222
1450	0.01496	1 603	6.9337	1.226	0.01148	1 613	6.8502	1.229
1500	0.01544	1 669	6.9753	1.236	0.01185	1 679	6.8917	1.237
1600	0.01640	1 794	7.0560	1.257	0.01257	1 804	6.9721	1.258
1700	0.01736	1 920	7.1323	1.278	0.01329	1 931	7.0490	1.281
1800	0.01832	2 049	7.2057	1.298	0.01401	2 059	7.1226	1.301
1900	0.01928	2 178	7.2760	1.314	0.01473	2 189	7.1931	1.318
2000	0.02024	2 310	7.3435	1.330	0.01545	2 321	7.2607	1.333
2100	0.02119	2 443	7.4086	1.346	0.01617	2 454	7.3258	1.349
2200	0.02215	2 578	7.4713	1.362	0.01688	2 589	7.3887	1.364
2300	0.02311	2 715	7.5321	1.378	0.01760	2 726	7.4491	1.379
2400	0.02406	2 853	7.5909	1.395	0.01832	2 864	7.5083	1.395
2500	0.02502	2 993	7.6482	1.413	0.01903	3 004	7.5655	1.412
2600	0.02597	3 135	7.7039	1.433	0.01975	3 146	7.6211	1.431
2700	0.02693	3 279	7.7583	1.454	0.02047	3 290	7.6754	1.450
2800	0.02790	3 426	7.8115	1.476	0.02118	3 436	7.7284	1.470
2900	0.02886	3 574	7.8638	1.502	0.02191	3 584	7.7804	1.493
3000	0.02983	3 726	7.9151	1.529	0.02263	3 734	7.8315	1.518
3100	0.03080	3 880	7.9658	1.560	0.02336	3 887	7.8817	1.546
3200	0.03178	4 038	8.0159	1.594	0.02409	4 043	7.9313	1.576
3300	0.03277	4 199	8.0655	1.631	0.02483	4 203	7.9803	1.609
3400	0.03375	4 365	8.1148	1.672	0.02557	4 366	8.0290	1.645
3500	0.03476	4 534	8.1640	1.716	0.02631	4 532	8.0772	1.683
3600	0.03577	4 708	8.2130	1.763	0.02707	4 703	8.1253	1.725
3700	0.03680	4 887	8.2620	1.812	0.02783	4 878	8.1732	1.769
3800	0.03784	5 071	8.3111	1.865	0.02860	5 057	8.2211	1.815
3900	0.03889	5 260	8.3603	1.919	0.02938	5 241	8.2689	1.863
4000	0.03997	5 455	8.4096	1.975	0.03018	5 430	8.3168	1.913
4100	0.04106	5 656	8.4591	2.037	0.03099	5 624	8.3647	1.963
4200	0.04217	5 862	8.5088	2.086	0.03181	5 823	8.4126	2.014
4300	0.04331	6 073	8.5585	2.141	0.03264	6 027	8.4607	2.064
4400	0.04447	6 290	8.6084	2.194	0.03349	6 236	8.5088	2.112
4500	0.04564	6 512	8.6583	2.243	0.03435	6 450	8.5568	2.159
4600	0.04684	6 739	8.7082	2.289	0.03523	6 669	8.6048	2.203
4700	0.04807	6 970	8.7579	2.330	0.03613	6 891	8.6477	2.244
4800	0.04931	7 205	8.8074	2.366	0.03704	7 117	8.7007	2.281
4900	0.05058	7 444	8.8366	2.396	0.03797	7 348	8.7478	2.313
5000	0.05186	7 685	8.9053	2.421	0.03891	7 581	8.7949	2.341
5200	0.05448	8 173	9.0010	2.453	0.04083	8 064	8.8877	2.383
5400	0.05716	8 666	9.0940	2.466	0.04280	8 534	8.9783	2.408
5600	0.05989	9 159	9.1837	2.467	0.04481	9 017	9.0662	2.421
5800	0.06265	9 653	9.2704	2.468	0.04685	9 503	9.1514	2.429
6000	0.06544	10 148	9.3543	2.478	0.04891	9 990	9.2340	2.442
	$p=500$ bar				$p=600$ bar			
1300	0.008537	1 438	6.6579	1.215	0.007289	1 447	6.6054	1.219
1350	0.008823	1 499	6.7004	1.221	0.007527	1 508	6.6424	1.225
1400	0.009111	1 561	6.7429	1.226	0.007760	1 570	6.6896	1.231
1450	0.009400	1 622	6.7851	1.233	0.008009	1 632	6.7316	1.238
1500	0.009690	1 689	6.8265	1.238	0.008251	1 699	6.7731	1.247
1600	0.01027	1 814	6.9071	1.265	0.008734	1 824	6.8538	1.267
1700	0.01085	1 941	6.9842	1.281	0.009218	1 951	6.9311	1.289
1800	0.01143	2 070	7.0580	1.306	0.009699	2 080	7.0050	1.310
1900	0.01200	2 200	7.1286	1.322	0.01018	2 211	7.0758	1.326
2000	0.01258	2 332	7.1964	1.337	0.01065	2 343	7.1437	1.341
2100	0.01315	2 460	7.2616	1.352	0.01114	2 477	7.2090	1.354
2200	0.01372	2 601	7.3245	1.366	0.01161	2 612	7.2720	1.368
2300	0.01430	2 737	7.3853	1.381	0.01209	2 748	7.3328	1.382
2400	0.01487	2 875	7.4441	1.396	0.01257	2 887	7.3917	1.397
2500	0.01544	3 015	7.5013	1.412	0.01303	3 026	7.4489	1.412
2600	0.01601	3 157	7.5569	1.429	0.01352	3 168	7.5044	1.428

continued

T, °K	v	i	s	c_p	v	i	s	c_p
2700	0.01659	3 300	7.6111	1.447	0.01400	3 311	7.5586	1,445
2800	0.01716	3 446	7.6640	1.466	0.01447	3 457	7.6114	1.463
2900	0,01774	3 594	7.7159	1.487	0.01496	3 604	7.6631	1.483
3000	0.01832	3 743	7.7667	1.511	0.01544	3 753	7.7138	1.505
3100	0.01890	3 896	7.8168	1.536	0.01592	3 905	7.7636	1.528
3200	0.01948	4 051	7.8659	1.563	0.01641	4 059	7.8126	1.554
3300	0.02007	4 208	7.9145	1.593	0.01689	4 216	7.8609	1.572
3400	0.02066	4 370	7.9626	1.626	0.01738	4 376	7.9086	1.612
3500	0.02125	4 534	8.0104	1.661	0.01788	4 538	7.9632	1.644
3600	0.02185	4 702	8.0577	1.699	0.01838	4 705	8.0028	1.679
3700	0.02246	4 875	8.1049	1.738	0.01888	4 875	8.0494	1.716
3800	0.02307	5 051	8.1569	1.780	0.01938	5 049	8.0958	1.754
3900	0.02369	5 231	8.1988	1.824	0.01990	5 227	8.1420	1.795
4000	0.02432	5 416	8.2456	1.869	0.02042	5 409	8.1881	1.837
4100	0.02496	5 606	8.2925	1.915	0.02095	5 595	8.2341	1.879
4200	0.02560	5 800	8.3393	1.962	0.02148	5 785	8.2800	1.923
4300	0.02626	6 027	8.3861	2.008	0.02202	5 999	8.3258	1.966
4400	0,02693	6 202	8.4328	2.054	0.02257	6 179	8.3716	2.009
4500	0.02761	6 410	8.4796	2.098	0.02313	6 383	8.4173	2.051
4600	0.02830	6 622	8.5262	2.140	0.02370	6 590	8.4630	2.091
4700	0.02901	6 839	8.5728	2.180	0.02428	6 802	8.5085	2.130
4800	0.02972	7 059	8.6191	2.216	0.02487	7 017	8.5538	2.166
4900	0.03045	7 283	8.6652	2.250	0.02547	7 236	8.5989	2.199
5000	0.03119	7 509	8.7111	2.279	0.02607	7 457	8.6437	2.229
5200	0.03270	7 971	8.8015	2.326	0.02731	7 909	8.7323	2.279
5400	0.03425	8 440	8.8901	2.358	0.02858	8 370	8.8192	2.315
5600	0.03583	8 914	8.9764	2.378	0.02989	8 836	8.9040	2.341
5800	0.03744	9 392	9.0602	2.393	0.03121	9 307	8.9866	2.360
6000	0.03908	9 873	9.1417	2.409	0.03256	9 782	9.0671	2.380
		p=800 bar				p=1000 bar		
1300	0.005725	1 465	6.5224	1.229	0.004781	1 482	6.4578	1.234
1350	0.005903	1 526	6.5633	1.234	0.004924	1 544	6.4977	1.241
1400	0.006084	1 588	6.6050	1.240	0.005069	1 606	6.5389	1.248
1450	0.006265	1 650	6.6468	1.247	0.005215	1 669	6.5805	1.256
1500	0.006448	1 719	6.6882	1.256	0.005361	1 738	6.6218	1.264
1600	0.006812	1 844	6.7691	1.275	0.005654	1 863	6.7029	1.283
1700	0.007175	1 971	6.8468	1.297	0.005945	1 991	6.7809	1.304
1800	0.007537	2 101	6.9211	1.318	0.006236	2 121	6.8555	1.325
1900	0.007898	2 232	6.9922	1.334	0.006525	2 253	6.9270	1.340
2000	0.008258	2 365	7.0604	1.347	0.006814	2 386	6.9954	1.354
2100	0.008617	2 498	7.1259	1.360	0.007101	2 520	7.0611	1.365
2200	0.008975	2 634	7.1890	1.373	0.007388	2 656	7.1244	1.377
2300	0.009332	2 771	7.2499	1.385	0.007674	2 799	7.1854	1.388
2400	0.009690	2 909	7.3089	1.399	0.007960	2 931	7.2445	1.400
2500	0.01005	3 049	7.3661	1.412	0.008246	3 071	7.3016	1.413
2600	0.01041	3 190	7.4216	1.427	0.008532	3 212	7.3573	1.427
2700	0.01076	3 333	7.4757	1.442	0.008818	3 355	7.4113	1.441
2800	0.01112	3 478	7.5284	1.459	0.009104	3 499	7.4640	1.456
2900	0.01148	3 625	7.5799	1.477	0.009391	3 646	7.5154	1.473
3000	0.01184	3 773	7.6304	1.496	0.009678	3 794	7.5658	1.491
3100	0.01220	3 924	7.6799	1.517	0.009966	3 944	7.6151	1.510
3200	0.01256	4 077	7.7286	1.540	0.01025	4 096	7.6635	1.531
3300	0.01293	4 233	7.7765	1.565	0.01055	4 251	7.7111	1.553
3400	0.01329	4 391	7.8237	1.592	0.01084	4 408	7.7580	1.577
3500	0.01366	4 552	7.8704	1.620	0.01113	4 567	7.8042	1.603
3600	0.01403	4 716	7.9166	1.651	0.01143	4 730	7.8499	1.631
3700	0.01441	4 883	7.9624	1.683	0.01172	4 895	7.8953	1.660
3800	0.01478	5 053	8.0073	1.717	0.01202	5 063	7.9401	1.691
3900	0.01516	5 227	8.0531	1.753	0.01233	5 234	7.9847	1.723
4000	0.01555	5 405	8.0981	1.790	0.01263	5 409	8.0289	1.757
4100	0.01594	5 586	8.1429	1.828	0.01294	5 587	8.0729	1.791
4200	0.01634	5 771	8.1875	1.866	0.01326	5 768	8.1167	1.826
4300	0.01674	5 960	8.2321	1.905	0.01357	5 953	8.1600	1.862

continued

T, °K	v	i	s	c_p	v	i	s	c_p
4400	0.01714	6 153	8.2764	1.944	0.01389	6 142	8.2036	1.898
4500	0.01756	6 350	8.3207	1.982	0.01422	6 334	8.2468	1.933
4600	0.01797	6 551	8.3648	2.019	0.01455	6 530	8.2899	1.968
4700	0.01840	6 755	8.4087	2.055	0.01488	6 729	8.3327	2.002
4800	0.01883	6 963	8.4485	2.090	0.01522	6 931	8.3754	2.034
4900	0.01927	7 174	8.4960	2.122	0.01557	7 137	8.4178	2.065
5000	0.01971	7 388	8.5393	2.152	0.01592	7 345	8.4600	2.094
5200	0.02062	7 825	8.6250	2.204	0.01663	7 771	8.5434	2.147
5400	0.02155	8 271	8.7092	2.245	0,01737	8 212	8.6256	2.190
5600	0.02251	8 724	8.7917	2.278	0.01812	8 649	8.7062	2.226
5800	0.02348	9 184	8.8722	2.304	0.01888	9 099	8.7851	2.256
6000	0.02447	9 648	8.9510	2.328	0.01966	9 554	8.8622	2.284

Molecular weight M of dissociated air [143]

p, bar → / T, °K	0.1	0.2	0.4	0.6	0.8	1	2	3	4
2000	28.95	28.96	28.96	28.96	28.96	28.96	28.96	28.96	28.96
2100	28.94	28.95	28.95	28.95	28.96	28.96	28.96	28.96	28.96
2200	28.91	28.93	28.94	28.94	28.95	28.95	28.95	28.96	28.96
2300	28.87	28.89	28.91	28.92	28.93	28.93	28.94	28.95	28.95
2400	28.79	28.84	28.88	28.89	28.90	28.91	28.93	28.93	28.94
2500	28.68	28.76	28.82	28.85	28.86	28.87	28.90	28.91	28.92
2600	28.52	28.65	28.74	28.78	28.80	28.82	28.86	28.88	28.89
2700	28.29	28.48	28.62	28.68	28.72	28.74	28.81	28.84	28.85
2800	27.99	28.26	28.45	28.54	28.60	28.63	28.73	28.77	28.80
2900	27.62	27.97	28.24	28.36	28.44	28.49	28.63	28.69	28.72
3000	27.19	27.62	27.97	28.14	28.24	28.31	28.49	28.58	28.63
3100	26.71	27.22	27.65	27.86	27.99	28.08	28.32	28.43	28.50
3200	26.22	26.78	27.28	27.53	27.70	27.81	28.12	28.26	28.35
3300	25.76	26.33	26.88	27.17	27.36	27.50	27.87	28.05	28.16
3400	25.35	25.89	26.46	26.78	27.00	27.15	27.59	27,81	27.95
3500	25.02	25.50	26.05	26.39	26.61	26.79	27.28	27.54	27.70
3600	24.75	25.17	25.68	26.00	26.24	26.42	26.95	27.24	27.42
3700	24.56	24.90	25.35	25.65	25.88	26.06	26.62	26.93	27.13
3800	24.41	24.68	25.07	25.34	25.56	25.73	26.28	26.61	26.83
3900	24.30	24.52	24.84	25.08	25.27	25.43	25.96	26.29	26.52
4000	24.21	24.39	24.66	24.86	25.03	25.17	25.67	25.99	26.22
4100	24.13	24.29	24.51	24.68	24.83	24.95	25.41	25.71	25.94
4200	24.05	24.20	24.39	24.54	24.66	24.77	25.18	25.46	25.67
4300	23.98	24.12	24.29	24.42	24.53	24.62	24.98	25.24	25.44
4400	23.90	24.04	24.20	24.32	24.41	24.49	24.81	25.04	25.23
4500	23.81	23.96	24.12	24.22	24.31	24.38	24.67	24.87	25.04
4600	23.71	23.87	24.03	24.14	24.21	24.28	24.54	24.73	24.88
4700	23.59	23.77	23.94	24.05	24.12	24.19	24.43	24.60	24.73
4800	23.44	23.66	23.85	23.96	24.03	24.10	24.32	24.48	24.61
4900	23.27	23.53	23.74	23.86	23.94	24.00	24.22	24.37	24.49
5000	23.07	23.37	23.62	23.75	23.84	23.91	24.13	24.27	24.38
5200	22.55	22.98	23.32	23.49	23.60	23.68	23.92	24.07	24.18
5400	21.86	22.47	22.93	23.15	23.29	23.40	23.69	23.85	23.96
5600	21.04	21.80	22.42	22.71	22.90	23.04	23.40	23.60	23.73
5800	20.06	21.00	21.78	22.17	22.41	22.58	23.05	23.29	23.44
6000	19.01	20.08	21.03	21.51	21.81	22.03	22.62	22.92	23.10

p, bar / T, °K	5	6	8	10	12	14	16	18	20
2000	28.96	28.96	28.96	28.96	28.96	28.96	28.96	28.96	28.96
2100	28.96	28.96	28.96	28.96	28.96	28.96	28.96	28.96	28.96
2200	28.96	28.96	28.96	28.96	28.96	28.96	28.96	28.96	28.96

continued

T, °K \ p, bar →	4	6	8	10	12	14	16	18	20
2300	28.95	28.95	28.95	28.96	28.96	28.96	28.96	28.96	28.96
2400	28.94	28.95	28.95	28.95	28.95	28.95	28.95	28.95	28.95
2500	28.92	28.93	28.93	28.94	28.94	28.94	28.94	28.94	28.95
2600	28.90	28.91	28.91	28.92	28.92	28.93	28.93	28.93	28.93
2700	28.86	28.87	28.89	28.89	28.90	28.90	28.91	28.91	28.92
2800	28.82	28.83	28.85	28.86	28.87	28.87	28.88	28.89	28.89
2900	28.75	28.77	28.78	28.79	28.80	28.81	28.82	28.83	28.84
3000	28.66	28.69	28.72	28.74	28.77	28.78	28.79	28.80	28.81
3100	28.55	28.58	28.63	28.66	28.69	28.71	28.73	28.74	28.75
3200	28.41	28.45	28.52	28.56	28.60	28.62	28.65	28.66	28.68
3300	28.23	28.30	28.38	28.44	28.48	28.52	28.54	28.57	28.59
3400	28.04	28.11	28.22	28.29	28.34	28.39	28.43	28.45	28.48
3500	27.81	27.90	28.03	28.12	28.18	28.24	28.28	28.32	28.35
3600	27.56	27.66	27.81	27.92	28.00	28.06	28.11	28.16	28.20
3700	27.28	27.40	27.57	27.70	27.79	27.87	27.93	27.98	28.02
3800	26.99	27.12	27.31	27.45	27.56	27.65	27.72	27.78	27.83
3900	26.69	26.83	27.04	27.20	27.32	27.42	27.50	27.57	27.63
4000	26.40	26.54	26.77	26.93	27.06	27.17	27.26	27.34	27.40
4100	26.11	26.26	26.49	26.66	26.80	26.92	27.01	27.10	27.17
4200	25.85	25.99	26.22	26.40	26.54	26.66	26.76	26.85	26.93
4300	25.60	25.74	25.97	26.14	26.29	26.41	26.52	26.61	26.69
4400	25.38	25.51	25.73	25.90	26.04	26.17	26.27	26.37	26.45
4500	25.18	25.30	25.51	25.68	25.82	25.94	26.04	26.14	26.22
4600	25.01	25.12	25.31	25.47	25.60	25.72	25.82	25.92	26.00
4700	24.85	24.96	25.13	25.28	25.41	25.52	25.62	25.71	25.90
4800	24.72	24.81	24.98	25.11	25.23	25.34	25.43	25.52	25.60
4900	24.59	24.68	24.83	24.96	25.07	25.17	25.26	25.34	25.42
5000	24.48	24.56	24.70	24.82	24.93	25.02	25.11	25.18	25.25
5200	24.26	24.34	24.47	24.58	24.67	24.75	24.88	24.90	24.96
5400	24.05	24.13	24.25	24.35	24.44	24.52	24.59	24.65	24.71
5600	23.82	23.90	24.03	24.13	24.22	24.29	24.36	24.42	24.48
5800	23.56	23.65	23.79	23.90	23.99	24.06	24.13	24.19	24.25
6000	23.24	23.35	23.51	23.64	23.74	23.82	23.89	23.95	24.01

T, °K \ p, bar →	25	30	35	40	50	60	70	80	90	100
2000	28.97	28.97	28.97	28.97	28.97	28.97	28.97	28.97	28.97	28.97
2100	28.96	28.96	28.96	28.96	28.96	28.96	28.96	28.96	28.96	28.96
2200	28.96	28.96	28.96	28.96	28.96	28.96	28.96	28.96	28.96	28.96
2300	28.96	28.96	28.96	28.96	28.96	28.96	28.96	28.96	28.96	28.96
2400	28.96	28.96	28.96	28.96	28.96	28.96	28.96	28.96	28.96	28.96
2500	28.95	28.95	28.95	28.95	28.95	28.95	28.95	28.96	28.96	28.96
2600	28.94	28.94	28.94	28.94	28.94	28.95	28.95	28.95	28.95	28.95
2700	28.92	28.92	28.93	28.93	28.93	28.93	28.94	28.94	28.94	28.94
2800	28.90	28.90	28.91	28.91	28.91	28.92	28.92	28.93	28.93	28.93
2900	28.87	28.87	28.88	28.89	28.89	28.90	28.91	28.91	28.91	28.92
3000	28.83	28.84	28.85	28.86	28.86	28.88	28.88	28.89	28.89	28.90
3100	28.77	28.79	28.80	28.81	28.83	28.84	28.85	28.86	28.86	28.87
3200	28.71	28.73	28.75	28.76	28.78	28.80	28.81	28.82	28.83	28.83
3300	28.63	28.65	28.68	28.69	28.72	28.74	28.76	28.77	28.78	28.79
3400	28.53	28.56	28.59	28.62	28.65	28.68	28.70	28.72	28.73	28.74
3500	28.41	28.45	28.49	28.52	28.56	28.59	28.62	28.65	28.66	28.68
3600	28.27	28.33	28.37	28.41	28.46	28.50	28.54	28.56	28.59	28.61
3700	28.11	28.18	28.23	28.28	28.35	28.40	28.44	28.47	28.50	28.52
3800	27.94	28.02	28.08	28.13	28.21	28.27	28.32	28.36	28.39	28.42
3900	27.75	27.84	27.91	27.97	28.06	28.13	28.19	28.24	28.27	28.31
4000	27.54	27.64	27.72	27.79	27.90	27.98	28.05	28.10	28.14	28.18
4100	27.32	27.43	27.52	27.60	27.72	27.82	27.89	27.95	28.00	28.04
4200	27.09	27.21	27.32	27.40	27.53	27.64	27.72	27.79	27.85	27.90
4300	26.86	26.99	27.10	27.19	27.34	27.45	27.54	27.62	27.68	27.74
4400	26.63	26.76	26.88	26.98	27.13	27.25	27.35	27.44	27.51	27.57

continued

T, °K \ p, bar →	25	30	35	40	50	60	70	80	90	100
4500	26.40	26.54	26.66	26.75	26.92	27.06	27.16	27.25	27.33	27.39
4600	26.18	26.32	26.44	26.56	26.72	26.85	26.97	27.06	27.14	27.21
4700	25.97	26.11	26.23	26.34	26.51	26.65	26.77	26.87	26.95	27.03
4800	25.77	25.91	26.03	26.14	26.31	26.46	26.58	26.68	26.77	26.84
4900	25.58	25.72	25.84	25.94	26.12	26.25	26.38	26.49	26.58	26.67
5000	25.41	25.54	25.66	25.76	25.93	26.08	26.20	26.31	26.40	26.48
5200	25.10	25.23	25.33	25.43	25.59	25.73	25.85	25.96	26.05	26.13
5400	24.84	24.95	25.05	25.14	25.29	25.42	25.54	25.64	25.73	25.81
5600	24.60	24.70	24.79	24.88	25.02	25.14	25.25	25.35	25.43	25.51
5800	24.37	24.46	24.56	24.63	24.77	24.89	24.99	25.08	25.17	25.24
6000	24.13	24.23	24.32	24.40	24.53	24.65	24.75	24.83	24.91	24.99

T, °K \ p, bar →	125	150	200	250	300	400	500	600	800	1000
2000	28.97	28.97	28.97	28.97	28.97	28.97	28.97	28.97	28.97	28.97
2100	28.97	28.97	28.97	28.97	28.97	28.97	28.97	28.97	28.97	28.97
2200	28.97	28.97	28.97	28.97	28.97	28.97	28.97	28.97	28.97	28.97
2300	28.96	28.96	28.96	28.96	28.96	28.97	28.97	28.97	28.97	28.97
2400	28.96	28.96	28.96	28.96	28.96	28.96	28.96	28.96	28.96	28.96
2500	28.96	28.96	28.96	28.96	28.96	28.96	28.96	28.96	28.96	28.96
2600	28.95	28.95	28.95	28.96	28.96	28.96	28.96	28.96	28.96	28.96
2700	28.95	28.95	28.95	28.95	28.95	28.95	28.96	28.95	28.96	28.96
2800	28.94	28.94	28.94	28.94	28.95	28.95	28.95	28.95	28.95	28,96
2900	28.92	28.93	28.93	28.93	28.94	28.94	28.94	28.95	28.95	28.95
3000	28.90	28.91	28.92	28.92	28.92	28.93	28.93	28.94	28.94	28.94
3100	28.88	28.89	28.90	28.90	28.91	28.92	28.92	28.93	28.93	28.93
3200	28.85	28.86	28.87	28.88	28.89	28.90	28.91	28.91	28.92	28.92
3300	28.81	28.82	28.84	28.86	28.86	28.88	28.89	28.89	28.90	28.91
3400	28.76	28.78	28.80	28.82	28.83	28.85	28.86	28.87	28.89	28.89
3500	28.71	28.73	28.76	28.76	28.80	28.82	28.83	28.85	28.86	28.87
3600	28.64	28.67	28.71	28.73	28.75	28.78	28.80	28.81	28.83	28.85
3700	28.56	28.60	28.64	28.68	28.70	28.74	28.76	28.78	28.80	28.82
3800	28.47	28.51	28.57	28.61	28.64	28.68	28.71	28.73	28.76	28.78
3900	28.37	28.42	28.49	28.54	28.57	28.62	28.66	28.68	28.72	28.76
4000	28.26	28.31	28.40	28.45	28.49	28.56	28.60	28.63	28.67	28.70
4100	28.13	28.20	28.29	28.36	28.41	28.48	28.53	28.56	28.61	28.65
4200	27.99	28.07	28.18	28.25	28.31	28.39	28.45	28.49	28.55	28.59
4300	27.85	27.93	28.06	28.14	28.21	28.30	28.36	28.41	28.48	28.53
4400	27.69	27.78	27.92	28.02	28.09	28.20	28.27	28.33	28.41	28.46
4500	27.53	27.63	27.78	27.89	27.97	28.09	28.17	28.24	28.33	28.39
4600	27.36	27.47	27.63	27.75	27.84	27.97	28.07	28.14	28.24	28.31
4700	27.18	27.30	27.48	27.61	27.71	27.85	27.95	28.03	28.14	28.22
4800	27.01	27.13	27.32	27.46	27.57	27.72	27.83	27.92	28.04	28.13
4900	26.83	26.96	27.16	27.31	27.42	27.59	27.71	27.80	27.94	28.04
5000	26.65	26.79	27.00	27.15	27.27	27.45	27.58	27.68	27.83	27.93
5200	26.31	26.45	26.67	26.84	26.97	27.17	27.31	27.43	27.59	27.71
5400	25.98	26.13	26.35	26.53	26.67	26.88	27.04	27.16	27.35	27.49
5600	25.68	25.82	26.05	26.23	26.37	26.60	26.76	26.90	27.10	27.25
5800	25.40	25.54	25.77	25.94	26.09	26.32	26.49	26.63	26.85	27.01
6000	25.15	25.28	25.50	25.67	25.82	26.05	26.22	26.37	26.59	26.76

Speed of sound u (m/s) and adiabatic exponent k for dissociated air [143]

T, °K \ p, bar →	0.1		0.2		0.4		0.6	
	u	k	u	k	u	k	u	k
1300	700.8	1.316	700.8	1.316	700.8	1.316	700.9	1.316
1350	713.3	1.313	713.3	1.313	713.4	1.313	713.4	1.313
1400	725.6	1.310	725.6	1.310	725.6	1.310	725.7	1.310

continued

p, bar → / T, °K	0.1		0.2		0.4		0.6	
	u	k	u	k	u	k	u	k
1450	737.6	1.307	737.6	1.307	737.7	1.307	737.7	1.307
1500	749.4	1.304	749.4	1.304	749.4	1.304	749.5	1.304
1600	772.2	1.298	772.3	1.298	772.3	1.299	772.4	1.299
1700	794.0	1.292	794.2	1.292	794.3	1.293	794.4	1.293
1800	814.8	1.285	815.1	1.286	815.4	1.287	815.5	1.287
1900	834.2	1.276	834.9	1.278	835.5	1.280	835.7	1.280
2000	853.1	1.267	854.2	1.270	854.9	1.273	855.3	1.274
2100	870.0	1.255	871.8	1.260	873.1	1.264	873.8	1.266
2200	885.5	1.239	888.1	1.247	890.2	1.253	891.1	1.256
2300	899.9	1.222	903.9	1.233	906.1	1.241	907.4	1.245
2400	913.7	1.204	917.6	1.217	921.1	1.228	922.9	1.233
2500	927.7	1.187	931.7	1.201	935.5	1.213	937.6	1.220
2600	942.9	1.173	946.2	1.186	950.0	1.199	952.1	1.207
2700	959.9	1.161	961.9	1.174	964.9	1.187	966.9	1.194
2800	979.2	1.153	979.3	1.164	980.9	1.176	982.4	1.183
2900	1001.0	1.148	998.6	1.157	998.4	1.167	999.1	1.174
3000	1025.5	1.146	1020.3	1.153	1017.7	1.161	1017.3	1.167
3100	1052.3	1.148	1044.2	1.151	1039.0	1.158	1037.2	1.163
3200	1081.1	1.152	1070.2	1.153	1062.2	1.157	1058.9	1.160
3300	1111.3	1.159	1097.9	1.156	1087.3	1.158	1082.4	1.160
3400	1142.2	1.170	1127.0	1.163	1113.9	1.161	1107.6	1.162
3500	1173.6	1.184	1156.8	1.173	1141.8	1.167	1134.1	1.166
3600	1204.8	1.200	1187.1	1.185	1170.5	1.175	1161.7	1.172
3700	1235.0	1.218	1217.2	1.199	1199.6	1.185	1189.9	1.180
3800	1263.1	1.232	1246.5	1.214	1228.6	1.197	1218.3	1.190
3900	1288.0	1.243	1274.1	1.227	1257.1	1.210	1246.6	1.202
4000	1308.9	1.246	1299.2	1.238	1284.2	1.223	1274.2	1.213
4100	1326.0	1.244	1320.9	1.243	1309.4	1.232	1300.4	1.224
4200	1339.9	1.237	1339.2	1.243	1331.8	1.239	1324.6	1.239
4300	1351.5	1.225	1354.4	1.237	1351.3	1.240	1346.4	1.238
4400	1361.8	1.212	1367.3	1.228	1367.9	1.238	1365.3	1.239
4500	1371.8	1.198	1378.6	1.217	1382.1	1.231	1381.7	1.236
4600	1382.2	1.184	1389.2	1.204	1394.6	1.222	1395.9	1.229
4700	1393.5	1.172	1399.9	1.192	1406.1	1.211	1408.6	1.221
4800	1406.1	1.161	1411.2	1.180	1417.2	1.200	1420.4	1.211
4900	1420.3	1.152	1423.4	1.170	1428.6	1.189	1431.8	1.200
5000	1436.3	1.145	1436.9	1.161	1440.6	1.179	1443.5	1.190
5200	1474.2	1.134	1468.5	1.146	1467.6	1.162	1468.7	1.172
5400	1520.9	1.127	1507.2	1.137	1500.1	1.149	1498.3	1.157
5600	1577.2	1.124	1554.0	1.131	1539.0	1.140	1533.5	1.147
5800	1643.2	1.123	1609.4	1.128	1585.2	1.135	1575.1	1.140
6000	1718.0	1.125	1673.5	1.127	1639.2	1.132	1623.7	1.136

p, bar → / T, °K	0.8		1		2		3	
	u	k	u	k	u	k	u	k
1300	700.9	1.316	701.0	1.316	701.2	1.317	701.4	1.317
1350	713.4	1.313	713.5	1.313	713.7	1.314	713.9	1.314
1400	725.7	1.310	725.8	1.310	726.0	1.311	726.2	1.311
1450	737.7	1.307	737.7	1.307	738.0	1.308	738.2	1.308
1500	749.5	1.305	749.5	1.305	749.8	1.305	750.0	1.305
1600	772.4	1.299	772.5	1.299	772.7	1.299	772.9	1.300
1700	794.5	1.293	794.5	1.293	794.7	1.294	794.9	1.294
1800	815.6	1.287	815.7	1.287	816.0	1.288	816.2	1.289
1900	835.9	1.281	836.0	1.281	836.4	1.282	836.7	1.283
2000	855.6	1.275	855.7	1.275	856.3	1.276	856.5	1.277
2100	874.1	1.267	874.4	1.268	875.2	1.270	875.6	1.271
2200	891.7	1.258	892.1	1.259	893.3	1.263	893.9	1.264
2300	908.3	1.248	908.9	1.250	910.6	1.255	911.4	1.257
2400	924.0	1.236	924.8	1.239	927.0	1.245	928.2	1.249
2500	939.0	1.224	940.0	1.227	942.8	1.235	944.2	1.239
2600	953.6	1.211	954.7	1.215	958.0	1.225	959.7	1.230

continued

p, bar → / T, °K	0,8 u	0,8 k	1 u	1 k	2 u	2 k	3 u	3 k
2700	968.3	1.199	969.5	1.203	972.9	1.214	974.8	1.220
2800	983.6	1.188	984.6	1.193	987.9	1.204	989.8	1.210
2900	999.8	1.179	1000.5	1.183	1003.2	1.194	1005.0	1.201
3000	1017.3	1.171	1017.6	1.175	1019.3	1.186	1020.7	1.193
3100	1036.9	1.166	1036.4	1.169	1036.3	1.180	1037.1	1.186
3200	1057.2	1.163	1056.1	1.166	1054.5	1.175	1054.5	1.180
3300	1079.6	1.162	1077.8	1.164	1074.1	1.175	1073.0	1.176
3400	1103.7	1.163	1101.1	1.164	1095.0	1.170	1092.8	1.174
3500	1129.3	1.166	1123.8	1.167	1117.3	1.170	1113.8	1.173
3600	1155.9	1.171	1151.8	1.171	1140.9	1.172	1136.0	1.174
3700	1183.4	1.178	1178.6	1.177	1165.6	1.175	1159.4	1.176
3800	1211.3	1.186	1206.0	1.184	1191.2	1.180	1183.7	1.180
3900	1239.3	1.197	1233.7	1.193	1217.3	1.186	1208.8	1.184
4000	1266.8	1.208	1261.1	1.203	1243.8	1.194	1234.4	1.190
4100	1293.5	1.218	1287.9	1.214	1270.2	1.202	1260.3	1.197
4200	1318.6	1.228	1313.4	1.224	1296.3	1.211	1286.0	1.205
4300	1341.6	1.234	1337.2	1.231	1321.4	1.220	1311.3	1.213
4400	1362.1	1.238	1358.8	1.236	1345.3	1.227	1335.8	1.221
4500	1380.1	1.237	1378.0	1.237	1367.5	1.232	1359.1	1.227
4600	1395.7	1.233	1394.8	1.235	1387.7	1.235	1380.8	1.232
4700	1409.6	1.226	1409.7	1.230	1405.9	1.235	1400.7	1.235
4800	1422.1	1.218	1422.9	1.222	1422.1	1.232	1418.8	1.234
4900	1433.9	1.208	1435.2	1.213	1436.8	1.227	1435.2	1.232
5000	1445.6	1.198	1447.1	1.204	1450.2	1.220	1450.0	1.227
5200	1470.1	1.179	1471.2	1.185	1475.1	1.204	1476.9	1.214
5400	1498.0	1.164	1498.2	1.169	1500.2	1.187	1501.9	1.198
5600	1530.8	1.153	1529.4	1.157	1527.7	1.173	1528.1	1.183
5800	1569.5	1.145	1566.0	1.148	1559.0	1.162	1557.1	1.171
6000	1614.6	1.140	1608.6	1.143	1594.9	1.153	1589.9	1.161

p, bar → / T, °K	4 u	4 k	5 u	5 k	6 u	6 k	8 u	8 k
1300	701.6	1.318	701.9	1.318	702.1	1.319	702.5	1.320
1350	714.1	1.314	714.4	1.315	714.6	1.315	715.0	1.316
1400	726.4	1.312	726.6	1.312	726.8	1.312	727.2	1.313
1450	738.4	1.308	738.6	1.308	738.8	1.309	739.2	1.310
1500	750.2	1.306	750.4	1.306	750.6	1.306	751.0	1.307
1600	773.1	1.300	773.3	1.300	773.4	1.301	773.8	1.301
1700	795.1	1.294	795.3	1.295	795.5	1.295	795.9	1.296
1800	816.6	1.289	816.7	1.289	816.8	1.290	817.2	1.290
1900	836.9	1.283	836.7	1.284	837.3	1.284	837.7	1.285
2000	856.8	1.278	857.1	1.278	857.3	1.279	857.7	1.279
2100	876.0	1.272	876.2	1.272	876.5	1.273	876.9	1.274
2200	894.4	1.265	894.7	1.266	895.0	1.267	895.5	1.268
2300	912.0	1.258	912.4	1.259	912.8	1.260	913.4	1.262
2400	928.9	1.251	929.5	1.252	930.0	1.253	930.7	1.255
2500	945.2	1.242	945.9	1.244	946.5	1.245	947.4	1.248
2600	960.8	1.233	961.7	1.235	962.4	1.237	963.4	1.240
2700	976.1	1.224	977.1	1.227	977.9	1.229	979.1	1.232
2800	991.2	1.215	992.2	1.218	993.1	1.220	994.4	1.224
2900	1006.3	1.206	1007.4	1.209	1008.3	1.212	1009.6	1.216
3000	1021.8	1.198	1022.8	1.201	1023.6	1.204	1024.9	1.208
3100	1037.9	1.191	1038.7	1.194	1039.3	1.197	1040.5	1.201
3200	1054.8	1.185	1055.2	1.188	1055.7	1.191	1056.6	1.195
3300	1072.7	1.180	1072.7	1.184	1072.9	1.186	1073.3	1.190
3400	1091.7	1.178	1091.2	1.180	1091.0	1.183	1090.8	1.187
3500	1111.9	1.176	1110.8	1.178	1110.0	1.181	1109.2	1.184
3600	1133.2	1.176	1131.4	1.178	1130.2	1.180	1128.7	1.183
3700	1155.7	1.177	1153.2	1.179	1154.4	1.180	1149.1	1.182
3800	1179.1	1.180	1175.9	1.181	1173.6	1.182	1170.4	1.183
3900	1203.4	1.184	1199.5	1.184	1196.6	1.184	1192.6	1.185

continued

p, bar → / T, °K	4		5		6		8	
	u	k	u	k	u	k	u	k
4000	1228.3	1.189	1223.9	1.188	1220.5	1.188	1215.6	1.188
4100	1253.6	1.195	1248.6	1.194	1244.8	1.193	1239.2	1.192
4200	1278.9	1.202	1273.6	1.200	1269.4	1.199	1263.2	1.197
4300	1304.1	1.209	1298.6	1.207	1294.1	1.205	1287.4	1.203
4400	1328.7	1.217	1323.1	1.214	1318.6	1.212	1311.6	1.209
4500	1352.4	1.224	1347.0	1.221	1342.6	1.218	1335.5	1.215
4600	1374.9	1.229	1370.0	1.227	1365.7	1.224	1358.8	1.221
4700	1396.0	1.233	1391.6	1.231	1387.7	1.229	1381.3	1.227
4800	1415.2	1.234	1411.6	1.234	1408.4	1.233	1402.7	1.231
4900	1432.8	1.234	1430.1	1.234	1427.6	1.234	1427.8	1.233
5000	1448.8	1.231	1447.0	1.232	1445.2	1.233	1441.4	1.234
5200	1477.1	1.220	1476.9	1.224	1476.3	1.227	1476.7	1.230
5400	1502.9	1.205	1503.4	1.210	1503.7	1.215	1503.5	1.220
5600	1528.7	1.190	1529.3	1.196	1529.6	1.201	1530.1	1.208
5800	1556.5	1.177	1556.5	1.183	1556.3	1.187	1556.5	1.195
6000	1587.5	1.167	1586.1	1.172	1585.3	1.176	1584.4	1.183

p, bar → / T, °K	10		12		14		16	
	u	k	u	k	u	k	u	k
1300	702.9	1.320	703.4	1.321	703.9	1.322	704.3	1.323
1350	715.4	1.317	715.9	1.318	716.3	1.319	716.7	1.320
1400	727.6	1.314	728.1	1.315	728.5	1.316	728.9	1.316
1450	739.6	1.310	740.0	1.311	740.4	1.312	740.8	1.312
1500	751.4	1.308	751.8	1.309	752.3	1.309	752.5	1.310
1600	774.2	1.302	774.6	1.303	775.0	1.303	775.3	1.304
1700	796.2	1.286	796.6	1.297	797.0	1.297	797.3	1.298
1800	817.5	1.291	817.9	1.291	818.2	1.292	818.6	1.292
1900	837.1	1.285	838.4	1.286	838.8	1.286	839.1	1.287
2000	858.0	1.280	858.4	1.280	858.7	1.281	859.1	1.281
2100	877.3	1.274	877.7	1.275	878.0	1.276	878.4	1.276
2200	895.9	1.269	896.3	1.269	896.7	1.270	897.1	1.271
2300	913.9	1.263	914.4	1.263	914.8	1.264	915.2	1.265
2400	931.3	1.256	931.8	1.257	932.3	1.258	932.7	1.259
2500	948.1	1.249	948.7	1.251	949.2	1.252	949.7	1.253
2600	964.3	1.242	965.0	1.244	965.6	1.245	966,2	1.246
2700	980.1	1.234	980.9	1.236	981.5	1.238	982.2	1.239
2800	995.5	1.227	996.4	1.229	997.1	1.231	997.8	1.232
2900	1010.8	1.219	1011.7	1.222	1012.5	1.224	1013.2	1.225
3000	1026.0	1.212	1027.0	1.214	1027.8	1.217	1028.5	1.219
3100	1041.5	1.205	1042.4	1.208	1043.2	1.210	1043.9	1.212
3200	1057.4	1.199	1058.1	1.202	1058.8	1.204	1059.5	1.206
3300	1073.8	1.194	1074.4	1.197	1074.9	1.199	1075.5	1.201
3400	1091.0	1.190	1091.3	1.192	1091.6	1.195	1091.9	1.197
3500	1109.0	1.187	1108.9	1.189	1109.0	1.191	1109.1	1.193
3600	1127.8	1.185	1127.4	1.187	1127.1	1.189	1127.0	1.191
3700	1147.6	1.184	1146.7	1.186	1146.1	1.188	1145.7	1.190
3800	1168.3	1.185	1166.9	1.186	1165.9	1.188	1165.1	1.189
3900	1189.9	1.186	1187.9	1.188	1186.5	1.189	1185.4	1.190
4000	1221.2	1.189	1209.8	1.190	1207.9	1.190	1206.4	1.191
4100	1235.3	1.192	1232.3	1.193	1229.9	1.193	1228.1	1.194
4200	1258.8	1.197	1255.3	1.196	1252.6	1.196	1250.4	1.197
4300	1282.5	1.202	1278.7	1.201	1275.6	1.201	1273.1	1.201
4400	1306.4	1.207	1302.2	1.206	1298.9	1.205	1296.2	1.205
4500	1330.1	1.213	1325.8	1.212	1322.2	1.211	1319.3	1.210
4600	1353.4	1.219	1349.0	1.217	1345.4	1.216	1342.3	1.215
4700	1376.1	1.224	1371.8	1.223	1368.1	1.221	1365.0	1.220
4800	1397.9	1.229	1393.7	1.227	1390.2	1.226	1387.2	1.225
4900	1418.5	1.232	1414.8	1.231	1411.5	1.230	1408.6	1.229
5000	1437.9	1.234	1434.7	1.233	1431.7	1.233	1429.1	1.232
5200	1472.7	1.232	1470.7	1.233	1468.7	1.234	1466.7	1.234
5400	1502.9	1.224	1502.0	1.227	1500.9	1.229	1499.8	1.231

continued

p, bar → / T, °K	10		12		14		16	
	u	k	u	k	u	k	u	k
5600	1530.2	1.213	1530.0	1.217	1529.7	1.220	1529.3	1.222
5800	1556.6	1.200	1556.7	1.205	1556.7	1.208	1556.6	1.211
6000	1584.0	1.188	1583.0	1.193	1583.6	1.196	1583.4	1.200

p, bar → / T, °K	18		20		25		30	
	u	k	u	k	u	k	u	k
1300	704.8	1.324	705.2	1.325	706.3	1.327	707.5	1.329
1350	717.2	1.321	717.6	1.321	718.7	1.323	719.8	1.325
1400	729.3	1.317	729.7	1.318	730.8	1.320	731.8	1.322
1450	741.2	1.314	741.6	1.315	742.6	1.316	743.7	1.318
1500	752.9	1.311	753.3	1.311	754.3	1.313	755.3	1.315
1600	775.7	1.305	776.1	1.305	777.0	1.307	777.9	1.308
1700	797.7	1.299	798.0	1.299	798.9	1.301	799.8	1.302
1800	818.9	1.293	819.3	1.293	820.1	1.295	821.0	1.296
1900	839.5	1.287	838.1	1.288	840.7	1.289	839.8	1.291
2000	859.4	1.282	859.8	1.283	860.6	1.284	861.4	1.285
2100	878.7	1.277	879.1	1.277	879.9	1.278	880.8	1.280
2200	897.5	1.271	897.8	1.272	898.7	1.273	899.5	1.274
2300	915.6	1.266	916.0	1.266	916.8	1.268	917.7	1.269
2400	933.2	1.260	933.5	1.260	934.5	1.262	935.4	1.263
2500	950.2	1.254	950.6	1.254	951.6	1.256	952.5	1.258
2600	966.7	1.247	967.1	1.248	968.2	1.250	969.2	1.252
2700	982.7	1.241	983.2	1.242	984.4	1.244	985.5	1.246
2800	998.4	1.234	999.0	1.235	1000.2	1.238	1001.3	1.240
2900	1013.8	1.227	1014.4	1.228	1015.8	1.231	1016.9	1.234
3000	1029.2	1.220	1029.8	1.222	1031.1	1.225	1032.3	1.227
3100	1044.5	1.214	1045.1	1.216	1046.5	1.219	1047.7	1.222
3200	1060.1	1.208	1060.6	1.210	1061.9	1.213	1063.1	1.216
3300	1076.0	1.203	1076.5	1.204	1077.7	1.208	1078.7	1.211
3400	1092.3	1.198	1092.3	1.200	1093.7	1.204	1094.6	1.207
3500	1109.3	1.195	1110.0	1.197	1110.2	1.200	1110.9	1.203
3600	1127.0	1.193	1127.0	1.194	1127.3	1.197	1127.8	1.200
3700	1145.4	1.191	1145.2	1.192	1145.1	1.195	1145.2	1.198
3800	1164.6	1.190	1164.1	1.192	1163.5	1.194	1163.3	1.197
3900	1184.5	1.191	1183.8	1.192	1182.7	1.194	1182.1	1.196
4000	1205.2	1.192	1204.3	1.193	1202.6	1.195	1201.5	1.196
4100	1226.6	1.194	1225.4	1.195	1223.1	1.196	1221.5	1.198
4200	1248.6	1.197	1247.1	1.197	1244.2	1.198	1242.2	1.199
4300	1271.0	1.201	1269.3	1.201	1265.8	1.201	1263.3	1.202
4400	1293.8	1.205	1291.8	1.205	1287.8	1.205	1284.9	1.205
4500	1316.7	1.209	1314.5	1.209	1310.1	1.209	1306.8	1.209
4600	1339.6	1.214	1337.2	1.214	1332.5	1.213	1328.9	1.219
4700	1362.2	1.219	1359.8	1.219	1354.8	1.217	1351.0	1.217
4800	1384.4	1.224	1382.0	1.223	1376.9	1.222	1372.9	1.221
4900	1405.9	1.228	1403.6	1.227	1398.6	1.226	1394.5	1.225
5000	1426.6	1.231	1424.4	1.231	1419.6	1.230	1415.6	1.229
5200	1464.9	1.234	1463.1	1.234	1459.1	1.234	1455.7	1.234
5400	1498.7	1.232	1497.6	1.233	1494.8	1.234	1492.2	1.235
5600	1528.7	1.224	1528.2	1.226	1526.6	1.229	1524.9	1.232
5800	1556.4	1.214	1556.2	1.216	1555.5	1.221	1554.6	1.224
6000	1583.3	1.203	1583.2	1.205	1582.8	1.210	1582.4	1.215

p, bar → / T, °K	35		40		50		60	
	u	k	u	k	u	k	u	k
1300	708.6	1.331	709.7	1.333	712.0	1.337	714.2	1.342
1350	720.8	1.327	721.9	1.329	724.1	1.333	726.2	1.337
1400	732.9	1.324	733.9	1.326	736.0	1.330	738.1	1.334
1450	744.7	1.320	745.7	1.323	747.7	1.326	749.7	1.330
1500	756.3	1.317	757.3	1.318	759.2	1.322	761.2	1.325

continued

T, °K \ p, bar	35		40		50		60	
	u	k	u	k	u	k	u	k
1600	778.9	1.310	779.8	1.312	781.7	1.315	783.5	1.318
1700	800.7	1.304	801.6	1.305	803.4	1.308	805.2	1.311
1800	821.9	1.298	822.7	1.299	824.5	1.302	826.2	1.304
1900	842.4	1.292	841.5	1.293	843.2	1.296	844.9	1.298
2000	862.3	1.286	863.1	1.288	864.7	1.290	866.3	1.292
2100	881.6	1.281	882.4	1.282	884.0	1.284	885.6	1.287
2200	900.3	1.276	901.1	1.277	902.7	1.279	904.3	1.281
2300	918.5	1.270	919.3	1.271	920.9	1.274	922.5	1.276
2400	936.2	1.265	937.0	1.266	938.6	1.268	940.2	1.271
2500	953.4	1.259	954.3	1.261	955.9	1.263	957.5	1.265
2600	970.1	1.254	971.0	1.255	972.7	1.258	974.3	1.260
2700	986.4	1.248	987.3	1.249	989.1	1.252	990.7	1.255
2800	1002.4	1.242	1003.3	1.243	1005.1	1.246	1006.8	1.249
2900	1018.0	1.236	1019.0	1.238	1020.8	1.241	1022.6	1.244
3000	1033.4	1.230	1034.5	1.232	1036.3	1.235	1038.1	1.238
3100	1048.8	1.224	1049.8	1.226	1051.7	1.230	1053.5	1.233
3200	1064.2	1.218	1065.2	1.221	1067.1	1.224	1068.8	1.228
3300	1079.7	1.214	1080.7	1.216	1082.5	1.220	1084.2	1.223
3400	1095.5	1.209	1096.4	1.211	1098.1	1.215	1099.7	1.219
3500	1111.7	1.205	1112.4	1.208	1113.9	1.212	1115.4	1.215
3600	1128.3	1.202	1128.9	1.205	1130.2	1.208	1131.5	1.212
3700	1145.5	1.200	1145.9	1.202	1146.9	1.206	1147.9	1.209
3800	1163.3	1.199	1163.5	1.201	1164.5	1.204	1164.8	1.207
3900	1181.7	1.198	1181.6	1.200	1181.7	1.203	1182.2	1.206
4000	1200.8	1.198	1200.4	1.200	1200.0	1.203	1200.1	1.205
4100	1220.4	1.199	1219.7	1.200	1218.9	1.203	1218.6	1.205
4200	1240.7	1.201	1239.6	1.202	1238.3	1.204	1237.5	1.206
4300	1261.5	1.203	1260.0	1.204	1258.2	1.205	1257.0	1.207
4400	1282.7	1.205	1280.9	1.206	1278.5	1.208	1276.9	1.209
4500	1304.3	1.209	1302.2	1.209	1299.3	1.210	1297.3	1.211
4600	1326.2	1.213	1323.8	1.213	1320.3	1.213	1317.9	1.214
4700	1347.9	1.216	1345.4	1.216	1341.5	1.217	1338.8	1.217
4800	1369.7	1.221	1367.0	1.220	1362.8	1.220	1359.7	1.220
4900	1391.2	1.225	1388.4	1.224	1384.0	1.224	1380.7	1.224
5000	1412.3	1.228	1409.5	1.228	1404.9	1.227	1401.5	1.227
5200	1452.7	1.234	1450.1	1.234	1445.7	1.233	1442.2	1.233
5400	1489.8	1.236	1487.7	1.236	1483.9	1.237	1480.7	1.237
5600	1523.4	1.233	1521.8	1.235	1519.0	1.236	1516.5	1.238
5800	1553.7	1.227	1552.8	1.229	1550.9	1.232	1549.2	1.235
6000	1581.9	1.218	1581.4	1.221	1580.3	1.225	1579.2	1.228

T, °K \ p, bar	70		80		90		100	
	u	k	u	k	u	k	u	k
1300	716.5	1.346	718.7	1.350	721.0	1.354	723.2	1.358
1350	728.4	1.342	730.6	1.345	732.7	1.349	734.9	1.353
1400	740.2	1.338	742.2	1.341	744.3	1.345	746.4	1.348
1450	751.7	1.333	753.7	1.337	755.8	1.339	757.8	1.344
1500	763.1	1.329	765.1	1.332	767.0	1.336	769.0	1.339
1600	785.4	1.321	787.2	1.324	789.1	1.327	791.0	1.330
1700	807.0	1.314	808.8	1.317	810.5	1.319	812.3	1.322
1800	827.9	1.307	829.6	1.310	831.3	1.312	833.0	1.315
1900	846.5	1.301	848.2	1.303	849.9	1.306	851.5	1.308
2000	868.0	1.295	869.6	1.297	871.2	1.299	872.8	1.302
2100	887.2	1.289	888.7	1.291	890.3	1.293	891.9	1.296
2200	905.8	1.284	907.4	1.286	908.7	1.288	910.5	1.290
2300	924.0	1.278	925.6	1.280	927.1	1.282	928.6	1.284
2400	941.7	1.273	943.3	1.275	944.8	1.277	946.3	1.279
2500	959.0	1.267	960.5	1.270	962.0	1.272	963.5	1.274
2600	975.8	1.262	977.4	1.264	978.9	1.266	980.3	1.268

continued

T, °K ↓ / p, bar →	70		80		90		100	
	u	k	u	k	u	k	u	k
2700	992.3	1.257	993.8	1.259	995.3	1.261	996.8	1.263
2800	1008.4	1.251	1009.9	1.254	1011.5	1.256	1012.9	1.258
2900	1024.2	1.246	1025.8	1.248	1027.3	1.251	1028.8	1.253
3000	1039.7	1.241	1041.3	1.243	1042.9	1.246	1044.4	1.248
3100	1055.1	1.236	1056.7	1.238	1058.3	1.240	1059.8	1.243
3200	1070.5	1.231	1072.0	1.233	1073.6	1.236	1075.1	1.238
3300	1086.8	1.226	1087.4	1.229	1088.8	1.231	1090.3	1.233
3400	1101.2	1.222	1102.7	1.224	1104.2	1.227	1105.6	1.229
3500	1116.9	1.218	1118.3	1.221	1119.7	1.223	1121.1	1.226
3600	1132.8	1.215	1134.1	1.217	1135.4	1.220	1136.7	1.222
3700	1149.0	1.212	1150.2	1.215	1151.4	1.217	1152.6	1.219
3800	1165.7	1.210	1166.7	1.212	1167.7	1.215	1168.8	1.217
3900	1182.9	1.208	1183.6	1.211	1184.5	1.213	1185.4	1.215
4000	1200.5	1.208	1201.0	1.210	1201.7	1.212	1202.4	1.214
4100	1218.6	1.207	1218.9	1.210	1219.3	1.212	1219.9	1.214
4200	1237.3	1.208	1237.2	1.210	1237.4	1.212	1237.7	1.213
4300	1256.4	1.209	1256.1	1.211	1255.9	1.212	1256.1	1.214
4400	1275.9	1.211	1275.3	1.212	1275.0	1.214	1274.9	1.215
4500	1295.9	1.213	1295.0	1.214	1294.4	1.215	1294.0	1.216
4600	1316.4	1.216	1315.0	1.216	1314.1	1.217	1313.5	1.218
4700	1336.7	1.218	1335.2	1.219	1334.1	1.220	1333.3	1.221
4800	1357.4	1.221	1355.7	1.221	1354.3	1.222	1353.3	1.223
4900	1378.1	1.224	1376.2	1.225	1374.6	1.225	1374.4	1.226
5000	1398.8	1.227	1396.6	1.228	1394.9	1.228	1393.5	1.229
5200	1439.3	1.233	1437.0	1.233	1435.1	1.234	1433.5	1.234
5400	1478.1	1.237	1475.8	1.238	1473.9	1.238	1472.3	1.239
5600	1514.3	1.239	1512.3	1.239	1510.7	1.240	1509.2	1.241
5800	1547.6	1.236	1546.1	1.238	1544.8	1.239	1543.6	1.240
6000	1578.2	1.231	1577.2	1.234	1576.3	1.235	1575.5	1.237

T, °K ↓ / p, bar →	125		150		200		250	
	u	k	u	k	u	k	u	k
1300	728.2	1.368	733.5	1.378	743.0	1.397	754.0	1.417
1350	740.0	1.363	744.5	1.372	754.7	1.392	765.5	1.411
1400	751.6	1.357	756.8	1.366	766.0	1.383	776.0	1.402
1450	763.0	1.352	768.0	1.360	777.5	1.377	787.5	1.395
1500	773.9	1.347	778.7	1.355	788.4	1.371	798.0	1.388
1600	795.6	1.338	800.2	1.346	809.4	1.361	818.5	1.377
1700	816.7	1.329	821.2	1.337	830.0	1.351	838.7	1.365
1800	837.3	1.322	841.6	1.328	850.0	1.341	858.5	1.354
1900	857.3	1.314	853.2	1.320	861.4	1.333	869.6	1.345
2000	876.8	1.308	880.8	1.313	888.8	1.325	896.7	1.336
2100	895.8	1.301	899.7	1.307	907.5	1.318	915.2	1.329
2200	914.3	1.295	918.1	1.301	925.7	1.311	933.2	1.321
2300	932.4	1.290	936.1	1.295	943.5	1.305	950.9	1.315
2400	950.0	1.284	953.6	1.289	960.9	1.299	968.1	1.308
2500	967.9	1.279	970.8	1.283	978.0	1.293	985.1	1.302
2600	984.0	1.273	987.6	1.278	994.7	1.287	1001.6	1.296
2700	1000.5	1.268	1004.0	1.273	1011.0	1.282	1017.9	1.291
2800	1016.6	1.263	1020.1	1.268	1027.0	1.277	1033.9	1.285
2900	1032.4	1.258	1035.9	1.263	1042.8	1.272	1049.6	1.280
3000	1048.0	1.253	1051.5	1.258	1058.4	1.267	1065.0	1.275
3100	1063.4	1.248	1066.9	1.253	1073.7	1.262	1080.3	1.270
3200	1078.7	1.243	1082.1	1.248	1088.9	1.257	1095.4	1.265
3300	1093.9	1.239	1097.3	1.244	1104.0	1.253	1110.4	1.261
3400	1109.1	1.235	1112.5	1.240	1119.0	1.249	1125.4	1.257
3500	1124.4	1.231	1127.7	1.236	1134.1	1.245	1140.3	1.253
3600	1139.9	1.228	1143.1	1.232	1149.3	1.241	1155.4	1.249
3700	1155.6	1.225	1158.6	1.229	1164.6	1.238	1170.5	1.246
3800	1171.6	1.222	1174.4	1.227	1180.1	1.235	1185.8	1.243
3900	1187.9	1.220	1190.4	1.225	1195.8	1.233	1201.2	1.241

continued

T, °K \ p, bar →	125		150		200		250	
	u	k	u	k	u	k	u	k
4000	1204.5	1.219	1206.9	1.223	1211.8	1.231	1217.0	1.239
4100	1221.6	1.218	1223.6	1.222	1228.1	1.230	1233.0	1.237
4200	1239.1	1.218	1240.7	1.222	1244.8	1.229	1249.2	1.236
4300	1256.9	1.218	1258.3	1.222	1261.7	1.229	1265.8	1.235
4400	1275.2	1.219	1276.2	1.222	1279.1	1.229	1282.7	1.235
4500	1293.9	1.220	1294.4	1.223	1297.7	1.229	1299.9	1.235
4600	1312.9	1.221	1313.0	1.224	1314.7	1.230	1317.5	1.236
4700	1332.1	1.223	1332.9	1.226	1333.0	1.231	1335.2	1.237
4800	1351.7	1.225	1351.9	1.228	1351.5	1.233	1353.3	1.238
4900	1371.4	1.228	1370.4	1.230	1370.2	1.234	1371.5	1.239
5000	1391.1	1.230	1389.8	1.232	1389.1	1.236	1390.0	1.241
5200	1430.5	1.235	1428.7	1.237	1427.1	1.240	1427.1	1.244
5400	1469.1	1.240	1467.0	1.241	1464.8	1.244	1464.2	1.248
5600	1506.2	1.242	1504.1	1.244	1501.6	1.247	1500.7	1.250
5800	1541.1	1.243	1539.3	1.245	1537.0	1.247	1536.1	1.252
6000	1573.7	1.240	1572.3	1.243	1570.5	1.248	1569.8	1.252

T, °K \ p, bar →	300		400		500		600	
	u	k	u	k	u	k	u	k
1300	764.5	1.438	784.5	1.477	804.0	1.516	823.2	1.552
1350	776.0	1.429	795.2	1.467	814.5	1.503	833.1	1.539
1400	787.0	1.420	806.0	1.457	825.0	1.492	843.0	1.526
1450	797.6	1.412	817.0	1.447	835.0	1.481	852.5	1.513
1500	807.6	1.405	826.5	1.438	845.1	1.471	862.4	1.501
1600	827.6	1.392	845.5	1.422	863.8	1.451	880.5	1.479
1700	847.4	1.379	864.6	1.406	882.5	1.432	898.0	1.458
1800	866.8	1.367	883.4	1.392	899.7	1.417	915.7	1.441
1900	885.9	1.357	901.9	1.380	917.7	1.403	933.2	1.425
2000	904.6	1.348	920.1	1.360	935.5	1.392	950.6	1.413
2100	922.8	1.339	938.0	1.360	952.9	1.381	967.7	1.401
2200	940.7	1.332	955.5	1.352	970.1	1.371	984.5	1.391
2300	958.2	1.324	972.6	1.344	986.9	1.363	1001.0	1.381
2400	975.3	1.318	989.5	1.336	1003.4	1.354	1017.2	1.372
2500	992.1	1.311	1006.0	1.329	1019.7	1.347	1033.2	1.364
2600	1008.5	1.305	1022.2	1.323	1035.7	1.340	1048.9	1.356
2700	1024.7	1.299	1038.1	1.316	1051.4	1.333	1064.4	1.349
2800	1040.6	1.294	1053.8	1.310	1066.8	1.326	1079.7	1.342
2900	1056.2	1.288	1069.2	1.305	1082.1	1.320	1094.7	1.335
3000	1071.6	1.283	1084.4	1.299	1097.1	1.314	1109.6	1.329
3100	1086.8	1.278	1099.5	1.294	1111.9	1.309	1124.2	1.323
3200	1101.8	1.275	1114.4	1.289	1126.7	1.303	1138.8	1.317
3300	1116.7	1.269	1129.1	1.284	1141.3	1.298	1153.2	1.312
3400	1131.6	1.265	1143.8	1.279	1155.8	1.293	1167.6	1.307
3500	1146.5	1.261	1158.5	1.275	1170.3	1.289	1181.9	1.302
3600	1161.4	1.257	1173.2	1.271	1184.8	1.285	1196.2	1.298
3700	1175.3	1.253	1187.5	1.268	1199.3	1.281	1210.5	1.294
3800	1191.4	1.251	1202.7	1.264	1213.9	1.277	1224.9	1.290
3900	1206.6	1.248	1217.7	1.261	1228.6	1.274	1239.4	1.287
4000	1222.2	1.246	1232.8	1.259	1243.4	1.271	1254.0	1.283
4100	1237.9	1.244	1248.1	1.257	1258.4	1.269	1268.7	1.281
4200	1253.9	1.243	1263.7	1.255	1273.7	1.267	1283.7	1.279
4300	1270.2	1.242	1279.5	1.254	1289.1	1.265	1298.8	1.277
4400	1286.8	1.241	1295.5	1.253	1304.7	1.264	1314.1	1.275
4500	1303.6	1.241	1311.8	1.252	1320.6	1.263	1329.7	1.274
4600	1320.8	1.241	1328.4	1.252	1336.7	1.263	1345.4	1.273
4700	1338.2	1.241	1345.2	1.252	1353.1	1.262	1361.4	1.272
4800	1355.8	1.243	1362.3	1.253	1369.7	1.262	1371.6	1.272
4900	1373.7	1.244	1379.5	1.253	1386.5	1.263	1394.0	1.272
5000	1391.8	1.245	1397.0	1.254	1403.4	1.263	1410.6	1.272
5200	1428.2	1.248	1432.3	1.256	1437.7	1.264	1444.2	1.273
5400	1464.8	1.251	1467.8	1.259	1472.5	1.266	1478.1	1.274

continued

T, °K ↓ p, bar →	300		400		500		600	
	u	k	u	k	u	k	u	k
5600	1500.9	1.254	1503.2	1.261	1507.1	1.268	1512.1	1.275
5800	1536.1	1.255	1537.9	1.262	1541.3	1.269	1545.8	1.276
6000	1569.8	1.255	1571.5	1.262	1574.6	1.269	1578.8	1.276

T, °K ↓ p, bar →	800		1000	
	u	k	u	k
1300	860.0	1.620	896.6	1.685
1350	869.5	1.603	905.0	1.665
1400	878.6	1.586	913.0	1.645
1450	887.8	1.571	921.5	1.627
1500	896.9	1.556	930.0	1.610
1600	914.2	1.530	946.7	1.580
1700	930.4	1.508	962.3	1.555
1800	947.0	1.487	977.1	1.531
1900	963.6	1.469	992.9	1.511
2000	980.1	1.454	1008.7	1.493
2100	996.5	1.440	1024.4	1.478
2200	1012.6	1.428	1040.0	1.464
2300	1028.6	1.417	1055.4	1.451
2400	1044.2	1.407	1070.6	1.440
2500	1059.8	1.397	1085.6	1.429
2600	1075.0	1.388	1100.4	1.419
2700	1090.0	1.380	1115.0	1.410
2800	1104.9	1.372	1129.3	1.401
2900	1119.5	1.365	1143.7	1.393
3000	1134.0	1.358	1157.9	1.385
3100	1148.3	1.351	1171.9	1.378
3200	1162.5	1.345	1185.7	1.371
3300	1176.6	1.339	1199.5	1.364

T, °K ↓ p, bar →	800		1000	
	u	k	u	k
3400	1190.7	1.333	1213.3	1.358
3500	1204.7	1.328	1226.9	1.352
3600	1218.6	1.323	1240.6	1.347
3700	1232.6	1.318	1254.2	1.342
3800	1246.6	1.314	1268.0	1.337
3900	1260.7	1.310	1281.7	1.333
4000	1274.9	1.307	1295.6	1.329
4100	1289.3	1.303	1309.5	1.325
4200	1303.7	1.300	1323.6	1.322
4300	1318.4	1.298	1337.8	1.319
4400	1333.2	1.296	1352.2	1.316
4500	1348.2	1.294	1366.8	1.314
4600	1363.4	1.293	1381.5	1.312
4700	1378.7	1.291	1396.4	1.310
4800	1394.3	1.290	1411.5	1.309
4900	1410.1	1.290	1426.8	1.307
5000	1426.0	1.289	1442.2	1.307
5200	1458.3	1.286	1474.5	1.305
5400	1491.0	1.289	1505.2	1.305
5600	1523.9	1.290	1537.1	1.304
5800	1556.6	1.290	1569.0	1.304
6000	1588.9	1.289	1600.5	1.303

Viscosity of gaseous air at $p = 1$ bar [70]

t, °C	0	100	200	300	400	500	600	700	800
$\eta \cdot 10^7$, N · s/m²	171	219	260	297	330	362	391	417	443
t, °C	900	1000	1100	1200	1400	1600	1800	2000	
$\eta \cdot 10^7$, N · s/m²	466	490	512	534	576	616	655	681	

Viscosity $\eta \cdot 10^7$ (N · s/m²) of liquid and gaseous air [141, 142]

T, °K ↓ p, bar →	1	10	20	30	40	50	60	70	80
75	226.6	2310	2360	2409	2460	2511	2564	2615	2668
80		1816	1859	1901	1943	1985	2028	2073	2117
85	60.4	1447	1481	1516	1536	1585	1621	1658	1695
90	64.1	1177	1205	1233	1261	1290	1318	1348	1379
95	67.6	981.7	1005	1027	1050	1074	1098	1122	1146
100	71.1	837.8	857.4	876.5	896.1	916.2	936.1	956.5	977.3
105	74.5	724.6	743.2	761.3	779.4	797.3	815.2	833.0	850.8
110	77.9	83.0	646.1	665.3	683.5	701.2	718.7	735.6	752.4
115	81.2	85.8	554.9	577.1	597.8	617.0	635.5	653.3	670.3
120	84.5	88.8	98.1	491.9	516.2	538.6	559.1	578.6	596.9

continued

T, °K \ p, bar →	1	10	20	30	40	50	60	70	80
125	87.7	91.7	99.3	416.9	437.7	464.6	488.0	509.6	529.5
130	90.9	94.6	101.2	115.9	359.7	405.0	437.4	446.7	468.3
135	94.1	97.6	103.4	114.1	149.3	305.6	353.2	386.0	411.8
140	97.2	100.5	105.8	114.4	131.8	190.8	276.7	322.8	355.7
145	100.3	103.5	108.3	115.6	128.0	152.8	205.6	261.4	301.4
150	103.4	106.4	110.8	117.3	127.2	143.4	171.7	213.2	253.8
160	109.4	112.2	116.1	121.3	128.5	138.6	152.7	172.0	193.8
170	115.3	117.9	121.3	125.8	131.6	139.1	148.6	160.6	174.1
180	121.1	123.5	126.6	130.5	135.4	141.4	148.8	157.5	167.1
190	126.8	129.1	131.9	135.4	139.6	144.7	150.7	157.7	165.1
200	132.5	134.6	137.2	140.4	144.1	148.6	153.7	159.5	165.6
210	138.1	140.1	142.5	145.4	148.8	152.7	157.2	162.1	167.4
220	143.6	145.5	147.8	150.4	153.5	157.0	161.0	165.4	170.0
230	149.1	150.9	153.0	155.5	158.3	161.5	165.1	169.0	173.1
240	154.4	156.1	158.1	160.4	163.0	166.0	169.3	172.8	176.5
250	159.6	161.2	163.1	165.2	167.7	170.4	173.5	176.7	180.1
260	164.6	166.2	168.0	170.0	172.3	174.8	177.7	180.6	183.8
270	169.6	171.1	172.8	174.8	176.9	179.3	181.9	184.6	187.5
280	174.6	176.0	177.7	179.5	181.6	183.8	186.2	188.8	191.4
290	179.6	181.0	182.6	184.3	185.3	188.3	190.6	193.0	195.5
300	184.6	185.9	187.4	189.1	191.0	192.9	195.1	197.3	199.7
310	189.6	191.0	192.3	193.9	195.7	197.6	199.6	201.7	204.0
320	194.5	195.8	197.1	198.6	200.3	202.1	204.0	206.1	208.2
330	199.2	200.4	201.7	203.2	204.8	206.5	208.4	210.3	212.3
340	203.8	204.9	206.2	207.7	209.2	210.8	212.6	214.4	216.3
350	208.2	209.3	210.4	211.9	213.4	215.0	216.6	218.4	220.2
400	230.1	231.1	232.1	233.3	234.5	235.8	237.2	238.7	240.2
450	250.7	251.6	252.5	253.5	254.5	255.7	256.8	258.0	259.3
500	270.1	270.9	271.7	272.6	273.5	274.5	275.4	276.5	277.6
550	288.4	289.1	289.9	290.6	291.5	292.3	293.2	294.1	295.1
600	305.8	306.4	307.1	307.8	308.6	309.4	310.2	311.0	311.8
650	322.5	323.1	323.7	324.4	325.1	325.8	326.6	327.2	328.0
700	338.8	339.4	339.9	340.5	341.2	341.8	342.5	343.1	343.8
750	354.6	355.1	355.6	356.2	356.8	357.4	358.0	358.6	359.2
800	369.8	370.3	370.8	371.3	371.8	372.4	372.9	373.5	374.1
850	384.3	384.8	385.2	385.7	386.2	386.7	387.2	387.8	388.3
900	398.1	398.5	399.0	399.4	400.0	400.4	400.9	401.4	401.9
1000	424.4	424.8	425.2	425.6	426.0	426.4	426.9	427.3	427.8
1100	449.0	449.3	449.7	450.0	450.4	450.7	451.2	451.6	452.0
1200	473.0	473.2	473.6	473.9	474.3	474.6	474.9	475.3	475.7
1300	496.0	496.3	496.6	496.9	497.2	497.5	497.9	498.2	498.5

T, °K \ p, bar →	90	100	125	150	175	200	250	300	350
75	2721	2776	2914	3053	3199	3346			
80	2161	2207	2324	2444	2568	2697	2827	2960	3098
85	1731	1770	1868	1968	2072	2182	2292	2409	2525
90	1410	1440	1521	1604	1692	1783	1878	1973	2076
95	1172	1197	1264	1333	1404	1480	1558	1640	1724
100	997.8	1019	1074	1131	1190	1253	1319	1387	1458
105	869.0	887.1	933.5	981.9	1031	1083	1138	1195	1254
110	769.3	785.8	827.2	869.2	912.0	957.0	1003	1051	1101
115	686.8	703.0	742.5	781.3	820.2	859.3	899.7	940.7	983.7
120	614.5	631.4	671.3	709.0	745.8	782.1	818.3	855.1	892.8
125	548.5	566.4	608.2	646.5	682.8	717.5	751.7	785.7	819.9
130	488.4	507.3	550.6	590.1	626.7	661.3	694.4	726.9	758.9
135	434.1	453.8	497.9	537.6	574.1	608.2	642.3	675.0	705.9
140	382.2	404.5	450.9	490.1	526.9	561.2	594.5	625.4	657.1
145	332.3	357.8	406.9	449.2	485.2	518.6	551.0	581.4	610.8
150	287.4	315.2	365.0	412.3	448.5	481.2	512.3	542.6	571.4
160	222.7	248.5	295.6	349.0	386.7	419.7	449.2	475.5	503.0

continued

T, °K \ p, bar →	90	100	125	150	175	200	250	300	350
170	192.4	211.0	252.5	300.1	337.0	369.7	426.0	474.9	
180	179.8	193.0	225.7	265.6	299.4	330.5	385.1	432.7	475.2
190	174.7	184.6	210.4	242.8	272.5	300.8	352.4	398.2	439.2
200	173.3	181.2	202.0	228.5	253.9	279.1	326.5	369.9	409.5
210	173.8	180.4	197.8	219.7	241.5	263.7	306.5	346.9	384.5
220	175.5	181.1	196.0	214.6	233.4	252.8	291.5	328.8	364.1
230	177.9	182.9	195.9	212.0	228.4	245.5	280.4	314.6	347.6
240	180.8	185.2	196.7	210.9	225.4	240.6	272.0	303.4	334.1
250	184.0	187.9	198.3	210.9	223.9	237.6	265.9	294.7	323.2
260	187.3	190.8	200.3	211.6	223.4	235.8	261.5	288.1	314.5
270	190.7	194.1	202.7	213.0	223.7	235.0	258.6	283.1	307.7
280	194.4	197.6	205.5	215.0	224.8	235.1	256.9	279.5	302.5
290	198.3	201.2	208.6	217.3	226.4	235.9	256.0	277.0	298.5
300	202.3	205.0	211.9	220.0	228.4	237.3	256.0	275.5	295.6
310	206.4	208.9	215.5	223.0	230.8	239.1	256.6	274.8	293.7
320	210.5	212.9	219.0	226.1	233.4	241.1	257.5	274.7	292.4
330	214.5	216.7	222.5	229.2	236.1	243.3	258.7	274.9	291.6
340	218.4	220.5	226.0	232.3	238.9	245.6	260.2	275.5	291.3
350	222.2	224.2	229.5	235.4	241.6	248.0	261.7	276.2	291.2
400	241.8	243.4	247.6	252.3	257.2	262.1	272.9	284.2	296.1
450	260.6	262.0	265.5	269.6	273.3	277.5	286.3	295.6	305.6
500	278.7	279.9	282.9	286.2	289.6	293.1	300.5	308.4	316.6
550	296.1	297.1	299.7	302.5	305.5	308.6	315.0	321.8	328.8
600	312.7	313.6	315.9	318.4	321.0	323.7	329.4	335.3	341.5
650	328.8	329.6	331.7	333.9	336.3	338.6	343.7	349.0	354.5
700	344.6	345.3	347.2	349.2	351.3	353.4	358.0	362.8	367.7
750	359.9	360.6	362.3	364.2	366.1	368.0	372.2	376.5	381.0
800	374.7	375.4	376.9	378.6	380.4	382.2	386.0	389.9	394.0
850	388.9	389.5	390.9	392.5	394.1	395.8	399.3	402.9	406.7
900	402.4	403.0	404.3	405.8	407.3	408.8	412.0	415.4	418.9
1000	428.2	428.7	429.9	431.2	432.5	433.8	436.7	439.6	442.6
1100	452.4	452.8	453.9	455.1	456.3	457.6	460.1	462.6	465.4
1200	476.1	476.5	477.4	478.4	479.4	480.6	482.8	485.2	487.6
1300	498.9	499.2	500.1	501.0	502.0	502.9	504.9	507.0	509.2

T, °K \ p, bar →	400	450	500	600	700	800	900	1000
85	3169							
90	2630	2874	3131					
95	2199	2411	2636					
100	1859	2043	2237					
105	1595	1750	1920					
110	1389	1523	1668					
115	1230	1343	1468					
120	1104	1203	1310					
125	1006	1091	1185					
130	925.6	1000	1081					
135	859.1	925.2	996.0					
140	801.8	961.3	924.2					
145	751.1	807.5	862.7					
150	706.4	760.1	810.6					
160	631.3	676.7	719.5					
190	477.2	512.7						
200	445.8	480.3	512.3					
210	419.4	452.7	483.8					
220	397.4	428.9	459.1	515.7				
230	379.1	409.2	438.2	492.5				
240	363.8	392.4	420.0	472.1	521.3			
250	351.2	378.2	404.5	454.5	501.8			
260	340.7	366.2	391.2	439.2	484.6	528.6		
270	332.2	356.2	379.9	425.9	469.6	511.7	552.3	

continued

T, °K \ p, bar →	400	450	500	600	700	800	900	1000
280	325.4	348.1	370.4	414.4	456.6	497.1	536.4	
290	320.0	341.5	362.7	404.6	445.2	484.3	522.2	559.4
300	315.9	336.2	356.4	396.3	435.1	473.0	509.7	545.5
310	312.8	332.0	351.2	389.2	426.4	463.0	498.5	533.2
320	310.5	328.7	346.9	383.1	418.8	454.0	488.3	522.1
330	308.7	326.0	343.3	377.9	412.2	445.9	479.1	511.8
340	307.5	323.9	340.4	373.4	406.3	438.7	470.8	502.4
350	306.6	322.2	337.9	369.6	401.1	432.3	463.3	493.9
400	308.3	320.8	333.4	359.2	385.2	411.3	437.4	463.4
450	315.4	325.7	336.2	357.6	379.5	401.6	423.9	446.1
500	325.1	333.8	342.7	361.0	379.8	398.8	418.1	437.5
550	336.3	343.7	351.4	367.3	383.6	400.3	417.2	434.3
600	348.0	354.6	361.3	375.3	389.7	404.5	419.5	434.7
650	360.2	366.1	372.1	384.5	397.4	410.6	424.1	437.7
700	372.9	378.1	383.5	394.8	406.3	418.2	430.4	442.7
750	385.6	390.4	395.3	405.5	416.0	426.8	437.9	449.1
800	398.3	402.7	407.1	416.4	426.0	435.9	446.1	456.4
850	410.6	414.7	418.8	427.3	436.1	445.2	454.5	464.1
900	422.5	426.3	430.1	437.9	446.1	454.5	463.2	472.0
1000	445.8	449.0	452.3	459.1	466.2	473.5	481.0	488.7
1100	468.1	470.9	473.9	479.8	486.2	492.6	499.1	505.8
1200	490.0	492.5	495.2	500.5	506.1	511.8	517.6	523.7
1300	511.5	513.8	516.1	520.9	525.9	531.1	536.4	541.8

Viscosity $\eta \cdot 10^7$ (N · s/m²) of dissociated air [353]

T, °K \ p, bar →	0.001	1	10	100	T, °K \ p, bar →	0.001	1	10	100
1500	557	557	557	557	3800	1216	1200	1176	1161
1600	584	584	584	584	3900	1243	1230	1206	1189
1700	611	611	611	611	4000	1269	1259	1236	1217
1800	637	637	637	637	4100	1296	1288	1267	1245
1900	663	663	663	663	4200	1323	1316	1296	1273
2000	690	689	689	689	4300	1349	1343	1326	1301
2100	717	715	715	715	4400	1375	1370	1355	1330
2200	745	740	740	740	4500	1401	1396	1383	1358
2300	774	766	766	766	4600	1426	1422	1412	1387
2400	806	792	792	792	4700	1450	1448	1439	1415
2500	839	818	817	817	4800	1473	1474	1466	1443
2600	874	844	843	843	4900	1494	1499	1493	1471
2700	907	871	869	869	5000	1512	1524	1519	1499
2800	940	898	896	895	5100	1529	1550	1545	1526
2900	970	926	922	921	5200	1546	1575	1571	1553
3000	999	955	949	947	5300	1561	1600	1596	1580
3100	1027	984	976	973	5400	1578	1624	1621	1606
3200	1055	1013	1003	999	5500	1595	1649	1646	1633
3300	1082	1044	1031	1026	5600	1613	1674	1671	1658
3400	1109	1075	1059	1052	5700	1632	1698	1695	1684
3500	1136	1107	1088	1079	5800	1652	1723	1720	1709
3600	1163	1138	1117	1106	5900	1673	1747	1744	1734
3700	1189	1169	1146	1133	6000	1694	1771	1768	1759

Thermal conductivity λ (W/m · deg) of gaseous air at $p = 1$ bar [15]

T, °K	λ · 10³	T, °K	λ · 10³	T, °K	λ · 10³	T, °K	λ · 10³
90	8.4	230	20.4	370	31.5	600	46.9
100	9.3	240	21.2	380	32.3	650	49.7
110	10.2	250	22.1	390	33.0	700	52.4
120	11.1	260	22.9	400	33.8	750	54.9
130	12.0	270	23.8	420	35.2	800	57.3
140	12.9	280	24.6	440	36.6	850	59.6
150	13.8	290	25.4	460	38.0	900	62.0
160	14.7	300	26.2	480	39.4	950	64.3
170	15.5	310	26.9	500	40.7	1000	66.7
180	16.4	320	27.7	520	42.0	1050	69.1
190	17.2	330	28.5	540	43.3	1100	71.5
200	18.0	340	29.2	560	44.5	1150	73.9
210	18.8	350	30.0	580	45.7	1200	76.3
220	19.6	360	30.8				

Thermal conductivity λ · 10³ (W/m · deg) of liquid and gaseous air from 75 to 300 °K [15]

p, bar → / T, °K	1	10	20	30	40	50	60
75	154.1	154.8	155.6	156.4	157.2	158.0	158.8
80		146.0	146.9	147.8	148.6	149.4	150.3
85	7.93	137.2	138.2	139.1	140.1	141.0	141.9
90	8.41	128.4	129.5	130.6	131.6	132.6	133.6
95	8.88	119.7	120.9	122.1	123.2	124.3	125.4
100	9.34	110.9	112.3	113.6	114.9	116.2	117.4
105	9.80	102.1	103.7	105.2	106.7	108.1	109.5
110	10.2	12.0	94.9	96.7	98.1	100.1	101.7
115	10.7	12.3	85.6	88.0	90.1	92.1	93.9
120	11.1	12.6	15.2	78.5	81.4	83.9	86.1
125	11.6	12.9	15.2	66.6	71.6	75.2	78.1
130	12.0	13.3	15.2	18.8	59.2	65.3	69.4
135	12.5	13.7	15.4	18.1	25.6	52.3	59.5
140	12.9	14.1	15.7	17.9	21.8	33.3	47.8
145	13.3	14.5	15.9	17.9	20.8	26.0	35.8
150	13.8	14.9	16.2	17.9			
160	14.7	15.7	16.8	18.3	20.1		
170	15.5	16.4	17.5	18.8	20.3	22.0	
180	16.4	17.2	18.2	19.3	20.6	22.1	23.8
190	17.2	18.1	18.9	20.0	21.1	22.4	23.8
200	18.1	18.9	19.7	20.6	21.7	22.8	24.0
210	18.9	19.7	20.4	21.3	22.2	23.2	24.3
220	19.8	20.5	21.2	22.0	22.9	23.8	24.8
230	20.6	21.3	22.0	22.7	23.5	24.4	25.3
240	21.4	22.1	22.7	23.4	24.2	25.0	25.8
250	22.3	22.9	23.5	24.2	24.9	25.6	26.4
260	23.1	23.7	24.3	24.9	25.6	26.3	27.0
270	23.9	24.5	25.1	25.7	26.3	27.0	27.6
280	24.7	25.3	25.8	26.4	27.0	27.6	28.3
290	25.5	26.0	26.6	27.1	27.7	28.3	28.9
300	26.3	26.8	27.3	27.9	28.4	29.0	29.6

p, bar → / T, °K	70	80	90	100	150	200	250
75	159.5	160.3	161.0	161.8	165.4	168.9	
80	151.1	151.9	152.7	153.5	157.4	161.1	164.7
85	142.8	143.7	144.5	145.4	149.5	153.5	157.3
90	134.5	135.5	136.5	137.4	141.8	146.1	150.0

continued

T, °K \ p, bar →	70	80	90	100	150	200	250
95	126.5	127.5	128.6	129,6	134.4	138.9	143.1
100	118.6	119.7	120.8	122,0	127.2	132.0	136.5
105	110.8	112.1	113.3	114,6	120.3	125.4	130.1
110	103.2	104.6	106.0	107.4	113.6	119.1	124.1
115	95.7	97.3	98.9	100.4	107.2	113.1	118.4
120	88.2	90.1	91.9	93.6	101.1	107.4	113.0
125	80.7	83.0	85.1	87.0	95.3	102.0	107.9
130	72.8	75.7	78.2	80.5	89.6	96.8	103.0
135	64.3	67.9	71.1	73.8	84.0	91.6	98.3
140	54.9	59.8	63.7	66.9	78.5	86.8	93.5
145	45.3	54.6	56.3	60.1	73.2	82.0	89.2
150					68.0	77.5	84.9
160					58.8	69.1	76.9
170					51.2	61.8	70.0
180	24.1	27.8	30,2	32.7	45.5	55.9	64.1
190	24.1	27.1	28.9	30.9	41.6	51.2	59.2
200	24.3	26,8	28,3	29.9	38.9	47.6	55.2
210	24.6	26.8	28.1	29.5	37.3	44.9	52.0
220	25.1	26.9	28.1	29.3	36.0	42.9	49.5
230	25,6	27.2	28.3	29.3	35.3	41.5	47.6
240	26.1	27.6	28.5	29.5	34.8	40.5	46.0
250	26.7	28.1	28.9	29.8	34.6	39.8	44.9
260	27.3	28.6	29.4	30.2	34.6	39.3	44.1
270	27.9	29.1	29.8	30.6	34.7	39.1	43.5
280	28.5	29.6	30.3	31.1	34.9	38.9	43.0
290	29,2	30.2	30.8	31.5	35.1	38.9	42.7
300	29.8	30.8	31.4	32.0	35.4	38.9	42.6

T, °K \ p, bar →	300	400	500	600	700	800	900	1000
80	168.1							
85	160.8	167.7						
90	153.8	161.0	167.7					
95	147.1	154.6	161.5					
100	140.7	148.5	155.7					
105	134.6	142.7	150.2					
110	128.8	137.2	144.9					
115	123.3	132.1	140.0					
120	118.1	127.2	135.4					
125	113.2	122.6	131.0					
130	108.5	118.2	126.7					
135	104.0	114.0	122.6					
140	99.6	109.8	118.6					
145	95,4	105.8	114.7					
150	91.2	101.9	110.9					
160	83.5	94.6	103.9					
170	76.8	88.0	91.6					
180	71.0	82.2	86.6					
190	66.0	77.3	82.2	94.7				
200	61.9	72.9	78.3	90.3				
210	58.4	69.2	74.9	86.3	93.4			
220	55.5	66.0	72.0	82.8	89.8	96.3		
230	53.2	63.3	69.4	79.7	86.6	93.1	99.0	
240	51.4	61.0	67.2	76.9	83.7	90.1	96.0	
250	49.9	59.0	65.3	74.5	81.2	87.5	93.2	
260	48.7	57.4	63.6	72.4	78.9	85.0	90.7	98.7
270	47.8	56.1	62.2	70.5	76.9	82.8	88.4	96,1
280	47.1	55.0	60.9	68.9	75.1	80.9	86.4	93.7
290	46.6	54.0	59.9	67.4	73.5	79.2	84,5	91.5
300	46.2	53.3	59.1	66.2	72.0	77.6	82.8	89.6
								87.8

Thermal conductivity $\lambda \cdot 10^3$ (W/m · deg) of gaseous air from 300 to 800 °K [15]

p, bar \ T, °K →	300	350	400	450	500	550	600	650	700	750	800
1	26.2	30.0	33.8	37.3	40.7	43.9	46.9	49.7	52.4	54.9	57.3
50	28.4	31.8	35.4	38.7	42.0	45.0	47.9	50.6	53.2	55.7	58.0
100	31.4	34.1	37.3	40.3	43.3	46.2	49.0	51.6	54.1	56.5	58.8
150	34.9	36.7	39.4	42.0	44.9	47.6	50.2	52.7	55.2	57.4	59.6
200	38.5	39.5	41.8	44.0	46.5	49.0	51.5	53.9	56.2	58.4	60.5
250	42.0	42.3	44.1	46.0	48.3	50.5	52.9	55.1	57.3	59.4	61.4
300	45.5	45.1	46.4	48.0	50.1	52.2	54.3	56.3	58.4	60.4	62.4
350	48.9	47.8	48.6	49.9	51.8	53.7	55.7	57.6	59.6	61.5	63.4
400	52.2	50.5	50.9	51.9	53.5	55.2	57.1	58.9	60.8	62.6	64.4
450	55.3	53.1	53.1	53.8	55.2	56.7	58.4	60.2	62.0	63.7	65.4
500	58.4	55.5	55.2	55.8	56.8	58.2	59.8	61.4	63.1	64.8	66.4
550	61.4	58.0	57.3	57.6	58.4	59.7	61.1	62.6	64.2	65.9	67.4
600	64.4	60.3	59.4	59.4	60.0	61.1	62.4	63.8	65.3	66.9	68.4
650	67.4	62.7	61.5	61.2	61.6	62.5	63.7	65.0	66.4	67.9	69.4
700	70.3	65.1	63.6	62.9	63.2	64.0	65.0	66.2	67.5	68.9	70.4
750	73.2	67.6	65.6	64.6	64.7	65.4	66.3	67.4	68.6	69.9	71.3
800	76.0	70.0	67.6	66.2	66.2	66.8	67.6	68.6	69.7	70.9	72.2
850	78.6	72.5	69.6	67.8	67.7	68.2	68.9	69.7	70.8	71.9	73.1
900	81.1	74.9	71.6	69.4	69.4	69.2	69.5	70.1	71.9	72.9	74.0
950	83.7	77.4	73.6	71.0	70.5	70.8	71.3	72.0	73.0	73.9	74.9
1000	86.2	79.8	75.6	72.6	71.8	72.0	72.5	73.2	74.1	74.9	75.8

Thermal conductivity $\lambda \cdot 10^3$ (W/m · deg) of dissociated air [353]

T, °K \ p, bar →	0.001	0.01	0.1	1	10	100	T, °K \ p, bar →	0.001	0.01	0.1	1	10	100
1500	100	100	100	100	100	100	3800	637	394	439	722	653	489
1600	109	107	106	106	106	106	3900	808	446	419	672	682	459
1700	121	115	114	113	113	113	4000	1035	520	417	620	701	489
1800	140	126	122	120	120	120	4100	1327	618	432	574	709	518
1900	174	142	131	128	127	127	4200	1692	747	463	538	707	546
2000	232	165	144	137	135	134	4300	2137	910	510	515	696	572
2100	328	202	161	147	143	141	4400	2659	1112	574	505	680	595
2200	473	260	184	160	152	149	4500	3243	1360	656	509	660	615
2300	666	344	218	175	162	157	4600	3858	1655	760	525	640	631
2400	874	459	265	196	173	166	4700	4451	2000	886	554	623	643
2500	1024	603	328	222	187	175	4800	4953	2393	1037	595	610	653
2600	1030	758	409	256	203	186	4900	5267	2824	1216	650	603	659
2700	879	890	508	299	222	197	5000	5330	3281	1424	718	604	663
2800	662	956	617	352	245	209	5100	5108	3739	1662	780	612	666
2900	481	926	725	414	272	223	5200	4626	4167	1929	897	629	667
3000	367	812	813	486	304	238	5300	3983	4522	2223	1010	655	669
3100	310	663	863	558	341	255	5400	3289	4769	2539	1140	689	672
3200	288	528	862	632	382	274	5500	2638	4861	2872	1287	731	676
3300	291	432	810	699	427	295	5600	2087	4785	3209	1452	784	683
3400	313	374	725	750	475	319	5700	1651	4538	3537	1634	845	693
3500	354	347	630	779	523	344	5800	1322	4158	3839	1832	916	708
3600	418	344	545	782	571	371	5900	1082	3690	4096	2046	997	726
3700	510	360	481	762	615	399	6000	911	3191	4287	2272	1087	749

Chapter 11

DIFFUSION IN GASES

EQUATIONS FOR THE CALCULATION OF DIFFUSION COEFFICIENTS IN GASES

Rigorous kinetic theory leads in first approximation to the following equation for the diffusion coefficient [246]:

$$[D_{12}]_1 = 0.002628 \frac{\sqrt{T^3(M_1+M_2)/2M_1M_2}}{p\sigma_{12}{}^2\Omega_{12}{}^{1,1*}(T_{12}{}^*)} \text{ cm}^2/\text{s} \tag{1}$$

where p is the pressure in atmospheres, $T_{12}{}^*$ $(=kT/\epsilon_{12})$–reduced temperature, M_1 and M_2–molecular weights of the diffusing gases; σ_{12} and ϵ_{12}/k–are parameters of the intermolecular potential describing interaction between the molecules of components 1 and 2 of the mixture and expressed, respectively in Ångstrom units and degrees Kelvin; k– the Boltzmann constant; $\sigma_{12} = 1/2\,(\sigma_1 + \sigma_2)$, $\epsilon_{12} = \sqrt{\epsilon_1 \epsilon_2}$, $\Omega_{12}{}^{(1,1)*}(T_{12})$–reduced collision integral, whose value depends on the interaction potential and whose values are given in Ref [246] for various potentials.

Approximate values of the Lennard-Jones potential are calculated from equations [177, 246]:

$$\varepsilon/k = 0.77\ T_{cr} \text{ and } \sigma = 0.833\,V_{cr}^{1/3}\ \text{Å}, \tag{2}$$

where T_{cr} and V_{cr}–are critical temperature (°K) and critical volume (cm³/mole).

A higher approximation be found by multiplying $[D_{12}]_1$ by the function $f_D{}^{(k)}$ which differs little from unity.

The temperature dependence of the diffusion coefficient can be obtained from

$$D = D_0(T/T_0)^n, \tag{3}$$

or

$$D = BT^n. \tag{3a}$$

The table on page 634 gives values of D_0 and of n for various gaseous systems.

The table also indicates the temperature range for the experimental data.

Holleran and Hubbert [160] proposed an exponential equation of the form

$$D = D_0 T^{[a_1 + a_2 \ln T + a_3 (\ln T)^2 + \dots]}, \tag{4}$$

which describes well self-diffusion by the first two terms of the exponent [161].

Saxena and Saxena [162] proposed a modified Sutherland formula for the calculation of the diffusion coefficient:

$$D_{12} = \frac{AT^{3/2}\left(\frac{1}{M_1} + \frac{1}{M_2}\right)^{1/2}}{p(V_{k_1}{}^{1/3} + V_{k_2}{}^{1/3})[1 + (BT_{k_{12}}/T)]} \text{ cm}^2/\text{s} \tag{5}$$

where V_k, and T_k–are critical volume (cm³/mole) and temperature (°K), p–pressure in atmospheres, $T_{k_{12}} = (T_{k_1} \cdot T_{k_2})^{1/2}$. For nonpolar gases $A = 0.02023$ and $B = 1.1756$, while for systems including combinations of both polar and nonpolar gases, $A = 0.02023$ and $B = 0.90116$.

Slattery and Bird [163 proposed

$$D_{12}=\frac{1}{p}\left[aT_{\text{red}}^{b}\left(P_{K_1}P_{K_2}\right)^{1/3}\left(T_{K_1}T_{K_2}\right)^{5/12}\left(\frac{1}{M_1}+\frac{1}{M_2}\right)^{1/2}\right], \qquad (6)$$

where the reduced temperature $T_{\text{red}} = (T/T_{k_1} \cdot T_{k_2})^{1/2}$, and the subscript k indicates that the value of the given physical quantity corresponds to the critical state, p–pressure in atmospheres.

Chen and Othmer [164] proposed the equation

$$D_{12}=\frac{0{,}43(T/100)^{1{,}81}\left(\frac{1}{M_1}+\frac{1}{M_2}\right)^{1/2}}{p\left(\frac{T_{k_1}\cdot T_{k_2}}{10^4}\right)^{0{,}1405}\left[\left(\frac{V_{k_1}}{100}\right)^{0{,}4}+\left(\frac{V_{k_2}}{100}\right)^{0.4}\right]^2}\ \text{cm}^2/\text{s} \qquad (7)$$

Here V is expressed in cm³/mole and p in atmospheres.

Carswell and Stryland [165] using the law of corresponding states obtained the following formula for the dimensionless diffusion coefficient D_{12}^*:

$$D_{12}^* \cdot n^* = 3/8T^*[\Omega_{12}^{(1,1)*}(T^*)]^{-1}, \qquad (8)$$

where $n^*=n\sigma^3$, $T^*=kT/\varepsilon$, $D_{12}^*=(D_{12}/\sigma)(2\mu/\varepsilon)^{1/2}$;

$$\Omega_{12}^{(1,1)*}(T^*)=[\Omega_{12}^{(1,1)}(T)]\sigma^{-2}(2\mu/\varepsilon)^{1/2},$$

where the reduced mass $\mu=\dfrac{M_1M_2}{M_1+M_2}$, ϵ and σ –Lennard-Jones parameters [42, 224] n–number of molecules in 1 cm³.

Kosov [224], using dimensional analysis obtained the formula:

$$D_{12}=2{,}188\cdot 10^{-3}\left(\frac{1}{M_1}+\frac{1}{M_2}\right)^{1/2}\frac{T^{5/2}}{p\sigma_{1\infty}\sigma_{2\infty}\sqrt{(T+C_1)(T+C_2)}}\ \text{cm}^2/\text{s} \qquad (9)$$

where σ_∞–is the effective diameter of the molecule at infinitely high temperature, C is the Sutherland constant and p is the pressure in atmospheres.

Equation (9) yields simple relationships between the coefficients of diffusion and self-diffusion [166, 167, 190], measured at the identical temperature:

$$D_{12}=\sqrt{\frac{M_1+M_2}{2\sqrt{M_1M_2}}}\sqrt{D_{11}D_{22}}\ \text{cm}^2/\text{s} \qquad (10)$$

and

$$D_{12}=\frac{D_{13}D_{23}}{D_{33}}\sqrt{\frac{2M_3(M_1+M_2)}{(M_1+M_3)(M_2+M_3)}}\ \text{cm}^2/\text{s} \qquad (11)$$

If the temperatures at which the coefficient of diffusion was measured are different, then the right-hand sides of Eqs, (10) and (11) must be multiplied by the "temperature coefficient" which can be found from Eq. (9).

Usmanov [168–170] extended the method of the theory of similarity to the phase and space, and found a relationship between transfer coefficients and entropy s, which, in the case of diffusion, takes the form:

$$\frac{D}{D_{\Delta s}}=\varphi\left(\frac{s_1-s_0}{R}\right), \qquad (12)$$

where, D, $D_{\Delta s}$ are diffusion coefficients within the interval of entropy change s–s_0 and $\Delta s = s' - s_0$ (scalar change in entropy) and s_0 is a conveniently selected reference entropy.

This method correlates well a large amount of experimental data on diffusion of binary mixtures.

Equations for groups of gases, turn out to be much simpler. For example, Mathur and Thodos [171] using the theory of similarity, obtained the following formula for the coefficients of self-diffusion for monoatomic gases (helium, neon, argon, krypton and xenon):

$$PD = 32{,}82\cdot 10^{-5}T_{\text{red}}^{1{,}792}. \qquad (13)$$

In the equations, D is expressed in cm² /sec, p in atmosphere and $T_{\text{red}} = T/T_{\text{cr}}$.

The table on pages 634–665 gives experimental values of diffusion coefficients of gases and gas mixtures. Throughout the table, if not otherwise stated, the pressure is 1 atmosphere (760 mm Hg).

Table of values of D_0 and n in the equation $D = D_0 \left(\frac{T}{273}\right)^n$ at $p = 1$ atmosphere†

Gas	D_0, cm²/s	n	Experimental temperature range, °K
N_2—N_2	0.178	1.90	77— 353
N_2—H_2	0,689	1.72	137—1083
N_2—He	0.621	1.73	293—3000 *
N_2—CO_2	0.144	1.73	288—1200
Ar—Ar	0.157	1.92	77— 353
Ar—H_2	0.715	1.89	273— 418
Ar—He	0.638	1.75	250—3000 *
H_2—H_2O	0.734	1.82	290— 370
H_2—CO_2	0,575	1.76	250—1083
H_2—O_2	0.661	1.89	142—1000
H_2O— air	0.216	1.80	273—1493
H_2O—CO_2	0.146	1.84	298— 434
H_2O—O_2	0.240	1.73	298—1000
Air–benzene	0.0783	1.89	273— 617
Air–hexane	0.0646	1.60	273— 575
Air–heptane	0.0594	1.60	373— 573
Air–CO_2	0.142	1.70	273—1533
Air–decane	0.0461	1,60	454— 537
Air–nonane	0.0490	1.60	425— 525
Air–octane	0.0544	1.60	298— 528
Air–tetralin	0.0536	1.90	484— 507
Air–fuel T-5	0.0287	1.96	523— 673
Air–toluene	0.0709	1.90	273— 332
Air–ethyl alcohol	0.105	1.77	273— 340
He—He	1.62	1.71	14— 296
He—CO_2	0.494	1.80	250— 404
CO_2—CO_2	0.0965	1.90	273— 362
CO_2—O_2	0.138	1.80	273—1000
O_2—O_2	0.186	1.92	77— 353
O_2—CO	0.188	1.68	273—1000
CH_4—CH_4	0.200	1.69	90— 353

*Up to 1200° K, direct experiments on diffusion; from 1200 to 3000° K, the potential of intermoleculaı action determined experimentally from dissipation of a gaseous beam in a medium of a different gas [199, 214].

Coefficient of Diffusion in Gases D (cm²/s) at a pressure of 1 atmosphere.*

Gas	T, °K	D	Ref.	Gas	T, °K	D	Ref.
I. Nitrogen N_2							
Nitrogen N_2	293	0.221	179	Nitrogen N_2	3 500	13.8	182 *)
	273	0.172	181		4 000	17.6	
	318	0.222			4 500	21.9	
	77.5	0.0168	180		5 000	26.6	
	194.5	0.104			5 500	31.8	
	273	0.185			6 000	37.3	
	298	0.212			6 500	43.2	
	353	0.287			7 000	49.6	
	1 000	1.56	182*)		7 500	56.5	
	1 500	3.08			8 000	63.5	
	2 000	5.05			8 500	71.0	
	2 500	7.48			9 000	78.9	
	3 000	10,4			9 500	87.0	
					10 000	95.5	

*The notation in the present table is as follows: * denotes the fact that dissociation, ionization, and excited state have not been taken into account; *a* denotes the Lennard-Jones potential; *b* denotes a modified Buckingham potential; *c* denotes the potential $\varphi(r) = d/r^3$, with d and s are constants; *d* denotes the potential $\varphi(r) = A \exp(-r/\rho)$, where A and ρ are constants. (Quantities in parentheses denote pressure in atmospheres).

An alphabetical listing of all substances for this table will be found in the index under *Diffusion in Gases*, starting on page 753.

continued

Gas	T, °K	D	Ref.
Nitrogen, N_2	11 000	113	182 *)
	12 000	133	
	13 000	153	
	14 000	174	
	15 000	197	
Ammonia, NH_3	273	0.214	183
Argon, Ar	293	0.204	184
	293	0.194	185
	244.2	0.1348	329
	274.6	0.1689	
	303.5	0.2433	
Benzene, C_6H_6	273	0.0823	186
	311.3	0.1022	187
n-butane, C_4H_{10}	298	0.0960	188
Isobutane, C_4H_{10}	298	0.0908	
cis-2-butene C_4H_8	298	0.095	
Hydrogen, H_2	289.2	0.737	189
	293	0.80	190
	373	1.25	
	435	1.61	
	473	1.86	
	483	1.92	
	573	2.56	
	583	2.64	
	673	3.36	
	705	3.54	
	773	4.15	
	873	5.12	
	973	6.06	
	1 000	6.30	
	1 083	7.20	
	137	0.173	191
	153	0.208	
	193	0.368	192
	253	0.600	
	273	0.708	
	303.5	0.852	
	335.5	1.001	
	288	0.743	193
	200	0.401	194
	273	0.689	
	300	0.800	
	400	1.270	
	293	0.759	184
	298	0.780	198
	315.8	0.849	173
	347.6	0.991	
	373.0	1.15	
	401.0	1.30	
	436.0	1.45	
	471.0	1.71	
Water vapor, H_2O	297.93	0.232	195
	312.79	0.268	
	327.95	0.290	
	307.1	0.257	196
	328.8	0.313	
	349	0.354	
	273	0.260	186
	307.4	0.256	197
	328.4	0.303	
	352	0.359	

Gas	T, °K	D	Ref.
Helium, He	289.4	0.651	189
	293	0.705	185
	298	0.71	198
	300	0.743	199
	600	2.40	
	900	4.76	
	1 200	7.74	

At 300 °K < T < 1200 °K, the following equation holds: $D = 4.81 \cdot 10^{-5} \cdot T^{1,691}$

Gas	T, °K	D	Ref.
	1 200	7.67	199
	1 500	11.41	
	1 800	15.80	
	2 100	20.79	
	2 400	26.39	
	2 700	32.56	
	3 000	39.28	

At 1300 °K < T < 3000 °K, the following equation holds: $D = 2.48 \cdot 10^{-5} \cdot T^{1,788}$

Gas	T, °K	D	Ref.
	243.2	0.477	329
	275.0	0.596	
	289.4	0.651	173
	298.2	0.687	330
	303.5	0.719	329
	315.6	0.788	173
	323.2	0.766	330
	332.5	0.811	329
	348.4	0.915	173
	353.2	0.893	330
	374.5	1.07	173
	383.2	1.08	330
	400.0	1.15	173
	413.2	1.20	330
	433.0	1.31	173
	443.2	1.29	330
	470.0	1.53	173
	473.2	1.569	330
	498.2	1.65	330
n-hexane, C_6H_{14}	288.6	0.0753	200
	263	0.0630	201
	273	0.0684	
	283	0.0734	
	293	0.0784	
1,5-hexadiene, C_6H_{10}	288.1	0.0772	202
n-heptane, C_7H_{16}	303.3	0.0740	203
	303.0	0.0743	202
	263	0.0561	204
	273	0.0600	
	283	0.0653	
	293	0.0702	
	303	0.0758	
	313	0.0807	
Carbon dioxide, CO_2	288	0.158	193
	293	0.163	184
			185
	298	0.165	188
	293	0.154	190
	373	0.256	
	435	0.323	
	473	0.355	
	483	0.387	
	573	0.509	

continued

Gas	T, °K	D	Ref.
Carbon dioxide, CO_2	583	0.55	190
	673	0.683	
	705	0.75	
	773	0.898	
	873	1.067	
	973	1.253	
	1 000	1.33	
	083	1.46	
	300	1,173	199
	600	0.605	
	900	1.217	
	1 200	1.976	
	290.4	0.135	173
	315.4	0.184	
	348.0	0.223	
	373.0	0.258	
	410.0	0.307	
	455.0	0.361	
	473.0	0.386	
2,3-dimethyl-1,3-butadiene, C_6H_{10}	288.1	0.0748	202
n-decane, $C_{10}H_{22}$	363.9	0.0763	200
2,3-dimethyl-2-butene, C_6H_{12}	288.3	0.0705	202
2,3-dimethyl-butane, C_6H_{14}	288.7	0.0751	200
2,4-dimethyl-pentane, C_7H_{16}	303.1	0.0744	203
Cyanogen gas, C_2N_2	273	0.0895	205
	1 073	1.000	
	1 273	1.346	
n-dodecane, $C_{12}H_{26}$	399.4	0.0829	200
Isooctane, C_8H_{18}	253	0.0484	204
	263	0.0546	
	273	0.0587	
	283	0.0630	
	293	0.0682	
	303	0.0729	
	313	0.0776	
Iodine, I_2	273	0.070	206
	583	0.275	251
	705	0.377	
	773	0.445	
	873	0.558	
Oxygen, O_2	293	0.219	284
Xenon, Xe	242.2	0.0854	329
	274.6	0.1070	
	303.45	0.1301	
	334.2	0.1549	
Methylcyclo-pentane, C_6H_{12}	285.9	0 0758	200
Sodium, Na	526.5	0.68	208
	655	0.91	207
n-nonane, C_9H_{20}	339.8	0.0737	202
Nitric oxide, NO	273	0.1379	205
	1 073	1.532	
	1 273	2.073	
Carbon monoxide CO	273	0.192	176
	288	0.211	193
	194.7	0.105	283
	273.2	0.186	
	319.6	0.242	
	373.0	0.318	
n-octane, C_8H_{18}	303.1	0.0726	200
Pyridine, C_5H_5N	317.9	0.1068	187
Piperidine, $C_5H_{11}N$	314.9	0.0953	
Mercury, Hg	273	0.1190	206
Thiophene, C_4H_4S	302.1	0.0992	187
2,2,4-trimeth-ylpentane, C_8H_{18}	303.1	0.0713	200. 203
2,3,3-trimeth-ylpentane, C_8H_{18}	363.8	0.0681	200
Carbon tetra-chloride, CCl_4	273	0.0737	186
Hydro-cyanic acid HCN	273	0.1290	205
	1 073	1.435	
	1 273	1.940	
Cyclohexane, C_6H_{12}	288.5	0.0746	200
Sulfur hexafluoride, SF_6	289.8	0.103	189
	328.0	0.115	173
	348.0	0.130	
	373.0	0.147	
	410.0	0.179	
	455.0	0.218	
	473.0	0.231	
Ethane, C_2H_6	298	0.148	188
Ethylene, C_2H_4	273	0.144	183
	298	0.163	188
Ethyl alcohol, C_2H_5OH	273	0.111	186

II. Argon

Gas	T, °K	D	Ref.
Ammonia, NH_3	254.7	0.150	281
	275.1	0.175	
	308.1	0.222	
	333.0	0.253	331
Argon, Ar	295	0.180	209
	77.5	0.0134	180
	90	0.0180	
	194	0.0830	
	273	0.156	
	295	0.178	
	353	0.249	
	194.5	0.0833	210
	273	0.158	
	295	0.180	
	326.5	0.212	
	1 000	1.51	182 *)
	1 500	3.00	
	2 000	5.03	

continued

Gas	T, °K	D	Ref.
Argon, Ar	2 500	7.50	182*)
	3 000	10.4	
	3 500	13.9	
	4 000	17.8	
	4 500	22.1	
	5 000	26.8	
	5 500	31.9	
	6 000	37.4	
	6 500	43.3	
	7 000	49.5	
	7 500	56.1	
	8 000	62.8	
	8 500	69.9	
	9 000	77.4	
	9 500	85	
	10 000	93.2	
	11 000	111	
	12 000	129	
	13 000	148	
	14 000	169	
	15 000	190	
	322.4	0.00272 (68,0)	
		0.00194 (88,8)	211
		0.00145 (151,2)	
		0.000875 (243)	
		0.00270 (95,0)	
		0.00161 (117,7)	
		0.000950 (194,0)	
		0.000659 (291,0)	
		0.00115 (156,5)	
	287.0	0.152	
Acetylene, C_2H_2			189
Hydrogen, H_2	273	0.674	
	293	0.772	176
	291.0	0.764	184
	287.9	0.828	189
	354.2	1.111	212
	418	1.714	
	242.2	0.562	
	295.0	0.83	331
	274.2	0.698	332
	303.9	0.830	331
	313.0	0.874	
	341.2	1.010	173
	344.8	1.05	331
	373.0	1.26	173
	404.0	1.46	
	418.0	1.55	
	436.0	1.68	332
	448.0	1.76	173
	473.0	1.96	332
	628.0	3.21	173
	806.0	4.86	332
	958.0	6.81	
	1 069.0	8.10	
	118	0.151	
	154	0.247	391
	197	0.391	
	231	0.510	
	295	0.807	
	296	0.821	
Hydrogen, H_2	380	1.261	391
	476	1.918	
	523	2.275	
	573	2.619	
	692.5	3.684	
Helium, He	273	0.641	176
	287.0	0.684	189
	287.9	0.697	212
	354.2	0.979	
	418.0	1.398	
	273	0.640	213
	288	0.701	
	303	0.760	
	318	0.825	
	300	0.76	214
	500	1.86	
	1 000	6.25	
	1 100	7.38	

At 300 °K $< T <$ 1100 °K, the following equation holds: $D=3.61 \cdot 10^{-5} \cdot T^{1.746}$

Gas	T, °K	D	Ref.
	1 000	5.98	214
	1 100	7.08	
	1 500	12.29	
	2 000	20.49	
	2 500	30.45	
	3 000	42.11	

At 1000 °K $< T <$ 3000 °K, the following equation holds: $D=2.81 \cdot 10^{-5} \cdot T^{1.778}$

Gas	T, °K	D	Ref.
	1 000	5.95	182*)
	1 500	12.3	
	2 000	20.3	
	2 500	30.0	
	3 000	41.3	
	3 500	54.3	
	4 000	68.6	
	4 500	84.2	
	5 000	101	
	5 500	120	
	6 000	139	
	6 500	160	
	7 000	182	
	7 500	205	
	8 000	230	
	8 500	256	
	9 000	284	
	9 500	313	
	10 000	343	
	11 000	406	
	12 000	474	
	13 000	546	
	14 000	624	
	15 000	705	
	251	0.544	215
	259	0.583	
	269	0.639	
	280	0.703	
	289	0.731	
	296	0.744	

continued

Gas	T, °K	D	Ref.
Helium, He	328	0.851	215
	337	0.889	
	354	1.000	
	366	1.060	
	372	1.122	
	387	1.165	
	405	1.288	
	418	1.344	
	169.2	0.285	333
	181.2	0.313	
	194.7	0.347	
	202.2	0.384	
	214.7	0.390	
	223.2	0.414	
	250.2	0.545	
	273.0	0.629	
	273.2	0.645	172
	276.2	0.646	334
	291.0	0.715	335
	292.2	0.736	333
	313.0	0.815	173
	315.2	0.833	172
	317.2	0.797	334
	323.1	0.853	172
	323.2	0.81	330
	333.2	0.932	172
	343.0	0.961	173
	346.2	0.924	334
	353.2	0.985	172
	353.2	0.978	330
	353.3	1.005	172
	373.0	1.11	173
	383.2	1.12	330
	393.9	1.203	172
	401.0	1.26	173
	413.2	1.24	330
	434.0	1.45	173
	443.2	1.40	330
	464.0	1.61	173
	473.2	1.61	330
	498.2	1.73	
	118	0.153	391
	143	0.212	
	177	0.304	
	225	0.463	
	296	0.735	
	301	0.755	
	374	1.084	
	479.5	1.652	
	676.5	2.958	
n-hexane, C_6H_{14}	288.6	0.0662	200
n-heptane, C_7H_{16}	303.2	0.0658	203
Carbon dioxide, CO_2	273	0.144	176
	288.6	0.135	189
	293	0.139	184
	328.0	0.185	173
	348.0	0.208	
	373.0	0.235	
	410.0	0.280	
	455.0	0.336	
	473.0	0.363	
2,3-dimethylbutane, C_6H_{14}	288.9	0.0652	200
2,4-dimethylpentane, C_7H_{16}	303.2	0.0655	203
Isooctane, C_8H_{18}	253	0.0407	204
	263	0.0473	
	273	0.0500	
	283	0.0509	
	293	0.0575	
	303	0.0614	
	313	0.0657	
Potassium, K	723.0	1.03	347
Oxygen, O_2	273	0.181	176
	293	0.200	184
	243.2	0.135	280
	274.7	0.168	
	304.5	0.202	
	334.0	0.239	
Krypton, Kr	273	0.119	216
	288	0.128	
	303	0.140	
	318	0.153	
	199.5	0.072	217
	273	0.126	
	353	0.197	
	373	0.216	
	473	0.327	
	297	0.142	279
	343	0.179	
	381	0.227	
	407	0.254	
Xenon, Xe	273	0.0943	213
	288	0.102	
	303	0.114	
	318	0.128	
	329.9	0.137	218
	194.7	0.0518	219
	273.2	0.0975	
	329.9	0.138	
	378.0	0.178	
	273.3	0.0935	172
	315.0	0.1326	
	354.1	0.1620	
	394.1	0.1920	
Methylcyclopentane, C_6H_{12}	288.6	0.0715	200
Sodium, Na	655	0.88	207
Neon, Ne	273	0.276	216
	288	0.300	
	303	0.327	
	318	0.357	
	90	0.036	217
	194.5	0.159	
	273	0.285	
	353	0.442	
	473	0.738	
	118	0.0606	391
	154	0.0984	
	197	0.155	
	231	0.207	
	296	0.317	

continued

Gas	T, °K	D	Ref.
Neon, Ne	300	0.325	391
	374	0.474	
	479	0.721	
	573	0.973	
	680	1.302	
n-octane, C_8H_{18}	303	0.0626	200
	303.2	0.0587	203
	273	0.0497	204
	283	0.0516	
	293	0.0561	
	303	0.0594	
	313	0.0639	
	323	0.0667	
	333	0.0735	
Toluene, C_7H_8	273	0.071	220
	301.1	0.087	
	273	0.0718	204
	283	0.0783	
	293	0.0826	
	303	0.0885	
	313	0.0942	
	323	0.0998	
	333	0.1062	
2,2,4-trimethyl-pentane, C_8H_{18}	303	0.0605	200
	303.2	0.0599	203
	288.7	0.0721	200
Cesium, Cs	299	0.19	348
	723	0.67	347
Cyclohexane, C_6H_{12}	287.2	0.0791	189
Sulfur-hexafluoride, SF_6	328.0	0.100	173
	348.0	0.112	
	373.0	0.127	
	410.0	0.151	
	447.0	0.183	
	472.0	0.200	
Ethylene C_2H_2	298	0.170	279
	317	0.184	
	340	0.210	
	379	0.258	
	407	0.288	
III. Hydrogen			
Ammonia, NH_3	273	0.736	183
Acetylene, C_2H_2	273	0.458	205
Acetone, C_3H_6O	273	0.361	206
Benzene, C_6H_6	273	0.3177	
	292.9	0.3406	221
	318	0.3993	
	311.3	0.4036	187
	253	0.2451	204
	263	0.2722	
	273	0.2946	
	283	0.3161	
	293	0.3373	
	303	0.3576	
Bromine, Br_2	273	0.402	205
n-butane, C_4H_{10}	287.9	0.361	212
	354.2	0.507	
	430	0.763	

Gas	T, K	D	Ref.
cis-2-butene, C_4H_8	298	0.378	188
Hydrogen, H_2	20.4	0.00816	222
	85	0.172	
	273	1.285	
	288.2	1.43	336
	293.2	1.40	337
Water vapor H_2O	307.1	1.020	197
	328.4	1.121	
	352.2	1.200	
	322.5	1.000	221
	365.4	1.179	
	307.0	0.915	196
	328.5	0.961	
	297.93	0.802	195
	312.79	0.937	
	327.95	0.998	
	292.95	0.850	206
	324.5	1.012	
	365.4	1.25	
	372.34	1.28	
Air	273	0.66	223
	289	0.596	224
	291.5	0.700	189
Helium, He	52	0.076	191
	58	0.093	
	137	0.344	
	153	0.421	
	273	1.21	223
	292.4	1.383	189
	118	0.318	391
	143	0.443	
	177	0.657	
	225	0.985	
	295	1.550	
	296	1.550	
	380	2.401	
	476	3.554	
	573	4.89	
	692	6.76	
n-hexane, C_6H_{14}	288.7	0.288	200
	253	0.2225	201
	263	0.2415	
	273	0.2597	
	283	0.2795	
	288.6	0.2914	
	293	0.3008	
1,5-hexadiene, C_6H_{10}	288.1	0.298	202
n-heptane, C_7H_{16}	303.1	0.283	203
	303.0	0.286	202
	263	0.2122	204
	273	0.2263	
	283	0.2433	
	293	0.2848	
	313	0.3008	
Carbon dioxide CO_2	273	0.58	223
	273	0.550	176
	293	0.603	184
	288	0.619	193
	298	0.646	188
	293	0.654	190
	373	1.02	
	435	1.35	

continued

Gas	T, °K	D	Ref.
Carbon dioxide, CO_2	473	1.54	190
	483	1.66	
	573	2.18	
	583	2.29	
	673	2.82	
	705	3.06	
	773	3.57	
	873	4.47	
	973	5.24	
	1 000	5.56	
	1 083	5.70	
	259	0.50	225
	282	0.52	
	358	0.84	
	250	0.481	215
	257	0.488	
	258	0.502	
	267	0.548	
	279	0.606	
	288	0.680	
	296.5	0.635	
	296.6	0.662	
	332	0.885	
	348	0.893	
	368	0.991	
	291.9	0.599	173
	313.0	0.701	
	344.8	0.850	
	373.0	0.968	
	404.0	1.15	
	436.0	1.28	
	473.0	1.47	
Deuterium, D_2	288	1.24	226
	65.1	0.081	227
	76.6	0.116	
	192	0.583	
	296	1.27	
	293	1.21	184
	273	1.13	176
	115	0.253	391
	155	0.418	
	197	0.649	
	232	0.857	
	295	1.280	
	295.5	1.289	
	378	1.952	
	485	2.938	
n-decane, $C_{10}H_{22}$	363.8	0.293	200
2,3-dimethyl-butane, C_6H_{14}	288.8	0.299	
2,3-dimethyl-2-butene, C_6H_{12}	288.1	0.296	200
2,3-dimethyl-1,3-butadiene, C_6H_{10}	288.1	0.312	
2,4-dimethyl-pentane, C_7H_{16}	303.3	0.297	203
Cyanogengas, C_2N_2	273	0.407	205
Ethyl ether, $C_4H_{10}O$	273	0.299	206
	292.9	0.354	
n-dodecane, $C_{12}H_{26}$	399.6	0.311	200

Gas	T, °K	D	Ref.
Nitrous oxide, N_2O	273	0.535	176
Isooctane, C_8H_{18}	253	0.2045	204
	263	0.2251	
	273	0.2400	
	283	0.2580	
	293	0.2760	
	303	0.2945	
	313	0.3162	
Oxygen, O_2	142	0.174	191
	153	0.215	
	273	0.697	176
	273	0.688	228**
	300	0.824	
	500	2.07	
	1 000	7.02	
	1 500	a) 13.7	
		b) 14.1	
		c) 14.5	
		d) 14.9	
	2 000	a) 22.2	
		b) 23.1	
		c) 24.3	
		d) 25.2	
	2 500	a) 32.1	
		b) 34.0	
		c) 36.1	
		d) 38.1	
	3 000	a) 43.4	
		b) 46.6	
		c) 50.0	
		d) 53.6	
Xenon, Xe	242.2	0.410	331
	274.2	0.508	
	303.9	0.612	
	341.2	0.751	
Methane, CH_4	273	0.625	222
	298	0.726	188
Methyl alcohol, CH_3OH	263	0.4690	204
	273	0.5033	
	283	0.5402	
	293	0.5786	
	303	0.6229	
	313	0.6656	
Methylcylo-pentane, C_6H_{12}	288.5	0.312	200
Sodium Na	655	3.14	207
Neon, Ne	242.2	0.792	331
	274.2	0.974	
	303.2	1.150	
	341.2	1.405	
	115	0.225	391
	155	0.392	
	197	0.588	
	232	0.778	
	295	1.170	
	295.5	1.161	
	379	1.768	
	484	2.688	
	575	3.585	
	680.5	4.68	
n-nonane, C_9H_{20}	339.8	0.284	202

continued

Gas	T, °K	D	Ref.
Nitric oxide, NO	273	0.643	205
Carbon monoxide, CO	273	0.651	176
	295.6	0.743	173
	315.0	0.856	
	345.0	0.979	
	374.5	1.14	
	401.0	1.27	
	436.0	1.49	
	471.0	1.68	
n-octane, C_8H_{18}	303.2	0.277	200
			203
	273	0,2060	201
	283	0.2370	
	293	0.2533	
	303	0.2718	
	313	0.2908	
	323	0.3100	
	333	0.3330	
Pyridine, C_5H_5N	317.9	0.437	187
Piperidine, $C_5H_{11}N$	314.7	0.403	
Propane, C_3H_8	273	0.385	183
Carbon disulfide, CS_2	292.9	0.4255	221
	305.8	0.4626	
Sulfur dioxide, SO_2	273	0.480	176
Sulfur trioxide, SO_3	273	0.379	205
Hydrocyanic acid, HCN	273	0.565	
Thiophene, C_4H_4S	302.2	0.400	187
2,3,3-trimethyl-pentane, C_8H_{18}	363.9	0.271	200
2,2,4-trimehyl-pentane, C_8H_{18}	303.0	0.292	203
	303.1	0.292	
Toluene, C_7H_8	273	0.469	220
	301.0	0.570	
	273	0.4632	201
	283	0.5000	
	293	0.5327	
	303	0.5765	
	313	0.6044	
	323	0.6428	
	333	0.6844	
Acetic acid, CH_3COOH	273	0.4096	
	283	0.4441	
	293	0,4851	
	303	0.5142	
	313	0.5455	
	323	0.5827	204
	333	0.6161	
	343	0.6654	
Chlorine, Cl_2	273	0.438	205
Methyl-chloride, CH_3Cl	273	0.453	
Carbon tetrachloride, CCl_4	273	0.293	206
Cyclohexane, C_6H_{12}	288.5	0.319	200
	288.5	0.319	187
	253	0.2459	201
	263	0.2671	
	273	0.2861	
	283	0.3070	
	293	0.3265	
	303	0.3477	
	313	0.3731	
Sulfur-hexafluoride, SF_6	290.0	0.434	189
	298	0.418	188
	286.2	0.396	212
	306.9	0.458	
	370.8	0.647	
	418	0.838	
	313.0	0.488	173
	344.4	0.570	
	376.0	0.662	
	401.0	0.750	
	429.0	0.855	
	473.0	1.03	
Ethane, C_2H_6	298	0.537	188
Ethylacetate, $C_4H_8O_2$	253	0.2432	204
	263	0.2542	
	273	0.2730	
	283	0,2979	
	293	0.3161	
	303	0.3400	
Ethylene, C_2H_4	273	0.625	176
	298	0.602	188
Ethylpropio-nate, $C_5H_{10}O_2$	273	0.326	220
	300.9	0.409	
	300.8	0.372	
Ethyl alcohol, C_2H_5OH	313.4	0.503	221
	339.9	0.5430	
	273	0.377	206
	340	0.586	
	263	0.3229	204
	273	0.3760	
	283	0.4016	
	293	0.4346	
	303	0.4673	
	313	0,5045	
	323	0,5465	
IV. Water vapor H_2O			
Air	273	0.251	186
	297.8	0.257	229
	298	0.260	178
	297.93	0.257	195
	289	0.244	206
	372.3	0.377	
	365.4	0.360	
	365.4	0.357	
	315	0.288	230
	298.9	0.258	231
	312.4	0.277	
	332	0.305	
	322.5	0.2827	221
	365.4	0.3451	
	381	0.376	232

continued

Gas	T, °K	D	Ref.
Air	382	0.382	232
	420	0.452	
	425	0.472	
	476	0.586	
	483	0.623	
	489	0.630	
	519	0.690	
	528.5	0.709	
	542	0.754	
	575	0.787	
	584.5	0.861	
	618.5	0.905	
	634	0.961	
	675	1.08	
	677.2	1.10	
	677.5	1.05	

Experimental data are correlated by equation of the type

$$D=D_0(T/273)^n,$$

where D_0 and n have the following values:
in the range $273\ ^\circ\text{K} < T < 677.5\ ^\circ\text{K}$
$D_0 = 0.2106$ and $n = 1.82$; 232
in the range $273\ ^\circ\text{K} < T < 370\ ^\circ\text{K}$
$D_0 = 0.2232$ and $n = 1.81$; 233
in the range $378\ ^\circ\text{K} < T < 575\ ^\circ\text{K}$
$D_0 = 0.2165$ and $n = 1.80$. 234

Gas	T, °K	D	Ref.
	373	0.353	235
	573	0.849	
	773	1.556	
	923	2.191	
	1 073	2.650	
	1 093	2.808	
	1 273	3.253	
	1 373	3.938	
	1 463	4.480	
	1 493	4.490	
Water vapor, H_2O	273	0.277	205
Helium, He	298	0.908	178
	307	0.902	197
	328.3	1.011	
	352.3	1.121	
Carbon dioxide, CO_2	328.5	0.198	196
	307.3	0.202	197
	328.4	0.211	
	352.2	0.245	
	297.7	0.164	206
	365.4	0.249	
	372.4	0.2594	
	322.5	0.1811	221
	365.4	0.2384	
	432.5	0.3399	234
	433.0	0.3418	
	433.7	0.3431	
	434.0	0.3488	
Oxygen, O_2	298.0	0.270	198
	307.9	0.282	197
	328.8	0.318	
	352.2	0.352	
	307.9	0.301	228**
	328.8	0.338	
Oxygen, O_2	352.2	0.381	228**
	500	0.691	
	1 000	2.21	
	1 500	a) 4.32	
		b) 4.31	
		c) 4.35	
		d) 4.37	
	2 000	a) 6.96	
		b) 6.93	
		c) 7.05	
		d) 7.11	
	2 500	a) 10.09	
		b) 10.00	
		c) 10.24	
		d) 10.38	
	3 000	a) 13.65	
		b) 13.48	
		c) 13.90	
		d) 14.16	
Methane, CH_4	297.8	0.251	229
	313.0	0.278	
	323.0	0.297	
	333.0	0.313	
	307.5	0.292	197
	328.6	0.331	
	352.1	0.356	
Propane, C_3H_8	297.8	0.156	229
Freon-12, CF_2Cl_2	298	0.105	178
Ethane, C_2H_6	297.8	0.177	229
Ethylene, C_2H_4	297.8	0.178	
	307.6	0.204	206
	328.3	0.233	
	352.4	0.247	

V. Air

Gas	T, °K	D	Ref.
Aviation gasoline	283	0.0845	236
	293	0.091	
	303	0.097	
	313	0.102	
sec-amyl alcohol $C_5H_{11}OH$	298.9	0.071	231
	312.4	0.076	
	332	0.086	
Ammonia, NH_3	293	0.227	237
Aniline, $C_6H_5NH_2$	298	0.0726	238
	298.9	0.074	231
	312.4	0.079	
	332	0.090	
Anthracene, $C_{14}H_{10}$	372.2	0.0783	238
Acetylene, C_2H_2	287.6	0.206	189
	289	0.191	224
Acetone, C_3H_6O	273	0.109	239
Benzene, C_6H_6	283	0.0834	236
	293	0.0900	
	303	0.0920	
	313	0.0993	
	323	0.1075	
	343	0.1170	
	315	0.102	230

continued

Gas	T, °K	D	Ref.
Benzene, C_6H_6	340	0.124	230
	263	0.0711	240
	273	0.0768	
	283	0.0828	
	293	0.0882	
	303	0.0941	
	313	0.0994	
	323	0.1044	
	298	0.0962	
	292.9	0.0877	178
	318	0.1011	221
	273	0.0794	186
	363.8	0.135	240
	377.8	0.147	
	418.0	0.179	
	440.2	0.187	
	451.5	0.199	
	473.0	0.222	
	526.8	0.272	
	530.2	0.269	
	530.8	0.271	
	573.8	0.318	
	579.2	0.332	
	617.5	0.361	
o-benzidine, $C_{12}H_{12}N_2$	372	0.0555	238
Bromine, Br_2	293	0.091	237
Butyl alcohol, C_4H_9OH	298.9	0.087	231
	312.4	0.092	
	332	0.104	
sec-butyl alcohol, C_4H_9OH	298.9	0.089	
	312.4	0.096	
	332	0.108	
Butyl stearate $C_{22}H_{44}O_2$	293	0.030	241
Helium, He	273	0.63	223
	287	0.689	189
	287.0	0.689	173
	315.6	0.785	
	348.4	0.920	
	374.5	1.04	
	400.0	1.17	
	430.0	1.32	
	469.0	1.52	
n-hexane, C_6H_{14}	273	0.0655	236
	293	0.0755	
	303	0.0793	
	263	0.0608	204
	273	0.0661	
	283	0.0709	
	293	0.0755	
	361.9	0.102	240
	399.0	0.120	
	415.4	0.125	
	453.9	0.143	
	487.3	0.161	
	526.7	0.180	
	571.2	0.210	
	575.4	0.217	
n-hexadecane, $C_{16}H_{34}$	287.97	0.0384	242
	289.97	0.0392	
	293.01	0.0392	
	297.98	0.0402	
	302.98	0.0425	
	307.88	0.0435	
n-heptadecane, $C_{17}H_{36}$	287.97	0.0403	
	293.01	0.0422	
	297.98	0.0423	
	302.98	0.0436	
	307.88	0.0453	
	312.94	0.0463	
n-heptane, C_7H_{16}	377.5	0.100	240
	377.5	0.102	
	410.2	0.119	
	414.2	0.111	
	434.5	0.126	
	445.8	0.127	
	462.5	0.133	
	469.2	0.138	
	474.8	0.148	
	498.2	0.151	
	527.2	0.168	
	564.5	0.190	
Carbon dioxide, CO_2	273	0.138	176
	288.6	0.156	189
	293	0.165	237
	290	0.152	235
	293	0.151	
	373	0.257	
	473	0.321	
	573	0.507	
	673	0.670	
	773	0.921	
	873	1.062	
	973	1.270	
	1 073	1.447	
	1 273	1.835	
	1 388	2.148	
	1 473	2.432	
	1 533	2.446	
Dibutyl-phthalate, $C_{16}H_{22}O_4$	293	0.031	241
	288	0.034	243
	292.9	0.0386	
	298	0.0415	
	303	0.0426	
	308	0.0442	
	313	0.0473	
n-decane, $C_{10}H_{22}$	453.8	0.105	240
	464.5	0.110	
	467.0	0.111	
	467.8	0.112	
	478	0.114	
	482.2	0.115	
	484.3	0.113	
	485	0.116	
	490.8	0.114	
	492.2	0.115	
	507.7	0.122	
	514.8	0.128	
	527.2	0.131	
	536.8	0.137	
Dibromo-methane $C_2H_4Br_2$	273	0.0708	244
	280.1	0.0736	
	288	0.0778	
	293	0.0813	

continued

Gas	T, °K	D	Ref.	Gas	T, °K	D	Ref.
Diphenyl,	298	0.0727	238	Propyl acetate,	315	0.092	230
$C_{12}H_{10}$	491	0.0160	231	$C_5H_{10}O_2$	340	0.101	
Cyanogen gas,	273	0.0970	205	Mercury, Hg	614	0.473	231
C_2N_2	1 073	1.080		Sulfur	293	0.122	237
	1 273	1.458		dioxide,			
Ethyl ether,	283.4	0.0835	221	SO_2			
$C_4H_{10}O$	292.9	0.0893		Carbon	292.9	0.1015	221
	292.9	0.090	206	disulfide, CS_2	305.8	0.1120	
Iodine, I_2	273	0.0692			253	0.0785	201
	298	0.0108	238		263	0.0836	
Isooctane,	323	0.060	236		273	0.0887	
C_8H_{18}					283	0.0939	
Isopentane,	288	0.0774			293	0.0983	
C_5H_{12}	293	0.0782			303	0.1022	
	303	0.0843		Tetrahydro-	484.2	0.159	240
Isopropyl	298.9	0.099	231	naphthalene,	488.4	0.162	
alcohol,	312.4	0.107		$C_{10}H_{22}$	493.8	0.166	
C_3H_7OH	332.0	0.121			501.2	0.170	
Oxygen, O_2	273	0.178	176		503.6	0.172	
Methane, CH_4	273	0.196			507.0	0.175	
Methylcyclo-	283	0.0571	236	Fuel T-5	523	0.103	232
hexane,	293	0.0615			573	0.123	
C_7H_{14}	303	0.0660			623	0.145	
	313	0.0706			673	0.168	
Methyl	263	0.1249	201	Toluene, C_7H_8	273	0.0709	236
alcohol,	273	0.1342			293	0.080	
CH_3OH	283	0.1424			298	0.0844	238
	293	0.1533			298.9	0.086	231
	303	0.1627			312.4	0.092	
	313	0.1725			332	0.104	
	323	0.1808			273	0.081	220
Naphthalene,	298	0.0611	238		300.7	0.098	
$C_{10}H_8$				Water	297.8	0.247	229
Nitrobenzene,	298	0.0855	178	(heavy) vapor,	313.0	0.277	
$C_6H_5NO_2$				D_2O	318.0	0.288	
n-nonane	424.3	0.101	240		333	0.314	
C_9H_{20}	439	0.103		Acetic	273	0.1064	201
	474.8	0.119		acid,	283	0.1141	
	496.5	0.128		CH_3COOH	293	0.1215	
	525.5	0.139			303	0.1297	
n-octadecane,	287.97	0.0388	242		313	0.1379	
$C_{18}H_{38}$	293.01	0.0396			323	0.1477	
	297.98	0.0408			333	0.1574	
	302.98	0.0418			343	0.1615	
	307.88	0.0421		Phosgene,	273	0.095	247
	312.94	0.0445		$COCl_2$			
n-octane,	298	0.0602	238	Cyanogen	273	0.111	
C_8H_{18}	273	0.0497	201	chloride, ClCN			
	283	0.0534		Chloropicrine,	298	0.088	
	293	0.0576		CCl_3NO_2			
	298	0.0598		Chlorine, Cl_2	289	0.102	224
	303	0.0622			293	0.124	237
	313	0.0671		Chlorbenzene,	298.9	0.074	231
	323	0.0718		C_6H_5Cl	312.4	0.079	
	405.5	0.103	240		332.0	0.090	
	424.6	0.112			315	0.094	230
	465.2	0.127			340	0.100	
	495.2	0.141		Chloroform,	273	0.091	239
	510.8	0.150		$CHCl_3$			
	528.4	0.162		Hydrocyamic	273	0.173	247
Hydrogen	333	0.188	245	acid,			
peroxide,				HCN			
H_2O_2							

continued

Gas	T, °K	D	Ref.
Cyclohexane, C_6H_{12}	283	0.0696	236
	293	0.0745	
	303	0.0781	
	313	0.0829	
	318	0.086	239
	263	0.0600	204
	273	0.0646	
	283	0.0696	
	293	0.0745	
	303	0.0793	
	313	0.0835	
	358.5	0.108	240
	385	0.125	
	387.3	0.125	
	414.5	0.146	
	441	0.162	
	465.3	0.177	
	500.3	0.205	
	540.8	0.231	
Carbon tetrachloride, CCl_4	273	0.07	186
Sulfurhexafluoride, SF_6	289.8	0.096	189
Ethyl acetate, $C_4H_8O_2$	298.9	0.087	231
	312.4	0.094	
	332	0.106	
Ethyl propionate, $C_5H_{10}O_2$	273	0.069	220
	300.8	0.082	
	300.9	0.0852	
Ethyl alcohol, C_2H_5OH	273	0.105	186
	298	0.135	178
	313.4	0.1372	221
	339.9	0.1475	
	340	0.1534	206
VI. Helium			
Ammonia, NH_3	274.2	0.668	282
	308.2	0.783	
	333.1	0.881	
Acetylene, C_2H_2	289.8	0.585	189
Benzene, C_6H_6	298	0.384	178
Helium, He	273	1.945	248
	14.4	0.0124	227
	19.6	0.0199	
	64.8	0.147	
	76.1	0.187	
	192	0.843	
	296	1.68	
	1 000	13.3	182*)
	1 500	26.9	
	2 000	46.7	
	2 500	70.3	
	3 000	98.6	
	3 500	130	
	4 000	167	
	4 500	207	
	5 000	250	
	5 500	299	
	6 000	350	
	6 500	407	
	7 000	467	
	8 000	595	
	9 000	738	
	10 000	898	
	11 000	1070	
	12 000	1260	
	13 000	1460	
	14 000	1670	
	15 000	1890	
n-heptane, C_7H_{16}	303.2	0.265	203
	263	0.1967	204
	273	0.2169	
	283	0.2328	
	293	0.2508	
	303	0.2689	
	313	0.2887	
Carbon dioxide, CO_2	250	0.392	215
	259	0.433	
	268	0.469	
	280	0.515	
	288	0.576	
	298.4	0.600	
	321	0.626	
	342	0.752	
	365	0.821	
	382	0.867	
	404	1.005	

Data from 250 °K to 404 °K, are described by equation $D=1.60 \cdot 10^{-5} \cdot T^{1.84}$

Gas	T, °K	D	Ref.
	273	0.54	223
	260	0.50	225
	283	0.52	
	358	0.70	
	287.0	0.592	189
	287.0	0.592	173
	298.2	0.612	330
	318.0	0.684	173
	323.2	0.68	330
	344.8	0.782	173
	353.2	0.80	330
	373.0	0.897	173
	383.2	0.884	330
	400.0	1.02	173
	413.2	1.04	330
	429.0	1.13	173
	443.2	1.13	330
	464.0	1.28	173
	473.2	1.28	330
	498.2	1.41	330
2,4-dimethylpentane, C_7H_{16}	303.2	0.263	203
Potassium, K	723.0	2.22	347
Oxygen, O_2	287.0	0.585	189
	244.2	0.533	280
	274.0	0.646	
	298.2	0.73	330
	304.4	0.771	280
	323.2	0.809	330
	334.0	0.901	280
	353.2	0.987	330
	383.2	1.12	
	413.2	1.24	
	443.2	1.42	
	473.2	1.60	
	498.2	1.68	

continued

Gas	T, °K	D	Ref.
Krypton, Kr	273	0.556	248
	288	0.605	
	303	0.659	
	318	0.720	
Xenon, Xe	273	0.501	213
	288	0.550	
	303	0.604	
	318	0.655	
	273.3	0.473	172
	315.0	0.572	
	354.2	0.721	
	394.0	0.882	
Sodium, Na	655	2.17	207
Neon Ne	273	0.906	248
	288	0.986	
	303	1.065	
	318	1.158	
	118	0.232	391
	154	0.361	
	197	0.557	
	231	0.716	
	296	1.080	
	299	1.116	
	374	1.614	
	479.5	2.433	
	573.5	3.290	
	683	4.45	
Nitrobenzene, $C_6H_5NO_2$	298	0.372	178
Carbon monoxide, CO	295.6	0.702	173
	314.8	0.788	
	345.0	0.914	
	374.5	1.05	
	400.0	1.17	
	436.0	1.35	
	470.0	1.54	
n-octane, C_8H_{18}	303.2	0.248	203
	273	0.1993	204
	283	0.2112	
	293	0.2335	
	303	0.2496	
	313	0.2742	
	323	0.2867	
	333	0.3081	
2,2,4-trimethyl-pentane, C_8H_{18}	303.2	0.253	203
	253	0.1780	204
	263	0.1938	
	273	0.2062	
	283	0.2220	
	293	0.2379	
	303	0.2534	
	313	0.2732	
Cesium, Cs	299	0.37	348
	723	2.00	347
Sulfurhexa-fluoride, SF_6	290.5	0.388	189
	313.0	0.430	173
	344.4	0.517	
	376.3	0.601	
	399.4	0.669	
	430.0	0.755	
	464.6	0.865	
Ethyl alcohol, C_2H_5OH	298	0.494	178

Gas	T, °K	D	Ref.
VII. Carbon dioxide			
Ammonia, NH_3	273	0.151	205
Acetylene C_2H_2	273	0.098	
Benzene, C_6H_6	292.9	0.0609	221
	318	0.0715	
	263	0.0492	204
	273	0.0525	
	283	0.0561	
	293	0.0600	
	303	0.0640	
	313	0.0682	
Bromine, Br_2	273	0.0664	205
Carbon dioxide, CO_2	273	0.096	181
	318	0.129	
	194.6	0.0516	249
	273	0.0970	
	312.6	0.1248	
	362.4	0.1644	
	194.5	0.0500	180
	273	0.0974	
	298	0.113	
	353	0.153	
	273	0.00598 (14.30)	250
		0.01501 (6.06)	
		0.002902 (25.50)	
	273.2	0.01126 (7.80)	
	307.9	0.01016 (11.20)	
	308	0.002347 (40.98)	
		0.001378 (58.45)	
		0.004285 (24.79)	
		0.000942 (69.95)	
	308	0.0002869 (89.28)	
		0.000649 (78.59)	
		0.000594 (77.57)	
		0.000457 (79.34)	
		0.0002732 (98.05)	
		0.000309 (86.01)	
		0.000932 (69.68)	
		0.0002973 (88.26)	
		0.000926 (69.81)	
	373.0	0.00768 (21.61)	
		0.00390 (41.29)	
		0.00529 (30.98)	
		0.002088 (71.11)	
		0.001316 (102.2)	
		0.000888 (135.7)	
		0.000497 (204.8)	
		0.000638 (171.7)	
		0.01121 (14.54)	
	296.2	0.0847 (1.243)	
	296.9	0.0424 (2.49)	
	296.1	0.0320 (2.77)	
	296.6	0.0150 (6.38)	
	296.4	0.0104 (9.33)	
	296.5	0.0071 (18.49)	
	295.7	0.0163 (6.34)	
	296.2	0.0101 (9.24)	
	296.5	0.00494 (18.59)	
	296.0	0.00476 (21.4)	
	296.0	0.00384 (28.1)	
	297.1	0.2060 (0.506)	
	296.0	0.1030 (0.98)	

continued

Gas	T, °K	D	Ref.
Carbon dioxide, CO_2	295.7	0.0910 (1.18)	250
	295.9	0.0500 (2.18)	
	295.6	0.0437 (2.46)	
	296.0	0.0065 (16.05)	333
	317.7	0.0111 (9.70)	
	317.6	0.0131 (9.20)	
	297.9	0.0110 (9.50)	
	297.9	0.00577 (16.70)	
	317.8	0.00529 (16.30)	
	318.2	0.00519 (16.30)	
	317.8	0.00415 (27.20)	
	298.3	0.00325 (34.20)	
	318.3	0.00340 (34.30)	
	298.2	0.00271 (34.30)	
	298.1	0.00179 (47.60)	
	273.3	0.00131 (34.30)	
	273.4	0.00183 (34.30)	
	286.6	0.00119 (47.80)	
	294	0.00260 (36.40)	
	295	0.00197 (38.40)	
	303.2	0.00166 (47.20)	
	317.7	0.00197 (47.70)	
	303.2	0.00158 (47.70)	
	296.8	0.00410 (16.70)	
	273.75	0.00130 (34.30)	
	286.4	0.00114 (47.50)	
	316.8	0.00149 (61.20)	
	317.6	0.00105 (68.10)	
	317.5	0.00130 (68.10)	
	298	0.00106 (61.20)	
	295.8	0.00228 (36.40)	
	295.5	0.00250 (36.40)	
	295.4	0.00306 (30.60)	
	296.3	0.00150 (47.70)	
	303.2	0.00126 (59.50)	
	303.3	0.00105 (61.20)	
	303.3	0.000822 (65.50)	
	313.4	0.000638 (80.80)	
	296.8	0.00269 (70.60)	
	303.8	0.00192 (45.60)	
	313.6	0.00154 (57.60)	
	313.6	0.00113 (68.00)	
	314.5	0.000924 (75.0)	
	313.5	0.000804 (79.50)	
	313.4	0.000530 (85.60)	
	305.06	0.000563 (74.30)	
	305.06	0.000538 (74.65)	
	313.25	0.000507 (86.05)	
	313.25	0.000550 (86.05)	
	313.08	0.000293 (96.30)	
	298.3	0.000105 (124.90)	
	305.06	0.000345 (73.60)	
	313.26	0.000300 (86.05)	
	313.26	0.000182 (108.50)	
	313.26	0.000149 (129.90)	
	298.1	0.000216 (65.10)	
	298.1	0.000104 (90.20)	
	298.1	0.0000822 (90.20)	
	273.2	0.0000456 (71.07)	
	273.3	0.0000599 (38.40)	
	273.2	0.0000404 (137.90)	
	313.21	0.000104 (144.90)	
	298.1	0.000103 (89.05)	
	298.2	0.0000702 (149.90)	
	298.2	0.000133 (65.10)	
	313.1	0.000166 (107.90)	
	313.2	0.000130 (119.80)	
	298.4	0.000111 (65.10)	
	298.0	$9.05 \cdot 10^{-5}$ (113.2)	334
	302.1	$13.7 \cdot 10^{-5}$ (103.1)	
	300.6	$7.02 \cdot 10^{-5}$ (178.9)	
	298.1	$9.34 \cdot 10^{-5}$ (103.1)	
	297.9	$7.64 \cdot 10^{-5}$ (130.3)	
	298.1	$5.12 \cdot 10^{-5}$ (562.0)	
	323.2	$9.16 \cdot 10^{-5}$ (232.3)	
	323.2	$8.84 \cdot 10^{-5}$ (250.0)	
	323.1	$7.04 \cdot 10^{-5}$ (470.5)	
	298.0	$4.09 \cdot 10^{-5}$ (402.5)	
	298.2	$4.34 \cdot 10^{-5}$ (402.5)	
	298.0	$3.54 \cdot 10^{-5}$ (562.0)	
	298.2	$3.18 \cdot 10^{-5}$ (752)	
	298.2	$2.53 \cdot 10^{-5}$ (1023.0)	
	272.9	$4.04 \cdot 10^{-5}$ (137.1)	
	273.2	$3.2 \cdot 10^{-5}$ (307.1)	
	273.2	$2.46 \cdot 10^{-5}$ (512.0)	
	273.1	$1.98 \cdot 10^{-5}$ (802.5)	
	323.0	$4.98 \cdot 10^{-5}$ (470.3)	
	322.9	$4.53 \cdot 10^{-5}$ (596.5)	
	322.9	$3.92 \cdot 10^{-5}$ (837.0)	
		$3.48 \cdot 10^{-5}$ (1029.0)	
	298.2	$3.51 \cdot 10^{-5}$ (561.0)	
	298.1	$2.45 \cdot 19^{-5}$ (1030.5)	
	296	0.109	174
	298	0.109	
	1 103	1.63	175
	1 180	1.78	174
	1 204	1.78	175
	1 213	1.94	
	1 218	2.04	174
	1 250	2.12	175
	1 278	2.19	
	1 302	2.26	
	1 321	2.19	
	1 330	2.38	174
	1 338	1.99	175
	1 372	2.30	
	1 416	2.34	
	1 434	2.56	
	1 445	2.83	174
	1 450	2.56	
	1 451	2.47	175
	1 471	2.62	
	1 478	2.69	
	1 487	2.88	174
	1 490	2.98	
	1 498	2.49	175
	1 576	3.12	
	1 580	2.78	174
	1 580	3.33	174
	1 607	3.12	175
	1 610	2.95	
	1 654	3.21	
	1 665	3.29	174
	1 671	3.13	175
	1 680	3.50	174
	1 703	3.33	175
	1 719	3.45	
	1 745	3.31	

continued

Gas	T, °K	D	Ref.
	1 782	3.67	
	1 796	3.59	
	1 944	4.30	
Deuterium, D_2	250	0.337	215
	256	0.370	
	267	0.383	
	297	0.494	
	346	0.594	
	372	0.660	
Data are described by $D=1.35 \cdot 10^{-5} \cdot T^{1.84}$			
Dibromobenzene, $C_6H_4Br_2$	273	0.032	205
Cyanogen gas, C_2N_2	273	0.0788	
Ethyl ether, $C_4H_{10}O$	273	0.0541	206
	292.9	0.0632	
Nitrous oxide, N_2O	273	0.096	176
	288.6	0.107	193
	194	0.0531	249
	273	0.0996	
	312.6	0.128	
	362.4	0.168	
	298	0.117	252
Iodine, I_2	554	0.176	251
	583	0.189	
	705	0.264	
	773	0.320	
	873	0.407	
	1 000	0.522	
	1 083	0.585	
	1 136	0.63	
	1 223	0.723	
	1 275	0.79	
Oxygen, O_2	273	0.139	176
	287.8	0.154	189
	293	0.160	184
	273	0.137	228**)
	293	0.153	
	300	0.163	
	500	0.415	
	1 000	1.43	
	1 500	a) 2.84	
		b) 2.81	
		c) 3.00	
		d) 3.04	
	2 000	a) 4.59	
		b) 4.55	
		c) 5.04	
		d) 5.19	
	2 500	a) 6.66	
		b) 6.58	
		c) 7.54	
		d) 7.90	
	3 000	a) 9.01	
		b) 8.89	
		c) 10.48	
		d) 11.15	
Methane, CH_4	273	0.153	176
	298	0.180	219
Methyl alcohol, CH_3OH	273	0.110	205
	263	0.0824	204
	273	0.0884	
	283	0.0937	
	293	0.0996	
	303	0.1060	
	313	0.1125	
	323	0.1185	
Nitric oxide, NO	273	0.129	205
Carbon monoxide, CO	273	0.137	176
	298	0.160	219
	296.1	0.152	173
	315.4	0.185	
	348.0	0.222	
	373.0	0.253	
	410.0	0.295	
	455.0	0.359	
	473.0	0.381	
Ethylene oxide, C_2H_4O	298	0.0918	252
Propane, C_3H_8	298	0.0863	
Sulfur dioxide, SO_2	273	0.087	205
Sulfur anhydride, SO_3	273	0.0708	
Carbon disulfide, CS_2	292.9	0.0726	221
	305.8	0.0789	
Hydrocyanic acid, HCN	273	0.117	205
Acetic acid, CH_3COOH	273	0.0716	201
	283	0.0767	
	293	0.0831	
	303	0.0879	
	313	0.0938	
	323	0.1001	
	333	0.1066	
	343	0.1135	
Chlorine Cl_2	273	0.078	205
Methyl chloride, CH_3Cl	273	0.085	
Sulfur hexafluoride, SF_6	290.8	0.0647	189
	328.0	0.0774	173
	348.0	0.0872	
	373.0	0.0980	
	410.0	0.118	
	447.0	0.143	
	472.0	0.151	
Ethylene, C_2H_4	298	0.15	219
Ethyl acetate, $C_4H_8O_2$	253	0.0339	204
	263	0.0447	
	273	0.0483	
	283	0.0525	
	293	0.0564	
	303	0.0606	
	313	0.0647	
Ethyl alcohol, C_2H_5OH	273	0.0686	206
	340	0.1064	
	313.4	0.0898	221
	339.9	0.1026	

continued

Gas	T, °K	D	Ref.
	VIII. Deuterium D_2		
n-heptane, C_7H_{16}	303.2	0.218	203
	263	0.1667	204
	273	0.1757	
	283	0.1901	
	293	0.2047	
	303	0.2181	
	313	0.2342	
n-octane, C_8H_{18}	303.2	0.208	203
	273	0.1607	204
	283	0.1793	
	293	0.1957	
	303	0.2068	
	313	0.2295	
	323	0.2392	
	333	0.2555	
2,4-dimethyl-pentane, C_7H_{16}	303.2	0.224	203
2,2,4-trimethyl-pentane, C_8H_{18}	303.2	0.212	
	253	0.1482	204
	263	0.1587	
	273	0.1730	
	283	0.1858	
	293	0.1987	
	303	0.2118	
	313	0.2289	
	IX. Nitrous oxide N_2O		
Nitrous oxide, N_2O	273	0.0890	205
Ethylene oxide, C_2H_4O	298	0.0914	252
Propane, C_3H_8	298	0.0860	
	X. Oxygen O_2		
Ammonia, NH_3	273	0.224	183
Acetylene, C_2H_2	287.0	0.202	189
Benzene, C_6H_6	273	0.067	186
	273	0.0797	206
	298	0.073	219
	311.3	0.1010	187
n-hexane, C_6H_{14}	288.6	0.0754	200
2,3-dimethyl-butene, C_6H_{14}	288.4	0.0742	
Cyanogen gas, C_2N_2	273	0.1058	205
	1 073	1.177	
	1 273	1.592	
	283	0.0605	
	293	0.0664	
	303	0.0702	
	313	0.0748	
Oxygen, O_2	273	0.175	181
	318	0.230	
	77.5	0.0153	180
	194.5	0.104	
	273	0.187	
	298	0.232	
	353	0.301	
Krypton, Kr	298	0.146	279
	343	0.198	
	377	0.244	
	408	0.268	
Xenon, Xe	242.2	0.084	280
	274.75	0.100	
	303.55	0.126	
	333.6	0.149	
Methane, CH_4	300	0.229	228**)
	500	0.580	
	1 000	1.98	
	1 500	a) 3.86	
		b) 3.95	
		c) 4.11	
		d) 4.18	
	2 000	a) 6.23	
		b) 6.38	
		c) 6.88	
		d) 7.11	
	2 500	a) 9.03	
		b) 9.23	
		c) 10.26	
		d) 10.77	
	3 000	a) 12.22	
		b) 12.45	
		c) 14 23	
		d) 15.18	
Methylcyclo-pentane, C_6H_{12}	287.1	0.0744	200
Nitric oxide, NO	273	0.1754	205
	1 073	1.951	
	1 273	2.636	
Carbon monoxide, CO	298	0.21	198
	273	0.191	228**
	300	0.224	
	500	0,540	
	1 000	1.75	
	1 500	a) 3.40	
		b) 3.39	
		c) 3.52	
		d) 3.57	
	2 000	a) 5.48	
		b) 5.45	
		c) 5.76	
		d) 5.89	
	2 500	a) 7.93	
		b) 7.88	
		c) 8.44	
		d) 8.70	
	3 000	a) 10.72	
		b) 10.62	
		c) 11.53	
		d) 11.99	
n-octane, C_8H_{18}	303.1	0.0705	200
	263	0.0486	201
	273	0 0566	
	283	0.0606	
	293	0.0654	
	303	0 0705	
	313	0.0761	
	323	0.0816	
Pyridine, C_5H_5N	.318.3	0.1050	187

continued

Gas	T, °K	D	Ref.
Piperidine, $C_5H_{11}N$	315.0	0.0953	
Hydrocyanic acid, HCN	273	0.1563	205
	1 073	1.740	
	1 273	2.35	
Cyclohexane, C_6H_{12}	288.6	0.0731	200, 187
	253	0.0574	201
	263	0.0615	
	273	0.0663	
	283	0.0718	
	293	0.0761	
	303	0.0810	
Carbon tetrachloride, CCl_4	273	0.0651	186
Sulfur hexafluoride, SF_6	287.0	0.099	189
	317	0.109	279
	340	0.129	
	379	0.160	
	408	0.193	
Ethylene, C_2H_4	273	0.148	183
Ethyl alcohol, C_2H_5OH	273	0.096	186

XI. Krypton Kr

Gas	T, °K	D	Ref.
Ammonia, NH_3	254.7	0.121	281
	275.1	0.142	
	308.1	0.178	
	333.0	0.208	
Krypton, Kr	273	0.087	248
	293	0.093	253
	199	0.045	217
	273	0.0795	
	292.7	0.090	
	373	0.140	
	474	0.214	
	1 000	0.853	182*
	1 500	1.72	
	2 000	2,83	
	2 500	4.14	
	3 000	5,67	
	3 500	7.38	
	4 000	9.32	
	4 500	11.4	
	5 000	13.8	
	5 500	16.4	
	6 000	19.2	
	6 500	22.2	
	7 000	25.5	
	8 000	32.6	
	9 000	40.7	
	10 000	49.6	
	11 000	59.6	
	12 000	70.2	
	13 000	81.5	
	14 000	93.7	
	15 000	107	
Neon, Ne	273	0.223	216
	288	0.240	
	303	0.266	
	318	0.284	

XII. Xenon Xe

Gas	T, °K	D	Ref.
Ammonia, NH_3	274.2	0.114	282
	308.4	0.145	
	331.1	0.173	
Xenon, Xe	194.5	0.0257	254
	273	0.0480	
	329.7	0.0684	
	377.8	0.0900	
	300.3	0.058	255
	293	0.044	253
	1 000	0.502	182*
	1 500	1,01	
	2 000	1.65	
	2 500	2.43	
	2 000	3.32	
	3 500	4.32	
	4 000	5.42	
	4 500	6.64	
	5 000	7.97	
	5 500	9.43	
	6 000	10.9	
	6 500	12.6	
	7 000	14.4	
	8 000	18.2	
	9 000	22.5	
	10 000	27.2	
	11 000	32.4	
	12 000	37.7	
	13 000	43.4	
	14 000	49.4	
	15 000	55.7	
Neon, Ne	273	0.186	248
	288	0.202	
	303	0.221	
	318	0,244	

XIII. Methane CH_4

Gas	T, °K	D	Ref.
Ammonia, NH_3	273	0,1574	205
	1 073	1.752	
	1 273	2.368	
Methane, CH_4	90	0.0266	180
	194.5	0.0992	
	273	0.206	
	298	0.240	
	353	0.318	
Monotritium methane, CH_3T	323	0.00365 (40)	256
		0,00246 (60)	
		0.00160 (80,3)	
		0,00113 (100)	
		0.00094 (124.8)	
		0.000664 (150)	
	298	0.00291 (40.5)	
		0.00198 (60)	
		0.00138 (80)	
		0,00098 (100)	
		0,00087 (100)	
		0.00069 (125)	
		0.00071 (125)	
		0.00057 (150)	
		0,000368 (200)	
		0.00021 (300)	
	273	0.0053 (20)	
		0.00248 (40.2)	

continued

Gas	T, °K	D	Ref.
Monotritium methane, CH_3T	273	0.00151 (60)	256
		0.00109 (81)	
		0.00075 (100)	
		0.000575 (125)	
		0.00040 (150)	
		0.000248 (200)	
		0.000150 (300)	
Ethylene, C_2H_6	273	0.136	183

XIV. Neon Ne

Gas	T, °K	D	Ref.
Ammonia, NH_3	274.2	0.298	282
	308.4	0.378	
	333.1	0.419	
Deuterium, D_2	115	0.163	391
	155	0.286	
	197	0.434	
	232	0.569	
	295	0.875	
	295.5	0.866	
	379	1.308	
	484.5	2.013	
	575.5	2.688	
	667	3.444	
Neon, Ne	77.5	0.0492	180
	194.5	0.255	
	273.0	0.452	
	298.0	0.516	
	353.0	0.703	
	293	0.473	257
			258
	1 000	3.93	182*)
	1 500	7.76	
	2 000	12.7	
	2 500	18.5	
	3 000	25.2	
	3 500	32.6	
	4 000	41.1	
	4 500	50.4	
	5 000	60.7	
	5 500	72.0	
	6 000	83.8	
	6 500	96.5	
	7 000	110	
	8 000	139	
	9 000	172	
	10 000	207	
	11 000	244	
	12 000	284	
	13 000	325	
	14 000	368	
	15 000	414	

XV. Carbon monoxide CO

Gas	T, °K	D	Ref.
Ammonia, NH_3	233	0.108	284
	273	0.151	
	313	0.209	
	353	0.269	
Carbon monoxide, CO	273	0.175	257
	194.7	0.109	
	273.2	0.190	
	319.6	0.247	
	373.0	0.323	
Sulfur hexafluoride, SF_6	296.8	0.0887	173
	315.4	0.105	
	348.0	0.125	
	373.4	0.144	
	410.0	0.174	
	455.0	0.212	
	473.0	0.222	
Ethylene, C_2H_4	273	0.116	176

XVI. Ethylene C_2H_4

Gas	T, °K	D	Ref.
Ammonia, NH_3	273	0,177	183

XVII. Ethane C_2H_6

Gas	T, °K	D	Ref.
Propane, C_3H_8	273	0,074	

XVIII. Pentane C_5H_{12}

Gas	T, °K	D	Ref.
Sodium, Na	655	0,23	207

XIX. Carbon tetrachloride CCl_4

Gas	T, °K	D	Ref.
Borontrifluoride, BF_3	303	0.045	259
Borontrichloride, BCl_3	303	0.034	

Coefficients of diffusion D (cm²/s) for different systems at various temperatures and pressures

1. Nitrogen–hydrogen [285]

T, °K \ p, atm →	1	50	75	100	125	200	300
273	0.708	0.0114	0.00735	0.00570	0.00436	0.00281	0.00199
298	0.800	0.0134		0.00651		0.00328	
323	0.94	0.0157		0.00771		0.00401	
363	1.15	0.0187		0.00982		0.00499	0.0034
473	1.86	0.0289		0.0142		0.00737	

2. Argon–hydrogen [285]

T, °K \ p, atm →	1	50	100	125	150
298	0.802	0.0139	0.00704	0,00572	0.00464
323	0.920	0.0158	0.00749	0.00651	
363	1.13	0.0198	0.0100	0.00807	0.00684

3. Carbon dioxide–hydrogen [285]

T, °K \ p, atm →	1	25	50	100
323	0.770	0.0212	0.0108	0.00435
363	0.95	0.0304	0.0144	0.00651

4. Water vapor–hydrogen [45]

T, °K \ p, atm →	25,2	49,4	98.8	194.6	291,4
321,15	0.0316	0.0135	0.0065	0.0026	0.0021
341.15	0.0650	0.0338	0.0176	0.0101	0.0065

5. Methyl alcohol vapor–hydrogen [45]

T, °K \ p, atm →	25.2	49.4	98.8	194.6	291.4
302.15	0.0741	0.0444	0.0293	0.0168	
323.15	0.1064	0.0624	0.0349	0.0179	
346.15	0.1392	0.0818	0.0392	0.0241	0.0154

6. Argon–helium [285]

T, °K \ p, atm →	1	50	100	125
298	0.736	0.0121	0.00637	0.00475
363	1.05	0.0163	0.00831	0.00726

7. Methyl alcohol vapors–nitrogen [45]

T, °K \ p, atm →	25.2	49.4	98.8	194.6	291.4
300.15	0.0141	0.0084	0.0044	0.0028	0,0022
321.15	0.0155	0.0098	0.0057	0.0036	0.0028
346.15	0.0181	0.0118	0.0074	0.0042	0.0032

8. Benzene vapors–nitrogen [45]

p, atm → / T, °K	25.2	49.4	98.8	194.6	291.4
299.15	0.0105	0.0060	0.0038	0.0028	0.0022
322.15	0.0134	0.0086	0.0053	0.0035	0.0027
345.15	0.0175	0.0102	0.0063	0.0044	0.0034

Chapter 12

THERMODIFFUSION IN GASES

The molecular transfer of mass. cause by inhomogeneity of temperature is referred to as thermal diffusion. Thermal diffusion causes a system to reach steady state when separation and mixing reach an equilibrium. Separation is caused by temperature differences, mixing is caused by concentration gradient which, in turn, was created by the difference in temperatures. Thermal diffusion is described by the separation quantity $\Delta\lambda$, or by the thermal diffusion ratio K_T, related to each other by

$$\Delta\lambda = K_T \ln \frac{T_1}{T_2}, \tag{1}$$

$$\Delta\lambda = c_2 - c_1, \tag{2}$$

where c_1 – volumetric concentration of the lighter component in the region where the temperature is equal to T_1 and c_2 is the volumetric concentration in the region of T_2;

$$K_T = \frac{D_T}{D},$$

where D is the coefficient of normal (concentration) diffusion, and D_T is the coefficient of thermal diffusion.

The table on pages 654–665 gives the values of $\Delta\lambda$ and K_T for a number of gas mixtures. The values of c_1 are given for the lighter component. All values of $\Delta\lambda$ in this table are taken from Ref [204]. These data were used by Berzhnoy to calculate the values of K_T using Eq. (1). The table also gives the values of $\Delta\lambda$ and of K_T for some gas mixtures over a wide range of temperatures, obtained using the Usmanov method [201].

Data on Thermal Diffusion in Gas Mixtures

c_1, %	T_1, °K	T_2, °K	$\Delta\lambda$, %	K_T	Ref.
		He—Ne			
20	373	288	1.38	0,0531	73
30			1.87	0.0725	
40			2.23	0.0864	
50			2.50	0.0969	
60			2.59	0.1003	
77.9	293	90	8.0	0.068	260
78,7		69	10.1	0.070	
79,8		20	11.7	0,031	
69,6		90	8.5	0.072	
71.1		69	11.3	0.078	
71,5		20	14.4	0,038	
63.6		20	17.2	0.045	
59,5		90	9.7	0.082	
60.4		69	11.4	0.079	
47.9		20	16.0	0.042	
44,5		90	9.5	0.081	
45,0		69	10.5	0.073	
53.8	369	293	1,80	0.0783	261
	464		3.60	0.0783	
	585		5,42	0.0788	
	293	233	1,80	0.0783	
		185	3.60	0.0783	
		147	5.30	0.0770	
		117	7.02	0.0763	
		93	8.65	0.0752	
39.9	288	81	10.0	0,0792	262
		128	6.64	0.0820	
		147	5.43	0.0808	
		163	4,54	0.0799	
		189	3,41	0.0811	
		226	2.29	0.0946	
53.6		81	11,2	0,0885	
		133	7.30	0.0945	
		151	5,98	0.0925	
		171	4,95	0,0952	
		191	3.79	0,0925	
		214	2,67	0,0900	
25,5	287	81	7,71	0.0609	
		129	5.02	0,0629	
		144	4,22	0.0612	
		158	3.61	0.0606	
		176	2.98	0.0611	
		200	2.21	0,0616	
		226	1.45	0.0607	

continued

c_1, %	T_1, °K	T_2, °K	$\Delta\lambda$, %	K_T	Ref.
53.7	402	300	2.93	0.100	263
	463		4.00	0.0924	
	567		5.82	0.0918	
	638		7.36	0.0976	
43.3	410		2.69	0.0860	
	470		3.60	0.0803	
	567		5.44	0.0857	
	638		6.47	0.0857	
30.8	402		2.25	0.0771	
	463		3.23	0.0747	
	567		4.57	0.0720	
	638		5.52	0.0732	
19.6	402		1.80	0.0617	
	463		2.44	0.0563	
	567		3.52	0.0555	
	638		4.25	0.0563	
75.7	402		2.53	0.0867	
	463		3.48	0.0804	
	567		4.91	0.0773	
	638		5.85	0.0775	
89.9	402		1.62	0.0555	
	463		2.52	0.0582	
	567		3.40	0.0536	
	638		3.95	0.0524	
53.8	293	192	3.45	0.0814	
		146	5.28	0.0761	
		122	6.74	0.0750	
		112	7.38	0.0767	
		100	8.08	0.0753	
		92	8.87	0.0766	
53.8	609	293	5.87	0.0807	
	457		3.58	0.0807	
	385		2.35	0.0948	
			He – Ar		
3.3	329	290	0.11	0.0087	264
	373		0.20	0.0079	
	445		0.33	0.0078	
	500		0.42	0.0078	
	579		0.53	0.0077	
11.2	322	292	0.29	0.0299	
	383		0.70	0.0257	
	430		1.04	0.0269	
	508		1.23	0.0222	
	567		1.73	0.0260	
18.5	329	290	0.51	0.0404	
	384		1.25	0.0445	
	453		1.99	0.0447	
	523		2.56	0.0435	
	543		2.78	0.0438	
38.1	377	291	1.90	0.0737	
	450		3.38	0.0778	
	480		3.80	0.0762	
	553		4.88	0.0762	
70.8	387	290	2.85	0.0994	
	412		3.43	0.0975	
	485		5.00	0.0975	
10	373	288	0.65	0.0252	73
20			1.23	0.0477	
30			1.70	0.0659	
40			2.09	0.0810	
50			2.40	0.0930	
65			2.60	0.1009	
51.2	369	293	2.18	0.0949	261
	464		4.40	0.0957	
	585		6.70	0.0972	
	293	233	2.18	0.0949	
		185	4.40	0.0957	
		147	6.35	0.0921	
		117	8.35	0.0912	
		93	10.2	0.0889	
20.85	283	81	6.79	0.0542	262
		121	4.34	0.0512	
		145	3.76	0.0564	
		161	3.22	0.0571	
		176	2.74	0.0578	
		182	2.25	0.0511	
		206	1.85	0.0585	
		223	1.43	0.0604	
		241	0.95	0.0590	
38.1	282	80	10.6	0.0845	
		122	6.86	0.0819	
		150	5.71	0.0905	
		166	4.84	0.0916	
		184	4.00	0.0940	
		195	3.41	0.0927	
		213	2.67	0.0950	
		234	1.84	0.0990	
51.1	283	81	11.8	0.0948	
		130	7.99	0.1028	
		147	6.72	0.1027	
		162	5.62	0.1009	
		176	4.82	0.1014	
		187	4.19	0.1011	
		207	3.34	0.1067	
		229	2.27	0.1070	
57.2	402		3.15	0.1079	263
	463		4.65	0.1074	
	567		6.39	0.1005	
	638		8.00	0.1060	
44.4	402		2.93	0.1002	
	463		4.10	0.0948	
	567		6.15	0.0969	
	638		7.42	0.0983	
23.2	402		1.72	0.0590	
	463		3.31	0.0765	
	567		4.43	0.0698	
	638		5.40	0.0715	
11.5	402		0.95	0.0326	
	463		1.28	0.0296	
	567		2.67	0.0421	
	638		2.75	0.0364	
74.4	402		2.29	0.0785	
	463		3.54	0.0818	
	567		5.15	0.0811	
	638		6.00	0.0795	
90.6	402		1.31	0.0449	
	463		1.64	0.0379	
	567		2.83	0.0446	
	638		3.03	0.0401	
			He – Kr		
30	373	288	1.75	0.0678	73
40			2.20	0.0853	
50			2.58	0.1000	
60			2.79	0.1081	
70			2.76	0.1070	
63			2.80	0.1084	

continued

c_1, %	T_1, °K	T_2, °K	$\Delta\lambda$, %	K_T	Ref.
55.0	369	293	2.52	0.1097	261
	464		5.10	0.1109	
	585		7.64	0.1108	
	293	233	2.60	0.1131	
		185	5.10	0.1109	
		147	7.50	0.1087	
		117	9.70	0.1054	
			He – Xe		
10	373	288	0.53	0.0206	73
20			1.06	0.0411	
30			1.55	0.0601	
40			2.03	0.0787	
50			2.53	0.0981	
70			3.15	0.1222	261
53.6	369	293	2.52	0.1097	
	464		5.02	0.1091	
	585		7.53	0.1091	
	293	233	2.50	0.1088	
		185	4.90	0.1066	
45	373	288	0.10	0.0388	73
			Ne – Ar		
20	373	288	0.60	0.0233	73
30			0.85	0.0330	
40			1.05	0.0407	
50			1.18	0.0457	
60			1.21	0.0469	
58			1.20	0.0465	
51.2	369	293	1.09	0.0474	261
	464		2.20	0.0478	
	585		3.30	0.0478	
	293	233	0.95	0.0413	
		185	1.83	0.0398	
		147	2.63	0.0381	
		117	3.21	0.0349	
		93	3.68	0.0320	
19.1	283	79	2.22	0.0174	262
		135	1.52	0.0206	
		168	1.21	0.0233	
		190	0.96	0.0241	
		205	0.79	0.0245	
		233	0.51	0.0270	
36.1	282	81	3.40	0.0273	
		133	2.44	0.0325	
		141	2.16	0.0312	
		168	1.78	0.0345	
		184	1.53	0.0360	
		209	1.10	0.0368	
		226	0.82	0.0371	
51.7	283	81	3.71	0.0297	
		129	2.80	0.0357	
		152	2.30	0.0371	
		171	1.93	0.0386	
		194	1.52	0.0403	
		227	0.98	0.0444	
51.2	293	264	0.63	0.0612	261
		234	0.89	0.0399	
		196	1.63	0.0407	
		174	2.05	0.0394	
		145	2.61	0.0371	
		125	3.00	0.0207	
		116	3.26	0.0237	
		105	3.45	0.0271	
		91	3.65	0.0322	
51.2	635	293	3.80	0.0492	
	600		3.54	0.0494	
	522		2.78	0.0484	
	471		2.17	0.0458	
	408		1.59	0.0481	
	348		0.90	0.0530	
			Ne – Kr		
20	373	288	0.84	0.0326	73
30			1.15	0.0446	
40			1.44	0.0559	
50			1.72	0.0667	
60			1.90	0.0737	
63			1.80	0.0698	
53.0	369	293	1.75	0.0761	261
	464		3.58	0.0778	
	585		5.47	0.0793	
	293	233	1.62	0.0704	
		185	2.93	0.0637	
		147	4.02	0.0583	
		117	5.00	0.0547	
			Ne – Xe		
20	373	288	0.67	0.0260	73
30			0.99	0.0384	
40			1.26	0.0489	
50			1.49	0.0578	
60			1.69	0.0656	
70			1.70	0.0660	
54.2	369	293	1.85	0.0805	261
	464		3.88	0.0844	
	585		6.15	0.0892	
		233	0.172	0.0748	
		185	0.330	0.0718	
			Ar – Kr		
40	373	288	0.29	0.0112	73
50			0.36	0.0139	
60			0.40	0.0155	
70			0.37	0.0143	
80			0,30	0.0116	
58			0.40	0.0155	
53.5	369	293	0.52	0.0226	261
	464		1.23	0.0265	
	585		2.20	0.0319	
	293	233	0.38	0.0165	
		185	0.65	0.0141	
		147	0.84	0.0122	
		117	0.95	0.0105	
		197	0.54	0.0135	
		179	0.66	0.0130	
		144	0.82	0.0116	
		134	0.86	0.0110	
		122	0.86	0.0098	
		111	0.93	0.0092	
	634	293	2.65	0.0338	
	577		2.15	0.0323	
	507		1.55	0.0199	
	470		1.35	0.0286	
	442		1.06	0.0258	
	397		0.69	0.0227	

continued

c_1, %	T_1, °K	T_2, °K	$\Delta\lambda$, %	K_T	Ref.
		Ar – Xe			
30	373	288	0.33	0.0128	73
40			0.41	0.0159	
50			0.46	0.0178	
60			0.48	0.0186	
70			0.43	0.0167	
58			0.47	0.0182	
56.4	369	293	0.62	0.0269	261
	464		1.50	0.0326	
	585		2.60	0.0377	
	293	233	0.47	0.0204	
		185	0.83	0.0180	
		D_2 – Ne			
82.2	293	20	5.6	0.0147	260
81.3		90	4.7	0.0399	
81.65		69	5.4	0.0374	
70.55		20	7.3	0.0191	
62.55		90	6.1	0.0518	
69.9		69	6.8	0.0471	
58.3		90	6.4	0.0544	
58.9		69	7.6	0.0526	
59.25		20	8.3	0.0218	
46.1		90	6.8	0.0578	
46.5		69	7.6	0.0526	
46.8		20	8.0	0.0209	
34.6		20	7.6	0.0526	
33.5		90	5.8	0.0493	
34.0		69	7.0	0.0485	
		H_2 – Ar			
47	286	108	5.19	0.0533	265
		126	4.40	0.0538	
		130	4.24	0.0539	
		137	4.09	0.0556	
		142	3.91	0.0559	
		149	3.67	0.0565	
		165	3.42	0.0623	
		172	3.11	0.0611	
		190	2.47	0.0603	
		197	2.43	0.0652	
		218	1.79	0.0651	
		231	1.40	0.0654	
55.6	290	103	5.78	0.0559	
		112	5.43	0.0572	
		126	4.96	0.0595	
		130	4.81	0.0601	
		143	4.18	0.0593	
		161	3.72	0.0634	
		178	3.30	0.0676	
		193	2.80	0.0688	
		205	2.54	0.0732	
		216	2.01	0.0681	
		231	1.57	0.0853	
		H_2 – O_2			
29.8	290	102	4.07	0.0390	265
		115	3.74	0.0404	
		134	3.43	0.0448	
		147	3.15	0.0464	
		153	2.96	0.0463	
		167	2.62	0.0476	
		178	2.35	0.0480	
		187	2.09	0.0478	
		199	1.81	0.0481	
		213	1.45	0.0471	
		223	1.26	0.0481	
		242	0.88	0.0483	
		H_2 – Ar			
6	369	289	0.27	0.0111	264
	428		0.47	0.0120	
	493		0.65	0.0122	
11	369	290	0.46	0.0193	
	448		0.87	0.0200	
	507		1.17	0.0209	
	547		1.39	0.0219	
16.1	376	289	0.84	0.0320	
	447		1.40	0.0320	
	506		1.88	0.0336	
73.5	330	288	0.57	0.0420	
	375		1.07	0.0408	
	431		1.52	0.0377	
	499		2.15	0.0392	
	541		2.50	0.0397	
85	324	286	0.72	0.0581	
	365		1.46	0.0599	
	402		2.09	0.0614	
	441		2.62	0.0607	
	442		2.74	0.0630	
	518		3.64	0.0613	
		N_2 – Ar			
46	289	94	1.14	0.0102	265
		128	0.92	0.0113	
		154	0.83	0.0119	
		177	0.77	0.0157	
		195	0.65	0.0165	
		215	0.55	0.0186	
		222	0.50	0.0189	
		232	0.40	0.0184	
62.5		94	0.95	0.0085	
		139	0.87	0.0119	
		181	0.73	0.0156	
		201	0.59	0.0163	
		221	0.46	0.0172	
70	290	114	0.92	0.0099	
		148	0.77	0.0114	
		166	0.72	0.0129	
		169	0.72	0.0134	
		184	0.67	0.0147	
		191	0.59	0.0142	
		203	0.54	0.0151	
		217	0.42	0.0145	
		229	0.39	0.0164	
		H_2 – Ne			
27.8	283	82	7.84	0.0696	262
		128	5.43	0.0752	
		147	4.46	0.0682	
		162	3.70	0.0664	
		173	3.23	0.0657	
		197	2.47	0.0679	
		228	1.41	0.0653	
40.6	285	82	9.44	0.0760	
		138	6.66	0.0919	
		147	5.40	0.0814	
		163	4.63	0.0829	

continued

c_1, %	T_1, °K	T_2, °K	$\Delta\lambda$, %	K_T	Ref.
		176	3.97	0.0822	
		200	3.10	0.0877	
		228	1.90	0.0852	
49.6	282	81	10.0	0.0803	
		129	7.06	0.0902	
		144	5.87	0.0873	
		161	5.26	0.0941	
		171	4.40	0.0879	
		196	3.30	0.0908	
		205	2.85	0.0896	
		211	2.04	0.0704	
84	290	20	6.4	0.0242	260
76.8		90	7.7	0.0660	
77.3		69	8.2	0.0573	
66.1		90	8.4	0.0720	
66.9		69	9.8	0.0685	
65.0		20	10.7	0.0404	
57.8		90	8.8	0.0754	
58.6		69	10.0	0.0698	
45.8		20	11.3	0.0426	
41.8		90	7.3	0.0625	
42.6		69	9.0	0.0629	
28.2		90	5.7	0.0488	
28.9		69	7.0	0.0489	
24.9		20	7.5	0.0283	
		H_2–He			
53.6	615	293	2.93	0.0396	261
	549		2.02	0.0324	
	432		1.52	0.0390	
54	293	90	4.20	0.0355	260
		20	10.1	0.0265	
		20	9.9	0.0260	
66		20	9.4	0.0246	
50	373	288	1.24	0.0481	226
60			1.14	0.0442	
70			0.90	0.0349	
80			0.64	0.0248	
90			0.34	0.0132	
32.78	763	273	2.50	0.0244	267
40.33	753		3.21	0.0317	
47.82	758		3.22	0.0319	
60.30	763		3.02	0.0295	
53.6	293	139	2.52	0.0338	268
		115	3.40	0.0365	
		93	4.00	0.0355	
		93	4.55	0.0398	
		67	5.75	0.0391	
		He–N_2			
34.5	284	81	9.35	0.1176	262
		122	5.99	0.0709	
		146	5.15	0.0775	
		170	4.05	0.0789	
		185	3.30	0.0771	
		198	2.78	0.0775	
		218	2.16	0.0815	
		240	1.40	0.0833	
		81	11.86	0.1493	
		133	7.77	0.1028	
		146	6.78	0.1020	
		165	5.59	0.1028	
		180	4.72	0.1038	
		192	4.05	0.1037	
		204	3.32	0.1040	
		227	2.44	0.1093	
		H_2–N_2			
32.7	328	284	0.76	0.0535	264
	379		1.71	0.0616	
	418		2.26	0.0592	
	456		2.50	0.0530	
	479		3.03	0.0580	
	510		3.46	0.0591	
	547		3.67	0.0560	
4.7	324	285	0.12	0.0079	
	369		0.23	0.0089	
	412		0.30	0.0082	
	450		0.43	0.0095	
	500		0.52	0.0092	
	543		0.60	0.0093	
10.7	325	283	0.28	0.0202	
	366		0.53	0.0208	
	411		0.76	0.0206	
	448		0.97	0.0211	
	499		1.23	0.0218	
	538		1.32	0.0206	
25.7	321	284	0.44	0.0355	
	373		1.21	0.0446	
	415		1.72	0.0456	
	450		2.01	0.0437	
	500		2.67	0.0474	
	543		2.92	0.0452	
37.4	326		0.85	0.0616	
	328		0.92	0.0648	
	374		1.70	0.0616	
	411		2.22	0.0603	
	445		2.79	0.0621	
	492		3.45	0.0611	
	539		4.25	0.0664	
50.5	324	282	1.03	0.0737	
	369		1.95	0.0731	
	418		2.81	0.0713	
		468	3.98	0.0782	
		506	4.56	0.0780	
		540	4.77	0.0734	
29.4	289	81	5.02	0.0396	265
		99	4.47	0.0418	
		116	4.04	0.0444	
		123	3.84	0.0451	
		138	3.22	0.0436	
		148	3.05	0.0457	
		174	2.48	0.0491	
		187	2.23	0.0513	
		193	2.04	0.0506	
		203	1.79	0.0509	
		242	0.95	0.0537	
42		81	6.62	0.0521	
		97	5.87	0.0539	
		130	4.74	0.0594	
		139	4.48	0.0613	
		149	4.17	0.0632	
		159	3.77	0.0633	
		179	3.06	0.0639	
		189	2.85	0.0671	
		198	2.61	0.0691	

continued

c_1, %	T_1, °K	T_2, °K	$\Delta\lambda$, %	K_T	Ref.
		203	2.41	0.0685	
		224	1.82	0.0720	
		240	1.30	0.0699	
77.5	288	81	6.15	0.0486	
		99	5.89	0.0552	
		114	5.42	0.0587	
		129	4.79	0.0598	
		136	4.67	0.0622	
		143	4.38	0.0627	
		152	4.14	0.0647	
		166	3.77	0.0685	
		191	2.96	0.0722	
		244	1.15	0.0693	
5.2	373	283	0.26	0.0094	269
9.6			0.45	0.0163	
18.9			0.97	0.0352	
25.4			1.34	0.0486	
36.9			1.80	0.0652	
46.6			2.25	0.0815	
54.7			2.54	0.0920	
55.8			2.60	0.0942	
61.0			2.63	0.0953	
62.1			2.58	0.0935	
66.4			2.62	0.0950	
68.2			2.54	0.0920	
76.4			1.98	0.0718	
81.6			2.03	0.0736	
85.0			1.45	0.0525	
87.2			1.21	0.0438	
39.8	293	254	0.73	0.0515	268, 270
		238	1.41	0.0681	
		202	2.47	0.0740	
		191	2.62	0.0612	
		182	3.03	0.0639	
		163	3.56	0.0609	
		153	3.89	0.0599	
		135	4.55	0.0588	
		123	4.85	0.0561	
		110	5.38	0.0549	
		98	5.60	0.0512	
		90	6.32	0.0536	
28	283	230	1.17	0.0566	271
		214	1.59	0.0572	
		195	1.91	0.0512	
		178	2.42	0.0525	
		151	3.05	0.0486	
		133	3.67	0.0486	
		89	4.79	0.0415	
		82	5.04	0.0407	
42.7		217	2.09	0.0793	
		188	2.94	0.0718	
		166	3.62	0.0678	
		147	4.14	0.0633	
		137	4.46	0.0616	
		134	4.76	0.0639	
		82	6.83	0.0552	
39.8	655	293	5.89	0.0734	268, 270
	513		4.08	0.0731	
	410		2.49	0.0741	
	357		1.66	0.0839	
	329		0.93	0.0810	
46	293	93	10.10	0.0882	272
		193	3.64	0.0876	

c_1, %	T_1, °K	T_2, °K	$\Delta\lambda$, %	K_T	Ref.
79.9		93	7.80	0.0681	
		193	3.10	0.0746	
46	393	293	2.53	0.0867	
	443		3.23	0.0784	
79.9	393		2.02	0.0692	
	443		2.77	0.0672	
		$H_2 - CO$			
24	284	81	4.13	0.0330	265
		131	3.14	0.0409	
		149	2.71	0.0405	
		171	2.29	0.0450	
		183	1.92	0.0437	
		197	1.62	0.0443	
		210	1.38	0.0457	
		233	0.92	0.0465	
32.5	285	81	6.12	0.0487	
		103	5.19	0.0510	
		115	4.80	0.0529	
		133	4.13	0.0543	
		147	3.78	0.0572	
		156	3.54	0.0587	
		170	3.08	0.0597	
		185	2.60	0.0600	
		208	1.94	0.0616	
53	286	81	7.32	0.0581	
		106	6.33	0.0640	
		128	5.22	0.0650	
		143	4.55	0.0643	
		166	3.60	0.0652	
		184	3.34	0.0755	
		190	3.46	0.0844	
		210	2.29	0.0744	
		$H_2 - CO_2$			
5.5	373	283	0.28	0.0102	269
8.0			0.41	0.0149	
15.7			0.84	0.0304	
24.4			1.21	0.0439	
30.1			1.49	0.0540	
35.7			1.69	0.0613	
42.4			1.95	0.0707	
48.5			2.18	0.0790	
55.0			2.54	0.0921	
61.7			2.53	0.0917	
63.3			2.64	0.0957	
65.3			2.62	0.0950	
70.4			2.46	0.0892	
77.8			2.19	0.0794	
81.9			1.65	0.0598	
83.4			1.57	0.0569	
		$D_2 - N_2$			
28.1	283	234	0.97	0.0513	271
		205	1.62	0.0503	
		184	1.97	0.0459	
		162	2.52	0.0453	
		135	3.09	0.0418	
		88	4.47	0.0384	
		81	4.62	0.0370	
42.6		225	1.67	0.0726	
		204	2.24	0.0685	
		189	2.82	0.0700	
		166	3.28	0.0614	

continued

c_1, %	T_1, °K	T_2, °K	$\Delta\lambda$, %	K_T	Ref.
		151	3.89	0.0619	
		132	4.54	0.0596	
		83	6.21	0.0508	
		80	6.36	0.0505	
		H_2-D_2			
56.9	417	293	1.73	0.0489	271
	480		2.27	0.0460	
	585		3.06	0.0443	
	690		3.85	0.0450	
10	373	288	0.37	0.0143	266
20			0.68	0.0264	
30			0.92	0.0357	
40			1.07	0.0415	
50			1.11	0.0430	
60			1.07	0.0415	
70			0.94	0.0364	
80			0.73	0.0283	
90			0.42	0.0163	
65.5	293	234	0.81	0.0360	271
		194	1.61	0.0391	
		92	4.30	0.0372	
88.2		20	4.2	0.0110	260
86.6		90	1.6	0.0136	
76.0		90	3.0	0.0255	
76.7		69	4.4	0.0305	
66.0		20	8.3	0.0217	
54.3		20	8.7	0.0228	
52.4		90	5.6	0.0476	
53.1		69	6.8	0.0471	
41.9		20	7.1	0.0186	
38.4		90	5.6	0.0476	
38.6		69	6.0	0.0416	
		H_2-CO_2			
5.8	320	290	0.12	0.0121	264
	370		0.29	0.0119	
	414		0.43	0.0121	
	452		0.58	0.0132	
	499		0.70	0.0129	
	548		0.82	0.0129	
11.8	317	289	0.23	0.0250	
	365		0.53	0.0228	
	373		0.64	0.0250	
	417		0.82	0.0224	
	459		1.07	0.0233	
	502		1.30	0.0235	
	530		1.47	0.0243	
	557		1.60	0.0244	
24.3	317	288	0.32	0.0232	
	368		1.00	0.0244	
	378		1.12	0.0414	
	405		1.38	0.0406	
	443		1.71	0.0398	
	488		2.22	0.0422	
	518		2.45	0.0418	
	570		2.91	0.0427	
65	318	291	0.59	0.0679	
	370		1.80	0.0754	
	372		1.89	0.0775	
	410		2.57	0.0756	
	449		3.21	0.0742	
	488		3.72	0.0721	
	514		4.14	0.0729	

c_1, %	T_1, °K	T_2, °K	$\Delta\lambda$, %	K_T	Ref.
	547		4.53	0.0719	
53	305	288	0.34	0.0618	273
	314		0.62	0.0713	
	321		0.75	0.0695	
	330		0.99	0.0713	
	343		1.26	0.0720	
	350		1.37	0.0710	
	367		1.69	0.0693	
	388		2.07	0.0693	
	398		2.24	0.0697	
	414		2.50	0.0693	
	430		2.81	0.0702	
	445		3.20	0.0739	
	457		3.36	0.0731	
	472		3.63	0.0705	
	488		3.98	0.0755	
	516		4.44	0.0760	
	538		4.78	0.0765	
	561		5.14	0.0773	
54.3	353	300	1.27	0.0780	263
	371		1.33	0.0628	
	404		2.00	0.0669	
	415		2.27	0.0701	
	419		2.50	0.0749	
	435		2.64	0.0708	
	454		3.14	0.0759	
	492		4.00	0.0808	
	561		5.20	0.0832	
	597		5.82	0.0845	
	612		6.00	0.0841	
	717		7.66	0.0881	
	836		9.66	0.0922	
	863		9.87	0.0934	
	882		10.00	0.0929	
42.9	759	273	6.94	0.0681	267
50.0	753		8.01	0.0687	
54.4	759		8.68	0.0851	
59.9	748		8.60	0.0855	
66.9	767		8.40	0.0815	
72.3	755		7.19	0.0806	
86.2	766		5.45	0.0529	
48.1	393	293	1.61	0.0552	272
	443		2.32	0.0560	
37.3	393		1.37	0.0470	
	443		2.02	0.0488	
88.6	393		0.85	0.0291	
	443		1.23	0.0297	
18.4	284	197	1.18	0.0322	265
		202	1.06	0.0311	
		206	1.00	0.0311	
		212	0.91	0.0312	
		221	0.78	0.0315	
		234	0.63	0.0326	
		239	0.54	0.0314	
		256	0.34	0.0327	
34	285	197	1.74	0.0473	
		201	1.69	0.0488	
		208	1.53	0.0486	
		213	1.42	0.0490	
		219	1.29	0.0492	
		225	1.14	0.0485	
		234	0.96	0.0485	
45.2	286	197	2.34	0.0628	

continued

c_1, %	T_1, °K	T_2, °K	$\Delta\lambda$, %	K_T	Ref.
		198	2.30	0.0625	
		202	2.09	0.0603	
		208	1.97	0.0620	
		213	1.82	0.0620	
		223	1.55	0.0625	
		229	1.41	0.0613	
		235	1.28	0.0657	
3.5	373	283	0.16	0.0058	269
8.4			0.43	0.0156	
13.6			0.68	0.0246	
15.7			0.83	0.0301	
19.2			0.95	0.0344	
22.2			1.15	0.0417	
23.0			1.18	0.0428	
24.4			1.21	0.0439	
28.3			1.43	0.0518	
32.8			1.56	0.0565	
34.0			1.54	0.0558	
37.1			1.74	0.0631	
42.1			1.94	0.0703	
46.7			1.99	0.0722	
63.5			2.18	0.0790	
71.4			2.10	0.0762	
78.0			1.95	0.0707	
80.0			1.83	0.0663	
54.3	670	293	6.57	0.0795	274
	604		5.54	0.0766	
	525		4.51	0.0775	
	490		3.97	0.0773	
	478		3.77	0.0768	
	431		2.88	0.0746	
	385		1.95	0.0712	
	362		1.51	0.0712	
	347		1.15	0.0677	
	316		0.51	0.0671	
	293	250	0.91	0.0573	
		224	1.53	0.0573	
		217	1.56	0.0522	
		197	2.16	0.0546	
50.89	676	299	7.04	0.0865	275
53.22	373	302	1.52	0.0717	
	477		3.29	0.0723	
	487		3.51	0.0738	
	487		3.53	0.0752	
	531		4.63	0.0822	
	583		5.46	0.0831	
	639		6.37	0.0871	
	681		7.22	0.0884	
	737		8.05	0.0904	
		N_2-CO_2			
76.5	367	284	0.25	0.0980	264
	405		0.40	0.0113	
	458		0.53	0.0111	
	521		0.73	0.0120	
59.4	326	282	0.24	0.0166	
	371		0.58	0.0212	
	412		0.68	0.0181	
	442		0.95	0.0209	
	493		1.19	0.0214	
	500		1.13	0.0197	
88.6	378	284	0.17	0.0597	
	418		0.26	0.0672	
	473		0.33	0.0647	
	475		0.38	0.0741	
	531		0.48	0.0769	
39.3	309	288	0.08	0.0116	
	322		0.11	0.0102	
	338		0.20	0.0124	
	354		0.23	0.0111	
	390		0.37	0.0123	
	402		0.42	0.0126	
	422		0.49	0.0128	
3.7	373	283	0.04	0.0015	269
12.5			0.13	0.0047	
17.6			0.19	0.0069	
26.9			0.28	0.0101	
35.3			0.37	0.0134	
40.6			0.39	0.0141	
44.9			0.41	0.0149	
45.1			0.40	0.0145	
49.8			0.42	0.0152	
57.0			0.41	0.0149	
67.2			0.36	0.0130	
80.8			0.20	0.0072	
92.9			0.09	0.0033	
			$He-CO_2$		
38.0	764	273	8.41	0.0818	267
52.2	763		9.80	0.0956	
62.3	758		10.23	0.1001	
66.6	750		10.30	0.1020	
75.4	760		9.51	0.0930	
78.8	765		8.90	0.0863	
			$CO-CO_2$		
11.8	373	283	0.13	0.0047	269
26.4			0.27	0.0098	
32.1			0.33	0.0120	
39.9			0.40	0.0145	
44.6			0.40	0.0145	
50.3			0.42	0.0152	
51.2			0.43	0.0156	
59.8			0.40	0.0145	
67.8			0.34	0.0123	
77.0			0.26	0.0094	
			N_2-N_2O		
45	307	288	0.09	0.0141	273
	318		0.11	0.0111	
	335		0.18	0.0118	
	353		0.23	0.0114	
	373		0.33	0.0119	
	389		0.37	0.0124	
16.3	373	283	0.16	0.0058	269
24.4			0.22	0.0080	
34.7			0.31	0.0112	
39.3			0.34	0.0123	
41.0			0.35	0.0127	
41.0			0.36	0.0130	
45.6			0.39	0.0141	
49.0			0.39	0.0141	
54.8			0.38	0.0138	
56.6			0.38	0.0138	
59.6			0.37	0.0134	
72.6			0.27	0.0098	
84.1			0.16	0.0058	

continued

c_1, %	T_1, °K	T_2, °K	$\Delta\lambda$, %	K_T	Ref.
			$CO-N_2O$		
11.4	373	283	0.11	0.0040	269
23.0			0.21	0.0076	
33.3			0.32	0.0116	
40.8			0.36	0.0130	
47.8			0.39	0.0141	
51.7			0.40	0.0145	
55.3			0.40	0.0145	
62.0			0.35	0.0127	
68.0			0.31	0.0112	
80.7			0.20	0.0072	
			O_2-CO_2		
20.0	373	283	0.20	0.0073	269
32.9			0.32	0.0116	
39.8			0.36	0.0130	
43.3			0.38	0.0138	
45.5			0.40	0.0145	
47.0			0.38	0.0138	
49.4			0.40	0.0145	
53.8			0.39	0.0141	
55.8			0.39	0.0141	
57.3			0.39	0.0141	
58.5			0.39	0.0141	
61.1			0.37	0.0134	
68.7			0.32	0.0116	
76.6			0.28	0.0101	
79.6			0.29	0.0105	
87.5			0.20	0.0073	
90.4			0.17	0.0062	
			O_2-N_2O		
17.1	373	283	0.16	0.0058	269
23.1			0.24	0.0087	
27.0			0.28	0.0101	
33.3			0.35	0.0127	
35.0			0.38	0.0138	
38.6			0.38	0.0138	
42.4			0.39	0.0141	
46.1			0.39	0.0141	
47.9			0.39	0.0141	
50.2			0.41	0.0149	
52.9			0.40	0.0145	
57.9			0.40	0.0145	
64.5			0.37	0.0134	
80.0			0.25	0.0091	
85.7			0.20	0.0073	
93.8			0.13	0.0047	
			H_2-N_2O		
55.3	312	288	0.55	0.0618	273
	327		0.88	0.0691	
	339		1.18	0.0724	
	368		1.69	0.0693	
	379		1.89	0.0690	
	398		2.25	0.0758	
	401		2.38	0.0723	
	414		2.54	0.0698	
	415		2.67	0.0729	
	431		2.88	0.0715	
	447		3.18	0.0723	
	461		3.45	0.0703	
	493		4.08	0.0762	
	503		4.25	0.0763	
	520		4.47	0.760	
35	288	195	1.68	0.0432	265
		207	1.43	0.0435	
		220	1.18	0.0442	
		228	0.98	0.0419	
		244	0.72	0.0434	
42.5	286	187	2.02	0.0478	
		193	1.87	0.0475	
		198	1.81	0.0492	
		213	1.49	0.0507	
		230	1.08	0.0495	
		235	0.98	0.0503	
		243	0.84	0.0522	
59	287	187	2.31	0.0540	
		199	2.03	0.0555	
		207	1.81	0.0559	
		220	1.47	0.0534	
		234	1.13	0.0560	
2.0	377	283	0.12	0.0044	
9.4			0.45	0.0163	
11.1			0.57	0.0206	
12.5			0.61	0.0221	
18.7			0.93	0.0337	
25.6			1.24	0.0449	
31.0			1.44	0.0522	
36.4			1.58	0.0573	
38.1			1.63	0.0591	
40.8			1.71	0.0620	
43.9			1.83	0.0663	
50.1			1.93	0.0700	
53.2			1.99	0.0721	
61.0			2.07	0.0751	
69.0			2.02	0.0732	
72.7			1.97	0.0714	
78.6			1.88	0.0681	
83.5			1.52	0.0551	
			$H_2-C_2H_4$		
17	288	183	1.35	0.0298	265
		187	1.23	0.0288	
		199	1.08	0.0294	
		208	0.99	0.0303	
		215	0.90	0.0310	
		228	0.68	0.0291	
		239	0.54	0.0290	
28	287	175	2.14	0.0435	
		180	2.07	0.0446	
		189	1.90	0.0457	
		202	1.61	0.0460	
		213	1.36	0.0458	
		223	1.15	0.0458	
		242	0.82	0.0483	
58.5		175	3.27	0.0663	
		180	3.10	0.0667	
		176	3.19	0.0654	
		192	2.70	0.0675	
		201	2.38	0.0669	
		222	1.74	0.0680	
		225	1.66	0.0680	
5.4	373	283	0.24	0.0087	269
10.5			0.47	0.0170	
17.7			0.79	0.0286	
25.1			1.11	0.0402	
29.0			1.28	0.0464	

continued

c_1, %	T_1, °K	T_2, °K	$\Delta\lambda$, %	K_T	Ref.
39.6			1.60	0.0580	
48.2			1.73	0.0627	
58.3			2.16	0.0783	
64.4			2.40	0.0870	
74.5			2.34	0.0848	
74.8			2.28	0.0826	
82.0			2.23	0.0808	
84.6			1.69	0.0613	
85.1			1.52	0.0551	
89.6			1.37	0.0497	
			H_2-O_2		
33.8	294	90	4.00	0.0339	270
34.3		66	4.90	0.0329	
48.2		90	5.50	0.0465	
48.9		66	6.60	0.0443	
63.1		90	6.00	0.0508	
63.6		66	6.80	0.0456	
73.7		90	5.30	0.0449	
74.1		66	5.70	0.0382	
84.6		90	3.70	0.0313	
84.8		66	3.80	0.0255	
			H_2-N_2		
40.2	292	90	6.30	0.0537	270
40.9		64	7.60	0.0501	
50.0		90	7.20	0.0614	
50.4		77	8.00	0.0447	
50.8		64	8.40	0.0555	
51.0		55	8.30	0.0495	
57.4		90	7.40	0.0631	
58.1		64	8.50	0.0561	
62.8		90	7.40	0.0631	
63.1		77	7.50	0.0419	
63.5		64	8.10	0.0535	
63.8		55	8.10	0.0483	
70.6		90	6.50	0.0554	
70.9		77	7.00	0.0391	
71.5		55	7.50	0.0447	
77.4		90	5.60	0.0477	
77.7		77	5.90	0.0329	
78.0		64	6.30	0.0416	
78.1		55	6.50	0.0387	
82.4		77	5.40	0.0301	
82.9		55	5.70	0.0340	
81.3		90	5.00	0.0426	
82.3		64	5.70	0.0376	
90.3		90	3.40	0.0290	
90.5		77	3.70	0.0206	
90.7		64	3.90	0.0257	
90.8		55	3.90	0.0232	
90.3		90	3.40	0.0290	
90.5		77	3.70	0.0206	
90.7		54	3.90	0.0231	
90.8		55	3.90	0.0232	
			H_2-CO		
39.9	293	90	5.60	0.0476	270
40.2		66	6.20	0.0416	
51.7		90	6.60	0.0561	
52.3		66	7.00	0.0470	
62.6		90	6.60	0.0561	
63.1		66	7.00	0.0470	
73.7		90	5.70	0.0484	
74.1		66	6.20	0.0416	
81.7		90	4.50	0.0382	
82.1		66	4.90	0.0329	
88.7		90	3.20	0.0272	
89.1		66	3.90	0.0262	
			H_2-Ne		
21.6	290	90	5.50	0.0471	
22.0		66	6.20	0.0419	
23.4		20	7.20	0.0270	
35.6		90	6.90	0.0591	
36.3		66	8.40	0.0568	
38.3		20	10.00	0.0375	
50.9		90	8.20	0.0702	
51.7		66	9.20	0.0622	
53.8		20	10.90	0.0409	
66.7		90	7.70	0.0659	
67.5		66	8.90	0.0602	
69.2		18	9.80	0.0353	
69.3		20	10.10	0.0378	
84.8		90	4.70	0.0402	
85.2		66	5.40	0.0365	
86.2		17	5.70	0.0201	
86.3		20	5.90	0.0221	
			H_2-He		
19.4	292	90	2.50	0.0213	270
19.8		65	3.50	0.0233	
21.3		20	5.90	0.0220	
32.3		90	3.40	0.0290	
32.8		65	4.60	0.0307	
35.0		20	8.20	0.0306	
44.8		90	4.00	0.0341	
44.8		65	5.40	0.0360	
50.5		90	4.60	0.0392	
51.1		65	5.80	0.0387	
53.7		20	9.90	0.0370	
65.4		90	3.70	0.0317	
65.0		65	5.00	0.0334	
68.4		20	9.20	0.0344	
81.8		90	2.50	0.0213	
81.9		65	3.20	0.0213	
83.3		20	5.40	0.0202	
78.8	290	228	0.50	0.0209	
66.2			0.90	0.0377	
52.0			1.20	0.0503	
46.6			1.10	0.0461	
26.0			1.00	0.0419	
89.0	291	90	1.60	0.0136	
67.4			4.10	0.0349	
65.3			4.10	0.0349	
45.4			4.70	0.0400	
32.8	290		3.90	0.0334	
17.8	288		2.30	0.0198	
86.4	291	77	2.90	0.0219	
65.5	290		4.40	0.0332	
47.7	291		5.20	0.0392	
43.4	288		4.80	0.0364	
41.4	289		4.80	0.0364	
18.6	288		3.40	0.0258	
54.0	290	288	1.20	0.0502	
	291	90	4.44	0.0379	
	290	77	4.99	0.0377	

continued

c_1, %	T_1, °K	T_2, °K	$\Delta\lambda$, %	K_T	Ref.
		He – He			
61.0	295	90	6.20	0.0522	270
62.1		66	8.50	0.0568	
61.0		90	6.20	0.0522	
62.1		66	8.50	0.0568	
		$H_2 - N_2$			
89.9	291	90	3.20	0.0273	276
81.0			5.00	0.0427	
66.7			6.40	0.0546	
57.1			6.20	0.0529	
49.4			6.10	0.0521	
40.1			5.50	0.0469	
24.5			4.00	0.0341	
		H_2 – Cl			
62.40	473	293	3.68	0.0768	277
	473		3.82	0.0798	
	613		5.31	0.0718	
	613		5.75	0.0778	
	673		6.31	0.0759	
	673		6.81	0.0820	
	773		7.07	0.0730	
	773		7.35	0.0759	
	923		8.50	0.0741	
	923		8.61	0.0751	
		$CO - CO_2$			
60.71	588	283	0.96	0.0137	277
	773		1.35	0.0139	
	1073		1.82	0.0140	
	1273		2.20	0.0150	
		$O_2 - CO_2$			
60.80	515	293	0.84	0.0149	277
	515		1.01	0.0179	
	515		1.01	0.0179	
	701		1.40	0.0161	
	876		1.75	0.0160	
	1034		2.02	0.0160	
	1034		2.14	0.0170	
	1250		2.32	0.0160	
		$H_2 - H_2S$			
45.95	433	293	2.51	0.0646	277
	538		4.19	0.0690	
	658		5.68	0.0705	
	738		6.18	0.0669	
	963		7.73	0.0651	
	1075		8.59	0.0662	
	1085		8.90	0.0680	
	1158		9.21	0.0671	
		$H_2 - CO_2$			
59.95	473	293	3.83	0.0800	277
	473		4.02	0.0840	
	580		5.79	0.0850	
	580		5.87	0.0862	
	698		7.29	0.0840	
	698		7.55	0.0871	
	798		8.42	0.0841	
	798		8.61	0.0860	
		$H_2 - CH_4$			
59.10	483	293	2.80	0.0541	277
	628		5.04	0.0662	
	773		6.57	0.0690	

Data on thermal diffusion at high temperatures calculated using the Usmanov method [278]

c_1, %	T_1, °K	T_2, °K	$\Delta\lambda$, %	K_T
		$CO - CO_2$		
10	373	283	0.14	0.0051
	650		0.44	0.0053
	1200		0.84	0.0058
	1900		1.17	0.0062
20	373	283	0.24	0.0087
	650		0.77	0.0093
	1200		1.49	0.0103
	1900		2.06	0.0108
30	373	283	0.32	0.0116
	650		1.03	0.0124
	1200		1.95	0.0135
	1900		2.57	0.0140
50	373	283	0.41	0.0148
	650		1.33	0.0160
	1200		2.45	0.0170
	2000		3.51	0.0180
70	373	283	0.31	0.0112
	650		0.90	0.0118
	1200		1.78	0.0124
	1900		2.45	0.0129
90	378		0.11	0.0040
	650	283	0.33	0.0041
	1200		0.64	0.0043
	1900		0.83	0.0044
		$O_2 - CO_2$		
10	373	283	0.10	0.0036
	650		0.30	0.0039
	1200		0.63	0.0044
	1900		0.88	0.0047
20	373	283	0.20	0.0072
	650		0.66	0.0079
	1273		1.25	0.0087
	1900		1.74	0.0092
30	373	283	0.30	0.0100
	650		0.89	0.0117
	1200		1.84	0.0128
	1900		2.54	0.0134
50	373	283	0.41	0.0148
	650		1.32	0.0159
	1200		2.49	0.0173
	1900		3.44	0.0181
70	373	283	0.35	0.0127
	650		1.17	0.0141
	1200		2.07	0.0144
	1900	283	2.86	0.0150
90	373	283	0.19	0.0069
	650		0.57	0.0070
	1200		1.05	0.073
	1900		1.43	0.075

continued

c_1, %	T_1, °K	T_2, °K	$\Delta\lambda$, %	K_T
		N_2-CO_2		
10	400	283	0,17	0.0049
	700		0,47	0.0052
	1200		0,80	0,0055
	2000		1,17	0.0060
20	400		0,29	0,0084
	700		0,85	0.0094
	1200		1.40	0.0097
	2000		2,00	0.0102
30	400	283	0.42	0.0122
	700		1.15	0.0127
	1200		1.98	0.0138
	2000		2.78	0.0142
50	400		0.52	0.0151
	700		1.46	0.0161
	1200		2.50	0.0173
	2000		3.55	0.0182
70	400		0,44	0.0128
	700		1,18	0,0130
	1200		1,91	0.0133
	2000		2.73	0,0140
90	400	283	0,16	0.0046
	700		0.45	0,0050
	1200		0,74	0,0051
	2000		1.05	0.0054
		H_2-CO_2		
10	400	293	0.76	0,0245
	700		2.17	0.0250
	1200		3,72	0.0264
	2000		5,34	0.0278
20	400	293	1,32	0.0425
	700		3.77	0.0434
	1200		6,53	0.0464
	2000		9.43	0.0492
30	400	293	1.80	0.0580
	700		5.22	0.0601
	1200		8.49	0.0603
	2000		12.82	0.0668
40	400	293	2.24	0.0722
	700		6.36	0.0732
	1200		10.89	0,0773
	2000		15.45	0.0805
50	400	293	2.56	0.0824
	700		7.21	0.0829
	1200		12.25	0.0870
	2000		17.37	0.0908
60	400	293	2.64	0.0818
	700		7.47	0.0859
	1200		12.54	0.0891
	2000		17.82	0.0929
70	400	293	2.46	0.0792
	700		7.02	0.0807
	1200		11.69	0.0830
	1900		16.51	0.0861
80	400	293	2.03	0.0654
	700		5.79	0.0656
	1200		9.57	0.0680
	2000		13.54	0.0706
90	400	293	1.34	0,0432
	700		3.75	0,0433
	1200		6.13	0.0436
	2000		8.64	0.0450

Chapter 13

THERMOPHYSICAL PROPERTIES OF GAS MIXTURES AND SOLUTIONS

VISCOSITY OF BINARY GAS MIXTURES

Viscosity $\eta \cdot 10^6$ (g/cm · s) of mixtures given at a pressure of 1 atmosphere; concentration given in volume-percent; η_1 –viscosity of lighter gas [154]

Mixture	T, °K	Concentration of heavier gas					η_2/η_1
		0	25	50	75	100	
H_2—D_2	293.1	88.6	98.4	107.8	115.5	123.0	1.39
	229.0	75.7	83.8	91.4	98.2	104.3	1.38
	196.0	67.6	75.0	81.8	87.9	93.6	1.38
	90.1	38.6	42.8	46.7	50.1	53.3	1.38
	71.5	32.5	35.8	38.9	41.7	44.4	1.37
	20.4	10.9	11.7	12.4	13.1	13.7	1.26
	14.4	8.0	8.5	9.0	9.5	10.0	1.25
H_2—HD	293.1	88.3	93.1	97.9	102.4	106.9	1.21
	229.0	74.5	78.9	83.2	87.2	91.0	1.22
	196.0	67.0	70.8	74.6	78.2	81.6	1.22
	90.1	39.2	41.4	43.6	45.6	47.5	1.21
	71.5	32.6	34.5	36.2	37.9	39.5	1.21
	20.4	11.1	11.5	11.8	12.1	12.4	1.12
	14.4	7.9	8.1	8.4	8.6	8.8	1.11
HD—D_2	293.1	107.5	111.7	115.9	119.9	124.0	1.15
	229.0	91.0	94.6	98.1	101.5	104.8	1.15
	196.0	82.2	85.2	88.3	91.2	94.0	1.14
	90.1	47.4	49.0	50.8	52.4	54.0	1.14
	71.5	39.3	40.6	42.0	43.4	44.7	1.11
	20.4	12.7	13.1	13.4	13.8	14.1	1.10
	14.4	9.1	9.4	9.7	9.9	10.0	

H_2—O_2 [286]

T, °K \ % H_2 →	0	20	40	60	70	75	80	85	90	95	100
300	205.7	201.1	193.5	178.8	165.3	155.2	145.0	134.4	122.0	105.5	88.9
400	256.8	250.0	238.1	219.9	204.9	193.5	179.9	156.7	147.7	128.0	108.7
500	301.7	293.7	279.2	256.3	236.6	223.0	218.0	187.8	170.5	148.9	125.9
550	322.0	314.0	298.0	278.3	252.0	237.3	221.1	199.1	183.8	158.9	138.1

*Thermal conductivity of non-aqueous solutions, multicomponent gas mixtures and heat capacities of aqueous solutions from Refs. [298, 302–305, 316, 372, 373, (72, 73) (72, 301)]

H_2—Ar [287]

t, °C \ % H_2 →	0	20	40	60	70	80	90	100
20	221.1	217.4	208.8	192.3	177.7	156.8	128.9	87.5
100	268.4	263.3	252.7	232.8	213.9	185.0	150.5	102.9
200	320.8	312.2	298.6	274.0	254.8	225.2	184.1	121.1
250	344.8	336.9	321.3	293.3	271.0	238.7	194.4	129.6

H_2—NO [289]

t, °C \ % NO →	0	10	20	30	40	60	80	100
0	84.9	127.2	140.3	149.9	156.6	167.2	174.0	179.7

H_2—N_2O [288]

T, °K \ % H_2 →	0	20	40	60	80	90	95	100
300	148.8	148.7	147.9	145.1	137.6	124.5	105.6	89.1
400	194.3	193.9	192.2	185.2	172.1	152.4	136.7	108.1
500	235.5	233.9	230.1	225.3	202.2	173.9	152.6	125.6
550	255.5	254.1	250.4	238.8	215.9	189.8	166.3	134.1

H_2—He [287]

t, °C \ % H_2 →	0	20	40	60	80	100
20	197.4	172.4	148.8	126.7	106.5	87.5
100	232.0	203.6	175.9	149.3	124.9	102.9
200	271.5	237.7	205.1	174.4	146.7	121.1
250	290.3	255.7	219.8	186.8	156.9	129.6

H_2—Ne [52]

t, °C \ % H_2 →	0	20	40	60	80	90	95	100
20	309.2	286.7	258.9	210.7	160.8	129.6	110.0	87.5
100	362.3	332.9	298.7	248.1	191.2	149.9	128.8	102.9
200	422.0	392.7	348.6	288.4	219.9	174.8	146.7	121.1
250	450.1	417.9	370.8	311.2	236.8	190.5	159.7	129.6

H_2—N_2 [291]

t, °C \ % H_2 →	0	20	40	60	70	80	90	95	100
−78	126.3	124.6	121.0	114.5	105.9	92.8	78.2	72.9	67.6
−38	146.4	144.0	139.1	130.9	123.2	112.7	96.5	86.8	75.4
19	173.9	170.3	164.9	154.4	145.1	132.9	114.8	101.2	87.4
100	208.4	204.9	196.9	182.5	171.4	154.9	132.9	118.7	103.0
200	246.1	240.0	230.6	214.2	201.2	182.0	155.7	139.8	121.2
250	262.9	256.3	246.6	230.8	215.9	195.1	167.5	150.1	129.7

H_2—CO [291]

t, °C \ % H_2 →	0	20	40	60	70	80	90	95	100
−78	126.4	124.2	122.5	114.1	106.5	96.1	83.9	75.9	67.6
−38	147.6	145.7	141.1	131.0	123.6	111.3	96.0	86.1	75.4
19	174.5	171.9	165.1	153.3	144.6	130.2	111.8	100.5	87.4
100	208.5	204.3	196.9	180.9	167.5	150.4	129.1	116.6	103.0
200	246.6	240.0	230.1	215.9	201.6	182.1	156.9	140.8	121.2
250	263.6	256.5	246.5	230.2	214.7	194.4	167.3	149.2	129.7

H_2—CO_2 [288]

T, °K \ % H_2 →	0	20	40	60	70	75	80	85	90	95	100
300	149.3	150.3	150.2	147.7	143.6	140.0	135.5	129.2	121.5	107.7	89.1
400	194.4	195.9	194.4	188.1	181.7	176.5	170.0	161.7	148.9	128.8	108.1
500	235.3	236.1	232.0	223.9	214.7	207.7	200.3	188.9	173.9	152.4	125.6
550	255.6	254.1	251.4	245.7	233.9	225.3	213.9	201.5	183.7	160.0	134.1

H_2—HCl [289]

t, °C \ % H_2 тФ →	0	20	40	60	80	90	95	100
21	143.4	146.1	148.4	146.5	134.6	116.6	103.8	89.5
54	160.0	162.5	163.4	159.8	147.5	125.1	111.1	96.3
99	183.2	186.2	185.4	181.3	162.6	144.3	128.9	105.5
154	209.5	211.6	207.1	201.2	179.7	156.6	136.8	116.3
200	230.2	231.3	228.1	220.5	193.9	167.0	149.1	124.3
250	253.6	252.9	249.2	243.3	210.9	182.6	163.1	132.2

H_2—SO_2 [289]

t, °C \ % H_2 →	0	20	40	60	70	80	90	95	100
17	125.9	129.3	133.4	136.6	137.5	132.6	120.3	109.3	88.8
45	138.6	142.6	146.7	149.1	149.2	144.3	129.1	114.9	94.5
70	149.8	154.1	157.5	160.2	159.9	154.1	138.2	122.6	99.4
92	159.9	163.2	167.6	168.1	167.7	161.5	147.4	130.5	103.7
124	173.9	177.8	180.8	181.2	179.5	173.5	155.5	137.6	110.2
159	189.7	192.6	195.0	195.6	193.1	184.5	162.1	143.1	116.9
199	207.1	210.2	212.0	211.8	208.5	201.8	182.6	162.3	123.7

H_2—NH_3 [288]

t °C \ % H_2 →	0	20	40	60	70	80	90	100
20	98.2	103.8	108.2	109.8	108.9	106.9	100.5	87.6
100	127.9	132.4	134.7	134.1	133.0	128.7	120.5	103.3
200	164.6	167.8	168.0	164.9	161.2	154.5	143.4	121.3
250	181.3	183.1	188.1	178.8	173.7	165.3	150.9	129.6

H_2—CH_4 [288]

t, °C \ % H_2 →	0	20	40	60	80	90	100
20	108.7	110.0	110.0	108.5	103.2	98.1	87.6
100	133.1	134.2	134.8	130.6	122.7	115.3	103.3
200	160.3	161.5	159.8	155.2	144.5	135.9	121.3
250	172.5	172.2	171.1	166.2	153.9	144.1	129.6

H_2—C_2H_4 [292]

t, °C \ % C_2H_4 →	0	10	20	40	60	80	90	100
−78	67.0	72.4	75.3	77.2	74.2	73.1	72.2	71.8
−40	74.0	82.2	85.7	86.8	85.3	84.0	82.9	81.8
− 1	83.0	94.3	98.1	100.1	98.4	96.5	94.5	94.3
20	87.3	101.1	106.2	108.0	106.3	103.9	102.1	101.2
55	94.3	108.7	115.1	118.1	116.8	114.9	113.4	112.2
100	103.0	118.6	126.7	131.2	130.9	129.2	128.0	126.4
150	112.3	132.6	140.1	145.4	146.0	143.9	142.5	140.8
200	121.1	141.2	152.3	159.3	158.9	157.5	156.3	154.7
250	129.4	150.8	161.6	170.0	170.9	170.0	169.2	168.1

H_2—C_2H_6 [288]

t, °C \ % H_2 →	0	20	40	60	80	85	90	95	100
20	90.9	94.1	97.5	100.2	99.9	99.3	97.0	92.8	87.6
100	114.2	118.2	120.1	122.9	121.2	118.8	116.1	110.7	103.3
200	140.9	144.1	146.2	147.1	144.0	141.2	137.7	131.2	121.3
250	152.6	156.2	158.3	159.0	153.5	151.1	148.5	140.9	129.6

H_2—C_3H_6 (propylene) [52]

t, °C \ % C_3H_6 →	0	10	20	40	60	80	90	100
20	87.6	96.7	100.0	97.3	92.1	89.1	86.2	84.4
100	103.1	113.9	121.7	120.1	114.8	112.3	110.4	107.6
200	121.0	134.6	144.4	144.5	141.7	138.2	136.7	133.9
250	129.6	146.1	154.5	158.2	154.8	150.4	148.8	146.7

H_2—C_3H_6 [288]

T, °K \ % H_2 →	0	20	40	60	80	85	90	95	100
300	81.7	84.1	88.2	93.8	99.4	99.1	98.0	95.2	89.1
400	107.0	109.5	114.3	118.1	122.5	122.4	121.3	116.7	108.1
500	130.8	132.5	138.0	142.9	146.1	143.2	140.6	135.0	125.6
550	142.2	143.7	148.3	154.1	157.2	154.1	151.8	143.9	134.7

H_2—C_4H_8 (2-butene) [52]

t, °C \ % C_4H_8 →	0	10	20	40	60	80	100
20	87.6	93.4	94.1	88.8	82.2	77.9	74.7
100	103.1	112.1	114.6	108.7	102.9	98.2	94.4
200	121.0	133.7	136.0	133.5	128.7	123.6	119.2
250	129.6	141.8	148.7	145.2	140.0	135.0	130.1

CO—O_2 [286]

T, °K \ % O_2 →	0	20	40	60	80	100
300	177.6	184.1	189.8	195.1	200.9	205.7
400	218.3	226.3	234.4	242.0	249.1	256.8
500	254.8	264.5	273.6	282.7	292.5	301.7

CO—N_2 [286]

T, °K \ % CO →	0	20	40	60	80	100
300	178.1	178.1	178.0	177.9	177.7	177.6
400	219.0	219.0	218.9	218.6	218.5	218.3
500	256.0	256.0	255.5	255.1	254.9	254.8
550	272.7	272.7	272.5	272.0	271.6	271.4

CO—C_2H_4 [286]

T, °K \ % C_2H_4 →	0	20	40	60	80	100
300	177.6	160.5	144.3	128.9	115.7	103.3
400	218.3	199.5	179.8	162.3	147.1	134.2
500	254.8	234.3	213.9	194.9	177.9	162.2
550	271.4	249.1	228.4	208.7	191.0	175.3

CO_2—air [293]

t, °C \ % air →	0	10	20	40	60	80	100
17.0	145.5	148.9	152.3	159.1	166.0	173.0	179.7

CO_2—SO_2 [293]

t, °C \ % SO_2 →	0	10	20	40	60	80	90	100
15.8	145.8	144.5	142.8	138.8	134.6	129.9	127.1	124.3

CO_2—HCl [293]

% CO_2 → / t, °C	0	10	20	40	60	80	90	100
18.0	142.6	144.0	145.3	147.3	148.3	148.1	147.6	146.4

CO_2—N_2O [288]

% CO_2 → / T, °K	0	20	40	60	80	100
300	148.8	148.8	148.9	148.7	148.5	149.3
400	194.3	194.3	194.3	194.5	194.4	194.4
500	235.5	235.6	235.6	235.6	235.4	235.3
550	255.5	255.5	255.5	255.6	255.6	255.6

CO—C_2H_4 [52]

% C_2H! → / T, °K	0	10	20	40	60	80	100
300	177.7	168.8	160.0	143.1	128.9	115.7	103.3
400	218.3	209.3	199.9	180.0	162.4	146.9	134.2
500	254.8	244.2	234.1	213.2	194.3	176.9	162.2
550	271.4	260.3	249.2	238.1	209.1	190.9	175.3

CO_2—C_3H_8 [288]

% CO_2 → / T, °K	0	20	40	60	80	100
300	81.7	93.1	104.9	118.3	133.7	149.3
400	107.0	121.9	138.2	155.5	174.1	194.4
500	130.8	148.8	167.0	190.4	210.3	235.3
550	142.2	161.4	180.9	205.1	228.9	255.6

Air–NH_3 [293]

% air → / t, °C	0	10	20	40	60	80	90	100
15.0	97.5	108.6	118.8	138.4	155.5	169.1	174.1	178.7

Air–H_2S [293]

% air → / t, °C	0	10	20	40	60	80	90	100
17.2	124.3	131.4	138.5	151.5	163.4	173.2	177.1	180.2

Air–water vapor at $p \leqslant p_s$ [370]

% H_2O → / t, °C	0	10	20	30	40	50	60	70	80	90	100
20	181.4										
30	186.5										
40	190.8										
50	195.5	191.4									
60	200.1	196.0	190.4								
70	204.6	200.5	195.0	188.0							
80	209.1	205.1	199.5	192.5	184.3	175.0					
90	213.5	209.5	203.5	196.9	188.7	179.2	168.9	157.7			
100	218.0	214.0	208.4	201.4	193.1	183.6	173.2	161.8	149.9	137.5	124.7
110	222.3	218.4	212.8	205.8	197.5	187.9	177.4	166.0	153.9	141.3	128.4
120	226.6	222.7	217.2	210.1	201.8	192.2	181.6	170.1	157.9	145.2	132.1
130	230.9	227.1	221.6	214.5	206.1	196.4	185.8	174.2	161.9	149.0	135.8
140	235.0	231.2	225.8	218.7	210.3	200.6	189.8	178.4	165.8	152.9	139.5
150	239.2	235.5	230.1	223.1	214.7	204.9	194.2	182.4	169.9	156.8	143.3

Air–HCl [289]

% air → / t, °C	0	10	20	40	60	80	90	100
16.5	140.7	147.0	153.5	161.6	169.3	175.5	177.7	179.4

He—Ne [287]

% He → / t, °C	0	20	40	60	80	100
20	309.2	301.2	285.9	264.8	235.9	194.9
100	362.3	353.0	336.2	312.1	278.4	228.1
200	422.0	410.1	391.9	364.0	324.0	267.2
250	450.1	436.2	418.5	388.4	346.2	285.3

He—Ne [154]

% He → / T, °K	0	25	50	75	100	η_2/η_1
20.4	35.0	36.7	36.9	36.1	35.1	1.00
65.8	74.5	91.1	99.3	103.2	104.5	1.40
90.2	91.2	113.5	125.4	131.8	135.0	1.48
194.0	149.3	188.7	212.2	226.8	236.0	1.58
294.1	196.1	246.0	277.3	297.1	309.7	1.58

He—Ar [287]

% He → / t, °C	0	20	40	60	80	100
20	221.1	226.1	228.4	226.0	214.5	194.9
100	268.4	274.2	274.3	270.1	238.9	228.1
200	320.8	325.6	324.6	318.1	301.9	267.2
250	344.8	350.2	348.1	338.2	318.8	285.3

NH_3—CH_4 [293]

t, °C \ % NH_3 →	0	10	20	40	60	80	90	100
14.5	107.7	108.5	109.1	108.5	106.3	102.5	99.4	96.6

NH_3—O_2 [293]

t, °C \ % NH_3 →	0	20	40	60	80	100
20	202.3	187.1	168.4	147.5	124.3	98.2
100	244.0	227.7	206.9	182.9	156.2	127.9
200	290.2	271.9	249.1	223.7	195.4	164.6

NH_3—N_2 [288]

t, °C \ % NH_3 →	0	20	40	60	80	100
20	174.5	164.0	151.2	135.5	117.9	98.2
100	208.5	198.1	183.9	167.7	148.3	127.9
200	246.2	235.7	222.1	205.8	186.4	164.6
250	262.7	252.3	238.0	222.1	203.6	181.3

N_2—C_2H_4 [286]

T, °K \ % C_2H_4 →	0	20	40	60	80	100
300	178.1	160.0	142.9	122.4	114.6	103.3
400	219.0	197.9	180.0	163.1	147.1	134.8
500	256.0	232.7	212.8	197.2	176.9	162.2
550	272.7	249.5	227.5	207.7	189.5	175.3

Ne—Ar [287]

t, °C \ % Ar →	0	20	40	60	80	100
20	309.2	288.1	269.1	247.0	235.0	194.1
100	362.3	339.4	318.3	296.0	284.0	228.1
200	422.0	392.5	373.4	348.3	336.0	267.2
250	450.1	428.4	400.9	375.5	361.4	285.3

CH_4—C_2H_6 [288]

t, °C \ % C_2H_6 →	0	20	40	60	80	100
20	90.9	94.4	97.1	100.5	104.1	108.7
100	114.2	118.0	121.3	125.0	128.2	133.1
200	140.8	144.8	148.5	152.2	156.3	160.3
250	152.6	156.1	160.0	164.1	168.0	172.5

CH_4—C_3H_8 [288]

t, °C \ % CH_4 →	0	20	40	60	80	100
20	80.1	84.0	88.5	93.9	100.4	108.7
100	100.8	105.2	109.7	117.1	124.9	133.1
200	125.5	131.0	136.2	142.9	151.1	160.3
250	136.3	141.5	147.5	154.4	162.2	172.5

C_2H_4–air [293]

t, °C \ % C_2H_4 →	0	20	40	60	80	100
15,0	178.7	163.8	146.9	131.0	115.1	99.3
99,3	217.7	199.6	181.1	163.9	144.9	125.8

C_2H_4—NH_3 [288]

t, °C \ % C_2H_4 →	0	20	40	60	80	100
20	98.2	101.4	102.9	102.5	102.0	100.8
100	127.9	130.2	131.0	130.0	128.2	125.7
200	164.6	164.7	163.9	160.5	158.4	154.1
250	181.3	180.0	178.0	175.4	171.1	166.6

C_2H_4—O_2 [286]

t, °C \ % C_2H_4 →	0	20	40	60	80	100
20	201.9	177.7	155.0	134.5	116.3	101.0
50	218.1	192.5	168.5	145.4	127.5	110.7
100	243.3	215.0	189.3	166.7	145.0	126.2

C_2H_6—C_3H_8 [288]

t, °C \ % C_2H_6 →	0	20	40	60	80	100
20	80.1	82.2	84.2	86.9	88.8	90.9
100	100.8	103.1	106.3	108.5	111.4	114.2
200	125.3	128.8	131.5	134.6	137.7	140.8
250	136.3	139.0	142.5	146.1	149.2	152.6

C_3H_8—C_3H_6 (propylene) [289]

t, °C \ % C_3H_8 →	0	20	40	60	80	100
40	90.4	89.8	89.1	88.6	87.8	87.3
60	96.0	95.4	94.9	94.6	94.0	93.2
80	101.6	101.0	100.5	100.1	99.6	98.8
100	107.0	106.4	105.9	105.6	104.6	104.0

$NO—N_2$ [289]

% NO → / t, °C	0	20	40	60	80	100
20	174.7	175.5	180.0	182.9	185.5	188.2
100	208.4	212.9	216.6	220.4	224.1	227.2

$N_2—O_2$ [286]

% N_2 → / T, °K	0	20	40	60	80	100
300	205.7	200.2	194.8	189.9	184.1	178.1
400	256.8	249.9	242.1	234.9	227.5	219.0
500	301.7	292.5	283.4	274.8	265.0	256.0
550	322.0	313.0	303.1	292.9	283.2	272.7

$N_2O—C_3H_8$ [288]

% N_2O → / T, °K	0	20	40	60	80	100
300	81.7	92.1	104.3	118.1	133.9	148.8
400	107.0	121.1	137.0	154.8	173.1	194.3
500	130.8	147.5	166.2	187.5	209.2	235.5
550	142.2	160.9	180.4	202.9	228.6	255.6

Vapor of ethyl alcohol and water vapor [294]

% ethanol	Condensation temperature, °C	η, 10^{-6} g/cm · s		% ethanol	Condensation temperature, °C	η, 10^{-6} g/cm · s	
		at condensation temperature	at 100 °C			at condensation temperature	at 100 °C
0.0	100.0	125.5	125.5	69.8	79.51	111.6	118.3
9.0	97.71	125.1	125.8	83.4	78.51	108.8	116.3
17.4	95.17	123.3	125.2	91.9	78.0	107.7	113.9
25.7	92.5	122.0	123.8	96.8	78.0	107.0	111.4
37.4	88.62	118.4	122.6	100.0	78.0	101.6	108.0
54.0	82.72	114.9	119.7				

Vapor of methyl alcohol and water vapor [294]

% methanol	Condensation temperature, °C	η, 10^{-6} g/cm · s		% methanol	Condensation temperature, °C	η, 10^{-6} g/cm · s	
		at condensation temperature	at 100 °C			at condensation temperature	at 100 °C
0.0	100.0	125.5	125.5	69.0	76.73	118.0	126.8
15.0	96.39	124.8	126.1	85.0	70.1	114.6	124.9
36.5	89.73	122.5	126.5	98.0	65.22	111.2	122.8
52.5	83.89	120.7	126.7	100.0	64.61	109.7	122.3

Viscosity $\eta \cdot 10^6$ (g/cm · s) of binary gas mixtures at different temperatures and pressures (concentration given in volume percent) [52]

CH_4—C_3H_8

% C_3H_8	20.0						46.4				75.6			
p, atm \ t, °C →	75	100	125	150	200	250	100	150	200	250	100	150	200	250
1	116.9	124.1	131.0	137.7	150.4	162.0	115.2	128.4	140.7	151.8	106.4	119.3	131.5	142.7
20	118.5	126.3	133.2	139.5	152.2	163.5	120.9	132.0	143.5	154.0	113.5	124.5	135.0	145.5
40	121.7	130.0	136.2	141.7	154.7	165.2	127.0	137.5	147.0	156.5	124.5	131.5	140.0	150.0
60	126.5	133.8	139.6	145.0	157.5	167.2	137.0	143.4	150.7	160.2	141.7	141.8	147.5	155.6
80	130.8	138.4	144.0	148.6	160.9	169.5	146.5	150.5	156.5	163.4	202.0	158.0	156.2	163.2
100	136.3	143.4	148.5	152.5	163.4	172.0	159.0	159.3	162.3	168.8	260.5	183.0	167.0	171.0
120	143.7	149.5	153.1	156.7	167.3	174.5	173.6	169.2	169.5	174.6	305.5	211.0	181.5	182.5
140	152.0	157.1	160.1	162.5	171.5	177.7	190.7	179.0	177.3	180.4	343.3	242.0	201.0	196.0
160	161.7	165.0	167.4	168.5	176.1	181.7	208.5	191.5	184.5	187.2	378.7	271.5	223.0	210.5
180	171.7	173.3	173.7	175.0	181.1	185.6	226.5	201.8	192.2	194.0	410.8	298.0	247.0	225.5
200	184.0	184.0	183.0	182.3	186.7	189.1	242.5	212.3	200.9	201.8	438.5	323.0	269.3	240.0
300	241.0	232.7	226.0	221.7	215.7	214.7	318.6	273.5	247.3	240.1	555.4	430.7	364.7	313.0
400	290.1	278.5	267.0	260.0	248.0	242.6	384.5	331.4	297.5	281.3	651.5	518.6	446.3	381.5
500	335.7	320.9	307.5	298.0	281.5	270.1	446.0	385.4	343.2	321.1	731.3	593.7	516.5	445.6
600	377.7	360.5	347.2	335.0	315.3	298.3	502.5	438.5	388.3	360.8	808.0	664.0	583.0	510.0

C_2H_6—C_2H_4 [52]

% C_2H_6	18.65				50.1				64.6			
p, atm \ t, °C →	50	100	150	200	50	100	150	200	50	100	150	200
1	101.8	116.4	129.9	143.3	105.0	119.9	133.6	147.0	106.6	121.7	135.4	149.1
20	104.5	118.5	131.0	144.1	110.5	123.5	136.0	148.0	112.5	126.2	138.5	151.0
40	114.0	123.4	134.0	145.5	119.4	130.0	140.5	152.0	120.3	132.5	143.5	152.5
60	146.5	134.9	145.5	149.5	136.0	141.0	148.3	156.6	132.7	140.2	150.0	160.0
80	232.0	157.0	151.4	156.5	183.5	155.0	158.0	163.5	173.0	153.0	159.0	166.5
100	310.0	185.6	166.8	166.0	251.5	179.0	172.5	172.5	241.0	174.5	171.5	175.0
120	353.5	218.5	186.4	176.5	307.0	208.5	189.0	182.5	302.5	203.0	184.7	184.7
140	387.5	251.0	207.0	189.5	352.5	241.0	207.0	193.0	341.0	232.5	200.6	195.0
160	417.0	283.5	227.5	203.0	385.8	271.7	226.4	204.5	373.0	260.7	216.0	206.8
180	443.5	312.3	248.5	216.5	414.5	301.5	243.5	216.5	403.1	286.5	232.5	217.5
200	463.5	340.5	268.0	230.5	438.1	326.5	261.0	228.0	427.0	311.0	250.2	229.0
300	569.5	446.5	351.5	296.5	525.0	416.4	333.0	284.5	521.0	407.5	327.5	284.5
400	648.5	524.5	421.2	354.5	587.0	478.0	390.0	337.0	591.5	476.5	392.0	336.5
500	718.5	588.6	484.2	407.7	640.0	533.5	440.0	381.8	653.7	536.0	448.5	386.5
600	784.5	646.5	543.0	458.5					706.3	590.0	501.1	434.0

C_2H_6—C_3H_6 [52]

% C_2H_6	18.65			50.1			64.6		
p, atm \ t, °C →	100	150	200	100	150	200	100	150	200
1	111.9	125.4	138.5	110.3	123.9	136.9	108.9	122.5	135.4
20	113.5	126.5	139.5	112.4	127.5	140.0	110.4	123.3	137.0
40	116.5	129.5	142.0	118.0	132.5	144.0	119.8	128.0	139.5
60	129.0	136.5	147.5	129.5	141.0	150.0	175.0	141.0	147.3
80	161.5	149.0	155.5	190.0	155.5	159.5	287.0	173.0	159.2
100	239.0	170.5	166.0	291.0	186.0	174.0	389.0	233.0	181.0
120	301.5	203.5	180.5	348.0	224.0	192.5	444.0	288.0	207.0
140	345.5	235.5	196.0	395.0	262.0	212.5	488.0	333.5	237.0
160	382.0	267.0	213.0	435.0	301.0	233.5	524.5	374.0	267.0
180	413.5	295.0	231.5	469.5	337.5	255.0	559.0	410.0	295.0

continued

% C_2H_6	18.65			50.1			64.6		
t, °C → / p, atm	100	150	200	100	150	200	100	150	200
200	441.5	322.0	250.0	500.0	370.0	277.5	590.0	443.0	321.7
300	553.0	433.0	344.5	626.0	493.0	387.0	721.0	572.0	447.0
400	642.5	523.0	423.1	729.5	590.5	478.0	833.0	679.0	549.0
500	719.0	598.0	494.0	813.5	675.5	556.5	927.0	770.0	634.0
600	789.0	666.4	561.2	887.0	750.0	630.0	1006.0	850.0	712.0

N_2—He [338]
($\eta \cdot 10^6$, kg · s/m^2); r_i–volume fractions

t, °C → / p, kg/cm^3	0	100	200	300	400	500	600	700	800	1000
					$r_{N_2}=0.222$					
1	2.03	2.52	2.95	3.37	3.74	4.09	4.43	4.75	5.08	5.69
50	2.06	2.53	2.96	3.38	3.75	4.15	4.43	4.75	5.08	5.69
100	2.08	2.55	2.98	3.40	3.76	4.11	4.44	4.76	5.09	5.70
150	2.11	2.58	2.99	3.41	3.77	4.12	4.45	4.77	5.10	5.71
200	2.15	2.60	3.01	3.42	3.78	4.13	4.46	4.78	5.10	5.71
					$r_{N_2}=0.412$					
1	1.96	2.43	2.86	3.25	3.62	3.96	4.28	4.58	4.89	5.46
50	2.00	2.45	2.88	3.26	3.63	3.97	4.29	4.59	4.90	5.47
100	2.05	2.48	2.91	3.28	3.65	3.99	4.30	4.60	4.91	5.48
150	2.10	2.52	2.93	3.33	3.67	4.00	4.31	4.62	4.92	5.48
200	2.16	2.56	2.96	3.35	3.69	4.02	4.33	4.62	4.93	5.49
					$r_{N_2}=0.565$					
1	1.89	2.35	2.75	3.15	3.51	3.83	4.13	4.41	4.72	5.23
50	1.95	2.39	2.79	3.17	3.53	3.85	4.15	4.43	4.73	5.24
100	2.03	2.44	2.83	3.20	3.56	3.87	4.17	4.44	4.75	5.25
150	2.12	2.50	2.87	3.24	3.59	3.90	4.19	4.46	4.77	5.26
200	2.22	2.56	2.92	3.27	3.62	3.92	4.21	4.48	4.79	5.28
					$r_{N_2}=0.778$					
1	1.79	2.23	2.63	2.99	3.33	3.64	3.93	4.19	4.47	4.95
50	1.87	2.28	2.67	3.02	3.35	3.66	3.95	4.21	4.49	4.96
100	1.99	2.35	2.72	3.06	3.39	3.69	3.97	4.23	4.51	4.98
150	2.17	2.44	2.78	3.09	3.42	3.72	3.99	4.25	4.53	5.00
200	2.28	2.53	2.84	3.15	3.46	3.74	4.02	4.27	4.55	5.01

H_2—Ar [12, 295]
($\eta \cdot 10^8$, kg · s/m^2)

Mole fraction	p, atm → / t, °C	20	100	200	300	400	500
$r_{H_2}=0,8$; $r_{Ar}=0,2$	0	1515	1575	1645	1710	1795	1870
	15	1565	1625	1690	1755	1830	1905
	25	1605	1665	1730	1795	1865	1935
	50	1695	1750	1810	1865	1935	1995
	100	1875	1915	1965	2025	2070	2135
	200	2205	2235	2280	2320	2360	2400
	300	2510	2540	2570	2600	2640	2670
	400	2790	2815	2835	2875	2905	2935
	500	3060	3080	3105	3135	3155	3185
	650	3435	3455	3475	3495	3515	3535
	800	3805	3815	3835	3855	3875	3895

continued

Mole fraction	t, °C \ p, atm →	20	100	200	300	400	500
$r_{H_2}=0.6$; $r_{Ar}=0.4$	0	1850	1930	2055	2195	2375	2535
	15	1920	1995	2105	2250	2405	2560
	25	1970	2045	2150	2285	2430	2580
	50	2085	2150	2240	2360	2480	2625
	100	2310	2365	2440	2540	2640	2765
	200	2730	2770	2830	2890	2950	3050
	300	3110	3140	3190	3230	3290	3335
	400	3465	3495	3530	3570	3615	3660
	500	3795	3815	3850	3885	3920	3960
	650	4255	4280	4300	4335	4365	4395
	800	4705	4725	4745	4770	4795	4820
$r_{H_2}=0.4$; $r_{Ar}=0.6$	0	2005	2140	2365	2620	2905	3185
	15	2090	2210	2420	2660	2915	3175
	25	2145	2260	2460	2690	2925	3170
	50	2275	2375	2545	2745	2950	3170
	100	2530	2615	2745	2905	3100	3250
	200	2995	3060	3155	3265	3390	3525
	300	3415	3465	3535	3615	3710	3810
	400	3805	3845	3905	3985	4050	4125
	500	4170	4205	4255	4315	4375	4435
	650	4670	4700	4740	4785	4835	4890
	800	5156	5180	5215	5255	5295	5335
$r_{H_2}=0.2$; $r_{Ar}=0.8$	0	2090	2295	2690	3105	3605	3990
	15	2185	2370	2720	3105	3565	3965
	25	2240	2415	2755	3115	3545	3945
	50	2380	2535	2810	3125	3445	3790
	100	2655	2780	2995	3245	3495	3770
	200	3115	3220	3350	3525	3715	3920
	300	3595	3685	3775	3905	4075	4260
	400	4010	4065	4135	4260	4370	4490
	500	4390	4440	4510	4600	4695	4795
	650	4915	4955	5015	5080	5155	5235
	800	5415	5450	5500	5555	5610	5680

H_2—N_2 [12, 295]
($\eta \cdot 10^8$, kg · s/m²)

Mole fraction	t, °C \ p, atm →	20	100	200	300	400	500
$r_{H_2}=0.75$; $r_{N_2}=0.25$	0	1335	1370	1430	1500	1595	1670
	15	1380	1465	1465	1535	1620	1695
	25	1415	1450	1500	1565	1645	1710
	50	1495	1525	1565	1625	1695	1770
	100	1645	1670	1705	1750	1810	1870
	200	1935	1955	1980	2010	2050	2095
	300	2200	2215	2240	2260	2290	2320
	400	2445	2460	2480	2495	2520	2545
	500	2680	2690	2710	2720	2735	2760
	650	3005	3015	3030	3040	3055	3070
	800	3325	3330	3345	3355	3365	3380
$r_{H_2}=0.5$; $r_{N_2}=0.5$	0	1555	1630	1775	1915	2105	2305
	15	1605	1680	1810	1950	2120	2300
	25	1650	1715	1845	1975	2130	2285
	50	1740	1800	1915	2030	2165	2310
	100	1920	1970	2055	2155	2270	2380
	200	2255	2290	2355	2420	2510	2595

continued

Mole fraction	p, atm → / t, °C	20	100	200	300	400	500
$r_{H_2}=0.5$; $r_{N_2}=0.5$	300	2565	2595	2635	2690	2760	2825
	400	2850	2875	2910	2955	3010	3065
	500	3120	3140	3170	3205	3250	3295
	650	3490	3505	3530	3555	3590	3625
	800	3845	3865	3885	3905	3930	3960
$r_{H}=0.25$; $r_{N_2}=0.75$	0	1655	1805	2050	2285	2535	2660
	15	1715	1810	2085	2300	2570	2855
	25	1760	1890	2105	2315	2565	2850
	50	1830	1950	2105	2325	2550	2755
	100	2045	2145	2295	2445	2630	2800
	200	2405	2485	2585	2690	2830	2960
	300	2730	2790	2870	2955	3060	3160
	400	3030	3085	3150	3220	3305	3370
	500	3310	3355	3425	3470	3540	3610
	650	3695	3725	3780	3825	3885	3935
	800	4065	4095	4135	4175	4220	4265

THERMAL CONDUCTIVITY OF BINARY GAS MIXTURES

Thermal conductivity λ (10^{-4} W/m · deg) given at $p = 1$ bar, concentration in volume-percent

% He → / t, °C	0	10	20	30	40	50	60	70	80	90	100
0	51	90.2	136	191	257	338	441	576	758	1020	1430
50	59.9	105	158	221	296	413	508	661	868	1163	1605
100	68.5	120	179	250	336	441	573	744	975	1303	1791
150	77.0	134	200	279	374	491	637	826	1078	1430	1919
200	85.5	148	221	308	412	540	700	905	1186	1558	2128
250	93.8	163	242	337	450	588	762	984	1279	1686	2291
300	102.0	176	262	364	486	634	820	1058	1372	1814	2454
350	110.2	190	283	392	522	682	860	1132	1465	1931	2605
400	119	204	302	419	557	729	937	1210	1558	2047	2756
450	127	216	321	445	592	772	996	1279	1651	2153	2896
500	135	230	341	471	627	816	1051	1349	1744	2279	3047

He—Ar [315]

% He → / t, °C	0	20	40	60	80	100
0	163	267	402	587	877	1405

H_2—Ar [306]

% H_2 → / t, °C	0	18.0	40.0	60.0	80.2	100
0	163.4	305.8	527.8	783.0	1130.1	1692

H_2—D_2 [306]

% H_2 → / t, °C	0	18.7	39.5	49.6	65.5	80.2	100
0	1290	1354	1428	1468	1528	1600	1692

H_2—CO [306]

% H_2 → / t, °C	0	16.3	27.2	56.6	63.4	79.4	100
0	222.2	335.1	431.2	754.6	875.6	1130.1	1692

H_2—CO_2 [306]

% H_2 → / t, °C	0	14.2	35.5	50.0	75.0	90.1	100
0	150.7	238.8	418.8	565.0	950.0	1319	1692

H_2—CO_2 [306]

% H_2 → / t, °C	0	4.7	19.3	49.6	90.59	96.38	100
25	170.8	185.5	317.2	633.4	1465	1684	1831

H_2—CO_2 [307]

% H_2 → / t, °C	0	23.1	23.2	25.0	38.7	41.5	43.4	53.5	74.8	100
75	207	419.5	420.5	447.2	620.8	666.7	681.5	877.1	1296	2058

H_2—CO_2 [307]

% H_2 → / t, °C	0	28.85	48.6	56.0	76.8	100
620	635	1228	1772	2035	2952	4338

H_2—N_2 [306]

% H_2 → / t, °C	0	15.9	39.0	65.2	80.3	100
0	230.3	335.1	645.5	811.7	1075.5	1692

H_2—O_2 [306]

% H_2 → / t, °C	0	20	40	60	80	100
22	249	414	645	922	1257	1675

H_2 — N_2O [306]

t, °C \ % H_2 →	0	20.9	38.6	59.9	81.2	100
0	159.2	297.3	448.2	711.3	1138.7	1692

H_2 — C_2H_4 [306]

t, °C \ % H_2 →	0.1	16.98	31.40	51.37	61.10	86.49	100
25	221.0	360.3	480.8	707.8	862.7	1377	1831

Air — CH_4 [308]

t, °C \ % CH_4 →	0	20	40	60	80
22	258.2	268.5	278.9	289.1	299.5

Air — C_2H_2 [308]

t, °C \ % C_2H_2 →	0	10	20	30	40	60	80	100
20	257.0	255.9	253.6	250.6	247.0	239.6	231.3	222.4
65	288.4	290.4	291.0	289.8	288.4	283.8	277.5	269.7

Air — CO [308]

t, °C \ % CO →	0	20	40	60	80	100
18	255.9	254.1	252.0	249.7	246.9	243.9

Air — H_2O [308]

t, °C \ % H_2O →	0	10	20	30	40	60	80	100
80	298.9	306.9	310.3	307.8	301.9	281.8	254.0	221.2

Air — NH_3 [308]

t, °C \ % NH_3 →	0	10	20	30	40	60	80	100
20	257.0	264.7	268.5	269.4	267.5	260.6	246.7	235.2
80	298.9	303.3	316.8	325.2	326.1	325.5	319.8	298.9

$CO—NH_3$ [308]

t, °C \ % NH_3 →	0	10	20	30	40	60	80	100
22	246.0	252.4	254.9	257.4	258.0	254.3	250.0	238.2

$NH_3—C_2H_4$ [306]

t, °C \ % NH_3 →	0	26.4	58.79	77.32	100
25	221.0	241.1	256.4	262.1	263.9

$N_2—Ar$ [306]

t, °C \ % N_2 →	0	20.38	35.87	61.08	78.04	100
0	161.1	174.8	185.7	205.0	219.2	237.0

$H_2O—N_2$ [309]

t, °C \ % H_2O →	0	10	20	30	40	60	80	100
65	281	287	285	283	276	256	234	209
330	440	472	490	492	493	492	480	462

$H_2O—CO_2$ [309]

t, °C \ % H_2O →	0	10	20	30	40	60	80	100
65	192	201	209	213	214	216	213	209
330	405	431	447	457	465	469	468	462

$N_2—CO_2$ [310]

t, °C \ % CO_2 →	17	25	33	44	47	50	67	75
369		12.82			12.69	12.73		
372	13.85		13.75			13.50	13.21	
375	14.05		13.96			13.70	13.41	
471				14.61				
569			16.21			16.14	16.03	
573			16.50			16.48	16.32	
677						18.92		
688		18.94				19.20		19.12
774						21.26		

VISCOSITY OF AQUEOUS SOLUTIONS

Viscosity $\eta \cdot 10^2$ (gm/cm · s) showing concentration of dissolved substance [313]

Ethanol–water

Weight %	10	20	30	40	50	60	70	80	90	100
Volume % → / t, °C	12.36	24.09	35.23	45.83	55.93	65.56	74.80	83.59	92.01	100
0	3.311	5.319	6.94	7.14	6.58	5.75	4.762	3.690	2.732	1.773
5	2.577	4.065	5.29	5.59	5.26	4.63	3.906	3.125	2.309	1.623
10	2.179	3.165	4.05	4.39	4.18	3.77	3.268	2.710	2.101	1.466
15	1.792	2.618	3.26	3.53	3.44	3.14	2.770	2.309	1.802	1.332
20	1.538	2.183	2.17	2.91	2.87	2.67	2.370	2.008	1.610	1.200
25	1.323	1.815	2.18	2.35	2.40	2.24	2.037	1.748	1.424	1.096
30	1.160	1.553	1.87	2.02	2.02	1.93	1.767	1.531	1.279	1.003
35	1.006	1.332	1.58	1.72	1.72	1.66	1.529	1.355	1.147	0.914
40	0.907	1.160	1.368	1.482	1.499	1.447	1.344	1.203	1.035	0.834
45	0.812	1.015	1.189	1.289	1.294	1.271	1.189	1.081	0.939	0.764
50	0.734	0.907	1.050	1.132	1.155	1.127	1.062	0.968	0.848	0.702
55	0.663	0.814	0.929	0.998	1.020	0.997	0.943	0.867	0.764	0.644
60	0.609	0.736	0.834	0.893	0.913	0.902	0.856	0.789	0.704	0.592
65	0.554	0.666	0.752	0.802	0.818	0.806	0.766	0.711	0.641	0.551
70	0.514	0.608	0.683	0.727	0.740	0.729	0.695	0.650	0.589	0.504
75	0.476	0.559	0.624	0.663	0.672	0.663	0.636	0.600	0.546	0.471
80	0.430	0.505	0.567	0.601	0.612	0.604				

Methyl alcohol–water

t, °C → / Weight %	0	10	20	30	t, °C → / Weight %	0	10	20	30
10	2.59	1.78	1.32	1.03	60	2.89	2.11	1.60	1.24
20	3.23	2.17	1.58	1.21	70	2.37	1.79	1.39	1.09
30	3.61	2.46	1.76	1.32	80	1.76	1.42	1.14	0.92
40	3.65	2.54	1.84	1.37	90	1.19	1.00	0.86	0.72
50	3.35	2.89	1.76	1.34	100	0.82	0.68	0.58	0.51

Propyl alcohol–water

t, °C → / Weight %	20	30	t, °C → / Weight %	20	30	t, °C → / Weight %	20	30
10	1.59	1.17	60	3.14	2.30	90	2.53	1.93
20	2.14	1.54	70	3.00	2.21	100	2.20	1.72
30	2.62	1.85	80	2.79	2.09			

Glycerin–water

t, °C → / Weight %	20	25	30	t, °C → / Weight %	20	25	30
0	1.005	0.893	0.800	9	1.274	1.121	0.997
1	1.029	0.912	0.817	10	1.311	1.153	1.024
2	1.055	0.935	0.836	15	1.517	1.331	1.174
3	1.083	0.959	0.856	20	1.769	1.542	1.360
4	1.112	0.984	0.877	25	2.095	1.810	1.590
5	1.143	1.010	0.900	30	2.501	2.157	1.876
6	1.175	1.037	0.924	35	3.040	2.600	2.249
7	1.207	1.064	0.948	40	3.750	3.181	2.731
8	1.239	1.092	0.972	45	4.715	3.967	3.380

continued

Weight % \ t, °C →	20	25	30
50	6.050	5.041	4.247
55	7.997	6.582	5.494
60	10.96	8.823	7.312
65	15.54	12.36	10.02
70	22.94	17.96	14.32
75	36.46	27.73	21.68
80	62.0	45.86	34.92
85	112.9	81.5	60.05
90	234,6	163.6	115.3
91	278.4	189.3	134.4
92	328.4	221.8	156.5
93	387.7	262.9	182.8
94	457.7	308.7	212.0
95	545	336.0	248.8
96	661	435.0	296.7
97	805	522.9	354.0
98	974	629	424.0
99	1197	775	511
100	1499	945	624

HNO_3 — water

Weight % \ t, °C →	10	20	30	40
20	1.32	1.05	0.86	0.71
40	1.60	1.30	1.08	0.91
60	2.62	2.00	1.63	1.36
80	2.37	1.88	1.54	1.26

H_2SO_4 — water

Weight % \ t, °C →	15	20	30	40	50
10	1.47	1.12	0.99	0.76	0.58
20	1.83	1.38	1.19	0.95	0.76
30	2.44	1.82	1.52	1.21	0.99
40	3.24	2.48	2.10	1.62	1.39
50	4.65	3.58	2.72	2.30	1.90
55	5.74	4.48	3.38	2.88	2.28
60	7.15	5.52	4.08	3.42	2.77
65	9.32	7.10	5.78	4.55	3.55
70	12.8	9.65	7.90	6.10	4.20
75	18.6	13.9	10.6	8.10	5.90
80	31.3	23.2	15.2	10.7	7.72
85	32.3	23.7	16.1	12.4	8.48
90	31.7	23.1	15.55	11.8	8.45
95	32.1	23.4	15.75	12.33	8.71
100	37.2	27.8	18.5	14.2	9.80

Acetic acid–water

Weight % \ t, °C →	0	10	20	30	40	50	60	70	80	90	100
10	2.21	1.60	1.22	0.97	0.78	0.65	0.56	0.47	0.41	0.36	0.32
20	2.70	1.93	1.45	1.15	0.92	0.76	0.64	0.54	0.47	0.41	0.36
30	3.24	2.28	1.70	1.33	1.05	0.87	0.73	0.61	0.52	0.46	0.40
40	3.83	2.68	1.96	1.52	1.20	0.99	0.82	0.68	0.59	0.51	0.45
50	4.35	3.03	2.21	1.70	1.35	1.11	0.92	0.76	0.65	0.57	0.50
60	4.76	3.33	2.43	1.89	1.48	1.23	1.03	0.84	0.73	0.63	0.54
70	5.13	3.57	2.66	2.05	1.63	1.33	1.10	0.91	0.78	0.67	0.58
80	5.26	3.70	2.75	2.09	1.69	1.35	1.12	0.94	0.81	0.69	0.59
90	4.35	3.23	2.43	1.87	1.49	1.22	1.04	0.89	0.77	0.65	0.57
95	3.45	2.48	1.89	1.52	1.26	1.07	0.92	0.78	0.69	0.59	0.52
100			1.22	1.04	0.90	0.79	0.70	0.63	0.56	0.51	0.46

Na_2SO_4 — water

Weight % \ t, °C →	20
5	1.17
10	1.29
15	1.43
20	1.85

HCl — water

Weight % / t, °C →	0	10	20	Weight % / t, °C →	0	10	20
5	1.84	1.38	1.08	20			1.36
10	1.89	1.45	1.16	30			1.70
15			1.24				

NaCl — water

Weight % / t, °C →	—10	0	10	20	30	40	50	60	70	80
5		1.86	1.39	1.07	0.87	0.71	0.60	0.51	0.45	0.40
10		2.01	1.51	1.19	0.95	0.78	0.67	0.57	0.51	0.45
15	3.37	2.27	1.69	1.34	1.07	0.89	0.75	0.64	0.56	0.50
20	4.08	2.67	1.99	1.56	1.24	1.03	0.87	0.74	0.64	0.57
25	5.19	3.31	2.38	1.86						

NaOH — water

Weight % / t, °C →	20	30	40	Weight % / t, °C →	20	30	40
5	1.30	1.05	0.85	20	4.48	3.30	2.48
10	1.86	1.45	1.16	25	7.42	5.25	3.86
15	2.78	2.10	1.65				

THERMAL CONDUCTIVITY OF AQUEOUS SOLUTIONS

Thermal conductivity λ of aqueous solutions of salts, acids and bases in W/m · deg* [294, 296]

Aqueous solutions of salts

Solute	Weight % → / t, °C	0	10	20	30	40	50
NaBr	20	0.599	0.580	0.558	0.534	0.504	
NaI	20	0.599	0.579	0.556	0.528	0.494	0.452
$NaCH_3COO$	20	0.599	0.570	0.537	0.502		
NaCl	20	0.599	0.590	0.578			
	30	0.618	0.604	0.590			
$NaClO_3$	20	0.599	0.585	0.569	0.550	0.529	
$NaClO_4$	20	0.599	0.583	0.566	0.547	0.523	0.498
$NaNO_2$	20	0.599	0.592	0.584	0.574	0.561	
$NaNO_3$	20	0.599	0.591	0.580	0.569	0.556	
$NaBrO_3$	20	0.599	0.588	0.577			
$Na_2S_2O_3$	20	0.599	0.593	0.585	0.570	0.544	
Na_2SO_4	20	0.599	0.600				
	30	0.618	0.619				
Na_2CO_3	20	0.599	0.607				
Na_2SiO_3	20	0.599	0.607	0.618			
$Na_2Cr_2O_7$	20	0.599	0.593	0.585	0.577	0.568	0.558
Na_3PO_4	20	0.599	0.613				
KF	20	0.599	0.588	0.572	0.545		
KCl	20	0.599	0.580	0.559			
KCl	30	0.618	0.595	0.574			
KBr	20	0.599	0.576	0.550	0.519	0.484	
KI	20	0.599	0.576	0.550	0.519	0.481	0.436
KC_2H_5COO	20	0.599	0.587	0.573			

*The tables gives concentration of the dissolved substances (solute).

continued

Solute	Weight % → / t, °C	0	10	20	30	40	50
KNO_2	20	0.599	0.584	0.566	0.547	0.527	0.508
KNO_3	20	0.599	0.584	0.566			
K_2SO_4	20	0.599	0.590				
K_2CO_3	20	0.599	0.592	0.583	0.564	0.540	0.509
$K_4Fe(CN)_6$	20	0.599	0.584	0.568			
$MgCl_2$	20	0.599	0.573	0.547	0.516		
$MgSO_4$	20	0.599	0.592	0.583			
$MgBr_2$	20	0.599	0.573	0.542	0.505	0.459	0.407
$Mg(NO_3)_2$	20	0.599	0.583	0.564	0.542		
$CaCl_2$	20	0.599	0.587	0.576	0.561	0.545	
$Ca(NO_3)_2$	20	0.599	0.590	0.578	0.565	0.550	0.533
$CaBr_2$	20	0.599	0.579	0.556	0.529	0.495	0.454
$BaCl_2$	20	0.599	0.590	0.578			
$BaCl_2$	30	0.618	0.605	0.593			
$BaBr_2$	20	0.599	0.583	0.564	0.542	0.515	
BaI_2	20	0.599	0.580	0.559	0.534	0.502	0.463
$SbCl_3$	20	0.599	0.588	0.576	0.562		
$SbBr_3$	20	0.599	0.582	0.561	0.536	0.506	0.468
$Sb(NO_3)_3$	20	0.599	0.590	0.579	0.566	0.550	
$ZnSO_4$	20	0.599	0.587	0.574	0.559		
$ZnSO_4$	30	0.618	0.604				
$ZnCl_2$	20	0.599	0.577	0.551	0.521	0.486	
LiCl	20	0.599	0.577	0.554	0.538		
LiBr	20	0.599	0.572	0.542	0.507	0.471	
LiI	20	0.599	0.572	0.537	0.506	0.469	0.427
$LiSO_4$	20	0.599	0.593	0.587			
$CuSO_4$	20	0.599	0.587				
$Al_2(SO_4)_3$	20	0.599	0.566	0.531			
NH_4Cl	20	0.599	0.566	0.531			
$AgNO_3$	20	0.599	0.587	0.574	0.558	0.540	0.514
$Pb(NO_3)_2$	20	0.599	0.590	0.579	0.566		
$Co(NO_3)_2$	20	0.599	0.584	0.565	0.544	0.520	
$Th(NO_3)_2$	20	0.599	0.583	0.563			

Aqueous solutions of acids [296]

Nitric acid HNO_3

t, °C → / Weight %	0	20	40	60	80	100
0	0.551	0.599	0.634	0.659	0.674	0.683
25	0.504	0.534	0.556	0.576	0.587	0.592
50	0.443	0.458	0.469	0.479	0.484	0.486
75	0.360	0.360	0.360	0.360	0.360	0.360
96	0.265	0.260	0.256	0.251	0.248	0.243

Sulfuric acid H_2SO_4

t, °C → / Weight %	0	20	40	60	80	100
0	0.551	0.599	0.634	0.659	0.674	0.683
25	0.491	0.531	0.563	0.587	0.609	0.624
50	0.436	0.469	0.493	0.513	0.529	0.538
75	0.381	0.400	0.420	0.438	0.454	0.462
96	0.317	0.326	0.333	0.340	0.347	0.352

Hydrochloric acid HCl

Weight % \ t, °C →	0	10	20	30	35
10	0.574	0.535	0.488	0.442	0.419
30	0.618	0.576	0.518	0.465	0.440
50	0.648	0.611	0.548	0.490	0.460
70	0.668	0.64	0.57		
90	0.680	0.65	0.59		

Chromic and phosphoric acids H_2CrO_4 and H_3PO_4

Solute	Weight % → / t, °C	0	10	20	30	40	50
H_2CrO_4	20	0.599	0.582	0.562	0.541	0.529	0.488
H_3PO_4	20	0.599	0.579	0.557	0.533	0.509	0.486

Aqueous solutions of bases [296]

Solute	Weight % → / t, °C	0	10	20	30	40	50
KOH	20	0.599	0.604	0.599	0.584	0.564	0.536
KOH	30	0.618	0.620	0.613	0.595	0.574	0.549
NaOH	20	0.599	0.627	0.640	0.645	0.645	
NH_4OH	20	0.599	0.635	0.484	0.445		
LiOH	20	0.599	0.621				

Aqueous solutions of organic liquids [298, 299, 314]

Ethyl alcohol

Weight % \ t, °C →	−40	−20	0	20	40	60	80
0			0.565	0.599	0.628	0.652	0.670
20			0.451	0.471	0.490	0.505	0.516
40		0.343	0.352	0.364	0.373	0.381	0.386
60	0.266	0.270	0.273	0.276	0.279	0.283	0.285
80	0.216	0.214	0.213	0.212	0.209	0.208	0.206
100	0.183	0.178	0.172	0.167	0.162	0.157	0.152

Methyl alcohol

Weight % \ t, °C →	−40	−20	0	20	40	60
0			0.565	0.599	0.628	0.652
20			0.465	0.485	0.505	0.524
40	0.357	0.368	0.377	0.387	0.398	0.407
60	0.300	0.304	0.307	0.310	0.314	0.316
80	0.254	0.251	0.249	0.246	0.244	0.242
100	0.223	0.216	0.209	0.202	0.195	0.188

n-Propyl alcohol

Weight % \ t, °C →	−40	−20	0	20	40	60	80
0			0.565	0.599	0.628	0.652	0.670
20			0.443	0.463	0.483	0.500	0.513
40			0.336	0.348	0.358	0.369	0.378
60	0.270	0.273	0.276	0.278	0.280	0.284	0.286
80	0.220	0.217	0.216	0.214	0.212	0.209	0.207
100	0.187	0.180	0.174	0.167	0.162	0.156	0.150

Isopropyl alcohol

Weight % \ t, °C →	−40	−20	0	20	40	60	80
0			0.565	0.599	0.628	0.652	0.670
20			0.437	0.456	0.474	0.491	0.505
40		0.321	0.330	0.341	0.350	0.359	0.368
60		0.238	0.243	0.248	0.252	0.257	0.262
80	0.185	0.184	0.181	0.179	0.177	0.176	0.173
100	0.151	0.148	0.144	0.141	0.137	0.134	0.130

Glycerin

Weight % \ t, °C →	−20	0	20	40	60	80	100
0		0.565	0.599	0.628	0.652	0.670	0.680
20		0.497	0.522	0.547	0.569	0.585	
40		0.434	0.452	0.471	0.488	0.502	
60	0.364	0.376	0.387	0.399	0.410	0.420	
80	0.319	0.324	0.330	0.336	0.342	0.348	0.354
100			0.283	0.285	0.287	0.291	0.293

Ethylene glycol

Weight % \ t, °C →	−40	−20	0	20	40	60	80	100
0			0.565	0.599	0.628	0.652	0.670	0.680
20			0.485	0.508	0.531	0.550	0.568	0.577
40		0.393	0.408	0.423	0.438	0.454	0.469	0.477
60	0.328	0.337	0.346	0.356	0.365	0.374	0.384	0.391
80	0.284	0.288	0.293	0.298	0.302	0.307	0.312	0.316
100			0.252	0.255	0.257	0.259	0.262	0.264

1,2-propylene glycol

Weight% \ t, °C →	−40	−20	0	20	40	60	80	100
0			0.565	0.599	0.628	0.652	0.670	0.680
20			0.472	0.493	0.514	0.531	0.547	0.556
40		0.376	0.388	0.401	0.414	0.427	0.440	0.449
60	0.301	0.308	0.315	0.322	0.330	0.337	0.344	0.350
80	0.246	0.249	0.251	0.254	0.257	0.259	0.263	0.265
100	0.200	0.200	0.199	0.199	0.199	0.198	0.198	0.198

Acetone

Weight % \ t, °C →	−40	−20	0	20	40	60
0			0.565	0.599	0.628	0.652
20			0.444	0.464	0.481	0.495
40			0.343	0.352	0.360	0.369
60		0.262	0.263	0.265	0.266	0.267
80	0.214	0.210	0.206	0.201	0.196	0.192
100	0.184	0.177	0.170	0.162	0.154	0.146

Acetic acid [372]

t, °C \ % acid →	10	20	30	40	50	60	70	80	90
20	0.5464	0.4918	0.4458	0.4011	0.3546	0.3081	0.2674	0.2331	0.1976
30	0.5650	0.5046	0.4511	0.4046	0.3575	0.3133	0.2699	0.2325	0.1842
40	0.5685	0.5139	0.4592	0.4081	0.3689	0.3197	0.2761	0.2360	0.1994
60	0.5836	0.5336	0.4697	0.4185	0.3767	0.3261	0.2778	0.2302	0.2011

Formic acid [372]

t, °C \ % acid →	10	20	30	40	50	60	70	80	90
20	0.5627	0.5232	0.4906	0.4581	0.4220	0.4011	0.3703	0.3371	0.3127
40	0.5836	0.5394	0.5115	0.4732	0.4348	0.4022	0.3674	0.3383	0.3104
60	0.6069	0.5590	0.5174	0.4894	0.4488	0.4115	0.3755	0.3441	0.3081

Oleic acid [372]

t, °C \ % acid →	10	20	30	40	50	60	70	80	90
20	0.5278	0.4592	0.4046	0.3511	0.3075	0.2656	0.2255	0.1976	0.1645
40	0.5487	0.4883	0.4208	0.3726	0.3209	0.2743	0.2348	0.1976	0.1651
60	0.5743	0.5069	0.4406	0.3802	0.3220	0.2790	0.2348	0.1930	0.1610

Acetic anhydride [372]

t, °C \ % anhydride →	10	20	30	40	50	60	70	80	90
30	0.5383	0.4790	0.4220	0.3743	0.3157	0.2668	0.2203	0.1846	0.1662

Thermal conductivity λ (W/m · deg) of aqueous solutions of ethanol at different temperatures and pressures (c_g = weight concentration of alcohol [371]

t, °C \ p, bar →	1	50	100	150	200	250	300
				$c_g = 100\%$			
0	0.1688	0.1708	0.1728	0.1748	0.1767	0.1786	0.1805
25	0.1602	0.1630	0.1652	0.1676	0.1697	0.1719	0.1739
50	0.1530	0.1556	0.1582	0.1608	0.1632	0.1657	0.1679
75	0.1468	0.1496	0.1524	0.1551	0.1578	0.1604	0.1627

continued

t, °C \ p, bar →	1	50	100	150	200	250	300
100		0.1446	0.1477	0.1502	0.1530	0.1556	0.1579
150		0.1358	0.1390	0.1424	0.1455	0.1484	0.1508
200		0.1261	0.1300	0.1338	0.1377	0.1411	0.1439
250			0.1182	0.1228	0.1274	0.1314	0.1348
300				0.1085	0.1143	0.1197	0.1240
				c_g=94%			
0	0.1792	0.1817	0.1842	0.1865	0.1886	0.1906	0.1925
25	0.1724	0.1751	0.1777	0.1800	0.1824	0.1845	0.1866
50	0.1660	0.1689	0.1716	0.1742	0.1766	0.1790	0.1812
75	0.1605	0.1635	0.1663	0.1691	0.1718	0.1742	0.1766
100		0.1588	0.1618	0.1647	0.1675	0.1702	0.1726
150		0.1503	0.1534	0.1565	0.1600	0.1629	0.1656
200		0.1406	0.1440	0.1477	0.1516	0.1552	0.1583
250			0.1316	0.1360	0.1405	0.1447	0.1483
300				0.1204	0.1265	0.1317	0.1361
				c_g=80%			
0	0.2112	0.2146	0.2180	0.2214	0.2245	0.2272	0.2298
25	0.2075	0.2108	0.2143	0.2178	0.2210	0.2239	0.2266
50	0.2033	0.2065	0.2101	0.2137	0.2171	0.2202	0.2229
75	0.1992	0.2024	0.2060	0.2097	0.2132	0.2165	0.2193
100		0.1985	0.2021	0.2058	0.2095	0.2129	0.2159
150		0.1901	0.1938	0.1976	0.2016	0.2053	0.2087
200		0.1791	0.1829	0.1871	0.1913	0.1953	0.1991
250			0.1680	0.1727	0.1775	0.1820	0.1862
300				0.1536	0.1595	0.1652	0.1702
				c_g=60%			
0	0.2707	0.2754	0.2801	0.2846	0.2887	0.2925	0.2960
25	0.2733	0.2781	0.2829	0.2876	0.2919	0.2957	0.2991
50	0.2737	0.2786	0.2834	0.2881	0.2924	0.2964	0.2999
75	0.2727	0.2776	0.2823	0.2870	0.2914	0.2954	0.2992
100		0.2751	0.2799	0.2846	0.2890	0.2931	0.2972
150		0.2669	0.2716	0.2763	0.2808	0.2851	0.2896
200		0.2528	0.2578	0.2628	0.2676	0.2722	0.2768
250			0.2374	0.2432	0.2488	0.2540	0.2588
300				0.2152	0.2226	0.2294	0.2354
				c_g=40%			
0	0.3485	0.3542	0.3597	0.3649	0.3697	0.3741	0.3782
25	0.3605	0.3663	0.3720	0.3773	0.3823	0.3868	0.3908
50	0.3680	0.3739	0.3796	0.3850	0.3900	0.3945	0.3984
75	0.3721	0.3779	0.3835	0.3888	0.3938	0.3983	0.4023
100		0.3787	0.3842	0.3895	0.3945	0.3990	0.4031
150		0.3721	0.3775	0.3827	0.3877	0.3924	0.3967
200		0.3546	0.3604	0.3661	0.3714	0.3765	0.3813
250			0.3325	0.3393	0.3458	0.3519	0.3575
300				0.2993	0.3084	0.3168	0.3245
				c_g=20%			
0	0.4471	0.4528	0.4582	0.4634	0.4682	0.4727	0.4770
25	0.4721	0.4779	0.4835	0.4888	0.4937	0.4982	0.5022
50	0.4900	0.4958	0.5014	0.5066	0.5115	0.5159	0.5199
75	0.5018	0.5075	0.5129	0.5181	0.5229	0.5273	0.5312
100		0.5136	0.5189	0.5239	0.5286	0.5330	0.5370
150		0.5112	0.5164	0.5233	0.5261	0.5306	0.5348
200		0.4908	0.4966	0.5022	0.5075	0.5126	0.5174
250			0.4597	0.4672	0.4742	0.4808	0.4869
300				0.4119	0.4228	0.4328	0.4418

Chapter 14

LIQUID FUELS

KEROSINE

Pressure p (mm Hg) of saturated vapor (ratio of volumes of gas and liquid phases $V''/V' = 4$) [317]

t, °C	p	t, °C	p	t, °C	p	t, °C	p
20	35	70	210	120	572	170	1218
30	56	80	270	130	670	180	1398
40	84	90	333	140	777	190	1600
50	117	100	406	150	906	200	1851
60	160	110	485	160	1040		

Heat capacity of kerosine vapor at $p \approx 1$ bar [318]

°C	150	160	170	180	190	200	210	220	230	240	250	260	270
c_p, kJ/kg · deg	2.37	2.39	2.41	2.43	2.45	2.47	2.49	2.51	2.53	2.55	2.57	2.60	2.62

Heat capacity (kJ/kg · deg) of liquid kerosine [322]

t, °C	c_p	t, °C	c_p	t, °C	c_p	t, °C	c_p
20	2.00	90	2.33	160	2.68	220	3.00
30	2.04	100	2.38	170	2.73	230	3.05
40	2.09	110	2.43	180	2.79	240	3.11
50	2.14	120	2.48	190	2.84	250	3.16
60	2.18	130	2.53	200	2.89	260	3.21
70	2.23	140	2.58	210	2.94	270	3.26
80	2.28	150	2.63				

Density ρ (kg/m^3) of liquid kerosine [322]

t, °C	$\varrho \cdot 10^{-3}$	t, °C	$\varrho \cdot 10^{-3}$	t, °C	$\varrho \cdot 10^{-3}$	t, °C	$\varrho \cdot 10^{-3}$
20	0.819	90	0.774	160	0.720	220	0.668
30	0.814	100	0.766	170	0.711	230	0.658
40	0.808	110	0.759	180	0.703	240	0.649
50	0.801	120	0.751	190	0.694	250	0.638
60	0.795	130	0.744	200	0.685	260	0.628
70	0.788	140	0.736	210	0.676	270	0.618
80	0.781	150	0.728				

Viscosity of kerosine vapor at $p = 1$ bar [319]

t, °C	100	120	140	160	180	200	220	240	260	280
$\eta \cdot 10^7$, N · s/m²	66.2	73.8	81.4	89.0	96.6	104.2	111.6	118.4	125.0	131.2

Viscosity η (N · s/m²) of liquid kerosine [319]

t, °C	$\eta \cdot 10^3$	t, °C	$\eta \cdot 10^3$	t, °C	$\eta \cdot 10^3$	t, °C	$\eta \cdot 10^3$
−50	11.5	−15	3.14	40	1.08	180	0.296
−45	9.04	−10	2.75	60	0.832	200	0.262
−40	7.26	−5	2.42	80	0.664	220	0.234
−35	5.96	0	2.15	100	0.545	240	0.211
−30	4.98	5	1.92	120	0.457	260	0.191
−25	4.22	10	1.73	140	0.390	280	0.174
−20	3.62	20	1.49	160	0.338	300	0.159

Thermal conductivity λ of kerosine vapor [320]

t, °C	200	225	250	275	300	325
$\lambda \cdot 10^4$, W/m · deg	276	313	346	381	415	449

Thermal conductivity λ of liquid kerosine [321]

t, °C	−50	0	50	100	150	200	250	300
λ, W/m · deg	0.127	0.1192	0.1114	0.1042	0.0965	0.0891	0.0816	0.0738

Surface tension σ (N/m) of kerosine [323]

t, °C	$\sigma \cdot 10^3$	t, °C	$\sigma \cdot 10^3$	t, °C	$\sigma \cdot 10^3$	t, °C	$\sigma \cdot 10^3$
−50	33.7	40	24.9	130	17.2	220	10.40
−40	32.7	50	24.0	140	16.4	230	9.70
−30	31.6	60	23.2	150	15.6	240	9.07
−20	30.7	70	22.2	160	14.8	250	8.48
−10	29.7	80	21.4	170	14.1	260	7.87
0	28.7	90	20.5	180	13.3	270	7.29
10	27.7	100	19.6	190	12.5	280	6.75
20	26.8	110	18.8	200	11.8	290	6.28
30	25.8	120	18.0	210	11.1	300	5.76

Gasoline*

Saturated vapor pressure p (ratio of vapor and liquid volumes $V''/V' = 4$) [317]

t, °C	20	30	40	50	60	70	80	90	100	110
p, mm Hg	80	123	148	206	286	404	566	755	973	1230

Heat capacity of gasoline vapor at $p \approx 1$ bar [318]

t, °C	130	140	150	160	170	180	190	200	210	220	230	240	250
c_p, kJ/kg · deg	2.28	2.31	2.34	2.36	2.39	2.41	2.43	2.46	2.48	2.51	2.53	2.56	2.58

*Soviet fuel designation B-70.

Heat capacity c_p (kJ/kg · deg) of liquid gasoline [322]

t, °C	c_p	t, °C	c_p	t, °C	c_p	t, °C	c_p
20	2.06	70	2.30	120	2.57	170	2.86
30	2.11	80	2.35	130	2.62	180	2.92
40	2.15	90	2.41	140	2.68	190	2.98
50	2.20	100	2.46	150	2.74	200	3.04
60	2.24	110	2.51	160	2.80	210	3.11

Density ρ (kg/m³) of liquid gasoline [322]

t, °C	$\varrho \cdot 10^{-3}$	t,°C	$\varrho \cdot 10^{-3}$	t, °C	$\varrho \cdot {-10^{3}}$	t,C°	$\varrho \cdot 10^{-3}$
20	0.751	70	0.708	120	0.660	170	0.605
30	0.743	80	0.699	130	0.650	180	0.594
40	0.735	90	0.690	140	0.639	190	0.582
50	0.721	100	0.681	150	0.628	200	0.570
60	0.717	110	0.671	160	0.617		

Viscosity of gasoline vapor at $p = 1$ bar [319]

t, °C	100	120	140	160	180	200	220	240	260	280
$\eta \cdot 10^7$, N · s/m²	49.2	55.4	61.6	67.8	73.8	80.0	86.4	92.4	98.0	103.0

Viscosity η (N · s/m²) of liquid gasoline [319]

t, °C	$\eta \cdot 10^3$	t, °C	$\eta \cdot 10^3$	t, °C	$\eta \cdot 10^3$	t, °C	$\eta \cdot 10^3$
−50	1.71	−15	0.916	40	0.411	180	0.126
−45	1.54	−10	0.849	60	0.328	200	0.111
−40	1.40	−5	0.789	80	0.269	220	0.099
−35	1.28	0	0.735	100	0.225	240	0.089
−30	1.17	5	0.687	120	0.191	260	0.081
−25	1.07	10	0.643	140	0.165	280	0.073
−20	0.990	20	0.529	160	0.146	300	0.067

Thermal conductivity λ of gasoline vapor at $p = 1$ bar [320]

t, °C	150	175	200	225	250
$\lambda \cdot 10^4$, W/m · deg	266	284	306	333	364

Thermal conductivity λ of liquid gasoline [321]

t, °C	−50	0	50	100	150	200
λ, W/m · deg	0.131	0.1204	0.1105	0.1005	0.0919	0.0800

Surface tension σ (N/m) of gasoline [323]

t, °C	$\sigma \cdot 10^3$	t, °C	$\sigma \cdot 10^3$	t, °C	$\sigma \cdot 10^3$	t, °C	$\sigma \cdot 10^3$
−50	29.9	40	20.6	130	12.3	220	5.16
−40	28.9	50	19.6	140	11.5	230	4.48
−30	27.8	60	18.7	150	10.6	240	3.91
−20	26.8	70	17.7	160	9.80	250	3.36
−10	25.8	80	16.7	170	9.00	260	2.84
0	24.7	90	15.8	180	8.15	270	2.38
10	23.7	100	14.9	190	7.41	280	2.00
20	22.6	110	14.0	200	6.65	290	1.64
30	21.6	120	13.2	210	5.89	300	1.34

Fuel T-5*

Saturated vapor pressure (mm Hg) (ratio of vapor and liquid phase volumes $V''/V' = 4$) [317]

t, °C	p	t, °C	p	t, °C	p	t, °C	p	t, °C	p
20	44	80	60	140	108	200	350	250	915
40	47	100	71	160	160	225	520	260	1090
60	52	120	84	180	238	240	765	270	1284

Heat capacity c_p of T-5 fuel vapor at $p \approx 1$ bar [318]

t, °C	150	160	170	180	190	200	210
c_p, kJ/kg · deg	2.31	2.32	2.34	2.36	2.37	2.39	2.41
t, °C	220	230	240	250	260	270	280
c_p, kJ/kg · deg	2.42	2.44	2.46	2.47	2.49	2.51	2.52

Heat capacity c_p (kJ/kg · deg) of liquid fuel T-5 at $p \approx 1$ bar [322]

t, °C	c_p	t, °C	c_p	t, °C	c_p	t, °C	c_p	t, °C	c_p
20	1.95	80	2.21	140	2.50	200	2.79	260	3.09
30	1.99	90	2.26	150	2.54	210	2.84	270	3.14
40	2.03	100	2.31	160	2.59	220	2.89	280	3.20
50	2.08	110	2.35	170	2.64	230	2.94		
60	2.13	120	2.40	180	2.69	240	2.99		
70	2.17	130	2.45	190	2.74	250	3.04		

Density ρ (kg/m³) of liquid fuel T-5 [322]

t, °C	$\varrho \cdot 10^{-3}$	t, °C	$\varrho \cdot 10^{-3}$	t, °C	$\varrho \cdot 10^{-3}$	t, °C	$\varrho \cdot 10^{-3}$	t, °C	$\varrho \cdot 10^{-3}$
20	0.842	80	0.801	140	0.759	200	0.715	260	0.668
30	0.835	90	0.794	150	0.752	210	0.707	270	0.660
40	0.828	100	0.787	160	0.745	220	0.699	280	0.652
50	0.821	110	0.780	170	0.737	230	0.692		
60	0.814	120	0.773	180	0.730	240	0.684		
70	0.807	130	0.766	190	0.722	250	0.676		

*Reprinted for information only.

Viscosity η of liquid fuel T-5 vapor at $p \approx 1$ bar [319]

t, °C	160	180	200	220	240	260
$\eta \cdot 10^7$, $N \cdot s/m^2$	74.2	82.7	90.2	100.8	108.0	118.1

Viscosity η ($N \cdot s/m^2$) of liquid fuel T-5 [319]

t, °C	$\eta \cdot 10^3$	t, °C	$\eta \cdot 10^3$	t, °C	$\eta \cdot 10^3$	t, °C	$\eta \cdot 10^3$
−50	87.3	−15	10.1	40	2.03	180	0.340
−45	55.9	−10	8.27	60	1.39	200	0.294
−40	38.3	−5	6.87	80	1.01	220	0.250
−35	27.6	0	5.79	100	0.771	240	0.220
−30	20.6	5	4.93	120	0.604	260	0.194
−25	15.9	10	4.23	140	0.490	280	0.171
−20	12.5	20	3.27	160	0.406	300	0.153

Thermal conductivity λ of fuel T-5 vapor at $p = 1$ bar [320]

t, °C	250	275	300	325
$\lambda \cdot 10^4$, W/m · deg	320	348	376	404

Thermal conductivity λ of liquid fuel T-5 [321]

t, °C	−50	0	50	100	150	200
λ, W/m · deg	0.123	0.119	0.1126	0.1072	0.1021	0.0958

Surface tension σ of fuel T-5 [323]

t, °C	$\sigma \cdot 10^3$	t, °C	$\sigma \cdot 10^3$	t, °C	$\sigma \cdot 10^3$	t, °C	$\sigma \cdot 10^3$	t, °C	$\sigma\ 1 \cdot 0^3$	t, °C	$\sigma \cdot 10^3$
−40	34.1	10	29.4	60	25.0	110	21.0	160	17.0	210	13.5
−30	33.1	20	28.5	70	24.2	120	20.2	170	16.3	220	12.8
−20	32.1	30	27.6	80	23.4	130	19.4	180	15.6	230	12.1
−10	31.2	40	26.7	90	22.6	140	18.6	190	14.9	240	11.4
0	30.3	50	25.9	100	21.8	150	17.8	200	14.2	250	10.7

Diesel fuel

Thermophysical properties of diesel fuel [324]: ρ (kg/m^3), λ (W/m · deg) and ν (cm^3)

t, °C	ϱ	λ	ν	t, °C	ϱ	λ	ν
20	878.7	0.1169	8.94	80	838.5	0.1099	2.14
40	865.4	0.1146	4.80	100	825.1	0.1076	1.62
60	852.0	0.1122	3.04				

Chapter 15

HIGH-TEMPERATURE HEAT TRANSFER AGENTS

Diphenyl mixture (Dow therm)**

$t_{melt} = 12$ °C; $t_{boil} = 258$ °C at $p = 1$ atm; $t_{cr} = 528$ °C;
$p_{cr} = 40.2$ bar

Thermodynamic properties of saturated Dowtherm [325] : v' (dm³/kg), v'' (m³/kg), ρ (kg/m³), i and r (kJ/kg)

t, °C	p, bar	v'	v''	ϱ'	ϱ''	i'	i''	r
20		0.943		1060		13	389	376
30		0.951		1052		29	402	373
40		0.959		1044		46	414	368
50		0.966		1036		63	427	364
60		0.973		1028		80	440	360
70		0.981		1020		96	454	358
80		0.988		1012		115	469	354
90		0.997		1003		134	484	350
100	0.006	1.005	28	995	0.035	153	498	345
110	0.010	1.014	18	987	0.056	172	513	341
120	0.017	1.022	11.5	978	0.087	190	527	337
130	0.024	1.030	8.2	970	0.12	211	546	335
140	0.037	1.040	5.6	961	0.18	232	563	331
150	0.052	1.050	4.2	953	0.24	253	582	329
160	0.074	1.058	3.0	945	0.33	274	601	327
170	0.108	1.067	2.2	937	0.45	297	620	323
180	0.147	1.077	1.7	928	0.60	318	638	320
190	0.196	1.087	1.2	920	0.81	341	657	316
200	0.245	1.096	1.0	912	0.99	364	678	314
210	0.323	1.106	0.76	904	1.3	389	699	310
220	0.412	1.116	0.62	896	1.6	414	720	306
230	0.510	1.126	0.50	887	2.0	440	741	301
240	0.627	1.137	0.41	879	2.4	465	762	297
250	0.843	1.148	0.31	871	3.2	490	781	291
260	1.029	1.159	0.25	863	3.9	515	802	287
270	1.31	1.170	0.20	854	5.0	540	820	280
280	1.63	1.184	0.165	845	6.1	567	842	275
290	1.95	1.197	0.14	835	7.2	596	866	270
300	2.33	1.211	0.115	825	8.7	626	890	264
310	2.76	1.226	0.096	815	10.4	655	912	257
320	3.25	1.243	0.082	804	12.2	682	936	254
330	3.82	1.260	0.069	794	14.5	712	959	247
340	4.47	1.277	0.059	783	17.0	741	984	243

*The term high temperature heat transfer agent (coolant) also refers to alkali metals (pp. 86–141), mercury (pp. 141–153), naphthalene (pp. 358, 359), diphenyls (359–362), and silicone-organic compounds (pp. 699–702).

**Dowtherm is an eutectic mixture of 73.5% phenyl ether and 26.5% diphenyl.

continued

t, °C	p, bar	v'	v''	ϱ'	ϱ''	i'	i''	r
350	5.20	1.295	0.050	772	20.0	770	1005	235
360	6.02	1.314	0.044	761	23.0	800	1030	230
370	6.94	1.333	0.038	750	26.0	829	1055	226
380	7.99	1.354	0.032	739	30.0	858	1078	220
390	9.13	1.380	0.028	725	36.0	888	1102	214
400	10.43	1.410	0.024	709	42.0	917	1124	207

Thermophysical properties of saturated Dowtherm [325] : c_p (kJ/kg · deg), λ (W/m · deg), η (N · s/m²), ν (m²/s) and Prandtl number Pr

t, °C	c_p'	λ'	$\eta' \cdot 10^5$	$\eta'' \cdot 10^5$	$\nu' \cdot 10^6$	$\nu'' \cdot 10^6$	Pr
20	1.59	0.137	435		4.11		50
30	1.63	0.135	333		3.19		40
40	1.67	0.134	263		2.51		33
50	1.67	0.133	215		2.07		27
60	1.72	0.131	178		1.73		23
70	1.76	0.129	152		1.49		20.5
80	1.80	0.128	130		1.29		18.5
90	1.84	0.127	114		1.14		16.5
100	1.88	0.126	101	0.68	1.01	192	15
110	1.92	0.123	89.5	0.70	0.907	123	14
120	1.97	0.122	80.4	0.72	0.822	82	13
130	2.01	0.121	72.2	0.74	0.746	60	12
140	2.05	0.120	65.8	0.75	0.686	42	11.3
150	2.14	0.119	60.3	0.77	0.633	32	10.9
160	2.18	0.116	55.2	0.79	0.574	24	10.3
170	2.22	0.115	50.9	0.81	0.544	18	9.8
180	2.26	0.114	47.0	0.83	0.508	14	9.4
190	2.30	0.113	43.7	0.85	0.476	10.5	9.0
200	2.34	0.110	40.7	0.87	0.446	8.8	8.6
210	2.39	0.109	37.9	0.89	0.421	6.8	8.3
220	2.43	0.108	35.6	0.91	0.397	5.6	8.0
230	2.47	0.107	33.5	0.93	0.378	4.7	7.7
240	2.55	0.105	31.6	0.95	0.360	3.9	7.6
250	2.60	0.104	29.7	0.97	0.341	3.0	7.4
260	2.64	0.102	28.1	0.99	0.326	2.5	7.2
270	2.68	0.101	26.6	1.01	0.313	2.0	7.1
280	2.68	0.100	25.3	1.03	0.299	1.7	6.9
290	2.72	0.098	24.0	1.05	0.287	1.4	6.7
300	2.76	0.096	22.7	1.07	0.276	1.2	6.5
310	2.80	0.095	20.7	1.09	0.266	1.0	6.4
320	2.80	0.094	20.8	1.11	0.259	0.90	6.2
330	2.85	0.092	19.9	1.13	0.251	0.78	6.1
340	2.89	0.091	19.0	1.15	0.243	0.68	6.0
350	2.89	0.090	18.2	1.17	0.236	0.59	5.9
360	2.93	0.088	17.3	1.18	0.229	0.52	5.8
370	2.93	0.086	16.7	1.20	0.223	0.46	5.7
380	2.97	0.085	16.1	1.22	0.218	0.39	5.6
390	2.97	0.084	15.5	1.24	0.214	0.35	5.5
400	3.01	0.083	14.9	1.26	0.210	0.31	5.4

Surface tension σ (N/m) of Dowtherm [64]

t, °C	$\sigma \cdot 10^3$	t, °C	$\sigma \cdot 10^3$	t, °C	$\sigma \cdot 10^3$	t, °C	$\sigma \cdot 10^3$
20	40.3	120	29.5	220	20.0	320	11.3
30	39.2	130	28.5	230	19.1	330	10.5
40	38.1	140	27.5	240	18.2	340	9.7
50	37.0	150	26.5	250	17.3	350	8.9
60	35.9	160	25.6	260	16.4	360	8.1

continued

t, °C	σ · 10³	t, °C	σ · 10³	t, °C	σ · 10³	t, °C	σ · 10³
70	34.8	170	24.6	270	15.5	370	7.3
80	33.7	180	23.7	280	14.6	380	6.5
90	32.7	190	22.8	290	13.7	390	5.7
100	31.6	200	21.8	300	12.9	400	5.0
110	30.5	210	20.9	310	12.1		

GAZOIL*

Thermophysical properties of liquid gazoil [326]: ρ (kg/m³), c_p (kJ/kg · deg), λ (W/m · deg), η (N · s/m²) and Prandtl number Pr

t, °C	p, mm Hg	ϱ	c_p	λ	η · 10³	Pr
20		848	1.900	0.121	5.02	78.8
40		838	1.967	0.119	2.95	48.8
60		826	2.039	0.117	1.95	34.0
80		814	2.114	0.114	1.43	26.5
100	17.4	801	2.189	0.112	1.05	20.5
120	34.3	788	2.265	0.109	0.832	17.3
140	62.7	774	2.344	0.107	0.665	14.6
160	107.8	761	2.424	0.105	0.553	12.8
180	175.8	747	2.507	0.102	0.463	11.4
200	273.9	733	2.591	0.100	0.401	10.4
220	410.4	718	2.675	0.097	0.337	9.29
240	593.9	704	2.769	0.094	0.295	8.69
260	834.1	688	2.863	0.092	0.259	8.06
280	1140	672	2.964	0.089	0.228	7.60
300	1523	656	3.064	0.086	0.206	7.34

*Gazoil consists of aromatic, paraffinic and naphthenic hydrocarbons, containing 28.31, 45.54 and 26.15 percent, respectively.

PAB*

Thermophysical properties of PAB [326]: ρ (kg/m³), c_p (kJ/kg · deg), λ(W/m · deg), η (N · s/m²) and Prandtl number Pr

t, °C	p, mm Hg	ϱ	c_p	λ	η · 10³	Pr
20		990	1.842	0.119	58.2	905.5
40		980	1.888	0.117	17.4	329.2
60		971	1.938	0.115	7.83	136.8
80		961	1.988	0.113	4.46	78.5
100	2.2	950	2.039	0.111	2.69	49.4
120	4.9	939	2.093	0.109	1.82	34.9
140	9.9	925	2.147	0.107	1.32	26.5
160	18.8	912	2.206	0.105	0.977	20.5
180	33.8	898	2.260	0.103	0.794	17.4
200	57.8	883	2.319	0.101	0.676	15.5
220	94.6	868	2.382	0.099	0.537	12.9
240	149	853	2.445	0.097	0.457	11.5
260	227	837	2.512	0.095	0.389	10.3
280	335	821	2.587	0.092	0.339	9.5
300	482	804	2.63	0.090	0.305	8.9
320	675	787	2.75	0.087	0.266	8.3
340	926	769	2.83	0.085	0.234	7.8
360	1.246 bar	750	2.93	0.082	0.209	7.5
380	1.645	730	3.01	0.079	0.193	7.4
400	2.136	710	3.05	0.076	0.182	7.3

*Liquid PAB represents a mixture of aromatic hydrocarbons, derivatives of diphenylalkanes and diphenyl (70%), alkyl benzenes (7%) and alkylated condensed aromatic hydrocarbons (21%), the remaining 2% are an admixture of saturated hydrocarbons.

ORGANIC SILICONE COMPOUNDS

Tetracresyloxysilance

$(CH_3C_6H_4O)_4Si$

$t =_{melt} - 36$ °C; $t_{boil} > 400$ ° C at $p = 1$ atm

Thermophysical properties of tetracresyloxysilance [139]: ρ (kg/m³), c_p (kJ/kg · deg), i (kJ/kg), λ (W/m · deg), η (N · s/m²), ν and α (m²/s) and Prandtl number Pr

t, °C	ϱ	c_p	i	λ	$\eta \cdot 10^5$	$\nu \cdot 10^6$	$a \cdot 10^6$	Pr
10	1135	1.80	17.6	0.124	19 286	170	219	2800
20	1128	1.84	36.0	0.123	5 958	52.9	214	890
30	1120	1.93	54.8	0.122	2 832	25.3	204	450
40	1113	2.01	74.5	0.121	2 244	20.7	194	370
50	1105	2.09	95.0	0.121	1 597	14.5	189	280
60	1097	2.14	116.4	0.120	1 009	9.20	184	180
70	1089	2.22	138.2	0.119	751	6.90	177	140
80	1080	2.30	160.8	0.117	605	5.60	170	118
90	1072	2.39	184.2	0.116	495	4.62	164	101
100	1064	2.47	208.5	0.115	407	3.82	158	87.2
110	1057	2.55	233.6	0.114	349	3.30	152	78.2
120	1050	2.64	260.0	0.114	294	2.80	148	68.1
130	1043	2.76	287.2	0.113	250	2.40	141	61.3
140	1035	2.85	315.3	0.112	220	2.13	136	56.4
150	1027	2.97	344.2	0.110	196	1.91	130	52.9
160	1019	3.06	374.3	0.110	181	1.78	128	50.1
170	1011	3.14	405.3	0.109	165	1.63	124	47.3
180	1003	3.27	437.5	0.108	151	1.51	119	45.7
190	995	3.39	470.6	0.107	140	1.41	114	44.5
200	987	3.48	504.9	0.106	129	1.31	111	42.5
210	978	3.60	540.5	0.106	119	1.21	108	40.3
220	970	3.73	576.9	0.105	112	1.15	104	39.8
230	961	3.81	614.6	0.104	103	1.08	102	38.1
240	953	3.94	653.6	0.102	95	1.00	98	36.8
250	944	4.06	693.3	0.101	86	0.91	95	34.5
260	936	4.14	734.4	0.100	78	0.84	93	32.5
270	928	4.27	776.6	0.100	72	0.78	91	30.8
280	919	4.40	820.2	0.099	66	0.72	88	29.4
290	910	4.52	865.4	0.098	61	0.67	86	28.0
300	902	4.65	911.5	0.096	58	0.64	84	27.4
310	893	4.77	958.4	0.095	55	0.62	82	27.2
320	884	4.86	1048.4	0.095	53	0.60	80	27.0
330	875	4.98	1055.9	0.094	50	0.58	78	26.3
340	866	5.11	1106.2	0.093	47	0.55	76	26.1
350	858	5.23	1157.6	0.092	45	0.53	74	26.0

Diethylsiloxane (silicone)

Molecular weight 400

$t_{boil} = 282$ °C at 760 mm Hg; $t_{melt} = -70$ °C

Thermophysical properties of diethylsiloxane [140]: ρ (kg/m³), c_p (kJ/kg · deg), λ (W/m · deg), η (N · s/m²). r (kJ/kg) and Prandtl number Pr

t, °C	p, mm Hg	ϱ	c_p	λ	$\eta \cdot 10^3$	r	Pr
0		971	2.04	0.137	19.7	131.5	293
10		964	2.05	0.135	13.2	131.0	215
20		956	2.06	0.133	9.71	130.6	144
30		949	2.06	0.130	7.35	130.6	111
40		942	2.07	0.128	5.78	130.2	91.5
50		935	2.08	0.127	4.66	130.2	76.7
60		928	2.10	0.124	3.87	129.8	65.0
70		921	2.11	0.122	3.25	129.4	57.0
80		914	2.12	0.120	2.79	129.4	50.0

continued

t, °C	p, mm Hg	ϱ	c_p	λ	$\eta \cdot 10^3$	r	Pr
90		907	2.14	0.117	2.41	129.0	44.5
100	4.0	900	2.15	0.116	2.11	128.5	39.0
110	5.0	893	2.16	0.114	1.86	128.5	35.5
120	7.5	886	2.18	0.112	1.66	128.1	32.2
130	11.5	879	2.19	0.109	1.49	128.1	29.8
140	18.5	871	2.21	0.107	1.34	127.7	27.8
150	25.0	863	2.23	0.105	1.22	127.3	25.9
160	38.0	856	2.24	0.104	1.11	127.3	24.5
170	50.0	848	2.26	0.100	1.02	126.9	23.4
180	70.0	840	2.28	0.098	0.94	126.4	22.2
190	90.0	832	2.30	0.095	0.86	126.4	21.4
200	125.0	825	2.32	0.094	0.80	126.0	19.8
210	175.0	817	2.34	0.092	0.74	126.0	18.5
220	199.0	809	2.36	0.090	0.70	125.6	17.5
230	258.0	802	2.38	0.087	0.65	125.2	17.0
240	368.0	794	2.40	0.085	0.61	124.8	16.8
250	408.0	786	2.43	0.084	0.57	124.3	16.5
260	490.0	779	2.45	0.081	0.54	123.9	16.0
270	587.0	771	2.48	0.079	0.51	123.1	15.5
280	700.0	762	2.50	0.077	0.48	122.7	15.0
290	880.0	753	2.53	0.074	0.45	122.2	14.9
300	1080.0	744	2.55	0.073	0.43	121.8	14.8

Polyorganosiloxane liquids*

Thermophysical properties of polyorganosiloxane liquids [374]: λ (W/m · deg), ρ (kg/m³), c_p (kJ/kg' · deg) and ν (m²/s)

t, °C	λ	ϱ	$\nu \cdot 10^6$	λ	ϱ	c_p	$\nu \cdot 10^6$
		PMS-1.5			PMS-10		
20	0.108	850.0	1.503	0.137	936.2	1.538	9.772
40	0.105	830.8	1.142	0.134	919.0	1.605	7.292
60	0.103	811.5	0.8983	0.131	901.9	1.670	5.333
80	0.100	791.9	0.7440	0.127	884.9	1.734	3.983
100	0.097	772.0	0.6507	0.124	867.9	1.799	3.031
120	0.095	752.4	0.5571	0.121	850.4		2.401
140	0.092	732.9		0.118	833.0		2.078
160				0.115	815.6		1.563
180				0.111	798.0		1.398
200				0.108	780.2		1.269
220				0.105			1.119
240				0.102			0.9692
260							0.8161
		PMS-5			PMS-50		
20	0.124	911.4	5.146	0.155	959.0	1.469	42.23
40	0.121	893.6	3.812	0.151	942.3	1.528	28.98
60	0.118	875.8	2.871	0.148	925.8	1.587	23.16
80	0.115	857.8	2.338	0.144	908.9	1.644	18.48
100	0.112	839.7	1.855	0.141	892.1	1.702	14.41
120	0.109	821.6	1.540	0.137	875.2		11.64
140	0.106	803.3	1.248	0.134	858.1		9.532
160	0.103	785.2	1.085	0.130	841.0		7.421
180	0.100	766.9		0.127	823.9		5.974
200	0.097	748.4		0.123	806.9		5.034
220				0.120			4.112
240				0.116			3.387
260				0.113			2.952

*Soviet designations.

continued

t, °C	λ	ϱ	c_p	$\nu \cdot 10^6$	λ	ϱ	c_p	$\nu \cdot 10^6$
	PMS-100				PMS-400			
20	0.161	967.4	1.421	107.9	0.165	970.4	1.392	395.3
40	0.157	951.0	1.481	69.1	0.161	954.2	1.447	277.9
60	0.154	934.1	1.540	48.85	0.158	937.7	1.500	201.8
80	0.150	917.4	1.597	36.96	0.154	921.0	1.552	148.9
100	0.147	900.9	1.655	28.00	0.151	904.3	1.605	110.3
120	0.143	884.0		22.42	0.147	887.9		86.89
140	0.140	867.6		18.02	0.144	871.0		65.64
160	0.136	850.5		14.69	0.140	854.4		51.38
180	0.133	833.7		12.91	0.137	838.0		40.30
200	0.129	817.0		11.09	0.133	821.8		32.07
220	0.126			9.311	0.130			25.83
240	0.122			8.030	0.127			22.23
260	0.119			7.105	0.123			20.18
280	0.115				0.120			
	PMS-200				PMS-476			
20	0.163	969.2	1.408	216.0	0.166	971.4	1.383	466.1
40	0.160	952.8	1.464	143.6	0.162	955.0	1.438	314.5
60	0.156	936.0	1.518	101.5	0.158	938.6	1.491	230.2
80	0.153	921.0	1.572	75.23	0.155	922.2	1.543	173.9
100	0.149	902.5	1.628	56.21	0.151	905.8	1.597	133.3
120	0.145	885.6		45.10	0.147	889.1		103.2
140	0.142	868.9		34.62	0.144	872.5		82.65
160	0.138	852.1		26.22	0.140	856.0		66.73
180	0.135	835.4		21.54	0.137	839.6		51.64
200	0.131	819.0		16.51	0.133	823.4		41.09
220	0.128			14.93	0.129			32.95
240	0.124			13.54	0.126			26.91
260	0.121			12.51	0.122			23.42
280	0.117				0.119			
300	0.113				0.115			
	PMS-700				PFMS-4			
20	0.167	972.0	1.373	697.9	0.148	1101.5		658.7
40	0.163	956.0	1.427	476.8	0.146	1086.7		198.8
60	0.159	939.4	1.479	341.6	0.143	1072.2		96.58
80	0.156	923.0	1.530	254.6	0.141	1057.8		49.92
100	0.152	906.9	1.584	196.4	0.138	1043.6		31.44
120	0.149	890.6		156.0	0.136	1029.0		20.47
140	0.145	874.0		124.2	0.133	1015.0		14.68
160	0.142	857.8		101.8	0.131	1000.6		12.10
180	0.138	841.6		83.53	0.128	986.4		9.69
200	0.134	825.5		69.72	0.126	972.0		7.215
220	0.131			57.04	0.124			6.238
240	0.127			47.91	0.121			5.254
260	0.124			42.85	0.119			4.283
280	0.120				0.116			
300	0.117				0.114			
	PMS-1000				PFMS-2/5 1			
20	0.167	972.4	1.372	1013.3	0.131	1019.6		16.93
40	0.163	956.6	1.424	684.4	0.128	1003.9		9.88
60	0.160	940.7	1.474	492.4	0.125	988.4		6.263
80	0.156	924.1	1.523	375.0	0.122	972.9		4.342
100	0.153	908.0	1.575	283.0	0.119	957.1		3.17
120	0.149	891.9		220.1	0.117	941.6		2.54
140	0.146	875.2		171.0	0.114	926.0		1.969
160	0.142	859.0		139.7	0.111	910.5		1.647
180	0.139	843.3		114.6	0.108	894.9		1.409
200	0.135	827.4		93.23	0.105	879.3		1.171
220	0.132			78.92	0.103			1.088
240	0.128			66.43	0.100			1.003
260	0.125			56.17	0.097			0.9211
280	0.121				0.094			
300	0.118				0.092			

continued

t,°C	λ	ρ	c_p	$\nu \cdot 10^6$	λ	ρ	c_p	$\nu \cdot 10^6$
	VM-1322				PES-2			
20	0.142	999.5		23.25	0.135	921.5	1.773	11.40
40	0.139	983.2		14.58	0.132	905.1	1.828	7.688
60	0.136	967.0		10.05	0.128	888.9	1.881	5.098
80	0.133	951.1		7.421	0.125	872.6	1.933	3.715
100	0.130	935.0		5.63	0.122	856.0	1.986	2.832
120	0.127	919.0		4.553	0.119	839.9		2.282
140	0.124	903.0		3.582	0.116	823.4		1.785
160	0.121	887.0		2.914	0.112	807.0		1.506
180	0.118	870.7		2.411	0.109	791.1		
200	0.115	854.6		1.987				
220	0.112			1.798				
240	0.109			1.522				
260	0.106			1.299				
280	0.103							
300	0.100							
	PES-1				PES-3			
20	0.130	869.8	1.837	3.135	0.138	947.4	1.722	13.76
40	0.127	853.8	1.898	2.224	0.135	932.0	1.770	8.784
60	0.123	838.4	1.957	1.625	0.132	916.8	1.816	6.011
80	0.120	822.9	2.014	1.263	0.129	901.3	1.862	4.562
100	0.117	807.0	2.073	1.068	0.126	886.4	1.908	3.376
120	0.113	791.9		0.8695	0.123	871.0		2.711
140	0.110	775.7			0.119	855.9		2.048
160					0.116	841.0		1.722
180					0.113	826.1		1.435
200								1.148
220								1.007
240								0.8582
260								0.7074
	PES-4				PES-5			
20	0.142	965.6	1.679	41.52	0.157	998.0	1,586	267.8
40	0.140	950.9	1.723	25.34	0.154	984.1	1,622	143.6
60	0.137	936.0	1.766	15.85	0.152	970.6	1,658	83.61
80	0.134	921.2	1.808	10.78	0.149	956.8	1,694	52.85
100	0.131	906.5	1.852	7.832	0.146	943.0	1,729	32.92
120	0.128	892.0		5.741	0.144	929.0		22.01
140	0.125	877.2		4.426	0.141	915.4		17.05
160	0.122	862.9		3.534	0.138	901.7		12.95
180	0.119	848.3		2.784	0.135	888.1		10.98
200	0.116	834.0		2.259	0.133	874.3		7.284
220	0.113			1.901	0.130			6.101
240				1.538	0.127			4.983
260				1.185	0.125			3.754

SALTPETER MIXTURE *

$t_{melt} = 148\ °C$

Thermophysical properties of saltpeter mixture [327]: ρ (kg/m³), λ (W/m · deg), η (N · s/m²), *i* (kJ/kg) and Prandtl number Pr

t, °C	ρ	λ	$\eta \cdot 10^3$	i	Pr
150	1975	0.441	17.76	337.9	57.4
160	1967	0.440	14.65	352.1	47.5
170	1959	0.438	12.28	366.3	39.9
180	1951	0.437	10.47	380.6	34.1

*40% $NaNO_2$, 53% KNO_3 and 7% $NaNO_3$.

continued

t, °C	ϱ	λ	$\eta \cdot 10^3$	i	Pr
190	1943	0.436	9.03	394.8	29.5
200	1934	0.435	7.88	409.0	25.8
210	1926	0.434	6.95	423.3	22.8
220	1919	0.433	6.18	437.5	20.4
230	1911	0.430	5.56	451.8	18.4
240	1903	0.428	5.02	466.0	16.7
250	1895	0.426	4.57	480.2	15.3
260	1887	0.419	4.18	494.5	14.2
270	1879	0.413	3.85	508.7	13.3
280	1871	0.407	3.56	522.9	12.4
290	1864	0.400	3.31	537.2	11.8
300	1856	0.393	3.09	551.4	11.2
310	1849	0.387	2.90	565.6	10.7
320	1841	0.381	2.71	579.9	10.1
330	1834	0.374	2.57	594.1	9.76
340	1826	0.369	2.43	608.3	9.39
350	1819	0.362	2.31	622.6	9.11
360	1812	0.356	2.18	636.8	8.74
370	1804	0.349	2.09	651.0	8.52
380	1797	0.343	2.00	665.3	8.30
390	1790	0.336	1.91	679.5	8.10
400	1783	0.330	1.834	693.8	7.91
410	1776	0.323	1.761	708.0	7.76
420	1769	0.317	1.695	722.2	7.60
430	1762	0.310	1.635	736.5	7.50
440	1754	0.305	1,578	750.7	7.37
450	1748	0.298	1.525	764.9	7.29
460	1741	0.292	1.477	779.2	7.20
470	1734	0.285	1.432	793.4	7.16
480	1728	0.279	1.390	807.6	7.09
490	1721	0.272	1.349	821.9	7.06
500	1715	0.266	1.312	836.1	7.02
510	1708	0.259	1.277	850.3	7.01
520	1701	0.254	1.246	864.6	7.00
530	1695	0.248	1.214	878.8	7.00
540	1688	0.241	1.186	892.6	7.00
550	1681	0.235	1.157	906.9	7.00

Sodium-potassium Alloy*

$t_{melt} = -11$ °C; $t_{boil} = 784$ °C at $p = 1$ atm

Thermophysical properties of NaK [394] : ρ (kg/m^3), c_p (kJ/kg · deg),

t, °C	ϱ	c_p	λ	$\nu \cdot 10^8$	$\mathrm{Pr} \cdot 10^2$
20	872	1.30	22.1	93.0	4.76
50	865	1.23	22.7	78.5	3.69
100	852	1.14	23.3	60.7	2.51
150	840	1.09	23.8	51.7	1.98
200	828	1.07	24.5	45.2	1.64
250	815	1.06	25.1	40.3	1.38
300	803	1.04	25.8	36.6	1.18
350	790	1.02	26.4	33.4	1.02
400	778	1.00	27.1	30.8	0.89
450	765	0.984	27.7	28.2	0.77
500	753	0.967	28.4	26.7	0.69
550	741	0.950	29.0	25.2	0.61
600	729	0.934	29.6	23.7	0.54
650	716	0.917	30.2	22.5	0.49
700	704	0.900	30.9	21.4	0.44

*) 25% Na and 75% K.

Lead-bismuth Alloy*

$t_{melt} = 123.5$ °C; $t_{boil} = 1670$ °C

Thermophysical properties of Pb-Bi [394]: ρ (kg/m^3), c_p (kJ/kg · deg), λ (W/m · deg), ν (m^2/s) and Prandtl number Pr

t, °C	ϱ	c_p	λ	$\nu \cdot 10^8$	Pr · 10^2
130	10 570	0.146	10.9	31.4	4.45
150	10 547	0.146	11.2	28.9	4.00
200	10 486	0.146	11.7	24.3	3.18
250	10 425	0.146	12.2	21.0	2.62
300	10 364	0.146	12.7	18.7	2.24
350	10 300	0.146	13.1	17.1	1.97
400	10 242	0.146	13.7	15.7	1.72
450	10 180	0.146	14.2	14.6	1.54
500	10 120	0.146	14.6	13.6	1.37
550	10 060	0.146	15.2	12.9	1.25
600	10 000	0.146	15.8	12.4	1.15
650	9 940	0.146	16.3	11.8	1.06
700	9 876	0.146	16.7	11.4	0.99

*45% Pb and 55% Bi.

Chapter 16

OILS

Oil MS-20

Thermophysical properties of oil MS-20 [328]: ρ (kg/m^3), c_p (kJ/kg · deg), λ (W/m · deg), η (N · s/m^2), β (bar^{-1}) and Prandtl number Pr

t, °C	ϱ	c_p	λ	$\eta \cdot 10^3$	$\beta \cdot 10^4$	Pr
0	903.6	1.98	0.136	6860	6.27	100 000
10	898.0	2.01	0.135	2430	6.31	36 200
20	892.5	2.04	0.134	999.6	6.35	15 400
30	886.5	2.07	0.133	466	6.38	7 300
40	881.0	2.11	0.131	235	6.42	3 780
50	875.5	2.14	0.130	131	6.46	2 140
60	869.6	2.16	0.129	78.7	6.51	1 320
70	864.0	2.20	0.128	50.2	6.55	860
80	858.5	2.23	0.127	33.8	6.60	590
90	852.5	2.26	0.126	23.7	6.64	424
100	847.0	2.29	0.126	17.2	6.69	316
110	841.5	2.32	0.124	13.0	6.73	244
120	835.5	2.35	0.123	10.1	6.77	194
130	830.0	2.38	0.122	8.04	6.82	157
140	824.5	2.42	0.121	6.52	6.87	130
150	818.5	2.44	0.120	5.38	6.92	110

Transformer oil (Standard 982–68)

Thermophysical properties of transformer oil [384]: λ (W/m · deg), c_p (kJ/kg · deg), ρ (kg/m^3), η (N · s/m^2), ν and α (m^2/s) and Prandtl number Pr

t, °C	$\lambda \cdot 10^3$	$c_p \cdot 10^2$	ϱ	$\eta \cdot 10^3$	$\nu \cdot 10^6$	$a \cdot 10^{10}$	$\mathrm{Pr} \cdot 10^{-2}$
−50	116	170	922	29 320	31 800	742	4286
−45	116	170	919	15 164	16 500	742	2224
−40	116	168	916	3 866	4 220	750	563
−35	115	167	913	2 004	2 195	755	291
−30	115	165	910	1 183	1 300	764	170
−25	114	163	907	691.3	762.2	773	98.5
−20	114	162	904	365.6	404.4	778	52.0
−15	114	160	901	189.7	210.5	788	27.0
−10	113	160	898	108.1	120.4	788	15.3
− 5	113	160	895	70.79	79.10	787	10.0
0	112	162	891	55.24	67.45	778	8.67
5	112	163	888	43.73	49.25	772	6.38
10	111	165	885	33.45	37.80	763	4.95
15	111	168	882	26.37	29.90	749	3.99
20	111	171	879	21.10	24.00	736	3.26
25	110	175	876	16.60	18.95	720	2.63
30	110	178	873	13.44	15.40	707	2.18
40	109	183	867	9.364	10.80	688	1.57

*Reprinted for information only.

continued

t, °C	$\lambda \cdot 10^3$	$c_p \cdot 10^3$	ϱ	$\eta \cdot 10^3$	$\nu \cdot 10^6$	$a \cdot 10^{10}$	$Pr \cdot 10^{-2}$
50	108	187	860	6.708	7.80	673	1.16
60	108	191	854	5.338	6.25	659	0.95
70	107	194	848	4.070	4.80	648	0.74
80	106	198	842	3.242	3.85	635	0.61
90	105	201	835	2.588	3.10	625	0.50
100	104	204	829	1.741	2.10	616	0.34

Oil AMG-10

Thermophysical properties of oil AMG-10[324]: ρ (kg/m³), c_p (kJ/kg · deg), λ (W/m · deg) and ν (cm³)

t, °C	ϱ	c_p	λ	ν	t, °C	ϱ	c_p	λ	ν
20	835.6	1.844	0.1192	21.00	80	794.2	2.135	0.1111	6.13
40	821.8	1.943	0.1163	12.62	100	780.2	2.232	0.1087	4.68
60	808.4	2.039	0.1140	8.48					

Oil TM-1 (VTU–M3–11–62)

Thermophysical properties of oil TM-1 [384]: λ (W/m · deg), c_p (kJ/kg · deg), ρ (kg/m³), η (N · s/m²), ν and α (m²/s) and Prandtl number Pr

t, °C	$\lambda \cdot 10^3$	$c_p \cdot 10^2$	ϱ	$\eta \cdot 10^3$	$\nu \cdot 10^6$	$a \cdot 10^{10}$	$Pr \cdot 10^{-2}$
−50	125	158	934	57 440	61 500	849	7244
−45	125	158	931	29 050	31 200	848	3679
−40	124	158	928	7 888	8 500	849	1001
−35	124	159	925	4 357	4 710	843	559
−30	124	159	922	1 992	2 160	843	256
−25	123	160	918	1 088	1 185	838	141
−20	123	160	915	582.8	637	837	76.1
−15	122	160	912	307.7	337.5	837	40.0
−10	122	161	909	152.3	167.5	831	20.0
− 5	121	161	906	86.80	95.8	831	11.5
0	121	162	903	56.93	63.05	825	7.6
5	120	163	899	40.14	44.65	820	5.4
10	120	163	896	30.55	34.10	820	4.1
15	119	164	893	23.71	26.55	820	3.2
20	119	164	889	18.67	21.00	815	2.6
25	118	165	887	14.90	16.80	809	2.1
30	118	166	884	12.20	13.75	804	1.7
40	117	168	877	8.288	9.45	794	1.2
50	116	170	871	6.097	7.00	784	0.89
60	115	172	864	4.752	5.50	774	0.71
70	114	175	858	3.518	4.10	761	0.54
80	113	178	852	2.897	3.40	747	0.45
90	112	180	845	2.366	2.80	738	0.38
100	111	182	838	1.760	2.10	730	0.29

Oil VM-4 (Standard 7903–56)

Thermophysical properties of oil VM-4 [384]: λ (W/m · deg), c_p (kJ/kg · deg), ρ (kg/m³), η (N · s/m²), ν and α (m²/s) and Prandtl number Pr

t, °C	$\lambda \cdot 10^3$	$c_p \cdot 10^2$	ϱ	$\eta \cdot 10^3$	$\nu \cdot 10^6$	$a \cdot 10^{10}$	$Pr \cdot 10^{-2}$
−30	132	144	933	765 200	820 200	982	83 520
−25	131	146	930	306 900	330 000	968	34 090
−20	131	146	927	46 630	50 300	967	5 201
−15	130	146	924	13 770	14 900	967	1 541

continued

t,°C	$\lambda \cdot 10^3$	$c_p \cdot 10^2$	ϱ	$\eta \cdot 10^3$	$\nu \cdot 10^6$	$a \cdot 10^{10}$	$\Pr \cdot 10^{-2}$
−10	130	146	921	7 239	7 860	966	814
− 5	130	146	918	3 392	3 695	966	382
0	129	146	916	2 006	2 190	966	227
5	129	146	913	1 337	1 465	966	152
10	128	146	910	919.1	1 010	966	104.5
15	128	147	907	564.5	622.5	965	64.5
20	127	148	904	300.8	332.8	952	35.0
25	127	149	901	219.2	243.3	945	25.7
30	126	150	898	145.3	161.8	939	17.2
35	126	151	895	101.4	113.3	932	12.1
40	126	152	892	78.50	88.00	926	9.5
45	125	152	889	59.83	67.30	926	7.3
50	125	152	886	45.63	51.50	926	5.5
55	124	153	883	36.47	41.30	920	4.5
60	124	154	880	29.92	34.00	914	3.7
65	123	155	877	24.55	28.00	907	3.1
70	123	156	874	20.36	23.30	902	2.6
80	122	158	868	14.58	16.80	890	1.9
90	121	160	862	10.51	12.20	878	1.4
100	120	162	856	7.618	8.90	868	1.0

Oil KhF-22 (Standard 5546–66)

Thermophysical properties of oil KhF-22 [384]: λ (W/m · deg), c_p (kJ/kg · deg), ρ (kg/m^3), η (N · s/m^2), ν and α (m^2/s) and Prandtl number Pr

t, °C	$\lambda \cdot 10^3$	$c_p \cdot 10^2$	ϱ	$\eta \cdot 10^3$	$\nu \cdot 10^6$	$a \cdot 10^{10}$	$\Pr \cdot 10^{-2}$
−55	166	163	1050	108 800	103 600	969	10 690
−50	165	164	1045	77 750	74 400	963	7 726
−45	164	164	1042	45 850	44 000	962	4 574
−40	164	164	1039	13 610	13 100	960	1 365
−35	163	164	1035	5 382	5 200	960	542
−30	162	164	1032	3 168	3 070	958	320
−25	161	164	1028	2 157	2 098	957	219
−20	161	164	1024	1 418	1 385	957	145
−15	160	164	1020	905.7	888.0	956	93.0
−10	159	164	1017	569.5	560.0	954	59.0
− 5	158	164	1013	372.7	368.0	953	37.0
0	158	164	1010	266.6	264.0	952	28.0
5	157	164	1006	202.9	201.7	952	21.0
10	156	164	1002	138.7	138.5	950	14.6
15	156	164	999	83.56	83.65	949	8.8
20	155	164	995	61.78	62.10	948	6.5
25	154	165	992	47.61	48.00	941	5.1
30	153	166	988	38.04	38.50	935	4.1
40	152	168	980	24.97	25.45	921	2.8
50	150	168	973	17.22	17.70	919	1.9
60	149	170	966	12.36	12.80	906	1.4
70	147	170	958	9.436	9.85	905	1.0
80	146	170	951	7.313	7.65	903	0.85
90	144	170	944	5.853	6.20	900	0.69
100	143	170	936	5.569	5.95	897	0.66

REFERENCES

1. Serdiuk, L. S., *Zhurnal Fiz. Khim,* No. 2 (1969).
2. Liquid Hydrogen, Mir Press, 1964.
3. Serdiuk, L. S., *Kholodil'naya tekhnika i tekhnologiya,* No. 7 (1968), Kiev.
4. Kazavchinskiy, Ya. Z. and Serdiuk, L. S. Collection GSSD No. 2, Standards Press, 1970.
5. Serdiuk, L. S., Collection GSSD, Standards Press, No. 2, 1970, No. 3, 1971.
6. Serdiuk, L. S., *Zhurnal Fiz. Khim.* No. 3 (1969).
7. Serdiuk, L. S., Cand. dissertation, Odessa Institute of Naval Engineers, 1969.
8. Gorykin, S. F. Cand. dissertation, Odessa Technological Institute (Lomonosov), 1968.
9. Gorykin, S. F. et al, *Teplo- i massoperenos,* 7, 142 (1968).
10. Timrot, D. L., Liusternik, V. E. and Teterina, I. N., *Trudy metrologicheskikh institutov SSSR* (VNIIFTRI), No. 92 (152), 102 (1967).
11. Tsederberg, N. V., Popov, V. N. and Andreev, I. I., *Teploenergetika,* No. 4 (1965).
12. Andreev, I. I., Cand. dissertation, Moscow Energetics Institute, 1968.
13. Vargaftik, N. B., Vasilevskaya, Iu. D., *Teplofizika vysokikh temperatur,* 7(5), 913 (1969).
14. Belov, V. A., *Teplofizika vysokikh temperatur* 5(1), 37 (1967).
15. Vargaftik, N. B. and Filippov, L. P. Thermal Conductivity of Gases and Liquids (Data Book), Standards Press, 1970.
16. Johnson, V. J., Properties of Materials at Low Temperatures, N. Y., 1961.
17. Vukalovich, M. P., Rivkin, S. L. and Aleksandrov, A. A., Tables of Thermodynamic Properties of Water and Steam, Standards Press, 1969.
18. Rivkin, S. L., *Teploenergetika,* No. 7 (1968).
19. Vargaftik, N. B., Volyak, L. D. and Volkov, B. N., Transactions of the VII International Conference on the Properties of Water and Steam, Tokyo, 1968, Transactions of All-Union Conference on Thermodynamics, Thermophysical Properties of Substances, Leningrad, 1970.
20. Kessel'man, P. M. and Blank, Yu. I. Transaction of the VII International Conference on the Properties of Water and Steam, Tokyo, 1968.
21. Kessel'man, P. M., Blank, Yu. I. and Mogilebskii, V. I., *Teplofizika vysokikh temperatur* 6(4), 658 (1968).
22. Kessel'man, P. M. et al. *Teplo- i massoperenos* 7, 132 (1968).
23. Kessel'man, P. M. *Teploenergetika,* No. 3, 4 (1960).
24. Kirillin, V. A. and Ulybin, S. A., *Teploenergetika,* No. 4 (1959).
25. Kirillin, V. A. (ed.) Heavy Water, Gosenergo Press, 1963.
26. Agaev, N. A. and Iusibova, A. D., *Atomnaya energiya* 23(2), 149 (1967).
27. Rivkin, S. L., and Egorov, B. N., *Atomnaya energiya* 7(5), (1959).
28. Volyak, L. D., Doctoral dissertation, Moscow Aviation Institute, 1969.
29. Volyak, L. D., Collection GSSD. No. 1, Standards Press, 1968.
30. Rybakov, V. V. Thermodynamic properties of gases at high temperatures, Mashinostroenie Press, 1968.
31. Solov'ev, A. N. Studies of thermophysical properties of substances, Nauka Press, Siberian Division, 1967.
32. Shpil rain, E. E. and Kraynova, I. F., *Thermofizika vysokikh temperatur* 5(1), 58 (1967); 6(3), 451 (1968).
33. Kraynova, I. F., Candidate dissertation, High Temperature Institute of the Academy of Sciences of the USSR, 1968.
34. Vargaftik, N. B. and Voshchinin, A. A., *Teplofizika vysokikh temperatur* 5(5), 802 (1967).
35. Rowlinson, J., *Physica* **19**, 303 (1953).
36. Tarzimanov, A. A. and Lozovoi, V. S. Trudy of the Kazan Chemical Engineering Institute, No. 45, 241 (1970).

37. Kirillin, V. A. (ed.) Thermophysical properties of alkali metals, Standards Press, 1970.
38. Lozovoy, V. S., Candidate Dissertation, Kazan Chemical Engineering Institute, 1971.
39. Avilova, I. V. and Belov, V. A., *Teplofizika vysokikh temperatur* **5**(3), 433 (1967).
40. Vukalovich, M. P. and Fokin, R. V., Thermophysical properties of mercury, Standards, Press, 1972.
41. Stone, J., Eving, C., Spann, J., *Chem. Eng. Data* **11**(3), 315 (1966).
42. Vargaftik, N. B. (ed.) Thermophysical Properties of Substances. A Handbook, Gosenergo Press, 1956.
43. Wolling, I., *J. Phys. Chem.* **67**, 1380 (1963).
44. Vargaftik, N. B. and Yakush, L. V., *Teplofizika vysokikh temperatur* **8**(6), 1182 (1970).
45. Golubev, I. F., Physico-chemical studies, No. 24, State University of Nitogen Industry (1969).
46. Zagoruchenko, V. A., Theory of Designing Naval Refrigeration Equipment, 1969, with Nguen Tan, Transactions of All-Union Conference on Thermophysical Properties of Gases, Leningrad, 1969.
47. Golubev, I. F., and Gnezdinov, N. E., *Gazovaya promyshlennost',* 12 (1965).
48. Tsederberg, N. V., *Teploenergetika,* 4 (1965).
49. Dawe, R. A., Smith, E. B., *J. Chem. Phys.* **52**(2), 693 (1970).
50. Hilsenrath, J., Tables of Thermal Properties of Gases, NBS, Circular 564, 1955.
51. Din, F., Thermodynamic Functions of Gases, Vol. 1, 2, 3, 1956. Butterworths, London.
52. Golubev, I. F., Viscosity of Gases and Gas Mixtures, Fizmat Press, 1959.
53. Golovskiy, E. A., and Tsymarnyi, A. L., Collection of GSSD, No. 2, Standards Press, 1969.
54. Golovskiy, E. A., and Tsymarnyi, A. L., *Teploenergetika,* 1 (1970).
55. Parks, G. S., Todd, S. S., Shomate, C. H., *J. Am. Chem. Soc.* **58**(12), 2505 (1936).
56. Kessel'man, P. M. et al.,*Inzhenerno-fizicheskii zhurnal* **5**, 4 (1965).
57. Kotliarevskiy, P. A. Candidate Dissertation, Odessa Technological Institute (Lomonosov), 1966.
58. Kessel'man, P. M. and Kotlyarevskiy, P. A. Thermodynamic properties of Carbon dioxide in the temperature range from 273–4000 °K and pressures up to 600 bar. Odessa Technological Institute, 1965.
59. Vukalovich, M. P. and Altunin, V. V. Thermophysical properties of carbon, Atom Press, 1965.
60. Bonilla, C. F., Brooks, R. D., Walker, P. Z., *Proc. of General Discussion of Heat Transfer, The Inst. of Mech. Eng.,* 167 (1951).
61. Zagoruchenko, V. A., and Zhuravlev, A. M. Thermophysical properties of methane, Standards Press, 1969.
62. Rossini, F. D. et al., Selected Values of Physical and Thermodynamic properties of Hydrocarbons and Related Compounds, NBS, Pittsburg, 1953.
63. Gelperin, I. I., Handbook on separation of gas mixtures, Goskhim Press, 1953.
64. Volyak, L. D., *Teploenergetika,* 7 (1958).
65. Tatevskiy, V. M. (ed.) Physico-chemical Properties of Individual Hydrocarbons, Gostoptech Press, 1960.
66. Mamedov, A. M. Doctoral dissertation, Ac. Sciences Azervaydzhan SSR 1959; Doklady Ac. Scie. AzSSR **4**(10), (1948); Izv. MVO SSSR: Series: Petroleum and Gas **3**(7), (1958); **6**(5), (1961).
67. Olds, R., Reamer, H., Sage, B., *Ind. Eng. Chem.* **36**(3), 279 (1944).
68. Golubev, I. F., and Agaev, N. A. Viscosity of limiting hydrocarbons, Azerbaydzhan State Press, Baku, 1964.
69. Kazavchinskiy, Ya. Z. and Katkhe, O. I. *Zhurnal fizicheskoi khmii* **29**(12), (1955).
70. Bonilla, C., Weiner, H., *Trans.ASME* 78(6), 1285 (1956).
71. Timmermans, J., Physico-Chemical Constants of Pure Organic Compounds, Interscience, N. Y., 1950.
72. Vargaftik, N. B., Handbook of Thermophysical properties of gases and liquids, Fizmat Press, 1963.
73. Atkins, B. E., Bastick, R. E., Ibbs, T. L., *Proc. Roy. Soc.* **A172**, 142 (1939).
74. Doulsin, D. R., Huffman, H. M., *J. Am. Chem. Soc.* **68**(9), 1704 (1946).
75. Parks, G. S., Huffman, H. M., Thomas, B., *J. Am. Chem. Soc.* **52**, 1032 (1930).
76. Osborn, N. S., Ginnings, D. C., *J. Res. NBS* **39**(5),453 (1947).
77. Huffman, H. M., Parks, G. S., Bormore, M., *J. Am. Chem. Soc.* **53**, 3876 (1931).
78. Mukhamedzianov, G. Kh, et al., Izv. MVO USSR, Series: Petroleum and Gas, No. 9, 75 (1963).
79. Mukhamedzianov, G. Kh., Candidate dissertation, Kazan Chemical Engineering Institute, 1962.
80. Doulsin, D. R., Huffman, H. M., *J. Am. Chem. Soc.* **68**(2), 173 (1946).
81. Aston, J. G., Szasz, G. J., Fink, H. L., *J. Am. Chem. Soc.* **65**(6), 1135 (1943).
82. Huffman, H. M., Todd, S. S., Oliver, G. D., *J. Am. Chem. Soc.* 71(2), 584 (1949).
83. Golubev, I. F. and Petrov, V. A., Trudy of GIAP, No. 2 (1953).
84. Naziev, Ya. M. and Abasov, A. A., Transaction of the Third All–Union Conference on Thermophysics, Thermophysical properties of Gases, Nauka Press, Moscow, 1970, Izvestiya MVO SSSR, Series Petroleum and Gas **13**(3), (1968); *Khimiya i tekhnologiya topliv i masel,* No. 3, 22 (1970).
85. Borovik, E. et al., *Zhurnal tekhnicheskoi fiziki* **10**(12) (1940).
86. Michels, A., Wassernaar, T., Louwers, K., *Appl. Scient. Res.* **A4**(1), 34 (1953).
87. Marchmann, H., Prengle, H., Motard, P., *Ind. Eng. Chem. 41,* 2658 (1949).

88. Olds, R., Sage, B., Lacey, W., *Ind. Eng. Chem.* **38**(3), 301 (1946).
89. Todd, S. S., Parks, G. S., *J. Am. Chem. Soc.* **58**(1), 134 (1936).
90. Day, F., Felsing, M., *J. Am. Chem. Soc.* 73(10), 4839 (1951).
91. Todd, S. S., Oliver, G. D., Huffman, H. M., *J. Am. Chem. Soc.* **69**(6), 1579 (1947).
92. Scott, R. B. et al., *J. Res. NBS* **35**(1), 39 (1945).
93. Kessel'man, P. M. et al., Transaction of the Third All–Union Conference on Thermophysics, Thermophysical Properties of Gases, Nauka Press, Moscow, 1970.
94. Henning, F., Wärmetechnische Richtwerte, Phys.-Technische Reichsanstalt, Berlin, 1938.
95. Mamedov, A. M. et al., Izv. MVO SSSR: Series: Petroleum and Gas **12**(6), 72 (1967).
96. Huffman, H. M., Parks, G. S., Daniels, A. C., *J. Am. Chem. Soc.* **52**(4), 1547 (1930).
97. Vargaftik, N. B., Izvestiya VTI, No. 8 (1949).
98. Corruccini, R. I., Ginnings, D. C., *J. Am. Chem. Soc.* **68**(2), 153 (1946).
99. Gutrie, G. B., Ralph, I. R., Spitzer, W., *J. Am. Chem. Soc.* **66**(12), 2120 (1944).
100. Kurbatov, V. Ya., *Zhurnal obshchey khimii* 18(11), 1999 (1947).
101. Vukalovich, M. P. et al., Thermophysical properties of organic coolants, Atom Press, 1969.
102. Matveev, I. G. et al., *Zhurnal prikladnoi khimii* **31**(6), 868 (1958).
103. Vargaftik, N. B. et al., Izv. MVO SSSR, Series: Petroleum and Gas, No. 3 (1963).
104. Volkov, B. N. *Zhurnal fizicheskoi khimii,* **45**(1), 182 (1971).
105. Badylkes, I. S. Kholodilnaya tekhnika, Encyclopedic Dictionary, Vol. 1, Gosenergo Press, 1960.
106. Kletskii, A. V., Kholodilnaya tekhnika, No. 1 (1967); Tables of thermodynamic properties of Freon-11, Leningrad Technological Institute of Refrigeration Industry, 1967.
107. Tsvetkov, O. B., Izv. MVO; Series: Energetika, No. 5 (1965); *Kholodilnaya tekhnika,* No. 4 (1965); *Inzhenerno-fizicheskii zhurnal,* No. 1 (1965); Candidate dissertation, Leningrad Technological Institute, 1965.
108. Zeise, H., Thermodynamik Tabellen, B.III/1, S. Hirzel, Leipzig, 1954.
109. Geller, Z. I. et al., *Kholodilnaya tekhnika,* No. 4, 60 (1969).
110. Kletskii, A. V., Tables of thermodynamic properties of Freon-22, Standards Press, 1969.
111. Babushian, M. G. Candidate dissertation, Moscow Energetics Institute, 1953.
112. Guthrie, G. B., Huffman, H. M., *J. Am. Chem. Soc.* **65**, 1139 (1943).
113. Kletskii, A. V., *Kholodilnaya tekhnika,* No. 4 (1967); Tables of thermodynamic properties of Freon-C-318, Leningrad Technological Institute of Refrigeration Industry.
114. Vold, R. D., *J. Am. Chem. Soc.* **59**, 1515 (1937).
115. Stull, D., *Ind. Eng. Chem.* 39(4), 517 (1947).
116. Woolf, I. K., Sibbit, W. L., *Ind. Eng. Chem.* **46**(9), 1947 (1954).
117. Erdly, M., Garret, L., Benignus, P., *Ind. Eng. Chem.* **41**(7) (1949).
118. Kopylov, N. I., *Inzhenerno-fizicheskii zhurnal,* No. 11, (1960).
119. Golubev, I. F., and Vasilkovskaya, T. N., *Teploenergetika,* No. 5 and 6 (1969).
120. Vukalovich, M. P. et al., *Teploenergetika,* No.2, 70 (1960); No. 10, 63 (1960).
121. Zubarev, V. N. and Aleksandrov, A. A. *Teploenergetika,* No. 3 (1963).
122. Rivkin, S. P. and Egorov, B. N *Teploenergetika,* No. 7 (1961).
123. Rivkin, S. L. and Vinnikova, A. N. *Teploenergetika,* No. 6 (1964).
124. Fiock, E., Ginnings, D., Helton, W., *J. Res. NBS* **6**, 881 (1931).
125. Khalilov, Kh. M. *Zhurnal tekhnicheskoi fiziki* 8(13–14), 1249 (1938).
126. Martin, J. J., *J. Chem. Eng. Data* 8, 4 (1963).
127. Cosner, J. L., Gadliardo, J. E., Storvick, T. S., *J. Chem. Eng. Data* **6**, 360 (1961).
128. Harrison, R. H., Williamson, K. D., *J. Chem. Phys.* **26**, 1409 (1957).
129. Hales, J. L., Cox, J. D., Lees, E. B., *Trans. Faraday Soc.* **59**, 7 (1963).
130. Berman, N. S., Larkam, C. W., McKetta, J. J., *J. Chem. Eng. Data* **9**, 2 (1964).
131. Kagan, S. E. and Chechetkin, A. V. Organic high-temperature coolants, Goschem Press, 1951.
132. Trehin, R., *Ann. Phys.* 9 (15), 2461 (1921).
133. Parks, G. S., Kelley, K. K., *J. Am. Chem. Soc.* **47**, 2089 (1925).
134. Burriel-Marti, A., *Bull. chim. Belg.* **39**, 590 (1930).
135. Ginnings, D. C., Furukawa, G. T., *J. Am. Chem. Soc.* 75(3), 522 (1953).
136. Lang. H., *Proc. Roy. Soc.* **A118**, 138 (1928).
137. Blacet, A., Leighton, B., Bartlett, E., *J. Phys. Chem.* **35**, 1935 (1931).
138. Ferguson, A., Miller, J., *Proc. Phys. Soc.* **45**, 194 (1933).
139. Baklastov, A. M. and Grigoryev, V. A., *Promyshlennaya energetika,* 6 (1956).
140. Sokolov, S. N. et al., *Teploenergetika,* No. 1 (1961).
141. Vasserman, A. A. et al., Thermophysical properties of air and its components, Nauka Press, 1965.
142. Vasserman, A. A. and Rabinovich, V. A. Thermophysical properties of liquid air and its components, Standards Press, 1968.
143. Bestuzhev, A. S. Candidate dissertation, Odessa Lomonosov Technological Institute, 1968.
144. Martinek, F., Thermodynamic and Transport Properties of Gases, Liquids and Solids, Symp. on Thermal Properties, Purdue Univ., 1959.
145. Vukalovich, M. P. et al., *Teploenergetika,* No. 1 (1960).

146. Needham, D. P., Ziebland, H., *J. Int. Heat Mass Transfer,* 1387 (1965).
147. Kudashev, Kh. Kh., Candidate dissertation, OIIMF, 1964.
148. Shchekotalina, S. A. Candidate dissertation, Odessa Lomosov Technological Institute, 1967.
149. Elverum, G., Doescher, R., *J. Chem. Phys.* **20**(12), 1834 (1952).
150. Kapoor, R. M., Martin, J. J., Thermodynamic Properties of Chlorine, Univ. of Michigan, 1957.
151. McCarty, R. D., Stewart, R. B., Second Symp. on Thermophysical Properties, ASME, 1962, p. 1071.
152. Tsederberg, N. V. et al., Thermophysical properties of Helium, Atom Press, 1969.
153. Kemp. J. D., Egan, C. J., *J. Am. Chem. Soc.* **60**(7), 1521 (1938).
154. Rieveld, A. O., van Itterbeek, A., Velds, C. A., *Physica* **25**(3), 205 (1959).
155. McCarty, R. D., Stewart, R. B., Third Symp. on Thermophysical Properties, ASME, 1965, p. 84.
156. Sengers, J. V., Bolk, W. T., Stigter, C. J., *Physica* **30**, 1018 (1964).
157. Löchtermann, E., *Cryogenic,* **44** (March 1944).
158. Kulik, P. P. et al., *Teplofizika vysokikh temperatur* **1**(1), (1963), Kulik, P. P. op. cit. 8(2), (1971).
159. Vukalovich, M. P. et al., Transactions of All-Union Conference on Thermodynamics, Thermophysical Properties of Substances, Leningrad, 1969.
160. Holleran, E. M., Hubbert, A., *J. Phys. Chem.* **56**, 1034 (1952).
161. Holleran, E. M., *J. Chem. Phys.* **21**(12), 2184 (1953).
162. Saxena, M. P., Saxena, S. C., *Indian J. Pure and Appl. Phys.* **4**(3), 109 (1966).
163. Slattery, J. C., Bird, R. B., *AJChE J.* **4**(2), 137 (1954).
164. Chen, N. H., Othmer, D. F., *J. Chem. Eng. Data* 7(1), 37 (1962).
165. Carswell, A. J., Stryland, J. C., *Canad. J. Phys.* **41**(4), 708 (1963).
166. Kosov, N. D., Studies of Transfer Processes, Transactions of the Kazakh State University, Alma-Ata, 1959.
167. Vyshenskaya, V. F. and Kosov, N. D., *Teplo- i massoperenos* **1** (1962).
168. Usmanov, A. G., Trudy of the Kazan Chemical Engineering Institute, No. 22, 154 (1957); No. 22, 99 (1958); *Zhurnal fizicheskoi khimii* 37(1), 179 (1963).
169. Usmanov, A. G. and Berezhnoy, A. N., Trudy of the Kazan Chemical Engineering Institute, No. 22, 115 (1958); *Zhurnal fizicheskoi khimii* **37**, No. 1, 179 (1963).
170. Nafikov, E. M. and Usmanov, A. G. Trudy of the Kazan Chemical Engineering Institute, No. 31, 36 (1963); No. 22, 17 (1964).
171. Mathur, G. P., Thodos, G., *AJChE J.* **11**(1), 164 (1955).
172. Malinauskas, A. P., *J. Chem. Phys.* **42**(1), 159 (1965).
173. Ivakin, B. A. and Suetin, P. E., *Zhurnal tekhnicheskoi fiziki* **34**(6), 1115 (1964).
174. Ember. G., Ferron, J. R., Wohl, K., *J. Chem. Phys.* **37**(4), 891 (1962).
175. Pakurar, T. A., Ferron, J. R., *J. Chem. Phys.* **43**(8), 2917 (1965).
176. Chapman, S. and Cowling, T. Mathematical Theory of Inhomogeneous Gases (Translation into Russian), Foreign Press, 1960.
177. Hirschfelder, J. O., Bird, R. B., Spotz, E. L., *Chem. Rev.* **44**(1), 205 (1949).
178. Lee, C. J., Wilke, C. R., *Ind. Eng. Chem.* **46,** 2381 (1954).
179. Winn, E. B., *Phys, Rev.* **74**(6), 698 (1948).
180. Winn, E. B., *Phys. Rev.* **80**(6), 1024 (1950).
181. Winter, E. R. S., *Trans. Faraday Soc.* **47**, 342 (1951).
182. Amdur, J., Mason, E. A., *Phys. Fluids* **1**(5), 370 (1958).
183. Almasy, G., Pallai, J., *Acta Chim. Ac. Sci. Hung.* **20**(4), 419 (1959).
184. Waldman, L., *Z. Phys.* **124,** 1 (1947).
185. Westenberg, A. A., Walker, R. E., *J. Chem. Phys.* **26**(6), 1753 (1957).
186. Bose, N. K., Chakraborty, R. N., *Trans. Ind. Inst. Chem. Eng.* **8,** 67 (1955).
187. Hudson, G. H., McCoubrey, J. C., Ubbelohde, A. R., *Trans. Faraday Soc.* **56**(8), 1184 (1960).
188. Boyd, C. A. et al., *J. Chem. Phys.* **19**(5), 549 (1951).
189. Suetin, P. E. and Ivakin, B. A., *Zhurnal tekhnicheskoi fiziki* **31**(4), 499 (1961).
190. Vyshenskaya, V. F. and Kosov, N. D., Studies of Transport Processes, Transactions of the Kazakh State University, Alma-Ata, 1959.
191. Van Itterbeek, A., Nihoul, J., *Acustica* 7(3), 180 (1957).
192. Schäfer, K., Cote, H., Moesta, H., *Elektrochem.* **55**(7), 662 (1951).
193. Boardman, L. E., Wild, N. E., *Proc. Roy. Soc.* **A162**(911), 511 (1937).
194. Schäfer, K., Moesta, H., *Z. Elektrochem.* **58,** 743 (1954).
195. Nelson, E. T., *J. Appl. Chem.* **6**(7), 286 (1956).
196. Crider, W. L., *J. Am. Chem. Soc.* 78(5), 924 (1956).
197. Schwertz, F. A., Brow, J. E., *J. Chem. Phys.* **19,** 640 (1951).
198. Westenberg, A. A., *Combustion and Flame* **1**(3), 346 (1957).
199. Walker, R. E., Westenberg, A. A., *J. Chem. Phys.* **29**(5), 1147 (1958).
200. Cummings, G. A., Ubbelohde, A. R., *J. Chem. Soc.,* No. 12, 3751 (1953); No. 7, 2524 (1955).
201. Usmanov, A. G. and Berezhnoy, A. N., *Zhurnal fizicheskoi khimii,* **34**(4), 907 (1960).
202. Cummings, G. A., McLaughlin, E., Ubbelohde, A. R., *J. Chem. Soc.,* 1141 (1955).

203. Clarke, J. K., Ubbelohde, A. R., *J. Chem. Soc.,* 2050 (1957).
204. Berezhnoy, A. N., Candidate dissertation, ENIN, Ac. Sciences of the USSR, 1960.
205. Andrussow, L., *Z. Elektrochem.* **54**, 556 (1950).
206. Trautz, M., Müller, W., *Ann. Phys.* **22**, 333 (1935).
207. Hartel, H., Meer, N., Polanyi, M., *Z. Phys. Chem.* **198**(2–3), (1932).
208. Cvetanovic, R. J., Roy, D. I., *J. Chem. Phys.* **20**, 343 (1952).
209. Hutchinson, F., *Phys. Rev.* **72**(12), 1256 (1947).
210. Hutchinson, F., *J. Chem. Phys.* **17**(11), 1081 (1949).
211. Mifflin, R. K., Bennett, C. O., *J. Chem. Phys.* **29**(5), 975 (1958).
212. Strehlow, R. A., *J. Chem. Phys.* **21**, 2101 (1953).
213. Srivastava, K. P., *Physica* **25**(7), 571 (1959).
214. Walker, R. E., Westenberg, A. A., *J. Chem. Phys.* **31**(2), 519 (1959).
215. Saxena, S. C., Mason, E. A., *Molec. Phys.* **2**(4), 379 (1959).
216. Srivastava, B. N., Srivastava, K. P., *J. Chem. Phys.* **30**(4), 984 (1959).
217. Schäfer, K., Schuhman, K., *Z. Elektrochem.* **61**(2), 246 (1957).
218. Amdur, J., Schatzki, T. F., *J. Chem. Phys.* **29**(6), 1425 (1958).
219. Srivastava, K. P., *J. Chem. Phys.* **28**(4), 543 (1958).
220. Fairbanks, D. F., Wilke, C. R., *Ind. Eng. Chem.* **42**(3), 471 (1950).
221. Winkelmann, A., *Ann. Phys. Chem.* **23**, 203 (1884).
222. Harteck, P., Schmidt, H. W., *Z. Phys. Chem.,* **21B**, 447 (1933).
223. Suetin, P. E. et al., *Zhurnal tekhnicheskoi fiziki* **29**(8), 1058 (1959).
224. Kosov, N. D. Study of physical fundamentals of operation of ovens and firing pits, Transactions of the Kazakh State University, Alma-Ata, 1957.
225. Londsdale, H. K., Mason, E. A., *J. Phys. Chem.* **61**, 1544 (1957).
226. Heath, H. R., Ibbs, T. L., Wild, N. E., *Proc. Roy. Soc.* **A178**(974), 380 (1941).
227. Bendt, P. J., *Phys. Rev.* **110**(1), 85 (1958).
228. Walker, R. E., Westenberg, A. A., *J. Chem. Phys.* **32**(2), 436 (1960).
229. Kimpton, D. D., Wall, F. T., *J. Phys. Chem.* **56**(6), 715 (1952).
230. Le Blanc, M., Wupperman, G., *Z. Phys. Chem.* **91**, 143 (1916).
231. Gilliland, E. R., *Ind. Eng. Chem.* **26**(6), 681 (1934).
232. Vasilevskaya, Yu. D. Trudy of the Moscow Aviation Institute, No. 132, 144 (1961).
233. Schirmer, R., *Z. VDI* **6**, 170 (1938).
234. Rosie, K., *Forsch. Geb. Ingenierwesens* **19**, 49 (1935).
235. Klibanova, Ts. M. et al., *Zhurnal tekhnicheskoi fiziki* **12**(1), 14 (1942).
236. Irisov, A. S. Evaporation of fuels for cylindrical engines and methods of study, State Toptech Press, 1955.
237. Andrew, S. P. S., *Chem. Engng Sc. 4,* No. 6, 269 (1955).
238. Mack, E., *J. Am. Chem. Soc.* **47**, No. 10, 2468 (1925).
239. Goriunova, N. A. and Kuvshinskiy, B. E., *Zhurnal tekhnicheskoi fiziki* **28**, 11, 1421 (1948).
240. Vasilevskaya, Yu. D., Izvestiya MVO SSSR, Series: Petroleum and Gas, No. 1 (1962).
241. Bradley, R. S., Evants, M. G., Whytlaw-Gray, R. W., *Proc. Roy. Soc.* **A186**, 388 (1946).
242. Bradley, R. S., Shellard, A. D., *Proc. Roy. Soc.* **A198**, 239 (1949).
243. Birks, J., Bradley, R. S., *Proc. Roy. Soc.* **A198**, 226 (1949).
244. Call, F., *J. Sci. Food and Agricult.* **8**(2), 86 (1957).
245. McMurtie, R., Keyes, F. G., *J. Chem. Soc.* **70**(11), 3755 (1948).
246. Hirshfelder, G. O. Curtiss, K. F. and Byrd, R. B. Molecular Theory of Gases and liquids, (Russian Translation) Foreign Press, 1961.
247. Klotz, J. M., Miller, D. K., *J. Am. Chem. Soc.* **69**(10), 2557 (1947).
248. Srivastava, K. P., Barua, *Indian J. Phys.* **33**(5), 229 (1959).
249. Amdur, J. et al., *J. Chem. Phys.* **20**(3), 437 (1952).
250. O'Hern, H. A., Martin, J. J., *Ind. Eng. Chem.* **47**, 2081 (1955).
251. Vyshenskaya, V. F., Study of Transport Processes, Transactions of the Kazakh State University, 1960; Candidate dissertation, Energetics Institute, Kazakh SSR, 1961.
252. Wall, F. T., Kidder, G. A., *J. Phys. Chem.* **50**(3), 235 (1946).
253. Groth, H. W., Harteck, P., *Z. Elektrochem.* **47**, 167 (1941).
254. Amdur, J., Schatzki, T. F., *J. Chem. Phys.* **27**, 1049 (1957).
255. Visnep, S., *Phys. Rev.* **82**(2), 297 (1951).
256. Jeffries, P. R., Drickamer, H. G., *J. Chem. Phys.* **21**, 1358 (1953).
257. Winter, E. R. S., *Trans. Faraday Soc.* **46**, 81 (1950).
258. Groth, W., Suscner, E., *Z. Phys. Chem.* **193A**, 296 (1944).
259. Raw, C. J. G., *J. Chem. Phys.* **23**(5), 973 (1955).
260. De Troyer, A., van Itterbeek, A., Berg, G. I., *Physica* **16**, 669 (1950).
261. Grew, K. E., *Proc. Roy. Soc.* **A189**, 402 (1947).
262. Ibbs, T. L., Grew, K. E., *Proc. Phys. Soc.* **43**, 142 (1931).
263. Puschner, M., *Z. Phys.* **106**, 597 (1937).

264. Ibbs, T. L., *Proc. Roy. Soc.* **A107,** 470 (1925).
265. Ibbs, T. L., Grew, K. E., Hirsk, A. A., *Proc. Phys. Soc.* **41,** 456 (1929).
266. Mason, E. A., Rice, W. E., *J. Chem. Phys.* **22**(5), 843 (1959).
267. Elliot, G. A., Mason, J., *Proc. Roy. Soc.* **A108,** 378 (1925).
268. Grew, K. E., *Proc. Phys. Soc.* **62,** 655 (1949).
269. Ibbs, T. L., Underwood, L., *Proc. Phys. Soc. 39,* 227 (1927).
270. Van Itterbeek, A., van Paemel, O., van Kierde, I., *Physica* **138,** 231 (1947).
271. Grew, K. E., *Proc. Roy. Soc.,* **A178,** 390 (1941).
272. Blueh, G., Blueh, O., *Z. Phys.* **90,** 12 (1934).
273. Bastick, R. E., Heath. H. R., Ibbs, T. L., *Proc. Roy. Soc.* **A173,** 543 (1939).
274. Grew, K. E. and Ibbs, T. A., Thermal Diffusion in Gases, (Russian Translation) Foreign Press, 1956.
275. Lugg, I. W. H., *Phil. Mag.* **8,** 1019 (1929).
276. Van Itterbeek, A., Forrez, G., Mariens, P., *Physica* **19,** 525 (1953).
277. Schmahl, W. G., Schewe, I., *Z. Elektrochem.* **46,** 203 (1940).
278. Usmanov, A. G. and Berzhnoy, A. N., Transactions of the Kazan Chemical Engineering Institute, 1961.
279. Ivakin, B. A. et al., *Zhurnal tekhnicheskoi fiziki* **37**(10), 1913 (1967).
280. Paul. R., Srivastava, J. B., *Indian J. Phys.* **35**(9), 465 (1961).
281. Srivastava, B. N., Srivastava, J. B., *J. Chem. Phys.* **36**(10), 2616 (1962).
282. Srivastava, J. B., *Indian J. Phys.* **36**(4), 193 (1962).
283. Amdur, J. Schuler, L. M., *J. Chem. Phys.* **38**(1), 188 (1963).
284. Paul, R., Watson, W. W., *J. Chem. Phys.* **45**(7), 2675 (1966).
285. Bondarenko, A. G. Candidate dissertation, GIAP, 1964.
286. Trautz, M., Melster, A., *Ann. Phys.* **5**(7), 409 (1930).
287. Trautz, M., Binkele, H., *Ann. Phys.* **5**(5), 561 (1930).
288. Trautz, M., Sorg, K., *Ann Phys.* **10,** 81 (1931).
289. Landolt-Börnstein, Physikalisch-chemische Tabellen, Bd. 1, Springer, 1927, S. 146.
290. Agaev, N. A. and Yusibova, A. D., *Gozovaya promyshlennost,* No. 6, 46 (1966)
291. Trautz, M., Baumann, P., *Ann. Phys.* **5**(5), 733 (1929).
292. Trautz, M., Stautz, F., *Ann. Phys.* **2,** 737 (1925).
293. Jung, C., Schmick, H., *Z. Phys. Chem.* **7B**(130), 147 (1930).
294. Silgardo, R., Storrog, J., *J. Am. Chem. Soc.* **69**(8), 261 (1950).
295. Andreev, I. I. et. al., *Teploenergetika,* No. 8 (1966).
296. Vargaftik, N. B. and Osminin, Yu. P. *Teploenergetika,* No. 7, 11 (1956).
297. Riedel, L., *Chem.-Ingr.-Techn.* **23,** 59 (1951); **22,** 54 (1950).
298. Filippov, L. P. and Novoselova, N. S., Vestnik of the Moscow State University, No. 3, 37 (1955).
299. Riedel, L., *Chem.-Ingr.-Techn.* **23,** 465 (1951); **30,** 189 (1958).
300. Ulybin, S. A. *Teploenergetika,* No. 6 (1962).
301. Kovalevskaya, N. S., Candidate dissertation. Moscow Energetics Institute, 1954.
302. Eldarov, F. G., *Zhurnal fizicheskoi khimii* **34**(6), 1205 (1960).
303. Eldarov, F. G., *Zhurnal fizicheskoi khimii* **34**(7), 1414 (1960).
304. Filippov, L. P., Vestnik of the Moscow State University, No. 2, 43 (1960).
305. Filippov, L. P., Vestnik of the Moscow State University, No. 8, 67 (1955).
306. Lindsay, A. L., Bromley, L. A., *Ind. Eng. Chem.* **42,** 1508 (1950).
307. Vargaftik, N. B. Doctoral dissertation, ENIN SSSR, 1952.
308. Grüss, A., Schmick, B., *Wissensch. Veröffentl. aus Siemens-Konzern* **7,** 202 (1928).
309. Kulakov, I. A., Izv. of the Voronezh Pedagogical Institute, No. 17 (1955).
310. Rothman, A. J., Bromely, L. A., *Ind. Eng. Chem.* **47,** 89 (1955).
311. Standards for the Design of Boilers, State Energy Press, 1956.
312. Shingarev, R. V. Collection of Research Works of the Ivanov Textile Institute, No. 7, 108 (1955).
313. Chemists Handbook, Vol. 3, State Chem Press, 1952.
314. Tsederberg, N. V., *Teploenergetika,* No. 9, 42 (1956).
315. Wachsmut, J., *Phys. Z.* **9,** 235 (1908).
316. Filippov, L. P., Vestnik of the Moscow State University, No. 3, 61 (1960).
317. Sokolov, S. N. and Tarlakov, Yu. V. Trudy of the Moscow Aviation Institute, No. 132, 116 (1961).
318. Sokolov, S. N. and Tarlakov, Yu. V., Trudy of the Moscow Aviation Institute, No. 132, 15 (1961).
319. Kopylov, N. I., Trudy of the Moscow Aviation Institute, No. 132, 45 (1961).
320. Zaytseva, L. S., Trudy of the Moscow Aviation Institute, No. 132, 79 (1961).
321. Kozyukov, A. V., Trudy of the Moscow Aviation Institute, No. 132, 94 (1961).
322. Piatibratov, S. N., Trudy of the Moscow Aviation Institute, No. 132, 31 (1961).
323. Volyak, L. D., Trudy of the Moscow Aviation Institute, No. 132, 63 (1961).
324. Zenkevich, V. B., Izvestiya MVO SSSR, *Energetika,* No. 2, 8 (1961).
325. Kagan, S. E. and Chechetkin, A. V. Organic high-temperature coolants, State Chem Press, 1960.
326. Vargaftik, N. B. et al., *Teploenergetika,* No. 7 (1968).
327. Vargaftik, N. B. et al., Izvestiya VTI, No. 9 (1952).

328. Petukhov, B. S., Mechanical Engineering Handbook, Vol. 2, Machine Press, 1960.
329. Paul, R., Srivastava, J. B., *Indian J. Phys.* **35**(10), 523 (1961).
330. Seager, S. L., Geertson, L. R., Giddings, J. C., *J. Chem. Eng. Data* 8(2), 168 (1963).
331. Paul, R., Srivastava, J. B., *J. Chem. Phys.* **35**(5), 1621 (1961).
332. Westenberg, A. A., Frazier, G., *J. Chem. Phys.* **36**(12), 3499 (1962).
333. Kosov, N. D. and Karpushin, A. G., Problems in general and applied physics, Transactions of the Kazakh State University, Alma-Ata, 1966.
334. Holsen, J. N., Strunk, M. K., *Ind. Eng. Chem.* **3**, 143 (1964).
335. Fedorov, E. B. et al., *Zhurnal tekhnicheskoi fiziki* **36**(3), 569 (1966).
336. Heath, H. R., Ibbs, T. L., Wild, N. E., *Proc. Roy. Soc.* **A178**, 380 (1941).
337. Waldmann, L., *Z. Naturforschung* **1**, 59 (1946).
338. Makaveckas, R. A. et al., *Teplofizika vysokikh temperatur,* **1**(2), (1963).
339. Blagoi, Yu. P. *Ukr. fiz. zhurnal* **5**(1), 109 (1960).
340. Naziev, Ya. M. and Abasov, A. A. Izvestiya MVO SSSR: Petroleum and Gas, No. 11, 63 (1968); No. 1, 81 (1969).
341. Kang, T. L. et al., *J. Chem. Eng. Data* **6**(2), 220 (1961).
342. Altunin, V. V. et al., *Teploenergetika,* No. 1, (1969).
343. Gateev, S. B. Izvestiya VTI, No. 10 (1950); *Promyshlennaya energetika,* No. 3 (1952).
344. Kessel'man, P. M., *Teplofizika vysokikh temperatur* **2**, 879 (1964).
345. Kessel'man, P. M. Doctoral dissertation, Odessa Lomonosov Technological Institute, 1966.
346. Glushko, V. P. et al. (eds.), Thermodynamic properties of Substances, Science Press, 1962.
347. Khomchenkov, B. N. et al., *Teplofizika vysokikh temperatur* **6**(6) (1968).
348. Legobsky, I., *J. Chem. Phys.* **41**, 1313 (1964).
349. Lyusternik, V. E. Transactions of the Third All–Union Conference on Thermophysics. Thermophysical Properties of Gases, Nauka Press, Moscow, 1970.
350. Shpilrayn, E. E. and Nikanorov, E. V., *Teplofizika vysokikh temperatur,* **9**(2), 434, (1971).
351. Lee, D. I., Bonilla, C. F., *Nuclear Engng. and Design* **7**, 455 (1968).
352. Kamenetskiy, V. P., Candidate dissertation, Odessa Technological Institute, 1969; with Kessel'man et al., Transactions of All-Union Conference on Thermodynamics. Thermodynamics of Phase Changes and Thermophysical Properties of Substances, Leningrad, 1970.
353. Tsitelauri, N. N., Candidate dissertation, ENIN Academy of Sciences of the USSR, 1969.
354. Sengers, I. V., Dissertation, Univ. of Amsterdam, 1962; Michels, A., Sengers, I. V., van der Gulik, *Physica* **28**, 1201, 1216 (1962).
355. Doolittle, A. K., *J. Chem. Eng. Data* **9**(2), 275 (1964).
356. Cherneyeva, L. I., Kholodilnaya teknika, VNII Kholodilnoi tekhniki, State Torg Press, 1955.
357. Rombusch, U. K., Geisen, H., *Kältetechnik,* No. 2 (1968).
358. Rombusch, U. K., Geisen, H., *Kältetechnik,* No. 3 (1968).
359. Popovskiy, Yu. M. and Deryagin, B. V., Doklady Acad. Sci. USSR **159**(4), 897 (1964).
360. Frank, E. U., *Z. Elektrochemie,* No. 7, 636 (1951).
361. Collins, D. T., Greif, R., *J. Heat Mass Transfer,* No. 8, 9 (1965); No. 1, 56 (1966).
362. Trappeniers, N., Botzen, A., van der Berg, H., van Oosten, J., *Physica* **30**(5), 985 (1964).
363. Di Pipo, R., An Absolute Determination of the Viscosity of Seven Gases to High Temperatures, Dissertation, Brown Univ., 1966.
364. Kestin, J., Di Pipo, R., *Physica* **33**, 762 (1968).
365. Michels, A., Wassernaar, T., Louwerse, P., *Physica 26,* 539 (1960).
366. Hanley, H. J. M., Childs, G. E., *Science* **159**,1114 (1968).
367. Reynes, E. G., Thodos, G., *Physica* **30**, 1529 (1964).
368. Ho, C. Y., Powell, R. W., Liley, P. E., Standard Reference Data on the Thermal Conductivity of Selected Materials, NBS, 1968.
369. Leadbetter, A. I., Thomas, H. E., *Trans Faraday Soc.* **61**(505), 12 (1965).
370. Studnikov, E. L., *Inzhenerno-fizicheskii zhurnal* **19**(2), 337 (1970).
371. Popov, V. N. and Malov, B. A., *Teploenergetika,* No. 6 (1969).
372. Usmanov, I., Candidate dissertation, Azerbaydzhan Institute of Petroleum Chemistry, 1970.
373. Bashirov, M. Ya., Candidate dissertation, Azerbaydzhan State Pedagogical Institute, 1969; Doklady Ac. Scie. Azerb. SSR, No. 2, (1966).
374. Rastorguev, Yu. L. and Nemzer, V. G., *Teploenergetika,* No. 5 (1969).
375. Kessel'man, P. M. et al., *Teplofizika vysokikh temperatur* **6**(2), 348 (1968); *Teplofizika vysokikh temperatur* **6**(3), 427 (1969).
376. Vargaftik, N. B. et al., *Inzhenerno-fizicheskii zhurnal,* No. 5, 882 (1968).
377. Vargaftik, N. B. and Yakush, L. V., *Inzhenerno-fizicheskii zhurnal,* No. 9, 3, 491 (1971).
378. Ikkenberry, L., Rice, S., *J. Chem. Phys.,* **39**(6), 1561 (1963).
379. Förster, S., *Cryogenics* **3**(3), 172 (1963).
380. Kestin, I., Whitelaw, I., *Physica* **29**, 335 (1963).
381. Reynes, E., Thodos, G., *J. Chem. Eng.* **11**, 137 (1963).
382. Rediger, A., *Chem. Ind. Technik,* No. 23 (1951).

383. Liley, P. E., Proc. Fourth Symp. on Thermophysical Properties, ASME, April 1968, p. 323.
384. Usmanov, A. G. et al., Trudy of the Kazan Chemical Engineering Institute (Aspirant Collection), 1970.
385. Kao, I., Kobayashi, R., *J. Chem. Phys.* **47**(8), 2836 (1967).
386. Tsymarnyy, V. A. and Potienko, N. F., *Inzhenerno-fizicheskii zhurnal,* No. 2 (1970).
387. Timrot, D. L. and Shuyskaya, K. F., *Atomnaya energiya* 7(5), 459 (1959).
388. Vargaftik, N. B. and Oleshchuk, O. N., *Teploenergetika,* No. 12 (1962).
389. Vargaftik, N. B. and Zaytseva, L. S., *Inzhenerno-fizicheskii zhurnal,* No. 5 (1963).
390. Vargaftik, N. B. et al., *Atomnaya energiya* 7(5), 465 (1959).
391. Kalinin, B. A. and Suetin, P. E., *Inzhenerno-fizicheskii zhurnal,* No. 6 (1970).
392. Van Itterbeek, A., van Dael, W., Cobs, A., *Physica* **29**, 365 (1963).
393. Lyusternik, V. E. et al., Transactions of All-Union Conference on Thermodynamics. Thermodynamics of Phase Changes and Thermophysical Properties of Substances, Leningrad, 1970.
394. Nikolskii, I. A. et al., Problems of Heat Transfer, ENIN Ac. Sci. USSR, No. 1, 11 (1959).
395. Blagoi, Yu. P. and Pashkov, V. V., *Zhurnal eksperimentalnoi i tekhnicheskoi fiziki* **49** 1453 (1969).
396. Eselson, B. N. et al., Properties of Liquid and Solid Hydrogen. Standards Press, 1969.
397. Grigoriev, B. N., *Zhurnal eksperimentalnoi i tekhnicheskoi fiziki* **47**, 484 (1964).
398. Rabinovich, V. A. and Veksler, L. S., Collection GSSD, No. 2, Standards Press, 1970.
399. Goodwin, R. D., *Cryogenics* **2**, 353 (1962).
400. Goodwin, R. D., Roder, H. M., *Cryogenics* **3**, 12 (1963).
401. Kessel'man, P. M. and Kotlyarevskiy, P. A., Collection GSSD, No. 2, Standards Press, 1970.
402. Akhundov, T. S. and Imanov, Sh. Yu., Transactions of the Third All–Union Conference on Thermophysics, Thermophysical Properties of Liquids, Nauka Press, Moscow, 1970.
403. Abas-Zade, A. K. et al., Transactions of the Third All-Union Conference on Thermophysics, Thermophysical Properties of Liquids, Nauka Press, Moscow, 1970.
404. Ewing, C. T., Spann, I. R., *J. Chem. Eng. Data* **15**(4), 508 (1970).
405. Vinogradov, Yu. K and Volyak, L. D., *Izmeritelnaya tekhnika,* No. 3, 43 (1967).
406. Vargaftik, N. B. et al., *Inzhenerno-fizicheskii zhurnal,* **15**(5), 893 (1968).
407. Tango, W. J., Link, J. K., *J. Chem. Phys.* **49**, 4264 (1968).
408. Velasko, R., Oftinger, C., Zare, R., *J. Chem. Phys.* **51**, 5522 (1969).
409. Demtröder, W., McClintock, R., Zare, R., *J. Chem. Phys.* **51**, 5495 (1969).
410. Kusch, R., Hessel, M., *J. Mol. Spectroscopy* **32**(2), 181 (1969).
411. Dillon, J., Nelson, P., Swanson, B., *J. Chem. Phys.* **44**(11), 4229 (1966).
412. Renkert, H., Hensel, F., Frank, E., *Phys. Letters* **30A**(9), 494 (1969).
413. Korshunov, Yu. et al. *Teplofizika vysokikh temperatur* 8(6), 1288 (1970).
414. Silver, J., Bonilla, C., Fifth Symposium on Thermal Properties of Gases, Liquids and Solids, Chicago, 1970, p. 105.
415. Melnichenko, N. I., *Zhurnal fizicheskoi khimii* **41**(7), 1826 (1970).
416. Bowles, K., Rosenblum, L., *J. Chem. Eng. Data* **10**(4), 321 (1965).
417. Bowles, K., NASA Report TN-D–4535, 1968.
418. Vargaftik, N. B. and Kerzhentsev, V. V., *Teplofizika vysokikh temperatur,* **10**(1), 56 (1972).
419. Vargaftik, N. B. and Studnikov, E. L., *Teploenergetika* **2**, 81 (1971).
420. Anisimov, V. M. Candidate dissertation, MAI, 1968.
421. Anisimov, V. M. and Volyak, L. D., *Teplofizika vysokikh temperatur* 7(2), 369 (1969).
422. Bodansky, J., Sching, H., *J. Phys. Chem.* **71**(2), 215 (1967).
423. Shpilrayn, E. E. and Belova, A. M., *Teplofizika vysokikh temperatur* **6**(2), 342 (1968).
424. Vargaftik, N. B. and Sidorov, N. I., *Teplofizika vysokikh temperatur,* No. 6 (1972).
425. Guevara, F., McInteer, B., Wageman, W., *Phys. Fluids,* **12**(12), 2493 (1969).

INSTRUCTIONS FOR USE OF THE INDEX

The index to this volume consists of four parts:

The **first part** is an alphabetical index of all substances (except aqueous solutions and mixtures) listed in the volume. The basic information for each substance, such as **boiling** and **melting points, critical values, chemical formulas, molecular weights,** etc., is given immediately following the heading in the main text and can be located by looking up the earliest page number for the desired substance (printed in bold type). Additional properties for each substance, further separated into **liquid** and **vapor** states, are indicated under the bold-type entry.

In order to conserve space, certain properties presented throughout the book in combined tables are listed under the common heading of **thermodynamic properties.** These properties usually include the following:

- adiabatic exponent
- compressibility
- density
- enthalpy
- entropy
- heat capacity
- heat of melting
- heat of vaporization
- molar fraction
- Prandtl number
- speed of sound
- specific volume
- volume fraction

The **second part** is an alphabetical index of properties with an indented, alphabetized index of substances. Again, as in part 1, above, **thermodynamic properties** are listed as a single entry.

The **third part**, Diffusion in Gases, is essentially an alphabetical index of values listed in a table starting on page 634.

Finally, the **fourth part**, lists properties of aqueous solutions and is self-explanatory.

The editors believe that the readers will find the index to be an enormous help in locating the desired properties.

ELEMENTS, COMPOUNDS, AND MIXTURES, AND THEIR PROPERTIES*

*Instructions on the use of the index may be found on page 717.

PROPERTIES OF ELEMENTS, COMPOUNDS, AND MIXTURES*

*Instructions on the use of the index may be found on page 717.

DIFFUSION IN GASES*

*Instructions on the use of the index may be found on page 717.

AQUEOUS SOLUTIONS AND GAS MIXTURES AND THEIR PROPERTIES*

*Instructions on the use of the index may be found on page 717.